Lecture Notes in Artificial Intelligence 546

Subseries of Lecture Notes in Computer Science
Edited by J. Siekmann

Lecture Notes in Computer Science

Edited by G. Goos and J. Hartmanis

O. Herzog   C.-R. Rollinger   (Eds.)

Text Understanding in LILOG

Integrating Computational Linguistics
and Artificial Intelligence
Final Report on the
IBM Germany LILOG-Project

Springer-Verlag

Berlin Heidelberg New York
London Paris Tokyo
Hong Kong Barcelona
Budapest

Series Editor

Jörg Siekmann
Institut für Informatik, Universität Kaiserslautern
Postfach 3049, W-6750 Kaiserslautern, FRG

Volume Editors

Otthein Herzog
IBM Deutschland GmbH, Wissenschaftliches Zentrum, IWBS
Postfach 80 08 80, W-7000 Stuttgart 80, FRG

Claus-Rainer Rollinger
Universität Osnabrück
FB 7, Arbeitsbereich Computerlinguistik und Künstliche Intelligenz
Postfach 44 69, Sedanstraße 4, W-4500 Osnabrück 1, FRG

CR Subject Classification (1991): A.1, D.1.6, D.2.m, F.4.3, H.2.3, I.2.3-4, I.2.7

ISBN 3-540-54594-8 Springer-Verlag Berlin Heidelberg New York
ISBN 0-387-54594-8 Springer-Verlag New York Berlin Heidelberg

Typesetting: Camera ready by author
Printing and binding: Druckhaus Beltz, Hemsbach/Bergstr.
45/3140-543210 - Printed on acid-free paper

Preface

IBM Germany has a long–standing tradition in research in natural language. Already in the 1960s there was a world–wide project on machine translation. I myself remember very well having demonstrated one of the earliest IBM machine translation systems at the New York World Fair in 1964! Our Heidelberg Scientific Center has continued the work in the area of natural language since then. Very good examples of these well–positioned efforts under the direction of Dr. A. Blaser were the USL and later projects which finally provided the technology basis for the IBM product Language Access. This provides a true natural–language interface for English and German to IBM relational databases.

New technologies like the new AI language Prolog and new results in mathematical logic were employed to reach further in computational linguistics: in the LEX project an expert system for the treatment of legal texts (1983–1986) was implemented. In the course of this project it became clear that more fundamental research was necessary to make substantial progress in the extremely complex field of the semantics of natural language. To this end an initial proposal was submitted in 1984 by Dr. A. Blaser to Prof. Ganzhorn who was resonsible for Research and Development in IBM Germany at that time. The management Board of IBM Germany set up the LILOG project ("LInguistic and LOGic methods and tools") to develop technologies for the evolving need of natural language as an end user interface – German in this case. From the beginning, it was planned as a large–scale cooperation with German universities with a planning horizon of five years. Dr. O. Herzog was given the task of starting up this project in April 1985.

A team of bright young scientists was hired within a few months and wrote a scrupulous project outline by fall 1985. A parallel careful search for research partners led to the participation of five universities in LILOG so that the project work could start in spring 1986. The project prospered under the management of A.E. Esslinger and Dr. W. Glatthaar and was extended in 1988 for another three years.

From the start, LILOG proved to be a successful project in every respect. The research cooperation between universities and industry came to full fruition. It was the interdisciplinary approach which marked the ultimate goal and combined the forces: developing theoretical concepts and sound experimental tools to build a software system which should be capable of deriving, storing and retrieving the meaning of texts written in German. Research in the following areas had to be focused: computer science, artificial intelligence, computational linguistics, mathematical logic and philosophy.

The project results are outlined in this book. Therefore, it need only be mentioned that the influence of LILOG to the scientific community is not directly related just to the project itself: LILOG had more the character of a research program than just of a simple project. During its course it involved approximately 200 of the scientists presently working in Germany in the fields of computational linguistics, natural language understanding systems and artificial intelligence. This already gives an impression of the very close cooperation between industry and universities. Another indication is provided by the fact that up to 1990 ten professorships at German universities were accepted by LILOG research staff members, that many project results were worked out in several dozens of Master's theses, eight doctoral theses and three "Habilitation" theses. The basic research effort "Theoretical Foundations of Computational Linguistics" of the universities of Stuttgart and Tübingen in cooperation with the IBM Germany Scientific Center was initiated in 1989. It was the first time in the history of the "Deutsche Forschungsgemeinschaft" (DFG) that a private enterprise was an official partner of such a long–term research project ("Sonderforschungsbereich").

LILOG proves that the cooperation between universities and industry is not only possible but that there can be a host of useful results – both in "pure" research" as well as in "implemented" methods and tools. Therefore I do hope that more industrial enterprises will follow this example in order to drive innovation in shorter cycles than hitherto: economies driven by technological advances can no longer afford to wait until new technologies trickle through in a time frame of ten to fifteen years; this process has to be actively driven by the ones whose task it is to develop innovative products.

I would like to express my acknowledgements and sincere gratitude to Dr. Herzog and all the scientists and students of our university partners as well as all the IBM researchers. They achieved this valuable breakthrough in understanding and processing the German language in close cooperation and motivated by their technological vision and their remarkably high personal involvement.

Stuttgart, August 1991

Hans–Olaf Henkel
Vice President
IBM Corporation
Chairman of the Management Board
IBM Germany

LILOG at the Transition between Information and Knowledge

The project LILOG as presented in this volume deals not only with a basic step beyond the scope of computer science as it has been understood up to now. In addition, it has shed light on conjectured basic interrelations of knowledge processing and language definition and has deepened insights.

The transition from data and information processing to knowledge processing implies a categorical step in computer science, namely of syntactically defined information to its semantic processing, to the elaboration of the meaning of language expressions behind their informational representation.

As it already becomes obvious when translating between two natural languages, there is no one–to–one correspondence between the meaning of individual words in two languages. Meaning is dependent on grammatical forms, and furthermore, the meaning of language expressions can often be mirrored only in the context of whole sentences or even chains of arguments. Therefore, semantic content of texts, i.e. the contained knowledge, depends on the specific language.

This resulted in a first proposition: Knowledge processing, i.e., the processing of the semantic meaning of a text, is strongly coupled to the natural language used and even to its cultural environment.

Knowledge processing supposes that the natural language has to be formally defined as far as necessary if it is to be used to represent knowledge and to process it. Moreover, the semantic interrelations of words have to be determined and have to be computable. This requires an information base for the language itself and necessitates the exact formal definition of linguistic knowledge about the natural language. This implies
- a linguistic dictionary,
- a concept lexicon which represents the word meanings,
- a computational grammar,
- a process capable of determining the meaning with respect to grammatical values and to the context.

Language definitions with this universal approach did not exist hitherto. Their volume becomes manageable only by computational methods.

More than 20 years ago it became evident through research undertaken in the IBM Vienna laboratory in the area of formal definition of programming languages that such a definition becomes very large and, in addition, requires a separate definition language. As a consequence, it was not usable for practical purposes such as compiler verification. At the same time it appeared that there may never be a complete formal definition for a natural language for two reasons: Any natural language lives and is in permanent evolution, and the meanings of expressions are open–ended in all their potential contexts. Ultimately, this is also one of the sources of poetry.

Thus, a second proposition arose: For applied knowledge processing we need a large though restricted information base which defines the semantic contents and interrelations of a language. Nevertheless, it constitutes an open entity. Knowledge–based systems technology is suited to match this by restricted, though extendable, application fields.

Yet the objective of LILOG consisted not only in the implementation of the needed information base. There was also a need for a set of tools in order to be able to work with this system. These include structuring of man–machine interfaces using natural language, dialogue mechanisms, inference algorithms, and a complete subsystem to acquire and store the required knowledge.

Following these lines the LILOG project came to experience a third proposition: Dependent on the application of a knowledge–based system it is always necessary to balance the extent of the system's functions – its application domain – against the desired performance. Knowledge processing systems will remain tools made by people to serve their intellect.

Stuttgart, August 1991   K. E. Ganzhorn

Contents

3 Spatial Knowledge

4 Generating Natural Language

5 LEU/2

3 Spatial Knowledge

4 Generating Natural Language

5 LEU/2

Chapter 0

Introduction

Introducing LILOG

Claus-Rainer Rollinger, Otthein Herzog

The various reasons for IBM to perform LILOG - outlined in the opening remarks by Mr. Henkel and Mr. Ganzhorn - resulted in the practical goal to develop a system capable of understanding German texts means able to extract knowledge from these texts and to represent it in such a way that enables further processing. The "LILOG Experimentier Umgebung" LEU (LILOG experimental environment) should have the characteristics of a workbench, to enable scientists to test and modify theories or to integrate new ones. In addition to the implementation of LEU, the central questions of LILOG concerned the domain-independent representation and processing of spatial and temporal knowledge, the internal structure of the dictionary, and dealing with unknown words. LILOG has remained faithful to this momentous task together with its ancilliaries for a period of almost 6 years, by no means a small feat.

The choice of text understanding as the main theme of LILOG also stems from considerations that there are problems with the acceptance of dialogue interfaces (to a certain degree a traditional alternative to text understanding) based on written, natural language, apart from the fact that with dialogue components, the application fields are already predominantly in the foreground. If, however, information can wholly or partially be extracted from natural language texts and made usable, then a field of applications opens up which is far superior to that of dialogue components.

Before reviewing the organisation and operation of the whole project, the following explains the basic parameters assumed, by which the project was defined, the task definitions arising therefrom and the results as laid out in this book.

Aspects of Text Understanding

The process of text understanding whereby the word text includes not only sentence sequences but also discourse can be divided into four main tasks:

1) The analysis of natural language.
This encompasses not only the morphological, lexical and syntactical analysis but also the semantic analysis, in which, should it prove necessary, not only the context is to be taken into consideration but also background knowledge.

2) The construction of semantic representations.
In order to express the meaning of the natural language utterances, the results of the analyses are mapped into a formal knowledge representation language.

3) The inferential processing of semantic representation.
In cases of text understanding, coherence and consistency tests are to be carried out, in cases of questions the answers must be selected or inferred from knowledge previously accumulated.

4) The generation of natural language.
In order to prove that the system has understood a text it is reasonable to present the answers to questions in natural language. On a high level this makes clear what information can be extracted from a text.

The task of dealing with temporal and spatial phenomena is difficult to classify with respect to the above mentioned fields although major proportions may be allotted to fields 2 and 3.

LILOG's beginnings saw the making of several basic decisions which were not to be modified or revoked. One of these was the decision to adhere to the paradigm of unification grammar, as it were to favour a lexicalised approach which is able to execute the syntax analysis parallel to compositional semantics (the rule-to-rule hypotheses). In order to do this the unification formalism "STUF" (Stuttgart Type Unification Formalism) was developed as an abstract data type (ADT) which was employed especially in the realization of the analysis process. A further decision was in favour of an inferential processing of the semantic representation to develop a logic oriented knowledge representation language on the basis of a formal semantics which met the requirements of linguistic components.

As STUF represents the basis for almost all linguistic components, we shall begin the presentation of LILOG results in Sect. 1.1 with this formalism and the workbench developed for it. Both STUF and STUF ADT (an extension of PROLOG) have undergone several development stages. The third and most up-to-date version, with a very wide range of functionality which well meets the requirements of those linguists developing a grammar, is presented in the paper by Dörre and Seiffert. Dörre explaines in the next the language of STUF and Seiffert presents afterwards the chart-parsing of STUF grammars. In the same section Dörre and Raasch discuss the workbench that has been created for STUF to support the writing and testing of grammars to a high degree. The next papers in this section discuss advanced topics as the formalization and parsing of unification ID/LP grammars (Seiffert) and GAP-handling mechanisms in categorial grammars (König). During the project a whole row of parsers (e.g., Definite Clause Grammar Parser, Bottom Up Parser, Chart Parser) have been implemented and applied. Erbach's paper is about a flexible parser for a linguistic developement environment that found its place in LEU/2.

One of the approaches to morphological processing which was inspired by Kaplan and Kay's paper on phonological rules as finite state transducers came to be known as the "two-level model". This model, which was developed by Koskenniemi, makes two fundamental assumptions: that the morphology of a language can be modeled by finite state techniques and that two levels of representation suffice to account for the phonological properties of a language. The success which the two-level model has had over the last few years is due to the fact that it not only provides a language-independent formalism for representing morphological knowledge but that it can also be applied both to the task of word form recognition and to the task of word form production. Under this paradigm and on the basis of STUF the morphological component for German was implemented. In Sect. 1.2 about the lexicon, Steffens and Schiller describe the morphological processing in LILOG.

Unknown words especially compounds pose a serious problem for natural language understanding systems (= NLU systems) regardless of the application field. In normal cases an NLU system cannot analyse a sentence which contains an unknown word. The exception to this rule is proper names. Part of this problem can be solved by accessing external, machine-readable dictionaries (e.g., a synonym lexicon). Of course, no guarantee can be given that the information required will be found there. But if some information is found there it is necessary to transfer the respective dictionary entries into the appropriate NLU system format. The paper by Ludewig in Sect. 1.2 about incremental vocabulary extensions deals with such points. This does not solve the problem of ad hoc compounds which cannot be found in any dictionary. In normal cases their meaning cannot be taken as the sum of the meanings of the components. In his paper in Sect. 1.2 Gust deals with the representation of word semantics in dictionaries for NLU systems with regard to nominal composition. In the same section Emde describes how both aspects of dealing with unknown words have been tackled in the Lexicon Manager of LEU/2.

The first LEU realized by LILOG was confronted with an actual text from a guide book for walkers and passed its test in, among other things, succeeding in writing a grammar, on the basis of the text as well as the possible questions to it, adequate for this specific fragment of German. The categorial unification grammar (CUG) was chosen here. LILOG demonstrated that it is possible to analyse very complicated real texts with literary elements. But some very special solutions were needed to reach this goal. Because most of them couldn't be applied to other problems (that means to other texts) LILOG was defined to concentrate on a more domain-independent fragment of German and to do so with respect to syntactic constructions that have been well studied. On the basis of the definition of this fragment on the one hand and the research questions of LILOG on the other, some texts were constructed by LILOG for LEU/2 in order to demonstrate the processing of a sequence of texts.

After it became clear that CUG itself contained some limitations which did not allow it to formulate certain phenomena with the desired generality, for LEU/2 the HPSG (Head-driven Phrase Structure Grammar) approach was chosen (see Kiss' paper about the grammars of LILOG in Sect. 1.3 on syntax). Special topics of LILOG in syntax were the phenomena of coordination (the paper by Wesche) and verb order (the paper by Kiss and Wesche).

When dealing with semantic analysis, there are basically two processes to be differentiated from each other: compositional semantics, built up during syntax analysis, and the analysis processes which start with the parsing results and cannot be carried out in compositional semantics up to now. The parsing results are transformed in a special language which is an extension of the Discourse Representation Structures (DRSs) based on Kamp's Discourse Representation Theory (DRT) and has therefore been named EDRS. Processes at this level are concerned for example with reference determination.

Reference determination (or anaphora resolution) has to do with the analysis of constructions within a text which refer to a later stage in the discourse, and which determin the respective entities. The choice of which construction is chosen by a text producer, in order to refer to an entity, is dependent on the entity itself to a certain extent. One can differentiate between two large classes of linguistic referentiality: firstly object reference, i.e., linguistic reference to individuals, quantities, prototypes, and generics and secondly event reference i.e., linguistic reference to actions, events, states, propositions, relations, characteristics, locations/positions both temporal and spatial, etc. The following questions are in the foreground in object reference: under what circumstances does a nominal phrase form a referable entity, a so-called dicourse referent? And for how long in a text may a discourse referent be referred to before it goes out of focus? And how can the "correct" candidate be selected from a number of possible candidates for anaphoric elements?

Some of the classic problems of referentiality are the following: on the one hand we can refer by name and definite description to objects which do not exist and have never existed, whereas on the other hand there are names which in almost all cases refer to more than one object of reality, e.g., Christian names and surnames, and which therefore show no unity. We may refer to objects which consist of several parts, e.g., "Fritz and Franz who are carrying a piano". This plural referent cannot be divided in two in the context of carrying a piano, but in the context of carrying coffee cups, this presents no problem. Mayer's paper, Sect. 1.4, deals with anaphora and domain restriction whereas van der Sandt and Geurts discuss in the same section the relation between presupposition, anaphora and lexical content.

Both directly tangible objects of reality and less tangible entities such as events, states, actions and the like have, as a rule, a limited lifespan, even if not all of them can be exactly defined. These as well as the intervals of the public time axis belong to the potential class of formal temporal objects and can be seen as labelled data structures. Such labels give information about a) whether we are dealing with a temporal object of public time (such as a certain week) or an event, b) in what relationship they stand to the time-indicative zero point, i.e., whether we are dealing with past, present, future, or a mixture of two or more, and c) if the temporal object is of duration- or point-form. Further labels are not excluded. The interpretation or processing of such data structures is known as "temporal reasoning".

The question is how much semantic and syntactic knowledge must be taken into account within the analysis so that a semantic representation of the temporal information may be built up. In more specific form this is a problem of the granularity of the representation: how elaborately or roughly should temporal knowledge be represented: according to what viewing method would a point form change to a duration form and vice versa? To what level should a made-up event be divided into a temporal sequence of event parts? Even the arrangement of events or states of any kind along the public or any other temporal axis cannot be undertaken without a certain degree of inference. Likewise the use of frequency adverbs and negation can can be achieved within the foreseeable future. Additionally, there are the results for the filling of gaps in the temporal structure, gaps caused by implicitly mentioned events.

Until the beginning of the 1980s, linguistic interpretations of such temporal structures was undertaken within the framework of model-theoretic semantics with the temporal structures of single sentences as limiting factors. From the beginning of the 1980s onwards, temporal structures have been interpreted in a contexttual relation, i.e., previous discourse and background knowledge are taken into account in the interpretation. Eberle's paper in Sect. 1.4 on representing the temporal structure of texts gives details of LILOG's chosen starting point to solve these problems.

As well as work on anaphora resolutions and the interpretation of temporal structures, work has also been carried out on the treatment of plurals (Link and Schütze's paper, Sect. 1.4) and comparatives. The first especially makes clear how all the participating components are affected when such a phenomenon is to be taken into account. Not only must the lexical and grammatical information be in readiness, but constructions must be made available also for knowledge representation, and they must be adequately pictured for plurals as well as for axioms which fix the meanings of these constructions.

We do not need to expound the central role of knowledge representation and processing within the context of language understanding systems here. It is clear that a very high degree of background knowledge is necessary for the analysis and disambiguation of natural language, and especially so for the interpretation of the semantic representations so produced. L-LILOG, also called L_{LILOG}, is the representation language developed in LILOG. Its task is to represent the domain knowledge necessary to understand texts of this domain on the one hand and the knowledge extracted from these texts on the other. Apart from this it must offer suitable constructions for semantic phenomena, upon which such phenomena may be mapped. In any case it is important to lay down the semantics of the formalism and to know complexity characteristics if one wishes to achieve suitable implementation. Pletat's paper, Sect. 2.1, presents L-LILOG as a logic-oriented order-sorted representation language together with its semantics, whereas Bollinger et al. describe the inference engine of L-LILOG in the same section.

The structuring of background and linguistic knowledge (e.g. the dictionary) plays an important part in view of the question of when which knowledge is to be activated. The supposition that only a certain part of the knowledge is always active and is being searched through or modified is supported not only by the argument for efficiency but also by that for cognitive adequacy. The choice of a suitable structure and distribution of knowledge prevents the activation of word-meanings within a context not being in focus: e.g., in the context of a financial transaction the meaning "riverside" is not available as a meaning for the word "bank", and should only be reachable under special circumstances. Wachsmuth's paper, Sect. 2.1, presents a method of structuring used in LILOG with which a row of experiments were executed.

The necessary incompleteness of natural knowledge systems, expressed in the line "I know there is a lot I don't know", is at least partially responsible (relative to the knowledge system) for its not being able to reach a decision of 100 % precision when dealing with certain statements concerning whether they are true in reality or not. This means that the system must be capable of representing and processing inexactitude in at least three dimensions: the dimension of incompleteness, that of vagueness and that of insecurity. Although in natural language these forms of inexactitude may be eminently well represented and placed in relation to each other, no satisfactory solution is available for their adequate and integrated treatment within the framework of formal representation languages and the interpretation mechanisms belonging thereto. Schmitt's paper, Sect. 2.1, presents a three-valued logic with which the aspects of inexactitude may be treated with respect to future events.

When the knowledge system is incomplete in an aspect which is important for deducing a knowledge entity, help can be found by using defaults insofar as these are available and these suppositions may be used to continue the work. If, however, the reality turns out differently than was assumed we are forced to retract the steps already taken. This means that "default reasoning" presupposes truthmaintenance. Moreover, natural knowledge systems can be inconsistent, although able to manage very well with such inconsistencies by the ability to isolate infected facts or to undertak correction. Such a system has at its disposal processes which may investigate the reasons for the contradictions. This is not trivial in as much as the reasons for it may be found in the field of inferential knowledge or in that of factual knowledge. Systems behaving in such a manner and one can be relatively sure of this in natural knowledge systems are known as non-monotonic and attempts are being made to describe such behavior with non-monotonic logic systems. The paper on the inference engine by Bollinger et al., Sect. 2.1, describes among other aspects how far a truthmaintenance system could be realized in the inference engine.

The search space of an inference engine can be very large, especially as the first order logic in L-LILOG has been realized to a very high degree. That's why there is the need to limiting the spaces to be searched. Here, the structuring of knowledge is only a means to an end. LILOG employed and developed forward and backward chaining mechanisms as well as a depth limiter, but most of all it employed the concept of entry points that trigger rules in a knowledge based manner. An aspect processed in LILOG is the development of a declarative control language as a metalanguage but on the basis of L-LILOG which enables the choice of task-oriented control strategies and the modification of the control knowledge without modifying the whole background knowledge. The paper of Bläsius, Sect. 2.1, describes the entry point followed in LILOG.

As well as a clear predicate logical part, L-LILOG has a component similar to KL-ONE, in which sorts can be defined and equipped with roles and features which are inherited down to the subsorts. This part of L-LILOG is related to STUF and different attempts have been made to unite these two languages. Nebel and Smolka, both of whom worked on both languages, describe in their paper, Sect. 2.1, the similarities between these languages and employ the experience collected during attempts at unification of the two languages.

In order for one to be able to act in the world (linguistically), one must know how the world "functions", which means that the knowledge system itself can be seen as a model of the world and that the individual must be given access to the model using it plans may be made and decisions reached. As a human being does not enter the world with a fully equipped model and never can have one because the world always changes, he/she has to build it up and keep it up-to-date. Correspondingly, within Artificial Intelligence there is a field of research named "machine learning" which is occupied with the problems of inductive and concept-driven learning, learning by anology and many other types of learning. In contrast there is the field of "knowledge engineering" which became relevant within the framework of expert system development. In the context of natural language understanding systems there is the necessity of modelling both linguistic and background knowledge into coherent forms, which is much more complex than merely filling the shell of an expert system. The complexity results from the necessity to relate linguistic knowledge to world knowledge in such a way that not only both syntactic and semantic analysis but also the generation of natural language may be systematically carried out. In Sect. 2.2 work on this task is detailed in which the fixing of an ontology in the sorting system plays a central role. The aspect of machine learing undoubtedly a very important one has only been marginally discussed in LILOG.

Besides these basic characteristics and abilities, taken into account in LILOG, the aspect of memory itself is drawn to attention. The differentiation between ultra short-term memory (or sensory memory), short-term and long-term memory is well known to all. However, there has up to now been a shortage of findings and theories capable of being formalized which have in a suitable way concerned themselves with the processing of information and which regulate the classification into one of these three memories. The decision about what was to be transferred from a short-term memory into a long-term memory is not rationally controlled but is dependent upon valuations which themselves reflect favoritism, aversion and interests. A further substantial capability of natural knowledge systems, as important as that of "learning" information (as part of a world model), is the ability to forget. This field, too, shows a shortage of theories capable of being formalized. LILOG has not undertaken work in either field.

However, at an early stage, it was ensured that methods and processes would be developed which would in the long term enable LILOG to externally administer even large inventories of knowledge for complex applications, whether it be linguistic or background knowledge or both. As it was at that time clear that we were dealing with formalisms which were more powerful than those which had gained access into data bank technology and we were further dealing with data structures which modified themselves dynamically and could become very complex, it was obvious that the traditional data bank technology was not in a position to offer us suitable solutions to the above. The database support developed for for knowledge based systems like that of LILOG is described by Benzschawel et al., Sect. 2.3.

It is not only the temporal classification of objects and events but also their spatial attributes and relations which can be expressed in natural language. Language concepts are available for this which can be excellently interpreted by natural speaker-listeners. Habel's paperon processing of spatial expressions in LILOG, Chap. 3, deals with the basic task of making clear by which method spatial knowledge can be represented so that these representations can be interpreted in a manner corresponding to a natural speaker-listener situation. An integral part of this is the ability to imagine spatially and the possibility to operate on it. To achieve such by propositional representation would appear to be unrealistic because of the over-proportionality of the amount of calculation and its cognitive adequacy. Therefore, in cognitive science or cognitive psychology this question would arise for a specific representation's format for spatial imagination which differs from propositional representation (Dual Coding Theory). Khenkhar's paper, Chap. 3, presents depictions together with operations for construction, modification and inspection as the inventory necessary to the modelling of two-dimensional spatial imagination.

This does not exclude that certain aspects may also be propositionally represented and evaluated by traditional inference processes (see Pribbenow's paper, Chap. 3). The existence of two differing representation forms leads to a row of questions. One of them is: Can everything expressed in one representation format also be expressed in the other? There are indications which would contradict such an assumption; it would be completely impossible to describe verbally an abstract painting by Kandinsky for example, in such a way that your conversation partner could build up a picture of this work more or less identical to the imaginary picture in your ownmind. Both representation formalisms have different, specific interpretation processes. We may therefore say, and only this allows the thesis of two formalisms to appear sensible, that there are problems which are solved easily in one formalism, but in the other only with great difficulty or not at all. The relationship between the two formalisms then becomes the central question for the interpretation of spatial expressions and spatial knowledge.

It is obvious that the results achieved with respect to text understanding, and with analysis in focus, can only be relied on in the long term when they suitably meet the demands of generation. During the development of the first prototype, generation played a very subordinate role. As a result of the findings that the whole modularity of a system suffers when one component must be subservient to all others, generation was moved up the priority list and made independent during the development of LEU/2 (see Novak's paper, Chap. 4). It would not otherwise have been possible to integrate a planning component that uses the inference engine which decides what to say. This is followed up in the generation process by the transfer of knowledge structures into text structures (see Dobes and Novak, Chap. 4) and then followed by the formulator (see Wendholt, also Chap. 4). Now there is the prospect of using not only the same lexicon as the analyses which is already realized in LEU/2 but also the same grammar.

LILOG had to implement a system that not only contains all the above mentioned single theories but enables their interaction to be tested, modified and replaced. The realization of such a text understanding workbench is a task for which there is a shortage of substantial experience. It is more difficult than traditional software developement because the single formal theories are being developed or modified during implementation: We are after all dealing here with scientific software. It is for this reason that classic software engineering methodology is only useful to a limited degree. Likewise the arrangement, first the implementing shell with all its tools and then building up the knowledge bases, is to a degree questionable. Apart from the fact that this separation, given such a complex system with its numerous knowledge sources and numerous developers, cannot be maintained, the question arises: What actually should be the center of interest? The knowledge necessary to understand natural language texts and their (declarative) representation or the algorithms which process this knowledge. Both are objects of research and both are competing for the position of central interest, at least as far as the building of a system is concerned. LEU/2 as a workbench is described in Chap. 5 with the context in which text understanding takes place (von Luck and Pirlein). Wilms describes its functionality in examples and Arning describes the experiences gathered during the implementation of LEU/2.

The Organization of LILOG

The scope of this volume, which presents a variety of the results achieved in LILOG and which especially endeavors to record the state of the art, has already made clear that LILOG was a voluminous project. In the course of the 5-1/2 years with a constantly changing staff whose average number was approx. 60 ranging from participating students up to management level, approx. 200 persons "passed through" LILOG. This necessitated special organizational measures to keep the staff up to date concerning the associated fields, to acquire and work in new members and especially to make sure that scientists coming from widely varying fields did actually co-operate with each other. It was here that LILOG showed one great advantage over comparable projects: The LILOG-group at IBM was not only the sponsor for all part projects and responsible for the organizational running of the whole project, but also the IBM LILOG-group did approximately half of the technical work and this half was basic to the project. This ensured that the measures regarding content, organization, personnel, and finances could be integrated with each other to a very high degree. It helped very much that IBM is considerably more flexible concerning the application of funds than for instance a govermental authority. Using these pre requisites as a starting point the project was divided into ten part projects of which five were sub contracted to universities. The vertical structure of the part projects was complemented by horizontal integration and work groups. IBM undertook the part projects "Computational Linguistics", "Knowledge Representation and Processing", "Natural Language Generation", "Knowledge Engineering" and "Implementation". The following part projects were sub contracted: "Spatial Knowledge" (Prof. Dr. C. Habel, University of Hamburg), "Tense in Natural Language and Temporal Reasoning" (Prof. Dr. C. Rohrer, University of Stuttgart), "Knowledge Structures and Lexical Structures" (Prof. Dr. S. Kanngießer, University of Osnabrück), until 1988 "Discourse Analyses" (Prof. Dr. F. Günthner, University of Tübingen), from 1989 on "Unification, Formalism and Parsing" (Prof. Dr. H. Uszkoreit, University of Saarbrücken) and "Database Support for Knowledge Based Systems" (Prof. Dr. B. Walter, University of Trier). The groups were drawn in early, at the definition stage, a stage at which it was not clear if LILOG would lift off or not. This ensured that the groups identified themselves with the content plan for LILOG as soon as the green light came.

The choice of the project groups was not a matter of formal application, LILOG was a project on an invitation basis. The selection of the university partners was multifaceted. A high priority was the scientific competence of the group or group leader in their respective fields. Another important point to which attention was paid was whether the groups were familiar with each other or had done any joint work previously. The latter could only be fulfilled to some degree because of the greatly varying fields from which the groups came. It proved to be advantageous that not only well established groups were taken into consideration but that through LILOG chances were available to establish and build up groups. In this way it was ensured that LILOG played a very central role for this circle of participants. Lastly, all the groups had to show strong interest in interdisciplinary work. It was also important that any significant progress achieved in one's own field was seen in the results of the interdisciplinary work.

As well as the company's internal review board to which the IBM group had to report annually, an external advisory board was set up, on which Professors Brauer, Lockemann and Schnelle thankfully decided to participate. Every six months saw a four-day workshop in which everybody involved in LILOG took part, including the advisory board. Beside all the important informal discussions, individual groups' progress reports were read in these workshops, fine planning was undertaken, project results were made public, demonstrations given, and guest speakers invited to lecture on special subjects. The groups themselves organized these workshops in turn and the group whose turn it was, was given the possibility to present itself in more detail.

The necessary infrastructure was placed at the disposal of the groups by IBM. This began with the creation of EARN-nodes to improve communications, the provision of workstations and the publication by IBM of a series named the LILOG Reports. In the course of the LILOG project in 1988, IBM created the "Institute for Knowledge Based Systems" (IKBS) in the IBM Germany Scientific Centre, and the LILOG Reports appeared in the IKBS Technical Report Series.

A further measure which was also one of the important aims of the whole project was to find a solution to the task of translating in a certain rhythm the individual results into a mutual complex text understanding system, because only by such a method could evaluable final results be evolved. This was undertaken twice, first in 1987 with a prototype written in PROLOG under VM and then in 1990 with LEU/2 written in PROLOG under AIX on PS/2. On the occasion of CeBIT 91 it was also available on RS/6000. Beside the enormous gains in findings resulting therefrom, this measure led to project members being forced to formalize their results, on the one hand to such an extent that they became implementable, and on the other hand to take into account the constraints imposed by other results when producing interfaces. The latter led to intensive discussion among the project staff which in itself led to a degree of understanding for the tasks and problems of the others, which had not existed at LILOG's beginnings. The implementation work was carried out and completed on schedule with remarkable motivation and even more remarkable engagement. It is due to this that there is now the system LEU/2, unique in its total functionality and created without compromising our demands concerning modularity and expandability.

Results

As well as the scientific results which this book documents among other things, the success of an undertaking such as LILOG will be measured by the undertaking's side effects, and we should say a few words about these here. During LILOG great pains were taken to ensure that the scientists and students participating could achieve higher formal qualifications as far as possible within the framework of the project's contents. At the project's conclusion approx. 65 diploma theses, 26 dissertations and 3 habilitations had been written. The value of this work may be measured by the fact that no less than 10 members of the IBM LILOG group were awarded professorships during the course of the project. LILOG members gave courses at many different universities. A large number of monographs, anthologies and essays (approx. 40 per year) were published and made available to the scientific public through the IKBS Technical Report Series. As well as the LILOG workshops, two IBM Symposia were held by LILOG. Special workshops took place, and last but not least, LILOG members have participated in the organization of many national and international conferences and summer schools.

A further, highly desirable side effect is the presentation of scientific achievements within IBM to their development divisions who, applying these results, will improve products or develop new ones. LILOG has by suitable measures intensively participated in market development and has tried to make clear what functionality can be achieved within the foreseeable future. Additionally, there are the results such as L-LILOG and the inference engine which have, in the meantime, been introduced into development projects as powerful knowledge representation and knowledge processing components.

Conclusions

LILOG was a project that produced more than could have been expected at the outset. Not only were a large number of scientific papers, implemented systems, diplomas, dissertations and professors produced, but also a large part of a whole generation of scientists working on language understanding was brought together. The present book on LILOG makes clear that LILOG represents a great step forward in the development of a theory of text understanding. Futhermore this step forward is not only to be found on paper but also in the fact that a large part of the theoretical results have been integrated into an operational system, LEU/2. Without any doubt there is still a great deal to be done, but LILOG has already shown how worthwhile it is to go on in this direction.

Acknowledgements

There are so many people who contributed to LILOG that it's impossible to name them all. In addition to the authors of this volume there are about 150 more people we have to thank. We all together learned a lot about text understanding and we had a great time in an excellent environment. Although fun and results were greatly supported by this setting and the atmosphere, it's the people who made everything happen. So thank you all very much.

Special thanks go to Prof. Dr. Dr. hc K. Ganzhorn, the initiator of LILOG, to the Senior Executives G. H. Müller and A. E. Esslinger of IBM Germany responsible for LILOG and to the Director of Science and IBM Fellow Prof. Dr. O. Folberth and his successor Dr. W. Glatthaar. They all supported LILOG to a very high degree and saw the value of basic research for spin offs and future products in this special area. We hope that LILOG may fulfill the expectations that were put on it.

Text Understanding - The Challenges to Come

W. Brauer

P. C. Lockemann

H. Schnelle

1. Scenarios

Everyone has faced this situation one time or another. Suppose you arrive by train in a city that you are not familiar with. Before leaving the station you look for a street map, and a plan of the public transportation network to find the best way to get to your destination. You wonder whether it is best just to walk, to take a bus or streetcar and if so which one, or to jump into a taxicab. Indeed, you find a city map right by the exit. You consult the alphabetic street guide which identifies the grid in which to search further. Examining the grid on the map you finally locate the desired street, but alas it is a very long one, and it takes considerable searching for the fine print to identify a house number close to the one of your destination. Now you scan the neighborhood to find the red line signifying a streetcar line close by, and the red dot which indicates a stop. Unfortunately, it is several streets and corners away so that you now memorize the directions and turns to take after alighting from the streetcar. Finally you make an educated guess as to the name of the streetcar stop.

Walking out of the station you discover a streetcar stop in front of you. You hope to find a network plan there and a timetable, and indeed you do. On closer inspection you detect the streetcar stop – you guessed its name right. Unfortunately, there is no direct connection so you must change cars. Worse, there seem to be several possibilities to do so. Which one is the best? And how long do you have to wait for the next streetcar? How long would you have to wait for the connecting car? Turning to the timetable you determine that – since it is long after rush-hour – the streetcar runs every twenty minutes, and the previous one left just five minutes ago.

By that time you probably become conscious of the taxistand right across, you walk over and take a cab which brings you to your destination within fifteen minutes and without more ado.

How much easier it would be if the city had an information desk at the station where you could just ask for the best way. But staffing such desks is an expensive affair these days, so you never seem to find one. But why have a person there? All you really need is a microphone close to the street map where you explain in your own language where you wish to go. A loudspeaker may convey to you the various alternatives you have, you may ask questions for clarification, an illumination may appear on the map to show you the route you should take, and finally a printer my provide you with a written log of the final recommendation. You may even go on and ask for further advice on where to obtain the most suitable ticket, whether you need exact change or may use bills, and so on.

Does this sound like a far-away future to you? The purpose of this book is to show that it is not. Admittedly, the book concentrates on the written word rather than oral communication, but much of what is has to say is of profound value to both. The book identifies the major issues of truly two-way natural-language communication between human persons and machines, where both have some common understanding of the universe of discourse. For the most part it then offers detailed conceptual and technical solutions for these issues, and raises numerous open questions that should stimulate a wealth of further research.

But what are some of these issues? Before we attempt a first crude answer, let us suggest a few further scenarios. Our scenario above is of the inquiry-at-the-information-desk variety. Services of this kind seem to abound in everyday life where one faces uncommon situations with a sharply limited discourse world. Take inquiries on train or flight connections and particular schedules. Services of this type are already partly automated but still require a human interlocutor who first clarifies the question or delineates the space of potential solutions, then types the request into a form display and hands over the printed reply. Reservations on flights or trains are another example where an interlocutor is the rule but nonetheless seems superfluous or at best needed for mediation. More generally and perhaps more futuristically, all kinds of teleshopping would benefit from a natural language dialogue. Even in situations with much more latitude such as in a hotel reservation where rooms have different prices, furnishing, orientation, proximity to stairs and elevators, and where the hotel has different restaurants, menues, health and shopping facilities, natural-language conversation with an automatic reservation system has been demonstrated as feasible at least on an experimental basis.

Take as another class of scenarios the world of sightseeing, hiking or museum visits. Instead of constantly consulting a travel guide while spending a few hours in a city, one may carry a computerized information system in one's pocket, ask for the next steps to take from a given point, obtain explanations of the object currently in sight, even describe it to the system in order to find out what it might be, or ask whether it is worthwhile to visit the interior or to take a certain detour. Similar technical support may make sense while hiking through the mountains with various viewpoints, historic sites and refreshment places. In a museum one may not necessarily wish to follow the directions of a tape recorded guide but wander around at one's own pace and obtain information on objects encountered spontaneously.

Information systems may also play a more active role as guides. Our initial example provided guidance only by laying out a plan that one then had to follow. Suppose, however, that you drive by car into a city. If you give your current position and desired destination, an information system may then, e.g., via radio link, give step-by-step directions on which streets to take, and may even take into account up-to-date information on traffic volume. The driver may communicate his observations, e.g., an accident in front of him, in order to receive directions on how to bypass the spot. Directions and guidance may also be useful in other conditions such as diagnostics of machinery and the subsequent repair actions.

Conversation need not be limited to a single language. Consider a more recent research scenario where a native speaker of, say, German, wishes to communicate with a Japanese partner, where neither of the two speaks the other's language. While the German speaks in German, his input is translated into Japanese and will be audible to his partner in his native tongue. In turn, the partner answers in Japanese, but by subsequent translation his response will be received by the German speaker in German. A bit more modest is a pocket information system where a tourist in a foreign contry, while trying to ask simple questions from a pedestrian or waiter, could present the question to the system which would then respond, e.g., in written form, with a translation of the question. The same system could also be used to query on the customs to be observed in a given situation, e.g., whether one should give tips and how big they should be.

While solutions to these scenarios still seem highly ambitious, more modest goals dealing with schematic procedures appear within reach. Take consultancy systems on taxes, insurance, or investment portfolios which one may access in a minitel or videotex fashion. While the dialogue takes place in a strictly formatted way, the final explanations and recommendations by the system may be easier to understand if provided in narrative form – perhaps printed and mailed to the questioner.

All the scenarios represent situations where a person needs help in the form of directives on how to overcome a given difficulty. The impulsive reaction is to turn to some person nearby to obtain the necessary information. Often such a person will not be available or turn out not to be knowledgeable enough to provide instantaneous relief. Computerized information systems may in the not-too-distant future substitute for such persons and may even render much more help than what could be expected from the average person. Before these prospects will materialize, though, a number of issues must first be resolved. In the next section we shall try to identify the major ones among them.

2. Topics

Solutions for each of the scenarios involve an information system designed for giving advice. The system must be able to interpret an input text, that is, determine its meaning in a way which is suited to invoking a desired response from the information system and, correspondingly, generate an output text expressing the advice or another meaningful reaction of the machine, such as a request for clarification of the input request. In between interpreting and generating language the machine will make use of internal processes which reflect concepts and manipulate the corresponding stored data (timetables, information about maps, distances, possible actions and conditions on actions). As this suggests, one is dealing with a transformation process between word strings and what they refer to, namely complexes of conceptual, numerical or graphical and perhaps pictorial information.

It is an absolutely nontrivial task to determine how the bits and pieces of questions relate to appropriate answers and how both relate to the meaning representations in the machine. For a machine, texts are merely sequences of letters segmented by blanks and punctuation marks. So, how does it come to know – to take the example of the first scenario – that the sentences

"How do I get to Goethestrasse?"

"We are looking for Goethestrasse."

"Do you know Goethestrasse? How do we get there?"

express the *same request*, whereas

"I'm looking for a street crossing Goethestrasse near its end. I forgot its name."

also contains the word *Goethestrasse* but does not make a request about it but rather asks for names of certain streets whose enumeration may help to recall the name of the street one is looking for. Note that even where the same request is posed it may be formulated as a question or as a statement of intent, or it may be packed into a single of several questions. Moreover, it may be lumped together with further information needs, as in

"What is the cheapest way to get to Goethestrasse?"

which asks primarily for price-related information and not directly – though, perhaps, indirectly – for an information about a location. Thus the fact that the word *Goethestrasse* occurs in the request is no sufficient indication about what the request is for.

Let us assume that, after suitable interpretation and internal manipulation of concepts, numerical lists and maps, the machine has found an internal specification of the route to Goethestrasse which it now wants to communicate to the requester. What is the appropriate wording? Suppose Goethestrasse is long but one of its ends is not far from the information desk (at the station, say). An answer like

"Goethestrasse is long. There are several possibilities to get there."

would be correct but not very informative as it stands. Much better would be a combination of a question for clarification together with a partial answer like

"Where in Goethestrasse do you want to go? The beginning of Goethestrasse can be reached by a five-minute walk."

The answer might be:

"Mannesmann-Hochhaus!"

The machine should now conclude that the requester assumes that the Mannesmann-Hochhaus is in Goethestrasse and must check whether this is true and where it is.

But what would the text understanding machine do if the answer were

"I have heavy luggage."

A good answer would involve a request for further clarification:

"In this case you may prefer to take the underground for one station. Which number in Goethestrasse are you looking for?
By the way, a taxi may may be cheaper than the underground. How many of you are there?"

The dialogue may be continued by quite different answers, such as:

"Four," or "No taxi! We're just two."

As the dialogue proceeds, more and more incomplete sentences are likely to occur. The requester will assume that the system keeps track of what was said before, as a human would do. In many cases, explicit clarification may be appropriate in the answer:

"You are four [i.e., I assume that "four" is not the answer to my request which number you are looking for]. Then a taxi is definitely cheaper. Taxis are to the left of the station's exit."

It should have become clear from these examples that a language understanding system, which has to cope with the problems of interpreting requests and assertions and must generate intelligent answers, involves several complex components that fall into the broad range of *linguistic processing*, and internal *storage and manipulation of symbolic meanings and facts*, the latter ranging from numerical values and lists to spatial layouts to pictorial information.

The linguistic part constitutes the user interface and must obviously include two mechanisms which operate on the basis of *knowledge of linguistic rules* (lexical and grammatical rules and semantic rules of meaning assignment), one for *interpreting* sentences, the other for *generating* answers or questions asking for clarification or additional information.

Linguistic knowledge involves an understanding of the word forms which must be applied to determine the lexical form from the form occurring in the text (heard -> hear, went -> go), the inflectional information (tense, case, number, etc.), knowledge about the grouping and syntactic categorizations and constructions in a sentence, and the semantic information about synonymy, paraphrasing, etc. As an example, consider the question containing the phrase "a street crossing Goethestrasse near its end". The analysis must find out that this is no question about a street crossing but about an x (a street) such that x crosses y (Goethestrasse) and that the crossing occurs near the end of y (Goethestrasse).

The lexicon is very important for organizing the relation to the internally represented knowledge. The correspondence between street names and locations is a trivial case. But common words are an entirely different matter. The *get* used in

"How do I get to Goethestrasse?"

is definitely different from the one used in

"How do I get change for the underground?"

An ordinary dictionary lists 24 different readings for *get*. How does the text understanding system know which one applies in a given sentence?

Linguistic knowledge also comes into play after the internal representation for the meaning of an answer has been computed. A generating mechanism will have to transform the representation into a sentence. But which one among the many possible ways of expressing the same contents is to be generated in a given situation?

The kernel of the system is a mechanism operating on the meanings. Thus, after having extracted the meaning of a request from its wording, the system must apply an *inferential mechanism* in order to compute the *possible* answers to the request on the basis of stored data, tables, structures, and maps. This presupposes that the knowledge relevant for answering the questions – the "*relevant world knowledge representation*" – is appropriately encoded and stored in the machine, such as the geographic descriptions of the town in which the position of the machine is marked.

World knowledge, however, is more than collections of domain-specific factual data, even if these are so diversified and complex that they do not fit into standard formats (just take the geographic descriptions of the town). A great amount of everyday knowledge is needed in addition – for example that a tall building (like the Mannesmann-Hochhaus) can usually be seen from far away but that this would not be the case if one used the underground, or that using the underground implies walking to and from the station using staircases or elevators, neither of which are not necessary when taking a taxi, or that the underground has a timetable, a taxi not. Further, contextual knowledge plays a role, such as a clear marking on a map of the position of the machine because words and phrases such as "nearby" or "a short distance" must be interpreted or generated in relation to this position. It also determines preferences among possible ways to be asked for: a machine located at a railway station is likely to be asked for information relevant for a pedestrian, whereas a device at a highway exit is rather consulted by car drivers.

Clearly, then, depending on circumstances there will be different answers. Listing all alternatives is of little use. In order to select an intelligent answer, the machine must have a user model of the requester which accounts for her/his possible needs and habits. In our example, the machine at the station must know that, usually, a requester would prefer a five-minute walk but that with heavy luggage (or heavy rain) even a three-minute walk may not be the right thing. Or consider the different meanings a business person and a backpack traveller will associate with words like cheap, quick, comfortable. Thus the internal models represented in the machine must be evaluated relative to a range of user needs and expectations.

Tying all this information – linguistic knowledge, domain-specific knowledge, common-sense everyday knowledge, contextual knowledge, user models – together and extracting the information pertinent to a given situation requires a powerful inferential mechanism which makes logical deductions, consistency checks, plausibility tests, etc.

Some of the inference rules may be represented by formal statements of the if.. then.. type: "If [to Goethestrasse] then [by foot to the initial part of Goethestrasse] or [by underground no. 5] or [by taxi]". "If [someone wants to take underground no. 5] then [description of finding the entrance to the underground]", etc., where inside the brackets formal representations appropriate for automatic processing must be entered. The rules must also account for semantic ambiguities such as in "near the end of Goethestrasse". Is it the far end as seen from the requester's position? Or the end with the highest house numbers? It is precisely these ambiguities that give rise to or provide hints for questions for clarification. Other rules are needed which tell what is the consequence of doing this or that, or what is necessary to reach this or that goal – such as "in order to use the underground you have to buy a ticket", or "if you take the underground then you will not see the Mannesmann-Hochhaus".

The inferential mechanism may also play a role during the linguistic analysis. Processing can often be done more efficiently if the knowledge base is used as soon as possible – for example, if somebody erroneously asks for Schillerplatz instead of Goethestrasse and Schillerplatz does not exist, one might (as an intelligent German) assume that the requester mixed up Goethe with his colleague Schiller and street with square.

Where does all the information – linguistic knowledge, domain-specific knowledge, common-sense everyday knowledge, contextual knowledge, user models, inference rules – come from, and how is it acquired? Much of it, we fear, must be manually collected in a tedious process requiring close attention to minute details. Fortunately, part of it is already available in the vast body of our scientific knowledge. This is not true, though, for the domain-specific factual data which, unfortunately, comprise the largest portion of the knowledge base. To be successful, acquisition of these data must be automated. Hence, text understanding does not start with the analysis of questions but much earlier with the analysis of the material from which the data are to be extracted. Take again our scenario where the information may be gleaned from one or more travel guides and municipal brochures. Indeed, whereas the individual traveller may have just one of them in his or her pocket, our information system may hold the combined knowledge of all of them all at once.

Once solutions have been developed for each of these topical areas they must be merged into a single coherent system which can serve a definite purpose. From what was said before, we observe a broad range of components that make up such a system: a large and diverse knowledge base (linguistic, lexical, domain-specific, common-sense everyday, contextual, and user models); a rule base (inferences, consistency checks, plausibility tests); knowledge base handlers; linguistic interpreters and generators; inference mechanisms; computational units for calculating prices, distances, time; a knowledge base extender, which adds new knowledge acquired in the course of dialogues; handlers for graphics, pictures, etc. As always, the real difficulties come when all the beautiful solutions developed in isolation must be merged into a single integrated system. A careful design of the modularity of the architecture is essential in a system of this complexity.

In view of this complexity, then, was it realistic and wise to start a project (even an experimental one) with the goal of building a first version of a text understanding system? Is there any hope of seeing some of the scenarios (alluded to earlier) come true soon? Before trying to give an answer we look at the major research issues at the time when the LILOG project was planned (next section), at the solutions developed in the course of the project (Sect. 4) and at some important open problems (Sect. 5).

3. Issues

Suppose that we are back in 1985 and wish to build a computer-based information system for visitors to a city as discussed above. This was by no means a "dark age", and our work could rely on the enormous progress in formalisms and procedures made in logical research since the early parts of this century, in computer science since the 1950s and in theoretical and computational linguistics during the same period. There certainly was enough hope for a coherent theory and a systematic implementation involving linguistic processes, knowledge representation and inference, and interfaces between the two.

In linguistic processing, the traditional grammars and dictionaries that were designed for intelligent readers and learners but not for machines had been augmented by a strand of theoretical linguistics which was more amenable to computerization. Its purpose was to make explicit the complete body of knowledge on language and its combinatorial and inferential possibilities, and not merely some data which a reader can be assumed to understand in applying his general intelligence. In order to do so it had to inject a high degree of formalization, thus providing the methodologies and theoretical principles for programming this knowledge on machines. Computational linguistics, in combination with informatics, had by 1985 made great strides towards the principles for programming linguistic structure (syntax, morphology, lexicon).

With all this progress, some deficiencies made themselves acutely felt as well. For example, the emphasis was on syntactically complete but otherwise isolated sentences. As our scenarios amply demonstrated, both restrictions should be softened, though the former not without the latter. Moreover, the high degree of ambiguity within sentences becomes combinatorially unbearable when several sentences are considered in connection. This raised two research issues:

- Implementing linguistic knowledge on parts of sentences, i.e., the structure of words and their meaning, and the relationships between different words in a language. This imposes a new burden on lexicon construction. For example, a lexicon should be able to inform on the relation of words where this is not obvious from the pure textual representation, as well as their independence where the representation would suggest otherwise. Take the word "stop". The lexicon should indicate that to *stop doing* something is equivalent to *not continuing to do* something, whereas *to stop something* (such as a car) is to *cause it not to continue* its way (perhaps indirectly by causing the driver to stop his/her car). The lexicon will have to make explicit the relation between the words *stop*, *continue* and *cause* as well as the independent meanings of *stop*. As a second example, take the German way of constructing composites where the same syntactic arrangement may lead to quite different meanings such as in "Schweineschnitzel" and "Zigeunerschnitzel".

Work on the maturation of lexica by, e.g., Kanngießer, Gust, and others., provided a convenient starting point for attack.

- Analysing the structure of dialogues, discourses and texts, their meanings, and the relationships between the meanings of their constituents - namely complete and incomplete sentences and questions. In view of the high degree of formalization needed for computerization, the analysis should result not merely in a collection and classification of linguistic phenomena but in a more profound discourse theory. Here as well, some initial work had already been done before LILOG started; in particular there was Kamp's discourse representation theory.

A system that integrates the many components mentioned above needs unifying formalisms that are adept at supporting all of them. Classical formalisms were already known to be inadequate for that purpose. Hence, LILOG faced several further challenges.

- An integration of formalisms or, better, the development of a single basic representation formalism, in which structures and meanings of words, sentences, texts can be coded in such a way that all components of the system can use the coded information directly. Several ideas for some of the aspects were around but a widely usable formalism did not exist.

- Algorithms for the transformation of texts into formal representations (i.e., for analysing the structures of words, sentences, texts), for associating meanings with the components of the structures and with the complete structure, including the application of an appropriate mechanism for logical deduction and correctness checking. Many ideas were available but no comprehensive system had been developed.

Many of these issues become particularly acute when textual material must be understood that includes spatial aspects as in our scenarios, or temporal aspects, that may come into play in our scenario as well when a sequence of steps is to be described. Indeed, both aspects develop their full power only in connection with sequences of sentences.

- Consider the treatment of time in a natural language and the representation of temporal knowledge in a logic formalism. Some work on the sentence level had been done, for German in particular by R. Bäuerle. For French, Kamp and Rohrer had analysed the tenses within the theoretical framework of Kamp's discourse representation theory. Example: "The trains leave every 20 minutes. If you hurry now, you'll get one". What conclusions on temporal aspect can be drawn from these two sentences? Think of all the possible circumstances in which these sentences may be uttered.

- Consider instead the treatment of spatial information in a natural language and the representation of spatial knowledge in the computer. Here the fundamental question arises whether we, in our own memory, use "mental" images and do reasoning about spatial relations by operations on these images, or whether we apply logical deductions on propositions describing spatial relations and properties. While there had already been considerable debate on this in Artificial Intelligence there had as yet been very little linguistic research done on how spatial knowledge is represented in a natural language. The problem of how to represent spatial knowledge in the computer and how to relate this representation to natural language text was a completely open question.

Somewhat simplified, semantics in traditional linguistics deals with standard, discourse-independent meaning. As we have seen, however, systems that are to serve a specific purpose must address themselves to domain-specific and contextual knowledge, and can act naturally only on the basis of common-sense everyday knowledge and user models. What is an adequate representation formalism that treats all this knowledge in a uniform fashion – even including temporal and spatial aspects – and that may therefore be subjected to the same uniform inferential mechanisms? And what is this mechanism? What was known around 1985?

In Artificial Intelligence a number of projects had tried to build experimental natural language dialogue systems. One of the most advanced was the HAM-ANS system of von Hahn, Wahlster and others from Hamburg University. These projects had concentrated on some specific aspects or restricted application domains. Major problems had not been solved, however:

– representation of everyday knowledge and common sense reasoning;

– automatic extraction of new knowledge from texts;

– development of one single formal representation language for all types of knowledge in the computer – including vague, incomplete, uncertain or hypothetical knowledge;

– construction of a flexible, universally usable inferential mechanism, i.e., a set of algorithms which can do all kinds of logical deductions, proofs, checks, etc., for reasoning about time or space, and for drawing conclusions from the meanings of texts and from the stored knowledge.

Thus, other problems are lurking behind the clarification of the theoretical basis. How do we select the words of the dictionary, how do we encode their grammatical information and their meaning? How do we encode the information for the particular knowledge base? This may be trivial in cases where information exists in tabular form, but it is far from trivial in the case of spatial relationships in a city. How do we check whether the meanings of complex sentences computed from the words by grammatical and semantic procedures of our theory and based on the stored knowledge are indeed the meanings the expressions have? How do we encode those grammatical rules or constraints of form and meaning which are actually appropriate for a specific language understanding system serving a particular task? Even more problematic is the acquisition of information relevant for the user model. Here we need certain areas of encyclopedic knowledge, knowledge about the typical behavior of people, their preferences, etc. And finally, how do we identify and collect the rules that determine the inferential capability?

Another weakness had evolved from these projects. As the lexicon, the amount of grammatical and inference rules and, above all, the facts of the discourse worlds (just think of our scenarios) grew, primitive methods of data storage like files became more cumbersome to use, or too insecure, or failed altogether.

Database technology seemed like a panacea, but first attempts to adapt data base systems for use in a large language understanding and knowledge representation system were discouraging. Neither their functionality nor their performance was up to expectations. True, a concerted effort had already started worldwide in the area of deductive databases. But results were still scarce in 1985, and none of the research was oriented towards supporting the ambitious linguistic goals of LILOG.

What functionality is expected from the database system? And what information is to be collected into the database? Even in English, systems developed so far contained only a subset of the linguistic rules or of the knowledge relevant for the domain, and very small subsets of the dictionary. For German, the situation was much worse. An enormous amount of linguistic and non-linguistic knowledge must be encoded according to the methods and principles now judged to be most fruitful. Appropriate methods for knowledge acquisition, integration and retrieval must be developed. This may easily turn into a mass problem. Just consider that even a basic dictionary involves 5,000 to 10,000 words whereas a flexible dictionary requires 50,000 to 100,000 words. The amount of non-linguistic knowledge relevant in a domain is difficult to judge, but it appears to be huge as well. Experience with the first LILOG prototype showed that a background knowledge of 10,000 lines of code is far too small for deeply understanding a one-page text about a hiking tour.

Finally, the integration of all the solutions into a coherent system raises intricate architectural issues. What are the system components? How can one avoid overlapping functions? What does an optimal division of labor between the components look like? How should the components collaborate? Often there is no single answer, thus leaving wide latitude for decisions. For example, how much of the linguistic processing should take place during lexical analysis, how much during syntactic analysis, and how much should be deferred to the inferential mechanisms? Should the three steps be taken in succession or be interleaved? This looked like a real engineering challenge on a scale never attempted before.

Each of these difficult research issues seemed to deserve its own long-term project. It was more challenging, however, to bring in people from different fields working on specific research problems and to have them cooperate with one another on the implementation of a comprehensive, integrative system – people who covered a wide range of ways of thinking, of different scientific attitudes, of philosophies, and of languages ranging from the humanities to formal logic to software engineering.

4. A Solution: LILOG

The LILOG project was intended to meet this challenge. To attack most of the aforementioned issues all at once seemed like a bold, if not unrealistic decision. But then, if scenarios like the ones introduced earlier are ever to become real, one must have the courage to assemble all that is currently known into a system, to experiment with it, to learn from the successes and failures, to identify the shortcomings of the present state of the art, and to try to overcome them by leading research into new directions. To start the LILOG project back in 1985, then, was also a farsighted decision, despite the fact that it had no comparison or precursor, either in Germany or worldwide.

To attack a complete system solution for a natural language information system even in a restricted domain of discourse requires the meeting of many of the best minds, the husbanding of many forces, a truly interdisciplinary and cooperative effort by many groups of scientists. This is exactly what the LILOG project has done with great success. Its overall objective was to build an integrated prototypical natural language understanding system with the goal of deep understanding of texts covering a large fragment of the German language applied to a broad domain within the everyday world. (That is, the goal was not simply to master a technical language in some limited domain of expertise).

In the course of doing this the project members had to sift through the state of the art, adapt it to the problem at hand, develop new solutions, attend to the very minute details mentioned above, struggle with the technicalities of programming the computerized solutions, develop tools for supporting their work, and finally integrate all the solutions into a single coherent system. Clearly, all this could not be done overnight. This book reflects more than five years of intensive work on basic and applied logic, linguistic knowledge, artificial intelligence, software engineering, data base systems and other topics in informatics, and their successful collection into one whole.

Scientifically, the project set off into virgin lands, not only as a whole but also with respect to several of the above mentioned goals. New ideas were needed. In some cases the project had to base its work on novel theories which were not yet accepted but still under debate (like the discourse representation theory). Nevertheless, LILOG not only reached its goals but accomplished much more – as can be seen from this book.

In the first phase of the project two representation formalisms were developed which were both quite powerful and useful and gave rise to a number of very interesting theoretical results on the properties of knowledged representation formalisms: STUF for the linguistic and L_{LILOG} for the semantic knowledge. Towards the end of the project, after much practical experience and deep theoretical study, the two (or at least their latest versions) were shown to be closely related and could be merged into one single formalism.

In the field of spatial knowledge the project started almost from scratch; it tried a dual approach: linguistic-logic analysis and representation of spatial expressions, and pragmatic use of analogue representations (depictions) for representing mental images of spatial scenes. The two finally coalesced into an elaborate theory integrating both aspects, and a concomitant implementation of a hybrid system. Also towards the end, the project succeeded at integrating spatial and temporal concepts, at least with respect to position changes of objects in the course of time. This will form the basis for techniques which in our scenario are used to find a route in mental maps, thus permitting answers to questions on how to reach a given place.

The lexicon assumed a more central role within LILOG than what one would have expected in the beginning, and the functionality of the lexicon was ultimately pushed way beyond its traditional limits. The discourse representation theory was greatly extended and has now become a powerful and versatile tool which integrates well with other linguistic approaches. These approaches had to be applied not only to the analysis of language entities. While LILOG started with the problem of text analysis, some of the emphasis shifted towards the generation of natural language utterances, since truly natural man-machine dialogue is inconceivable without it as our scenarios amply demonstrated. LILOG provided an ideal environment to abandon the present ad-hoc solutions in favor of more systematic approaches.

Perhaps one of the greatest achievements was the matching of all the linguistic theories and practical solutions with knowledge representation formalisms and techniques and inference mechanisms. From the beginning, it was clear that the inference mechanism would be a key part of the system and that it would have to serve a multitude of purposes. Therefore a completely new and highly modular approach was tried − with great success. A comparable achievement which blends into the inference mechanism is the development of a complete deductive database system with a data model specifically geared to the needs of this mechanism.

What legacy will LILOG leave after the project finishes? The legacy is not just the wealth of scientific results documented by a host of publications and collected into this book. Nor is it just the prototypical natural language understanding system which was uniquely responsible for the coherence of the project and which demonstrated the feasibility and integrability of the individual solutions. Above all, what is left is a modular system which should serve in future as a workbench for linguists and knowledge engineers, with a versatile collection of tools for the fields of language or knowledge processing. It is our hope, therefore, that the results of LILOG will become widely available.

In the final analysis, however, any success rests on people. The LILOG project was a collaborative effort between scientists from academia and industry, between experienced professors and managers on the one hand and young, enthusiastic and creative graduates and students on the other, between linguists and computer scientists. Most admirably, there were a few visionary people who provided guidance throughout the project, who stubbornly believed in its success, who were quick at adapting to changing research priorities and implementation issues, and who always struck the proper balance between freedom to pursue promising scientific avenues and pressure to submit one's own interest to the common goal.

It is often said that the best way to transfer knowledge is through the heads of people. If this is true, LILOG will have a lasting effect. The project produced no fewer than 10 university professors, around 20 young scientists completed their dissertations as part of the project, and countless students were exposed to the project during their master's thesis work or contributed in other capacities.

In a way, the LILOG project was an exeptional case, a stroke of luck if you will. Nevertheless, we believe that this type of industry-sponsored research could serve as a model for collaboration between industry and academia in the early stages of high-risk research – even on a smaller scale.

5. What Remains to be Done

Neil Armstrong, as he stepped onto the surface of the moon, exclaimed "One small step for man, one great leap for mankind!" One is tempted to reverse his words when judging how far we have closed in toward our scenarios: despite its achievements, LILOG is but a stepping stone towards our loftier goals.

In other words, LILOG is not the last piece in a linguistic puzzle, but rather the end of a climb to an intermediate vantage point which opens broad new vistas to future goals. Many of these goals have to do with the issues of Sect. 3 for which LILOG provides a much better understanding but which it by no means resolves. In linguistics, these have to do with the long-distance relationships between components of a text in a longer discourse, some of them expressed explicitly by referents, others contained implicitly in the contents, and with no a priori defined direction, e.g., with a possibility of forward references so that it becomes necessary first to understand the following sentence before understanding the current one. Lexica and grammars should bear with incorrect use of language. Lexica must learn to accomodate the change of language over time, e.g., the change of word semantics or of expressions of metaphors. Lexica should also be able to start from a basic vocabulary and to extend it into new knowledge domains by sophisticated learning and teaching models. Even in the presence of learning, however, larger computer lexica are needed. The present LILOG lexicon of a thousand words should be radically extended to several tens of thousands of words.

The current limits of linguistic expertise must simultaneously be transcended. Thus, world knowledge is not entirely textual but often supplemented by tabular, graphical, pictorial or animated material. Bridges must be established which connect these different types of material and permit to free movement among them. For example, a geometric layout should on request be describable in terms of natural language, but it should also become possible to transform a textual description of, say, a tour across a city into non-verbal communication such as visualization by a line moving across a street map. The inclusion of temporal and spatial aspects within the LILOG project has been a first step in this direction but has hardly scratched the surface so far.

Linguistic phenomena are the key to access the deeper world of knowledge and to invoke inference processes. LILOG still lives in a world where knowledge is well-defined, complete and certain. In real-life discourse, however, knowledge often is incomplete, uncertain, or vague. Also, knowledge is the result of integrating many different sources – just consider knowledge from one or more domains, common-sense knowledge, one or more user models, a variety of contexts and viewpoints. All this knowledge is to be assembled into one coherent knowledge representation accessible by the same inference mechanism, or at least into compatible representations with compatible mechanisms. As a particularly challenging example, take qualitative reasoning about space and time. How does one find an adequate level of abstraction and precision to convey just the information needed, how does one store imprecise and imcomplete knowledge such that it may be refined at some later stage? Think of humans who have little problem in reasoning about imprecise and qualitative statements expressed by words such as "early", "late", "small" or "large".

Common-sense, everyday knowledge often seems well expressed by default assumptions in language and knowledge processing. As far as the latter is concerned, default assumptions were studied quite intensively in the early 1970s in artificial intelligence in connection with schema-based approaches using the prototype concept, and in the 1980s on a more theoretical basis by many types of non-monotonic logic. In linguistics, however, little research has yet been done, although default assumptions should be particularly beneficial with respect to efficient resolution of ambiguities.

Besides its purely scientific results and perspectives, a unique contribution of the LILOG project is in its systems engineering aspect. Never has a complete solution for a linguistic system been attempted on such a scale. It is not surprising, then, that the project had to find its way through the myriad of engineering problems that came up – often surprisingly because lack of experience often precluded foresight. In the end there existed a working prototype – but as the saying goes, now that the project team knows how to build the system they wished they could start all over again. Many engineering issues will have to be attended to in the future: a suitable systems architecture, proper modularization of the functionality and interfacing of the system components, well-structured organization of the linguistic and knowledge base, automatic means for knowledge acquisition from textual, verbal and other sources, proper ergonomic interfaces to human users. Also the art of building such systems must be refined: how does one coordinate teams of researchers and engineers in a distributed environment of highly interdisciplinary teams?

A book such as this one does not serve its purpose if it is little more than an account of past achievements, no matter how successful these are deemed to be. It will only have lasting value if it has an impact on the curiosity and interests of its readers, if it stimulates them into activity, if it leaves an imprint on future directions of research. We are confident that this book has indeed all this potential.

Chapter 1

The Linguistic Point of View

Chapter 1.1

STUF and Parsing

Unification-based grammar formalisms have recently received great interest in computational linguistics because they allow for a very high-level, declarative and modular description of grammatical relations over linguistic objects. Feature structures are used to encode various kinds of information about any given linguistic object, e.g., certain syntactic properties or semantic content. Lexical entries and grammar rules define the relation between surface strings of a language and the information associated with it. Special purpose theorem provers – parsers and generators – operate on these grammars to compute this relation in either direction, from a string to a feature structure, or vice versa.

When we speak about "unification grammars" we should carefully distinguish between *unification-based theories of grammar* and *unification-based grammar formalisms*. Theories like Lexical-Functional Grammar, Categorial Unification Grammar, or Head-Driven Phrase Structure Grammar employ features structures to represent *linguistic objects*, and the actual form and content of these structures depends on the underlying linguistic theory. Most grammars also state a number of additional principles, which include universal principles that are deemed to hold for any natural language, as well as language-dependent principles, for instance concerning word order. These principles are either stated on a meta level, like, e.g., completeness and coherence in Lexical-Functional Grammar, or directly on the level of feature structures using implications, e.g., the Head-Feature Principle in Head-Driven Phrase Structure Grammar.

Formalisms like Functional Unification Grammar, PATR-II, or STUF are theory-neutral. They use feature structures as their central *data structure*, and they impose no restrictions on the actual use of these structures. These formalisms have the status of very high-level programming languages that are especially well-suited to encode linguistic theories. They provide the means to represent linguistic objects using feature structures, and to encode additional theory-specific principles. For instance, the Head-Feature Principle applies to all "phrasal signs" and is represented by the specification that a phrasal sign via the unification mechanism inherits all properties provided by the principle. To turn a formalism into a useful tool for linguists not only requires an adequate language, but also a helpful environment for the development and debugging of grammars. Therefore, a good deal of work in the LILOG project has been put into a workbench for the STUF formalism.

The first four articles in this chapter present the *Stuttgart Type Unification Formalism (STUF)*. This includes an introduction to and a detailled description of the language, basic parsing techniques, and an overview of the STUF workbench.

The three following articles address special research topics concerning the development of STUF. The first of those articles discusses a more general approach to grammar rules, called *Unification-ID/LP rules*, and provides a clear formalization of these grammars and a parsing algorithm. Next comes a description of the parser that is actually used in the STUF system. This parser is designed to support and encourage experimentation with different grammars, different styles of writing grammars, and with different parsing strategies and heuristics. The last article discusses the problem of *gap-handling* in Categorial Grammars. It suggests that mechanisms for dealing with problems of unbounded dependencies like gap-handling be integrated into the underlying calculus of the formalism instead of using hand-coded dependencies in lexical entries and grammar rules.

Roland Seiffert

A Formalism for Natural Language – STUF

Jochen Dörre
Roland Seiffert

In the following we give an introduction to the grammar formalism STUF (*Stuttgart Type Unification Formalism*) which is used in the LILOG project to develop a grammar for German.

The formalism STUF is most appropriately classified as belonging to the family of logic grammars, like Definite Clause Grammar [PW80], Functional Unification Grammar [Kay79], PATR-II [SUP+83] or the formalisms of Lexical Functional Grammar [KB82] or Head-Driven Phrase Structure Grammar [PS87], with PATR-II being its closest relative. In this family we distinguish logic-term-based from feature-based formalisms and STUF belongs to the latter ones. Another line of inheritance for STUF has been the influential work of Aït-Kaci [AK86, AKN86] and Kasper and Rounds [KR86], who explored the mathematical foundations of feature structures and their description languages. Actually, the grammar description language used in STUF is a symbiosis of Aït-Kaci's ψ-terms and Kasper's FML.

Characteristics of Unification-Based Grammar Formalisms

The purpose of all of these formalisms is to characterize a language, which is here meant to be a (possibly infinite) set of strings over an underlying set of elementy language units, e.g., the set of words of a natural language, by associating information in the form of structures to the well-formed strings of the language in a compositional way.

A distinguishing feature of these formalisms as compared to others is their *declarativity*. A grammar written in one of these formalisms does not predetermine the procedural realisation of the analysis or the generation of strings.[1] Instead, it only describes an abstract *relation* between strings and information structures. In this sense a grammar provides us with "knowledge" about a language, i.e., describes *what* the language is, but doesn't fix *how* it is put to use. The procedural application is entirely left to the modules for parsing, i.e., the association of information structures to a given string, or its inverse, generation.

Another characteristic of the abovementioned formalisms is their *directness* in the mapping between information structures and surface strings. Lexical entries and rules directly apply to surface strings. No transformations of the strings or their syntax trees, as they are performed, for example, by movement rules in Government and Binding Theory [Cho81], whose computational properties are problematic, are assumed. However, this does not mean that the theoretical insights about the structure of natural languages gained in that framework could not be a basis for our type of unification grammar. We just have to encode, for example, movement by using the level of the information structures.

A third characteristic property worth mentioning is the *modularity* of the abovementioned formalisms. Generalizations over lexical items or rules can often be expressed by using *templates*

---

[1]This holds only partially for DCGs, since there full procedural attachment to PROLOG is possible.

of common information structures, which we also call *types*. This not only helps in avoiding redundancies, but is also an aid for keeping critical decisions in the encoding of grammatical information in one place and preventing possible inconsistencies. Actually, these templates are most often not just random aggregations of information which happen to occur together more than once, but are themselves linguistically meaningful prototypical structures for a whole category of words, which explains our use of the name 'types'. Thus, for example, in a lexical entry for a proper name or for an auxiliary verb we use the prototypical structures for proper names or auxiliary verbs and have to add only a small amount of entry-specific information. Hence, not only can lexical entries be formulated much more concisely using templates, but also we obtain a higher independence of the pure lexicon from the actual encoding of the syntactic properties of words and phrases in information structures. The usefulness of templates cannot be overestimated in these formalisms, and actually the recent shift of interest in the computational linguistics society to more lexicalist approaches, i.e., approaches where most of the encoding of the combinatory potential of words and phrases is made on the side of the lexicon rather than with syntax rules and where syntax rules reduce to very few very general combination schemes, has only become practical through the use of template mechanisms in the unification framework, since they allow us to capture generalizations.

STUF vs. PATR-II

As already mentioned above, STUF is a unification grammar formalism which is closely related to PATR-II. Like this widespread formalism it has no adherence to any specific theory whatsoever in computional linguistics, i.e., it is *theory-neutral*, and different approaches to encode grammar, like Categorial Unification Grammar or Head-Driven Phrase Structure Grammar, can be expressed in STUF with ease.

STUF deviates from PATR-II in that it uses a much more flexible and more powerful description language for the information structures, i.e., the feature structures. Instead of specifying feature equations we use feature terms, whose structure directly reflects the described feature structures, but which can also embed disjunctions, simple negations, logical variables, and a simple kind of subsorting. Feature terms as a description language for feature structures go back to [KR86] and [AK86]. The semantics of such a language as it is used within STUF has been investigated by Smolka [Smo88, Smo89], who showed how such a language can be viewed as a notational variant of quantifier-free function-free first-order predicate logic with equality.

The other major deviation from PATR-II is the possibility to have *parametrized templates*. For example, we could have a template `PNAME(Name,Gender)` describing the prototypical structure of a proper name where the actual name and the gender are parameters. This allows for an even more abstract specification of lexical entries, thus enhancing modularity.

The Informational Domain: Recursive Feature Structures

In the enterprise of writing a formal grammar which can be employed computationally we have to model certain properties of parts of the language we deem relevant for the enterprise, e.g., words, phrases, but also more abstract things like word classes, in a mathematical sense. In STUF we assume that we can model these properties using a class of mathematically simple structures, called recursive feature structures. Such a kind of model simply consists of a set of objects, and everything we want to say about such an object, every property of it, is expressed in interrelations with other objects we assign to it. These interrelations are called features. Also, there is a subset of distinguishable primitive objects called atoms. The following simple restrictions hold:

- features are functional

- atoms are uniquely described by their names

- atoms have no features

For example, we could have an object that has a feature called 'gender' that relates it to another object, the atom 'feminine'. Due to the functionality of features the first object always has a unique value for its features.

Often feature structures are seen as graphs of a certain kind. Nodes in these graphs that represent atoms are labeled with atom names. Arcs are always labelled with feature names (also called attributes) and the value of a feature is the subgraph reachable via the so-labelled arc, which in the simplest case may consist of a single node. A convenient notation for feature structures is the attribute-value matrix. Figure 1 gives an example of a feature graph and its matrix notation.

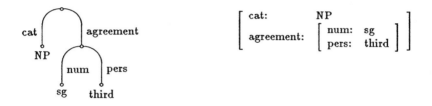

Figure 1: A feature graph and its matrix notation

The information contained in this feature graph is fully determined by specifying which "paths" of attributes lead to which atomic values. Hence the three equations

$$< cat > \;=\; NP$$
$$< agreement\ num > \;=\; sg$$
$$< agreement\ pers > \;=\; third$$

are another equivalent notation for our feature graph. This is so, because of the functionality of features, which implies that for every node the outgoing arcs have to carry different labels.

Feature graphs, however, may have a subgraph as the value of more than one attribute. They need not be trees. It is an important difference if two subgraphs of a graph are actually identical or just contain the same information in terms of their attributes and values. Compare for example the two graphs in Figure 2. In the matrix notation (see Figure 3) we use a numerical index preceding a multiply occurring substructure in the place of its first occurrence and the index in brackets as a reference to that structure for every subsequent occurrence. The second feature graph contains the same information as the first plus the additional fact that the values of f and g are identical, which can be expressed in the equation

$$< f > \;=\; < g > .$$

The difference between the two graphs becomes apparent when we want to add more information, e.g., about additional attributes, to the graphs. In the first case the subgraph beneath f

Figure 2: Type- vs. token-identical graph

$$\left[\begin{array}{ll} \text{f:} & \left[\begin{array}{ll} \text{h:} & \text{a} \end{array}\right] \\ \text{g:} & \left[\begin{array}{ll} \text{h:} & \text{a} \end{array}\right] \end{array}\right] \qquad \left[\begin{array}{ll} \text{f:} & \boxed{1}\left[\begin{array}{ll} \text{h:} & \text{a} \end{array}\right] \\ \text{g:} & [1] \end{array}\right]$$

Figure 3: Type- vs. token-identical graph, matrix notation

and the one beneath g can be extended with mutually inconsistent information, e.g., if we add an attribute i having an atomic value a in f's substructure and an i with value b in g's substructure. Since different atomic values are considered inconsistent with each other, we cannot do the same

Figure 4: Extending the graphs

extension with the second graph (see Figure 4). We cannot get a well-formed feature graph in which the equation above still holds. However, if we find an extension to the second graph, we always can apply it to the first graph. In fact, we see the second graph itself as an extension of the first, where the only addition to be made is expressed through the equation above.

Instead of considering one graph whose informational content is extended, we can actually think of the extension itself as a graph. Hence, we want to consider the informational combination of two graphs, which is called the unification of the two graphs. This concept of combining consistent information is the key concept of unification grammars.

How is feature graph unification related to the original notion of unification as used, for example, in theorem proving or logic programming? There unification of two terms means finding a substitution of variables which makes them syntactically equal. In fact, feature graphs are considered a generalization of first-order terms where arity is not fixed and arguments are identified by keyword rather than by position. Free arity means that we always can have new attributes, i.e., we need not have variables to extend a graph (but there are also variables, as we shall see later). Thus instantiation of terms corresponds to adding information to graphs, either new arcs or labels for anonymous nodes or identifications of nodes. Note that this information can always be expressed using equations of one of the following forms.

$$< path > \quad = \quad atom$$
$$< path > \quad = \quad < path >$$

From another point of view, we can think of feature graphs as a representation (or a solution) to a set of equational constraints as exemplified above. Corresponding to unification would be the question for a graph satisfying a combined set of constraints. This constrained-based point of view has the advantage that we can think of other types of descriptions without having to change the underlying structures which are used for the interpretation of the constraints.

Now that we have learned about the informational structures that a STUF or PATR-II grammar associates with the strings of a language, how is this association done? All we need are *lexical entries* which relate the strings considered indivisible, e.g., words in a grammar using a full-form lexicon, to features graphs and *grammar rules* which tell us how to combine associated feature graphs, if we want to concatenate strings. These combination schemes are themselves feature graphs as we shall see below.

Syntax Rules

If we want to assign properties to complex linguistic objects, e.g., a phrase, we first have to assign properties to the basic objects from which the complex ones are constructed and to state generally how the properties of the composed objects relate to those of their components. However, a purely compositional approach where we really construct models of complex objects only from models of their components does not account for linguistic reality. Most of the time linguistic information of a subphrase is highly dependent on the context in which it appears. In order to account for this fact, STUF's lexical entries and combination rules have a declarative status, i.e., a combination rule only describes a *relation* between information attached to a composed object and its components, without determining where this information comes from. Instead of specifying complete feature structures we only express *facts about* the feature structures which are to be the models of linguistic entities in a STUF grammar. In this way, information about a linguistic entity can be gathered to constrain its properties more and more, yielding an increasingly fine-grained description. This point of view also led to the name constraint-based formalism for STUF and similar formalisms (cf. [Shi89, Smo89]).

References

[AK86]   Hassan Aït-Kaci: An algebraic semantics approach to the effective resolution of type equations. *Theoretical Computer Science*, 45:293–351, 1986

[AKN86]   Hassan Aït-Kaci, Roger Nasr: LOGIN: A logic programming language with built-in inheritance. *Journal of Logic Programming*, 3:185–215, 1986

[Cho81]   Noam A. Chomsky: *Lectures on Government and Binding.* Foris, Dordrecht, 1981

[Kay79]   Martin Kay: Functional grammar. In *Proceedings of the Fifth Annual Meeting of the Berkeley Linguistics Society*, Berkeley Linguistics Society, Berkeley, CA, 1979

[KB82]   Ronald M. Kaplan, Joan Bresnan: Lexical-Functional Grammar: A formal system for grammatical representation. In J. Bresnan (ed.): *The Mental Representation of Grammatical Relations*, pp. 173–381. MIT Press, Cambridge, MA, 1982

[KR86]   Robert T. Kasper, William C. Rounds: A logical semantics for feature structures. In *Proceedings of the 24th Annual Meeting of the ACL, Columbia University*, pp. 257–265, New York, NY, 1986

[PS87]   Carl Pollard, Ivan A. Sag: *Information-Based Syntax and Semantics*. CSLI Lecture Notes 13. Center for the Study of Language and Information, Stanford University, Stanford, CA, 1987

[PW80]   Fernando C.N. Pereira, David H.D. Warren: Definite clause grammars for language analysis—a survey of the formalism and a comparison with augmented transition networks. *Artificial Intelligence*, 13:231–278, 1980

[Shi89]   Stuart M. Shieber: Parsing and type inference for natural and computer languages. Technical Note 460, SRI International, Artificial Intelligence Center, Menlo Park, CA, March 1989

[Smo88]   Gert Smolka: A feature logic with subsorts. LILOG Report 33, IWBS, IBM Deutschland, Stuttgart, May 1988. To appear in *Journal of Automated Reasoning*

[Smo89]   Gert Smolka: Feature constraint logics for unification grammars. IWBS Report 93, IWBS, IBM Deutschland, Stuttgart, November 1989. To appear in Jürgen Wedekind, Christian Rohrer (eds.): *Unification in Grammar*, MIT Press, Cambridge, MA, 1991

[SUP+83]   Stuart M. Shieber, Hans Uszkoreit, Fernando C.N. Pereira, J.J. Robinson, M. Tyson: The formalism and implementation of PATR-II. In J. Bresnan (ed.): *Research on Interactive Acquisition and Use of Knowledge*. SRI International, Artificial Intelligence Center, Menlo Park, CA, 1983

The Language of STUF

Jochen Dörre

In this section, the grammar formalism is introduced in an intuitive way. As described in the previous section, every kind of linguistic object mentioned in a STUF definition is modeled using feature structures. Hence, it is of central importance for the formalism how these structures are expressed. In STUF we use the very powerful language of *feature terms* (also called feature logic [Smo89]) for the description of feature structures, which allows for a (linearized) feature-matrix-like notation for feature terms. This kind of term language originates from Kasper and Rounds' seminal work on the semantics of feature structures [KR86].

The remainder of this section is structured as follows. After a motivating example we describe what feature terms are in general. Thereafter, it is shown how templates, lexical entries, and syntax rules are defined. Finally, we exemplify with an entire grammar how these different definitions work together.

A Motivating Example

Let us first consider an example of a term we might want to assign to the verb 'likes' in the reading where it can combine with a subject and an infinitive as in

> John likes to swim.

We want to model aspects like the tense form or number and person features which have to agree with those of the subject. Furthermore our special form of 'like' requires a verb complement which should be in infinitival form with 'to'. Our (simplistic) meaning representation of such a sentence will be a formula with the two-place predicate 'like', which we assume to be given, hence, we model an object having features 'rel(ation)', 'arg1' and 'arg2' as the value of feature 'pred' of our verb where 'rel' is the atom 'like' and the arguments are filled in by the subject and the verb complement appropriately (see Figure 1).

The constructs used in the feature term indicate that we are modeling with two types of information, namely information about what atomic values are found below which attributes, expressed using the selection operator ':', and information about which paths of attributes lead to the same object, expressed by equations of paths. The whole term has to be read as a conjunction which we write as a list of terms enclosed in brackets. So the whole term describes:

an object	whose 'tense' value is described by	the atomic value 'pres'	
and	whose 'subj' value is described by	an object	whose 'num' value is 'sg'
		and	whose 'pers' value ...
and	...		
and	whose 'pred's arg1' is identical to its 'subj' and its 'vcomp's subj'		
and	...		

Note that we can embed a conjunction of feature terms as the value of a feature by using brackets, i.e., the indentation in the example is not significant. This is what we mean by linearized

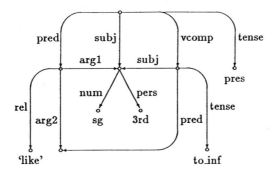

```
[ tense:   pres
  subj: [ num:      sg
          pers:     3rd ]
  vcomp:  tense:   to_inf
  pred:   rel:     like
  <pred arg1> = <subj> = <vcomp subj>
  <pred arg2> = <vcomp pred> ]
```

Figure 1: A feature structure for 'likes' and its description

matrix-like notation. We can pretty-print it as a feature matrix. The advantages of this notation will become clearer below, where we introduce the full syntax of feature terms including the possibility to embed other complex structures like disjunctions of feature terms, negated feature terms, logical variables, and domain expressions.

The point of view taken in unification grammar formalisms is to consider such a description not as an exhaustive one, but rather as a partial description of a linguistic object. The description will have to be refined when we consider the context, in which the word 'likes' occurs. In our example we could wish to incorporate information about the subject:

```
subj:   pred:   name:   john
```

which introduces a new feature with complex value at the subject node. Clearly this new information can itself be seen as describing a feature structure. Hence, we want to consider the (conjunctive) combination of feature terms. This information-combining operation is called unification of feature terms.

Feature Terms

The possible syntactic forms of feature terms are given in Figure 2.

Here *S, T, S1,...* are meant to be arbitrary feature terms, *Path* is a list of features enclosed in angle brackets, and *Domain* is a domain name.[1] Variables are identifiers that start with an underscore. Atoms, features and names of templates are the other identifiers.

---

[1] Currently the only domain supported is **sorts**.

```
_X                       a variable
atom                     an atom or template
templ(S1, ...,Sn)        parametrized template
feature :  S             feature selection
Path :  S                path selection
Path = Path = ...        path equation
[S T ...]                conjunction of terms
{S T ...}                disjunction of terms
atom @ Domain            domain expression
not S                    negation
```

Figure 2: Forms of feature terms

Atomic Values

An atom is a constant piece of information which we do not want to decompose further. The feature graph of an atom consists of a single node labeled with that atom. An atom (but not one of the special atoms below) doesn't unify with anything else. Examples of atoms are:

```
singular
noun
3
```

Special Atoms

The four special atoms are

$$\$S\$, \ \$T\$, \ \$U\$, \ \$F\$.$$

The meaning of these is as follows. T (the type 'true') denotes the entire universe, i.e., the set of all possible feature graphs, the empty constraint. U ('undefined') and S ('something') are duals (S is equivalent to: not U) denoting the undefined type and anything else, respectively. The undefined type is an atom usually used to state the undefinedness of a feature in a certain graph, e.g., f:U does not unify with a graph where the feature f has any other value than U. It is also used as the empty list. F ('false') denotes the empty set, i.e., no feature graph satisfies this description. It makes no sense to use the false type in a grammar.

Feature and Path Selections

Pairs of attribute (or path) and value terms are put together with the ':'-operator. Examples:

```
tense : past
<syntax value syntax> : noun
<syntax direction> : left
<syntax argument syntax> : s
```

Note that path selections are actually redundant, since we can iterate feature selections.

```
syntax : direction : left
```

means the same as the third line above. It is understood as

```
(syntax : (direction : (left))),
```

where any term in parentheses is a well-formed feature term.

Note also that we can embed arbitrary feature terms with feature (or path) selection. For example, we can rewrite the conjunction of the selections above as:

```
[ tense:  past
  syntax: [ value:     syntax: noun
            direction: left
            argument:  syntax: s
          ]
]
```

Path Equations

The special path notation is useful when we want to express the fact that two paths point to the same substructure, i.e., that this substructure is "shared" between these two paths. We do this by using an equation as in:

```
[ syntax: [ value:     syntax: s
            direction: left
            argument:  np
          ]
  <syntax value semantic_form> = <semantic_form>
]
```

Logical Variables

Variables in feature terms stand for specific nodes in the described feature graph. They can be used instead of path equations to express substructure sharing. We can thus rewrite the above example:

```
[ syntax:        [ value:    [ syntax:          s
                               semantic_form: _SEM ]
                   direction: left
                   argument:  np
                 ]
  semantic_form: _SEM
]
```

Variables have the same interpretation as the structure indeces in the matrix notation of feature graphs. We are allowed to conjoin information with them, e.g., if we use [_SEM T] in one place, the subgraph described by T is accessible everywhere in the structure where _SEM appears. Logical variables are also important when we want to define parameterized templates.

Sorts

STUF provides for a flexible way to extend its domain of structures with special-purpose structures, for which unification is to be defined differently. Sorts are an example of such an extension which has been implemented. Syntactically, sorts are considered to be atoms. However, the unification of two sorts s_1 and s_2 is defined with respect to a sort lattice. This means that sorts are ordered into a hierarchy of sorts and subsorts where every pair of sorts has a unique greatest common subsort. This greatest common subsort is taken to be the result of the unification of two sorts.

For this purpose we have define a sort lattice as described below. Now, if we have, for example, grammarian < human we can unify the two descriptions

```
agent : human@sorts
agent : grammarian@sorts
```

to yield the second description, since grammarian is the greatest common subsort of grammarian and human.

Conjunctions and Disjunctions

By surrounding a sequence of feature terms with brackets or with braces we express that these descriptions have to hold conjunctively or disjunctively for a described graph. In the following example the top-level syntax attribute has two possible values, a complex one or the atom pp.

```
syntax: { [ value:     syntax : s
            direction: left
            argument:  syntax : s
          ]
          pp
        }
```

The description of agreement and case features of the German article 'der' is a more complicated example for the use of disjunctions (comment lines are used between disjuncts to enhance readability):

```
head: [ <agree pers>: 3
        { [ <agree num>: pl
            case: gen
          ]
        % or
          [ <agree num>: sg
            { [ <agree gend>: fem
                case: {gen dat}
              ]
            % or
              [ <agree gend>: masc
                case: nom
              ]
            }
          ]
        }
      ]
```

This feature term specifies possible values for the four paths <head agree pers>, <head agree num>, <head case> and <head agree gend> using conjunction and disjunction. Four combinations are possible (person is 3 in any case):

(pl gen) (sg gen f) (sg dat f) (sg nom m)

Templates

In order to make things more compact and to organize information more clearly, we can assign a name to a complex feature term, i.e., we define a **template**, and refer to the term just by using its name instead of repeating the whole feature term whenever it is needed. We adopt the convention that if a feature term is a conjunction on the top level we may omit the outermost brackets.

```
intransitive_verb :=
    syntax: [ value:      syntax: s
              direction: left
              argument:  syntax: np ]
    <syntax value semantics> = <semantics>.

3rd_sg :=  agree: [ pers: 3
                    num:  sg ].
```

In these examples, intransitive_verb and 3rd_sg are the names of the feature terms which show up after the definition sign := . Syntactically we use templates just like atoms. An example of a template definition using another template is:

```
Noun_3rd_sg :=  syntax: noun
                3rd_sg.
```

If 3rd_sg had not been defined as a template, this definition would be inconsistent, since an atom and an attribute-value pair don't unify. They cannot conjunctively describe one and the same graph. However, together with the definition of 3rd_sg this definition is fine. It describes a feature graph with attributes syntax and agree, where agree has another two attributes.

As already mentioned, no syntactic difference between the use of an atom or of a template is enforced by the system. However, it is good style and increases readability to use different formats for templates and atoms, e.g., we let templates begin with capital letters. The system will recognize anything as an atom which is not defined somewhere as a template.

Functional Templates

Functional templates are templates which have parameters that are substituted for (or more precisely, unified with) actual values when applied. The definition of a functional template may consist of several defining clauses of the following format:

$$\text{templ}(T_1, T_2, \ldots, T_n) := T_0.$$

Here the T_i are arbitrary feature terms, templ is the name, and n is the arity of the defined template. Multiple definitions are taken disjunctively and templates with the same name of different arity are independent, like predicates in Prolog.

Examples:

```
NOUN( _NFORM ) :=
    syntax: local: head: [ major: n
                           nform: _NFORM
                           vform: $U$
                           aform: $U$
                           pform: $U$    ].

invert_boolean(plus)  := minus.
invert_boolean(minus) := plus.

cons( _X, _Y ) := first: _X, rest: _Y.
```

As can be seen from the examples, functional templates can be used to compute a feature term from other feature terms. For example, invert_boolean gives us back the value minus if called with plus. If called with a variable it gives us back the disjunction {minus plus}.[2] It should be clear that we can define arbitrary functions (or more precisely relations, since the result may be disjunctive) with this mechanism, e.g., a passivization function should be definable which, given the encoding of the syntax of an active form of a verb, gives us back the passive form.

In order to 'make feature terms do work' for us when parsing a sentence, they must be related with lexemes and with syntax rules which are described in the following subsections.

Lexical Entries

Syntactically a lexical entry is just a feature term definition, but its name is interpreted as a lexeme which may appear in the input sentence. A set of lexical entries is what we call a lexicon. Examples:

```
Otto :=
    syntax: np.

geht :=
    syntax: [ value:     syntax: s
              direction: left
              argument:  syntax: np ].
```

The definition of the feature term intransitive_verb allows us to rewrite the last lexical entry using less space:

```
geht :=
    intransitive_verb.
```

It is then easy to add similar lexical entries:

```
schläft :=
    intransitive_verb.

ißt :=
    intransitive_verb.
```

---

[2]Actually, as a side effect the variable will also be bound to a disjunction, which is synchronized with the one above, such that whenever the variable gets bound to plus the resulting disjunction is resolved to minus and vice versa.

Syntax Rules

Syntax rules or combination rules define how adjacent constituents (in a string of words) can be joined together into one constituent, or how the feature graphs associated with a certain substrings can be rebuilt into a feature graph associated with their concatenation.

cf-Rules

The form of a cf-rule definition is:

$$\texttt{Name} \; := \; \texttt{L} \; \text{->} \; \texttt{R}_1 \; \texttt{R}_2 \; ... \texttt{R}_n \; \text{--} \; T.$$

where $\texttt{Name}$, $\texttt{L}$, $\texttt{R}_i$ are identifiers and T is a feature term, where $\texttt{L}$ and $\texttt{R}_i$ appear as top-level attributes. An example is the application of a functor constituent to an appropriate argument constituent:

```
%% right application
ra :=
    value -> functor argument --
    < functor syn dir > : right
    < functor syn val > = < value >
    < functor syn arg > = < argument >.
```

'ra' is the name of this combination rule. The part which looks like a context-free rule gives names to the input feature graphs and to the output feature graph, and specifies also the order of the input feature graphs. After the double hyphen, there follows a feature term, which describes the relation between input and output feature graphs. The names appearing in the 'context-free' rule scheme are used as top-level attributes in the feature term T, i.e., we associate with a rule a feature graph which contains all of the input feature graphs as well as the output feature graph accessible via these attributes.

id-Rules

The form of an id-rule definition is:

$$\texttt{Name} \; := \; \texttt{L} \; \text{->} \; \{\texttt{R}_1, \; \texttt{R}_2, \; ... \texttt{R}_n\} \; \text{--} \; T.$$

The symbols mean the same as above. However, in this case the notation specifies that the right-hand side is an unordered set.

lp-Rules

The form of an lp-rule definition is:

$$\texttt{Name} \; := \; \texttt{L} \; \text{<<} \; \texttt{R} \; \text{--} \; T.$$

Again, $\texttt{Name}$, $\texttt{L}$, $\texttt{R}$ are identifiers and T is a feature term, where $\texttt{L}$ and $\texttt{R}$ appear as top-level attributes.

The Startgraph

As stated above, a STUF grammar relates feature structures to strings, either directly by the lexicon relation or indirectly using rules recurring on the relation established for substrings. However, the *language* of strings ultimately defined by a STUF grammar is not to be the entire set of strings that a STUF grammar associates some feature structure with, but instead a specific subset thereof. To define this subset we use a special template with the fixed name 'START_GRAPH'. This corresponds roughly to the start symbol of a context-free grammar. The language described by a STUF grammar is now the set of strings which are associated with some feature structure that is unifiable with this start graph.

Expansion of Templates

When STUF rules or lexical entries are put to use, an internal representation of their graphs is evaluated first. This means that any templates used to define these must be (recursively) expanded, until the full graph representation is found. For rules it makes sense to calculate all graphs of a rule section before this type of rules will be used. Lexical entries are expanded on demand and stored in a cache for future reuse.

When a functional template is expanded, its internal representation is first built without regard to actual parameters. This representation is stored in the internal template cache and is used with actual parameters whenever the functional template is called. A consequence of this optimized expansion strategy is that recursive templates cannot be expanded.

Defining the Sort Lattice

The sort lattice is defined in section sorts:sorts through the specification of the direct subsort relation <. Example:

```
section sorts:sorts.

%% definition of the lattice of sorts, which are used as atoms
%% of the domain sorts

Entity < $TOP$.
Animate < Entity.
Inanimate < Entity.
Human < Animate.
Building < Inanimate.
Dreiflügelanlage < Building.
```

We can use a sort which is not a subsort of other sorts by just defining it as a subsort of the built-in sort TOP, like Entity above. When sort sections are loaded using the STUF compiler the greatest common subsorts of each pair of sorts are evaluated (in an efficient incremental way) and stored efficiently. When a greatest common subsort of two sorts s_1 and s_2 is not unique, an error message is issued. This problem can be fixed by introducing a new sort as the greatest common subsort of s_1 and s_2, say s_3, and letting greatest common subsorts of s_1 and s_2 be subsorts of s_3.

```
section(example:lexicon).                section(example:templates).

john := name(john).                      'START_GRAPH' :=
mary := name(mary).                              cat: s.

a := determiner(exists).                 cons(_F,_R) := first:_F, rest:_R.
every := determiner(all).

man := noun(man).                        name(_X) := cat: name,
woman := noun(woman).                             sem: _X.

that := cat: that.                       determiner(_X) := cat: determiner,
                                                          quant: _X.

lives := ag_verb(live1).                 noun(_X) := cat: n,
loves := ag_pat_verb(love1).                       sem: rel: _X.

                                         ag_verb(_X) := cat: iv,
                                                        sem: (rel: _X,
                                                              ag: _Ag),
                                                        subj: _Ag.

                                         ag_pat_verb(_X) := cat: tv,
                                                            sem: (rel: _X,
                                                                  ag: _Ag,
                                                                  pat: _Pat),
                                                            subj: _Ag,
                                                            obj: _Pat.
```

Figure 3: Example grammar, lexicon and templates

An Example Grammar

In the following we present an example grammar consisting of cf-rules (see Figure 4), lexicon, and template definitions (see Figure 3). We do not claim that this grammar is very elegant or captures many relevant generalizations. We merely want to illustrate how a nontrivial relationship between syntax and semantics can easily be established.

```
section(example:cf).                        nr_rule :=
                                                n_bar -> n, relcl --
s_rule :=                                       n_bar: (cat: n_bar,
    s -> np, vp --                                     sem: cons(_NSem,_RSem),
    s: (cat: s,                                        ref: _X),
       sem: _NPSem),                            n: (cat: n,
    np: (cat: np,                                      sem: (_NSem,
         sem: _NPSem,                                        arg: _X)),
         pred: _P,                              relcl: (cat: relcl,
         ref: _R),                                     sem: _RSem,
    vp: (cat: vp,                                      ref: _X).
        sem: _P,
        subj: _R).                         relcl :=
                                               relcl -> that, vp --
np_rule :=                                      relcl: (cat: relcl,
    np -> det, n_bar --                                sem: _S,
    np: (cat: np,                                      ref: _X),
        sem: (quant: _Q,                        that: cat: that,
              var: _X,                          vp: (cat: vp,
              restr: _NSem, % is a list             sem: _S,
              body: _B),    % dto.                  subj: _X).
        pred: _B,
        ref: _X),                          vp_i :=
    det: (cat: determiner,                     vp -> iv --
         quant: _Q),                            vp: (cat: vp,
    n_bar: (cat: n_bar,                             sem: list(_S),
           sem: _NSem,                              subj: _X),
           ref: _X).                          iv: (cat: iv,
                                                   sem: _S,
np_pn :=                                           subj: _X).
    np -> name --
    np: (cat: np,                          vp_t :=
        sem: _P,                               vp -> tv, np --
        pred: _P,                               vp: (cat: vp,
        ref: _Name),                                sem: list(_NPSem),
    name: (cat: name,                               subj: _Subj),
         sem: _Name).                         tv: (cat: tv,
                                                  sem: _P,
n_rule :=                                         subj: _Subj,
    n_bar -> n --                                 obj: _Obj),
    n_bar: (cat: n_bar,                      np: (cat: np,
           sem: list(_NSem),                     sem: _NPSem,
           ref: _X),                             pred: list(_P),
    n: (cat: n,                                  ref: _Obj).
       sem: (_NSem,
             arg: _X)).
```

Figure 4: Example grammar, cf-rules

With this grammar we can parse sentences like

Every woman loves a man that loves Mary.

and assign to them their translation into predicate logic, encoded as a feature structure. In the present case we would get as the value of the semantics attribute an encoding of the formula

$$\forall W : (woman(W) \rightarrow \exists M : (man(M) \land love1(M, mary) \land love1(W, M)))$$

which is shown in Figure 5.

$$
\begin{bmatrix}
\text{cat: s} \\
\text{sem:} \begin{bmatrix}
\text{quant: all} \\
\text{var:} \quad \_0 \\
\text{restr: list(} \begin{bmatrix} \text{arg:}\_0 \\ \text{rel: woman} \end{bmatrix} \text{)} \\
\text{body: list(} \begin{bmatrix}
\text{quant: exists} \\
\text{var:} \quad \_1 \\
\text{restr:} \quad \text{list(} \begin{bmatrix} \text{arg:}\_1 \\ \text{rel: man} \end{bmatrix} , \quad \text{list(} \begin{bmatrix} \text{rel: love1} \\ \text{ag:} \quad \_1 \\ \text{pat: mary} \end{bmatrix} \text{))} \\
\text{body: list(} \begin{bmatrix} \text{rel: love1} \\ \text{ag:} \quad \_0 \\ \text{pat:}\_1 \end{bmatrix} \text{)}
\end{bmatrix} \text{)}
\end{bmatrix}
\end{bmatrix}
$$

Figure 5: Feature structure of 'Every woman loves a man that loves Mary'

Notice that although the main syntactic functor in this grammar is as usual the verb, its semantic translation may be deeply embedded in the semantic structure of a sentence, as it should be in the presence of quantified noun phrases. This is achieved by having the semantics of the sentence be passed up from the (subject) noun phrase in the rule s_rule, which in turn gets as 'input' the semantics of the verb phrase, the predicate (logical variable _P). Noun phrases may either have a quantifier structure as their semantics (rule np_rule), where the predicate is part of the body, or in the case of proper names just pass through the predicate (rule np_pn).

References

[KR86]   Robert T. Kasper, William C. Rounds: A logical semantics for feature structures. In *Proceedings of the 24th Annual Meeting of the ACL, Columbia University*, pp. 257–265, New York, NY, 1986

[Smo89] Gert Smolka: Feature constraint logics for unification grammars. IWBS Report 93, IWBS, IBM Deutschland, Stuttgart, November 1989. To appear in Jürgen Wedekind, Christian Rohrer (eds.): *Unification in Grammar*, MIT Press, Cambridge, MA, 1991

Chart-Parsing of STUF Grammars

Roland Seiffert

A STUF grammar defines a relation between the strings of a language and the information associated
with them. This information is expressed using feature terms. The *parsing problem* is the task
of computing this relation given one specific string of the language. In this section we provide an
informal description of the parsing algorithm[1] being used in the STUF system. It is important
to understand the basic ideas of this algorithm to be able to develop grammars using the STUF
workbench, since most of the tools are built around the central data structure of the parser, the
chart . For a more detailed and formal description see [Seiffert, this volume].

In the following, we will use for our explanations a very simple STUF grammar defining the
language $L = \{a^n b^n c^n | n \geq 1\}$, i.e. all strings consisting of any number of 'a's, followed by the same
number of 'b's, followed by again the same number of 'c's. L is a very simple example of a language
that cannot be described with a context-free grammar, and also a context-sensitive grammar is rather
tricky to write. However, a STUF grammar can be specified straightforwardly:

```
section anbncn:cf.

R1 :=      S -> An Bn Cn --
    [ <S  cat> : S
      <An cat> : A
      <Bn cat> : B
      <Cn cat> : C
      <S count> = <An count> = <Bn count> = <Cn count>
    ].

R2 :=      Xn -> X Xn_1 --
    [ <Xn cat> = <X cat> = <Xn_1 cat>
      <Xn count count> = <Xn_1 count>
      <X count> : one
    ].

section anbncn:lexicon.

a := [ cat : A
       count : one
     ].

b := [ cat : B
       count : one
     ].
```

---

[1]We consider only grammars using rules of type **cf**. The processing of rules in the sections **id** and **lp** is more
complicated and the interested reader should look at [Seiffert, this volume]. Also, we do not intend to give an
introduction to parsing of unification-based grammars or even describe advanced parsing techniques. We restrict our
description to the basic ideas of the standard parser included in the STUF system. A section on more sophisticated
parsing strategies by Gregor Erbach can be found later in this volume.

```
c := [ cat : C
       count : one
     ].
```

section anbncn:templates.

START_GRAPH := [cat : S].

A STUF grammar can be understood as a generalization of a context-free grammar. The section 'cf' contains rules very similar to productions in context-free grammars. The symbols on both sides of the arrow correspond to nonterminal symbols. The feature structure following '--' specifies the information associated with each nonterminal, i.e., the nonterminal symbols are generalized from atomic symbols to possibly very complex objects. Note that the nonterminals are allowed to share part of their informational contents. Rules also define implicitly the possible strings of terminal symbols related to the nonterminal on the left-hand side, which has to be the concatenation of one of the possible strings for each of the symbols on the right-hand side.

The task of the section 'lexicon' is to relate the possible terminal symbols, written on the left-hand side of ':=', to one of those complex-structured nonterminal symbols specified on the right-hand side of ':='.

There has to be defined one specific template: 'START_GRAPH'. It corresponds to the start symbol in context-free grammars. The information associated with a complete sentence of the language generated by a STUF grammar must be unifiable – and is indeed unified – with this feature structure.

In our example grammar the rule 'R2' together with the lexicon generates strings of arbitrary length that contain either 'a's, 'b's, or 'c's. The rule associates with the string as the informational content the type of the string, i.e., whether it contains as, bs, or cs and the length of the string. The length is encoded using the 'count'-feature. The rule 'R1' relates the concatenation of 'a's, 'b's, and 'c's to the feature structure containing the equation '<S count> = <An count> = <Bn count> = <Cn count>', thereby ensuring that the number of 'a's, 'b's, and 'c's is the same. The feature structure associated with a rule thus may impose further constraints on possible strings of the language. This shows that the possibility to share information between different nonterminals gives us a more powerful grammar formalism than context-free rules alone.

We now turn to the question how we can decide whether a given string of terminals is part of the language described by a given grammar and what is the information associated with it, i.e., how does a *parser* for STUF grammars work?

First, note that the only direct connection between terminals and nonterminals is encoded in the lexicon. Rules make no direct reference to terminals. The parser included in the STUF system therefore associates in a first processing phase each terminal symbol with the information specified in the lexicon. We call this *lexical lookup*. For each terminal w in the input string and each lexical entry $w := \phi$ an *item* $[N-1, N, \phi]$ is stored in the *chart*. The three components of an item are: the position where the spanned string starts ($N-1$), the position where it ends (N), and the information associated with this string (ϕ). Suppose we want to parse the string 'aaaabbbbcccc' using our example grammar. The lexical lookup puts 12 items into the chart:

lexical lookup:	(1)	$[0, 1, [\text{cat:A count:one}]]$
lexical lookup:	(2)	$[1, 2, [\text{cat:A count:one}]]$
...		
lexical lookup:	(11)	$[10, 11, [\text{cat:C count:one}]]$
lexical lookup:	(12)	$[11, 12, [\text{cat:C count:one}]]$

The chart serves as a *well-formed substring table* . Every item stored in the chart associates a substring of the input with the information related to it as defined in the grammar. These substrings are all well-formed in the sense that they are legalized by the lexicon and/or grammar rules. But they need not themselves be valid strings of the language, because they need not be unifiable with 'START_GRAPH'.

After the lexical lookup, the parser proceeds with the computation of information associated with (longer) substrings by using the grammar rules in a *bottom-up* way. The parser tries to unify the nonterminals, i.e., feature structures, stored in items for adjacent strings with the nonterminals on the right-hand side of a rule. If this succeeds, then a new item is built that spans the concatenated string and contains as information the nonterminal from the left-hand side of the rule including the information that it shares with the right-hand side structures. This is expressed in the rule shown in Figure 1.

if   there is a rule $X_0 \rightarrow X_1 \ldots X_n - \phi$
    and there are n items in the chart having the form:
             $[i_0, i_1, \phi_1], [i_1, i_2, \phi_2], \ldots, [i_{n-1}, i_n, \phi_n]$
    and the following unification succeeds:
             $\phi \sqcup [X_1 : \phi_1] \sqcup [X_1 : \phi_1] \sqcup \ldots \sqcup [X_n : \phi_n]$
             with ψ being the value of X_0 (i.e. the result of the unification contains $[X_0 : \psi]$)

then   add an item $[i_0, i_n, \psi]$ to the chart
             (if it is not already there)

Figure 1: Basic bottom-up rule for chart-parsing

In our example, the following two items built during lexical lookup are combined to yield a new item that is stored in the chart and can in turn be used for the construction of yet another item, and so on:

lexical lookup:	(3)	$[2, 3, [\text{cat:A count:one}]]$
lexical lookup:	(4)	$[3, 4, [\text{cat:A count:one}]]$
rule R2 using (3) & (4):	(28)	$[2, 4, [\text{cat:A count:[count:one]}]]$
lexical lookup:	(2)	$[1, 2, [\text{cat:A count:one}]]$
rule R2 using (2) & (28):	(30)	$[1, 4, [\text{cat:A count:[count:[count:one]]}]]$
...		

Finally, rule 'R1' becomes applicable:

rule R2 using (1) & (30):	(31)	$[0, 4, [\text{cat:A count:[count:[count:[count:one]]]}]]$
rule R2 using (5) & (46):	(47)	$[4, 8, [\text{cat:B count:[count:[count:[count:one]]]}]]$
rule R2 using (9) & (52):	(54)	$[8, 12, [\text{cat:C count:[count:[count:[count:one]]]}]]$
rule R1 using (31), (47) & (54):	(56)	$[0, 12, [\text{cat:S count:[count:[count:[count:one]]]}]]$

The parser keeps applying the above rule until no more new items can be built. Then it is checked whether there is an item spanning the whole input string. The information associated with such an item is unified with the 'START_GRAPH'. If this is successful then the input string belongs to the language generated by the STUF grammar and the result of this unification is a feature structure that encodes the information that the grammar associates with this string.

In our example, the string 'aaaabbbbcccc' is part of the language and the information associated with it is [cat:S count:[count:[count:[count:one]]]]. The complete chart for the analysis of the input string 'aaaabbbbcccc' as displayed by the STUF workbench is shown in Figure 2.

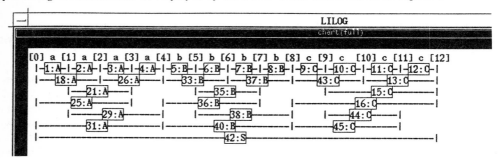

Figure 2: Chart as displayed by the STUF workbench for 'aaaabbbbcccc'

The STUF Workbench

Jochen Dörre

Ingo Raasch

The STUF workbench is a collection of tools running under XWindows to help a grammar author in developing and testing a STUF grammar. Developing formal grammars has many similarities to program development, and hence many of the methodologies used there can be applied. The main difference, however, lies in the fact that for most programs we can freely design their behavior, whereas a grammar for a natural language has to account for the very complex structure of the natural language. We cannot simply change the natural language like the formats used in a database, just because this would better meet the needs for processing it. Thus, we need a kind of software development technique which is suited to being driven by empirical data where we cannot fix the functionality of the product beforehand in detail. This kind of software development technique also applies to other branches of artificial intelligence software development, where it is often termed *explorative development*. Especially in this style of development a fast and incremental development cycle is crucial, while good support for comfort design decisions is not that important.

An aspect specific to the development of STUF grammars comes from their declarativity, i.e., STUF grammars state logical relationships between linguistic objects rather than operational instructions on how to proceed in parsing a sentence. Therefore tools that observe the progression of interpreters of STUF, e.g., tracing tools for a parser, are not that helpful. Instead our grammar development environment provides operations to inspect various logical aspects of the grammar and of the results of parses statically. In the resulting logical relationships the author may detect some bugs which he can correct using an editor integrated into the system; the updated parts of the grammar can be reloaded to iterate the inspection and thus to elaborate the grammar.

In the first section we mention some general ideas concerning the architecture of the STUF workbench and show how these ideas are realized in the current version. Then, we will step through a typical STUF session and will thereby explain the different STUF displays and their use.

The Architecture of the System

The STUF workbench running under XWindows is a collection of tools for the development of a STUF grammar dedicated to help the grammar author to test and elaborate his STUF grammar. The XWindows system already provides a lot of functionality that allows for a comfortable use of the system. However, we think that the following application-specific features integrated into the system are crucial for the usability of the STUF workbench:

- The possibility to access displays in an associative manner.

  Although there are some 'entry points' to the inspection of the grammar and of the results of parses (which can be accessed in a main menu), the author of a STUF grammar may want to inspect the different aspects of some objects in a nonhierarchical way.

In the STUF environment he can do this by selecting a so-called sensitive area in a display. He is offered a list of aspects available for the selected object in a pop-up. The corresponding STUF inspector display is created.

- The possibility to rapidly access previously created displays.

To guarantee a uniform environment all STUF displays are shown in the same window. But since the computation of an inspector window may take some time, the developer of a STUF grammar should be able to rapidly reaccess some of the recently created displays. These displays should not be recomputed but just raised, i.e., made visible again.

In the STUF environment there is a 'window stack' in which the names of the last ten previously created displays are listed; if one of the elements in the list is selected, the corresponding inspector window is raised.

- The integration of an editor including a locate function to get to the source code of an object.

During the inspection of results the developer may detect some bug in his grammar. To fix it, the system should locate the definition of a grammar object in the source code of the grammar where the author can make use of an editor. Then he should be able to load the updated part of the grammar.

In the STUF environment an emacs editor is available. The user can get to the source code of an object, e.g., via pop-ups from an inspector window. Then he can edit and reload the updated definitions using some special functions bound to key strokes in the editor. Thus, a fast incremental development of the grammar is made possible.

- The possibility to rerun parses.

In developing a grammar it may be useful to specify one or more sentences to be parsed as 'test sentences' for the grammar. Having updated the grammar it should be easily possible to rerun the parse of the test sentences or of some variations of them.

In the STUF system, the sentences to be parsed are specified in an editor buffer, and the parse of a sentence is invoked using some special editor function. Thus, previously parsed sentences can be easily parsed again or can be modified and rerun thereafter.

- The possibility to run batch files.

In the STUF system the grammar author can run batch files where he can start tests noninteractively.

In general, the development of a (STUF) grammar will follow the cycle shown in Figure 1. Any comfortable tool for the development of grammars should efficiently support each single step in this cycle. This implies, that an integrated editor must be available that interacts with the other tools: when the author detects some error in his grammar during the inspection of results, he should be able get directly to the STUF definition of objects in order to correct them. It should then be possible to reload the grammar. Most often the changes made to the grammar are very small. Hence, a good grammar development system must deal with small incremental changes very efficiently, i.e., allow for incremental loading of parts of the grammar.

A Typical Session

In this section we will step through the parts of the cycle described above by looking at a typical session in the STUF system and will explain the various kinds of inspector windows and their use

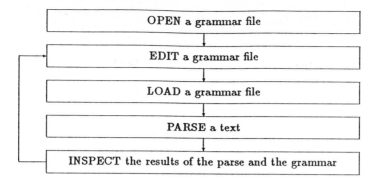

Figure 1: The grammar development cycle

in detecting errors in a grammar. During the session to be described we will consider the two most common symptoms of bugs in a grammar: the chart of a parsed sentence may contain some unexpected items or there may be some items missing in the chart. Both effects may be caused by different kinds of bugs, and we describe how one could proceed to find and fix them.

For a detailed description of the usage of the system, see [DR91].

When the STUF system is started a default grammar is loaded which can be specified by the user. If we specified a grammar, we can enter the cycle at 'PARSE a text'. Otherwise, we have to open a file for our grammar in the emacs running in one of the windows; the file may be new or may already contain some part of the grammar. We adjust the grammar according to our needs and hereafter invoke a special emacs function to pass the grammar to the STUF compiler.

Let us assume that a (somewhat buggy) grammar for some fragment of the German language has been loaded; now we might want to test the grammar by parsing the sentence

'Das Hetjensmuseum ist im Kirche untergebracht .'

which is syntactically ill-formed, since 'im Kirche' is no legal prepositional phrase: the gender of 'Kirche' is feminine and 'im' (short form for 'in dem') requires to be followed by a noun of gender masculine or neuter gender[1].

We enter that sentence in an emacs buffer and invoke the bottom-up chart parser integrated in the system.[2] The system tells us that the parse was successful and that the sentence is well-formed. This is not what we expected, and therefore we start inspecting the results of the parse to find out the bug in our grammar.

In most cases the inspection will start with looking at the chart. We select 'chart' in the main menu, and a STUF result display is created in which the chart is presented as follows (see Figure 2). In the first line the words of the input sentence are listed, separated by increasing numbers. In the lines below are given item numbers together with their syntactic category (or some other information; this can be specified by the user) and a line indicating by position and length the span of that item, i.e., the part of the input sentence that is 'covered' by the item.

---

[1] We do not consider other readings of 'im' here.

[2] see description in Seiffert: *Chart-Parsing for STUF Grammars* (in this chapter)

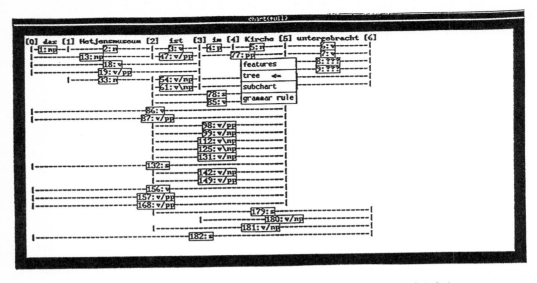

Figure 2: Chart of 'das Hetjensmuseum ist im Kirche untergebracht'

Figure 3: Tree of item 77

This chart contains some unexpected items which state a logical relationship between linguistic objects we did not want to establish. Obviously, item 77 spanning 'im Kirche' is not correct and responsible for the other incorrect items. We start fixing that bug by looking at the tree of that item, which we get via a pop-up menu.

A tree represents the 'history' of the construction of an item in form of an indented tree. Items are shown along with the name of the grammar rule, respectively lexical entry, that lead to the construction of the item. Subitems (or better: 'parent' items) are displayed indented below an item.

Figure 3 shows the tree of item 77. The reason for an unexpected item to be constructed is always that there is some rule application that succeeded, but shouldn't have succeeded, which in our case is the application of the rule 'RIGHT_COMPLEMENTATION2' to the lexical items of 'im' and 'Kirche'. We thus have three candidates which might be responsible for the ill-formedness. But since we know that the phrase is only ill-formed because of an agreement clash and that agreement is not handled explicitly within the rule, but rather stated as a subcategorization requirement, we will first inspect the subcategorization list of 'im', i.e., we select the feature structure display of item 4, which spans 'im' (Figure 4).

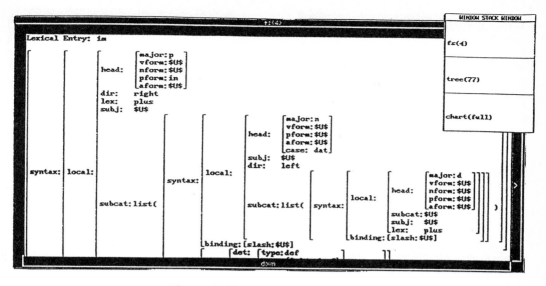

Figure 4: Feature structure of item 4

In this feature structure we observe that there is no restriction on the gender and the number of the noun phrase that 'im' subcategorizes for. There should be the features **gender** and **num** below the path <syntax binding> of the element of the subcat list. We now tell the system via a selection in a pop-up menu to open the grammar file with the STUF source code of the definition of 'im'. Here, we add the information that 'im' combines with nouns of gender 'neut' and 'masc' and of number 'sg', and reload that part of the grammar by invoking a STUF-specific emacs function. But let's suppose for expository reasons that we misspelled 'masc'. Figure 5 shows the grammar file with the 'corrected' definition of the lexical entry 'im'.

If we now parse the string 'im Kirche' there is no item spanning the whole string, as we expected. We start a further test for our grammar and parse 'im Museum' which works as desired (since 'Museum' is neutral). But if we parse 'im Hofgarten' ('Hofgarten' is masculine), it's not well-formed, in contrast to what would be correct. In the chart (see Figure 6) there is no item spanning 'im Hofgarten', i.e., no rule could be applied to the structures of 'im' and 'Hofgarten'. Hence, we are here in a situation where we have to find out why a certain rule application didn't work. In our case we would certainly remember the last change and would quickly find and correct the error by changing the source code again. In general, we would have to compare the structures of the three items and the rule that we want to be involved in the expected rule application to find out the reason for the failure. Finding the feature responsible for the clash, however, is only halfway to finding the erroneous definition. The structure where the feature occurs might have been constructed by rules from other structures and so on. Ultimately the erroneous feature must have been introduced by some lexical entry or some rule. An aid to fast access to all definitions that contribute directly or indirectly to the definition of a linguistic object is the display of the template hierarchy of that object.

The hierarchy of a grammar object consists of a tree which contains the atoms occuring in the definition of that object and the templates, which themselves may be defined using templates and atoms. The template hierarchy is displayed as an indented tree, and the user-defined templates in the hierarchy are highlighted. In the hierarchy of 'im' (see Figure 7) we also can observe that our mispelled atom 'masv' occurs directly in the definition of 'im'. We update the definition of 'im' in

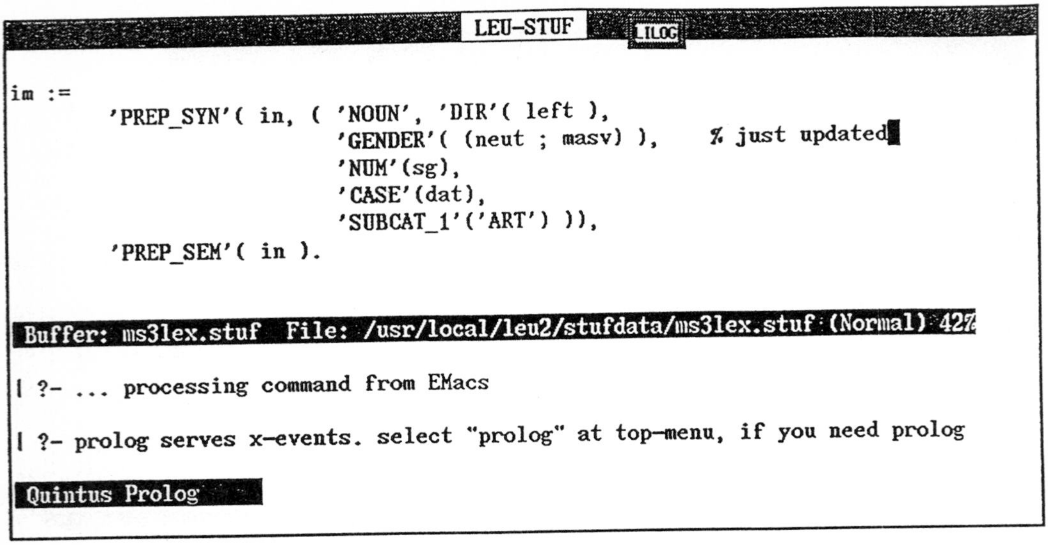
LEU-STUF
LILOG
im :=
'PREP_SYN'(in, ('NOUN', 'DIR'(left),
'GENDER'((neut ; masv)), % just updated
'NUM'(sg),
'CASE'(dat),
'SUBCAT_1'('ART'))),
'PREP_SEM'(in).
Buffer: ms3lex.stuf File: /usr/local/leu2/stufdata/ms3lex.stuf (Normal) 42%
| ?- ... processing command from EMacs
| ?- prolog serves x-events. select "prolog" at top-menu, if you need prolog
Quintus Prolog

Figure 5: Lexical entry of 'im'

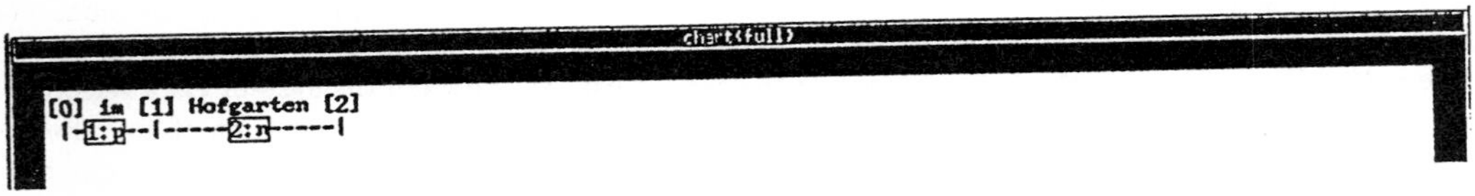
chart(full)
[0] im [1] Hofgarten [2]
|-1:p--|-----2:n-----|

Figure 6: Chart of 'im Hofgarten'

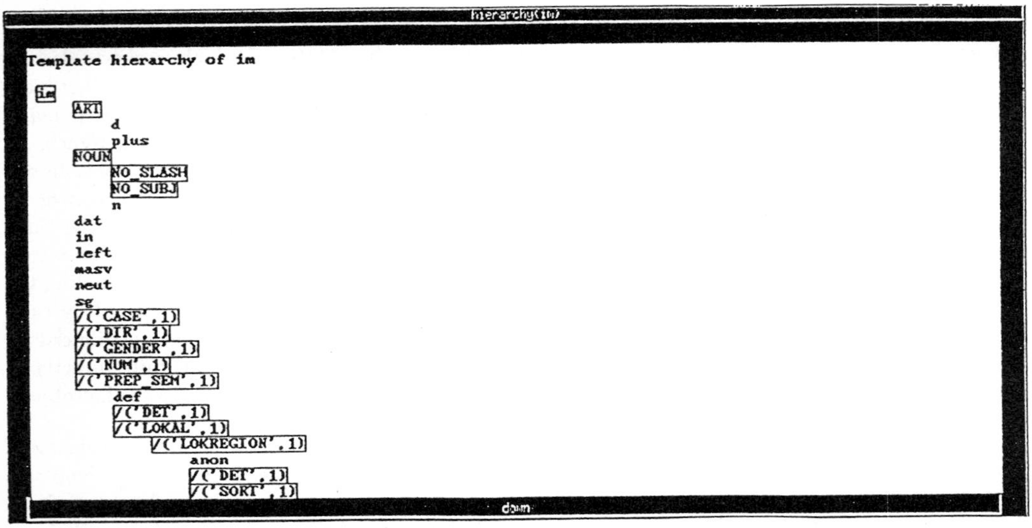
hierarchy(im)
Template hierarchy of im
im
ART
d
plus
NOUN
NO_SLASH
NO_SUBJ
n
dat
in
left
masv
neut
sg
/('CASE',1)
/('DIR',1)
/('GENDER',1)
/('NUM',1)
/('PREP_SEM',1)
def
/('DET',1)
/('LOKAL',1)
/('LOKREGION',1)
anon
/('DET',1)
/('SORT',1)
down

Figure 7: Hierarchy of 'im'

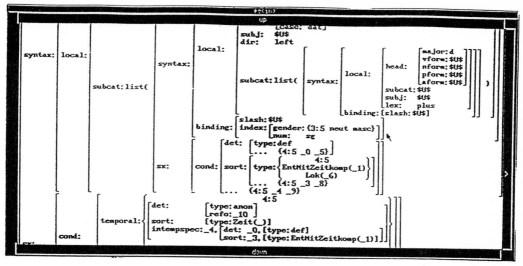

Figure 8: Corrected feature structure of 'im'

the grammar, reload that part of the grammar and get the desired results[3].

Figure 8 shows the relevant parts of the corrected feature structure for 'im'. Some words are in order here to explain the feature structure representation and displays used in our system. STUF uses a new method to represent compactly in one structure the whole set of alternative feature structures which are produced out of one feature description by freely embedding so-called distributed disjunctions as values of features [DE89, ED90, DE90]. This method helps us to avoid in most cases an exponential explosion in the size and number of the structures caused by disjunctions.

A disjunction like the one between neut and masc in our example can be kept local to the feature gender inside the subcat element. It only has to be multiplied out with another disjunction if the other disjunction also affects this gender feature. However, in general, disjunctions may affect more than one path. Take for instance the feature term

```
{ [ syn: arg: case: dat
     sem: rel: stat_in    ]
% or
  [ syn: arg: case: acc
     sem: rel: dir_in     ]
}
```

which might be used to express the dependency of the semantic interpretation of German prepositions like 'in' from the syntactic case of a following noun phrase. The directional reading (translated as 'into') goes along with the accusative case of its argument, whereas for the stative reading (English 'in'), the argument has to be of dative case. Such a disjunction is treated internally as two

---

[3]Since there are often spelling errors in grammars and since this kind of error is sometimes hard to detect, the system offers some further functions to verify the consistency of the grammar: you can get a list of all atoms occuring in the grammar currently loaded and you can get a list of all templates that are defined but never used, which.may also indicate some spelling error or some 'dead code'.

'synchronized' disjunctions embedded as deeply as possible in the feature structure representation. The fact that a choice in one affects the choice in the other is expressed by tagging both disjunctions with a 'disjunction name' which represents this unique choice (see Figure 9). The advantage of this

$$\left[\begin{array}{l} \text{syn:} \quad [\text{ arg:} \quad [\text{case:} \quad \{\text{d1:1 dat acc}\}]] \\ \text{sem:} \quad [\text{ rel:} \quad \{\text{d1:1 stat\_in dir\_in}\}]] \end{array}\right]$$

Figure 9: Distributed Disjunction

representation is that, because the disjunction is represented with the narrowest possible scope, we don't have to duplicate information that is independent of the disjunction, as we would have to do, if the disjunction were represented at the top level of the structure. So, for instance, we can add more features to the sem structure without having to duplicate this information. Notice that in our feature structure for 'im' above (Figure 8) the disjunction for gender (3:5) and another disjunction (4:5) which differentiates between the local and the temporal reading coexist without causing any reduplication of structure. Hence, the whole structure represents four different readings.

Since disjunctions are always binary in the internal format, each disjunction name represents a global choice between the left branches (l) for every disjunction with this name or the right branches (r). We call the assignment of r or l to a disjunction name a (committed) choice. A set of choices is called a context. If feature structures contain disjunction, the set of valid contexts is displayed also. It is often convenient to look at only one of the combined feature structures, i.e., to select one context under which the feature structure should be projected. This gives us a disjunction-free display.

Experiences

The STUF workbench is used within the LILOG project to develop grammars of rather broad coverage of the German language. The experiences the grammar authors had when using the system gave us a lot of hints on how to improve the usability of the tools. Furthermore, we profited greatly from ideas realized in development tools that were used before in the project, as well as from experience with the UNI-STUF system developed by Jochen Dörre at the University of Stuttgart.

References

[DE89] Jochen Dörre, Andreas Eisele: Determining consistency of feature terms with distributed disjunctions. In Dieter Metzing (ed.): *GWAI-89, 13th German Workshop on Artificial Intelligence*, pp. 270–279. Informatik Fachberichte 216, Springer-Verlag, 1989

[DE90] Jochen Dörre, Andreas Eisele: Feature logic with disjunctive unification. In *Proceedings of the 13th International Conference on Computational Linguistics*, Helsinki, Finland, 1990

[DR91] Jochen Dörre, Ingo Raasch: The Stuttgart type unification formalism – user manual. IWBS Report 168, IWBS, IBM Deutschland, Stuttgart, April 1991

[ED90] Andreas Eisele, Jochen Dörre: Disjunctive unification. IWBS Report 124, IWBS, IBM Deutschland, Stuttgart, May 1990. To appear in Jürgen Wedekind, Christian Rohrer (eds.): *Unification in Grammar*, MIT Press, Cambridge, MA, 1991

Unification-ID/LP Grammars: Formalization and Parsing

Roland Seiffert

Most of the grammar formalisms used in today's computational linguistics follow the *information approach* to language description. A grammar defines in a declarative way a relation between strings of a language and the information associated with this string. The information is usually encoded in complex term-like structures and the only operation for combining information is *unification*. Often, these formalisms are therefore called *unification-based*. The advantages of this approach have been widely hailed and we don't want to go into this discussion here.

It has been argued ([Gaz85], [Usz86]) that the two different pieces of information a grammar rule usually encodes simultanously, namely *immediate dominance* and *linear precedence* should be separated into two different types of rules, one rule type, *ID-rules*, describing only immediate dominance relations, and the other, *LP-rules*, describing all linear precedence constraints. This step made grammatical descriptions for languages with complicated word-order phenomena – like German – a good deal simpler and more general. GPSG is the most prominent formalism using ID/LP-rules, but the descriptive power of GPSG is limited to that of context-free grammars.

Since the LILOG project set out to develop a large grammar for German, we have tried to combine the ID/LP idea with the information approach of unification grammars. So we have investigated the descriptive possibilities and computational properties of *unification-ID/LP grammars*. We will have nothing to say on linguistic issues in this section. Instead we put the focus on the formalization of these grammars, and the main topic is to describe a *parsing algorithm* for unification-ID/LP grammars.

Before we start with this, we give precise formal definitions of our grammars and the languages generated by them. We try to keep these definitions very close to those of the well known theory of context-free grammars familiarity with which is ussumed here. This makes it seem reasonable that parsing algorithms used for unification grammars can be so similar to the standard algorithms and makes it much easier to understand how all this works.

Unification-CF Grammars

First, we define the basic notion of a *unification grammar*. The idea is to extend standard context-free grammars by using complex feature structures – STUF types – instead of atomic nonterminal symbols.

Definition 1 (Unification-CF Grammar) A *unification-CF grammar* – or *unification grammar for short* – is a triple $G = (\text{Lex}, \text{UCF}, \text{ST})$, where

- **Lex** is the *lexicon*. It is a set of *lexical entries* that have the form $Word := t$, where t is an arbitrary STUF type
- **UCF** is the set of *unification-CF rules*. Each rule has the form $t_0 \to t_1 \ldots t_n$, where all t_i are STUF types
- **ST** is the *start type*, an arbitrary STUF type

When using context-free grammars one usually states which are the terminal and nonterminal symbols of the grammar. In unification grammars we give a mapping from *words* – terminals – to *types* – nonterminals – in the lexicon and don't allow the use of words in rules. This is clearly not a restriction but improves the modularity of the grammar. The *start type* parallels the start symbol in context-free grammars, i.e., every derivation starts with it.

With the above definition, context-free grammars are just a special case of unification grammars, where the use of types is restricted to atoms. Unification grammars are more powerful than context-free grammars because they use complex types as nonterminal symbols and allow for structure sharing among different types in one rule. This allows us to express context-sensitive[1] conditions in the grammar rules.

In the following, we regard the words from the lexicon simply as distinguished STUF atoms. This allows for a very simple definition of *derivation* in unification grammars.

Definition 2 (derives directly, $\Rightarrow$) Let G = (Lex, UCF, ST) be a unification-CF grammar and all t_j and e_j be STUF types, then $e_0 \ldots e_{i-1} e_i e_{i+1} \ldots e_n \Rightarrow e'_0 \ldots e'_{i-1} t'_1 \ldots t'_m e'_{i+1} \ldots e'_n$ if and only if
(i) $t_0 \rightarrow t_1 \ldots t_m \in UCF$ or $(t_1 := t_0) \in Lex$ and

(ii)
$$
\begin{bmatrix} 0: & e_0 \\ \ldots & \\ \boxed{i}: & e_i \\ \ldots & \\ n: & e_n \end{bmatrix}
\sqcup
\begin{bmatrix} \boxed{i}: & t_0 \\ r1: & t_1 \\ \ldots & \\ rm: & t_m \end{bmatrix}
=
\begin{bmatrix} 0: & e'_0 \\ \ldots & \\ \boxed{i}: & e'_i \\ \ldots & \\ n: & e'_n \\ r1: & t'_1 \\ \ldots & \\ rm: & t'_m \end{bmatrix}
$$

The crucial point in this definition is the use of the same attribute $\boxed{i}$ in both types that are unified in condition (ii). In context-free grammars a derivation step simply replaces a nonterminal with the righthand side of a rule having the very same nonterminal on its lefthand side. In unification grammars we only require that the corresponding types are unified.

Note that there may be reentrancies among all types on the lefthand side of "$\Rightarrow$" and among all types of a rule. In consequence, the unification in condition (ii) not only works on the values of $\boxed{i}$ but might also change all other types. Therefore we have marked all types on the righthand side of "$\Rightarrow$" with a prime symbol.

We can now easily extend the definition of a single derivation step to an arbitrary sequence of such steps, called a *derivation*.

Definition 3 (derives, $\overset{*}{\Rightarrow}$) Let G = (Lex, UCF, ST) be a unification-CF grammar, B a STUF type, and α, β, γ, α', γ', μ_i (possibly empty) sequences of STUF types, then $\alpha B \gamma \overset{*}{\Rightarrow} \alpha' \beta \gamma'$ if and only if $\alpha B \gamma = \alpha' \beta \gamma'$ or $\alpha B \gamma = \mu_0 \Rightarrow \mu_1 \Rightarrow \ldots \Rightarrow \mu_n = \alpha' \beta \gamma'$

Now, we are ready to define the language generated by a unification grammar. For a sentence of the language we simply demand that there exists a derivation, beginning with the start type and finally yielding the sentence.

---

[1] "Context-sensitive" is not used in the technical sense. The computational power of unification grammars defined in this way is that of a Turing machine.

Definition 4 (L(G)) Let G = (Lex, UCF, ST) be a unification-CF grammar. Then we define the language generated by G as $L(G)=\{\ w = x_1 \ldots x_n \mid$ (i) $ST \overset{*}{\Rightarrow} w$, and (ii) $\forall i \exists t (x_i := t) \in Lex\ \}$

There might be many derivations for one sentence, but only some of them represent real ambiguities. Most of the derivations simply differ in the order in which the derivation steps are applied. Unification has the nice property of being a *monotonic* operation, so the resulting feature structure will not change if the order of the derivation steps is changed. A parser usually avoids multiple derivations by fixing the replacement order, e.g., do the leftmost possible derivation step first. A *parse tree* may be viewed as a graphical representation for a derivation that filters out the choice regarding replacement order. Parse trees in unification grammars are very much like those in context-free grammars, but the inner nodes of the tree are STUF types instead of simple nonterminal symbols. The leaves are words from the lexicon. The daughters of every node are ordered. If the order of the daughters of some node in two parse trees is different, the trees are different. A *local tree* is just one node in a parse tree with its immediate daughters.

Unification-ID/LP Grammars

We will now define unification-ID/LP grammars and give the precise conditions under which an input sentence is a member of the language generated by the grammar.

Definition 5 (Unification-ID/LP Grammar) A *unification-ID/LP grammar* is a quadruple G = (Lex, UID, ULP, ST), where

> **Lex** is the *lexicon*
>
> **UID** is the set of *unification-ID rules*. Each rule has the form $t_0 \rightarrow t_1, \ldots, t_n$, where all t_i are STUF types
>
> **ULP** is the set of *unification-LP rules*. Each rule has the form $t_0 \prec t_1$, where all t_i are STUF types
>
> **ST** is the *start type*, an arbitrary STUF type

For each unification-ID/LP grammar we define an induced unification-CF grammar that reflects only the immediate dominance relation of the unification-ID/LP grammar and does not account for linear precedence rules. We need this definition to be able to use the notion of derivation from unification-CF grammars in the definition of $L(G)$.

Definition 6 (Induced Unification-CF Grammar) Let G = (Lex, UID, UCF, ST) be a unification-ID/LP grammar. Then G' = (Lex, UCF, ST) is the *induced unification-CF grammar* of G if and only if UCF is the set of all grammar rules corresponding to all permutations of the righthand sides of all rules in UID

The language generated by a unification-ID/LP grammar is a subset of the language generated by the induced unification-CF grammar, namely all those sentences that can be derived using the induced unification-CF grammar – this is condition (i) in the definition of $L(G)$ – and also obey all linear precedence constraints imposed by the unification-LP rules – condition (ii).

Definition 7 (L(G)) Let G = (Lex ,UID ,ULP ,ST) be a unification-ID/LP grammar and G'=(Lex, UCF, ST) the induced unification-CF grammar of G. Then we define the language generated by G as $L(G)$={ $w = x_1 \ldots x_n$ | (i) $w \in L(G')$, and (ii) there exists a parse tree for w in G' such that every local tree in it is ULP-acceptable }

To complete the definition of $L(G)$ we need to clarify under which conditions a local tree is ULP-acceptable. This is done in the following two definitions.

Definition 8 (applies) A unification-LP rule $t_0 \prec t_1$ *applies* to a local tree
$$\begin{array}{c} e_0 \\ \diagup\diagdown \\ e_1 \ldots e_n \end{array}$$
if and only if there exist some i and j with $i \neq j$, $1 \leq i \leq n$, $1 \leq j \leq n$ and $\begin{bmatrix} 0: & t_0 \\ 1: & t_1 \end{bmatrix} \sqsubseteq \begin{bmatrix} 0: & e_i \\ 1: & e_j \end{bmatrix}$

Here the idea is that a linear precedence constraint should be relevant for a local tree only if the information in that tree is compatible with and at least as specific as the information in the unification-LP rule.

Now a local tree is ULP-acceptable if it does not contradict any applicable unification-LP rule.

Definition 9 (ULP-acceptable) A local tree
$$\begin{array}{c} e_0 \\ \diagup\diagdown \\ e_1 \ldots e_n \end{array}$$
is *ULP-acceptable* if and only if no unification-LP rule applies to the local tree with $j < i$

Suppose we believe in the strict subject–predicate–object ordering of English sentences and also that the subject is always the nominative NP. This could be easily encoded in a unification-ID/LP grammar, and the following example is part of such a grammar.

Example 1 (Unification-ID/LP grammar) To encode that a nominative NP – the subject – has to precede the VP in a sentence we write the following unification-ID/LP grammar:

UID: $\begin{bmatrix} cat: & S \end{bmatrix} \rightarrow \begin{bmatrix} cat: & NP \\ case: & nom \end{bmatrix}$, $\begin{bmatrix} cat: & VP \end{bmatrix}$

ULP: $\begin{bmatrix} cat: & NP \\ case: & nom \end{bmatrix} \prec \begin{bmatrix} cat: & VP \end{bmatrix}$

Lex: *John* $:= \begin{bmatrix} cat: & NP \\ case: & nom \end{bmatrix}$

sleeps $:= \begin{bmatrix} cat: & VP \end{bmatrix}$

The sentence *(1)*John **sleeps** is accepted since the local tree *(1)* is ULP-acceptable, whereas the sentence *(2*)*sleeps **John** is rejected since the unification-LP rule applies to the local tree *(2)* with $i = 2$ and $j = 1$:

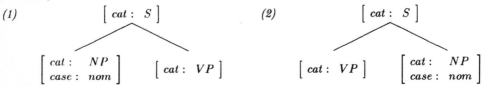

Parsing with Unification-ID/LP Grammars

There is a very simple and straightforward way of parsing with unification-ID/LP grammars: use the induced unification-CF grammar with an arbitrary parser for unification grammars and then check all parse trees for the sentence to see if there exists at least one tree in which every local tree is ULP-acceptable. This method directly implements the definition of $L(G)$. But clearly this cannot be efficient.

Another approach — adopted by the GPSG people – is *indirect parsing*: take the ID/LP grammar and compute an equivalent context-free grammar, then use the context-free grammar for parsing. Unfortunately, this does *not* work for unification-ID/LP grammars. It is not clear whether there is a way of computing an equivalent unification-CF grammar in every case. By no means would this be possible by considering the UID and ULP rules of the grammar alone. One would have to take into account all lexical entries!

Therefore, we propose a *direct parsing algorithm* that uses the unification-ID/LP grammar without any preprocessing. We want to attack the problem by extending the algorithm for direct parsing of ID/LP grammars given in [Shi83] to unification-ID/LP grammars similar to the extension of the Earley algorithm [Ear70] to unification-CF grammars as proposed in, e.g., [Shi85].

Unlike in standard ID rules, the information contained in the STUF types of UID rules is only partial, i.e., more information can be added to them while parsing. The following example will illustrate the resulting problems.

Example 2 Consider the following unification-ID/LP grammar G with $L(G) = \{abc\}$:

$$
\text{UID:} \quad \begin{bmatrix} cat: & S \end{bmatrix} \quad \rightarrow \quad \begin{bmatrix} cat: & A \\ f: & \langle 1 \rangle \end{bmatrix} \,, \quad \begin{bmatrix} cat: & B \\ f: & \langle 2 \rangle \end{bmatrix} \,, \quad \begin{bmatrix} cat: & C \\ f1: & \langle 1 \rangle \\ f2: & \langle 2 \rangle \end{bmatrix}
$$

$$
\text{ULP:} \quad \begin{bmatrix} f: & one \end{bmatrix} \quad \prec \quad \begin{bmatrix} f: & two \end{bmatrix}
$$

$$
\text{Lex:} \quad a \quad := \quad \begin{bmatrix} cat: & A \end{bmatrix}
$$

$$
b \quad := \quad \begin{bmatrix} cat: & B \end{bmatrix}
$$

$$
c \quad := \quad \begin{bmatrix} cat: & C \\ f1: & one \\ f2: & two \end{bmatrix}
$$

The input sentence $w = abc$ leads to the following local tree, which is ULP-acceptable:

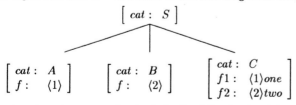

The input sentence $w = bac$ leads to the following local tree, which is *not* ULP-acceptable:

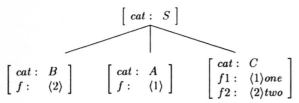

Suppose we are analyzing the input sentence $w = bac \notin L(G)$ from left to right and have processed ba. The parser will then produce an active item (1) which is still ULP-acceptable since no unification-LP rule applies to it. Then we build a constituent for (2) and detect that the passive item (3) is no longer ULP-acceptable since (4) and (5) are in the wrong order.

$$(1) \quad [0, 2, \begin{bmatrix} cat: & S \end{bmatrix} \rightarrow \begin{bmatrix} cat: & B \\ f: & \langle 2 \rangle \end{bmatrix} \begin{bmatrix} cat: & A \\ f: & \langle 1 \rangle \end{bmatrix} \cdot \{ \begin{bmatrix} cat: & C \\ f1: & \langle 1 \rangle \\ f2: & \langle 2 \rangle \end{bmatrix} \}]$$

$$(2) \quad \begin{bmatrix} cat: & C \\ f1: & \langle 1 \rangle \\ f2: & \langle 2 \rangle \end{bmatrix}$$

$$(3) \quad [0, 3, \begin{bmatrix} cat: & S \end{bmatrix} \rightarrow \begin{bmatrix} cat: & B \\ f: & \langle 2 \rangle \end{bmatrix} \begin{bmatrix} cat: & A \\ f: & \langle 1 \rangle \end{bmatrix} \begin{bmatrix} cat: & C \\ f1: & \langle 1 \rangle one \\ f2: & \langle 2 \rangle two \end{bmatrix} \cdot \{ \}]$$

$$(4) \quad \begin{bmatrix} cat: & B \\ f: & \langle 2 \rangle \end{bmatrix}$$

$$(5) \quad \begin{bmatrix} cat: & A \\ f: & \langle 1 \rangle \end{bmatrix}$$

Here, the problem is that there is only partial information available in the STUF types of the items that can be extended later on and lead to a ULP-violation in already "accepted" constituents. In standard ID/LP grammars such situations could not arise. Therefore it was safe for the parser to only check if a new constituent appended to an active item obeys all LP rules. For unification-ID/LP parsing we must check ULP-acceptability of the *whole item* each time a new constituent is appended.

This ensures that all ULP-violations are detected as soon as possible. It would also suffice to check ULP-acceptability only when a passive item is being built. But this would slow down parsing since all permutations of constituents would be allowed in active items and so a lot of unnecessary work would have to be done.

As [Shi85] pointed out we have to use *restriction* in the predictor step of an Earley-style parser for unification grammars to avoid infinite loops while predicting new active items. Clearly, this is also true for our unification-ID/LP parser. Thus, we have added this to our algorithm. For details see [Shi85].

We are now in a position to specify the first part of the unification-ID/LP parsing algorithm:

Algorithm 1 (Unification-ID/LP Parsing Algorithm, Part I) The first part of the parsing algorithm builds the chart representing all possible parse trees for an given input sentence.

Input	• Unification-ID/LP grammar $G = $ (Lex, UID, ULP, ST)
	• Restrictor R, a set of feature paths
	• Input sentence $w = x_1 \ldots x_n$

Output	• chart, containing all parse trees
Method	**(1) Initialization**

Clear the chart. Add an item $[0, 0, dummy \rightarrow .\{ST\}]$ to the chart

Repeat steps (2) and (3) with $j = 0$ until no more items can be added to the chart

(2) Completer

If $\qquad [i, j, d_0 \rightarrow d_1 \ldots d_r.\{\,\}] \in chart$

and $\quad [k, i, e_0 \rightarrow e_1 \ldots e_{m-1}.(\{e_m\} \cup \{e_{m+1} \ldots e_s\})] \in chart$

and $\quad e'_m = e_m \sqcup d_0$

and $\quad$ the (partial) local tree $\overset{e'_0}{\overset{\displaystyle\wedge}{e'_1 \ldots e'_m}}$ is ULP-acceptable

then $\qquad$ add the item $[k, j, e'_0 \rightarrow e'_1 \ldots e'_{m-1} e'_m.\{e'_{m+1} \ldots e'_s\}]$ to the chart,
$\qquad\qquad$ if it is not subsumed by another item in the chart

(3) Predictor

If $\qquad [i, j, d_0 \rightarrow d_1 \ldots d_{m-1}.(\{d_m\} \cup \{d_{m+1} \ldots d_r\})] \in chart$

and $\quad e_0 \rightarrow e_1, \ldots, e_s \in UID$

and $\quad e'_0 = e_0 \sqcup (d_m \diamond R)$

then $\qquad$ add the item $[j, j, e'_0 \rightarrow .\{e'_1 \ldots e'_s\}]$ to the chart,
$\qquad\qquad$ if it is not subsumed by another item in the chart

Repeat step (4) and then (2) and (3) for all j, $1 \leq j \leq n$,
until no more items can be added to the chart

(4) Scanner

If $\qquad (x_j := d) \in Lex$

then $\qquad$ add the item $[j - 1, j, d \rightarrow x_j.\{\,\})]$ to the chart,
$\qquad\qquad$ if it is not subsumed by another item in the chart

Note that unification-LP conditions are only tested in the completer. The direct parsing algorithm for ID/LP grammars given in [Shi83] also performs this test in the predictor step. This is not necessary for the correctness of the algorithm but could eventually lead to somewhat fewer items and thus better performance. But our tests have shown that the test for ULP-acceptability is rather expensive and the advantage of having fewer items is negligible compared to the reduction of the number of ULP-acceptability tests by avoiding them in the predictor.

The algorithm given above will accept every sentence of $L(G)$, i.e., it is complete. Unfortunately, it is a bit too generous and will sometimes also accept some sentences that are not in $L(G)$, i.e., it is *not* correct. Consider the following example:

Example 3 (Restriction is a problem) Consider the following unification-ID/LP grammar G with $L(G) = \{abcd\}$:

$$
\text{UID:} \quad \begin{bmatrix} cat: & S \end{bmatrix} \rightarrow \begin{bmatrix} cat: & T \\ f: & \langle 1 \rangle \end{bmatrix}, \begin{bmatrix} cat: & U \\ f: & \langle 1 \rangle \end{bmatrix}
$$

$$
\begin{bmatrix} cat: & T \\ f: & \begin{bmatrix} f1: & \langle 1 \rangle \\ f2: & \langle 2 \rangle \end{bmatrix} \end{bmatrix} \rightarrow \begin{bmatrix} cat: & A \\ f1: & \langle 1 \rangle \end{bmatrix}, \begin{bmatrix} cat: & B \\ f2: & \langle 2 \rangle \end{bmatrix}
$$

$$
\begin{bmatrix} cat: & U \\ f: & \begin{bmatrix} f1: & \langle 1 \rangle \\ f2: & \langle 2 \rangle \end{bmatrix} \end{bmatrix} \rightarrow \begin{bmatrix} cat: & C \\ f1: & \langle 1 \rangle \end{bmatrix}, \begin{bmatrix} cat: & D \\ f2: & \langle 2 \rangle \end{bmatrix}
$$

$$
\text{ULP:} \quad \begin{bmatrix} cat: & T \\ f1: & one \end{bmatrix} \prec \begin{bmatrix} cat: & U \end{bmatrix} \prec \begin{bmatrix} f2: & two \end{bmatrix}
$$

$$
\text{Lex:} \quad a := \begin{bmatrix} cat: & A \\ f1: & one \end{bmatrix}
$$

$$
b := \begin{bmatrix} cat: & B \\ f2: & two \end{bmatrix}
$$

$$
c := \begin{bmatrix} cat: & C \end{bmatrix}
$$

$$
d := \begin{bmatrix} cat: & D \end{bmatrix}
$$

The input sentence $w = abcd$ leads to the following structure of the parse tree, which is ULP-acceptable:

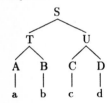

In this grammar we have a non-local dependency between the constituents A and C and between B and G, namely that A/C and B/D share the values of the features f1 and f2, respectively.

Now, suppose we are parsing an input sentence $w = abdc \notin L(G)$. When we have processed ab, the values of the features f1 and f2 in the item $[0, 2, T \rightarrow AB.\{\ \}]^2$ are known. These values are passed to the item $[0, 2, S \rightarrow T.\{U\}]$ by the completer. With this active item the predictor has to propose an active item for the constituent U: $[2, 2, U \rightarrow .\{C, D\}]$. Unification in the predictor would pass the values for f1 and f2 down to the constituents C and D, respectively. This allows us to detect the ULP-violation when we try to build the passive item $[2, 4, U \rightarrow DC.\{\ \}]$ and all seems to work fine.

The problem is that the predictor *must not* use all of the information solely through unification but has to use restriction on the information coming from the chart. The predictor will add an active item $[2, 2, U' \rightarrow .\{C'', D'\}]$, where U' is the result of unifying the UID rule for U with the *restricted* type for U from the item $[0, 2, S \rightarrow T.\{U\}]$. If we choose the restrictor to be $R = \{\langle cat \rangle\}$ this yields the following types for U', C' and D':

---

[2] In the following we refer to a complex category by giving the value of its *cat*-feature. The full structure should be clear from the context.

$$\text{U':} \quad \begin{bmatrix} cat: & U \\ f: & \begin{bmatrix} f1: & \langle 1 \rangle \\ f2: & \langle 2 \rangle \end{bmatrix} \end{bmatrix}$$

$$\text{C':} \quad \begin{bmatrix} cat: & C \\ f1: & \langle 1 \rangle \end{bmatrix}$$

$$\text{D':} \quad \begin{bmatrix} cat: & D \\ f2: & \langle 2 \rangle \end{bmatrix}$$

In these types exactly that information needed to detect the ULP-violation has vanished. Therefore the passive item $[2, 4, U \rightarrow DC.\{\ \}]$ will be ULP-acceptable, since no unification-LP rule applies to it any more.

If we had chosen the restrictor to be $R = \{\langle cat \rangle, \langle f1 \rangle, \langle f2 \rangle, \langle f\ f1 \rangle, \langle f\ f2 \rangle\}$, the ULP-violation would be detected. The choice of a most specific restrictor makes sense in any case, since it allows the predictor to be as precise as possible with its proposed items, which in turn leads to a more efficient parse because no unnecessary items are built. But it is very annoying that the choice of the restrictor has an influence on the correctness of the parsing algorithm!

An even more complicated situation arises if we change the lexicon of the above example to:

$$\text{Lex:} \quad \begin{array}{lll} a & := & \begin{bmatrix} cat: & A \end{bmatrix} \\ b & := & \begin{bmatrix} cat: & B \end{bmatrix} \\ c & := & \begin{bmatrix} cat: & C \\ f1: & one \end{bmatrix} \\ d & := & \begin{bmatrix} cat: & D \\ f2: & two \end{bmatrix} \end{array}$$

$L(G)$ is not changed, but if we parse the input sentence $w = bacd \notin L(G)$ we inevitably end up with the following situation: the analysis of the first part ba of w gives us no information about the value of the features f1 and f2. Therefore no unification-LP rule applies to the item $[0, 2, T \rightarrow BA.\{\ \}]$ and it it not possible to detect the ULP-violation in this (partial) local tree.

The information for f1 and f2 comes from the analysis of the rest of the input sentence cd. But at this point the passive item $[0, 2, T \rightarrow BA.\{\ \}]$ cannot be simply deleted, since it might already have triggered many other items. To cope with this situation directly in the Earley-based parser would make it necessary to introduce a very complex concept of backtracking into the algorithm. We shall refrain from doing this, however.

To justify this decision let us have a look on the critical properties of grammars that lead to a situation as outlined above. The crucial observation is that there must be some information relevant for the ULP-acceptability of a sentence which is found in some constituent and that tells us if some other already fully analyzed constituent to its left is ULP-acceptable or not. In German there are examples in which the verb determines the order of other constituents in the "Mittelfeld" in an unmarked construction[3]. This might be such a critical case if we have verb-last structure in subordinate clauses. But it turns out that this dependency is bound to one local tree since German syntacticians prefer a flat analysis of the "Mittelfeld". The order of imbedded parts of the constituents in the "Mittelfeld" is immaterial at this point of the analysis. Therefore the completer in our algorithm is able to check the order correctly when the verb is encountered.

---

[3]See [WR87].

If there are other phenomena that require similar, but non-local, dependencies, these would be the cases where ULP-violations could possibly go undetected while building the chart. But so far we do not know of such phenomena.

Therefore it seems reasonable to accept that the algorithm builds up a chart that might contain wrong analyses. We can easily filter out these analyses in a second step, and we expect that there are few or none such wrong trees.

Here we give the second step of the parsing algorithm that has to check whether there exists a parse tree that observes all ULP rules. To prove this, we extract one parse tree after the other from the chart and check it, until we find an acceptable one. If such a tree can be found then we accept the input sentence, otherwise it must be rejected. In the following we specify the algorithm for checking ULP-acceptability for a given parse tree.

Algorithm 2 (Unification-ID/LP Parsing Algorithm, Part II) This part checks whether a given parse tree is ULP-acceptable.

Input	• Unification-ID/LP grammar $G = ($Lex, UID, ULP, ST$)$	
	• parse tree T	
Output	• yes, if T is a ULP-acceptable; no, otherwise	
Method	If	T is a leaf, T is ULP-acceptable

If   T is $e_0 / e_1 \ldots e_n$

and   the local tree $e_0 / e_1 \ldots e_n$ is ULP-acceptable

then   apply this method to all subtrees of T recursively

         If   all subtrees are ULP-acceptable

         then T is ULP-acceptable

else   T is *not* ULP-acceptable

One crucial point for Part II of the algorithm is to have efficient access to all parse trees encoded in the chart. In our implementation, we have therefore adopted a technique from [Gra80] that encodes all trees in an explicit data structure and allows access to a single tree in linear time, whereas extracting a tree directly from the Earley-chart requires quadratic time. We have used our parser with several different test grammars and the results look quite promising. Processing time is comparable to that of a standard parser for a unification grammar generating the same language.

Conclusion

It has been shown that the ID/LP formalism from GPSG can be extended to take advantage of the full power of unification grammars. The problems that arise for a parsing algorithm have been pointed out. We propose a parsing algorithm for unification-ID/LP grammars consisting of two steps. We argue that in all practical cases most ULP-violations are detected in step one of the parser and step two has not much work to do. Therefore, this yields an efficient algorithm. If it turns out that none of our grammars use non-local backward feature passing with influence on ULP-acceptabilty, we can eventually switch off step two completely. This is especially feasible, if we don't use restriction in the predictor step, which is possible since most grammars will not use rules that lead to nontermination without restriction. In that case, no information is lost in the prediction step and there are no undetected ULP-violations like those in Example 3.

It is an open question whether all ULP-violations can be detected for any grammar at all while building the chart. There are similar problems with constraining equations in LFG or in handling the ANY-values of FUG. The source for these problems is that these constraints are really *meta-constraints* depending on the instantiation state of feature structures. The algorithm proposed here has the advantage that step one is not complicated through expensive constraint processing which in most cases will not be necessary. If it is needed for some special case, this work can be easily done in a separate second step. This gives a better performance in the typical case.

Another advantage of our approach is that we have a direct parsing algorithm that requires no compilation of the input grammar. This is especially useful for a grammar development environment where changes to the grammar are very frequent. For a realistic application using the grammar, efforts should be made to speed up processing through the use of advanced compiling techniques.

References

[Ear70] J. Earley: *An Efficient Context-Free Parsing Algorithm*. In: Communications of the ACM, Vol. 13, pp. 94-102, 1970

[Gaz85] G. Gazdar, E. Klein, G. Pullum, I. Sag: *Generalized Phrase Structure Grammar*. Blackwell, London, 1985

[Gra80] G. Graham, M.G. Harrison, W. L. Ruzzo: *An Improved Context-Free Recognizer*. In: ACM Transactions on Programming Languages and Systems 2 (3), pp. 415-462, 1980

[Sei87] R. Seiffert: *Chart-Parsing of Unification-Based Grammars with ID/LP-Rules*. In: E. Klein, J. v. Benthem (eds.): Categories, Polymorphism and Unification. Centre for Cognitive Science, University of Edinburgh, UK, 1987

[Shi83] S. Shieber: *Direct Parsing of ID/LP Grammars*. Technical Note 291R. SRI International, Menlo Park, CA, 1983

[Shi85] S. Shieber: *Using Restriction to Extend Parsing Algorithms for Complex-Feature-Based Formalisms*. In: Proceedings of the 22nd Annual Meeting of the Association for Computational Linguistics. University of Chicago, Chicago, IL, 1985

[SUP+83] S. Shieber, H. Uszkoreit, F. Pereira, J. Robinson, M. Tyson: *The Formalism and Implementation of PATR-II*. In: Research on Interactive Acquisition and Use of Knowledge. Artificial Intelligence Center, SRI International, Menlo Park, CA, 1983

[Usz86] H.Uszkoreit: *Constraints on Order*. Report No. CSLI-86-46. Center for the Study of Language and Information, Stanford University, Stanford, CA, 1986

[WR87] B. Wesche, I. Renz: *Word Order and Focus Projection*. LILOG-Report 13. IBM Deutschland, Stuttgart, 1987

A Flexible Parser for a
Linguistic Development Environment

Gregor Erbach

Abstract

We describe the parser of LEU/2, the Linguistic Experimentation Environment of the LILOG project. The parser is designed to support and encourage experimentation with different grammars, different styles of writing grammar, and with different parsing strategies.

Unlike the parser of the first LILOG prototype, which was designed specifically for Categorial Unification Grammars (Uszkoreit 1986a), the present parser places hardly any restrictions on the format of the grammar, and also supports rules in ID/LP-format (Gazdar et al. 1985) under two interpretations of LP statements. Empty categories can be processed. The parser includes a mechanism for processing unknown words, and for determining sentence boundaries in continuous text.

The parser is a bottom-up chart parser for grammars encoded in STUF, the Stuttgart Type Unification Formalism (Dörre, this volume, section 1.1). Although the emphasis of the parser is on experimentation with different grammars rather than efficient analysis of texts, we have tried to make the parser as efficient as possible in order to make it a powerful experimentation tool for the grammar designer. For the implementation of parsing strategies, the parsing process is decomposed into individual parsing tasks, which are placed onto an agenda (Kay 1980) according to their priority.

This paper consists of two parts. In the first part, we discuss various choices in parser design, and motivate our design decisions by the use of the parser in a linguistic development environment. In the second part, the parser is described in more detail. Some familiarity with chart parsing is assumed.[1]

Introduction

In order to understand some of the choices we made in the design of the parser, it is necessary to have some information about the process of grammar development, the software environment used by grammar developers, and about the place of the parser in such an environment.

State-of-the-art grammar development environments support the following activities:

— writing and editing a grammar,
— parsing one or more sentences to verify the grammar,
— inspection of the parse results.

This sequence of steps is repeated until the linguist is satisfied with the grammar, based on the parse results. This style of working imposes the following requirements on the parser:

---

[1] For an introduction to chart parsing, see (Kay 1980) or (Seiffert, this volume, section 1.1).

- It should be reasonably efficient so that the user is not kept waiting for parse results.
- It should be transparent to the user how the parse result was constructed, and what the analyses are for substrings of the sentence that was parsed.
- In case of failure to parse a string, it should be possible to give a reasonable output that helps with the diagnosis of the error and the debugging of the grammar.

Choices in Parser Design

Parsing technology provides various choices in the design of a parser, relating to

- the types of grammars that can be processed (specialization vs. generality),
- expectation-driven (top-down) vs. data-driven (bottom-up) processing,
- dealing with non-determinism (parsing strategies).

Each of these issues will be discussed in the following, and the choices taken will be motivated by the use of the parser in an environment for the development of grammars and experimentation with parsing strategies.

Types of Grammars

There are various degrees in which a parser can be specialized for particular grammars:

- The parser can be specialized for one particular grammar (according to a particular linguistic theory) of one particular language. In this case, there is no separation between grammer and parser. This is the most extreme degree of specialization, which would be appropriate for a commercial parser, used in a natural-language interface, which must operate under severe constraints of time and space.

- The parser can be specialized for one particular linguistic theory, like Government-Binding Theory (Chomsky 1981), Lexical-Functional Grammar (Kaplan, Bresnan 1982), and numerous others. This allows a gain in efficiency by exploiting the structural properties of these theories, while it makes it possible to use different grammars for different languages within the framework of a given grammatical theory.

- The parser can process any grammar encoded in a general formalism like Functional Unification Grammar (Kay 1985), PATR-II (Shieber et al. 1983), or STUF (Dörre, this volume, section 1.1). But even with such very general formalism, it is still possible to interpret rules in different ways. For example, a rewrite rule like

S -> A B C

can be interpreted as a rule of a context-free grammar, in which case S can only be rewritten as the sequence "A B C", or the rule can be interpreted as an immediate dominance rule, in which case S can be rewritten as any permutation of the right-hand-side (i.e., "A B C", "A C B", "B A C", "B C A", "C A B", or "C B A"). In this repect, grammar is an open-ended concept, and it is the grammatical formalism and its interpretation by the parser that limit the range of possible grammars that can be processed. This option is the most inefficient one, but it allows the highest degree of freedom in the development of different grammars.

Our parser is not restricted to any particular linguistic theory, and can process the types of grammar rules discussed below. While the grammars for the first LILOG prototype were Categorial Unification Grammars (Uszkoreit 1986a), the current grammar is based on HPSG[2].

Another option that needs to be considered is preprocessing or compilation of the grammar. Such preprocessing may range from conversion to some normal form to the generation of a parser for a particular grammar. We have chosen not to use any preprocessing, so that the parser operates directly on the grammar. This makes it easier to build tools to inspect the parse results, and to relate the parse results to the grammatical knowledge bases, i.e., the syntax rules and the lexicon.

Top-Down or Bottom-Up Analysis

There is in general a choice between data-driven (bottom-up) and expectation-driven (top-down) analysis. Both choices have their advantages and disadvantages:

Bottom-up analysis has the advantage that the choice of the grammar rules that are applied depends on the words present in the sentence and on analyses for substrings of the sentence. However, the disadvantage is that analyses for substrings are built up, which do not contribute to the overall analysis of the sentence.

Top-down parsing has the advantage that only such rules are applied which can be useful in proving that the sentence is grammatical. The disadvantage is that the rules are tried "blindly", without any regard to the lexical material present in the sentence.

The advantages of both top-down and bottom-up parsing are combined in "directed" parsing strategies (Kay 1980), as for example in left-corner parsers (Pereira, Shieber 1987), or head-driven parsers (Kay 1989).

We have chosen pure bottom-up parsing for two reasons:

— Our grammars do not need to have a context-free backbone to guide top-down analysis, or support the creation of a link table which is needed for the "directed" methods. Nor can we rely on any properties of the grammar to implement a "head-driven" parsing algorithm (Kay 1989), because the linguist has complete freedom in writing the grammar.
— In grammar development, one is not only interested in the overall parse of the sentence, but also in analyses of the substrings. So what is generally claimed to be a drawback of bottom-up parsers, the creation of analyses for substrings, which are never used in the analysis of the sentence, turns out to be an advantage for our purposes.

Dealing with Non-determinism

Non-determinism in parsing arises when several different parsing tasks can be performed at the same time. Since parallel processing is not available to us, we must have a way of choosing a parsing task.

---

[2]See Kiss, this volume, section 1.3 for an explication of the grammar

Deterministic parsing (Marcus 1980) is not appropriate for grammar development, because Marcus' deterministic parser requires a grammar format (of situation-action rules) which is not declarative and not very intuitive linguistically.

A simple backtracking parser cannot be used for reasons of efficiency. It does not store intermediate results so that a lot of work has to be done repeatedly.

We have chosen chart parsing because it stores intermediate results and avoids duplication of effort. Storage of intermediate results is useful because the linguist developing and debugging a grammar is not only interested in the overall parse result, but also in the analyses that his grammar produces (or does not produce) for substrings of the sentence.

Chart parsing leaves open the question of the search strategy, i.e., the selection of the next parsing task. Our chart parser allows for the definition of arbitrary parsing strategies, so that it is also a tool for experimentation with different strategies.

Description of the Parser

In the following, we will give a technical description of the parser, focusing on the data structures, the parsing algorithm, the processing of LP statements, empty categories, unknown words and the implementation of parsing strategies.

The parser can process grammars encoded in STUF, which may contain the following types of grammatical information:

— *lexical entries,* which associate word forms with feature structures.
— *lexical rules,* which create lexical entries from lexical entries.
— *CF rules,* which have information about both dominance and linear precedence; the order of the right-hand side of the rule reflects the order of the constituents in the string[3].
— *ID rules,* which just have information about dominance, not about linear precedence.
— *LP statements,* which constrain the linear precedence of constituents.
— the *Start Graph,* a feature structure which defines what a well-formed sentence of the language is; nothing counts as a parse result unless it unifies with the Start Graph.

The parser needs lexical entries, and a set of ID rules or CF rules. Lexical rules and LP statements can be processed, but they are not essential for the operation of the parser. It is possible to have both CF rules and ID rules in one grammar, so that it is possible to describe languages in which some constructions are fixed and others allow for permutation.

Data Structures

The central data structure of the parser is the **chart,** which is a set of chart items. Chart items may be passive (complete constituents) or active (constituents which are still missing something).

---

[3] They are called CF-rules because they share this property with context-free rewrite rules. However, the grammar formalism is equivalent to type-0-grammars.

Chart items:
passive: <Start, End, Item, FS, Daughters, Evaluation>
active: <Start, End, Item, FS, Daughters, Evaluation, LHS, RHS>

where

— *Start* is the starting position of the item.
— *End* is the ending position of the item.
— *Item* is a unique identifier of the item, a number.
— *FS* is the feature structure of the item. In the case of passive items, it represents a grammatical category, and in the case of active items, it represents a partially instantiated grammar rule. A grammar rule is a feature structure with an attribute for its left-hand side and and attribute for each of the elements of its right-hand side.
— *Daughters* is a list of identifiers of the items that were used in building the current item, and the name of the rule. This information is needed for reconstructing phrase structure trees for parse results.
— *Evaluation* is a numerical value that associates with the item a probability or qualitative rating, which will be discussed in the section on parsing strategies. This evaluation for an item must not be confused with the priority of a parsing task.
— *LHS* is a feature under which the left-hand side of the grammar rule is found after an active item has been completed.
— *RHS* is a list of features, which indicates how many more constituents are needed to make the active item passive, and with which features of the rule their feature structure must be unified.

The other fundamental data structure is the **agenda,** an ordered list of parsing tasks. A priority is associated with each parsing task. The parser can process the following **parsing tasks:**

— **a_and_p(act(X), Item1, Item2)**

Combine an active item (Item1) with a passive item (Item2). act(X) can have the values act(ID) or act(CF) depending on whether the active item originated from the application of an ID rule or an LP statement. If it originated from a CF rule, the next element of the remaining right-hand side of the active item must be unified with Item2; if it originated from an ID rule, **any** element of the remaining right-hand side may be unified with Item2.

— **unary_rule(RULE-NAME, Item1)**

Apply the unary rule with the RULE-NAME to the passive item Item1, thereby creating a new passive item if the rule application was successful.

— **binary_cf_rule(RULE-NAME, Item1, Item2)**

Apply the binary CF rule RULE-NAME to the passive items Item1 and Item2, creating a new passive item if the rule application was successful. Binary rules are treated specially for reasons of efficiency. The option for treating binary rules specially can be turned off, in which case binary rules are treated with the parsing task cf_rule(RULE-NAME, Item).

— **binary_id_rule(RULE-NAME, Item1, Item2)**

Apply the binary ID rule RULE-NAME to passive items Item1 and Item2. Since ID rules do not prescribe the order of the constituents, there will be two tasks on the agenda in the general case (binary_id_rule(NAME, Item1, Item2) and binary_id_rule(NAME, Item2, Item1)) . However, if we can tell beforehand by application of a filter (see below) that one of these options will fail anyway, it will not be put on the agenda.

— **cf_rule(RULE-NAME, Item1)**

Apply the CF rule RULE-NAME to the passive item Item1, creating an active item if the rule application was successful.

— **id_rule(RULE-NAME, Item1)**

Apply the ID rule RULE-NAME to the passive item Item1. Since ID rules do not prescribe the order of the constituents, any element on the right-hand side of the rule may be unified with the item Item1. Thus, the rule application may create as many active items as there are elements on the right-hand side of the rule.

The Parsing Algorithm

The parsing algorithm is rather simple: after initialization of the parser (and creation of an initial agenda), the task with the highest priority is taken from the agenda and executed. Successful execution of the task produces a new chart item. The addition of that item to the chart may produce new tasks which are added to the agenda. The parser will continue executing the highest-valued task of the agenda until a parse for the sentence has been found or the agenda is empty.

Phase 1: Initialization
unless there is a chart and agenda[4]:
read next sentence from input stream
for each word of the sentence, perform lexical lookup and add a passive item to the
    chart (thereby generating new parsing tasks)
order the parsing tasks and create an inital agenda

Phase 2: Parsing Loop
while the agenda is not empty
take the task with the highest priority off the agenda and *perform that task*
if it succeeds, *add a new item to the chart*(thereby generating new parsing tasks)
order new parsing tasks into the agenda
if that item is passive, covers the entire string and unifies with the Start Graph then
    stop

Perform a Parsing Task
See the above description of the parsing tasks.

---

[4] There may already be a chart and an agenda, if one parse result was found, and the parser is restarted in order to look for another analysis of the sentence. Before parsing a new sentences, the chart and agenda for the previous sentence are deleted.

Add an Item I to the Chart
store the item I
if the item I is passive, then
      — for every unary rule UR, create a task unary_rule(UR,I)
      — for every binary CF rule(BR), and every right-adjacent passive item RI, create a task binary_cf_rule(BR,I,RI)[5]
      — for every binary CF rule(BR), and every left-adjacent passive item LI, create a task binary_cf_rule(BR,LI,I)
      — for every binary ID rule, and every adjacent passive item AI, create tasks binary_id_rule(BIR,AI,I) and binary_id_rule(BIR,I,AI).
      — for every more than binary CF rule R, create a task cf_rule(R,I).
      — for every more than binary ID rule R, create a task id_rule(R,I).
      — for every left-adjacent active item A, create a task a_and_p(A,I).
else if the item I is active, then
      — for every right-adjacent passive item P, create a task a_and_p(I,P).

Order the Parsing Tasks
Each parsing task as assigned a priority based on any information which may be available about it, for example the rules involved, the feature structures of the items involved, the length of the resulting item, the position in the resulting item. In this way arbitrary parsing strategies can be implemented (see below).

LP Constraints

The grammar formalism STUF includes LP constraints which control the linear precedence of constituents. LP constraints can be interpreted in various ways. The classic interpretation (Gazdar et al. 1985) is that LP constraints determine the relative order of sister constituents. However, it is linguistically interesting to experiment with different interpretations which allow ordering constituents that are not sisters[6]. A domain in which to enforce LP constraints is defined by all complements and adjuncts of a lexical head.

It is up to the grammar writer to specify the domain within which LP constraints are enforced. For this reason, the grammar must be augmented in such a way that a list of constituents is built up in the feature structure of a constituent. The LP constraints are checked on the elements of the list every time an item is added to the chart.

The following example makes use of a difference list encoding which allows the concatenation of lists of arbitrary length by unification (Sterling, Shapiro 1986). The feature 'list' is used for the list, and the feature 'var' for the rest variable. The list is encoded with the features 'first' for the first element, and 'rest' for the rest of the list. In the example, the grammar rules of Right-Complementation and Left-Complementation are augmented such that they build up a list of the head's complements. The lexical head of the phrase has initially an LP-list containing only itself.

---

[5] We assume here that binary rules are treated specially, for reasons explained below.

[6] For a linguistic motivation of the need for interpreting LP constraints in hierarchical structures, see (Uszkoreit 1986b).

Right-Complementation :=

mother -> head comp
<mother, lp_list, list> = <head, lp_list, list>
<head, lp_list, var, first> = <comp>
<mother, lp_list, var> = <head, lp_list, var, rest>

Left-Complementation :=

mother -> comp head
<mother, lp_list, list, first> = <comp>
<mother, lp_list, list, rest> = <head, lp_list, list>
<mother, lp_list, var> = <head, lp_list, var>

Empty Categories

Linguistic theory makes use of empty categories for a constituent that has been 'moved' from one position on the phrase structure tree to another. Empty categories are not strictly necessary, because their effect can be simulated by adding more rules to the grammar. Nevertheless, their use may be more convenient to the grammar writer[7]. For working with empty categories, the grammar writer must specify what the information content (the feature structure) of possible empty categories is. Empty categories are implemented by adding an item from each position of the chart to the same position, thus covering no element of the input string. We do not constrain the introduction of empty categories, but this could be done by treating the introduction of an empty category at some position in the chart as a normal parsing task, which can be assigned a priority by a parsing strategy. Thus it would be possible to introduce empty categories only if certain conditions are met.

Unknown Words

If an unknown word is encountered during lexical lookup, the parser does not simply fail, but rather makes the assumption that the word is a member of one of the open word classes (nouns, verbs, adjectives) of the language in question. A disjunction of these categories is then used as a preliminary (highly underspecified) lexical entry, which the parser uses for analysis of the sentence.

If the parsing succeeds, the parse result will be somewhat underspecified (e.g., for the semantic contribution of the unknown word). It is then possible to compute the constraints of the parse on the unknown word, and thus obtain some information about the unknown word. This method and its applications for automatic extension of the lexicon are discussed in (Erbach 1990).

Sentence Boundaries

In a continuous text, it is not always clear where the sentence boundaries are. Punctuation is not a clear indication because (in German), the period is also used to indicate an abbreviation and an ordinal number. It is the job of the parser to

---

[7] As far as efficiency is concerned, a large number of unary rules is just as disastrous as having empty items in the chart.

determine sentence boundaries in a text. For this purpose, the algorithm given above is somewhat extended. The parser is presented with a string of words up the next possible punctuation mark. If this string cannot be analyzed as a sentence, the parser requests the words up to the next punctuation mark, and extends the chart. The parsing process then proceeds with this longer sentence candidate.

Efficiency

Even though the parser is intended for use with a grammar development and experimentation environment, and not for large-scale text processing, efficiency has nevertheless been a major concern, because we want to minimize the waiting time for the user.

We consider two problems: the proliferation of active items which causes a waste of space, and the problem of useless parsing tasks which causes a waste of time.

The *proliferation of active items* is due to the fact that principle-based or categorial grammars use very general rules. It will often be the case that a rule can be applied to an item, resulting in an active item which then cannot be combined with any other item to form a complete constituent. A very large proportion of the storage space used in the parsing process is consumed by active items, which generally contain large feature structures. For this reason, we treat binary rules specially without introducing active items.

By not creating active items, there is some work that must be done repeatedly, however. Consider the following situation in the chart, which contains four passive items (A, B, C and D):

```
|——A——|——B——|
      |——C——|
      |——D——|
```

For every binary cf rule R, we can now create three parsing tasks: apply R to item A and item B, apply it to item A and item C, and apply it to item A and item D.

Applying the rule R to items A and B means unifying it *first* with the feature structure of item A, and then with the feature structure of item B. If the unification with item A fails, it will fail for the other two parsing tasks as well. Therefore the parser records that applying rule R to item A as the first element of the RHS has failed, and knows consequently that all tasks of the form

binary_cf_rule(R,A,?)

will fail as well.

Since the largest proportion of binary rule application fails, we retain one advantage of using active items, namely that we do not try a failing unification a second time. However, for unifications that do succeed, we do not store intermediate results, because this would be exactly the same as creating an active item, which we want to avoid because of the space problems mentioned above.

The second problem concerns *useless parsing tasks*, that is, parsing tasks that do not succeed. There are two reasons for filtering out these useless parsing tasks. The first is that the computational cost of executing these parsing tasks should be avoided, and the second is that there is no point in computing a priority for these failing tasks and adding them to the agenda.

While in general, there is no way of telling which task is going to fail and which is going to succeed (unless the task is performed!), a large proportion of rule applications can be eliminated by a computationally inexpensive filter. For every rule and every passive item we compute a Prolog term which contains only a subset of the information of its feature structure, i.e., it subsumes the feature structure. Before the task is added to the agenda, the Prolog terms associated with the rule and the items are unified. If this unification fails, we know that the task is also going to fail, and it is not added to the agenda. With this method, a large proportion of the failure-bound parsing tasks can be filtered out. Because Prolog unification is much cheaper than unification of STUF terms, a large amount of time is saved this way.

Parsing Strategies

By a parsing strategy, we mean a method for choosing among several possible parsing tasks by assigning a priority to a parsing task. There are three objectives for using explicit parsing strategies instead of simple depth-first or breadth-first search:

— reduction of the search space
— finding the intended reading for ambiguous sentences
— creating a model of human sentence processing

We will focus here only on the first two issues, and leave the third to psycholinguistic research. It should be noted that a parsing strategy is not useful if one wants to have all possible analyses of a sentence, because this requires exploration of the complete search space.

The motivation for using parsing strategies is mostly one of efficiency. First of all, the objective of a parsing strategy is to find an analysis of a sentence with minimal effort. Moreover, in the face of ambiguity, there are two sources of inefficiency: firstly the exploration of the complete search space and secondly the effort involved in deciding which reading is the intended one. We hope that the use of a parsing strategy will overcome both of these problems.

For reduction of the search space a strategy can be constructed automatically by measuring how many times rules are applied, and assigning a high priority to those parsing tasks which involve rules which frequently contribute to a successful analysis. In order to obtain the data necessary for the definition of parsing strategies, the parser collects statistics on how often each rule is attempted, how often it is successful, and how often it contributes to the final parse result.

Finding the intended reading can only be achieved by close interaction with semantics and discourse representation. The idea is to filter out semantically implausible readings as soon and as locally as possible. Such early semantic processing results in the evaluation of chart items according to their plausibility. These values of the items will then be used in the calculation of priorities for tasks involving these items. Another possible source providing input for the evaluation of chart items are LP constraints, whose violation decreases the acceptability of a sentence, but does not make it completely ungrammatical. The evaluation of chart items is still largely uncharted territory and a matter of future research.

The architecture of the parser provides a framework in which research on parsing strategies can be conducted. Our experimentation suggests that a parsing strategy which assigns tasks a priority according to the rule which is involved in the parsing task can reduce the search space significantly.

Let us now turn to the question how parsing strategies are implemented. A parsing strategy means choosing an order in which the different parsing tasks are executed. In order to achieve this, each parsing task is assigned a priority. This priority is a function of the information that is available about the parsing task (and other information about the chart as well). To illustrate the implementation of parsing strategies, we provide examples of some evaluation functions. The absolute value of the priority is irrelevant; only the relative value compared to the values of other parsing tasks is needed.

depth-first

Every new parsing task must be given higher priority than the older parsing tasks. This can be achieved, for example, by taking the system time as value for the priority[8].

priority(TASK) = system_time

breadth-first

Every new parsing task must be given lower priority than the older parsing tasks. This can be achieved by making the inverse of the system time the value for the priority.

priority(TASK) = 0 − system_time

right-to-left

priority(TASK) = 0 − starting_position of resulting item

long strings first

priority(TASK) = length of resulting item

unary rules first

priority(TASK) = 1 if a unary rule is involved, and 0 otherwise

frequently used rules first

In our experiments, this has proved to be the most successful and effective parsing strategy. See (Erbach 1991) for more details.

priority(TASK) = frequency of the rule involved in the task

Options of the Parser

The parser has a number of options which control its behaviour. Some options enforce a different interpretation of the grammar and add to the power of the parser, and may thus yield different parses, while others concern the internal representation of items and the order of enumeration of the parse results.

---

[8] In reality, we implement a depth-first-strategy by assigning the same priority to all tasks. When a task is added to the agenda, and there is already a task with the same priority, the new task is placed before the old one.

We will first consider those options that make the parser more or less powerful and cause it to yield different results:

LP constraints   LP constraints may be interpreted either for sister constituents or in user-defined domains (in hierarchical structures), as described above, or they may be ignored completely.

Empty categories   The introduction of empty categories may optionally be suppressed.

Punctuation   A grammar may or may not contain lexical entries and rules that deal with punctuation. This option specifies whether the parser ignores punctuation or treats each punctuation mark as one word.

Unknown words   The processing of unknown words may be turned off, in which case the analysis fails if an unknown word is encountered.

Addition of features While the parser is running, it may add features to the feature structure of new chart items.

There is one feature that gives each item a unique name, e.g., the number of that item.

Another feature for lexical items encodes whether or not the word was capitalized. This is useful if the grammar writer wants to exploit information about capitalization of a word at the start of a sentence.

The third dynamically added feature relates to the position of the item in the chart. The position feature has two features, one for the starting vertex of the item, and one for the ending vertex. This feature can be exploited to encode word order regularities, to check for adjacency of items.

For example, an equation like <cat1, pos, end> = <cat2, pos, start> would specify that cat1 is followed by cat2.

The following options do not change the language accepted by the parser, but rather its efficiency, and the order in which the parse results are enumerated.

Complete search   This option gives two choices:

—   All parses are enumerated, which is useful for testing the grammar, and finding out which ambiguities are present. This option is also useful if one has no way of knowing which reading is the correct one.

—   The parser stops after one analysis has been found. More analyses can be searched for by restarting the parser from the state in which the first parse had been found. For this purpose, the chart and the agenda are saved. This option is useful if a parsing strategy has been defined.

Binary rules	Binary rules can be processed with or without creation of active items. The consequences for the efficiency of the parser are discussed above.
Useless task filter	The filter for useless rule applications (see above) may be turned off. This is useful for checking the efficiency gain achieved by different filters. The user may choose which paths of the feature structure are included in the filter.
Parsing strategy	The user may select one of the parsing strategies. New parsing strategies can be defined by writing an evaluation function for parsing tasks.

Conclusion

We have given an overview of the choices in parser design, and motivated the choices we have taken in light of the use of the parser for a linguistic development environment. The use of a parser in a linguistic development environment is necessary in order to check whether the grammar accepts the sentences it should and assigns them the correct structures. State-of-the-art linguistic development environments consist of an editor, a parser, and a tool for inspecting parse results.

Such an parser-based environment does not offer means for checking whether the grammar overgenerates, nor does it offer any convenient way of checking why the analysis of a particular sentence has failed. For these purposes, a linguistic development environment must be extended by two components:

— A generator which will produce a representative sample of sentences for every grammar. The set of produced sentences is restricted to a manageable size by using only a subset of the lexicon with only one member for every word class, by limiting recursion and the length of the sentences produced. Such a system has been implemented and is described in (Arens, Erbach 1991)

— A means for selecting linguistic objects (lexical entries, chart items, grammar rules), and unifiying them with each other. In case of a unification failure, the system should indicate why the unification has failed. Such a functionality is useful for determining the source of an error in the grammar if the analysis of a sentence has failed unexpectedly.

References

Arens, R. G., Erbach, G. (1991): Evaluation von Grammatiken für die Analyse natürlicher Sprache durch automatische Generierung einer repräsentativen Satzmenge. In: Proceedings of GWAI '91.

Chomsky, N. (1981): Lectures on government and binding. Foris, Dordrecht

Erbach, G. (1990): Syntactic processing of unknown words. In: Jorrand, P., Sgurev, V. (eds.): Artificial Intelligence IV, methodology, systems, applications. North-Holland, Amsterdam

Erbach, G. (1991): An environment for experimenting with parsing strategies. In: Proceedings of IJCAI '91, Sydney

Gazdar, G., Klein, E., Pullum, G., Sag, I. (1985): Generalized phrase structure grammar. Basil Blackwell, Oxford

Kaplan, R., Bresnan, J. (1982): Lexical functional grammar: a formal system for grammatical representation. In: Bresnan, J. (ed.): The mental representation of grammatical relations. MIT Press, Cambridge, MA, pp. 173-281

Kay, M. (1980): Algorithm schemata and data structures in syntactic processing. Report CSL-80-12, XEROX PARC, Palo Alto, CA

Kay, M. (1985): Parsing in functional unification grammar. In: Dowty, D., Karttunen, L., Zwicky, M. (eds.): Natural language parsing. Cambridge University Press, Cambridge, UK

Kay, M. (1989): Head-driven parsing. In: Proceedings of the international workshop on parsing technology. Carnegie-Mellon University, Pittsburgh, PA

Marcus, M. (1980): A theory of syntactic recognition for natural language. MIT Press, Cambridge, MA

Pereira, F., Shieber, S. (1987): Prolog and natural language analysis. CSLI Lecture Notes 10, Stanford, CA

Shieber, S., Uszkoreit, H., Pereira, F., Robinson, J., Tyson, M. (1983): The formalism and implementation of PATR-II. In: Grosz, B., Stickel, M. (eds.): Research on interactive acquisition and use of knowledge. Stanford Research Institute International, Menlo Park, CA

Sterling, L., Shapiro, E. (1986): The art of Prolog. MIT Press, Cambridge, MA

Uszkoreit, H. (1986a): Categorial unification grammar. In: Proceedings of COLING, pp. 187 - 194, Bonn, Germany

Uszkoreit, H. (1986b): Linear precedence in discontinuous constituents: complex fronting in German. CSLI Report 86-47, Stanford, CA

Gap-Handling Mechanisms
In Categorial Grammars

Esther König

Abstract

We compare and evaluate three methods for handling extraposition phenomena with categorial grammars: one method which makes use of the extension of categorial grammars by features, the so-called gap- threading method, and two methods which rely on extensions of the deductive framework of the grammar formalism either by a rule of functional composition (Combinatory Categorial Grammar) or by a rule of functional abstraction (Lambek calculus).

1 Introduction

Grammar formalisms must allow for the description of many different aspects of the syntactic phenomena in a natural language. As the basic ingredients of a grammar formalism, one needs at least the means to describe

1. *Immediate Dominance* (ID), i.e., functor-argument structures, phrase structures

2. *Linear Precedence*, i.e., word order in local ID-trees

There are (among others) two grammar formalisms which allow for these kinds of structural descriptions: the context-free phrase structure grammars and the basic categorial grammars **B** ([BHGS60]).

Natural languages are more or less flexible concerning word order. Variations of word order which are local to one functor can still be treated in the simple grammar formalisms of the above kind. But they cannot deal (directly) with extraction phenomena, where a substructure is "moved" globally, i.e., over several borders of local functor-argument structures.

In order to handle certain kinds of extraction phenomena, the context-free phrase structure grammars and their relatives have been augmented with so-called gap-threading or gap-percolation mechanisms ([KB82], [GKPS85], [PS87b], etc.). If one imposes certain structural restrictions on these mechanisms they do not exceed the power of context-free grammars, i.e., the corresponding gap-handling mechanism corresponds to a *finite* extension of a context-free grammar ([Gaz88]).

The *gap-threading* method can be applied in categorial grammars as well. It was the method of choice in the LILOG prototype no. 1 and is described in [Bou87] and [Wes88]. Steedman and his colleagues argue for an extension of the deductive capacity of categorial grammars by rules of *functional composition*, which they call "partial combination rules" ([AS82], [Ste85] and cf. [Dow88]). Their approach is named "Combinatory Categorial Grammar" (**CCG**). More recently, the Lambek calculus (**L**) ([Lam58]), whose rule of *functional abstraction* represents an elegant generalization of the **CCG** approach has been rediscovered for linguistic application ([Moo88], [Mor89b], [OZ89], etc.). From a theorem-proving point of view, the Lambék calculus is an instance of a logical system where hypothetical reasoning is used. There are other methods for gap handling or variations of the above methods (see, e.g., [Mor88], [BG89], [Par89]) but we want to limit our investigation to the three mentioned ones in order to show the principles of gap handling in categorial grammars.

The paper is organized as follows: The basic categorial grammars and their augmentation by feature structures are introduced. Then the fundamentals of the three different gap-handling methods are presented in such a way that their similarities become obvious. The paper concludes with a list of the differences which nevertheless exist in order to give a basis for further discussion and systematic experimentation.

2 Basic Categorial Grammars

The following parameters define the basic categorial grammars **B** and will be the core of all the grammar definitions in this paper:

- A finite set C_0 of basic categories is given

- The set of categories C is defined by
  $$C := C_0 \cup \{z \mid z = x/y \text{ or } z = x \backslash y; \ x, y \in C\}$$

- The *goal category* or start symbol of the grammar is a basic category

- A *lexicon* is a function from a finite set of lexemes onto a set of finite sets of categories. These finite sets can be given either extensionally, or intensionally by lexical rules with finite output and applicability.

- The two combination rules "leftward application" ($app_\backslash$) and "rightward application" ($app_/$):

  $$\begin{aligned} (app_\backslash) \quad & y, \ x\backslash y \to x \\ (app_/) \quad & x/y, \ y \to x \end{aligned}$$

The category y is usually referred to as the *argument category*, and the category x is called *value category*. Complex categories are named *functor categories*.

Derivation trees in basic categorial grammar look quite similar to phrase structure trees. Figure 1 shows the tree for the example:

daß	eine	Frau	ein	Buch	liest
that	*a*	*woman*	*a*	*book*	*reads*

For the sake of simplicity, we assume that the verb-final and the verb-first positions are the two alternative standards which are encoded with the lexical entries for verbs.

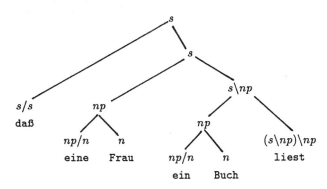

Figure 1: A syntax tree in a basic categorial grammar

2.1 Adding Feature Unification

Since features and feature unification have become indispensable tools for linguistic description, categorial grammars have been augmented with feature structures ([Kar89, presented in 1986], [Usz86], and [ZKC86]).

Here we define how the basic categorial grammars and feature unification can be married. For the feature terms, we adopt a STUF-like (or PATR-II-like, [SUP$^+$83]) notation. The following example shows how the construction of the logical form of a two-place verb is defined.

$$(s(\begin{bmatrix} lf : & subj : \langle 1 \rangle \\ & obj : \langle 2 \rangle \end{bmatrix})\backslash np([lf : \langle 1 \rangle]))/np([lf : \langle 2 \rangle])$$

The definition of the combination rules $(app_\backslash)$ and $(app_/)$ must be extended in such a way that feature structures are handled appropriately. We give an informal definition for the required extensions in the case of the rule $(app_\backslash)$:

$$(app_\backslash) \qquad y', \ x\backslash y \rightarrow \sigma(x)$$

where the categories y and y' must be unifiable by a variable substitution σ.

3 Gap-Handling Mechanisms

In this section, we introduce the three gap-handling mechanisms to be compared. In order to work out the similarity between the three approaches, we omit any details which would obscure this relation. In particular, we demonstrate only the core ideas of the gap-threading method and of the Combinatory Categorial Grammar approach.

The three methods are described by showing how they encode the three parts of the extraction phenomenon: the gap filler, the consumer of the gap filler, and the "bridge" (cf. [GKPS85, p. 138]):

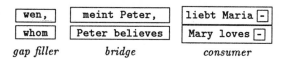

wen,	meint Peter,	liebt Maria $\boxed{\text{-}}$
whom	Peter believes	Mary loves $\boxed{\text{-}}$
gap filler	*bridge*	*consumer*

3.1 The Gap-Threading Approach

3.1.1 Gap Filler

Gap filler categories are given lexically, e.g.,

wen *(whom)*: $s/s([gap:np])$

This means that the category of the word "**wen**" expects as its argument a category s which lacks an np-argument.

3.1.2 Consumer

For every functor category which allows for extraction of its rightmost argument an alternative category is added by a lexical rule, e.g.,

(gap intro) $\quad s/np\,\vec{a} \rightarrow s(gap:np)\,\vec{a}$

The $\vec{a}$-sign[1] stands for all the other arguments of the category and their directionalities besides the mentioned argument np. The restriction to rightmost arguments (or leftmost ones) is for reasons of conformity with the other approaches which are presented here.

3.1.3 Bridge

The distance between the gap filler and the consumer is bridged over by explicit gap threading. Functor categories which allow for through-passing of a gap filler are augmented with a "gap threading statement", e.g.,

meint(*believes*) : $(s([gap:\langle 1\rangle])/s([gap:\langle 1\rangle]))/np$

3.2 Sample Tree

Figure 2 shows how the gap-threading mechanism works for the sentence

Wen,   meint   Peter,   liebt   Maria?
Whom   (believes   Peter)   loves   Maria

---

[1]This notation is due to [Hen87].

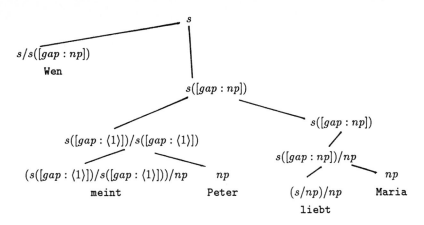

Figure 2: An example for gap-threading

3.3 The Deductive Approaches

Since the two deductive approaches **L** and **CCG** have a lot in common, they will be defined together in the same subsection.

3.3.1 Gap Filler

In the case of the deductive approaches, the lexical entry for a gap filler word is slightly different from the one used in the gap threading approach. The fact that, e.g., an argument category s with an np-gap is expected is not expressed in terms of features but in the category notation itself:

    wen: $s/(s/np)$

3.3.2 Consumer

No extra provisions are needed to designate the consumer category, i.e., any functor category which lacks, e.g., its rightmost np-argument can consume what the gap filler **"wen"** delivers (if the "bridge" mediates in the right way between the expected s-argument category and the innermost category of the consumer functor).

3.3.3 Bridge and Sample Trees

The two approaches can be distinguished by the means they use to "overcome" the bridge between the gap filler and the consumer.

The "bridge" in the Lambek calculus

In the Lambek calculus, the rules of *functional abstraction*[2] perform the task of mediating between a gap filler and its consumer (T non-empty sequence of categories):

---

[2]Care must be taken when defining the feature unification part for these rules in order not to lose the **variable** bindings of the hypothetically asserted category y.

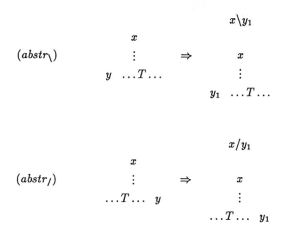

The rule $(abstr_\backslash)$ can be verbalized as:

> *If* the category x is derivable from a sequence of categories T plus an additional category y which has been put in front of T
>
> *then* consider the category $x\backslash y$ as being derivable from the sequence T alone.

In the context of the abstraction rules, the category y is called the *hypothetical category*. It is marked by an index which makes clear to which abstraction step in a derivation it belongs. Note that the introduction of such an "empty" constituent is caused by a category which is actually realized in the input.

For the presentation of the abstraction rules, we use the so-called "proof figure" notation (cf. [MLHB90]), which seems to be the most handy one for manipulation by humans.

Figure 3 shows the derivation tree for the previous German example.

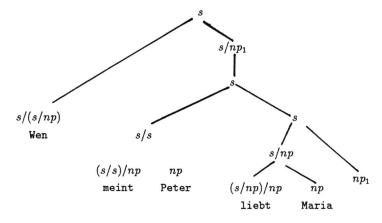

Figure 3: Gap-handling in **L**

The "bridge" in CCG

In **CCG**, the bridge is overcome by the use of the rules *leftward functional composition* and *rightward functional composition* in addition to the application rules:

$(fc_\backslash)$ $y\backslash z, x\backslash y \rightarrow x\backslash z$
$(fc_/)$ $x/y, y/z \rightarrow x/z$

Depending on the lexicon, a set of instances of the following two rules is necessary in order to turn categories which are not complex enough to participate in a certain functional composition step into more complex functor categories (*type raising*):

$(tr_\backslash)$ $y \rightarrow x\backslash(x/y)$
$(tr_/)$ $y \rightarrow x/(x\backslash y)$

For example, assume that a certain (non-linguistic) lexicon makes use of these three categories:

$s/(s/np), np, ((s\backslash np)\backslash np)/np$

This lexicon needs the following two instances of the type-raising rules as lexical rules in order to make the grammar work appropriately for extraposition cases:

$np \rightarrow s/(s\backslash np)$
$np \rightarrow (s\backslash np)/((s\backslash np)\backslash np)$

A non-linguistic example[3] shows how these rules interact to derive a "sentence" with an extraposed constituent:

$$
\begin{array}{llllll}
s/(s/np) & np & np & ((s\backslash np)\backslash np)/np & (tr_/) \\
& \overline{s/(s\backslash np)} & & & (tr_/) \\
& & \overline{(s\backslash np)/((s\backslash np)\backslash np)} & & (fc_/) \\
& & \overline{(s\backslash np)/np} & & (fc_/) \\
& & \overline{s/np} & & (app_/) \\
& & s & &
\end{array}
$$

The **CCG** version of the current linguistic example is given here:

$$
\begin{array}{lllllll}
\text{Wen} & \text{meint} & \text{Peter} & & \text{liebt} & \text{Maria} \\
s/(s/np) & (s/s)/np & np & (app_/) & (s/np)/np & np & (app_/) \\
& \overline{s/s} & & & & \overline{s/np} & (fc_/) \\
& & & & & & (app_/) \\
& & \overline{s/np} & & & & \\
& & s & & & &
\end{array}
$$

---

[3]We use the traditional **CCG** notation for the derivation tree.

4 Comparison of the Three Approaches

4.1 Feature-Based Gap-Handling Versus Deductive Extensions

First we want to compare the feature-based handling of gaps, i.e., the gap-threading approach, with the two deductive approaches CCG and L.

Observation 1 *The problem of spurious ambiguities in L (and CCG) is a spurious problem.*

When parsing with categorial grammars, the appearence of multiple analyses for one syntactic structure has been observed. This phenomenon has been called the problem of spurious ambiguities ([Kar89]) and has served as an argument against the use of categorial grammars. In the meantime, proof-theoretic solutions for the deductive approaches have been found. The solution for the case of the Lambek calculus ([Kön89]) can be adapted to the CCG-approach. In [PS87a], the two sources for the "spurious ambiguities" in CCG concerning the rules of functional composition have been determined as follows:

1. Underdetermination of the functional composition rule with regard to the question which of the two input functors "triggers" the use of the rule:
   "$(fc_/)(x_1, (fc_/)(x_2, x_3)) \equiv (fc_/)((fc_/)(x_1, x_2), x_3)$"

2. Uses of the functional composition rules where the use of application rules already would suffice:
   "$(app_/)(x_1, (app_/)(x_2, x_3)) \equiv (app_/)((fc_/)(x_1, x_2),x_3)$"

The first part of the problem can be solved by the requirement that the first functor category of the two functors to be composed must be directly available in order to trigger the use of the composition rule. The second source is eliminated if a functional composition rule is only put into action if its complex output category is needed as an *argument* in an application rule or as the second input category of a composition rule. These suggestions are incompatible with a pure bottom-up approach to parsing which gives preference to the use of the functional composition rules (hence to superfluous uses of these rules).

Observation 2 *The Lambek calculus L gets along with a smaller lexicon than the gap-threading approach without increasing the search space on the rule side.*

Since the gap-threading approach uses two different data structures for locally filled versus "long-distance" filled argument-slots, instead of only one representation in L (and CCG), the gap-threading approach needs bigger disjunctions of categories in the lexicon, created by the gap introduction rules.

The feature structures needed in the gap-threading approach are bigger: the gap-threading statements increase slightly the size of the feature structures of some categories. Furthermore, one needs additional features to avoid

1. Cases of overgeneration in Figure 4

96

2. Cases of spurious ambiguities in Figure 5 (This example is based on analyses of non-constituent coordination as proposed in [Wes89] or [Gaz81]).

One could argue that instead of augmenting the lexicon, the Lambek calculus increases the set of rules and therefore the search space for a parser/theorem prover. But, in spite of the fact that the number of rules has been doubled from 2 to 4, the search space stays practically the same. There are two easy-to-test criteria for when to use which rule:

- The application rules are used if one wants to derive a basic category

- The abstraction rules are applied if a complex category has to be derived

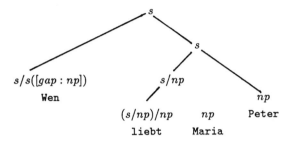

Figure 4: An example of overgeneration in the gap-threading approach

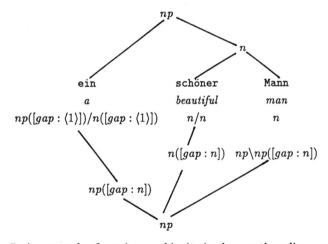

Figure 5: An example of spurious ambiguity in the gap-threading approach

4.1.1 Functional Composition Versus Functional Abstraction

Now the two deductive approaches will be compared.

Observation 3 L *includes* **CCG.**

The functional composition rules (and the type-raising rules) are theorems of the Lambek calculus ([Lam58]). This means that the functional abstraction rules are stronger than the composition rules. This additional strength is only used if the lexicon raises the need for it. See for example the category of the conjunction "und" in the example in Figure 6 where a possible L-analysis of the second half of the sentence "Martha las diese Bücher und Maria jene." (*Martha read these books and Mary those*) is shown.

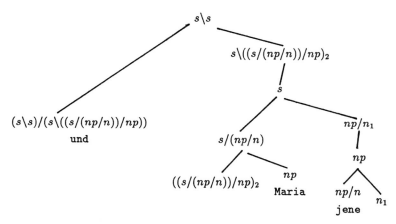

Figure 6: Use of the full power of the Lambek calculus by providing lexical categories with nested complex argument categories

Observation 4 *The L-approach gets along with a smaller lexicon than* **CCG.**

The type raising rules in CCG produce big disjunctive lexical entries, which have to be processed by the parser.

5   Conclusion

On the one hand, the four "observations" in the previous section imply the superiority of the deductive approach to gap handling in the guise of the Lambek calculus. The Lambek calculus constitutes a generalization of both the CCG and the gap-threading approach: the rule of functional abstraction makes most of the lexical manipulations of the latter approaches superfluous. On the other hand, this conclusion contradicts the arguments in the literature which support the gap-threading approach ([Bou87] and [Pol88]) against the CCG-style deductive approach. Bouma and Pollard critize the fact that the deductive approaches use the same data structure for both local functor-argument dependencies and long-distance dependencies. They warn that unwanted interactions cannot be excluded. We can turn this argument against the gap- threading approach itself: it needs extra features in order to avoid undesired side-effects of the gap-threading mechanism. The deductive approaches do not need these additional and unclear provisions, because they use two clearly distinct mechanisms for local versus long distance dependency. In the case of **L**, local dependencies are accounted for by the application rules, whereas long-distance dependencies are handled by the abstraction rules.

The Lambek calculus uses a logical technique for the handling of long-distance phenomena: hypothetical reasoning [GR84]. The fact that gap-threading by features and hypothetical reasoning are two sides of the same coin was first discussed in [Par89]. Pareschi shows how gap threading in GPSG can be simulated in Harrop Hereditary Logic, a first-order Horn Logic which allows for embedded implications in the body of a clause. The Lambek calculus is a rather restricted propositional variant of this logic.

A new picture of the design of grammar formalisms emerges:

1. On the one hand there is a specialized *propositional calculus* which states how, in principle, functor-argument structures are built, and, e.g., long-distance dependencies are handled.

2. On the other hand there is a highly structured lexicon which consists of

   (a) *propositions*, i.e., categories, which will cause uses of the inference rules of the grammar calculus during the parsing/theorem-proving process.

   (b) feature structures associated with these propositions which represent the *constraints* on certain of these combinatory inference steps.

Processing will be more efficient and grammar coding will be clearer if one does not try to do just about everything with feature structures and unification, i.e., on the level of the constraint language. It seems wise to separate out phenomena which can be described clearly in the logic part of the system.

The Lambek calculus is just the first, naked species created by the spirit of the grammar-as-logic paradigm, see [Mor89a] . . . .

References

[AS82]   Anthony E. Ades, Mark J. Steedman: On the order of words. *Linguistics and Philosophy*, 4:517–558, 1982

[BG89]   Gabriel Bès, Claire Gardent: French order without order. In *Proceedings of the Fourth Conference of the European Chapter of the Association for Computational Linguistics*, pp. 249–255, Manchester, UK, 1989

[BHGS60] Yehoshua Bar-Hillel, Chaim Gaifman, E. Shamir: On categorial and phrase structure grammars. *Bull. Res. Council Israel, Sec. F.*, 9:1–16, 1960. Reprinted in: Bar-Hillel, Y. (ed.): Language and Information. Selected Essays on Their Theory and Application. Addison-Wesley, Reading, MA, 1964, pp. 99–115.

[Bou87]   Gosse Bouma: A unification-based analysis of unbounded dependencies in categorial grammar. In Jeroen Groenendijk, Martin Stokhof, Frank Veltman, (eds.): *Proceedings of the Sixth Amsterdam Colloquium*, pp. 1–19. Institute for Language, Logic and Information, University of Amsterdam, 1987

[Dow88]   David R. Dowty: Type raising, functional composition, and non-constituent conjunction. In Richard T. Oehrle, Emmon Bach, Deirdre Wheeler (eds.): *Categorial Grammars and Natural Languages Structures*. Reidel, Dordrecht, 1988. Proceedings of the Conference on Categorial Grammar, Tucson, AZ, 1985

[Gaz81]   Gerald Gazdar: Unbounded dependencies and coordinate structure. *Linguistic Inquiry*, 12(2):155–183, 1981

[Gaz88]   Gerald Gazdar: Applicability of indexed grammars to natural languages. In Uwe Reyle, Christian Rohrer (eds.): *Natural Language Parsing and Linguistic Theories*, pp. 69–94. Reidel, Dordrecht, 1988

[GKPS85] Gerald Gazdar, Ewan Klein, G.K. Pullum, Ivan Sag: *Generalized Phrase Structure Grammar*. Blackwell, Oxford, UK, 1985

[GR84]   Dov Gabbay, Uwe Reyle: N-PROLOG: An extension of PROLOG with hypothetical implications. *Journal of Logic Programming*, 4:319–355, 1984

[Hen87]   Herman Hendriks: Type change in semantics: The scope of quantification and coordination. In Ewan Klein, Johan van Benthem (eds.): *Categories, Polymorphism and Unification*. Centre for Cognitive Science, University of Edinburgh, and Institute for Language, Logic and Information, University of Amsterdam, Edinburgh and Amsterdam, 1987

[Hep90]   Mark Hepple: Verb movement in Dutch and English. a categorial grammar analysis. Report 1.1.A, ESPRIT Basic Research Action 3175, Dynamic Interpretation of Natural Language (DYANA), Edinburgh, UK, 1990

[Kar89]   Lauri Karttunen: Radical lexicalism. In Mark Baltin, Anthony Kroch (eds.): *Alternative Conceptions of Phrase Structure*, pp. 43–65. University of Chicago Press, 1989

[KB82]   Ronald M. Kaplan, Joan Bresnan: Lexical-Functional Grammar: A formal system for grammatical representation. In Joan Bresnan (ed.): *The Mental Representation of Grammatical Relations*, pp. 173–281. MIT Press, Cambridge, MA, 1982

[Kön89]   Esther König: Parsing as natural deduction. In *Proceedings of the 27th Annual Meeting of Association for Computational Linguistics*, pp. 272–279, Vancouver, B.C., 1989

[Kön90]   Esther König: *Der Lambek-Kalkül. Eine Logik für lexikalische Grammatiken (The Lambek calculus. A logic for lexical grammars)*. PhD thesis, Stuttgart University, Stuttgart, Germany, 1990

[Lam58] Joachim Lambek: The mathematics of sentence structure. *American Mathematical Monthly*, 65:154–170, 1958. Reprinted in: W. Buszkowski, W. Marciszewski, J. van Benthem (eds.): Categorial Grammar. Amsterdam, 1988

[MLHB90] Glyn Morrill, Neil Leslie, Mark Hepple, Guy Barry: Categorial deductions and structural operations. In Guy Barry, Glyn Morrill (eds.): *Edinburgh Working Papers in Cognitive Science*, vol. 5, pp. 1–21. Centre for Cognitive Science, University of Edinburgh, Edinburgh, UK, 1990

[Moo88] Michael Moortgat: *Categorial Investigations. Logical and Linguistic Aspects of the Lambek Calculus.* Foris Publications, Dordrecht, 1988. Dissertation, University of Amsterdam

[Mor88] Glyn Morrill: *Extraction and Coordination in Phrase Structure Grammar and Categorial Grammar.* PhD thesis, University of Edinburgh, Centre for Cognitive Science, Edinburgh, UK, 1988

[Mor89a] Glyn Morrill: Grammar as logic. Technical Report EUCCS/RP-34, Centre for Cognitive Science, University of Edinburgh, Edinburgh, UK, 1989

[Mor89b] Glyn Morrill: Intensionality, boundedness, and modal logic. Technical Report EUCCS/RP-32, Centre for Cognitive Science, University of Edinburgh, Edinburgh, UK, 1989

[OZ89] Richard T. Oehrle, S. Zhang: Lambek calculus and preposing of embedded subjects. In C. Wiltshire (ed.): *CLS 25, Papers from the Twenty-Fifth Regional Meeting*, Chicago, IL, 1989. Chicago Linguistic Society

[Par89] Remo Pareschi: *Type-Driven Natural Language Analysis.* PhD thesis, University of Edinburgh, Edinburgh, UK, 1989

[Pol88] Carl Pollard: Categorial grammar and phrase structure grammar: An excursion on the syntax-semantics frontier. In Emmon Bach, Richard Oehrle, Deirdre Wheeler (eds.): *Categorial Grammars and Natural Languages Structures.* Reidel, Dordrecht, 1988. Proceedings of the Conference on Categorial Grammar, Tucson, AZ, 1985

[PS87a] Remo Pareschi, Mark Steedman: A lazy way to chart-parse with categorial grammars. In *Proceedings of the 25th Annual Meeting of the Association for Computational Linguistics*, Stanford, CA, 1987

[PS87b] Carl Pollard, Ivan Sag: *An Information-Based Syntax and Semantics. I. Fundamentals*, vol. 13 of *Lecture Notes.* Center for Study of Language and Information, Stanford, CA, 1987

[Ste85] Mark Steedman: Dependency and coordination in the grammar of Dutch and English. *Language*, 61(3):523–568, 1985

[SUP+83] Stuart Shieber, Hans Uszkoreit, Fernando Pereira, Jane Robinson, M. Tyson: The for-
          malism and implementation of PATR-II. In B. Grosz, M. E. Stickel (eds.): *Research on
          Interactive Acquisition and Use of Knowledge.* Stanford Research Institute International,
          Menlo Park, Ca., 1983

[Usz86]   Hans Uszkoreit: Categorial Unification Grammars. In *Proceedings of the 11th Interna-
          tional Conference on Computational Linguistics*, pp. 187–194, Bonn, Germany, 1986

[Wes88]   Birgit Wesche: German word order in the LILOG-system. In *Proceedings of the IBM
          Conference on Natural Language Processing*, pp. 90–96, Thornwood, NY, 1988

[Wes89]   Birgit Wesche: Spurious ambiguities - on the syntax-semantics relation in C(U)G. In
          Stephan Busemann, Christa Hauenschild, Carla Umbach (eds.): *Views of the Syntax-
          Semantics Interface*, pp. 133–166, Berlin, July 1989. KIT, Universität Berlin. Proceedings
          of the Workshop GPSG and Semantics

[ZKC86]   Henk Zeevat, Ewan Klein, Jo Calder: Unification categorial grammar. Technical Report
          EUCCS/RP-21, Centre for Cognitive Science, University of Edinburgh, Edinburgh, UK,
          1986

Chapter 1.2

Lexicon

Outlines of the LEU/2 Lexicology

Siegfried Kanngießer

Abstract

LEU/2 is a language processing computer system which is lexically creative and, therefore, able to form and to comprehend words which are not elements of the fixed inventory of the LEU/2 lexicon. The lexical creativity of the system arises from two features radically different from each other and, consequently, complementary to each other. On the one hand, the system is lexically creative because LEU/2 is able to extend its lexicon by means of its knowledge of certain rules of word formation. In this respect the LEU/2 lexicology has an explanatory force, as this lexicology gives, at least on a highly abstract level of representation, an answer to the question how the lexical creativity of the native speaker/hearer is structured. On the other hand, the system is able to extend its lexicon incrementally, namely by means of an access to external lexica and an interactive use of the user input. These mechanisms optimize the lexical power of the system, but, trivially, they do not induce explanations of the lexical creativity of the native speaker/hearer. The LEU/2 lexicology is, therefore, the result of a mixed methodology, as this lexicology is partly explanatory and partly a non-explanatory procedure to optimize the lexical capacity of the system.

1. The foundation of the LEU/2 lexicology is given by the insight that every native speaker/hearer SH of a language L is, whatever SH may be with regard to the entirety of his or her linguistic abilities, at least this: a linguistically creative system. As is well known, this linguistic creativity is manifested by the ability of SH to produce and to understand an unlimited number of L-sentences, L-phrases and, last but not least, L-texts. However, as is well known, too, the linguistic creativity of SH is not only demonstrated by these essentially sentence-grammatical abilities; it is also manifested by the faculty of SH to create and to comprehend an unlimited number of L-words. The fact that SH is a linguistically creative system means, therefore, in every case, that SH is a word-grammatical creative system. Obviously, this word-grammatical creativity rests upon the SH knowledge of the rules of word formation on the one hand, and upon his knowledge of the word meanings on the other hand. By means of these systems of knowledge the speaker/hearer is not only able to produce and to comprehend L-words which he has never previously heard or uttered and which are, in this sense, SH-new words, his word-grammatical creativity enables SH also to create and to understand L-words which are not elements of the fixed inventory of the L-lexicon and which are, therefore, in the strict sense of this concept, L-new words.[1] Evidently, the creation of L-new words changes the extent of the L-lexicon just as the creation of SH-new words changes the extent of the SH-lexicon; the creation of new words induces in both cases innovations of the lexicon. Therefore, the word-grammatical creativity of SH implies the lexical creativity of SH, and for this reason a native speaker/hearer of a natural language L is necessarily a lexically creative system. Furthermore, it should be clear that the lexical creativity of SH opens SH-new possibilities in the domain of sentence grammar, as SH's ability to form and produce L-sentences depends on the elements belonging to the L-lexicon: in this respect the cardinality of the lexicon determines the possibilities to generate and to interpret L-sentences. The lexical extensions, which SH is able to induce on the base of his word-grammatical knowledge, are

---

[1] That these words are L-new words in the strict sense of this concept means especially that they are L-new in a sense in which no sentence which is possible in L, but which has never been previously uttered, can be an L-new sentence. By this fact it becomes evident that there is a radical difference between sentence grammar and word grammar. This difference is explained in Kanngießer (1985) in detail; the study contains also a specification of the concept of novelty.

thus extensions of the power of the sentence grammar.[2] Insight into this relation, which exists between sentence grammar and word grammar, should make it obvious that lexical creativity, and likewise the system of word-grammatical knowledge which is the base of the lexical creativity of SH, is an essential component of the entirety of the linguistic achievements of a native speaker/hearer.

However, if this is the case, then there is no doubt that a computer system, which can be regarded as able to process a natural language L in a non-trivial manner and to a non-trivial extent, must be a system which is lexically creative too. In general, the attempt to develop such a system (a speaker/hearer machine, so to speak) has a chance to be successful only if this attempt is guided by the aim to develop a lexically creative speaker/hearer machine.[3] It is an explicit goal of the LEU/2 lexicology (and surely its most important one) to make it possible for the system to behave in a lexically creative manner. Of course, the question arises how this goal can be reached. The answer is that there are two ways of reaching this aim, at least in a non-trivial approximation. Therefore, the competent component of the system LEU/2, called LexMan, uses a set of different, but interacting strategies and knowledge sources which are complementary to each other.[4] What is meant by this answer is specified in the relevant details in the following sections of this paper.

2. First, LEU/2 is lexically creative because the system is equipped with a system of knowledge of word meanings and of certain rules of word formation. It is this knowledge system which enables LexMan to produce and to understand German words which are new in relation to the LEU/2 lexicon LEX/2, and it is this knowledge which enables LexMan to generate and to comprehend words which are even new-in-German, namely L-new, in the strict sense of this concept. The case of nominal composition may serve to illustrate how this lexical creativity of the system becomes possible. The mechanisms of nominal composition are structured within the framework of an order-sorted logic; consequently, these mechanisms make use of a sort hierarchy with inheritance of features and roles.[5] Of course, this allows sortal inferences; the system can, for instance, infer that if x belongs to the sort s_1, then also belongs to the sort s_2, and so on. Beside syntactic and morphological information, whose structure and processing are not the subjects of the present consideration, the mechanism of nominal composition uses, for the purpose of semantic

---

[2]It is easy to see that extensions of the lexicon systematically involve extensions, and often even refinements, of the conceptual knowledge of the speaker/hearer; cf. Emde (in this volume). An answer to the question how to represent conceptual knowledge is given by Gust (in this volume), cf. also Gust (1991) and Gust, Scheffczyk (1991).

[3]A system able to extend its lexicon bears the potential to accumulate information of a previously unforeseen diversity, density and depth, and this is one of the main reasons for the requirement that a natural language understanding system must be a lexically creative system. For further arguments see Emde (in this volume) and Ludewig (in this volume), cf. also Gust, Ludewig (1989).

[4]LexMan is described in detail by Emde (in this volume).

[5]On how far as the sort hierarchy is concerned with respect to word formation and the representation of word meanings, see Rickheit (in this volume) and Gust (in this volume).

interpretation, essentially sortal information of this kind.[6] In order to show how the system deals with this information it is sufficient to consider the extremely simple case of (N-N)-composition, which leads to compounds like "Kunstsammlung" (art collection). Syntactically, these compounds consist of two words w_1, w_2 of the category N, with w_2 as the head of the (N-N)-construction. The semantic interpretation of this construction takes into account the information supplied by the sort hierarchy, which means the relation r, which exists between the two N-meanings of the (N-N)-structure, is determined sortally. Obviously, in the case of nominal compounds like "Kunstsammlung" the relation r is induced by the meaning of the head element of the construction; that is the two N-meaning are related by the relation r = is_collection_of. Furthermore, the sort of art collections is a subsort of the sort of collections. From this specification of the relation r and from the sortal in-formation, the semantic interpretation of the (N-N)-structure results. Neglecting many details, the interpretational device can be represented as shown in the following figure:

$$N(w_1 + w_2, x: s_2 \mid r(x: s_2, y: s_3) \land (s_3 < s_1))$$
$$N(w_1, y: s_3, ?) \quad N(w_2, x: s_2 \mid r(y: s_1, x: s_2))$$

Figure 1

It seems unnecessary to discuss further details of the processes of nominal composition or to specify further mechanisms of word formation in this place.[7] It has been asserted that LEU/2 is a lexically creative system because its subcomponent LexMan is equipped with word formation knowledge. The above discussion and the example given in Fig. 1 should have made clear in general, if not on points of detail, what is meant by this assertion and why it is indeed permissible to attribute to the LEU/2 system a lexical creativity based on word formation knowledge.

3. LEU/2 is a lexically creative system because of its knowledge of rules of word formation. But, of course, it is not the privilege of LEU/2 to be equipped with knowledge of this kind. On the contrary, it is not reasonably possible to doubt that the native speaker/hearer SH is also equipped with knowledge of the rules of composition and of derivation. Furthermore, there is sufficient evidence to justify the assumption that with respect to the processes of word formation, SH is a sortal information processing system. This means, at least insofar as the abstract level of representation exemplified in Fig. 1 is concerned, there is no relevant difference between the native speaker/hearer SH and a speaker/hearer machine like LEU/2. The rules of derivation and of composition, which enable LEU/2 to be lexically creative, are, in principle, the

---

[6] The question of how LEU/2 processes morphological information is answered by Steffens, Schiller (in this volume).

[7] More complex cases of (N-N)-composition can be treated by additional specification of the relation r. For instance, r may be given by r = is_temporally_located_in, and so on. This hint shows how complex compounds can be represented by the use of specified relations. These specifications can be intrinsic or extrinsic in nature, in a sense of these concepts which is explained in Kanngießer (1985); cf. also the literature cited there. Rickheit (in this volume) shows especially how LexMan proceeds when extending its lexicon by means of derivation.

same rules which enable SH to be a lexically creative system. In this respect the LEU/2 system is, in fact, a simulation of the SH ability to extend his lexicon.

As far as the processes of word formation are concerned, LEU/2 has a simulative content. The devices which enable LEU/2 to extend its lexicon reflect the mechanisms that make it possible for SH to be a lexically creative system. Therefore, insight into these devices induces an insight into the mechanisms that constitute the lexical creativity of the native speaker/hearer SH.[8] This means that LexMan gives, at least in part, an answer to the question of how the native SH knowledge of word formation is structured. The simulation of the native SH knowledge by the system induces an explanation of this knowledge.[9] In this sense one can say that the lexical creativity of the system is a function of its simulative content.

Unfortunately, the explanations induced by the system in the mode of simulation are incomplete. They are incomplete because the system's knowledge of word formation in German is incomplete.[10] The immediate consequence of this incompleteness is, of course, that there are words new for the system which are outside the scope of the system's knowledge of word formation. There are LEX/2-new words which cannot be analysed and interpreted semantically by LexMan on the basis of its word-grammatical knowledge; the lexical creativity of the system is limited by gaps in its lexical knowledge.

Despite the first impression, this does not imply that LexMan is definitely not able to process LEX/2-new words which are beyond its word-grammatical knowledge. LexMan is able to extend its lexicon incrementally, and this second possibility to behave in a lexically creative manner is quite independent of its knowledge of the rules of word formation. Consequently, incremental extensions of the lexicon can serve to fill the gaps in the system's lexical creativity. How incremental extensions of LEX/2 become possible is sketched out in the following section of the paper.

4. The lexicon LEX/2 of the LEU/2 system consists initially of a fixed, finite inventory of structured vocabulary units; this subcomponent LEX/2A is called the permanent lexicon of the system. The lexical extensions by means of composition and derivation produce a second subcomponent LEX/2B of LEX/2;

---

[8] Nevertheless, it is, of course, possible to represent the structure of the processes of nominal composition by the use of other formal means than those used in Fig. 1. But if the representation in Fig. 1 gives a correct picture of a specific case of (N-N)-composition, every other correct representation of this case of (N-N) composition must be equivalent to the representation given in Fig. 1. And this must be the case for the simple reason that from the existence of possibilities of formal representation different from each other it does not follow that the represented processes of composition are different from each other. In other words, if it is a class of equivalences which fixes what can be said about compounds with explanatory force and descriptive content, then it does not follow that it is impossible to build up a unitary theory of composition, the possibility of building up a theory in different ways does not imply that there is no unitary theory. This holds, of course, not only with respect to the theory of composition, but rather with respect to linguistic theories in general.

[9] An attempt to give a systematic answer to the question of why simulations of this type should, or even must, be regarded as explanations is made by Kanngießer (1989). It is not necessary or even possible to repeat this attempt here.

[10] The main reason for this incompleteness is the incompleteness of the accessible linguistic knowledge about word formation and word meanings. Therefore, progress in linguistics is required to make further progress possible in the field of developing natural language processing computer systems.

this second subcomponent is called the temporary lexicon of the system. The problem is, of course, how LexMan can give an analysis and an interpretation of words which belong neither to LEX/2A nor to LEX/2B. The ability of the system to extend the lexicon LEX/2 = LEX/2A + LEX/2B incrementally solves this problem at least in part. In this case the system makes use of its access to (machine-readable) external lexica and extracts from these lexica the information which is required for the analysis and interpretation of a word w which does not belong to LEX/2. This extraction of information must comply with the information contained in LEX/2.[11] Following (Ludewig 1991) the structure of this access can be represented as shown in Figure 2.

It is, once again, not necessary to consider the details of this approach to making lexical extensions possible. It should be obvious that an access to external lexica is possible with some efficiency. Incremental extensions of the lexicon can increase the lexical capacity of a system to a remarkable degree; in fact they contribute significantly to the lexical power of the LEU/2 system.

It is obvious, too, that the incremental extensions of the LEU/2 lexicon LEX/2 are radically different from the lexical extensions which LexMan can induce using its knowledge of the rules of word formation. The incremental extensions are, quite unlike to the latter, evidently without explanatory force. They do not simulate the lexical creativity of the native speaker/hearer SH, as SH, confronted with a word w which is SH-new, does not, at least in the normal course of events, consult a dictionary in order to analyse and to interpret this word w. On the contrary, SH is able to analyse and to interpret w quite directly, without taking the roundabout way of consulting a dictionary. But to give such a direct analysis and interpretation of a LEX/2-new word goes beyond the word formation capacities of LEU/2; therefore, if these capacities are exhausted, the system takes the indirect way of consulting a dictionary, in this case the system makes use of the procedure of the incremental extension of the lexicon. Thus, lexical extensions of this type fill up, at least to a certain degree, the gaps of the word-formation based lexical creativity of the system. Incremental extensions of the lexicon do not explain anything, but they compensate for the deficiencies of the system with respect to its knowledge of the set of rules of word formation.[12]

5. LEU/2 is a natural language processing computer system which is lexically creative and, therefore, able to form and to understand words which are not elements of the fixed inventory of the LEU/2 lexicon. As shown, the lexical creativity of the system arises from two features which are radically different from each other and, consequently, complementary to each other.

---

[11] See Ludewig (in this volume) for a detailed discussion of incremental extensions of the lexicon.

[12] This contains a third possibility for the system to behave in a lexically creative way. This third possibility is given by the system's ability to make an interactive use of the user input; cf. Ludewig (in this volume). But this approach is basically just a variant of the strategy of access to external lexica, where the user is playing, in a certain sense, the role of an external lexicon. For this reason, this third strategy for extending the LEU/2 lexicon can be neglected here.

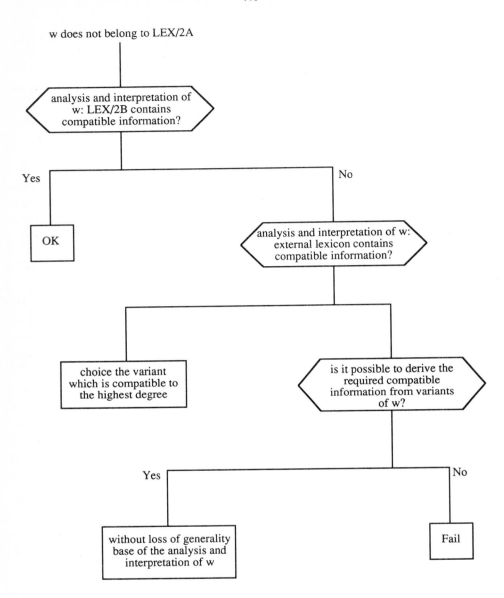

Figure 2

The lexical extensions, which are based on knowledge of rules of word formation, induce explanations, at least partial explanations, of the lexical creativity of the native speaker/hearer. The incremental extensions of LEX/2 do not induce such explanations; they become effective if such explanations, for whatever reasons, cannot (at least not yet) be induced by the system. In these cases they do fill up the gaps in the system of lexical knowledge of LexMan, and therefore it is justified to equip the system with the additional ability to extend its lexicon incrementally.

These remarks should have made clear what the LEU/2 lexicology constitutes, in outline. This lexicology is the result of a mixed methodology, a methodology which requires the integration of devices with explanatory force as well as the integration of mechanisms with its purpose of increasing the lexical functionality of the system.[13] The LEU/2 subcomponent LexMan can be seen as a proof that it is possible in the framework of such a mixed methodology to overcome the bottleneck concerning the lexical creativity of a language processing system.

References

Gust, H., Ludewig, P. (1989): Zielgerichtete Wortschatzerweiterung in natürlichsprachlichen Systemen. In:Metzing, G. (ed.): Proceedings of the 13th German Workshop on Artificial Intelligence (GWAI 89), Springer-Verlag, Berlin, Heidelberg, New York, pp. 224 - 233

Gust, H., Scheffczyk, A. (1991): Ein Ansatz zur Beschreibung von Konzeptstrukturen und Eigenschaftssystemen im Kontext wissensbasierter Systeme. In: Kognitionswissenschaft 1,71 - 82

Kanngießer, S. (1985): Strukturen der Wortbildung. In: Schwarze, Ch., Wunderlich, D. (eds): Handbuch der Lexikologie. Athenäum-Verlag, Königstein, Ts., pp. 134 - 183

Kanngießer, S. (1989): Korrespondenzen zwischen KI und Linguistik. In: von Luck, K. (ed.): Künstliche Intelligenz, 7. Frühjahrsschule, KIFS-89, März 1989, Informatik-Fachberichte 203, Springer-Verlag, Berlin, Heidelberg, New York, pp. 270 - 282

Ludewig, P. (1991): Incremental Vocabulary Extensions in Text Understanding Systems. IWBS Report 152, IBM Deutschland, Stuttgart

---

[13]Nevertheless, for general reasons specified in Kanngießer (1989) it seems to be justified to assume that it is possible, at least in principle, to build up a language processing computer system with a complete lexical creativity (L-complete, so to speak) resulting only from the word formation knowledge of the system.

On the other hand, it seems likewise reasonable to assume that this possibility does not deliver an aim for practical research in the field of computational linguistics and Artificial Intelligence (AI). The reason for this is quite clear: A language processing system requires only a limited linguistic functionality with respect to the purposes of its use. Therefore, the system must not necessarily be L-complete, and indeed it must not necessarily be explanatory at all, as neither L-completeness nor explanatory force is a necessary precondition for achieving the intended functionality of the system.

Therefore, a mixed methodology (in the sense of the concept explained above) seems to be the most suitable methodology for developing language processing systems. This means that the LEU/2 lexicology is an instance of the methodology which is most suitable in the field of computational linguistics and language-orientated AI.

Morphological Processing in the Two-Level Paradigm

Anne Schiller, Petra Steffens

Abstract

This article describes the architecture of LILOG/2LM, a development tool for two-level morphological descriptions. One of the predominant characteristics of this architecture is the modularization of the lexicon into three components: a morph lexicon containing morphologically relevant information, a base lexicon containing syntactically and semantically relevant information, and a layer of lexical rules which - depending on the outcome of morphological analysis - produce a syntactic and semantic description of the analyzed word form. To illustrate the individual components of LILOG/2LM examples of a two-level account of German inflectional morphology are provided. In addition, the algorithms performing recognition and production of word forms are outlined with respect to a sample of lexical entries and morphological rules.

1 Introduction

In 1981 Kaplan and Kay presented a paper on phonological rules as finite state transducers [Kaplan, Kay 1981]. One of the approaches to morphological processing which was inspired by Kaplan and Kay's ideas came to be known as the "two-level model". This model, which was developed by Koskenniemi [Koskenniemi 1984], [Koskenniemi 1983], makes two fundamental assumptions: that the morphology of a language can be modelled by finite state techniques and that two levels of representation suffice to account for the phonological properties of a language (see Sect. 2.3 of this paper). The success which the two-level model has had over the last years is due to the fact that it not only provides a language-independent formalism for representing morphological knowledge but that it can also be applied both to the task of word form recognition and to the task of word form production (see Sect. 3 of this paper). In addition, later work in the two-level paradigm showed how the two-level model can be embedded in a unification-based framework [Bear 1986] [Görz, Paulus 1988]. Such an integrated approach not only allows one to formulate the morphosyntactic regularities of a language in a more transparent way than this can be done with the continuation classes originally proposed by Koskenniemi [Koskenniemi 1983]; it also facilitates communication among different levels of linguistic processing (see, e.g., the treatment of German verbs with separable prefixes as described in [Schiller, Steffens 1990]).

At project LILOG, a tool for developing two-level descriptions – henceforth referred to as LILOG/2LM – was developed as part of the linguistic development environment LEU/2. LILOG/2LM is based on the two-level analyzer which John Bear presented at COLING 1986 [Bear 1986] and which he reimplemented at IBM Germany in 1988. It differs from John Bear's original implementation mainly in two respects:

- The lexicon of LILOG/2LM is partitioned into two parts: one that includes morphological information and one that provides information relevant for other levels of linguistic processing, e.g., syntactic and semantic information. This separation not only adds to the system's degree of modularity, but also makes it easier to employ the morphological component in combination with different grammar theories.

- An additional layer of lexical rules has been added to the system, which relate the morphological and syntactic level of description. These rules were motivated by the fact that a lexeme's syntactic and semantic characteristics may vary with its morphological form. They allow one to build syntactic and semantic feature structures that depend on the outcome of morphological analysis.

In Sect. 2 of this paper, we will describe the overall architecture of LILOG/2LM and we will provide examples to illustrate the various components of this architecture. In Sect. 3, we will outline the processes of morphological analysis and synthesis.

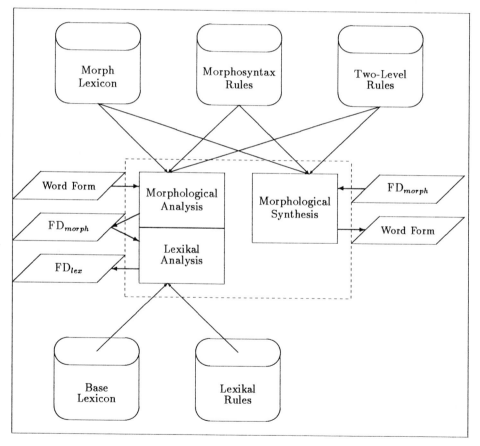

Figure 1: The Architecture of LILOG/2LM. The feature structure FD_{morph} represents morphological information, FD_{lex} describes morphological, syntactic and semantic properties of the input word form

2 The Architecture of LILOG/2LM

The architecture of LILOG/2LM is shown in Figure 1. This architecture distinguishes five sources of linguistic information.

- The **morph lexicon** lists individual morphs and provides information which is of relevance for morphological processing.

- The **morphosyntax rules** specify how the individual morphs can be combined to build inflected word forms.

- The **two–level rules** account for graphemic changes which result from affixing processes.

- The **base lexicon** provides an entry for every base, which includes syntactic and semantic information.

- The **lexical rules** operate on the outcome of the morphological analysis and the corresponding entry in the base lexicon and produce a feature structure which suits the needs of the syntactic and semantic analysis.

The morph lexicon, the base lexicon, and the lexical rules can be viewed as the system's main lexical resource. The lexicon as well as the morphosyntax rules are encoded in the unification grammar formalism STUF (see Sect. 1.1 of this book). The lexical and morphological knowledge is thus represented in a formalism that can also be employed to state syntactic and semantic regularities [Bouma et al. 1988]. Using the same formalism for the specification of morphological, syntactic, and semantic knowledge has several advantages:

- It allows for a uniform representation of lexical knowledge.

- It facilitates communication among the different levels of linguistic processing.

- It reduces the number of formalisms employed in a natural language understanding system.

In the subsequent sections, we will take a closer look at the different rule and lexicon components and we will explain how they are operated upon by the analysis and generation processes.

2.1 The Morph Lexicon

The morph lexicon provides at least one entry for every morpheme. Such an entry consists of a lexical string L which represents a given morph and of a STUF formula which describes all those properties of L that are of relevance for morphological processing. Lexical strings may include special characters which do not appear in surface word forms, but only serve to steer the application of the two-level rules (see Sect. 2.3). We will refer to these characters as "diacritics".

As examples of lexical entries, consider the entries for the adjective stems *rasch* 'quick', *kalt* 'cold' and *gut* 'good', for the comparison endings *-er* and *-st*, for the declension ending *-er*, for the verb stems *sammel* 'collect' and *bau* 'construct', for the finite verb ending *-st* '2nd person sing. present', for the non-finite verb ending *-end* 'present participle', and for the verb prefix *auf* 'on'.

```
section adj_stem.
rasch := [ root: rasch ].
kAlt  := [ root: kalt ].
gut   := [ root: gut          degree: positive ].


section comp_ending.
$er := [ degree: comparative ].
$st := [ degree: superlative ].


section decl_ending.
er := [ agr: [ decl: strong
              [ [ gender: masc      number: sg      case: nom ];
                [ gender: fem       number: sg      case: [ dat ; gen ] ];
                [ number: pl        case: gen ] ] ] ].


section verb_stem.
sammEl := [ root: sammeln    prefix: empty      stem: regular ].
bau    := [ root: bauen      stem: regular
            prefix: [ root: auf     separable: yes ] ].


section verb_fin_ending.
+St := [ agr: [ person: second    number: sg ]
         tense: present          mode: indicative ].


section verb_non_fin_ending.
+End := [ type: present_part ].


section verb_prefix.
auf := [ prefix: [ root: auf     separable: yes ].
```

The morph lexicon is subdivided into sections, which correspond to the categories referred to by the morphosyntactic rules.

There are two cases in which the comparison and declension morphemes have no phonological realization: if the degree of comparison is positive and if the adjective is used non-attributively. If we want to account for both forms without introducing additional morphosyntax rules, we have to provide lexical entries which have an empty surface realisation. We use the diacritic symbol + to represent these "empty morphs".

```
section comp_ending.
+ := degree: positive.

section decl_ending.
+ := agr: uninflected.
```

For processing reasons the lexicon is compiled into a letter tree, the "lexicon tree", with one subtree for each lexicon section. The subtrees for the sections adj_stem and comp_ending are shown in Figure 2. The use of the lexicon tree in morphological processing will be described in Sect. 3.

116

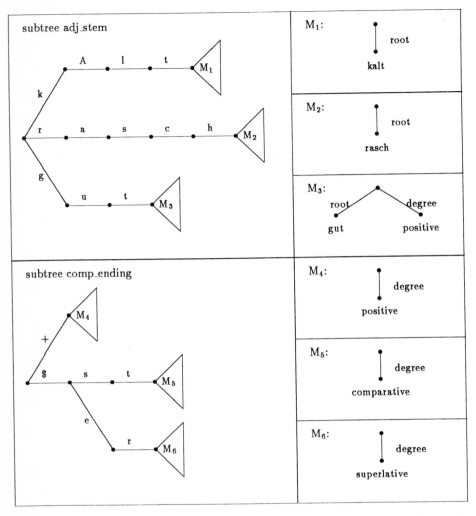

Figure 2: The lexicon subtrees for adjective stems and comparison endings. The leaves of the lexicon subtrees are associated with the feature descriptions M_i as they are specified in the lexical entries

2.2 The Morphosyntax Rules

It is the task of the morphosyntactic component to describe how the morphemes of a language can be combined to build inflected or derived word forms. The morphosyntactic rules have the following format:

```
Rule_Name :=
    X ⟶ Y₁ Y₂ ... Yₙ –
    FS .
```

A rule consists of two parts: a combinatory part and a feature structure. The combinatory part states how morphs $Y_1\ Y_2\ ...\ Y_n$ may be arranged in a larger unit X. X names the resulting category of the morph combination. Y_i is either the name of a lexicon section or an intermediate category, i.e., the left-hand side of a morphosyntax rule. In interpreting a morphosyntactic rule, the feature structures associated with the component morphs are unified with the feature structure FS. The resulting feature structure is associated with the resulting morphological category X. Here are some examples.

Adj_Inflection :=
    adj ⟶ adj_stem comp_ending decl_ending –
    [ ].

Verb_Inflection_1 :=
    verb ⟶ verb_stem verb_fin_ending –
    [prefix: empty ;
      [prefix: separable: yes
        prefix: attached: no]].

Verb_Inflection_2 :=
    verb ⟶ verb_prefix verb_stem verb_fin_ending –
    [prefix: attached: yes].

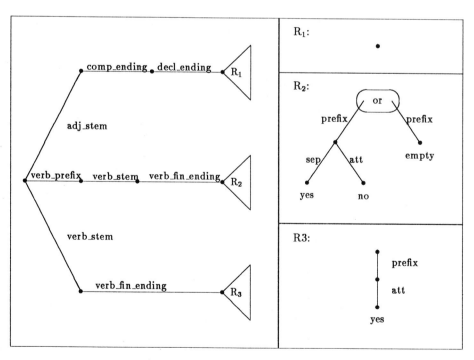

Figure 3: The morphosyntax tree. The leaves of the morphosyntax tree are associated with the feature descriptions R_i, which are part of the morphosyntax rules

      The feature structure associated with rule Adj_Inflection is empty. Thus, the feature structure resulting from the application of this rule is built from the feature structures associated with the adjective stem and the adjective endings in the lexicon. In order to avoid incorrect morph combinations like, e.g., *gutest, 'goodest', appropriate filters have to be included in the lexical entries of the morphs (e.g., degree: positive as part of the lexicon entry for the adjective stem morph *gut*).

The feature structure associated with rule Verb_Inflection_1 distinguishes two cases in which the rule may be applied: either the verb may in principle be affixed with a separable prefix ([prefix: separable: yes]), but the prefix is not attached to the verb ([prefix: attached: no]); or the verb is used without prefix ([prefix: empty]). Rule Verb_Infection_2 describes verb forms in which the stem is preceded by a prefix ([prefix: attached: yes]).

For the time being, LILOG/2LM is only applied to inflectional morphology. Therefore, no recursion in the morphosyntactic rules is required. This allows us to represent the morphosyntactic rules as a tree structure, the "morphosyntax tree". The edges of the morphosyntax tree are labelled with lexical morpheme categories (that is, with the names of lexicon sections) and every leaf L of the morphosyntax tree is associated with the feature description that results from applying the rules which are represented by the path leading to L. The morphosyntax tree for the rules Adj_Inflection, Verb_Inflection_1 and Verb_Inflection_2 would look as shown in Figure 3. The use of the morphosyntax tree in morphological processing will be described in Sect. 3.

2.3 The Two-Level Rules

When two morphs are combined with each other, the result is not always just a concatenation of the two as in (1); often additional processes such as reduplication, insertion, deletion or umlauting of a character may occur, as shown in (2)[1].

(1) *dunkel* 'dark' + *st* ([SUPERLATIVE])
       + e ([FEMININE SINGULAR NOMINATIVE]) $\longrightarrow$ *dunkelste*

(2) *alt* 'old'   + *st* ([SUPERLATIVE])
       + e ([FEMININE SINGULAR NOMINATIVE]) $\longrightarrow$ *älteste*

In the model of two-level morphology these processes are described by what are usually referred to as "two-level phonological rules". Since we are currently not concerned with spoken language but only with written language, we will use the term *orthographic* instead of *phonological* or simply speak about *two-level rules*.

Whereas in generative phonology the derivation of a word form is viewed as a multistep process involving several intermediate levels of representation[2], the main idea behind the two-level rules is that in order to describe the phonology or orthography of a language, two levels of representation suffice. These two levels are called the "lexical level" and the "surface level". On the surface level, words are represented just as they appear in written or spoken language; on the lexical level, their representation may include diacritic characters. It is the task of the two-level rules to perform a mapping between the lexical and the surface level. That is to say, in the case of word form recognition, the two-level rules map a surface form onto its lexical representation; in the case of word form generation, they derive a surface form from its underlying lexical representation.

---

[1]We use strings in capital letters enclosed by square brackets to indicate the morpheme which a given morph realises.

[2]For an introduction to the concepts of generative phonology, see, e.g., [Schane 1973].

LILOG/2LM distinguishes three types of two-level rules. To understand these rules, we first have to introduce the notion of a "default character": without any additional specification, every lexical character which is also included in the surface alphabet (i.e., the set of characters which may appear on the surface) is assumed to correspond to itself on the surface and every diacritic symbol is assumed to correspond to the empty character on the surface. It is, however, possible to override this default assumption by explicitly stating default correspondences between a lexical and a surface character. With the notion of default correspondence we can now state the three types of two-level rules available in LILOG/2LM.

- The **"allowed-type rule"**. This rule has the format:

  L:S allowed in LC _ RC.

  and says: in addition to its default correspondence, the lexical character L may correspond to the surface character S, if it occurs in the context LC _ RC[3].

- The **"disallowed-type rule"**. This rule has the format:

  L:S disallowed in LC _ RC.

  and says: the lexical character L must not correspond to the (otherwise allowed) surface character S, if it occurs in the context LC _ RC.

- The **"required-type rule"**. This rule has the format:

  L:S required in LC _ RC.

  and says: the lexical character L must not correspond to its default character Z, but has to be realised as S, if it occurs in the context LC _ RC. A rule of this type is equivalent to an allowed-type rule of the form

  L:S allowed in LC _ RC.

  and to a disallowed-type rule of the form

  L:Z disallowed in LC _ RC.

As an example for the use of two-level rules, consider the phenomenon of umlauting in German adjectives. As was already exemplified by (1) and (2), there are certain adjectives in German which require that their stem vowel a, o, or u be umlauted, if they are combined with a morpheme of comparison. We could account for this phenomenon in the following way:

- The stem vowel of adjectives that can be umlauted is represented on the lexical level by a diacritic symbol, e.g., by (capital) A, O, and U.

- Adjective endings which realise morphemes of comparison are prefixed with a diacritic symbol, e.g., $\$$, which distinguishes them from adjective endings that do not trigger umlauting.

---

[3]Contexts are specified as strings of character pairs $L_1:S_1 \ldots L_n:S_n$, where every L_i stands for a lexical character and every S_i for a surface character; if S_i is the default correspondence of L_i, it may be omitted.

- The following default correspondences are specified: A:a, O:o, U:u, and $:0[4].

- Phonological rules are provided, which stipulate that the lexical characters *A*, *O*, and *U* are realised as *ä*, *ö*, and *ü* respectively, if they are succeeded by a dollar sign:

```
Adj_A_Umlauting :=
    A:ä required in _ * $.[5]

Adj_O_Umlauting :=
    O:ö required in _ * $.

Adj_U_Umlauting :=
    U:ü required in _ * $.
```

As already mentioned, the two-level rules are not compiled into finite state machines but are processed by an interpreter. In designing the interpreter, we experimented with the two control strategies which John Bear outlined in [Bear 1986, p.275]. The first of these strategies considers the left context of a rule R only in case the correspondence pair of R matches a character of the input string. This requires that a stack of already processed character pairs matching the input string is maintained. The other strategy continually matches the input string against the left contexts of all two-level rules. Thus, a data structure is required which keeps track of all two-level rules which, at a given point in processing, are suitable. This strategy proved to be particularly inefficient if the left contexts of rules were formulated in a very general way (e.g., in terms of wild card characters or character sets). We therefore adopted the first strategy.

2.4   The Base Lexicon and the Lexical Rules

In the preceding sections, we described those sources of linguistic information that contribute to morphological analysis and generation. In this section we will explain the parts of the system that supply the information necessary for syntactic and semantic analysis. If the syntactic and semantic properties for a given lexeme were invariant with regard to its morphological characteristics, one could simply state these properties in the lexicon and unify them with the result of the morphological analysis. However, if other levels of linguistic processing require lexical information that varies with regard to a lexeme's morphological properties but can in a regular way be deduced from them, the lexicon would display a high degree of redundancy.

Consider for instance count nouns. In a clause, plural count nouns may be preceded by a determiner or they may occur on their own. Singular count nouns, on the other hand, have to be preceded by a determining element (e.g., article, quantifier, possessive phrase). If this phenomenon is considered a lexical property of the noun, as for example in an HPSG-based framework [Pollard, Sag 1987], then the lexicon has to supply subcategorization information that is different for singular and plural count nouns.

Assuming that subcategorization properties are described by a complex feature (syntax local subcat) (see [Pollard, Sag 1987]), the value of this feature would reflect the possible determiners in the case of singular and plural count nouns; for bare plurals it would indicate that no further determination is possible. If this difference was accounted for in the base lexicon, the entries of countable nouns would have to include a disjunctive feature structure describing these two cases. To

---

[4]The character *0* is used to represent the empty character.

[5]The asterisk *** is used as wild card character here.

avoid the resulting redundancy in the lexicon, we introduced an additional layer of rules: the lexical rules. The lexical rules are coded in STUF and have the following format:

```
Rule_Name :=
    Lex_Result ⟶ Lex_Entry Morph_Result –
    FS.
```

After a word form W has been morphologically analysed and after its corresponding entry in the base lexicon has been determined, one or more lexical rules are applied to the feature structure resulting from morphological analysis (Morph_Result) and to the feature structure retrieved from the base lexicon (Lex_Entry). The resulting feature structure (Lex_Result) describes the morphological, syntactic and semantic properties of W.

Assuming that (3) results from the morphological analysis of *Tische* 'tables', that (4) is the lexical entry for the lexeme *tisch* in the base lexicon, and that the rules noun_rule_1 and noun_rule_2 describe how syntactic information for nouns correlates with morphological information, the application of these rules to (3) and (4) results in the disjunctive feature description (5).

```
noun_rule_1 :=
    result ⟶ lexeme, morph_out –
    [ ⟨ result syntax ⟩ = ⟨ lexeme syntax ⟩ ].


noun_rule_2 :=
    result ⟶ lexeme, morph_out –
    [ ⟨ morph_out agreement number ⟩: pl
      ⟨ result syntax binding index number ⟩ = ⟨ morph_out agreement number ⟩
      ⟨ result syntax local head case ⟩ = ⟨ morph_out agreement case ⟩
      ⟨ lexeme syntax local head nform ⟩ : count
      ⟨ result syntax local subcat ⟩ : $U$[6]].
```

```
(3)  [ root: tisch
       agr: [ number: pl
              case: [ nom; gen; acc ] ].


(4)  Tisch :=
     [ syntax: local: head: gender: masc
       syntax: local: head: nform: count
       syntax: local: subcat: ART
       ... ].


(5)  [ syntax: local: head: gender: masc
       syntax: local: head: nform: count
       syntax: local: head: case: [ nom; gen; dat ]
       syntax: binding: index: number: pl
       [ [ syntax: local: subcat: ART ... ];
         [ syntax: local: subcat: $U$ ... ] ] ].
```

---

[6]U denotes the STUF-type 'undefined' which cannot be unified with any other type.

3 Recognition and Production of Word Forms

As shown in Figure 1, the recognition of an inflected word form W is performed in two steps. First, W is morphologically analysed and a feature description FD_{morph} is built that characterizes the morphological properties of W; then, one or more lexical rules are applied to FD_{morph} and to its corresponding features structure FD_{base} in the base lexicon to produce a comprehensive lexical description FD_{lex} of W.

The task of the morphological analysis consists in (1) mapping a surface word form W (input) onto a sequence L of morphs and in (2) building a morphological feature description FD_{morph}. If we did not have to consider the possibility of a lexical character having an empty surface realisation, this task could be achieved with the following straightforward algorithm:

1. Apply the two-level rules to W in order to map W onto one (or more) lexical string(s) Q.

2. Decompose Q into one (or more) sequence(s) L of substrings M_1 ... M_n such that every M_i represents a morph.

3. Apply the morphosyntax rules to L to verify its morphosyntactic correctness and build the corresponding feature description F.

However, the difficulty with this algorithm is that, at every position in the surface string W, an infinite number of empty characters may in principle occur. There would thus be no limit to the number of times that the first step is applied. To exclude the danger of an infinite loop, the interpretation of the two-level rules is intertwined both with a traversal of the lexicon tree and with a traversal of the morphosyntax tree: a sequence L of morphs M_1 ... M_n is only considered as a potential lexical representation for W, if

- for every M_i, there is a path in one of the lexicon subtrees and if

- for M_1 ... M_n (to be more precise: for the morphological categories associated with M_1 ... M_n), there exists a path in the morphosyntax tree.

Given the lexicon tree of Sect. 2.1, the two-level rules for umlauting in adjectives as stated in Sect. 2.3, and the morphosyntax tree of section 2.2, the following steps would lead to a recognition of the adjective *kälter* 'colder'.

Step 1.1 There are only three morphological categories, which label the initial edges of the morphosyntax tree: the categories verb_prefix, verb_stem, and adj_stem. Only the lexicon subtrees for these categories are therefore searched for candidate morphs. In applying the two-level rules to the input string *kälter*, it is found that only the lexicon subtree adj_stem includes a path which matches an initial substring of the input: the path labelled *kAlt*.

Step 1.2 The path of the morphosyntax tree which starts with category adj_stem continues with category comp_ending. For the remaining input string *er*, the lexicon subtree comp_ending allows two paths: the path labelled *$er* and the path labelled *+*. Only the first of these two alternatives is licensed by the two-level rules. In the first case, the umlaut rule can be applied successfully, whereas in the second case it fails. We have thus recognized the input substring *er* as surface realisation of the comparison morph *$er*.

Step 1.3 Even though the entire string *kälter* has now been mapped onto a lexical string, namely onto *kAlt$er*, the recognition process is not complete yet, because we have not reached a leaf in the morphosyntax tree. We are, therefore, left with the task of finding a morph of category decl_ending that has no surface realisation. Assuming that the corresponding lexicon subtree includes such a morph (+) and given that the two-level rules allow this morph to suffix the lexical string *kAlt$er*, the recognition process has arrived at a potential decomposition of the input string.

Step 1.4 It now remains to unify the feature description associated with the traversed path in the morphosyntax tree with the feature descriptions associated with the recognized morphs in the morph lexicon. If the unification succeeds, the first step of the word form recognition process terminates successfully, yielding as its result the morphological feature description FD_{morph}.

After morphological analysis, the lexical rules are applied.

Step 2.1 The morphological feature description FD_{morph} contains two features which are relevant to determining the appropriate entry in the base lexicon: the feature root and, for verb forms, the feature prefix (in the case of *kälter*, the value of root would be kalt, i.e., the lexeme's usual citation form). From the values of these features, a key is constructed which is used to retrieve the corresponding feature structure FD_{base} from the base lexicon.

Step 2.2 Once FD_{base} has been retrieved from the base lexicon, the lexical rules are applied. When applying a lexical rule, the feature description of the rule is unified with the feature description FD_{morph} augmented by the attribute Morph_Result and with the feature description FD_{base} augmented by the attribute Lex_Entry. If this unfication succeeds, the feature description assigned to the attribute Lex_Result is extracted.

The production of word forms reverses most of the processes outlined above. The input for morphological generation is supplied by the formulator (see Chap. 4 of this book). It is a STUF feature description F which indicates the lexeme and its morphological properties. The task of word form production consists in (1) decomposing the feature description F (input) of an inflected word form W into a set of morphs $M_1 ... M_n$ compatible with F and in (2) mapping the linear arrangement of $M_1 ... M_n$ onto a correct surface form. In contrast to the recognition process, the problem of empty characters does not arise for the production process. The following simple algorithm will therefore do:

Step 3.1 Find a path P in the morphosyntax tree whose associated feature structure matches the input structure.

Step 3.2 For every category labelling an edge of P, retrieve a corresponding morph M_i from the morph lexicon.

Step 3.3 Apply the two-level rules to map the sequence(s) $M_1 ... M_n$ onto a surface word form.

For a given feature description F, different surface word forms may be generated for the following reasons:

- F is underspecified.
- A given morpheme can be realised by several (synonymous) morphs.
- The two-level rules allow for different surface realisations (allowed-type rules).

4   Conclusion

In this paper, we described the architecture of the computational environment LILOG/2LM for implementing two-level morphological descriptions. We pointed out that LILOG/2LM differs from other two-level environments mainly in two respects: the lexicon of LILOG/2LM is divided into a morphological and a syntactic/semantic partition and an additional layer of lexical rules allows one to account for the interplay of the morphological and syntactic level of lexical description.

Whereas these extensions to the original architecture are mainly geared to improving the communication between the morphological and other levels of linguistic processing, another need for improvement arises from certain phenomena of German morphophonology. Consider for example the two-level rule E_Epenthesis_Dental, which inserts an *e* between a verb stem that ends in a dental-like *t* or *d* and a verb ending that begins with a consonant. Assuming that the set of dentals has been defined as Dental and the set of consonants as Consonant and that the lexical symbol +, which is by default to be realised as the empty character, prefixes verb endings, this rule can be formulated in the following way:

```
E_Epenthesis_Dental :=
    +:e required here:
    Dental _ Consonant.
```

This rule describes the following pairs of lexical and surface strings:

f i n d + s t   'find (second person singular present)'
f i n d e s t

e n d + t e   'ended (first person singular past tense)'
e n d e t e

a n b i e t + t   'offers (third person singular present)'
a n b i e t e t

It would, however, also license the pair

h ä l t + s t   'hold (second person singular present)'
h ä l t e s t

which is certainly incorrect, because e–epenthesis does not apply if the verb stem has been ablauted. The conclusion we have to draw from this is that the process of e–insertion after dentals is phonologically as well as morphologically conditioned and can only be adequately described if reference to both types of information is possible. The only mechanism which the two-level model provides to refer to morphological information in a two-level rule are diacritic symbols. To signal that a verb stem has been ablauted, we therefore have to suffix it with another diacritic symbol (e.g., with #), which by default is to be realised as the empty character. Since the set Dental does not include this character, the rule E_Epenthesis_Dental cannot be applied in the case of ablauted verb stems.

The need for diacritic symbols as a means to pass morphological information to the two-level component has been discussed and criticized by several authors working in the two-level context [Bear 1988], [Calder 1989], [Emele 1988], [Reinhard 1990], [Trost 1990]. In our view, the most

Representing Word Meanings

Helmar Gust

Abstract

Starting with an approach to lexical semantics proposed by Bierwisch, a structure of semantic information in lexical entries is sketched which takes into account lexical ambiguities and polysemy. Some phenomena will be discussed which show that the strict discrimination between context-specific conceptual interpretations and context-invariant semantic forms may not be adequate.

The proposed method for representing lexical meanings allows both, abstract context-invariant lexical entries which need specification during analysis by conceptual shifting and conceptual differentiation, and specific word meanings from which other meanings can be derived if needed.

On the one hand, this integrated approach supplies a framework which is suitable for modelling processes of learning abstract meanings from typical uses of words. On the other hand, derivation operations may be sensitive to world knowledge, therefore the scope of possible context-specific meanings can change following respective variations in world knowledge without any need to revise lexical entries.

1 Introduction

Words appear in a variety of contexts where they are assigned different interpretations. Verbs and nouns frequently are used to refer to concepts. An example given in (Bierwisch 1983) may serve to illustrate the idea. The word 'school' has different meanings in different contexts: inter alia 'institution', 'building', 'network of processes' or 'the very concept school' in sentences like

> *Die Schule hat einen neuen Direktor bekommen.*
> (The school has got a new director.)
> *Die Schule hat ein neues Dach bekommen.*
> (The school has got a new roof.)
> *Die Schule ist anstrengend.*
> (School is demanding.)
> *Die Schule ist eine Grundlage unserer Zivilisation.*
> (School is a basis of our civilization.)

This is not a simple ambiguity comparable to the meanings of the German word 'Bank'('financial institution' vs. 'seating accommodation') that are independent of each other. As far as the word 'school' is concerned, further contexts requiring other meanings are likely to exist. In suitable contexts, 'school' may also have the meaning of, for example, 'staff'.

> *Die Schule machte einen Betriebsausflug.*
> (The school took a staff outing.)

So lexical semantics has to cope with this effect, which demands a formalism to represent the vague context-invariant meaning of words in a compact form suitable for deriving an unpredictable number of context-specific readings. Computation of word meanings within a text-understanding system amounts to specifications of their conceptual interpretations in an actual discourse. General conceptual knowledge should support this process.

Subsequently we will often talk about concepts. We will use this term informally without exact defining it. In a first approximation, concepts correspond to sorts in the representation languag L-LILOG, and, as far as concrete implementations are concerned, every concept encountered her will be realized as a sort in L-LILOG. But our intuitive idea of concepts assigns them a riche structure than the one provided by a sortal system, namely a structure by which different aspects of typicality can be expressed. This would include the possibility of using examples for concept constitution. Thus, the attempt could be made to integrate procedures already explored within the fields of machine learning into the definition of concepts. Up to now an elaboration of the relevant theory is still missing, and we have to content with the approximation of concepts being sorts. Some ideas on how conceptual systems may be enriched to cope with problems like uncertain classification, similarity and constitution by examples and counterexamples can be found in (Gust, Scheffczyk 1991). Meanwhile we assume that qualities of concepts that cannot be represented by means of the sortal system have to be realized as general inference rules. This leads us to the following situation concerning the representation of concepts:

1. Word meanings refer to concepts or operations on concepts.

2. Essential parts of concepts comprise access structures to systems of inference rules in a very wide sense.

With respect to the LILOG lexicon, the following basic assumptions can be made:

1. The sortal system makes conceptual structures available which are independent of individual lexemes. It is the basis for context-sensitive interpretations.

2. References from words to sorts are carried out via sortal indices.

3. There is not a one-to-one but a many-to-many mapping from words to sorts.

In accord with a general idea of a certain flexibility in a word's meaning, sorts provide relevant conceptual knowledge. Putting sortal indices on words roughly corresponds to the usual procedure of lexica to break down different readings, but the expectation associated with the use of sorts is to make the motivation of the assignments transparent – via explicit sortal definitions within the sortal system.

2   Semantic Forms, Conceptual Interpretations and Primary Meanings

The following considerations mainly take into account words of certain word classes, namely nouns, verbs, and, with certain restrictions, adjectives, adverbs, and prepositions. They do not hold for articles, pronouns, conjunctions, etc.

The tasks of a lexical component as part of a language-understanding system consist in:

- Reducing the individual word form to the corresponding lexeme or stem,

- Assigning to this basic form a concept that comprises all context-specific meanings,

- Determining context-dependent specifications.

Applied to the school example these steps can be illustrated by the following schema:

schools —>   morphological analysis
        lexeme: school
        number: plural

school —>   meaning assignment
        concept: school'
        concept: school"

school' —>   contexual specifications
        school1 < INSTITUTION
        school2 < BUILDING
        school3 < PROCESS
        school4 < CONCEPT

school" ->
        school5 < a body of people adhering to a certain doctrine
        school6 < group of artists, writers linked by the same style

Some remarks concerning the notation are necessary. '<' indicates a subsort relation. The sort CONCEPT is used instead of ENTITY in (Bierwisch 1983), since ENTITY will serve as the uppermost node of a section of the sortal hierarchy which will be introduced later.

In order to explain our own conception of lexical meaning it is worth taking a closer look at the arguments presented in (Bierwisch 1983). Bierwisch opposes two possible approaches dealing with lexical ambiguities:

1. Primary meanings together with operations to construct derived meanings.

2. Semantic forms[1] representing abstract lexical meanings, from which context-specific conceptual interpretations may be derived by conceptual shifts and differentiations. In this approach, semantic forms and conceptual structures belong to different and strictly discriminated levels. To emphasize this fundamental distinction, we will henceforth refer to these levels as the semantic and the conceptual layers, respectively.

Bierwisch advocates the second approach. His main arguments against the first one are the following:

- The distinction between primary and derived meanings is arbitrary.

- Constraints for the operations to derive meanings are hard to formulate and must be coded into the lexical entries.

Bierwisch gives good arguments for believing the second approach to be more adequate, and he demonstrates that some of the mentioned problems with the vaguenes of lexical meaning may be solved in an elegant way. First we give an outline of our interpretation of Bierwisch's theory and then we discuss some remaining problems.

---

[1]In (Bierwisch 1983) Bierwisch does not yet use the term 'semantic form' introduced in (Bierwisch, Lang 1989). He uses the term 'semantische Einheit' instead.

What Bierwisch postulates can be made plain by the following schema:

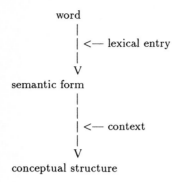

```
        word
          |
          |
          | <— lexical entry
          |
          V
  semantic form
          |
          |
          | <— context
          |
          V
conceptual structure
```

The lexicon supplies a semantic form for a word. This semantic form determines a function from contexts to conceptual structures. The layer of semantic forms is constituted by a logical representation language, while the layer of conceptual structures corresponds mainly to a set-theoretic structure analogous to interpretations in model theory. In his examples, however, Bierwisch uses the same structure, a kind of higher-order logic with lambda abstraction, for the representation of both layers. Consequently, the instantiation of this schema for the word 'school' in the first example sentence looks like this:

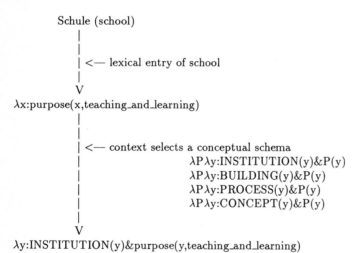

```
        Schule (school)
              |
              |
              | <— lexical entry of school
              |
              V
λx:purpose(x,teaching_and_learning)
              |
              |
              | <— context selects a conceptual schema
              |              λPλy:INSTITUTION(y)&P(y)
              |              λPλy:BUILDING(y)&P(y)
              |              λPλy:PROCESS(y)&P(y)
              |              λPλy:CONCEPT(y)&P(y)
              |
              V
λy:INSTITUTION(y)&purpose(y,teaching_and_learning)
```

Therefore, a hierarchy of concepts is needed on the conceptual layer which is determined by predicability constraints. Each node of the hierarchy serves as a sortal constraint for predicates used to describe the world. A small section of such a hierarchy may look like figure 1.

For cognitive reasons this hierarchy – being a hierarchy of natural kinds – should be tree-like (Osherson 1978). Therefore in the mentioned example INSTITUTION, PROCESS or BUILDING cannot be an element of this hierarchy together with a concept P represented by the predicate

λx:purpose(x,Lehr_und_Lernprozesse).

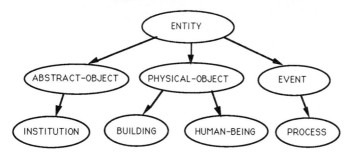

Figure 1: Part of a hierarchy of concepts

Examples of predicates taking these concepts as argument constraints:

ENTITY	exists
ABSTRACT_OBJECT	propose
PHYSICAL_OBJECT	located_at
EVENT	happen
INSTITUTION	$\lambda x{:}sponsor(x,state)$
PROCESS	duration
BUILDING	$\lambda x{:}height(x,three\text{-}storeyed)$
HUMAN_BEING	$\lambda x{:}actor(x,...)$

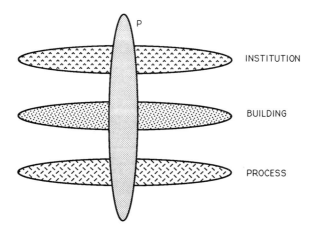

Figure 2: Extension of P

Since there are good reasons for sorts like INSTITUTION, PROCESS and BUILDING to be members of this hierarchy, P itself cannot be such a node. The extension of P is to some extent orthogonal to the extensions of sorts (see figure 2).

So a distinction has to be made between sortal concepts (members of the hierarchy) and other concepts (such things like P), which must be shifted to sorts during a conceptual interpretation process in a context. These operations of conceptual shifting have the general form

$$\lambda P \lambda y : sortal\_predicate(y) \& P(y) .$$

This gives rise to the question: Is there such a operation for every sort and are all of them applicable to all semantical forms? Presumably the answer is yes, since there are no criteria for restricting the application of such a schema.

The operation of conceptual specification of semantic forms corresponds to the instantiation of existentially quantified variables which leads to more specific conceptual structures. In the above example a more elaborated version may include the topic of teaching and learning as an argument:

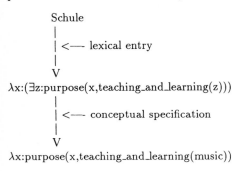

By means of a lexical entry a compound like 'Musikschule' (music school) could be mapped directly into this specified meaning.

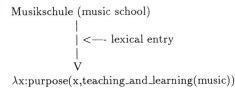

So one method of dynamically interpreting compounds, which don't have lexical entries, corresponds to this operation of conceptual specification, dynamically performed during lexical analysis.

The outlined theory presupposes, firstly, successful abstractions from a variety of different word usages, secondly, a method to scrutinize which conceptual features of an actual referent are relevant, and thirdly, a conceptual interpretation process filling up the empty meaning slots in the abstract semantic form. In spite of his convincing arguments, there remain some serious problems with this approach, a fact which Bierwisch himself partially concedes.

a) First there is the postulated strict discrimination of two basically different layers, namely the semantic forms and the conceptual structures. It is not this assumption which makes difficulties. The problem arises from the tasks Bierwisch assigns to these layers as well as the transition from the first to the second layer, especially if considered from the point of view of meaning representation in a natural-language AI system. Bierwisch, however, does not have this view in mind.

- The conceptual layer is difficult to cope with, especially when it is in fact treated as a set-theoretic structure.

- Bierwisch assigns two tasks to the transition from the semantic layer to the conceptual layer:

  (a) handling lexical ambiguities,

  (b) model theoretic interpretation of a logical representation language.

  For task (a) a language understanding system needs a representation mechanism for the conceptual layer which leads to a simulation of this layer within the semantic layer, and this is the way the given examples really work.

- There are continuous variations between semantic forms and conceptual structures. This contradicts the postulated strict discrimination of these layers.

On the other hand, lexical entries may be composed of more than semantic forms. There clearly is a distinction between the structure of representational expressions on the level of utterances and on the level of lexical entries; the latter accounts for syntactical knowledge as well, and the interdependencies of these knowledge types have to be expressed too. However, the aim of this paper is to emphasize the similarities between the representational structure of utterances and lexical entries.

b) Even for simple nouns it is hard to find unspecific and context-independent meanings, if the domain of artefacts is left aside. Since the semantic forms of words have to be specific enough te discriminate between the meanings of words like 'Berg' (mountain), 'Hügel' (hill), 'Anhöhe' (hill) and so on, they have to contain a lot of specific information. Artefacts seem to be determined essentially by the function intended by their creator, whereas perceptual properties may be more relevant for natural objects. A thing created for seating is a seat even if it looks like a cupboard.

But representing the creator's intention is not always sufficient to grasp all meaning aspects of artefacts, as the following example demonstrates:

Wir gehen die Straße entlang.
(We walk along the street.)
Die Straße, in der ich wohne, feiert am Samstag ein Fest.
(The street I live in will have a party on Saturday.)

We will hardly want to say that 'Straße' occurs in both sentences in two or more meanings. But different aspects of meaning are mentioned: firstly the distance, secondly an area and thirdly the social structure. Consequently the lexicon can only assign a word an interpretation – mostly underspecified both sortally and by the logical conditions – which still has to be completed by context-specific operations. But this procedure cannot go so far as to produce all possible uses of a word exclusively by putting the vague lexical frame in concrete form. To almost every word-meaning-pair we could construct a context in which the word would occur in the indicated meaning so that the lexical semantics of the word would become empty. In the context Nagel-in-die-Wand-schlagen (hitting-the-nail-into-the-wall) the word 'hammer' can refer to a shoe, but from this we cannot conclude that the meaning of 'hammer' has to subsume the meaning of 'shoe'. To conclude, it's a hard job to find a proper semantic form comprising all possible contextual meanings of a word.

c) Regarding proper names, Bierwisch proposes the same conceptual interpretation mechanism, e.g., for 'Hans' in a sentence like

Hans ist schwer zu verstehen.
(Hans is hard to understand/hear.)

Bierwisch does not discuss the point in detail, but it is not clear how the interpretation process would work here. Of course, the meaning of such an utterance is ambiguous, but its ambiguity is not due to the word 'Hans', which refers to an individual of the sort HUMAN-BEING in each case. It is unlikely to reach at the interpretation 'books written by Hans' or 'the prononciation of Hans' without using derivational operations acting on this basic meaning, and without using knowledge about the structure of the world or even about facts (e.g., that Hans has written some books).

d) Another point is the formally identical treatment of generic and nongeneric readings. The distinction between generic and nongeneric readings is regular to an extent that a special mechanism seems to be appropriate. Generic interpretations of nouns work in a way similar to interpretations of proper names. Therefore, as a preliminary attempt, generic readings of nouns could be treated as proper names for concepts.

e) The possibility of generic readings poses another problem. The natural candidate for a generic interpretation of the noun 'Schule' (as a name of a concept) is a concept described by the predicate

$$\lambda x : purpose(x, teaching\_and\_learning) \ .$$

As such, it has been introduced in the semantic form of 'Schule'. If this representation has to be interpreted as a concept on its own, it is hard to motivate the status difference with regard to concepts like INSTITUTION, BUILDING etc. On the other hand, if this concept does not have a different status, it is an excellent candidate for the primary meaning of 'Schule', from which all other possible meanings may be derived. Thus, the distinction between semantic forms and conceptual structures vanishes. In this case, using a unification-based order-sorted logic, conceptual shifting degenerates to a simple sort unification of constraints assigned to argument positions of predicates or functions with the sorts of the terms to be filled in.

f) Conceptual shifts do not uncover the relations between the different readings. The following example (taken from (Bierwisch 1983)) illustrates the importance of uncovering relations of this kinds. Here syntactic coreference does not correspond to semantic coreference:

Die Schule, die neben dem Sportplatz liegt, hat einen
größeren Beitrag gestiftet.
(The school next to the sports field donated
some considerable amount.)

g) A related problem occurs when conceptual shifts are not symmetric to an extent suggested by the theory. This may be demonstated again by the case of syntactic but not semantic coreference:

das dreistöckige staatliche Museum
(the three-storeyed state museum)
das staatliche dreistöckige Museum (?)
(the state three-storeyed museum) (*)

The second version is clearly less acceptable. Assuming an application from right to left, the adjective 'dreistöckig' forces a conceptual shift from the semantic form of 'Museum' to BUILDING which leads to a clash with the sortal constraint of the argument of 'staatlich'. Obviously this clash does not occur in the first version where 'staatlich' forces a conceptual shift from the semantic form of 'Museum' to INSTITUTION. A transition from INSTITUTION to BUILDING seems to work fine while the inverse transition fails. Conceptual shifts cannot explain this behavior while derivational processes do. They need not be symmetrical.

Some of the problems mentioned can be solved simply by weakening the strict discrimination between the semantic and the conceptual layers. This does not mean that these layers are not distinct.

But they should be viewed as not necessarily disjoint subsystems of a unique representational layer. The conceptual subsystem supplies concepts (and the relations between them) while the semantic subsystem supplies more or less abstract semantic forms for lexical entries and specifies derivational operations for the generation of contextual meanings. Since they need not be disjoint there is no problem with continuous variations (see figure 3).

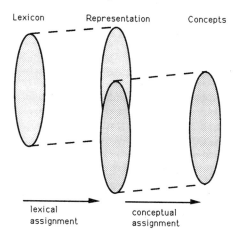

Figure 3:

Another reason for weakening the discrimination of the two layers follows from the fact that the main arguments against primary meanings do not hold in a strict sense. Firstly, as mentioned above, generic readings are excellent candidates for primary meanings and supply a criterion to specify what primary meanings are. But this criterion may seem to be too strong in many cases, since appropriate generic readings need to be available. Another criterion may be developed from well known technique in algebra. Certain sets with an algebraic structure may be specified by representative elements from which the whole structure can be reconstructed by the corresponding algebraic operations. Thus, a good candidate for a primary meaning is one from which all relevant contextual meanings can be derivationally obtained.

On a uniform representational level both approaches may coexist. The transition from primary meanings to abstract semantic forms can be viewed as a process of abstraction or a process of learning context-independent word meanings from specific uses of the respective words.

But there remain at least three fundamentally different aspects which should not be confused when talking about ambiguity and vagueness in this context:

- lexical ambiguities, which can be resolved by finding a context-specific conceptual interpretation,

- conceptual vagueness which is related to problems of classification,

- the correct designation of discourse referents (for example by noun phrases).

The distinction between these phenomena is not as clear as it seems to be at first glance. If the NP 'ein Fisch' (a fish) refers in a discourse to an individual which cannot be classified as an instance of a concept FISCH (for example a wooden fish) it may not be quite clear whether this should be treated (i) by a shifting operation and therefore during the process of constructing contextual meanings from lexical entries, or whether (ii) this is a phenomenon of vague classification and should therefore be treated within the conceptual subsystem, or whether (iii) this is a problematic designation of a discourse-referent and should be treated as a pragmatic aspect of discourse analysis. Perhaps none of these possibilities is adequate and such a situation should be solved dynamically by constructing a new concept.

3   A Representational Schema for Word Meanings in Lexical Entries

On the one hand, word meanings form the basis for computing the meanings of phrases and sentences. At the same time, our representation formalism are intended to be useful for describing morphological processes that become necessary in the transition to a more differentiated conception of the lexicon. Some examples dealing with this aspect can be found in (Rickheit, this volume). Ultimately there are inherent constraints within a lexical subsystem to be satisfied. Some of them have been discussed in the previous section. So a compromise must be found with regard to the implementation of a lexical component. This is a difficult task and not in all cases satisfactory. In this section, the basic ideas of a lexical representation schema used in LILOG will be outlined.

We will consider two levels of assigning meaning to words, which are to reflect the principled vagueness of word meaning. On the first level, which is mainly to be achieved by the lexicon, the words are assigned 'semantic frames' which are largely independent of the concrete context. These 'semantic frames' have to be able to represent the principled vagueness of word meaning.

On the second level, the words are assigned expressions of the representational language with regard to the current context. In the course of this, the vagueness is gradually eliminated. This process has to take place while the semantics of more complex units (phrases, sentences, but also complex nouns) is being constructed.

The base for the representation of word meanings is provided by the representation languages STUF and SORT-L-LILOG. STUF allows the definition of graphs by means of the unification and disjunction of subgraphs as well as by specifying values of paths (given by series of edges). Moreover, STUF puts a definition and administration mechanism for templates (the names for subgraphs) at the disposal of the user (Uszkoreit, this volume).

Order-sorted logics with inheritance of qualities and roles, such as SORT-L-LILOG, can be regarded as a first approximation of conceptual sytems. So the following expressions are possible for the representation of word meaning[2]:

1. sorted terms, especially variables, for the representation of reference,

2. formulas for the representation of restrictions on the reference.

As EVENT and STATE are special sorts, verbs can be treated like nouns in this respect. Adjectives are treated in the same way, although this is critical for many adjective classes, for example for grade adjectives.

---

[2](Gust et al. 1988) proposed representing word meanings as a pair consisting of a sort and a (i.a., indefinite) term:

  k := <s t>

There, such a pair was called a 'conceptual structure'. The sort-component controls the access to sort-inferences, whereas the operations occurring in the logical expression (predicates and functions) determine the access to the other inference-rule systems. Here we use a representation that is more compatible with the structures used in other areas of the project (e.g., DRSs). But the basic idea remains the same and the formalisms can be translated into one another to a large extent.

Over and above that, the semantic arguments play an essential part in the computation of word meanings. The assignment between semantic and syntactic arguments is important for analysis and especially for generation. That is why we need a representation formalism for word meanings which allows the representation of such argument-frames. Therefore, lexical entries consist of (at least) five parts:

syn: contains the description of the syntactic features.

index: contains a stand-in for the reference of the word and is represented by a variable of SORT-L-LILOG.

conds: contains a number of statements restricting the reference.

args: contains a set of (semantic) arguments represented by L-LILOG variables. They are available for reference-resolving processes and have to be interpreted in an implicitly existentially quantified way.

subcat: corresponds to the subcategorization frame. The elements have a structure similar to the structure of the lexical entries themselves, but without the components 'args', 'subcat' or 'conds'. Instead they have a component 'context', which describes the contribution of this argument to the semantics of the word.

Such entries can simply be taken as STUF-graphs. To represent the examples here we choose a simplified syntax, and we give below the edge 'syn' only minimal details which, in the case of realistic lexical entries, would have to be correspondingly extended:

```
werfen (to throw) ->
     syn:          V
     index:        x@THROW
     conds:        nil
     args:         nil
     subcat:       {
                   (syn:       NPnom
                   index:      y@HUMAN_BEING
                   context:    {(actor x y )})
                   (syn:       NPacc
                   index:      z@all)
                   context:    {(affected_object x z)})
                   }

wandern (to hike) ->
     syn:          V
     index:        x@HIKE
     conds:        nil
     args:         nil
     subcat:       {
                   (syn:       NPnom
                   index:      y@HUMAN_BEING
                   context:    {(actor x y )})
                   }
```

This lexical representation, among other things, provides the basis for derivational operations. Simple nominalizations, for example, can be interpreted as shifts from syntactically necessary arguments into only semantically necessary arguments:

```
Wanderung(hike) ->
     syn:        N
     index:      x@HIKE
     conds:      {(actor x y)}
     args:       {y@HUMAN_BEING}
     subcat:     nil
```

Or else 'index' is exchanged with an element from 'args' or 'subcat':

```
Wanderer (hiker) ->
     syn:        N
     index:      y@HUMAN_BEING
     conds:      {(actor x y)}
     args:       {x@HIKE}
```

However, it will be impossible to make the assignment between words and conceptual interpretations independent of the context. Therefore this assignment cannot be completely encoded in a lexical entry. On the one hand, as discussed in the previous section, the assignment of sorts is often ambiguous because in many cases there is a number of different interpretations which – concerning their sorts – are incompatible with one another. That is why the assignment of a sort becomes dependent on the context. On the other hand, on looking more carefully, many words prove to be functions which do not provide a conceptual meaning of their own unless applied to conceptual interpretations. For example, 'Beginn' (beginning) will provide different sortal interpretations depending on its argument.

```
begin(x@HIKE)
begin(x@STREET)
begin(x@CENTURY)
```

Nevertheless, in all three cases we have a uniform word meaning for 'Beginn'. But it can only be unsatisfactorily represented by the described formalism:

```
beginn ->
     syn:        N
     index:      x@POINT_OF_TIME
     conds:      {(beginning_time y x)}
     args:       {y@PERIOD_OF_TIME}
     subcat:     nil
```

```
beginn ->
      syn:          N
      index:        x@PLACE
      conds:        {(beginning_place y x)}
      args:         {y@PATH}
      subcat:       nil
```

Only if the specification of the sortal restrictions can be achieved by the relation 'beginning' itself do we get one single entry for 'Begin'.

```
beginn ->
      syn:          N
      index:        x
      conds:        {(beginning y x)}
      args:         {y}
      subcat:       nil
```

Normally, the elements of 'args' are not syntactically realized in the sentence, or cannot be syntactically recognized as arguments.

Wir gehen die Straße entlang und biegen an der Kreuzung rechts ab.
(We walk along the street and turn right at the crossroads.)

```
kreuzung (crossroads)->
      syn:          N
      index:        x@AREA
      conds:        {(cross x y z)}
      args:         {y@TRAFFIC_WAY, z@TRAFFIC_WAY}
```

4   Computation of Context-Specific Meanings

Conceptual shifting corresponds to a sortal specification. For the time being, the possible sortal specifications are scheduled to be extensionally given by a shifting graph whose leaves specify sorts (see figure 4). Such a graph can be represented in STUF by disjunction.

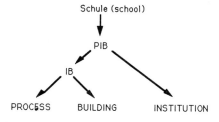

Figure 4:

The non-terminal nodes cannot be identified with sorts because they can connect disjunctive sorts with one another. Depending on the granularity of the sort-system, we may have to introduce three concepts, SCHULE1, SCHULE2 and SCHULE3, which occur as subsorts of the corresponding supersorts INSTITUTION, BUILDING and PROCESS. This is not adequate, because a completely extensional rendering is not possible. For example, in the above mentioned sentence there are contexts in which the word 'Schule' may refer to individuals that are incompatible with any of the three possibilities, as in the example 'Die Schule machte einen Ausflug' in the sense of 'The school took a staff outing'.

A more adequate realization can be achieved by (context-dependent) derivational operations which are iteratively applicable to a limited extent. This strategy corresponds to primary meanings together with derivational operations as discussed in the previous sections when considering the example:

> *das dreistöckige staatliche Museum*
> (the three-storeyed state museum)
> *das staatliche dreistöckige Museum* (*)

Both adjectives obviously cannot refer to the same object: 'state' requires an institution as argument, 'three-storeyed' a building, and these two sorts are disjunctive. The asymmetry of the two nominal phrases can be interpreted to the effect that 'institution' is a primary meaning of 'museum' and 'building' is achieved (asymmetrically) by a derivational operation. The corresponding lexical entries may have the form:

```
Museum (museum) ->
        syn:        N
        index:      x@MUSEUM
        conds:      nil
        args:       nil
        subcat:     nil


staatlich (state) ->
        syn:        Adj
        index:      x@INSTITUTION
        conds:      nil
        args:       nil
        subcat:     {
                    (syn:        N
                    index:       x@INSTITUTION
                    context:     {(sponsor x state)})
                    }

dreistöckig (three-storeyed) ->
        syn:        Adj
        index:      x@BUILDING
        conds:      nil
        args:       nil
        subcat:     {
                    (syn:        N,
                    index:       x@BUILDING
                    context:     {(height x three-storeyed)})
                    }
```

Combining them leads to the following intermediate structures for 'staatliche Museum' and 'dreistöckige staatliche Museum':

staatliche Museum:
syn:	N
index:	x@MUSEUM
conds:	{(sponsor' x@state)}
args:	nil
subcat:	nil

dreistöckige staatliche Museum:
syn:	N
index:	y@BUILDING
conds:	{(sponsor x state)
	(has_seat x y)
	(height y three-storeyed)}
args:	{x@MUSEUM}
subcat:	nil

This can be achieved by the following shifting rule:

syn:	SYN		syn:	SYN
index:	x@INSTITUTION		index:	y@BUILDING
conds:	C	====>	conds:	C u {(has_seat x y)}
args:	A		args:	A u {x@INSTITUTION}
subcat:	S		subcat:	S

This rule has to be interpreted as follows:

Whenever an argument of the sort BUILDING is required and instead something of the sort INSTITUTION is available, the argument can be filled after introduction of a new relation 'has_seat' linking the old term to a new variable of sort BUILDING.

Using the other sequence of adjectives gives the following structure (after application of the shifting rule):

dreistöckige Museum:
syn:	N
index:	y@BUILDING
conds:	{(has_seat x y)}
	(height y three-storeyed)}
args:	{x@MUSEUM}
subcat:	nil

There are obviously no derivational operations leading from a building to the institution it accommodates. It is evident that shifting operations are only possible along certain relations. Within the framework of LILOG such relations are defined in the sort system as features or roles. This example shows that 'is_seat_of' should not be a role of the concept (sort) BUILDING, whereas the concept INSTITUTION should have a role 'has_seat'. Not all the roles or features of a concept are suitable for shifting operations. As a first step we can extensionally add to each concept the set of features and roles which can be used for shifting operations.

Conceptual specifications bind variables in the component 'args'. These variables occur freely in the component 'conds'. The existential quantification of these variables is only one (and in general not the best) method for achieving conceptual interpretations. Further methods can be provided by reference resolution and discourse representation. Considering the crossroad example again, we get the following possibilities of specifications: from the context, one of the roads can at least be identified as the street we go along, and the second one has to be existentially quantified in a first step. But later this second road can be referred to if the text continues with a sentence like:

Diese Straße heißt Sternstraße.
(This street is called Sternstraße.)

5 Conclusions

With regard to the initially stressed flexibility of word meanings, which cannot be anticipated in many cases, a dynamic lexicon conception suggests itself whose lexical entries provide 'primary' meanings as a basis for derivational operations to construct 'derived' ones as well as the possibility to use abstract semantic forms together with conceptual shifting and specification. Such an approach would extend the approach put forward in (Bierwisch 1983) and elaborated in (Bierwisch, Lang 1989) where they propose that the semantic form of a lexical entry is the invariant of context-specific variants.

Since the derivation process may not be symmetrical, not every context-specific reading is a proper candidate for a 'primary' meaning. So 'primary' meanings are neither unique nor arbitrary. They are in some sense typical. In the context of the LILOG-lexicon, only first attempts could be realized. A compromise realistic for LILOG consists in encoding alternatives that

1. give sortal indices for common readings, and

2. offer – in cases of fine-grained meanings – a 'primary' concept plus contextual conditions plus derivation mechanism.

References

Bierwisch, M.(1983): Semantische und konzeptuelle Repräsentation lexikalischer Einheiten. In Motsch, W.; Ruzicka R. (eds.): "Untersuchungen zur Semantik", pp. 61-99, Akademie-Verlag, Berlin

Bierwisch, M.; Lang, E.(1989): Dimensional adjectives. Springer-Verlag, Berlin Heidelberg New York

Gust, H.; Scheffczyk, A.(1991): Ein Ansatz zur Beschreibung von Konzeptstrukturen und Eigenschaftssystemen. Kognitionswissenschaft, pp. 71-82

Gust, H.; Ludewig, P.; Rickheit M.(1988): Das Lexikon für LILOG. LILOG-Report 29.

Osherson, D.N.(1978): Three conditions on conceptual naturalness. Cognition 4, pp. 263-289

Sortal Information in Lexical Concepts

M. Rickheit

Abstract

Words are linguistic concepts whose definitions depend on specific semantic interests within a certain scope of linguistic description; relative to more or less controversial conceptions of words there furthermore exist different views on what word meanings are. However, there is a classical dead end in pure linguistic argumentation, namely the form-meaning problem of linguistic symbols, particularly of words. Cognitive arguments offer the possibility to decompose the question of a word's meaning into separable factors, each of them describable on the grounds of specific regularities, while being functional only in their interaction.

In this article a distinction is made between two different kinds of lexical concepts: (i) meaning representations of context-free lexicon words and (ii) meaning representations of words uttered in a discourse. Concepts that are linked with words conceived as part of the vocabulary are called *word concepts*, while concepts that are connected with words conceived as elements of an actual discourse are *reference concepts*. Since word concepts function as input for the generation of reference concepts, a closer look at the latter is necessary to develop ideas about the internal structure of the former. It will be evident that a reference concept requires not only specifications of a word's linguistic environment but also specifications of the relevant non-linguistic referential background. Taking this into account, sortal concepts play a crucial role in that they integrate world knowledge on both levels of lexical representation.

Sorts as Links Between World and Words

It is a common view that, in contrast to the descriptive function of sentences, words often have a referential function. Consequently, the notion of word meaning is closely related to the notion of reference. There exist, however, fundamental theoretical problems with each, and the relevant philosophical, linguistic, and psycholinguistic discussions have a long tradition. However, there are several possibilities to approach the question of what lexical concepts are, just as there are also different views on referentiality. In a text, words evidently combine to refer to some object or situation, but the interesting question is how the relationship between the level of words and the level of real-world entities can be explained.

Already in the early 1920s, Ogden and Richards (1923) stressed the fact that there is no direct relation between a linguistic symbol and a real-world entity. On the contrary, this relation is always established in the human brain and consequently determined by pragmatic factors concerning the person who attributes meaning. In his summary of psycholinguistic studies in word comprehension, Johnson-Laird (1987) comes to the conclusion that knowledge about the reference of a word is a decisive factor – in the context of his article, the term reference is replaceable by real-world entity. If a word's meaning is understood as a conceptual structure developing when a human uses or understands a word, then it is not something fixed and given a priori, but rather an individual mental construction dependent on specific communication conditions and probably different from one case to another. If word meanings are interpreted as mental representations, they vary relative to knowledge about the world entities referred to in an actual discourse.

The sortal approach which has been developed within the framework of the LILOG project can be interpreted as a central theoretical link between the level of linguistic symbols and the level of real-world entities. Sorts in LILOG primarily have the function of modeling world knowledge which is basic for inferences to be drawn during the process of computational text-understanding. They are conceptual structures organized in an ontological hierarchy: on higher levels of the ontology, they express general correlational constraints on features of objects and situations; on lower levels, they represent knowledge associated with entities referred to in given texts (cf. Klose, von Luck, in this chapter). In this article, the hypothesis is held that sortal concepts on a higher level of the hierarchy are crucial for lexical concepts, whereas there is little to be said about sorts on lower levels from a linguistic standpoint. The topic focuses a view on the matter which is complementary to knowledge engineering, but is related to it by problems of referentiality. Central aspects in word meanings cannot be grasped without the integration of sortal information.

Sorts in a Model of Reference Constitution

Sorts convey conceptual information that is not directly bound to linguistic entities in general, or words in particular. In principle, there is not a one-to-one, but a many-to-many mapping from sorts to words. This takes account of non-isomorphisms between lexical and sortal categories. For example, either the verb *wander* or the noun *hike* can be used to refer to an event, and conversely, a given word may have different sortal interpretations, such as *door* in the readings of "entrance" versus "panel".

Words appear in a multitude of verbal and nonverbal contexts and thus exhibit different meanings. So, for example, the semantics of the German predicate *gehen* changes depending on the conceptual category of its subject, i.e., it may be a human agent, a physical object, a track, etc.:

Sie geht auf Zehenspitzen (She tiptoes).
Die Uhr geht nicht richtig (The clock is wrong).
Das Fenster geht zur Straße (The window looks onto the street).
Die Straße geht durch den Wald (The street goes through the forest).

Apart from its subject, further complements or adjuncts influence the interpretation of this verb:

Er geht über die Straße (He walks across the street).
Er geht am Stock (He walks with a stick/He is dead-beat/...).
Er geht jeden Donnerstag ins Kino (Every Thursday, he goes to the movies).
Er geht zum Militär (He joins the army).

In the cognitive literature, the relation between a word percept (i.e., the complex of its perceptual features such as its phonological or graphematic structure) and a word concept is interpreted as a code relation usually activating several concepts and in this respect opening up different possibilities of establishing reference relations (Strohner 1990). The above sentences illustrate the general idea and present themselves for two additional remarks.

Firstly, the conceptual structure of a word has to contain meaning factors to allow the distinction of several readings. As mentioned above, sortal expressions like 'human agent', 'physical object', or 'track' can be used to constrain possible contexts of the verb *gehen*. To interpret the verb itself in accordance with its respective linguistic context, further sortal descriptions like 'change of location', 'physical state', 'habitual action', or 'intended state' may serve as global indicators of specific differences in the type of situation. Sortal concepts are obviously suitable to establish a relation between linguistic signs on the one hand, and real-world entities referred to in a text on the other.

Secondly, reference relations to real-world entities such as objects and situations are crucial for the meaning of words uttered in a discourse. However, from a linguistic point of view, they cannot be determined on the level of words, but only on the level of phrases. Word meanings are referentially vague unless words combine to form phrases and thus mutually restrict their possible readings.

In order to get some insights into the role of sorts in this respect, different conceptual levels that are involved in the constitution of reference have to be explained beforehand. The following schema summarizes a view of the matter which is more explicitly presented in Rickheit (1990).

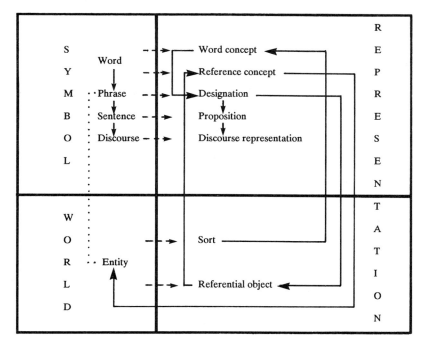

Figure 1: A model of reference constitution

Figure 1 proposes a structural model of reference constitution as far as word meanings are concerned. It presents an attempt to seize conceptual components central in this respect and essentially corresponds to the triangle model suggested in Ogden, Richards (1923). It makes a distinction between a level of linguistic symbols, a level of world entities, and a level of conceptual representations. Word, phrase, sentence, and discourse are common linguistic units, and the arrows between them express constituency. A dotted line connects phrases with entities. Phrases are taken to be the relevant linguistic units establishing reference relationships. Dots indicate an indirect connection, since reference constitution actually involves the interaction of several mediating conceptual representations. Two dashed lines mark relationships from the level of entities to the level of representations. One of them points to so-called referential objects, the other one to sorts. We first make a comment on sorts.

Within the framework of the proposed model of reference constitution, sorts have the function of specifying general knowledge about real-world entities. However, this knowledge comprises heterogeneous perspectives on the world. As a matter of fact, very often there is more than one possible view of objects and situations referred to by speech. A well known example is the possibility to conceive a given situation either as an event, a state, or even a combination of an event and a state:

When she came to the office, the door was (already) open/closed. (State)
When she came to the office, the door was being opened/closed (by the secretary). (Event)
When she came to the office, the door was opened/closed (by the secretary). (Resultative)

Here we see that the situation presented in the second clause of the first example is depicted as a state, in the second example as an event, and in the third example as an event which leads to a resulting state (cf. Andersen 1991, p.87ff.). In this respect, note that there is generally no formal distinction made in English (in contrast to German) between the expression of states and resultatives (a notable exception being *open* (state) vs. *opened* (resultative).

Without going into details of temporal semantics, the sentences should highlight the general possibility of characterizing a real-world situation from different points of view. Two persons who watch the scene may have different interpretations for it and consequently put it into different terms. With respect to the above examples, the distinction between events, states, and resultatives plays an important role and gives rise to controversal inferences. Generally speaking, events imply that some effect, result, or change has to be expected. Furthermore, they imply an entity affected by the change as well as an entity mediating it. If the situation is categorised as a state, however, these aspects are faded out. What counts is that there be an entity to whom a state is attributed. EVENT and STATE can be defined as two sortal categories, the difference consisting in the attributes 'result', 'medium', and 'affected object' which are obligatory of the category EVENT (resultatives included) and nonexistent within the sortal category STATE (cf. Rickheit 1990).

Likewise, sortal categorizations of objects depend on certain attributes in focus, e.g., perceptual or functional attributes. Features of this kind pertain to different sortal categories, such as HEAVY OBJECT versus MUSICAL INSTRUMENT. Relative to the entity in question, for example a piano, they do not necessarily exclude each other, but they are more or less important in certain contexts. An example already discussed in Barclay et al. (1974) and taken up in Hörmann (1976) may illustrate the point:

He carries the piano.
He tunes the piano.

In the context of *carry*, sortal characteristics such as the moveability of objects and the weight of heavy objects become relevant; in the context of *tune*, however, neither aspect seems to be pertinent – although both remain valid. The *relevance profile* (Hörmann 1976) in the structure of features associated with an entity has undergone a shift and, as a consequence, the actual meaning of the word *piano* has undergone a shift, too.

The approach implies that sortal concepts depend neither on individual words nor on individual entities. Instead, they function as categorial structures containing possible attributes of any entity whatever in a systematic way. As parts of a sortal hierarchy, they define correlational constraints on these attributes and thus restrict sortal categorisations of entities: some entity may be characterized either under the aspect of being alive or under the aspect of being heavy, but in case these attributes are applicable, the entity cannot be described as being vaporous, because living beings usually have a body. Constraints of this kind have to be put down in a sortal system. A level of sortal description which is distinct from the level of entities, distinct from the level of words, and distinct from the level of lexical concepts, can be organized consistently.

Following the continous line in figure 1, sorts enter into *word concepts*. One of their functions here is to indicate what Kanngießer (1985) calls the relation between words in the lexicon and extensions of possible referents. This short remark may suffice at the moment, since word concepts and the integration of sorts are treated in more detail below. Word concepts are conceptual structures associated with context-free lexicon words, and usually there exist several of them to constitute what is known as the notoriously vague meaning of words.

Word concepts, in turn, are the input for so-called designations (for the definition of this concept, cf. Habel 1986). Designations are meaning representations of phrases: on the one hand, they are determined by individual structures of word concepts; on the other hand, they are subject to specific conditions on the relevant representation language. Designations can be more or less complex, and the most important thing about them is that they open up the possibility to integrate knowledge about relationships to referents of other phrases.

Designations are not only meaning representations of phrases but also conceptual descriptions of objects and situations referred to in a discourse. Formal representatives of entities introduced into a discourse via phrases are so-called reference objects (Refos, Habel 1986). Reference objects form part of the episodic knowledge in that they directly depend on the respective phrases of a text. Since identical real-world entities may be referred to by various linguistic expressions in a discourse, reference objects serve the function of identification. Reference objects are specified by more or less complex designations, which, in turn, may include relationships to other reference objects. The model proposed in Figure 1 interprets designations as constituents of propositions which are representations of sentences. Finally, propositions serve as input for complex discourse representations. These concepts are only mentioned to complete the picture, but cannot be treated in this article.

Knowledge associated with reference objects is constitutive for the meaning of a text word, i.e., the *reference concept*. Reference concepts are unambiguos since they draw on reference relations which do not yet exist on the level of word concepts. Reference concepts presuppose the integration of the above mentioned concepts on different representational levels and in this are qualitatively different from word concepts. They have to be understood as functions with three arguments: their first argument consists of word concepts associated with a lexicon word, their second argument consists of the word concepts associated with words of the relevant phrase, and their third argument consists in knowledge about the respective referential entity. Meaning structures of text words turn out to be results of interactions on different conceptual levels, in particular on the levels of lexical, sortal, and referential knowledge.

Finally, unambiguos reference concepts lead to context-specific conceptualizations of real-world entities. The basis for this kind of conceptualization are lexical selection and combination processes that presuppose several matches among potential word concepts, on the one hand, and certain features of referential objects, on the other. In using words to refer to entities, only those features come into play which are enclosed in word concepts via sortal categories, whereas other features remain valid but unmentioned.

The Role of Sorts in Word Concepts

In this model, a word concept specifies linguistic and sortal knowledge associated with one possible reading of a word. It is a complex structure that restricts, firstly, the syntactic category of a word, secondly, the sortal category of a potential referent of the respective phrase the word may appear in, and thirdly, the word's linguistic context in its sortal aspects. By this, it represents one potential word meaning without a specific referential value. Unlike a reference concept, it does not contain these contextual restrictions in an instantiated, but only in a categorially given, form. The following example of a word concept may give an impression of what is meant:

waschen

synt_cat:	V
sort_index:	x @ AFFECT_2
subcat:	{

     (synt_cat: NPnom
      sort_index: y @ HUMAN
      context: { (actor x y) })

     (synt_cat: NPacc
      sort_index: b @ PHYSICAL_OBJECT
      context: { (aff_obj x b) })

     (synt_cat: PPmit
      sort_index: a @ LIQUID
      context: { (medium x a) })
     }

This structure adopts a proposal made by Gust (in this volume). A sortal index (sort_index) integrates general sortal knowledge about a potential referent of the relevant verbal phrase, e.g. *wäscht die Hose (washes the trousers)*. The category AFFECT occupies a certain position within a sort hierarchy and possesses an internal structure which can be paraphrased as being an EVENT characterized by the fact that a physical object A affects a physical object B. The effect is a physical change concerning B. AFFECT is a subclassification of EVENT. Neither are bound either to an actual situation or to a single word. The notion AFFECT_2 implies an additional actor and his intention.

Under 'subcat' ('subcategorization') some possible syntactic contexts in which this verb may appear receive specification. In a discourse they need not necessarily be realized, but in case they are, they are then subject to specific linguistic and sortal restrictions as well as to semantic instantiation conditions given at the position 'context'. If there are three syntactic arguments, namely a nominative phrase, an accusative phrase, and a prepositional phrase containing the preposition *mit*, they are not only constrained by sortal categories, but also by certain semantic relations such as 'actor of', 'affected object of', and 'medium of'. At first glance, these relations are very similar to what has widely been discussed as lexical cases (Fillmore 1968), thematic roles (Jackendoff 1972), and theta roles (Chomsky 1981), and there is no doubt that they show common traits. However, they do not belong to any of these grammatical paradigms, because they are sortal relations independent from syntactic arguments. They function as attributes of global sortal categories which do not exist in the mentioned syntactic theories. Possibly, discussing sortal attributes may finally lead to exact formal representations of thematic relations as well as to specifications of interrelationships between syntactic and morphological configurations (cf. Wilkins 1988).

The proposed example of a word concept is not very satisfying, however, since it equally applies for other German verbs, such as *gießen (water), nässen (wet), tränken (water), spülen (rinse), spritzen (splash)*. It does not express the fact that wash events usually consist in removing a substance C from a substance B, typically by means of water. If there is a corresponding sortal concept available, it is preferable to AFFECT. SEPARATE could be introduced as a subconcept of AFFECT and defined such that it additionally contains a physical object C being removed from B. C need not be syntactically instantiated, but in case it is, the following word concept applies:

waschen

synt_cat:	V
sort_index:	x @ SEPARATE_2
subcat:	{

(synt_cat:	NPnom	
sort_index:	y @ HUMAN	
context:	{ (actor x y) })	
(synt_cat:	NPakk	
sort_index:	c @ PHYSICAL_OBJECT	
context:	{ (sep_obj x c) })	
(synt_cat:	PPmit	
sort_index:	a @ LIQUID	
context:	{ (medium x a) })	
(synt_cat:	PPaus	
sort_index:	b @ PHYSICAL_OBJECT	
context:	{ (aff_obj x b) })	
}		

This possible word concept of *waschen* holds for contexts like: *Y wäscht C aus B (Y washes C from B)* or *Y wäscht C mit A aus B (Y washes C from B by means of A)*. It is likewise valid for the German verb *spülen*, but it excludes *gießen, nässen, spritzen, tränken* as well as every other German verb, because they do not comply with the specific combination of restrictions defined in this word concept. In particular, they cannot be used to refer to events categorized by the sort SEPARATE in connexion with LIQUID as an obligatory conceptual argument within the word concept.

So far, sortal classifications have been discussed as referential constraints on real-world situations via 'sort_index'. They have also been viewed as extralinguistic constraints on possible syntactic arguments of verbs. A further point is that sorts can be used to specify word-internal constituents in case the word is complex.

In the following two examples, a prefixation with *aus-* marks the sortal argument C which is the separated physical object of the sortal category SEPARATE. The relevant information is given under 'sem_marker'. C does not necessarily become realized word-externally (cf. *Y wäscht C aus B aus / Y wäscht B aus (Y washes B out from B/ Y washes out B)*), but it is an obligatory conceptual argument of the prefixed verb *auswaschen (wash out)*. If C is not specified at the position 'subcat', its conceptual presence – which is invoked by word formation – has to be determined somewhere else. It suggests itself to assign the information to two additional positions in the word concept, namely to the slot 'sem_arguments' ('semantic arguments'), and to the slot 'sem_conditions' ('semantic conditions'):

auswaschen

synt_cat:	V
sort_index:	x @ SEPARATE_2
sem_marker:	c @ PHYSICAL_OBJECT
subcat:	{

        (synt_cat: NPnom
         sort_index: y @ HUMAN
         context: { (actor x y) })

        (synt_cat: NPakk
         sort_index: c @ PHYSICAL_OBJECT
         context: { (sep_obj x c) })

        (synt_cat: PPmit
         sort_index: a @ LIQUID
         context: { (medium x a) })

        (synt_cat: PPaus
         sort_index: b @ PHYSICAL_OBJECT
         context: { (aff_obj x b) })
      }

auswaschen

synt_cat:	V
sort_index:	x @ SEPARATE_2
sem_marker:	c @ PHYSICAL_OBJECT
sem_arguments:	{ (c @ PHYSICAL_OBJECT) }
sem_conditions:	{ (sep_obj x c) })
subcat:	{

        (synt_cat: NPnom
         sort_index: y @ HUMAN
         context: { (actor x y) })

        (synt_cat: PPmit
         sort_index: a @ LIQUID
         context: { (medium x a) })

        (synt_cat: PPaus
         sort_index: b @ PHYSICAL_OBJECT
         context: { (aff_obj x b) })
      }

The slots 'sem_marker', 'sem_arguments', and 'sem_conditions' usually become instantiated within conceptual structures of words derived by word formation processes. They integrate sortal knowledge associated with the complex word's constituents which may be simple stems or affixes. If, for example, possible word concepts of *waschen* are given, and if, furthermore, certain functions of prefixed *aus-* and suffixed *-ung* are available, then it should not be difficult to generate new word concepts by simply instantiating the relevant slots:

Auswaschung

synt_cat:	N
sort_index:	x @ SEPARATE_2
sem_marker:	COMPLEX_EVENT
sem_arguments:	{ (y @ HUMAN)
	(a @ LIQUID)
	(b @ PHYSICAL_OBJECT)
	(c @ PHYSICAL_OBJECT) }
sem_conditions:	{ (actor x y)
	(medium x a)
	(aff_obj x b)
	(sep_obj x c) }
subcat:	nil

Word concepts of complex words provide for a cluster of sortal and linguistic knowledge which can be inferred and for this reason need not be given explicitly in a discourse. They may be very useful in cases when unknown complex words appear in a text. To illustrate the point, a text has been chosen which has been found on a label on jeans. It contains the noun *Auswaschung* in a reading presumably not yet to be found in a lexicon:

Sie haben eben eine modische, sandgewaschene Hose gekauft. Abgestoßene Kanten sind typisch für diese modische Auswaschung und somit gewollt. Diese Optik berechtigt deshalb nicht zur Reklamation. Viel Spaß beim Tragen!

(You have just bought fashionable, sand-washed trousers. Roughened edges are typical of this fashionable "wash-out" and are therefore intended. The optical effect does not justify complaint. Much fun wearing them!)

The text gives rise to the question what the German word *Auswaschung* means. The nominal phrase *diese modische Auswaschung* is related to the previous nominal phrase *fashionable, sandwashed trousers* in that both imply a reference to some wash event. Although *-ung* derivatives generally allow for an event-interpretation, the actual context does not comply well with this kind of reading. Without going into details concerning the constitution of the relevant reference concept, its result may be mentioned. A second function of the suffix *-ung* consists in nominalizing the result of the event indicated by the verbal constituent. A plausible result of a wash event is a specific state of the thing washed, an argument which finally leads to the following lexical concept:

Auswaschung

synt_cat:	N
sort_index:	r @ STATE
sem_marker:	nil
sem_arguments:	{ (x @ SEPARATE)
	(y @ HUMAN)
	(a @ LIQUID)
	(b @ PHYSICAL_OBJECT)
	(c @ PHYSICAL_OBJECT) }
sem_conditions:	{ (resultat x r)
	(thema r b)
	(actor x y)
	(medium x a)
	(aff_obj x b)
	(sep_obj x c) }
subcat:	nil

The derived concept does not contain all information necessary for the actual reference concept of the word in question – in particular, it cannot supply world knowledge with respect to the special instance of physical object B which consists of the color rinsed out from the trousers during the washing process. However, it signals a category switch from EVENT to STATE. It makes the underlying conceptual relations explicit and thus represents a step forward in constituting the meaning of the respective word.

Word concepts provide for a word-specific integration of sortal superstructures. Amazingly rough-grained sorts suffice to grasp central aspects in word meanings, an observation which leads to the conclusion that sortal categories should be aimed at which combine a minimum of definition effort with a maximum of lexical discrimination capacity.

References

Andersen, P.K. (1991): A New Look at the Passive. Peter Lang, Frankfurt a.M.

Barclay, J.R., Bransford, J.D.,Franks, J.J., McCarrell, N.S., Nitsch, K. (1974): Comprehension and semantic flexibility, J. Verb. Learn. Verb. Behav. 13, 471-481

Fillmore, C.J. (1968): The case for case, in: Bach, E., Harms, R.T.(eds.): Universals in Linguistic Theory. Holt, New York, 1-88

Habel, C. (1986): Prinzipien der Referentialität, Springer-Verlag, Berlin, Heidelberg, New York

Hörmann,H. (1976): Meinen und Verstehen. Grundzüge einer psychologischen Semantik. Suhrkamp, Frankfurt a.M.

Jackendoff, R. (1972): Semantic Interpretation in Generative Grammar. MIT Press, Cambridge, MA

Johnson-Laird, P.N. (1987): The meaning of words. Cognition, 25, 189-211

Kanngießer, S. (1985): Strukturen der Wortbildung, in: Schwarze, C., Wunderlich, D.(eds.): Handbuch der Lexikologie. Athenäum, Königstein/Ts, 134-183

Ogden, C.K., Richards, I.A. (1923): The Meaning of Meaning. Harcourt, Brace, & World, New York

Rickheit, M. (1990): Wortbedeutungen und lexikalische Repräsentationen. IWBS Report 127

Strohner, H. (1990): Textverstehen. Kognitive und Kommunikative Grundlagen der Sprachverarbeitung. Westdeutscher Verlag, Opladen

Wilkins, W. (ed.)(1988): Syntax and Semantics. Vol. 21: Thematic Relations. Academic Press, San Diego, CA

Incremental Vocabulary Extensions in Text Understanding Systems

Petra Ludewig

Abstract

Natural language understanding systems which have to prove good in interesting applications cannot manage without some mechanism for dealing with lexical gaps. In this paper four strategies appropriate for goal-directed vocabulary extensions – 'contextual' specification, use of morphological rules, access to external lexica and interactive user input – are outlined, directing the principal attention to the exploitation of machine-readable versions of conventional dictionaries (MRDs). These mechanisms complement each other as they are geared to different types of unknown words and may be used recursively. A temporary lexicon is introduced to cope with the uncertainty and partiality of the so-gained lexical information. The treatment of unknown words presented in this paper contributes to overcoming the bottleneck concerning lexical and, to some degree, conceptual knowledge.

1 Introduction

Natural language processing (NLP) systems – whether artificial or human – never reach the full extent of knowledge concerning language use, especially as far as vocabulary is concerned. Nonetheless, many systems do start from the assumption of a complete dictionary. However, even in restricted areas of application, as in, for example, expert systems, it would be hopeless to try to encode a complete dictionary: on the one hand there is an extensive number of synonyms and technical terms which, moreover, varies in the course of time; on the other hand the vocabulary of a single area of application cannot always be clearly delimited (Alshawi 1987).

Lexica are incomplete with regard to several aspects. Macro-structural incompleteness is given by missing lemmata. In this case we may talk about unknown words. Micro-structural incompleteness arises if some type of information, for example morphological characterization, is not included or some reading of a lemma is not taken into account, the latter corresponding to the problem of unknown word uses.

Consequently, in order to make knowledge acquisition from texts robust, procedures are needed which do not give up when confronted with gaps in vocabulary[1]. Against this background, macro-structural deficiencies seem to cause less problems than micro-structural ones insofar as they are easier to identify: unknown words usually can be revealed by the fact that they cannot be led back to a known lexical item (at least by inflectional morphology alone)[2] whereas an NLP system still finds some information in its lexicon when confronted with unknown word uses. For this reason, in the latter case the system may overread the problematic words and construct text representations whose inconsistencies might not become evident until it is already quite difficult to make out the corresponding reason. Thus, in a first step to tackle lexical gaps it seems to be advantageous to confine oneself primarily to those gaps given by unknown words. This decision permits one, for the time being, to take less account of revealing the gaps and to concentrate on closing them.

---

[1]'The impact of lexical gaps in generation is not as drastic'(Zernik 1989). Concerning text generation, lexical gaps may become visible as concepts for which there exist no words in the internal lexicon referring to them. Such concepts may be circumscribed with recourse to known words, for example, as in dictionary definitions or in compounds and derivatives.

[2]In order to prevent the system from taking a misspelt word for an unknown word, a spelling correction should be integrated (Erbach 1990, Wahlster 1982).

The only chance of coping with unknown words consists in:

1. being content with a partial text understanding, or

2. closing the gaps as they arise by shifting into a learning mode, which means extending the vocabulary on demand, whether by using morphological rules, by accessing external lexica, or by asking the user of the system.

These two strategies for bridging lexical gaps are closely connected. In order to ensure a meaningful partial text understanding, unknown words often have to be at least partly inferred by trying to derive the necessary lexical information from the context. This is an approach which, in the following, will be referred to as 'contextual' specification. When the information gained in this way is put into a lexicon, one might speak of word acquisition.

At the same time the vocabulary extensions that are carried out by means of the methods listed under 2) can only be of a partial nature. Neither the completeness of morphological rules nor the completeness of the available dictionaries or of the user's knowledge, nor the exhaustive processing of lexical information given more or less as natural language input can be taken for granted. Thus, the incompleteness of lexical knowledge cannot be remedied by dynamic vocabulary extensions, but it can be shifted to a different level.

An inflectional morphology capable of treating, at least to some extent, unknown words by building a list of their possible stems or basic forms seems to be a prerequisite for a successful and efficient use of the above mentioned strategies (Emde, this volume, following paper). How, for example, do you look up a noun in a traditional dictionary or an MRD if you only know its plural form? Furthermore it seems to be advantageous to take stems or basic forms as headwords under which the incrementally gained lexical information is stored.

Ineffective vocabulary extensions resulting from indiscriminate word acquisition can be at least partly avoided by restricting vocabulary learning to those words that, in the course of text understanding, turn out to be unknown (or used in an unknown reading) and by deciding not to cover the whole range of alternative readings but rather the variant that is the most plausible in the given context. To achieve the latter, the method of contextual specification will provide crucial clues. Thus, procedures of vocabulary extension such as those described in the following can ensure, at least partly, that beyond an initial vocabulary only those words or readings are included in an internal lexicon that are also relevant for the application at hand. In this context they help to overcome the knowledge acquisition bottleneck as it arises at the level of lexical and, to some degree, conceptual knowledge (cf. Emde, this volume, following paper).

Before discussing the different word acquisition strategies, it should be mentioned that they complement one another in two respects:

- The different approaches are more or less geared to different types of unknown words, so that quite a wide range of words can be covered.

- As the treatment of unknown words can be initiated recursively by the different procedures for word acquisition, the capabilities of the individual approaches themselves improve.

To avoid the danger of a never-ending attempt to deduce an unknown word, the depth of recursion has to be restricted. Besides, some control mechanism to co-ordinate the various methods appropriately is needed. It appears to be advantageous to modularize this mechanism in a lexicon manager. Since the treatment of unknown words seems to get better to the same extent as the co-operation of the various methods is improved, the lexicon manager should serve as an experimentation environment for optimizing this interaction[3].

---

[3]An experimental dialogue system has been implemented to study the four strategies presented in section 2 as well as heuristics controlling their interaction (Gust, Ludewig 1989).

2 Four Strategies to Deal with Unknown Words

2.1 Contextual Specification

Contextual specification in the present context means the ability to derive assumptions about the lexical qualities of an unknown word from the context in which it occurs. For example, the sentence 'Otto is eating an orange' deduces for 'orange' the part of speech noun. Moreover, with the help of suitable background knowledge the hypothesis can be put forward that 'orange' might refer to a kind of food.

Some good ideas on how to obtain syntactic information about unknown words from context can be found in Erbach (1990). If we want to build hypotheses about the meaning of unknown words it seems advisable to let the syntactic parsing run in parallel to the semantic analysis[4]. Thus, on the basis of presumed constituent structures and the number of slots of the semantic representation that still have to be filled, the subset of the slots may be identified to the instantiation of which the unknown word might contribute.

At this point, parser and semantic construction have to co-operate with the inference machine in order to build hypotheses about the rough semantic categories of unknown words by taking into account the restrictions that the slot-fillers have to satisfy. As the ranges of semantic slots usually turn out to be rather wide, the assumptions about the meaning of unknown words that are based on them are correspondingly rough. This, in turn, results in the demand on the mechanism building up the semantic text representation that it be able to continue its work even with partial representations of word meanings.

In this context it should be pointed out that if an initially unknown word occurs repeatedly, lexical information can be accumulated gradually. Erbach (1990, p.9) gives the valuable hint that the structure of lexical entries must be taken into account when we are trying to refine the content of these entries, since for 'specific word classes, there are some features which must have unique values, while others allow a disjunction of values'.

Considering the context that goes beyond the sentence in question often makes it possible to draw more specific conclusions concerning the semantic representation of its unknown words. For example, in some cases an early anaphor resolution may contribute, by means of reference identity, to putting up more detailed hypotheses about unknown nouns. Example:

> On the opposite side of the valley you can see the old castle Greifenstein. The ruin is one of the sights of the valley.

> Assuming that the word 'ruin' is unknown to the system, then, by means of anaphor resolution, 'ruin' could be analyzed in this context as referring to an old castle.

However, contextual specification involves the risk of not recognizing text-specific facts as such and of assuming their general validity. This may happen especially if the meaning is obtained with the help of reference identity. For example, 'ruin' can refernot only to the remains of castles, but also to those of other (historical) buildings.

In his approach to the syntactic processing of unknown words, Erbach (1990) introduces a filter taking into account the structure of lexical entries to extract overspecified information obtained from context before building a new entry. But obviously, it is incomparably more difficult to identify and correct excessively specific semantic assumptions.

---

[4]Lytinen and Roberts (1989, p.5) even propose to represent all linguistic knowledge in a uniform manner and to completely integrate the processing of syntax, semantics and pragmatics, which enables their NLP system 'to use a single mechanism, unification, to infer many different kinds of features of undefined words'.

The procedure of contextual specification is excellently suitable for co-ordination with the other methods for treating unknown words; it even seems to be an indispensible strategy:

- Both when using morphological rules and when accessing external lexica, the assumptions built up by contextual specification can be consulted in order to reduce the number of alternative readings. This mechanism considerably contributes to the efficiency and goal-directedness of these procedures.

- In connection with the interactive user input, the user can be guided and relieved of some work by means of contextual specification (cf. Sect. 2.4 of this paper).

- In case the remaining procedures fail, contextual specification constitutes the last possibility of providing lexical information.

2.2 Use of Morphological Rules

Within the domain of morphology one can distinguish between inflectional morphology and derivational morphology understood as word formation. The former treats word modifications concerning, for example, person, number, and tense. The latter tries to capture the type of meaning inheritance going along with affixation and compounding[5].

Thus, some of the unknown words an NLP system might be confronted with can be deduced by using word formation rules. For example the fact that 'wanderer' refers to the agent of an event that might be designated by 'to wander' can be explained by derivation, while compositional rules permit one to conclude that 'art exhibition' refers to an exposition where works of art are on display. Even basic rules – interpreting compounds as specializations of their word-internal heads and sometimes proposing simple relations which connect the concepts the single word-constituents are referring to – permit one to gain partial interpretations for quite a lot of compounds[6].

Beside such regular forms, there are lexicalized words such as 'Milky Way' which cannot be adequately analyzed by word formation rules. But there are also words which have a lexicalized reading as well as a reading that can be reconstructed compositionally. So, for example, the compound 'horse trading' refers to some kind of a clever business according to its lexicalized reading, whereas it designates a transaction, the subject of which is given by horses, when it is used rather as an ad hoc formation[7].

These examples should show that the morphological component and the external lexica complement each other because:

- Occasionally, morphological rules and external lexica offer different interpretations,

- Lexicalized forms, which cannot be reconstructed by morphological rules any more, are usually listed in dictionaries, and

- By means of morphological rules, numerous analyzable ad hoc formations can be deduced for which dictionary entries do not exist.

---

[5]In the context of this paper, word formation rules are only treated under the aspect of their usability for word interpretation and not in connection with word generation as the notion 'word formation' might suggest.

[6]Compounds which contain some kind of negation as their modifying constituent, as, for example 'half-full' and 'non-monotonic', have, of course, to be treated differently. But it seems that the set of such building-blocks is not too extensive and therefore should not lead to unsolvable problems.

[7]For a more detailed discussion of word formation problems see (Kanngießer 1985).

Word formation rules usually provide quite a lot of alternative readings for the same word. For example, 'printer' may refer to the agent as well as to the instrument of a print event (person whose job is printing vs. machine for printing (OALD 1989)) and 'tea house' may be analyzed as referring to a house where tea is sold or drunk or perhaps even as designating a little house built out of pressed tea and serving as decoration. As the decision about which of these readings is the adequate one in a particular case is to a high degree dependent on the given context, the use of word formation rules for the interpretation of complex words usually does not make sense without the integration of an efficient component for lexical disambiguation.

A conclusion to be drawn from this section should be that derivation and composition yield a mighty instrument for dynamically extending the vocabulary. They reduce at the same time the complexity of lexica needed for natural language processing and the amount of labor necessary for dictionary development (Aoe 1989).

2.3 Access to External Lexica

Subsequently it is proposed to use MRDs for gradual vocabulary extensions, a strategy which can be seen as one possible way of taking up the idea of 'reusability of lexical resources' (Boguraev, Briscoe 1989). The following reasons, in particular, favor this approach:

- Over the years, vast amounts of lexical knowledge have been accumulated in conventional dictionaries.

- Lexical entries can be regarded as special text variants. Within the bounds of systems for knowledge acquisition out of texts, such as treated in the LILOG-project, the obvious thing to do would be to make use of similar procedures for the analysis of lexical entries as well.

- In comparison with other texts, dictionary entries and dictionary definitions as parts of them can be considered as text segments that are highly structured and submitted to lots of restrictions (Byrd et al. 1987), (Chodorow et al. 1985).

But unfortunately the structure of lexical entries is of a rather implicit nature. For example, certain types of information are characterized by their position within the entry and/or by particular typefaces, the latter being represented by corresponding control codes in the machine-readable versions.

Procedures revealing the internal structure of such entries by explicitly labelling the different types of information have been applied successfully to numerous MRDs – above all to the Collins German dictionary: German-English, English-German (Byrd et al. 1987) and to the DUDEN Deutsches Universalwörterbuch (Bläser, Wermke 1990) – and should not cause too many problems. This is the reason why, in the following, we may assume our external lexica to be given by already simply prestructured versions of MRDs (from now on called lexical data bases or LDBs).

Apart from the fact that such external lexica are relatively unsuitable for the treatment of neologism anyway, there are no further restrictions for the group of open class words thus deducible. In the individual case, however, the number of words accessible via an external lexicon strongly depends on the choice of the underlying dictionary. As to the macro-structure, dictionaries not only vary in the number of words they include, but also in the selection criteria for lemmata. As to the micro-structure, they differ in the readings they differentiate. So, we can roughly distinguish between dictionaries that are domain-independent and those that are geared to special areas of application, for example medicine. But there is no reason not to admit more than one external lexicon as an additional source of information for an NLP system.

The overall purpose of an LDB used in the context of automatic word and knowledge acquisition is to give detailed information about the different readings of words. Dictionary definitions, synonyms, hyperonyms, hyponyms and antonyms give hints to form hypotheses about possible interpretations. No doubt that at this point the definitions will play a role of higher importance.

As English and German dictionary definitions follow similar principles, successful approaches to the analysis of English dictionary definitions might be transferred to the German language. The extraction of semantic information out of dictionary definitions can be done on the following assumptions (Chodorow et al. 1985):

- Dictionary definitions typically consist of one or more 'genus' terms and specifications (differentia).

- The semantic object which a 'genus' term refers to in the context of a definition already contains central features of the meaning to be defined.

- The differentia usually delimit the concept to be defined from other ones.

- In noun and verb definitions the 'genus' terms (semantic heads) typically coincide with the syntactic heads of the defining phrases. In order to identify the latter, heuristics can be used (Byrd et al. 1987).

- The patterns included in definitions rather systematically represent semantic relations (Binot, Jensen 1987). For example 'used for' indicates an instrument relation.

- Not all of the knowledge that is represented in definitions is of the same importance for an initial treatment of unknown words. Even only being able to locate the semantic head can be useful (Alshawi 1987).

However, the compact formulation of definitions, the variant status of specifications, the ambiguity expressed by sense entries referring to the different readings of a lemma (Wilks et al. 1988), and the ambiguity located in the definitions themselves cause problems when semantic information is to be filtered out automatically.

In order to save space, redundant or alternative definitions are formulated in a compact way. Example:

Küche: Raum zum Kochen, Backen, Zubereiten der Speisen
(kitchen: room for cooking, baking, preparing meals)

(DUDEN Bedeutungswörterbuch 1985)

The resulting requirements affect the parser's level as well as the level of knowledge processing. For example, the parser must be able to interpret punctuation adequately. During the semantic analysis of the definition of 'kitchen', for instance, cooking and baking have to be identified as two alternatives of preparing meals, which means that subsuming relations have to be made out.

The specifications given in definitions may refer not only to distinctive but also to typical features. For example:

Hagebutte: kleine hellrote Frucht der Heckenrose
(rose hip: small light-red fruit of the wild rose)

(DUDEN Bedeutungswörterbuch 1985)

The difficulty concerning these differentia essentially consists in identifying the respective status of the individual features: an unripe greeny fruit of the wild rose should be regarded as an instance of the concept of rose hip, whereas a ripe fruit of a mountain ash should not. The solution of this problem can only be approximated by integrating heuristics that deal with uncertain knowledge.

In the process of LDB-supported vocabulary extension, two types of disambiguation tasks occur. On the one hand the sense entry which goes best with a given context has to be chosen out of different ones. On the other hand there may occur ambiguities within the definition of a sense entry which have to be resolved.

Example of the double ambiguity problem:

John macht eine Hocke über das Pferd.
(John is squat-vaulting over the horse.)

Hocke: turnerische Übung ... (gymnastic exercise),
         Haltung (im Sitzen) ... (carriage when sitting)

Übung: das Üben (the act of exercising),
         ... Folge bestimmter Bewegungen
         (series of certain movements)

(DUDEN Bedeutungswörterbuch 1985)

The system should not only recognize that the first definition of 'Hocke' provides the interpretation that is relevant to the example but it also has to interpret the semantic head 'Übung' as a series of movements.

As to the choice of a suitable sense entry, the following strategies could be used among others:

1. The lexical information that is arranged in a sense entry should always be checked for its compatibility with the assumptions that are obtained for the unknown word by means of contextual specification. Concerning the sentence 'The church burnt down in the 16th century' the readings 'service' and 'institution' for church can be excluded because only something concrete can form the affected object of a process referred to by 'burning down'.

2. Diatechnical details included in lexical entries, such as 'linguistics' and 'commerce' can be consulted in a double respect to decide which alternative is the likeliest in the context of the unknown word:

   • in a positive way when a certain sense entry contains some domain information that is compatible with the context, and the sense entry can therefore be regarded as favored:

     Am 8. Januar gab es an der Börse einen großen Krach.
     (On January 8th there was a big crash on the stock market.)

     Details of the different sense entries for 'Krach':

     1. Lärm (noise)
     2. Streit (quarrel)
     3. (Wirtschaft) Preissturz, Bankrott
        ((economy) sudden fall in prices, bankruptcy)

     (DUDEN-Stilwörterbuch 1970)

- in a negative way when a sense entry contains subject information that is incompatible with the context and can therefore be excluded from closer examination:

> Hans geht einmal monatlich ins Theater.
> Er ist ein Mensch mit Sinn für Kultur.
> (Once a month John goes to the theatre.
> He is a man who appreciates culture.)

Details of the different sense entries for 'Kultur':

1. Gesamtheit der geistigen, gestaltenden Leistungen
    von Menschen-(gruppen)
    (all the mental, creative achievements of people
    (groups of people))
2. a) Ausbildung, Pflege (education, cultivation)
    b) Bildung, verfeinerte Lebensformen
       (scholarliness, distinguished customs)
3. (Landwirtschaft (agriculture))
    a) Bodenbearbeitung (farming)
    b) Anbau (cultivation)
    c) das Gepflanzte (culture)
4. (Biologie) Zucht
    ((biology) breeding, growing)

(DUDEN-Stilwörterbuch 1970)

It may be supposed that domain information can be used especially within the bounds of expert systems, because their domains are rather strictly limited and can be quite well related to the diatechnical details given in sense entries.

3. As to external lexica with a frequency-based order of sense entries, it may be assumed that the readings specified first are more likely than those mentioned later. However, there are two reasons for handling this assumption carefully. Firstly, the order is subject to a certain arbitrariness. Secondly, the relative frequency of word usages is domain-dependent and thus cannot be transferred without regard to the given context.

4. We may try to define a measure of semantic proximity between the context in which the unknown word occurs and the definitions and examples that are cited in a sense entry. Such approaches can be found in (Binot, Jensen 1987) as well as in (Wilks et al. 1989).

Like other natural language text fragments, dictionary definitions may also contain lexical ambiguities. As the 'genus' terms that are included in the definitions are assumed to form the crucial point for vocabulary extensions, their disambiguation is more important for an initial treatment of unknown words than the disambiguation of the differentia. For interpreting the semantic heads the following conditions can be made use of:

- The reading of the 'genus' term has to be compatible with the diatechnical details of the sense entry.

- The differentia, which delimit from other ones the concept to be specified and represent its typical qualities, can restrict the range of alternatives which the 'genus' term is capable of referring to in the context of the definition. The reason is that the differentia introduce features only defined for certain classes of concepts.

- The concept the 'genus' term refers to in the context of a definition has to subsume the concepts which the synonyms and hyponyms refer to in the context of the associated sense entry.

- The hypotheses derived from a definition can be checked with the examples listed in the associated sense entry. In the process of building up semantic representations for the examples, bad misinterpretations of the 'genus' terms should lead to contradictions.

The phrases and sentences that are included as examples sometimes can be regarded as additions to the definitions (Drysdale 1987) providing further information about the quality of the concepts outlined in the definitions. In this case they can be made usable for the acquisition of concepts by the knowledge-processing component of the NLP system. In its simplest form, the additional information may consist in details about instances or subconcepts:

Blume: die Tulpe, die Rose ist eine Blume
(flower: the tulip, the rose is a flower)

(DUDEN Bedeutungswörterbuch 1985)

2.4 Interactive User Input

As procedures for analyzing simply pre-structured dictionary entries exist, the user should be given the opportunity of providing lexical information in a similar way. To achieve this, he should be offered a frame for a quasi-natural dictionary entry in which as much contextually deduced information as possible is already included. The formulation of definitions and examples, such as given in traditional dictionaries, should not cause too much difficulty for the user. Besides, the user should be allowed to refuse the input information. In this case the system would have to go on working with the information inferred from the context.

Since the analysis of such a user input can essentially be carried out with the same methods as the analysis of the LDB-entries, the development required for the user interface might not take that much time and work. The user interface could equally be regarded as a by-product of the interface to the LDB and as a medium for developing the latter. However, the treatment of unknown words emerging in the user input should differ from that of unknown words in LDB-entries by additionally allowing inquiries to the user.

As a rule, the interactive user input should turn out to be superior to the access to external lexica both in its run-time behavior and in the reliability of the information obtained. Not only does the analysis of more than one subentry – usually required when analyzing LDB-entries – not take place, but also the choice of a suitable sense entry is not necessary, a difficulty that should not be underestimated. However, the fact that the user is describing with his input a reading compatible with the given context represents an important premise that should be supported as follows:

- The user input will only be claimed in the course of dialogues with the user so that he knows the context of the unknown word. A call during the analysis of LDB-entries can be dispensed with because under these circumstances the context of the unknown word might not be seen by the user.

- By offering a frame already including as much contextually obtained information as possible, the user can be guided and relieved of a lot of work.

If the decision is taken in favor of the guiding principle of doing everything within the possibilities inherent in the system itself before having recourse to external sources, then it seems reasonable to initialize an interactive user input only if both – using morphological rules and accessing the LDB – have failed. This measure would also have the advantage of not bothering the user with unnecessary questions. However, such a procedure involves the risk that the user has to accept longer waiting periods and that, in the end, the system might still be obliged to ask him for information.

3 The Temporary Lexicon

Because of their special uncertainty and partiality, dynamically obtained lexical entries should get a special status for the duration of the text processing that directly follows their generation. This status could consist in the following points:

1. The system has to provide evidence for compatibility of these entries with the analyzed text.

2. The entries have provisional character insofar as, in contrast to well established entries, they can be more easily modified or extended by the system.

3. The system has to provide clues about the importance of the entries as well as of the readings specified in them.

For this reason, the new entries should be stored apart from the already established entries in a separate lexicon that is built up incrementally. To fulfil the points 1) and 3), a statistical approach could be followed as a first attempt, according to the assumption that a newly constructed entry can be regarded the more reliable and relevant, the more often it is successfully used in the course of further text processing, offering a reading compatible with the expectations built up by the system. Of course, such a measure of importance is only meaningful with regard to a corresponding topic and to a certain degree even depends on the author of the analyzed texts.

Regarding this, it has to be pointed out that it is not always as easy as it may seem at first glance to verify or falsify the assumptions on the contextual meaning of an unknown word. This might be explained by the following example:

John heard the bells of the church ringing. He had to hurry. Church would begin at ten o'clock.

Here, the second occurrence of 'church' must not be interpreted as an indication that its first occurrence does not refer to a building. Besides, in this case it seems desirable not to have to start the analysis of the LDB-entry right from the beginning if the word occurs a second time.

On the whole, when revising a dynamically generated entry, the motto of rejecting as little information as possible should be followed. The preceding specification of the entry usually already includes a whole series of checkpoints successfully run through, and more drastic correction measures demand a lot from the truth-maintenance system.

But what can be done with the entries of the incrementally constructed lexicon in the long term? On the one hand, not all of them should get lost at the end of a working session. After all we might deal with entries

- that are necessary to answer questions about the stock of knowledge that has been acquired by means of the text just analyzed, or

- that play a significant role in the course of future text comprehension.

On the other hand, if we were to automatically adopt dynamically generated entries, there would be some danger that

- incorrect details would slip into the internal lexicon, making a correct maintenance of the lexicon impossible, or that
- the relevant entries or readings cannot be reasonably differentiated from the irrelevant ones.

There are two measures that might, at least basically, do justice to these problems. On the one hand, the dynamically generated entries are given a temporary status, and are not stored automatically at the end of a working session. On the other hand, the system offers the user the chance to transfer entries in an interactive manner to the permanent lexicon before bringing the session to an end[8].

To achieve this, the system could give the user a survey of all those words to which dynamically generated entries exist. In connection with this, a certain order should be kept in listing them. We might, for example, think of a frequency-based order in which the headwords will be listed according to their rate of occurrence in the analyzed texts.

Next, the user should have the chance of successively displaying all those entries that, in his opinion, are most likely to be taken into the permanent lexicon. At the same time he should have the possibility of modifying the indicated entries. Here, of course, the question arises of what will happen if an entry is so much changed that it stands in more or less complete contradiction to the preceding assumptions of the system.

Furthermore, the system could support the user by presenting on the screen – in addition to a dynamically generated entry – the statistical details won during the text analysis, and also, perhaps, the corresponding entry from the external lexicon. The latter should not only make checking the correctness of dynamically generated entries easier but also facilitate modifications of the same. In case of a domain-specific structured lexicon as outlined in Wachsmuth (1989), the diatechnical details of external lexica give hints as to which nodes in the knowledge base the entries or some of the readings specified in them might be assigned to.

4 Conclusions

In the long run the methods for incremental word acquisition presented in this paper will be of great importance for NLP systems usable in applications requiring more extensive semantic competence. The classical and somehow obsolete method of building up lexica for NLP systems according to which the entries are coded by hand and are recoded for each new system is uneconomical if not unrealizable, requiring too much time and being very expensive as well. The problem of providing large lexica – originally taken for just a quantitative one – turns out to be a problem only solvable with qualitatively new methods.

The approach to unknown words outlined in this paper can be seen as one possible way to face this challenge. The proposed incremental and task-driven vocabulary extensions may be of use to integrate just those words and readings into the system-internal lexicon that are relevant to the application in question, taking as basis an initial lexicon covering a domain-independent basic vocabulary and the core of an application-specific vocabulary.

A component performing the task of inferring the meaning of unknown words must, at least to some extent, be able to reconstruct extralinguistic knowledge. Since there seem to exist many

---

[8]In the long term, an integration of an intermediate lexicon in addition to the temporary and permanent ones should possibly be considered, where, at the end of a working session, the system user could store those entries about which he was uncertain whether or not to take them into the permanent lexicon.

more concepts than words referring to them, an NLP system often does not have at its disposal the concept corresponding to the meaning of an unknown word. Thus, adequate mechanisms for word acquisition are not only of use for extending the lexicon but even contribute in some degree to developing the general knowledge base (Emde, this volume, next paper). As the behavior of NLP systems with increased semantic capabilities considerably depends on both knowledge bases, an efficient development of lexica and general knowledge bases will become a major concern for the 'language industry of the future'.

Of course, automatic extensions of the conceptual knowledge base made by the system itself can only be of a rudimentary nature as long as corresponding inference rules are not elaborated. Even if perhaps feasible in principle, discovering these new inference rules will be expensive and require a depth of analysis which will often be intolerable while parsing a text. However, this shortcoming seems to be less serious than it might appear at first glance. The strategy of introducing even highly underspecified concepts seems to improve the system performance considerably without consuming too much time, though in some cases, the system might pretend to have understood more than it actually has. This might be illustrated by the following example:

input: The ceramics collection of Hetjensmuseum has more than 2, 000
           pieces.
question: How many pieces of ceramics does the collection include?
answer: More than 2, 000.
question: Where can you see ceramics?
answer: Presumably in Hetjensmuseum.

Such behavior can be achieved by the system even if the word 'ceramics' and all its possible forms are unknown. The impression might arise that the system knows what the meaning of 'ceramics' is. Actually, the system does know something about ceramics: it can serve to specify pieces of a collection. Of course, the system is not able to answer the question 'What exactly are ceramics?'. The answer 'pieces of a collection' suggested by the system's knowledge should be avoided.

Each dynamically produced lexical entry for an unknown word has to be assigned at least one reference to conceptual knowledge in order to be able to construct a semantic representation for the corresponding sentence. If a new word cannot be taken as a synonym for an already known word, there are two strategies to store the specific meaning of the new word in the system:

- The word meaning can be constructed using known concepts. For example, the word 'Kirchturm' (church steeple) may be analyzed as 'Turm einer Kirche' (tower of a church) using the concepts TURM (TOWER), KIRCHE (CHURCH) and the relation 'part_of'.

- The conceptual knowledge is extended by new concepts introduced as unspecified sub-concepts.

Against this background, the lexicon and the extralinguistic knowledge base should be divided into two parts, one containing (well) elaborated and sophisticated data, the other including data worked out rather superficially. The incrementally obtained shallow data may be refined by lexicographers and knowledge engineers in further steps.

References

Alshawi, H. (1987): Processing dictionary definitions with phrasal pattern hierarchies. In: Computational Linguistics 13 (3-4), pp. 195-202

Aoe, J. (1989): A method for building english dictionaries based on morphology. In: Zernik U. (ed.): Proceedings of the First International Lexical Acquisition Workshop, Detroit, MI

Binot, J., Jensen, K. (1987): A semantic expert using an online standard dictionary. In: Proceedings of the Tenth International Joint Conference on Artificial Intelligence (IJCAI-87), Los Altos, CA, pp. 709-713. Also appeared as IBM Research Report RC 12455, IBM Thomas J. Watson Research Center, Yorktown Heights, NY

Bläser, B., Wermke, M (1990): Projekt 'Elektronische Wörterbücher/Lexika', Abschlußbericht der Definitionsphase. IWBS Report 145, IBM Deutschland, Stuttgart

Boguraev, B., Briscoe, T. (eds.) (1989): Computational Lexicography for Natural Language Processing. London, UK

Byrd, R.J., Calzolari N., Chodorow M.S., Klavans, J.L., Neff, M.S. (1987): Tools and methods for computational linguistics. In: Computational Linguistics 13 (3-4), pp. 219-240

Chodorow, M.S., Byrd, R.J., Heidorn, G.E. (1985): Extracting semantic hierarchies from a large online dictionary. In: Proceedings of the 23rd Annual Meeting of the Association for Computational Linguistics (ACL), Chicago, IL, pp. 299-304

Drysdale, P.D. (1987): The role of examples in a learner's dictionary. In: Cowie, A. (ed.): The Dictionary and the Language Learner. Lexicographica Series Maior 17, Tübingen, pp. 213-224

DUDEN Bedeutungswörterbuch (1985): Der DUDEN in 10 Bänden, vol. 10. Mannheim

DUDEN Stilwörterbuch (1970): Der DUDEN in 10 Bänden, vol. 2. Mannheim

Erbach, G. (1990): Syntactic processing of unknown words. IWBS Report 131, IBM Deutschland, Stuttgart

Gust, H., Ludewig, P. (1989): Zielgerichtete Wortschatzerweiterungen in natürlichsprachlichen Systemen. In: Metzing, G. (ed.): Proceedings of the 13th German Workshop on Artificial Intelligence (GWAI 89), Eringerfeld, pp. 224-233

Kanngießer, S. (1985): Strukturen der Wortbildung. In: Schwarze, Ch., Wunderlich, D. (eds.): Handbuch der Lexikologie, pp. 134-183

Lytinen, S., Roberts, S. (1989): Lexical acquisition as a by-product of natural language processing. In: Zernik, U. (ed.): Proceedings of the First International Lexical Acquisition Workshop, Detroit, MI

OALD (1989): Oxford Advanced Learner's Dictionary. Oxford University Press

Wachsmuth, I. (1989): Zur intelligenten Organisation von Wissensbeständen in künstlichen Systemen, IWBS Report 91, IBM deutschland, Stuttgart

Wahlster, W. (1982): Natürlichsprachliche Systeme - Eine Einführung in die sprachorientierte KI-Forschung. In: Bibel, W., Siekmann, J. H. (eds.): Künstliche Intelligenz Frühjahrsschule (KIFS 82), Teisendorf, pp. 203-283

Wilks, Y.A., Fass, D., Guo, Ch., McDonald, J.E., Plate, T., Slator, B.M. (1988): Providing machine tractible dictionary tools. In: Pustejovsky, J. (ed.): Theoretical and Computational Issues in Lexical Semantics, Cambridge, MA

Wilks, Y.A., Fass, D., Guo, Ch., McDonald, J.E., Plate, T., Slator, B.M. (1989): A tractable machine dictionary as a resource for computational semantics. In: Boguraev, B., Briscoe, T. (eds.): Computational Lexicography for Natural Language Processing. London, UK, pp. 193-228

Zernik, U. (1989): Paradigms in lexical acquisition. In: Zernik, U. (ed.): Proceedings of the First International Lexical Acquisition Workshop, Detroit, MI

Managing Lexical Knowledge in LEU/2

Werner Emde

Abstract

This article deals with the problem of incomplete lexical knowledge in natural language systems. For several reasons, it is hard or even impossible to supply NL-systems in advance with all the lexical knowledge that may become necessary in an application. For example, it is difficult to predict which words will be used in what sense by its users. More important, natural language includes word formation rules allowing the creation of new words and new word usages. The paper describes the lexical component of the fully implemented NL text understanding system LEU/2. This component, called Lexicon Manager, is able to deal with unknown nouns and adjectives using a set of interacting strategies and knowledge sources and to acquire the lexical knowledge necessary to analyze and generate natural language text. It is argued that dealing with unknown words requires the ability to extend or to refine lexical knowledge as well as conceptual knowledge.

1 Introduction

Natural language systems usually possess different kinds of knowledge of varying generality. One might distinguish between linguistic knowledge including lexical and grammatical knowledge on the one hand and extra-linguistic knowledge including conceptual and assertional knowledge on the other.

The linguistic knowledge is required to construct the semantic representation of a natural language input and to generate the natural language output from a given internal representation. This does not mean that the extra-linguistic knowledge is not necessary in natural language understanding. On the contrary, the resolution of anaphoric references and the resolution of ambiguities is not possible without world knowledge in many cases. Nevertheless, it is important to draw a clear distinction between linguistic and extra-linguistic knowledge and to separate these kinds of knowledge in the knowledge base of natural language systems (Barnett et al. 1990).

The other distinction mentioned above concerns the generality of knowledge entities. The knowledge organization in natural language systems should reflect the fact that some knowledge entities are usually more general than others and hence useful in a broader set of problem classes and application domains, or even a broader set of languages.

One might object that neither distinction is telling us news. This is certainly true, but the point here is that the distinctions apply not only with respect to abstract classes of knowledge but also in the concrete case, especially with regard to the lexical knowledge necessary in natural language understanding. First, lexical knowledge entities do have counterparts in extra-linguistic knowledge. Second, lexical knowledge entities may differ in their generality and should therefore be represented separately.

This paper deals with the consequences of these two facts with respect to the organization, the use and the acquisition of lexical knowledge. First, it is argued that an independent component should be devoted to the task of providing the lexical information for natural language analysis and generation. The lexical component of the fully implemented text understanding system LEU/2 is described to show that providing lexical information is much more than making a single lookup in a lexical data base. Instead, the lexical component, called the Lexicon Manager, has to apply general rules to specific lexical information in order to deliver the required information.

The second issue has to do with the fact that it is difficult or even impossible to supply a natural language understanding system with all the lexical information which would be necessary to make it robust (Gust, Ludewig 1989), (Zernik 1989), (Ludewig 1991), not only because natural language usually offers a variety of ways to express even basic facts, but also because natural language offers word formation rules. Therefore, natural language understanding systems should be able to deal with unknown words and support the acquisition of lexical knowledge. The Lexicon Manager is described as a lexical component which is able to deal with unknown nouns, adjectives and adverbs using a set of interacting strategies and knowledge sources and to acquire the lexical knowledge necessary to analyze and generate natural language text. As lexical knowledge is related to conceptual knowledge, dealing with gaps in the lexical knowledge may reveal gaps in the extra-linguistic knowledge. Therefore, a system which must deal with unknown words should have the ability to deal with incomplete extra-linguistic knowledge.

The organization of this paper is as follows. First, the architecture of LEU/2 is sketched to give a rough understanding of the interaction of the Lexicon Manager with other components of LEU/2. In the next part it is described how lexical information is provide by the Lexicon Manager if the lexical information necessary to analyze natural language text is stored in the lexicons. Third, the different methods to handle unknown words and their interaction in the Lexicon Manager are described.[1] Then, the problem of refining the conceptual knowledge while dealing with unknown words is discussed and a first approach to handling this problem in LEU/2 is discussed. Finally, we describe some shortcomings and possible extensions of the present approach.

2 The General Task of Lexicon Manager

LEU/2 is a fully implemented, experimental natural-language text-understanding system for the German language. The rough architecture of LEU/2 is illustrated in Figure 1 to show the interaction of the Lexicon Manager with other components of LEU/2. The general task of the Lexicon Manager is to provide lexical information to the parser and the natural language generation component. In natural language analysis the Lexicon Manager is called by the parser and delivers information about syntax, semantic and morphology of the items (i.e., words and numbers) found in the input text. Called by the natural language generator, the Lexicon Manager is given the basic form of the words and delivers inflected words. An inference engine (IM) constitutes the interpreter for the knowledge representation language L_{LILOG} used in LEU/2.[2]

When LEU/2 tries to analyze a natural language input (i.e., text or question), the Lexicon Manager is called by the parser for each word found in the input. The lexical information necessary to parse a sentence and to construct a semantic representation is passed to the parser in a STUF feature graph representation.[3] In the current implementation, the Lexicon Manager is not supplied with any expectations about syntactic properties or the semantics of the words found in a text. Therefore, the Lexicon Manager is not able to resolve lexical ambiguities. They are passed to the analysis component (as a disjunctive feature description) and have to been resolved by the parser or the semantic construction.

The basic strategy to retrieve the lexical information when a sentence is analyzed is as follows:

- The morphology component, called 2LM (Schiller, Steffens, this volume), is called to make a morphological analysis of the word based on a morphology lexicon and a morphology rule

---

[1]This paper concentrates on the methods implemented in LEU/2, whereas (Ludewig, this volume) focuses on the theoretical background and also presents some more advanced (not yet realized) ideas.

[2]The knowledge representation system is described in (Bollinger, Pletat 1991) and L_{LILOG} is described in Pletat's paper in this volume.

[3]The unification-based grammar formalism STUF used to represent the linguistic knowledge in LEU/2 is described in (Seiffert, this volume).

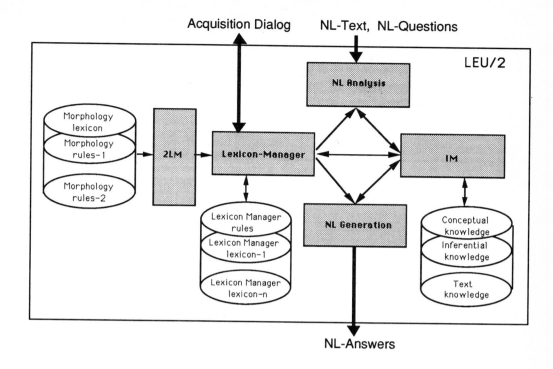

Figure 1: Rough architecture of LEU/2

knowledge base. The result delivered by this component is a list of lexemes (necessary to access the corresponding basic form lexicon entry) together the corresponding morphologic information (e.g., number and case).[4]

- Serving as keys, the lexemes are used to retrieve the corresponding entries from the basic form lexicon.

- Lexical rules describing some flexion-dependent but not lexeme-dependent syntactic properties are finally applied to these entries and the results are related disjunctively.[5] For example, one lexical rule for German represents the fact that count nouns in plural form do not require a determiner. Therefore, the syntactical property that a noun has to be preceded by a determiner cannot be specified in the basic form lexicon. Instead, the interpreter for lexical rules will add this syntactic property to the lexical information delivered to the parser only if the 2LM has analyzed that the noun is in singular form.

There are two cases not covered by this basic scheme: The handling of numbers (e.g., "12", "1113.") and words of the closed word classes (e.g., pronouns and determiners). If the parser requires lexical information for a cardinal number, the Lexicon Manager retrieves a general pattern containing the lexical information for year, mass and time specifications and instantiates a variable in the pattern with the actual cardinal. Ordinal numbers are handled by a corresponding scheme.

---

[4]It is a list of such tuples because an additional separable prefix may be found in the rest of the sentence. For example, the word 'kommen' may belong to 'ankommen' (arrive) or 'kommen' (come). Other morphological ambiguities are handled with a disjunction of feature descriptions.

[5]More details on lexical rules can be found in (Schiller, Steffens, this volume).

The lexical information on words belonging to closed word classes is retrieved by a single lookup in a full-form lexicon.

The natural language generation component (Novak 1991) of LEU/2 uses an inverted basic form lexicon. Thus, under normal circumstances (see below) the generation component is able to determine the lexemes necessary to build an internal semantic representation. The only thing the Lexicon Manager has to do in such cases is to call the 2LM morphology component in order to compute the inflected word forms.

In (Schiller, Steffens, this volume) a stand-alone version of the 2LM with an integrated basic form lexicon is described. The advantage of separating the morphological analysis and the basic form lexicon access is simply that within an overall system this allows one to differentiate between insufficient morphological information and insufficient syntactical/semantical information. The architecture shown above allows the Lexicon Manager to use the results of a successful 2LM analysis even if a corresponding entry is not stored in the basic form lexicon.

3 Dealing with Unknown Words

If the 2LM analysis fails or the lexical information cannot be retrieved from the basic lexicon, the Lexicon Manager but will not just fail, but try to obtain the required lexical information by:

- using (temporary) lexicon entries constructed by the Lexicon Manager in foregoing attempts to resolve a request,

- using a (pre-formatted) natural language dictionary describing synonyms between adjectives and nouns,

- applying word formation rules (derivation and nominal compound analysis), and/or

- asking the user to supply some information about the word.

With respect to the handling of unknown words, the task of the Lexicon Manager is twofold. First, it should to try acquire the lexical information necessary to understand sentences containing an unknown word and to generate NL answers concerning the acquired textual knowledge. Furthermore, the inverted basic form lexicon of the generation component should be extended. Second, the Lexicon Manager is supposed to support the manual acquisition of lexical and conceptual knowledge by giving hints to the knowledge engineer as to what knowledge is missing and what it might look like.

In the current version, the Lexicon Manager is able to construct lexical entries for unknown nouns, adjectives and adverbs (if the necessary information can be obtained with the strategies described above). The component is not able to deal with unknown verbs.

In Figure 2, a sample trace from the Lexicon Manager is shown to illustrate what may happen when an unknown word is encountered. The trace messages of the Lexicon Manager are prefixed by the string 'LEXMAN:'. The current version of LEU/2, the basic form lexicon and the morph lexicon of the morphology component do not contain the information necessary to analyze the word "Bootspartien" (boat trips). The word appears in the sentence: "Die Teilnehmer des Workshops machten Bootspartien." (The participants of workshop made boat trips). The Lexicon Manager analyses the unknown word by:

- first, decomposing the nominal compound into "Boots"-"partien".[6]

---

[6]As no lexical information for "Boot" (boat) is found, the Lexicon Manager is not able to recognize the 's' as linking morpheme.

```
Scanning phrase: Die Teilnehmer des Workshops machten Bootspartien

LEXMAN: Unknown word: Bootspartien
LEXMAN: Searching for entry in temporary lexicon ..
LEXMAN: No entry in temporary lexicon!
LEXMAN: Searching for a synonym which is known ..
LEXMAN: Can not build lexical entry using a synonym
LEXMAN: Trying to decompose word ..
LEXMAN: May I use: ' Ausflug ' instead of: ' Partien '?
LEXMAN: Please answer yes or no (yes/no).
-> yes
LEXMAN: Synonym found:  Ausflug
LEXMAN: Decomposed as  Boots - Partien
LEXMAN: New concept: #Bootspartie inserted as sub-concept of : Ausflug !
LEXMAN: Decomposition successful
LEXMAN: continuing calling process ..
Parsed: Die Teilnehmer des Workshops machten Bootspartien.
Phrase is well_formed
Constructing EDRS ...
```

Figure 2: A sample trace from the Lexicon Manager

- Using the (pre-formatted) natural-language synonym dictionary, the second constituent "Partien" is analyzed as a synonym of "Ausflüge" (trips). This word can be analyzed by the Lexicon Manager using the basic form lexicon. As the German word "Partie" can be used in the sense of "game" or "trip", the Lexicon Manager asks whether the reading "Ausflug" (trip) is an appropiate one.

- In the third step, a new lexical entry for "Bootsausflug" (boot trip) is constructed. This is done simply by copying most of the information found in the base form lexicon for the lexeme "Ausflug". As the gender of two synonyms may differ, the gender of the unknown word is acquired from the synonym lexicon. The semantics of the word is specified by a reference to a new concept "#Bootsausflug".[7]

- Finally, the information gained so far has to be completed with a declaration of the number and case of the unknown word. This is done using the information delivered by a morphology sub-component of the Lexicon Manager. This component delivers *hypotheses* about the possible base word forms of an unknown word together with corresponding hypotheses about the number and the case of the unknown word. The resulting values for case and number may be complex disjunctive expressions.

In the rest of this section, some details about the components and the strategies of the Lexicon Manager are presented. The components and knowledge sources of the Lexicon Manager are depicted in Figure 3.

---

[7]The reason for doing this is given in the next section.

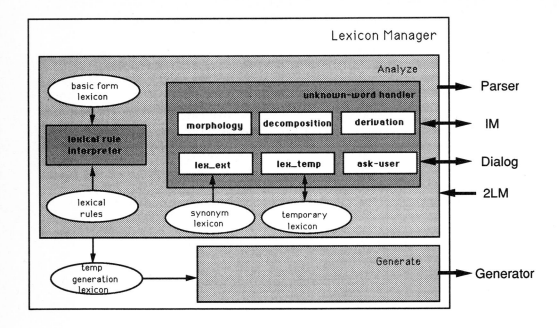

Figure 3: Components of the Lexicon Manager

3.1   Morphological Analysis of Unknown Words

The morphological analysis of the 2LM is based on morph lexicon which provides information about individual morphs (Schiller, Steffens, this volume). The component will fail if a word is encountered whose word stem is not stored in this lexicon. Therefore, the Lexicon Manger contains a distinct morphology sub-component to handle such cases. The analysis made by this component is based on a set of heuristics which deliver hypotheses about the base form of the unknown word together with corresponding hypotheses about the number and case of the word. In addition, the sub-component states hypotheses about the possible part of speech of the unknown word.

The part of speech analysis is done using the rule of German that nouns have to begin with a capital letter. The analysis requires information about the position of the unknown word in a sentence. For unknown words at the beginning of a sentence, the sub-component will state that the unknown word is an adjective, adverb or noun. A word beginning with a capital letter within a sentence is determined as a noun, and a lower-case word is stated to be an adjective or an adverb.

The hypotheses about the base form, the number and the case are stated with an analysis of the word endings. For example, a noun that ends with 'en' (like "Bootspartien") is regarded in the following steps as a word in plural form (with the basic form "Bootspartie" or "Bootsparti") *and* as a word in singular form (with the basic form "Bootspartien").[8]

---

[8]Heuristics like this one were adopted from the MICRO-LILOG system (Gust, Ludewig 1989), an experimental question-answering system especially designed to test ideas on incremental vocabulary extension (independent from the overall LEU/2 system) (Ludewig 1991).

3.2   The Temporary lexicon

If an unknown word has been analyzed, a new lexical entry is stored in the temporary lexicon. This entry will be used if the word occurs once more in the input text. The entry may also be used to complete the basic form lexicon. The entry constructed with the sentence containing the unknown word "Bootspartien" (boat trips) is shown in Figure 4.

```
'Bootspartie' :=
        'GENDER'( fem ),
        'NOUN_FEAT'( norm, plus ),
        ( ('SUBCAT_1'( 'ART' ),
            'NOUN_SUB_AGREE',
            'NOUN_SX'( '#Bootspartie' @ sorts ) );
          ('SUBCAT_2'( ( 'NP', 'CASE'( gen ) ), 'ART' ),
            '$S$',
            'NOUN_SUB_AGREE2') ),
        'NO_SLASH',
        'PERS'( third ).
```

Figure 4: A sample lexicon entry constructed by the Lexicon Manager

The syntactical and semantical information in the basic form entry is represented using so-called (parameterized) "templates" (cf. (Seiffert, this volume)) written in capital letters. For example, the semantics of the lexeme is specified using the template 'NOUN_SX' and a reference to the concept '#Bootspartie'. The feature graph representation required by the parser is gained by an expansion of the templates into feature descriptions (Seiffert 1991). Without going into further details here as to what the entry means[9], it should be mentioned that dynamically constructed entries fit the form of entries stored in the pre-supplied basic form lexicon. This way, the Lexicon Manger supports the *manual* acquisition of lexical knowledge, because the entries in the temporary lexicon can be used as a basis to complete the basic form lexicon.[10]

The template-based representation of lexical knowledge in the temporary lexicon also supports the automatic construction of new lexical entries. For example, the lexicon entry shown in Figure 4 can be used by the Lexicon Manager to construct an entry for the word "Flußbootpartie" (river boat trip) in the same way as the entry for "Ausflug" has been used to construct the lexicon entry for "Bootsausflug". The Lexicon Manager uses special operations to duplicate, change and extend template-based lexicon entries.

3.3   Using a NL Synonym Lexicon

Taking up the idea of the 'reuseability of lexical resources', Ludewig (1991, in this volume) has proposed the use of lexical data bases/knowledge bases for gradual vocabulary extensions. In order to illustrate the support gained by the use of external lexicons, we incorporated a (slightly pre-formatted) natural language synonym lexicon into the system.[11] Examples of (not pre-formatted) typical entries from the lexicon are shown in figure 5.

---

[9]See (Kiss, this volume) for examples of feature descriptions representing the syntactical information passed finally to the parser.

[10]See Ludewig's paper in this volume for a discussion of (representation-independent) problems that may occur when automatically constructed lexicon entries are used to extend the original lexicon.

[11]The current version of this lexicon specifies synonyms for 346 lexemes (nouns, verbs, adjectives and adverbs).

```
parallel adj: 1. gleichlaufend, nebeneinander, Seite an Seite
Partie (die), 1. der Ausflug, 2. das Spiel
passen verb: 1. harmonieren, sich eignen, stimmen, zusammenpassen
Preis (der), 1. die Gebühr, die Kosten, 2. der Großhandelspreis,
        der Kaufpreis, der Pauschalpreis, der Selbstkostenpreis,
        der Verkaufspreis, 3. der Kurs, der Tarif, 4. das große Los,
        der Hauptgewinn, der Haupttreffer, 5. das Pokal, die Trophäe,
        6. die Auszeichnung, die Belohnung, die Prämie, 7. die Medaille
```

Figure 5: Sample entries from the experimental synonym lexicon

If a request to deliver the lexical information for an unknown word cannot be resolved using the temporary lexicon, the Lexicon Manager tries to find a synonym for the unknown word in the synonym lexicon which can be analyzed. Only one-word synonyms are used by the Lexicon Manager. The synonyms are delivered together with information about some syntactical properties of the unknown word and the synonym by a pattern-directed entry analysis. In contrast to multi-purpose natural language lexicons (including morphological information, dictionary definitions, hyperonyms and antonyms), the structure of the pre-formatted synonym lexicon is simple and unambiguous.

If a known synonym can be found, the Lexicon Manager is able to restrict the hypotheses stated by the (unknown word) morphology to those which are compatible with the lexical information specified in the synonym lexicon entry (i.e., the basic word form and part of speech).

Although, in general, an unknown word which is found in an entry from a lexical data base may be analyzed by another lookup in the lexical data base (Ludewig, this volume), a recursive analysis of synonyms using a lexical data base is not very promising. The synonym relation specified in a lexical data base cannot be regarded as a transitive relation. Therefore, the Lexicon Manager only tries to analyze an unknown synonym with a lookup in the temporary lexicon, but not with another lookup in the synonym lexicon. Furthermore, the lexicon entries constructed using the synonym lexicon are marked as 'uncertain' in the temporary lexicon if the used entry in the synonym lexicon describes different readings of an unknown word.[12] These entries are only supposed to be helpful in the process of the manual acquisition of lexical knowledge. They are not used when the corresponding unknown words occur once more. Instead, the unknown word will be analyzed by another lookup in the external synonym lexicon.

3.4   Analyzing Nominal Compounds

The usefulness of lexical data bases is limited in the case of unknown words constructed by word formation rules. Only a limited number of words which can be constructed by word formation rules will be included in a lexical data base. Therefore, a natural language system should be able to analyze words using word formation rules.

An important class of words which can be analyzed by the use of word formation rules is that of nominal compounds. The Lexicon Manager uses a set of simple heuristics for a partial analysis of nominal compounds. Theses heuristics are invoked whenever an unknown word cannot be analyzed using the temporary lexicon or the synonym lexicon.

In the German language, nominal compounds are usually written as one word. Therefore, the first step in analyzing a nominal compound is to look for a segmentation of the compound. In general,

---

[12]Different readings are specified in the synonym lexicon (as usual) by an enumerated list.

the Lexicon Manager looks for the largest second constituent of a compound which can be analyzed using the basic form lexicon as well as the strategies to deal with unknown words.[13]

As the second constituent determines the syntactical properties of the compound, the Lexicon Manager is able to construct the syntax part of the lexicon entry of the compound after the segmentation step. Problems are brought about by the semantics. The Lexicon Manager could look for the semantics of the first constituent and combine them with the semantics of the second constituent as in the KBNL system (Barnett et al. 1990). Unfortunately, the meaning of compounds is not unambiguously determined by the semantic of their constituents, although the set of applicable word formation rules may be restricted to just a few (Meyer 1989), (Kanngießer 1985). For example, "olive oil" means an oil *made* of olives, whereas "baby oil" means an oil which can be *applied* to babies.

Before it is described how nominal compounds are interpreted in LEU/2, let us have a look at approaches chosen for other systems. In the MICRO-LILOG system, the first applicable rule which is found to construct the meaning of a compound is used. A more sophisticated solution was implemented in the KBNL system. The KBNL approach is based on the use of background knowledge (like "oil is not produced by processing humans") to discard faulty readings. As such knowledge may be unstated or not deducible or may not be sufficient to choose among all alternatives, a level of effort is assigned to lexical entries and rules. This assignment is used to apply specific rules before more general rules. Rules on a higher level are only used if a consistent interpretation of a sentence cannot be found with the rules of a lower level.

Both approaches have shortcomings and/or cannot be used in the LEU/2 system for other reasons. First, the analysis component (i.e., the parser and semantic construction) is not able to backtrack to another choice point in the lexical analysis if a sentence turns out to be ill-formed or a consistent interpretation is not possible. Second, a sentence context is not necessarily sufficient to determine the correct reading. Third, a faulty reading must not necessarily lead to an inconsistent sentence/text interpretion, and may instead merely cause an incoherent interpretation. Fourth, both approaches are only applicable if the semantics of the first constituent can be determined. If the semantics of the first constituent are unknown, the processing of the phrase containing the sentence has to be stopped.

Therefore, an alternative approach has been chosen for the Lexicon Manager and LEU/2. The Lexicon Manager will construct a lexicon entry for nominal compounds with shallow lexical semantics: Given that the semantics of the last constituent are specified by a reference to a concept from the extra-linguistic knowledge, the semantics of the compound are specified by a reference to an unspecified sub-concept which is dynamically added to the conceptual structure. An example has already be given with the trace presented in Figure 2. To specify the semantics of the compound "Bootspartie" a new sub-concept "#Bootspartie" (boat trip) was added to the already known concept "Ausflug" (trip). Thus, at least a partial understanding of a natural language text is rendered. The partial understanding in the boat-trip example may be demonstrated with a single question to the system: If the system is asked what the participants at the workshop undertook, it will answer the question with the utterance: "Trips".

It should be emphazised that this approach allows a demand-driven specification of the semantics of a compound and thereby a later refinement of natural language text interpretations. When we say that the semantics of a nominal compound are specified in the lexicon by a reference to a new sub-concept, it is not meant that the Lexicon Manager is not allowed to store hypotheses about the meaning of the compound as an axiom in the inference engine! Let us continue the oil example and

---

[13]Exceptions are made to analyze names of locations (e.g., street names). If a noun ends with a suffix such as '-straße' (street), -'platz' (place), or -'allee' (avenue), the compound is regarded as the name of a corresponding object and the Lexicon Manager constructs a lexical entry for the name. In rare cases, when more than two words are combined and the constituents at the beginning of the compound are more closely related, the general strategy leads to a faulty segmentation.

suppose that the Lexicon Manager stores its knowledge about possible readings of the compound "baby oil" by stating the axiom

"If an object is a baby oil it is either an oil produced by processing babies or it is an oil which can be applied to babies",

then the inference engine will automatically be able to deduce a specification of the semantics of the compound when more information becomes available (during manual knowledge acquisition or the processing of further natural language texts). For example, the system may encounter a text which describes the application of a particular 'baby oil' to a baby and the origin of that oil, so that the alternative reading is ruled out by text understanding. In such a case, the system would also be able to specify the semantics of the new sub-concept introduced during the analysis of the compound.

3.5 Derivation

Of course, word formation is not restricted to nominal compounds, and derivational processes are also subsumed by the term 'word formation'. For example, the use of the word "building" in order to refer to an event[14] can be explained by derivation.

A first step towards the use of derivation rules in order to handle unknown words in LEU/2 has been made with the inclusion of rules that allow the system to analyze nouns that begin with a verb stem and end with the string '-ung'.[15] These rules are applied when an unknown word cannot be analyzed as a compound with the strategy described in the previous section.

As is the case with nominal compounds, more than one derivation rule can usually be applied to explain the meaning of a word, e.g., the word "building" may refer to an event as well as to a house (cf. (Rickheit 1990)). Erbach (1990) describes an approach which allows the system to derive information about an unknown word from the syntactic structure of a parse. Such an approach seems to be well suited to choose among alternative readings of derived words.

3.6 Asking the User

If an unknown word cannot be analyzed by the use of the components described above, the Lexicon Manager will try to acquire the lexical information by asking questions. The unknown word is displayed and the user is asked if she is willing to answer some questions about the unknown word.

In the current version, the Lexicon Manager allows the user to specify an unknown word (noun, adjective or adverb) by entering a synonym, a hyperonym, or the specification of proper names. A sample trace of a dialog is listed in Figure 6.

The user is asked to answer some question about the unknown word "LEU2" which occurs in the sentence "Der LEU2 ist im Hetjensmuseum untergebracht." (The LEU2 is put into the Hetjensmuseum.). The unknown word is specified as a proper name and the system asks the user to specify the kind of the named object. The user inputs "KI-System" (AI system) which turns out to be another unknown word. As this word cannot be analyzed by the strategies described in the previous sections either, the Lexicon Manager asks for a specification of this new unknown word. The user decides to do this by entering the hyperonym "Objekt". This word can be analyzed using the basic form lexicon, and the system is able to construct a lexicon entry for the word "KI-System".

The semantics of the lexeme are specified by a reference to the concept "#KI-System" which is introduced as *sub-concept* of 'DepicObject', the concept used to describe the meaning of the known

---

[14]An example is: "The building took place in 1991".

[15]The ending '-ung' in German is very similar to the ending '-ing' in English.

```
Scanning phrase: Der LEU2
LEXMAN:  Unknown word: LEU2
                    :
LEXMAN: Could not find lexical information for LEU2
LEXMAN: Select kind of information you will provide or quit.
LEXMAN:  Choose one of
LEXMAN: proper_name hyperonym synonym correction quit
-> proper_name
LEXMAN: Please select proper article for LEU2
LEXMAN:  Choose one of
LEXMAN: none_or_der none_or_das none_or_die der die das quit
-> der
LEXMAN: What is LEU2 ?
-> KI-System
LEXMAN: Unknown word: KI-System
                    :
LEXMAN: Could not find lexical information for KI-System
LEXMAN: Select kind of information you will provide or quit.
LEXMAN:  Choose one of
LEXMAN: proper_name hyperonym synonym quit
-> hyperonym
LEXMAN: Please select proper article for KI-System
LEXMAN:  Choose one of
LEXMAN: der die das quit
-> das
LEXMAN: Please enter hyperonym of KI-System
-> Objekt
LEXMAN: New concept: #KI-System inserted as sub-concept of : DepicObjekt !
LEXMAN: New atom:  LEU2  of sort 'Name' inserted
LEXMAN: continuing calling process .
Scanning phrase: im Hetjensmuseum untergebracht
Parsed: Der LEU2 ist im Hetjensmuseum untergebracht.
Phrase is well_formed
Constructing EDRS ... Translating EDRS to L_Lilog ...
doing forward inferences ... Processing terminated.
```

Figure 6: An example for asking the user questions

word "Objekt". As a consequence, the new lexicon entry for "KI-System" can be used in order to determine the concept reference ("#KI-System") necessary to make the lexicon entry for "LEU2".

With this dialog, the Lexicon Manager is able to acquire new lexical entries as well as to complete its conceptual knowledge. After processing the sentence about LEU2, the system is able to understand the question "Welches KI-System ist im Hetjensmuseum untergebracht" (Which AI-system is put into the Hetjensmuseum?) without any question to the user and to produce the answer: "Der LEU2" (The LEU2). Obviously, the information gained by such a dialog cannot be complete or guaranteed to be correct. But in many case it allows the system to continue the text processing with a partial understanding and leads to suggestions what the necessary additions to the lexical and conceptual knowledge may look like. More sophisticated techniques used in other language acquisition tools (cf. (Barnett et al. 1990)) for the semiautomatic construction of lexicons are likely to be necessary in the future.

4   Discussion

In this paper, the Lexicon Manager, the lexical component of the experimental text understanding system LEU/2, has been described. The component is responsible for providing the lexical information necessary to analyze and generate natural language. The system uses a set of interacting strategies to deal with unknown words. Some tests with the Lexicon Manager have already shown a surprising degree of robustness gained by the interacting strategies. It should be emphasized that a number of important questions have been left untouched in the implementation of the Lexicon Manager. For example, we have not considered the problem of how to deal with incomplete lexical entries (in contrast to missing lexical entries). Some ideas of how to use contextual information in order to derive assumptions about the lexical qualities of an unknown word are presented in Ludewig's paper (in this volume). An approach to lexical semantics which takes into account lexical ambiguities and polysemy is presented in (Gust, this volume).

It should be obvious from the description of the Lexicon Manager that delivering lexical information is a distinct sub-task in the process of understanding and generating natural language. This task can only be adequately handled by a separate component within an overall natural language system. Furthermore, the acquisition of lexical knowledge has to proceed alongside with the development of the conceptual system. A system which is able to deal with missing lexical knowledge should also be able to deal with insufficiencies in conceptual knowledge.

Acknowledgements

The author wishes to thank Helmar Gust, Petra Ludewig, Andrea Meyering (who implemented parts of the Lexicon Manager) and Mechthild Rickheit for many helpful discussions. Thanks also the other members of the LILOG project for the help necessary to use (and understand) other components of LEU/2. The basic form lexicon and the lexical rules were supplied by the 2LM group at IBM in Stuttgart.

References

Barnett, J., Knight, K., Mani, I., Rich, E. (1990): Knowledge and natural language processing. In: Communications of the ACM, Vol. 33, No. 8, pp. 50–71

Bollinger, T., Pletat, U. (1991): The LILOG knowledge representation system. IWBS-Report 156, IBM Germany, Stuttgart

Erbach, G. (1990): Syntactic processing of unknown words. IWBS-Report 131, IBM Germany, Stuttgart

Gust, H., Ludewig, P. (1989): Zielgerichtete Wortschatzerweiterung in natürlich-sprachlichen Systemen. In: Metzing, D. (ed.): Proceedings GWAI-89. Springer, Berlin, pp. 224–233

Kanngießer, S. (1985): Strukturen der Wortbildung. In: Schwarze, Ch., Wunderlich, D. (eds.): Handbuch der Lexikologie.

Ludewig, P. (1991): Incremental Vocabulary Extensions in Text Understanding Systems. IWBS-Report 152, IBM Germany, Stuttgart

Meyer, R. (1989): Vagheitsaspekte der Komposition. IWBS-Report 77, IBM Germany, Stuttgart

Rickheit, M. (1990): Wortbedeutung und lexikalische Repräsentation. IWBS-Report 127, IBM Germany, Stuttgart

Zernik, U. (1989): Lexicon Acquisition: Learning from Corpus by Capitalizing on Lexical Categories. In: Proceedings of the 11th IJCAI-89, Morgan Kaufmann, San Mateo, CA, pp. 1556–1562

Chapter 1.3

Syntax

The two LILOG prototypes evolving out of the LILOG project employ different, though related, grammars. The first LILOG prototype is based on *Categorial Unification Grammar (CUG)*, while the second relates to *Head-driven Phrase Structure Grammar (HPSG)*. Both grammars find their origin in the family of lexicalist grammars, which are distinguished by a very small component of syntactic rules, complemented by a rich and complex lexicon component.

As to the architecture of the grammars, it should be mentioned that the first LILOG prototype contains a full-form lexicon, in which the lexical entries comprise syntactic and semantic, as well as morphological specifications. The second prototype is organized in a more modular way, and is equipped with a separate morphological component together with a lexicon which conveys an item's basic syntactic and semantic information. An independent morpho-syntax component merges the morphological and lexical features in question to yield actual surface structure word forms. The morpho-syntax component also accounts for word formation processes hitherto handled by specific lexical rules, such as – among others – passivization of given verbal items.

The article on the grammars of LILOG briefly introduces the two models of grammar, CUG and HPSG. Predominantly, it discusses the basic distinction between the type of rules employed within these two grammars. CUG in essence only relies on a type of *complementation*, which implies a uniform treatment of complementing categories (e.g., verbs, prepositions) and adjoining categories (e.g., adverbials) as functor categories. By contrast, HPSG clearly distinguishes between *complementation* on the one hand, and *adjunction* on the other – a move which, consequently, has its impact on the categorization of lexical items. Furthermore, the article addresses HPSG's general principle of modular representation of linguistic information, as opposed to CUG, which is characterized by a rather integrative approach.

Another article is dedicated to the treatment of so-called movement phenomena within non-transformational approaches to grammar, where CUG and HPSG are representatives of the latter. These surface-structure oriented approaches by definition lack the concept of a movement transformation. Hence, alternative devices have to be sought to account for such phenomena. This is discussed with German verb order regularities, which are known to be threefold: the finite verb can occupy a clause-final, a clause-initial or a clause-second position – the latter two hitherto assumed to be derivatives of the former.

The third article in this section addresses a linguistic construction challenging any non-transformational approaches to grammar: coordination. Especially those coordinate structures in which we encounter so-called reduced conjuncts pose difficulties for surface-structure oriented analyses, such as CUG and HPSG, where the semantics of an expression is derived (partially or entirely) in parallel with the syntactic analysis: though not available during syntactic processing, the "missing" constituents of reduced conjuncts are nevertheless relevant for semantic interpretation. The proposed approach, which uniformly covers constituent as well as non-constituent (reduced) coordination, is developed from the perspective of transformational analyses, whose modularity in levels of linguistic representation allows for the most lucid exposition of the regularities governing coordinate structures in general. However, the main tenets of the theory presented in this article are claimed to be transferable to any of the non-transformational frameworks, such as, e.g., HPSG. This is due to the fact that the level of abstractness reached within transformational and non-transformational grammars permits one to focus more on the commonalities than on the differences between each of the approaches, thus making way for viewing linguistic phenomena from a most general perspective.

Birgit Wesche

The Grammars of LILOG

Tibor Kiss

Abstract

In the first prototype of LILOG, Categorial Unification Grammar was used to model linguistic information, i.e., the grammar and the semantics. After reflecting upon the structure of the theory, we came to the decision that we should use Head-driven Phrase Structure Grammar to model the grammar and semantics of LILOG's current development environment (LEU/2). This paper compares the two approaches in several respects: the treatment of subcategorization, the utilization of data structures to gain more lucid representation, the treatment of complements and adjuncts, and the construction of semantic representations.

1 Introduction

The grammar and compositional semantics of LILOG's first prototype were encoded in *Categorial Unification Grammar[1]* (CUG), a blend of unification-based phrase structure grammar with Categorial Grammar.[2] In the current system, however, *Head-driven Phrase Structure Grammar[3]* (HPSG) is used to represent the grammar and compositional semantics of the fragment. This paper tries to compare the two approaches and gives arguments for the superiority of the latter approach. Thus, this article can be viewed as a partial description of the evolution of the LILOG project, focusing on linguistics aspects. In the following, we will discuss three topics which have led to the reorientation in grammar modelling: The first one considers the respective data structures, which are employed to represent subcategorization requirements. Whereas HPSG introduces list-structures as possible values, CUG is confined to category-valued attributes. Here, our conclusion will be that the list-valued subcategorization attribute of HPSG is more lucid and allows for a greater ease of representation than the cascade of RESULT-attributes in CUG.

The second problem centers around the negative effects of multicategorization in CUG. To illustrate this point, we will consider the treatment of PP-complements

---

[1] Several versions of Categorial Unification Grammar are introduced and described in Uszkoreit (1986) and Karttunen (1989). A description of the implementation of CUG in LILOG's first prototype is given in Wesche (1988).

[2] For an excellent overview of goals and analysis of Categorial Grammar, see Bach et al. (1985).

[3] The standard introduction to HPSG is Pollard/Sag (1987). Alternative proposals and further extensions of this basic model are found in Kathol (1991), Kiss (1991) and Sag/Pollard (1989).

and adjuncts in CUG and HPSG. Whereas the modularity of representation was a background assumption for the first two topics, it will be assessed in the last topic discussed here. The relevance of modular representation for linguistic knowledge will be illustrated by giving a brief overview of semantic construction in HPSG and CUG.[4]

After comparing CUG and HPSG in the three respective aspects mentioned above, we will come to the conclusion, that although the two grammar models share common roots in their attempt to utilize complex lexical information, HPSG still is preferable because it includes a greater range of data structures, is more adequate, and allows the grammar writer to use more elaborate modular representations which lead to a more compact and lucid representation of linguistic knowledge.

2 The Representation of Subcategorization in CUG and HPSG

One of the central features of *Categorial Grammar* (CG) is the lexical encoding of subcategorization requirements, which results in a large reduction of the rule system of the grammar, especially when compared with phrase-structure-based approaches. Let us quickly summarize how this reduction is achieved: CG introduces a set of basic categories (1), which is extended by induction to the set of all possible categories. This set includes so-called complex or functor categories (2) as well.

(1)   The set of basic categories consists of the following categories: S, N, NP, PP.

(2)   If X and Y are categories, then so are X/Y, and X\Y.[5]

---

[4]   It should be mentioned here that in the first, as well as in the current prototype of LILOG, the semantics were influenced by DRT (Kamp/Reyle forthcoming). Whereas most DRT-practitioners employ a top-down algorithm to build a semantic representation it was always a goal in LILOG to build semantic representation in a compositional manner, using bottom-up mechanisms. Thus, semantic construction is simply the bottom-up representation and projection of semantic information given in the lexicon. For a more detailed account of the semantics in LILOG, see the paper by Geurts in this volume.

[5]   Categorial grammarians usually do not pay much attention to the fact that definitions like (1) and (2) offer many more categories to the linguistic community than generally needed. For a discussion of this aspect in connection with Montague Grammar, where CGs were first employed for complex natural language analysis, see Dowty et al. (1981).
Interestingly, it would be possible to reduce the number of categories produced by a mechanism like (2) simply by adding sortal restrictions and phrase-structure-categorial information (the latter being introduced in Uszkoreit (1986) to cover overgenerations), and imposing the condition that only those categories have extensions, which can be inferred from the categorial information. Then, we would have a C(U)G which would be a mere notational variant of HPSG, thus further sustaining our main theme here that HPSG is more appropriate for adequate linguistic descriptions.

When considering a functor category, i.e., a category described by X/Y or X\Y, we will call Y the *argument* and A the *result* of the function X/Y. In the directional variants of CG discussed here, slash (/) and backslash (\) indicate the direction in which the functor category seeks its argument. To make this more clear, (3) gives a short comparison of traditional phrase-structure-grammar categories like determiners (Det), transitive (V-trans) and intransitive (V-intrans) verbs, as well as prepositions, and their respective CG counterparts.

(3)   Table of Comparison between PSG- and CG-Categories:

Example	PSG-Notation	CUG-Notation
the	Det	NP/N
loves	V-trans	(S\NP)/NP
sleeps	V-intrans	S\NP
in	P	PP/NP

Looking at (3), it should be clear why it is possible to reduce the rule set in CG to a minimum: The combinatorial potential of a sign is directly encoded in its categorial definition. Hence, there is no need to encode information pertaining to the syntactic combination in the lexicon, and the rule component. Take as an example intransitive verbs and determiners: Intransitive verbs, encoded as S\NP, combine with a single NP-argument to yield a sentence; an article (NP/N) combines with an N to yield an NP. Thus, the combination of complex categories with basic ones can be viewed from the vantage point of the application of a function to its argument. This is utilized in the following rule scheme, which is consequently dubbed *Functional Application*.

(4)   Rule of Functional Application:

$$X \rightarrow X/Y \ Y$$

This scheme is to be interpreted as follows. A *functor* of type X/Y and an *argument* of type Y can combine to a (not necessarily basic) category of type X. If X/Y is a syntactic head in the sense of X'-Theory (Jackendoff 1977), and Y is its complement, then (4) can be viewed as a kind of saturation scheme for complementation. This rule scheme, however, is not confined to complementation, but also serves as a skeleton for adjunction cases. Adjoining categories can be distinguished from complementing ones by comparing their respective values for *result* and *argument*. If the value of the *argument* matches the value of the *result*, we have an exocentric category which adjoins; if the value of the *argument* is distinct from the value of the *result*, the category is endocentric. Hence, all categories given in (3) are complementing ones, because their *arguments* are distinct from their *results*. In (5-1), some adjoining, i.e., exocentric, categories are listed, and the respective syntactic contexts are given in (5-2)

(5-1)   Adjoining Categories in CG and their Counterparts in PSG:

Example	**PSG-Notation**	**CG-Notation**
in New York	PP	(S\NP)\(S\NP)
red	A	N/N

(5-2)   Examples for Adjoining Categories:

He visited him in New York
the red door

Now, *Categorial Unification Grammar* combines the apparatus introduced so far with the mechanisms of unification and disjunction.[6] Thus, *functor* and *argument* categories can be represented by a set of features for *result, argument and direction*. Complex categories can be distinguished from basic ones by their respective value for *argument* – whereas the value for *argument* (ARG) and *direction* (DIR) is always non-empty in complex categories, both must be empty in case of basic ones. In our implementation, this distinction was covered by the special *U*-type of our representation formalism STUF. The *U*-type can be compared with the special NIL atom in LISP. An illustration of this strategy is given in (6-1) and (6-2). In (6-1) the representation of a transitive verb – say *love* – is given. (6-2) models a basic category of type NP.

---

[6]   A very instructing, as well as theory-neutral, introduction to the basics of unification grammar can be found in Pollard/Sag (1987, Chap. 2).

(6-1) Transitive Verb Representation in CUG:

$$
\begin{bmatrix}
\text{RES}: \begin{bmatrix} \text{RES}: \text{S} \\ \text{DIR}: \text{left} \\ \text{ARG}: \begin{bmatrix} \text{RES}: \text{NP} \\ \text{DIR}: *\text{U}* \\ \text{ARG}: *\text{U}* \end{bmatrix} \end{bmatrix} \\
\text{DIR}: \text{right} \\
\text{ARG}: \begin{bmatrix} \text{RES}: \text{NP} \\ \text{DIR}: *\text{U}* \\ \text{ARG}: *\text{U}* \end{bmatrix}
\end{bmatrix}
$$

(6-2) NP Representation in CUG:

$$
\begin{bmatrix}
\text{RES}: \text{NP} \\
\text{DIR}: *\text{U}* \\
\text{ARG}: *\text{U}*
\end{bmatrix}
$$

Let us briefly discuss (6-1). (6-1) introduces a category which seeks for an NP (see (6-2)) to its right. An application of (6-1) to (6-2) would result in a complex category again, viz. a functor, which awaits a second NP-argument to its right to yield a sentence as its final result. To make this intuitive combination mode precise, CUG introduces phrase-structure schemes, which mimic the rule schemes of CG. In this sense, the rules of CG can be viewed as a second class of complex signs in CUG, the class of rules. In contrast to the categories, (binary) rules introduce attributes for FUN-RESULT, FUNCTION and FUN-ARGUMENT, which stand for the categories of result, functor and argument, respectively.[7]

(7) Rule of Functional Application in CUG:

$$
\begin{bmatrix}
\text{FUNC-RES}: \boxed{1} \\
\text{FUNCTION}: \begin{bmatrix} \text{RES}: \boxed{1} \\ \text{DIR}: \text{right} \\ \text{ARG}: \boxed{2} \end{bmatrix} \\
\text{FUNC-ARG}: \boxed{2}
\end{bmatrix}
$$

---

[7] To represent the unification or structure-sharing of two value, indexed boxes are used in the following. In a representation like (i), the boxes serve to indicate that the value of the feature X is token-identical to the value of the feature Y:

(i) Structure-Sharing:

$$
\begin{bmatrix}
\text{X}: \boxed{1} \\
\text{Y}: \boxed{1}
\end{bmatrix}
$$

A translation of (7) into the more familiar rewrite-format would result in a phrase-structure rule, which – except for its internal structure formed from attributes – closely resembles the rule of *functional application* introduced in (4). It should be mentioned, however, that (7) is a rule which combines *rightward seeking* functors with its arguments. To cover cases of leftward seeking functors, an additional rule is introduced, which is differentiated from (7) by the respective value for the path FUNCTION|DIR. To see the rules work, consider the following derivation of the sentence **Bart hates jazz**. The verb *hates* is represented as in (6), so are the NPs.

(8-1) gives an instantiation of (7) for the verb *hates* and its object; (8-2) shows the complete structure. The particular information contributed by *hates* is indicated in boldface.[8]

(8-1)   Instantiation of (7):

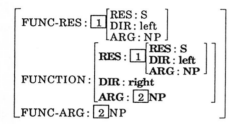

(8-2)   Full Structure of **Bart hates jazz**

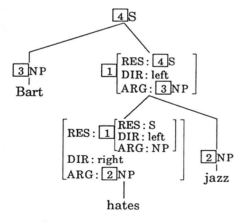

---

[8]   In the following derivation, NP and S are abbreviations for (i), and (ii) respectively:

(i)   Notational Convention for NP:
(ii) Notational Convention for S

One of the strange consequences of this combination of unification and categorial grammar is the assumption that the notion of a syntactic head can only be defined with respect to a lexeme. This is due to the fact that headedness is ultimately coded in the RESULT-cascades of the lexeme, or in other words, in CUG, the head of a phrase is determined by a daughter, the RESULT-attribute of which is identical to the mother. I consider this assumption particularly counter-intuitive and inadequate, because the notion of head in a given projection generally is considered to be a structural property of a tree, and thus should be represented as such. This point will be discussed more thoroughly in connection with the data structures employed in both approaches.

As another point of objection, readers may ask where the information pertaining to the subject-verb agreement, as well as the necessary case information, is stored. We cannot tackle these aspects here, mainly due to space limitation. However, centering around these aspects, another main problem of CUG can be formulated: CUG simply takes over the theory of combination from CG, but does not introduce adequate mechanisms for handling other important aspects of linguistic representation, such as a theory of case or a theory of agreement. Thus, a certain impression of ad hoc treatment surrounds these parts of linguistic representation in CUG. On the other hand, a number of intrinsic problems for CG, such as overgeneration problems which arise in combination with adjunct characterizations or as a consequences of the introduction of other combinatorial devices such as *functional composition* or *type raising* apparently can be eliminated in CUG. However, these advantages can mainly be traced back to the introduction of unification mechanisms. Now, because unification is a common mechanism for HPSG, as well as CG, any merit of unification in CUG ceteris paribus carries over to HPSG and will not enter into our discussion.[9]

It should be mentioned, however, that many disadvantages of CG still carry over to CUG. Before we consider these deficiencies, we will briefly discuss the treatment of subcategorization in HPSG.

One of the things that HPSG has in common with CUG is the small set of rules that both require. In contrast to CUG, however, where unconnected cascades of category-valued features are employed to represent the valency of a sign, HPSG uses

---

[9] As one of these advantages, Uzskoreit (1986) considers the implementation of *functional composition* in terms of variable ARGUMENT-restrictions on complex categories. A detailed account of *functional composition-like* mechanisms is given in Kiss (1991).

a list-valued feature called SUBCAT, in which the arguments are stored, which a sign requires to become saturated.

(9)   Partial Description of a Transitive Verb in HPSG:

[SYNTAX | SUBCAT ⟨ NP[nom], NP[acc]⟩]

Clearly, it does not follow from this representation of valency that the combinatorial potential of a lexeme determines its syntactic categorization – an assumption which does hold in CUG. In HPSG, neither projectional properties – which follow from the RESULT-cascades in CUG – nor the category of a sign is determined by its combinatorial potential. These information types are encoded in a different attribute, the so-called HEAD-attribute, which gives information, say, as to which major class a lexeme belongs or which case is assigned to a nominal element.[10] This gives rise to the more elaborate feature structure in (10).

(10)   Partial Description of a Transitive Verb in HPSG:

$$\left[\text{SYNTAX} \begin{bmatrix} \text{SUBCAT} \langle \text{NP[acc], NP[nom]} \rangle \\ \text{HEAD [VFORM FIN]} \end{bmatrix} \right]$$

Like CUG, HPSG proposes only a few rule schemata, the most prominent of which for our present concerns are the following *complementation* and *adjunction* rule schemes:

(11)   *Complementation Rule:*

X[SUBCAT: M] → X[SUBCAT: M + N], N

(12)   *Adjunction Rule:*

X[SUBCAT: M] → X[SUBCAT: M], N

---

[10] Readers may wonder why we do not mention the ubiquitous sortal restrictions, which are among the main characteristics of HPSG. That sortal information will be largely ignored in the following discussion is due to the assumption that – in contrast to common practice – only *implemented* aspects of both approaches should be mentioned in the present context. As discussed elsewhere in this volume, the representation formalism STUF did not support sorts, types, type inference and the like. Thus, aspects pertaining to sorts and type could not be employed in our current implementation, and are consequently not discussed herein.

These two rules are fairly general, in fact they are too general as they stand. So, nothing in (11) guarantees that the number and kind of arguments unify with the number and kind of elements on the list-valued SUBCAT-attribute, and we have no indication that the mother projection in (11) or (12) is actually headed. Now, instead of encoding information pertaining to the percolation of categorial information or the relationship between the arguments and the complements directly into the rules (or, as in CUG, directly into the lexical items), HPSG proposes so-called principles, which are to be interpreted as general constraints on feature structures. Thus, the information given in the rules is confined to rule-specific assumptions. To see how these principles work, consider the *HEAD Feature Principle*. This principle guarantees that in a given projection mother and head-daughter belong to the same category. An informal but complete statement of this principle is given in (13):

(13)   *Head Feature Principle:*
       The HEAD features of the head-daughter of a given phrase agree with the
       HEAD features of the phrase.

More important for our present concerns is the *Subcategorization Principle,* which requires a matching between kind and number of the elements on the *subcat list,* and the complements of the head.

(14)   *Subcategorization Principle:*
       The value of the SUBCAT attribute of a phrase equals the value of the
       SUBCAT attribute of the head-daughter of the phrase, except for those
       elements, which have been realized as complement-daughters.

The rather cryptic *Subcategorization Principle* can be reformulated as follows: If a given element is to be found on the *subcat list* of the head of a projection, but is absent from the *subcat list* of the mother, it must be realized as a complement-daughter.

It should be clear by now that the *Complementation* and *Adjunction* rule schemes are just two sides of the same coin, only differentiated by the application of the *Subcategorization Principle.* In the first case, viz. *Complementation,* the number of arguments of the phrase is different from the number of arguments of the head-daughter; whereas the number of argument of the phrase equals the number of the head-daughter's arguments in case of *Adjunction*. Thus, we find a certain kind of similarity between CUG and HPSG: in HPSG, we distinguish *Adjunction* and *Complementation* by a certain (in-)equality between head and phrase, whereas in CUG, lexemes are segregated into endocentric and exocentric ones.

However, one merit of the HPSG-treatment of *Complementation* and *Adjunction* is, that adjoining categories do not need to be described as functor, or head categories. This aspect will be further scrutinized in Chap. 3 of this paper. For the moment we will conclude our brief review of HPSG with a sample derivation, again of the sentence **Bart hates jazz**. In (15-1) we have an attribute-value-representation of our *Complementation Rule*, unified with the principles introduced so far; (15-2) is the phrase-structure representation of the whole sentence.

(15-1) *Complementation Rule:*

$$
\begin{bmatrix}
\text{SYNTAX} \begin{bmatrix} \text{HEAD } \boxed{1} \\ \text{SUBCAT } \boxed{3} \end{bmatrix} \\[2ex]
\text{DTRS} \begin{bmatrix} \text{HEAD-DTR} \mid \text{SYNTAX} \begin{bmatrix} \text{HEAD } \boxed{1} \\ \text{SUBCAT } \langle \boxed{2} \mid \boxed{3} \rangle \end{bmatrix} \\[2ex] \text{COMP-DTR } \boxed{2} \end{bmatrix}
\end{bmatrix}
$$

(15-2) Bart hates jazz

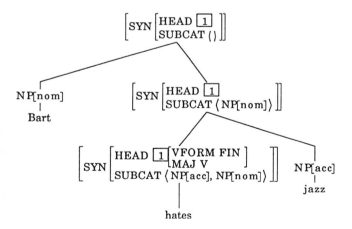

Now, our first point can be made by just comparing the representation in (15) with the one in (8). Whereas in HPSG the valency of a sign is represented in a unique as well as perspicuous list-valued attribute, which does not confine the categorial membership of the sign, in CUG the valency is split up into a number of category-valued RESULT-attributes. As a consequence of this, the percolation of categorial information must be traced by considering a number of RESULT-attributes, which are tied only by the lexemes. In HPSG, on the contrary, categorial information percolates via the *Head Feature Principle,* which is a principle of syntax – as it should be. For that matter, we can conclude that the data structures employed in HPSG are superior to the ones used in CUG, from a theoretical as well as an empirical perspective.

3 Multiple Categorizations in CUG

As mentioned several times, in CUG, complementation and adjunction are distinguished only by the structure of the functor categories. Complementing categories can be described by the endocentric scheme in (16-1), whereas adjoining categories are described as exocentric in (16-2):

(16-1) Endocentricity: X/Y where X $\neq$ Y.
(16-2) Exocentricity: X/Y where X = Y.

Thus we find a three-way categorial distinction in CUG: we have basic categories, where Y is *U*, exocentric and endocentric complex categories. However, what at first glance looks like a virtue of the theory becomes a serious problem under critical scrutiny. This problem can be described as multicategorization: it is not the case that *all* categories fit into the scheme introduced in (16). This problem becomes apparent when discussing prepositional phrases (PPs).

As (17) shows, PPs surely can be used as complements. In (18), however, the PP *neben der Quelle* ('beside the fountain') must be treated as an adjunct.

(17)   Peter geht in die Stadt.
        Peter walks to town
(18)   Peter fand den Hundertmarkschein neben der Quelle.
        Peter picked up the DM 100 bill beside the well.

In (17), the main verb should be treated as a simple transitive verb – in CG-notation (S\NP)\NP – and the prepositional object must be characterized as a basic category of type PP. But this will not do with (18). If the prepositional adjunct were encoded as a basic PP again, no mode of combination could be employed to combine this adjunct with the verbal projection, because neither of the two can be treated as an argument of the other one. A better categorization for the prepositional adjunct would be X/X, where X is instantiated to the respective verbal projection. This will serve as a solution for the adjunction case (18), but will not do in the complementation case, because, as an X/X, X cannot be instantiated to *U*. Consequently, in CUG, prepositional phrases must be treated by at least two categorizations, viz. as PP in complementation contexts and as X/X in adjunction contexts.[11]

Similar problems arise in postnominal complementation contexts. Consider the following example, in which the genitive object is to be categorized as an NP.

(19)   Wir gedachten des toten Vorstandsvorsitzenden.
        We commemorated the dead chairman.

But what would be the right category for the postnominal genitive NP in (20)?

(20)   der Vorstandsvorsitzende der Treuhandgesellschaft
        the chairman of the Treuhandgesellschaft

Two ways are open for investigation. First, we may assume that certain Ns are not categorized as basic, but as complementing categories of type N/NP[gen]. This assumption would be supported by the fact that the head N in (20) is a relational noun. The other possibility would be to re-categorize the postnominal NP as an N-modifier, i.e., as an adjunct of type N\N. Clearly, this would not be preferable in case of example (20), but would be the right direction, if non-argument postnominal NPs such as the genitive NP in (21) are tackled.

(21)   der Flaschenöffner des Vorstandsvorsitzenden
        the bottle-opener of the chairman

Thus, it seems to be the case that certain expressions may belong to at least *three different categories,* viz. to basic categories of type NP (19), to endocentric categories of type N/NP (20), and to exocentric categories of type N\N (21). It should be clear that even if empirical and theoretical considerations are left aside for the moment, this situation is at least unsatisfactory from an implementational vantage point.

---

11 Technically, this would be captured as a lexical rule, which maps entries of type PP/NP to (X/X)/NP.

In HPSG, similar problems do not arise. This is so because categorial membership and combinatorial potential of a lexeme are strictly segregated, as was shown above. Adjunction and complementation are implemented not as lexical structures but as syntactic combination schemes. From this point of view, an expression can only be ambigious because it can fill slots in adjunction, as well as in complementation schemes – still it is categorized as PP. In the case of postnominal genitive NPs, the fact that certain nouns do take postnominal complements is simply achieved by a different *SUBCAT attribute*. Thus, nouns like *Vorstandsvorsitzender,* which are inherently relational, are treated as subcategorizing for a postnominal NPs. But this is covered by a variation of the valency, not by recategorization.[12]

Coming to a conclusion, HPSG's *Subcategorization Feature* again proves as a useful tool to cover cases in which a lexeme exhibits different valencies. This feature, however, only covers cases of syntactic complementation. If a phrase must be treated as an adjunct, it is covered by the *Adjunction Rule,* thereby avoiding empirically unmotivated disjunctions. Finally, it should be mentioned that the *Subcategorization Feature* of HPSG is a further development out of the lexical encoding of valency in CG, but one which stays clear of CG's deficiencies.[13]

4 The Modularity of Representation

As a final point of consideration, we would like to mention a topic which has been one of our main themes throughout the investigation, i.e. the modular structuring of information in HPSG. In Chap. 2 we have introduced HPSG's principles. A first example of the modular structure of representation arose when we compared CUG's RESULT-cascades with the *HEAD Feature Principle* in HPSG. Whereas in CUG, projectional properties are encoded in the lexemes, HPSG 'extracts' this information and puts it into a principle, which then is applied to possible phrasal projections. Another example of modular structuring can be given, when semantic construction is discussed. I do not want to dive too deeply into semantic issues[14] in this article, but still consider the construction of a semantic representation which is carried out in parallel with the syntactic analysis. For the time being I will assume

---

[12] Technically, this is simply implemented by a disjunction over the *SUBCAT* attribute.
[13] This does not mean that in case of adjunction, no valency is involved at all. In Pollard/Sag (forthcoming), as well as in Jacobs (1989), adjunction is viewed as a mode of combination by which semantic valencies are saturated. For a more detailed account, the reader is referred to the sources mentioned above.
[14] See also Geurts (this volume).

that verbs (as well as NPs and other categories) exhibit an additional attribute called SX (for Semantics). This attribute locates the semantic contribution of the sign. As an example take the representation of the verb *hates* in (22). The abbreviation NP:[1] stands for an NP with SX-value [1]. Thus, in (22) the semantic contributions of the NPs are anchored to the respective roles introduced by the verb.

(22)   *hates*

$$
\begin{bmatrix}
\text{SYNTAX} & \begin{bmatrix} \text{SUBCAT } \langle \text{NP[acc]:}\boxed{2}, \text{NP[nom]:}\boxed{1} \rangle \\ \text{HEAD [VFORM FIN]} \end{bmatrix} \\
\text{SX} & \begin{bmatrix} \text{REL hate'} \\ \text{HATER } \boxed{1} \\ \text{HATEE } \boxed{2} \end{bmatrix}
\end{bmatrix}
$$

Now, to get the semantics construction to work in the right way, only the introduction of an additional principle, the so-called *Semantics Principle,* is necessary.[15] This is stated in (23).

(23)   Semantics Principle:
       The value of the SX-attribute of a phrase is equal to the SX-attribute of the phrase's head-daughter.

Very important in this respect is the fact that the *Semantics Principle* does not make any prediction concerning the actual merging of the semantic contribution of the complements with the semantics of the head. Indeed, there is no necessity to do so. Consider the *Subcategorization Principle.* This principle already says that the arguments of a head are unified with the complements-daughters of the head's projection. But by this operation, the respective semantics of the complements are unified as well. Consequently, the *Semantics Principle* need only take care of the projection of the semantic contribution of the head. This can be seen by the augmented representation of our sample sentence **Bart hates jazz** in (24).[16]

---

[15] For expository purposes, I have simplified matters quite a bit, thereby largely ignoring adjunction cases. But this clearly does not influence the point in question.

[16] The representation of Noun Phrase Semantics in (24) as well as in (25) should not be taken too seriously. It is just a convenient representation, which serves for expository purposes. The actual representation of Noun Phrase Semantics can be found in Geurts (this vol.).

(24)   Bart hates jazz

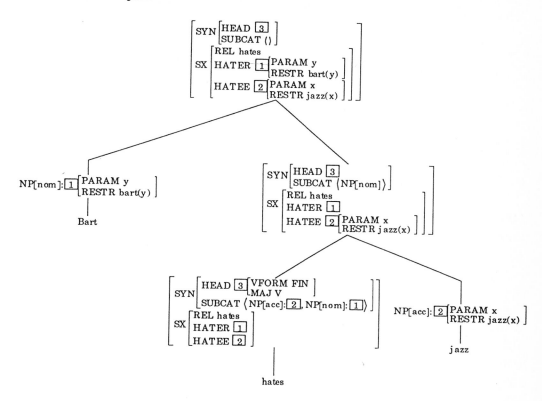

Here, the semantic contribution of the NP-complements is merged via saturation, i.e., the application of the *Subcategorization Principle,* whereas the projection of the semantic contribution of the head is carried out by the *Semantics Principle.* By the way, it should be mentioned that the order of the combination of the (semantic) functor with its arguments is not of relevance in unification grammar, because all unification grammars are declarative, monotone, and thus order independent.

In CUG, however, a very different picture arises. Here the rule scheme must explicitly take care of the semantics construction. Thus, not only the projection of semantic information, but the merging of information as well must either be encoded in the rules or in the lexemes. If we extend our simple representation of a transitive verb in CUG by including semantic information, matters becoming quite confused, as can be seen in (25). At least, it should be clear that an extraction of semantic information cannot be carried out so simply.

(25)   Semantics of transitive verb

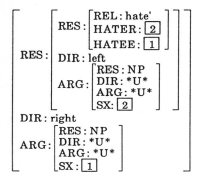

Again, it can be concluded that HPSG seems to provide better means to represent linguistic knowledge.

5   Conclusion

In this paper, we have compared CUG with HPSG. Our goal was to show that although CUG and HPSG have common ancestors, such as their foundation in lexicalism, or their use of unification mechanisms, HPSG still seems to be the better offspring. In particular, HPSG incorporates many advantages of CUG but tries to overcome the disadvantages of its rival. Several arguments have been given in favour of this thesis: HPSG extends CUG's data structures by employing lists, multiple categorizations are omitted due to more elaborate segregations between syntax and lexicon, and the semantics construction can be carried out in a more lucid way. The common theme of both grammars is the reduction of the rule systems. In this, HPSG's three-way distinction between the lexicon, the rule and the principle components seems to be more promising than CUG's two-way distinction between rules and the lexicon. Clearly, in the architecture of the latter, all the complexity which is eliminated from the rule component must be put into the lexicon, whereas HPSG's principles do their work in factorizing grammatical information, thus making way for more lucid knowledge representations – the main goal in the LILOG project.

References

Bach, E., R. Oehrle, D. Wheeler (eds.) (1985): *Categorial Grammar and Natural Language Structures*. Dordrecht: Kluwer Academic Publishers

Dowty, D., R. Wall, S. Peters (1981): *Introduction to Montague Semantics*. Dordrecht: Kluwer Academic Publishers

Jackendoff, R. (1977): *X'-Syntax: A Study of Phrase Structure*. Cambridge/London: MIT Press

Jacobs, J. (1989): *Skopus und Inkohärenz*. Ms. Bergische Universität-Gesamthochschule Wuppertal

Kamp, H., U. Reyle (forthcoming): *From Discourse to Logic*. Dordrecht: Kluwer Academic Publishers

Karttunen, L. (1989): *Radical Lexicalism*. In: Broch, A., M. Baltin (eds.): Alternative Conceptions of Phrase Structure. Chicago: University of Chicago Press

Kathol, A. (1991): *Verbal and Adjectival passives in German*. In: MIT Working Papers in Linguistics, Vol. 14

Kiss, T. (1991): *Variable Subkategorisierung – Eine Theorie der unpersönlichen Konstruktionen im Deutschen*. Forthcoming in: Linguistische Berichte

Pollard, C., I.A. Sag (1987): *Information-Based Syntax and Semantics. Vol. I: Fundamentals*. Chicago: University of Chicago Press

Pollard, C., I.A. Sag (forthcoming): *Information-Based Syntax and Semantics. Vol. II: Topic in Binding and Control*. To be published in Chicago, University of Chicago Press

Sag, I.A., C. Pollard (1989): *An Information-Based Theory of Agreement*. In: Proceedings of the Parasession of Grammatical Agreement, CLS 24, Chicago

Uszkoreit, H. (1986): *Categorial Unification Grammar*. CSLI Report 86-66

Wesche, B. (1988): *Dokumentation der Grammatik des ersten LILOG-Prototypen*. LILOG-Memo 9, 1988

An Alternative Phrase Structure Account of Symmetric Coordination

Birgit Wesche

Introduction

We present a uniform and coherent approach to symmetric coordination, which we take (along with, e.g., Sag 1976, Neijt 1980, or Hoehle 1990) to comprise the three universal coordination types *Phrasal Coordination* (PhC), *Right Node Raising* (RNR), and *Gapping*. The proposed treatment of coordinate structures is couched in the transformational framework of Government and Binding (GB) (as presented in Chomsky 1981 and Chomsky 1986). Our approach will not take recourse to any type of deletion transformation. Especially concerning RNR constructions, numerous counterarguments have been raised against a deletion treatment. In the course of these a preceding operation of raising was also questioned (see, e.g., Abbott 1976, Jackendoff 1977, Levine 1985). Consequently, we also deny the procedural interdependence hitherto assumed between the three coordination types, according to which the non-constituent coordination types RNR and Gapping are derived (via deletion transformations) from the base-generated constituent coordination type of PhC. Instead we will propose a direct phrase structure account which presents itself as a natural extension of the given X̄-scheme (as assumed in Chomsky 1986). This not only uniformly covers the syntactic structures of constituent coordination (CC) as well as non-constituent coordination (NCC), but, moreover, can be generalized to a unique X̄-scheme which is valid for both, simplex and coordinate structures.

Symmetric Coordination Types

Coordinate structures are classified as follows:

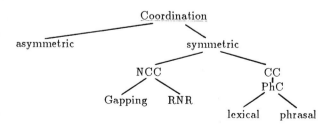

Roughly, symmetric coordination, as opposed to asymmetric coordination, is characterized by conjuncts of the same syntactic type.[1]

---

[1]See (Sag et al. 1984) for a discussion of the range of syntactic alikeness of conjuncts.

The representative of the class of constituent coordination (CC), the coordination type of PhC, is subdivided into phrasal PhC and lexical PhC, shown in (1) and (2), respectively:

(1) a. NP & NP:
         John likes [$_{NP}$ loud music] and [$_{NP}$ good films].
     b. IP & IP:
         [$_{IP}$ John is reading the newspaper] and [$_{IP}$ Mary is writing a letter].

(2)   N & N:
         John wants to buy a small [$_N$ bus] or [$_N$ car].

Instances of asymmetric coordination are often found with German coordinate constructions:

(3)   CP & C'(V-1):
         [$_{CP}$ In den Wald ging der Jäger] und [$_{C'}$ jagte einen Hasen].
         (Into the forest went the hunter and caught a hare.)
         (cf. Wunderlich 1988)

Example (3) displays a first conjunct of type CP, containing a preposed adverbial phrase, coupled with a verb-first (V-1) second conjunct of type C'. Nevertheless the interpretation of sentence (3) corresponds to that derived from its symmetric counterpart represented in (4):

(4)   C' & C':
         Der Jäger [$_{C'}$ ging in den Wald] und [$_{C'}$ jagte einen Hasen].
         (The hunter went into the forest and caught a hare.)

However, in the course of this paper we will only deal with symmetric coordination, leaving aside asymmetric coordination.[2]

Non-constituent coordination (NCC), as opposed to constituent coordination, is built up by conjuncts which usually do not display constituent status in the conventional sense. The class of NCC comprises the two major types of Gapping on the one hand, and RNR on the other. Both are assumed to be derived via deletion transformations from a base generated PhC structure according to the phrase structure rule:

X ⇒ X Conj X

---

[2] We take VP-Deletion or Sluicing constructions not to belong to the class of symmetric coordinate structures, since, among other reasons, they are not exclusively coordinate in nature, but also occur in subordinate contexts:

  i. VP-Deletion:
      I will leave when you do.

  ii. Sluicing:
      John is determined to buy a car on Saturday, although he cannot decide which.

in which the variable X can be any phrasal or lexical entity. Gapping constructions are distinguished by the second conjunct (or the non-first conjuncts in n-ary coordinate structures) missing the finite verb – and possibly further complements and adjuncts of the verbal projection. Since Gapping is bound to (at least) the finite verb, it operates in the phrasal domains of IP and CP only.[3] Classical Gapping affects the finite verb only, leaving two major constituents (maximal projections) behind as remnants (cf. example (5)). The Gapping construction in (6) shows the elision of a verbal projection, while in (7) we observe Gapping with only one remnant, which is also known as *Stripping*.

(5)   Classical Gapping:

       [John reads the newspaper] and [Mary ϕ a book].
       ϕ = reads

(6)   Gapping—verbal projection:

       [My sister reads the newspaper in the morning] and [my brother ϕ in the evening].
       ϕ = reads the newspaper

(7)   Stripping—Gapping with one remnant:

       [John reads the newspaper], and [Mary ϕ].
       ϕ = reads the newspaper

With RNR constructions on the other hand we meet deletion in the first (or non-last) conjunct(s). Deletion here affects a conjunct's rightmost constituents, irrespective of their syntactic nature.

(8)   [John loves ϕ] and [Mary hates oysters].
       ϕ = oysters (verbal complement)

(9)   [John is confident of ϕ] and [Peter is dependent on a successful outing at the track].[4]
       ϕ = a successful outing at the track (prepositional complement)

(10)   [Peter sells ϕ] and [Mary donates valuable books to the library].
       ϕ = valuable books to the library (verbal complements)

Apart from assuming simple deletion to be at work, some analyses of this type of coordinate structure (see in particular Postal 1974) furthermore assume the constituents in question to be raised to the coordinate node (i.e., a copy of them Chomsky-adjoined to the latter), prior to deleting them in their original conjunct's position. Both positions, relying on raising plus deletion or on deletion only, have been attacked in the literature with numerous counterarguments. The following sentence, for example (taken from Jackendoff 1977), questions any type of deletion approach:

(11) ?   [John whistled ϕ] and [Mary hummed the same tune].
     ? ϕ = the same tune

---

[3]Gapping in VP (as assumed by, e.g., Neijt 1980) will be denied. We subsume respective constructions also under Gapping in either IP or CP.

Here, the NP *the same tune* could not possibly have originated in the first conjunct. Similar effects can be observed with the next two sentences – noted by (Abbott 1976) – where each sentence contains one reading which evades an approach via deletion (plus raising):

(12)   a.   I borrowed, and my sister stole, a total of \$ 3000 from the bank.

      b.   John gave Mary, and Joan presented to Fred, books which looked remarkably similar.

Despite these counterexamples, however, to date no adequate alternative approach to RNR constructions has been proposed.

Shared Constituent Coordination

The assumption of the procedural interdependence between the three coordination types, as represented in

(13)

is based on semantic considerations. As a hypothesis, any type of coordination is attributed to coordination of complete propositions, predicates or arguments. In former models of grammar, semantic rules applied to the level of deep structure. Hence, for example, the RNR surface structure

(14)   [on the big ϕ] and [under the small table]

is assumed to be based on the PhC deep structure

(15)   [on the big table] and [under the small table]

      In the later GB-model of grammar, semantic rules are postponed to apply following S-structure representations, on the level of Logical Form (LF). The hypothesis of a PhC base for any type of coordination is retained – a permissible step, since deletion rules in this model of grammar also apply following S-structure representations, on the level of Phonetic Form (PF). The semantic representation of complete propositions, etc., is hereby still accounted for.

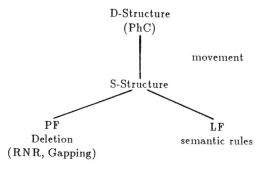

The account of symmetric coordinate structures we present here presupposes a change in perspective. Instead of focusing on semantic aspects, which enforces the distinction into the three mentioned coordination types – together with the assumption of their procedural interdependence – we will redirect the focus to syntactic aspects governing the generation of coordinate structures. Our emphasis will be on the constituents which can be *shared* in a given coordinate structure. The question then is which constituents can be shared where – given the condition that a shared constituent must simultaneously comply with the grammatical requirements of each of the conjuncts, resulting overtly in one unique surface structure form (requirement of *phonetic identity*). Under this *Shared Constituent Coordination* (SCC) perspective we achieve a re-classification of the given symmetric coordination types:

(16) **Shared Constituent Coordination**

a. **Non-SCC**   (formerly: complete phrasal PhC)

e.g.: (and) $\begin{bmatrix} \text{on the table} \\ \text{under the carpet} \end{bmatrix}$

(*on the table and under the carpet*)

b. **Right SCC**   (formerly: RNR; lexical PhC of rightward governing heads)

e.g.: (and) $\begin{bmatrix} \text{on the big} \\ \text{under the small} \end{bmatrix}$ *table*

(*on the big and under the small table*)

c. **Left SCC**   (formerly: lexical PhC of leftward governing heads)

e.g.: (sowohl ... als auch) *seiner Frau* $\begin{matrix} \text{treu} \\ \text{überdrüssig} \end{matrix}$

(*seiner Frau sowohl treu als auch überdrüssig*;
his wife (dat/gen) both, loyal to and tired of)

d. **'Medial' SCC**   (formerly: Gapping)

e.g.: (and) $\begin{matrix} \text{Susan} \\ \text{Mary} \end{matrix}$ *kisses* $\begin{matrix} \text{teddybears} \\ \text{frogs} \end{matrix}$

(*Susan kisses teddybears and Mary frogs*)

With this classification we obviate the need for a distinction between constituent coordination and non-constituent coordination (right SCC, for example, comprises both). The crucial factor is the position of the shared constituent, whether the conjuncts involved display constituent status or not. The main difference to the previous classification lies in the fact that we propose a mirror-image rule, viz. left SCC versus right SCC. Thus, we oppose lexical PhC of leftward governing heads with RNR constructions, which we could generalize to include also those instances of lexical PhC with rightward governing heads. Leftward governing heads do not occur in English, but can be found with German adjectives, and with German verbs in their basic subordinate position, where they occur clause-final. In (16c) the adjective *treu* (loyal to) assigns dative case, while the adjective *überdrüssig* (tired of) assigns genitive case. Other than within the masculine or neuter declension, in the femine declension both case endings result in the same surface structure form. Hence, the requirement of phonetic identity is satisfied for the shared constituent *seiner Frau* (his wife).

An essential consequence of this SCC view is that we explicitly deny any type of lexical coordination. In a left SCC construction, formerly lexical PhC, the affected shared constituent behaves analogously to the shared constituent in a right SCC construction, formerly RNR. Since for the latter the assumed domain is the phrasal level (including the shared constituent to the right), we will accordingly assume a phrasal level for left SCC, too. With Non-SCC and Gapping[5] ranging by definition over phrases, we conclude that the domain of any type of coordinate structure is the phrasal level.

The direct approach via phrase structure rules which we present in the next section accounts directly for the generalizations of coordinate structures drawn from the SCC perspective.

A Phrase Structure Account

Generalized $\overline{\overline{X}}$-scheme

The proposed $\overline{\overline{X}}$-scheme presupposes an extension of the data structures admitted as terminal nodes. We introduce *Ordered Lists* and *Factors*: Ordered Lists contain the contrasting elements of a coordinate structure, Factors are a one-element list (the shared elements in a coordinate structure), complying with the grammatical requirements of each of the respective ordered list elements.

Extended $\overline{\overline{X}}$-scheme:

$$X_{[coord]} \Rightarrow \langle X_1,..., X_m \rangle$$
$$X'_{[coord]} \Rightarrow X_{[coord]} \quad \langle Compl_1,..., Compl_m \rangle$$
$$X"_{[coord]} \Rightarrow \langle Spec_1,..., Spec_m \rangle \quad X'_{[coord]}$$

By this extended X-scheme we generate a *conflated tree*.[6] The conflated tree T consists of m simplex structure trees T', which are determined as follows:

i. Each sequence S in T is replaced by the ith element, with $1 \le i \le m$.

ii. A sequence of length one is an element of each of the simplex structures T'.

iii. Condition:
Each simplex structure tree T' must be wellformed with respect to the grammatical requirements on each level of syntactic representation.

Any coordinate structure is obligatorily determined by the existence of a sequence (i.e., Ordered List) of heads whose length is ≥ 2. Complements and specifiers may either be also Ordered Lists, which results in a PhC construction (i.e., a structure in which no element is shared). Or one of the two, or both, may be Factors, which results in a SCC construction – left, right or 'medial'. To take this concept one step further, one can also think of a pure Factor base generation, which would

---

[5]Though in its classical constellation Gapping shows a clear 'medial' sharing of a constituent, it becomes less obvious when considering the whole range of Gapping constructions. We will therefore retain the more common term Gapping here.

[6]Another way of looking at this tree structure is to say that we added a "third dimension" to a hitherto two-dimensional structure. See (Goodall 1984) for a three-dimensional treatment of Gapping structures, which is based on a separate component, deviating significantly from the conventional $\overline{\overline{X}}$-scheme.

then result in a conventional simplex structure. For the generation of a simplex structure, then, a head-Factor generation will be obligatory, just as for a coordinate structure we require an Ordered List head. Therefore, we generalize the above extended $\overline{X}$-scheme to the following form:

Generalized $\overline{X}$-scheme

$$
\begin{aligned}
X &\Rightarrow \langle X_1,..., X_m \rangle \\
X' &\Rightarrow X \ \langle Compl_1,..., Compl_m \rangle \\
X'' &\Rightarrow \langle Spec_1,..., Spec_m \rangle \ X'
\end{aligned}
$$

This generalized $\overline{X}$-scheme is instantiated alternatively by either of the two phrase structure rules:

(17) a. $X \Rightarrow X_{[simplex]}$

    b. $X \Rightarrow X_{[coord]}$

With this highly general $\overline{X}$-scheme, which we claim to be universal, we provide a representation incorporating both, simplex and coordinate structures, and hereby present a comprehensive account of any type of endocentric phrasal structures.

As outlined above, the general $\overline{X}$-scheme is conditioned such that an $X_{[simplex]}$-instantiation is bound to a Factor-head generation, while an $X_{[coord]}$-instantiation requires an Ordered List head. We subsume these conditions under the *head-drivenness constraint*. In case of a Factor-head, the remaining complements and specifiers must be Factors, too. Within the $X_{[coord]}$ paradigm, as mentioned, complements and specifiers can be instantiated arbitrarily as Factors or Ordered Lists.

In the following we will neglect simplex structures and take a more detailed look at the behavior of coordinate structures.

Linearization

According to the head-drivenness constraint, the coordinate constructions *on the table and under the carpet* (Non-SCC) on the one hand, and *on the big and under the small table* or *on and under the table* (right SCC) on the other, are licensed by the prepositional head sequence $\langle on, under \rangle$. The base generated tree structures[7] look as follows:[8]

(18) Non-SCC:

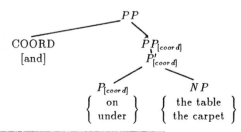

---

[7]Ordered Lists are given in braces, Factors are delimited by vertical lines.

[8]We in fact assume a DP-analysis of noun phrases, but for expository purposes we refer to the conventional NP-representation here.

(19) Right SCC:

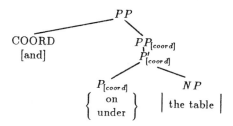

The actual surface structure output is achieved by *Linearization* on the level of PF:

Linearization I (Non-SCC, left and right SCC)

Provided the Ordered Lists are directly adjacent to each other, linearize the respective list elements line by line, connecting them by the given conjunction. Factors, preceding or succeeding, are realized as usual.

The constraint of direct adjacency of the Ordered Lists, by which we guarantee the coherent conjunct structure, is due, we claim, to a general principle governing coordinate structures:

Principle of Coordinate Structures

Contrasting elements are realized as close to each other as possible.

The conjunction is treated as an abstract COORD lexeme, adjoined to the coordinated maximal node, according to the condition that coordination always ranges over phrasal levels, i.e., maximal projections.

$$X" \Rightarrow COORD_{[conj]} \ X"_{[coord]}$$

The abstract COORD lexeme is annotated by a specification of the actually chosen conjunction, which will be overtly realized in the course of the Linearization process.[9] Specific structural requirements demanded by a given conjunction will be noted along with the conjunction feature, and also accounted for during the Linearization process. Thus we do not interfere with the general phrase structure of coordination.

With the above prepositional phrases the adjacency constraint is trivially fulfilled, since no movement operations occur within PP. Thus, either Ordered Lists are directly generated in an adjacent position, providing for a coherent conjunct structure, or they are not – which leads to grammatical structures in the first case, but to ungrammatical ones otherwise. Things look differently, though, for coordinate structures within the domain of IP or CP. This is illustrated by the German right SCC construction *Johann liebt und Maria haßt Austern* (John loves and Mary hates oysters). The range of coordination here is the domain of CP, the coordinate structure being licensed by a multiple C-head (originating from a base generated multiple I-head, passing on its tense and

---

[9]Since we deny asyndetic symmetric coordination, the conjunction feature must always be filled.

agreement features to the main verb list, which in turn is moved to the C-head position to yield a German verb-second construction). The following figure shows the corresponding D-Structure:[10]

(20)

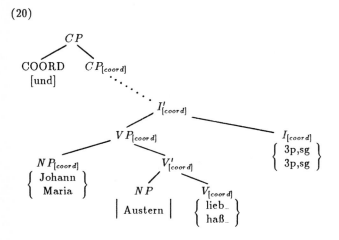

We presuppose movement of the verbal list to the head-IP position, where verbal stem and inflectional features are linewise synthesized. The above Linearization rule, then, correctly predicts that, given the base structure shown in (20), no German subordinate clause can be achieved, if we want to retain the meaning as intended by the constellation of the contrasting ordered lists:

(21) *   (...., daß) Johann Austern liebt und Maria haßt.
          ('... that Johann oysters loves and Maria hates.')

This surface structure will not permit an interpretation in which *Mary* is the agent hating the object *oysters*.

Movement applies to Lists and Factors as to atomic terminal elements. Hence, with empty nodes being irrelevant for Linearization, both the structures resulting first from moving the verb list to the head-CP position (verb-first (V-1): e.g., question) and second from subsequently moving the subject list to the Spec-CP position (verb-second (V-2): e.g., assertions) qualify for Linearization. The respective S-structures before Linearization look as follows:

---

[10]For the remainder of this article we ignore the specification of tense features at the head-IP position.

(22) <u>V-1:</u>

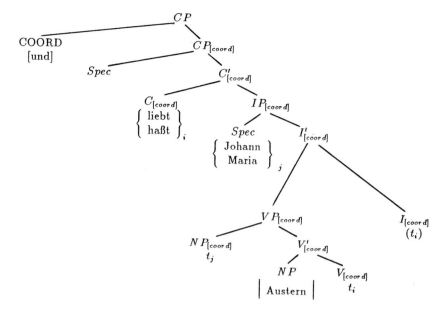

(23) <u>V-2:</u>

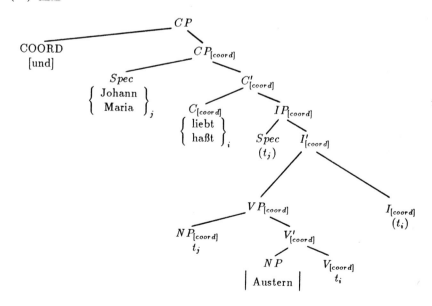

Since each time movement resulted in adjacent Ordered Lists, Linearization may apply:

(24) a. V-1:

[Liebt Johann] und [haßt Maria] Austern?
('[Loves Johann] and [hates Maria] oysters?')

b. V-2:

[Johann liebt] und [Maria haßt] Austern.
([Johann loves] and [Mary hates] oysters.)

Also, topicalizing the factor *Austern* will result in a grammatical structure, as can easily be verified:

(25)   Austern [liebt Johann] und [haßt Maria].
('Oysters [loves Johann] and [hates Maria].')

Treatment on LF

After given movement operations have taken place, the same structure which is input to PF is also input to the level of LF. Since via base generation the elements to be coordinated are already grouped together correctly, no reconstruction process in order to obtain the adequate interpretation is necessary. In case of a simple NP being factorized (like *Austern* (oysters) in the above examples), the input structure – in case of V-2 – for LF is:

$$\left\{ \left\{ \begin{array}{c} \text{Johann} \\ \text{Maria} \end{array} \right\} \left\{ \begin{array}{c} \text{liebt} \\ \text{haßt} \end{array} \right\} \right\} \left| \text{Austern} \right|$$

The factor *oysters* will be interpreted with each subtree in turn, which yields a semantics corresponding to *John loves oysters and Mary hates oysters* for the above sentence.

In case the Factor is a collective predicate, such as the NP *the same tune* in

(26)   [John whistled] and [Mary hummed] the same tune.

with the simplified LF-representation

$$\left\{ \left\{ \begin{array}{c} \text{John} \\ \text{Mary} \end{array} \right\} \left\{ \begin{array}{c} \text{whistled} \\ \text{hummed} \end{array} \right\} \right\} \left| \text{the same tune} \right|$$

this NP can (and, in fact, *must*) be directly interpreted, and assigned a semantic type of higher order, which reflects its taking scope over both of the conjuncts. Thus, the inadequacy of a base-generated PhC construction with subsequent deletion of the respective NP is overcome. In (26) there simply is no gap to be created in the first conjunct, neither could we possibly generate a complete PhC structure serving as input for LF. Our approach directly accounts for this fact.[11]

How a given Factor will be interpreted is simply a question of its semantic type. But no matter which the adequate semantic type will be, we are given a unique representation at LF, which allows for any type of interpretation.

---

[11] It is obvious from a Factor such as *the same tune* that the condition of a Factor being a constituent of each simplex tree contained in the conflated tree structure only holds for the syntactic levels of representation (e.g., on D-structure and S-structure θ-role and case assignment criteria must be satisfied).

Linearization with 'Medial' SCC – Gapping

Gapping requires a different Linearization principle. For a sentence such as *Johann liebt Austern und seine Eltern Krabben* (John loves oysters and his parents shrimps), we again assume a list of I-heads to determine this CP-coordination (in the sense outlined above). Within our framework the characteristics of Gapping will be captured by base-generating a verb factor (and possibly further factors according to Gapping conventions)[12], which receives its inflectional features as usual. During the Linearization process, however, only the first specification of the INFL-list will be spelled out. Thus, a finite verb factor, intervening between ordered lists, may present an exception to the above mentioned constraint of phonetic identity, since inflectional features need not be identical.[13]

(27) Gapping tree structure after movement:

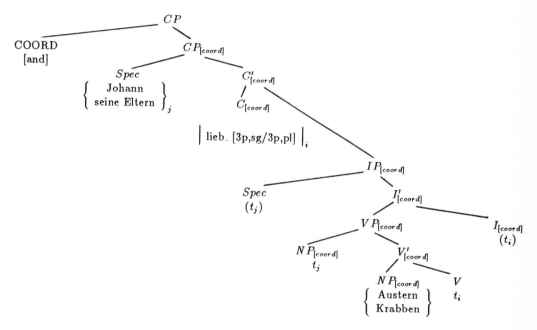

Linearization II (Gapping)

Provided the Ordered Lists are only interrupted by a finite verb Factor (and possibly further Factors according to Gapping conventions) linearize first the elements of the first line including all of the Factors, then the remaining elements line by line, connecting the lines by the given conjunction.

Hence we get the "gapped" surface structure output as desired:

---

[12]For a detailed summary of Gapping phenomena see, e.g., (Sag 1976, Neijt 1980, or Chao 1988).

[13]There are speakers, however, who have a strong intuition concerning phonetic identity here, too. For them, only Gapping structures with identical inflectional specifications are acceptable.

(28)   [Johann liebt Austern] und [seine Eltern Krabben].
        (Johann loves oysters and his parents shrimps.)

Interaction of Linearization Rules

Our rule system nicely explains a systematic interaction between right SCC and Gapping found in German subordinate clauses. Both of the following two structures:

(29) a. (..., daß) [Johann Austern] und [Maria Krabben] liebt.
          ('... that Johann oysters and Maria shrimps loves.')
      b. (..., daß) [Johann Austern liebt] und [Maria Krabben].
          ('... that Johann oysters loves and Maria shrimps.')

will be derived from the same base structure:

(30)

The sentence in (29a) is achieved via Linearization I (right SCC), the one in (29b) via Linearization II (Gapping).

A pitfall for any procedural approach are sentences in which we find all types of coordinate structures. For example, if we encounter a sentence which displays the characteristics of both, right SCC and Gapping, we are hard put to apply an analysis which presupposes a basic PhC construction on which deletion may operate. At some stage in the derivation either structure could only be obtained from an already reduced form. Thus, the question arises which type of deletion operation should apply first – in other words, we are faced with ordering paradoxes.

With our approach no such problems arise. All types of coordinate structures can be incorporated into a common sentential structure. Consider sentence (31):

(31) (and) John / his friends love_ green and red / yellow and white gummibears.

The adjectival phrases *green and red* and *yellow and white* are Non-SCC structures obtained by the above mentioned phrase structure rule:

$$AP \Rightarrow COORD_{[and]} \; AP_{[coord]}$$

Any maximal projection thus obtained distributes like a simplex phrase, and is treated as such during the Linearization process. Besides this Non-SCC structure in (31) we observe a shared finite verb (Gapping: *love_*), and a shared constituent to the right (right SCC: *gummibears*). Given this structure, we have two options for Linearization. The first is a strict Gapping Linearization:

(32) [John loves [$_{AP}$ green and red] gummibears] and [his friends [$_{AP}$ yellow and white] (ones)].

Here, the first line including all Factors (*love, gummibears*) has been realized first. However, we are not restricted to this possibility. In fact, in English the second version seems to be more natural:[14]

(33) [John loves [$_{AP}$ green and red]] and [his friends [$_{AP}$ yellow and white]] gummibears.

This shows that preferably this "first-line-first" condition applies only to two Ordered Lists between which a finite verb Factor intervenes (and possibly further Factors of the verbal projection). We linearize "first-line-first", including all of the intervening verbal Factors, only until we meet the first item of the second contrasting Ordered List. Afterwards we proceed as specified in Linearization I, hereby indirectly treating the respective Ordered Lists as displaying coherent conjunct structures. Thus, we conclude that Linearization II is embeddable, as a special case, into Linearization I, the latter being the predominant rule. This nicely supports the view that in a coordinate structure contrasting lists are realized as closely to each other as possible, as stated in the Principle of Coordinate Structures.

Applicability to Non-Transformational Frameworks

The proposed treatment of symmetric coordination is not necessarily bound to the GB framework. The main tenets of the approach presented here could also be captured in any of the non-transformational approaches to grammar, such as *Generalized Phrase Structure Grammar (GPSG)* (cf. Gazdar et al. 1984), *Lexical Functional Grammar (LFG)* (cf. Kaplan, Bresnan 1982), or *Head-Driven Phrase Structure Grammar (HPSG)* (cf. Pollard, Sag 1987). In essence, our approach affects the phrase structure component, introducing a generalized $\overline{X}$-scheme valid for both, simplex and coordinate structures. Apart from the transformation *move* α no further transformation, be it deletion or any other transformation, is invoked. Every grammatical framework relies on a phrase structure

---

[14]In German both solutions are equally acceptable:

i. [Johann liebt grüne und rote Gummibärchen] und [seine Freunde gelbe und weiße].

ii. [Johann liebt grüne und rote] und [seine Freunde gelbe und weiße Gummibärchen].

component, each after its own fashion. And the phenomena captured within the GB framework by employing *move α* are equally well accounted for within the non-transformational approaches, again each after its own fashion. So the necessary provision is made for an adaptation of the proposed approach to non-transformational frameworks.

Summary

Our SCC approach naturally overcomes the three basic problems hitherto encountered with non-constituent coordination, i.e., the problems arising from assuming, firstly, raising and secondly deletion, and thirdly from failing to provide an adequate input structure for semantic rules on LF. The proposed phrase structure account, according to which any coordination structure is licensed by the existence of coordinated heads (i.e., an Ordered List of heads), presents itself as a natural extension of the $\overline{X}$-scheme for simplex sentences. It not only equally accounts for the generation of any type of symmetric coordination. We, moreover, presented a *generalized* $\overline{X}$-scheme which uniformly covers the syntactic structures from simplex sentences (where only Factors are involved), over shared constituent coordination (involving Ordered Lists and Factors), up to non-shared constituent coordination (in which we find Ordered Lists only). In this respect, the proposed phrase structure account is a valid contribution to a general theory of sentence grammar.

References

[Abbott 1976]   Abbott, B.: Right Node Raising as a Test for Constituenthood *Linguistic Inquiry* Vol. 7.3, pp. 639–642

[Chao 1988]   Chao, W.: *On Ellipsis* Garland Publishing, New York

[Chomsky 1981]   Chomsky, N.: *Lectures on Government and Binding* Foris, Dordrecht

[Chomsky 1986]   Chomsky, N.: *Barriers* MIT Press, Cambridge, MA

[Gazdar et al. 1984]   Gazdar, G., Klein, E., Pullum, G.K., Sag, I.: *Generalized Phrase Structure Grammar* Blackwell, Oxford

[Goodall 1984]   Goodall, G.: *Parallel Structures in Syntax* Ph.D. thesis, University of California, San Diego, CA

[Hoehle 1990]   Hoehle, T.: On Reconstruction and Coordination, University of Tübingen, manuscript

[Jackendoff 1977]   Jackendoff, R.: $\overline{X}$-*Syntax: A Study of Phrase Structure* MIT Press, Cambridge, MA

[Kaplan, Bresnan 1982]   Kaplan, R., Bresnan, J.: Lexical-Functional Grammar: A Formal System for Grammatical Relations In: Bresnan, J.(ed.): *The Mental Representation of Grammatical Relations* MIT Press, Cambridge MA, pp. 173–281

[Levine 1985]   Levine, R.D.: Right Node (Non-)Raising *Linguistic Inquiry* Vol. 16.3, pp. 492–497

[Neijt 1980]   Neijt, A.: *Gapping—A Contribution to Sentence Grammar* Revised edition (first edition 1979), Foris, Dordrecht

[Pollard, Sag 1987]   Pollard, C., Sag, I.: *An Information-Based Syntax and Semantics, Vol. 1* Center for the Study of Language and Information, Lecture Notes 13, Stanford, CA

[Postal 1974]   Postal, P.: *On Raising: One Rule of English Grammar and its Theoretical Implications* MIT Press, Cambridge, MA

[Ross 1967]   Ross, J.R. *Constraints on Variables in Syntax* Ph.D. thesis, MIT

[Sag 1976]   Sag, I.: *Deletion and Logical Form* Ph.D. thesis, MIT

[Sag et al. 1984]   Sag, I., Gazdar, G., Wasow, T., Weisler, S.: *Coordination and How to Distinguish Categories* Center for the Study of Language and Information, Report No. 84-3, Stanford, CA

[Wesche 1990]   Wesche, B.: Coordination without Deletion In: Proceedings of the 2nd IBM–ITL Conference on Natural Language Processing, Paris

[Wunderlich 1988]   Wunderlich, D.: Some Problems of Coordination in German In: Reyle, U., Rohrer, C.(eds.): *Natural Language Parsing and Linguistic Theories* Reidel, Dordrecht, pp. 289–316

Verb Order and Head Movement

Tibor Kiss, Birgit Wesche

Abstract

This paper will focus on the treatment of so-called verb movement phenomena within non-transformational approaches to grammar, namely Categorial Grammar (CG) and Head Driven Phrase Structure Grammar (HPSG). We will discuss a number of recent proposals put forward by categorial grammarians, including one of the approaches taken within the LILOG project, which is a version of Categorial Unification Grammar (CUG). Subsequently, we will present a proposal for the treatment of finite verb positions in German within the framework of HPSG, which represents a further development of the original LILOG grammar and which can also be viewed as an extension to the theory of HPSG in general.

1   Introduction

German belongs to the class of SOV languages. For languages of this class it is assumed that in their basic word order subject and object precede the main verb. For German the basic word order is best exemplified with subordinate clauses such as:

(1)   ... , daß Hans seine Mutter anrief.
          (..... that Hans his mother 'up'called.)

If one looks at a question or a declarative sentence corresponding to this example, the motivation for assuming the verb-final construction as basic becomes evident.

(2)   Rief Hans seine Mutter an?
          (Called Hans his mother 'up'?)

(3)   Hans rief seine Mutter an.
          (Hans called his mother 'up'.)

In these sentences, which bear verb-initial (2) and verb-second (3) structures, respectively, the separable prefix *an* stayed behind in its basic position. This means that a verb form occurs continuously only in verb-final structure – therefore called the basic structure – while in verb-initial and verb-second structures it can be split. Finite verbal items change their position, while non-finite ones remain in place.

Within the realm of transformational grammar a convincing account for the different finite verb positions has been offered. It is assumed that the finite verb will be moved to the initial position for generating, e.g., a question. A second movement transformation accounts for topicalizing an arbitrary phrasal constituent, i.e., moving it before the finite verb, which results, e.g., in a declarative sentence.

The grammatical frameworks chosen for prototype development within the LILOG project are non-transformational approaches to grammar. Categorial Unification Grammar (CUG), a descendent of Categorial Grammar (CG; cf. Ajdukiewicz 1935; Bar-Hillel 1964), and Head Driven Phrase Structure Grammar (HPSG; cf. Pollard, Sag 1987) are surface-structure oriented grammatical frameworks. They do not resort to a concept where a sentence's surface structure is arrived at via transforming a basic deep structure, but search for a non-derivational account of a given sentence (movement is, i.a., simulated via structure sharing of feature structures). Still, they have to capture the generalizations observed for the different finite verb positions.

In this paper we will discuss a number of proposals addressing verb movement phenomena, which do not involve recourse to an overt movement transformation. After a brief overview of German sentence types, we will first take a look at recent approaches taken by categorial grammarians. The perspective we adopt toward these accounts is guided by the question to what extent the proposed treatment of finite verbs could be adopted for the LILOG framework. Second, we will present a proposal for verb movement within HPSG. The proposed treatment implies a number of extensions to the overall theory of HPSG. Each section is preceded by a brief introduction to the respective grammatical framework.

2 German Sentence Types

In German we distinguish between three different sentence types, according to the position that the finite verb takes:[1]

- verb-final (V-F)
  e.g.: subordinate clauses
  ..., daß Clara mit den Geistern gesprochen hat.
  (... that Clara to the spirits talked has.)

- verb-initial (V-1)
  e.g.: yes/no questions
  Hat Clara mit den Geistern gesprochen?
  (Has Clara to the spirits talked?)

- verb-second (V-2)
  e.g.: declarative sentences, wh-qestions
  Clara hat mit den Geistern gesprochen, um zu meditieren.
  (Clara has to the spirits talked, in order to meditate.)

A theoretical framework which offers a suitable model for describing the word order phenomena found in German, as in most Germanic languages,[2] is the positional field framework (PFF). The

---

[1]The following examples should not imply that there is a one-to-one correlation between V-1, V-2, and V-F structures and respective sentence modes such as declaratives, questions, or subordinate clauses. Thus, declaratives also display V-1 structure, and subordinate clauses can have V-1 or V-2 structure.

[2]English is an exception in this respect.

PFF divides the sentence into three topological regions, called the 'initial', 'middle' and 'final' fields (henceforth IF, MF, and FF, respectively). The MF is framed by the verbal bracket, which is so called because it predominantly contains elements of the verb cluster. Within the PFF, then, the above examples are assigned the following structure:

IF	VB$_{left}$	MF	VB$_{right}$	FF
	..., daß	Clara mit den Geistern	gesprochen hat.	
	Hat	Clara mit den Geistern	gesprochen?	
Clara	hat	mit den Geistern	gesprochen,	um zu meditieren.

The final field is mainly reserved for extraposed phrases, such as infinitival complements or subordinate clauses.

Transformational approaches to the description of German verb order have been attempted since the early sixties (see, e.g., Bierwisch 1963) Most of the more recent approaches to the varieties of German verb order go back to Thiersch and den Besten (Thiersch 1978; den Besten 1983). As for most Germanic languages it is generally assumed for German that the basic position of the finite verb is clause-final (recall 1). In these transformational proposals, V-1 and V-2 variants are derived by rule from V-F sentences.

As can be seen in the matrix above, complementizers and finite verbal elements are distributed complementarily over the left verbal bracket. Thiersch introduces a pair of fronting rules, the first of which moves the finite verb out of the final into the initial (left VB) position, provided the latter does not contain a complementizer. Given the constructions that result from applying this rule, the second rule makes possible the topicalization of an arbitrary phrasal constituent; i.e., it moves it out of the MF into the IF before the fronted finite verb. Fillers for this preverbal position may be any obligatory or optional argument to the main verb, including complex non-finite verbal clusters.

(4) $[_S \ldots \text{Vfin}] \rightarrow [_{S'} \text{Vfin}_i [_S \ldots t_i]]$

(5) $[_{S'} \text{Vfin}_i [_S \ldots \text{XP} \ldots t_i]] \rightarrow [_{S''} \text{XP}_j [_{S'} \text{Vfin}_i [_S \ldots t_j \ldots t_i]]]$

The sample derivation of V-1 and V-2 sentences given in (6) illustrates how these two rules[3] operate:

(6) a. weil Peter dem Jungen Schokolade gegeben hat →
         because Peter to the boy chocolate given has →
     b. hat$_i$ Peter dem Jungen Schokolade gegeben t$_i$ →
         has$_i$ Peter to the boy chocolate given t$_i$ →
     c. Peter$_j$ hat$_i$ t$_j$ dem Jungen Schokolade gegeben t$_i$
         Peter$_j$ has$_i$ t$_j$ to the boy chocolate given t$_i$

If we restate this standard treatment in Government and Binding (GB) terms (see, in particular Baker 1988 and Chomsky 1986a), rule (4) describes the movement of the finite verb into the

---

[3]The rules are given in X-bar notation. S, S', and S" here stand for V-F, V-1 and V-2 sentences, respectively. The symbols t$_i$ and t$_j$ are to be read as the traces left behind by the moved verb and the fronted constituent, respectively.

head position of C, and rule (5) describes the movement of a phrasal constituent into the specifier position of C. Three attractive consequences follow from this reformulation of the theory: First, both rules may be regarded as specific variants of the general transformation 'Move α'. They only differ in the phrasal type of the elements involved: either a lexical element – the head of a phrase – is being moved or an arbitrary phrasal constituent.

Second, in Thiersch's analysis, both rule (4) and rule (5) are adjunction rules. Accordingly, the intuition that some kind of dependency is established between the finite verb and the topicalized constituent cannot be captured in Thiersch's framework but must be stipulated independently. It *does* follow, however, from the GB-version of Thiersch's analysis that there is an inherent configurational dependency between the finite verb and the topicalized constituent, due to the fact that the finite verb occupies the head position of the C-projection of which the topicalized constituent is a specifier.[4]

Finally, since head movement is an instance of Move α, it is to be expected that it underlies the general restrictions on movement. In particular, it is predicted that verb gaps, being head gaps, must be antecedent-governed – because if they were not, an extraction of the head would always lead to a violation of the *Empty Category Principle* (ECP).[5] Chomsky's *Head Movement Constraint*, which is a theorem of the GB theory, makes explicit this generalization (cf. Chomsky 1986a):

(7)   *Head Movement Constraint* (HMC):
        Movement of a zero-level category β is restricted to the position of a head α that
        governs the maximal projection γ of β.

GB thus predicts, correctly, that a subordinated verb can never be moved out of a verbal chain over a maximally governing verb, because then it has to be moved across the maximal projection of its governor, as is indicated in (8). Hence the boundedness of verb movement is actually derived from the ECP.

(8)   a.   Peter wollte Claudia küssen
              Peter wanted-to Claudia kiss
        b. * Peter küssen Claudia wollte
           * Peter kiss Claudia wanted-to

During the discussion of non-transformational accounts in the following sections it should be kept in mind that any attempt which seriously tries to cope with verb order variations without resorting to transformational operations should be able to capture this generalization as well. The following categorial approaches, however, arrive at very different solutions pertaining to verb orders. Mainly, we find accounts given in terms of redundancy rules or lexical approaches. There has been only one approach which covers the generalization expressed in the *Head Movement Constraint*, viz. Jacobson's and Borsley's treatment of verb movement in terms of a deviant of the *slash* feature, the so-called *double slash* (DSL) (Jacobson 1987; Borsley 1989). Before turning to this treatment, however, we first take a look at accounts given within the categorial grammar framework.

---

[4]For a more detailed account of the relation between specifiers and heads in GB, see Fukui (Fukui 1986).

[5]Roughly, the ECP says that a trace must be either theta- or antecedent-governed. In GB Theory, theta-government means that the trace is a sister of a lexical head; antecedent-government on the other hand means that the antecedent of a trace c-commands this trace and there is no intervening possible governor which c-commands the trace but not the antecedent.

3   Introduction to CUG

Categorial Unification Grammar is a formalism that combines the central concepts of Categorial Grammar with the concept of unification (for a detailed introduction see, e.g., Uszkoreit 1986a or Zeevat et al. 1987). As far as its categorial component is concerned, the CUG variant employed in LILOG basically adheres to classical CG (Ajdukiewicz 1935; Bar-Hillel 1964).

An essential characteristic of CG is that its syntactic rule component is relatively small, whereas the lexicon is rich and complex. Besides the usual morphological information like case, gender, etc., each lexical entry carries detailed information about its syntactic behaviour, stating which elements it can combine with to render larger syntactic entities. The few syntactic combinatory rules merely carry out the combinations as specified in the lexicon.

Starting from a basic set of categories, which are syntactically inert (e.g., sentences (S) and noun phrases (NPs)), complex categories are built by the following condition: if X and Y are categories, then so is X/Y. A complex, or – in other terms – functor, category X/Y is to be read as a functor which combines with an argument of type Y to render a value of type X. Thus, S\NP would be the categorization for an intransitive verb, NP/N the one for a determiner. The LILOG grammar is based upon a directional categorial system, in which each functor category specifies whether its arguments are to be found to the right or to the left of the functor.[6] The argument as well as the value can be either a basic category or another functor category, hence, e.g., (S\NP)/NP for a transitive verb.

The rule of Functional Application, which divides into Left Application and Right Application, takes care of the actual combination of a functor with its arguments. A simple example will illustrate the basic idea. The lexical items *John* and *sleeps*, which are labeled 'NP' and 'S\NP' respectively, can be combined to form a sentence by the combinatory rule of Left Application.

(9)   Left Application:
      rule schema: B   A\B   →   A
      instantiation: NP   S\NP   →   S
                      John   sleeps →   John sleeps

An important principle of the LILOG-CG version is that – following, among others, Ades and Steedman (1982) – functor and argument must be directly adjacent to each other, otherwise the combinatory rules of Functional Application will not apply.

The grammar formalism STUF (Stuttgart Type Unification Formalism), developed within the LILOG project, belongs to the family of unification based grammar formalisms (see Shieber 1986 for an introduction). The central concepts of STUF are feature graphs and graph unification (cf. Bouma et al. 1988). STUF is flexible in that it not only allows for encoding CUG-based concepts but would also allow for developing phrase structure grammar concepts.

---

[6] The notation adopted here is that in a functor category the result, or value, will always appear on the left, followed by the slash indicating the position where the argument, which appears on the right, must be found. In a different notation value and argument are given in reversed order if a leftward oriented functor is specified (see, e.g., Bach et al. 1988).

4 Verb Movement in Extended CG

Being committed to a strictly lexicalist approach to grammar, neither classical CG nor CUG provide for such a device as 'movement'. Information pertaining to syntactic surface structure realizations is incorporated in a lexeme's functor-argument structure.

If one must deal with word-order variation in CG or CUG, the only option one has is to enrich the lexicon with disjunctive entries for the appropriate lexemes. For a language such as German, however, which allows for relatively free insertion of optional arguments, and where, furthermore, in V-2 declaratives any constituent – including complex verbal clusters – may be topicalized, this would entail an enormous expansion of the base lexicon, which is undesirable in itself. But moreover, this brute-force method of course fails to capture any generalization concerning the different verb positions.

It is clear, therefore, that the basic categorial scheme must be extended in some way or other. In this section we shall discuss a number of proposals for extending classical CG in order to deal with variations of word order, in particular with variable positioning of the finite verb. The discussion leads up to the treatment of word order that was implemented in the first LILOG prototype, and in the presentation of the alternative proposals we shall focus, on the one hand, on the problems that motivated us to adopt our own approach, and, on the other hand, on the aspects that were taken over into the LILOG version of CG.

4.1 Ades and Steedman

Among the first to explicitly discuss the relation of the finite verb to other constituents were Ades and Steedman (Ades, Steedman 1982). Ades and Steedman are mainly concerned with the positioning of the finite verb in English. Via a number of operations, which should not concern us here, they arrive at the following categorization for the tensed verb in V-1 and V-2 constructions, which are the only possible constructions in English:[7]

(10)   Finite verb: $S\$|NP_S$

Ades and Steedman's is a non-directional system, which is indicated by the use of vertical lines in the notation of functor categories. The rules of Left Application or Right Application combine two categories as usual, the only difference with a directional system being that the functor category does not prescribe which rule should apply in any given case. A non-directional approach, such as Ades and Steedman's, has several advantages. One is that one can achieve a higher level of generalization in describing linguistic regularities. For instance, the category that Ades and Steedman assign to the tensed verb nicely captures the fact that in English the subject NP will always be found directly adjacent to the tensed verb,[8] either to its right or to its left, depending on the type of sentence. This is also true for German (given normal word order): in a V-2 sentence either the subject NP has been moved to the initial field, or – in case another constituent has been topicalized – the subject remains in the middle field, occupying its canonical position, which, according to given word order

---

[7] The symbol '$\$$' is a variable standing for the canonical order of the remaining arguments, depending on the valency of the verb. 'NP$_S$', 'NP$_O$', and 'NP$_{IO}$' stand for 'subject noun phrase', 'direct object noun phrase', and 'indirect object noun phrase', respectively.

[8] This, of course, is modulo intervening adverbs modifying the verb.

constellations, is the leftmost one. In either case the subject NP and the tensed verb are immediately adjacent to one another. In a V-1 sentence no constituent has been topicalized. Thus the subject remains in its original MF position, and again subject and finite verb are directly adjacent.

If we wanted to capture these observations we could introduce the unary rule in (11), which is unlike the binary combination schemata of Left Application and Right Application in that it is simply a category-changing rule. This rule would take a V-F category as input and render as result a category à la Ades and Steedman. For transitive verbs such a rule would look like this:

(11)   Verb Rule: $(S\backslash NP_S)\backslash NP_O \rightarrow (S|NP_O)|NP_S$

This new category would permit the derivation both of V-1 and of V-2 sentences:

(12)

```
          Liebt        Johann       Maria?
          (Loves       Johann       Maria?)
          (S|NPo)|NPs   NPs          NPo
          ----------------------- RA
              S|NPo
          ------------------------------------- RA
                        S
```

(13)

```
          Johann       liebt        Maria.
          (Johann      loves        Maria.)
          NPs          (S|NPo)|NPs   NPo
          ------------------------- LA
              (S|NPo)
          ------------------------------------- RA
                        S
```

However, non-directional categorial systems have serious drawbacks. In such a CG, in principle, at each step in the derivation the parser has the choice of applying either Left or Right Application. This by itself suffices to slow down the parsing process significantly. [9]

Note, incidentally, that if we wanted to implement Ades and Steedman's proposal in a directional system, we would arrive at a version of CG as sketched in the introduction to this section. That is, in such a system each of the possible word orders would be encoded into the lexical entries of finite verbs. Considering the possibility of unlimited insertion of optional arguments, each one in turn giving rise to further complex fronting constructions, this could amount to a possibly infinite set of categorizations in the worst case.

---

[9] In later work Steedman gives up on non-directionality – partly for the reasons mentioned here, partly on the basis of further linguistic considerations.

4.2 Hepple

Hepple's proposals for V-2 phenomena in Dutch and English are not designed predominantly for a grammatical system in the sense of the above CG version, but rather within the setting of 'logic as grammar' (Hepple 1990b). His aim is to extend the frame of the Lambek Calculus by appropriate operations to grasp the word-order phenomena characteristic for Dutch and English. Hepple's system is based on a categorial lexicon and strings are analyzed via a flexible grammar calculus.

Though the derivational systems differ it is still worthwhile to ask whether Hepple's proposals, translated into a directional CG framework, would be suitable for the LILOG grammar. Our main concern therefore is with Hepple's treatment of Dutch verb phrases, because of the similarities to German.

Within his system Hepple presents one general verb movement rule for both V-1 and V-2 sentences, which translates into the LILOG-CUG as two distinct rules, according to the sentence type. If a finite verb occurs in a V-2 sentence the simulation of the verb movement amounts to type raising[10] this verb, irrespective of its valency, over an intransitive verb. If a finite verb occurs in V-1 constructions it will be raised over 'S'.

(14) a. V-2 movement rule:
$$(S \backslash NP_S) \backslash NP_O \rightarrow (S \backslash NP_S)/((S \backslash NP_S)/((S \backslash NP_S) \backslash NP_O))$$
    b. V-1 movement rule:
$$(S \backslash NP_S) \backslash NP_O \rightarrow S/(S/((S \backslash NP_S) \backslash NP_O))$$

Hepple also type raises the subject as well as the direct and indirect object:

(15) a. Type Raising subject (TR_S):
$$NP_S \rightarrow S/(S \backslash NP_S)$$
    b. Type Raising direct object (TR_O):
$$NP_O \rightarrow (S \backslash NP_S)/((S \backslash NP_S) \backslash NP_O)$$
    c. Type Raising indirect object (TR_{IO}):
$$NP_{IO} \rightarrow ((S \backslash NP_S) \backslash NP_O)/(((S \backslash NP_S) \backslash NP_O) \backslash NP_{IO})$$

Type raising of all of the arguments is needed, since the raised verb category cannot combine with simple NPs. During an analysis, arguments to the right of the finite verb are combined first. The raised verb, being the main functor of the sentence, will take this combination as its argument. This is best illustrated with a V-1 sentence:[11]

---

[10]The operations of Type Raising and Functional Composition, which will be introduced below, rest upon the notions developed by (Curry et al. 1958) in their combinatory logic.

[11]We leave aside V-2 sentences here, since this would involve the discussion of Hepple's problematic generalized type raising operation for topicalized phrases, which is not directly relevant for the present discussion.

(16)

$$
\begin{array}{ccc}
\text{Kent} & \text{Jan} & \text{dit boek?} \\
\text{(Knows} & \text{Jan} & \text{this book?)} \\
\text{S/S/((S\NPs)\NPo)} & \text{NPs} & \text{NPo}
\end{array}
$$

$$
\begin{array}{cc}
\Downarrow \text{ TR--s} & \Downarrow \text{ TR--o} \\
\text{S/(S\NP)} & \text{(S\NPs)/((S\NPs)\NPo)}
\end{array}
$$

$$
\underline{\hspace{10cm}} \text{ FFC}
$$

$$
\text{S/((S\NPs)\NPo)}
$$

$$
\underline{\hspace{10cm}} \text{ RA}
$$

$$
\text{S}
$$

To combine the arguments *Jan* and *dit boek* the operation of 'Forward Functional Composition' (FFC) is used. The general rule schema is:

(17) Forward Functional Composition (FFC): A/B B/C → A/C

Would Hepple's approach be suitable for the LILOG environment? The answer is no. For a system which does not rely on a calculus such as Hepple's the operation of Type Raising together with Functional Composition can introduce many unwanted effects. The number of derivations increases considerably, in that one and the same input string could be analysed structurally in several different ways, but all with identical semantic results. These so-called 'spurious ambiguities' are insignificant from a linguistic point of view, but evidently they have serious impacts on the efficiency of the parsing process.[12] So, neither Type Raising nor any type of Functional Composition (there are four kinds all together) are part of the chosen CUG version. Hence, neither of Hepple's proposals has been adopted.[13]

4.3 Hoeksema

Hepple shows that his approach to verbal regularities in Dutch entails the one taken by (Hoeksema 1985). Hepple, therefore, introduces into his proof system a category-changing rule to change his verb forms into Hoeksema's, for alternatively using either form. Hoeksema does not employ type-raising rules in his account of verb movement phenomena; i.e., he type-raises neither the finite verb nor any of the involved arguments. His rules more closely resemble the category-changing rules found with Ades and Steedman:

(18) Verb-Second Rule:
$$S\backslash X_1 \ldots X_n \rightarrow (S/X_n \ldots X_{i+1} X_{i-1} \ldots X_1)\backslash X_i$$

---

[12]See, e.g., (Wittenburg 1987) and (Wesche 1989) for detailed discussions of the various aspects of the 'spurious ambiguity' problem.

[13]It should be noted that in subsequent work Hepple abandons the approach of also type-raising the arguments. Instead he choses a natural deduction formulation of the Lambek Calculus, employing (slash) introduction rules (Hepple 1990a). See also König (this volume) for a discussion of this topic.

The leftward looking basic verb category is changed into a rightward looking one displaying the reversed order of the respective arguments except for an arbitrary topicalized argument which must be found to the left of the finite verb. This rule nicely captures the generalization that any of a verb's arguments can be fronted. Unfortunately, however, it carries over neither to optional arguments nor to complex fronting constructions.

Hoeksema does not explicitly state a V-1 rule, since it is contained in his V-2 rule. Still, a V-1 rule for his system could be singled out as:

(19)   Verb-First Rule:
        $S \backslash X_1 \ ..... \ X_n \to S / \ X_n \ ..... \ X_1$

A direct adaptation of Hoeksema's approach for the LILOG framework is not feasible. This is mainly due to the chosen configuration of the underlying grammar formalism STUF on the one hand together with parsing strategies on the other. With STUF there is no possibility of expressing such an 'if-then' relation as implied in Hoeksema's rule: X_1 can be any constituent; if it is a category of type A, the whole verb category will be instantiated accordingly; if it is B we will get a different result, etc. In the LILOG-CUG each variant would need to be encoded explicitly. And again – this would amount to a possibly infinite set of lexical categorizations for verbal entries in the worst case.

4.4   The LILOG Approach

In order to give a uniform account of topicalization – or, in other words, long distance dependencies in general – we have chosen to introduce a rule device, termed Gap Introduction (GI) and Gap Elimination (GE)[14]. With these rules not only can we keep the lexicon free from overabundant entries, but we can also account for the German word order regularities in terms of topological fields in a quite straightforward way. This device equally handles any type of fronting in declarative sentences, as well as wh-fronting in questions. In designing this gap mechanism we have made explicit use of CUG's unique representation of linguistic information in terms of feature structures.[15]

As with the accounts for Dutch verb regularities discussed in the previous section, in the LILOG lexicon every verb is encoded as verb-final, allowing for the direct analysis of subordinate clauses via successive application of Left Application. A unary rule changes the governing direction of the verb from left to right, simulating the fronting from the right to the left verbal bracket. A verb category thus changed triggers V-1 structures. For a transitive verb the unary rule would operate as follows:

(20)   V-1 rule:
        e.g.: $(S \backslash NP_S) \backslash NP_O \ \to \ (S/NP_O)/NP_S$

This change of a finite verb functor's direction is analogous to the Verb-First Rule à la Hoeksema, which in turn resembles Ades and Steedman's non-directional verb category. For deriving V-2 sentences the device of Gap Introduction and Gap Elimination comes into play. The operation

---

[14]Here we have drawn upon insights gained with the slash-mechanism employed in the Generalized Phrase Structure Grammar (Gazdar et al. 1985).

[15]This gap handling device will, roughly, also be adopted for handling V-2 constructions within the subsequent prototype (see Sect. 4.7 of this paper).

of Gap Introduction again is a unary rule, taking a V-1 category as input. Via Gap Introduction the information pertaining to the fronted constituent, which will be missing in its expected MF position, will be set into a feature structure headed by the attribute 'gap':

(21) Gap Introduction:

$$\text{e.g.:} \quad (S/NP_0)/NP_S \quad \rightarrow \quad \begin{array}{c} S/NP_0 \\ [gap : NP_S] \end{array}$$

Right Application can then proceed as usual, while a special gap-threading mechanism will guarantee the percolation of the gap feature. When reaching the final S-value, which still contains the gap feature, the rule of Gap Elimination applies:

(22) Gap Elimination:

	Argument	Functor	$\rightarrow$	Value
	X	S	$\rightarrow$	S
	$[[gap : X][vpos : first]]$			$[vpos : second]$

Example (23) represents a simplified sample parse of the sentence *Clara erzählt eine Geschichte* ('Clara tells a story') to illustrate the described treatment.

(23)

```
        Clara       erzählt         eine  Geschichte.
        NPs       (S\NPs)\NPo              NPo
                      \||/ V–1 rule
                       \/

                  (S/NPo)/NPs
                      \||/ Gap Introduction
                       \/

                   (S/NPo)
                   [gap: NPs]
        – – – – – – – – – – – – – – – – – – – – – – – –  RA
                       S
                   [gap: NPs]
        – – – – – – – – – – – – – – – – – – – – – – –  Gap Elimination
                       S
```

This treatment of V-2 phenomena also is like Hoeksema's. But it differs in one respect. What Hoeksema combines into a single rule is divided into two distinct steps in the LILOG approach. Each V-2 sentence is analyzed by first construing a V-1 structure, and then applying the gap mechanism for determining the topicalized constituent. Thus the simulation of the two fronting processes (finite verb and fronted constituent) is handled in situ, rather than approaching this twofold procedure in a single account. Thus a higher flexibility in treating the fronting to the initial field is achieved, accounting for all types of topicalization.[16] We do not need to encode countless disjunctions for

---

[16]In the lexicon only obligatory arguments are encoded with each verb. If an optional argument, such as a locative

verbal items, according to possible word order variations, thereby missing important generalizations pertaining to finite verb positioning in general. The device of Gap Introduction and Gap Elimination accounts for the various topicalization phenomena in a principled way. Furthermore, one of the most important advantages of this device lies in the fact that we do not encounter any spuriously ambiguous analyses with respect to the overall sentence structure. In contrast to a derivational system referring to the operations of Type Raising and Functional Composition, with Gap Introduction and Gap Elimination the analysis of a given V-2 construction will render a unique syntactic structure.

In one important respect, however, the treatment of V-1 and V-2 phenomena sketched in this section remains problematic. One objection to be raised against it is that the MF is restructured in the derivation of V-1 and V-2 sentences. Thereby one commits oneself to the assumption that scope relations – and interpretations – in the MF of V-1 and V-2 sentences are different from scope relations in V-F sentences, a view which evidently is inappropriate, as (24) indicates:

(24) a. darum heiraten die meisten Frauen mehr als einen Mann
         (therefore marry most women more than one man)
     b. weil die meisten Frauen mehr als einen Mann heiraten
         (because most women more than one man marry)

In both (24a.) and (24b.) the subject 'die meisten Frauen' has wide scope over the object 'mehr als einen Mann'. But in (24a.) the object c-commands the subject, thereby implying that the latter is in the scope of the former, because in restoring the canonical word order after application of the verb-first rule (21) it is necessary for subject and object to interchange their configurational positions.[17] Other objections against a derivation of V-1 and V-2 in terms of functor changing rules as sketched in (4.4) could be raised as well but are not mentioned here due to space limitations.[18]

As a consequence of these considerations, we decided to change the grammar formalism from pure categorial grammar (enriched by unification) to an approach in which the interesting

---

adverb, is involved in the fronting process, a slightly modified version of the account just presented comes into play. So, the device of Gap Introduction and Gap Elimination, in general, is maintained to account for all types of topicalization. We have to admit, however, that the instantiation of this device in case of topicalized optional arguments does not represent a principled account, but must be viewed as a purely descriptional one, manipulating the respective feature structures according to given conditions. See also the arguments raised below.

[17]C-command is a relation between nodes in a tree. A node A c-commands a node B if neither A nor B dominates each other and every node which dominates A dominates B as well.
C-command (first formulated by Reinhart (Reinhart 1983) to cover the local domains of anaphora in syntactic terms) is a necessary prerequisite for the determination of scope and binding relations between nominals. To give a short example, due to c-command it is predicted that the pronoun 'he' cannot be construed as coreferential with the proper noun 'John' in (i), because c-command holds between 'he' and 'John' whereas a coreferential construal between 'his' and 'John' actually is possible in (ii), where no c-command relationship holds:

(i) he likes John

(ii) his mother likes John

Pertaining to scope relationships it is generally assumed that if quantifier A c-commands quantifier B then A has scope over B.

[18]Among those are two prominent and and interconnected questions concerning adjunct treatment. First, Gap-Introduction cannot be used to cover adjuncts in a CG in a principled way, because adjuncts are not arguments of a verb. This leads to a stipulative solution of topicalization cases depending on whether the topicalized constituent is characterized as argument or as adjunct. Secondly, one and the same PP has to be categorized in multiple ways to permit its realization as argument, adjunct or (in cases of adjunction) topicalized element. Obviously, this is not preferable.

generalizations and neat mechanisms of CG are captured as well but in which such problematic aspects as the one sketched above are eliminated. Our choice in this was HPSG, an eclectic approach, descending – and borrowing – from both phrase structure and categorial grammars. Interestingly, to our knowledge, in its treatment of V-2 phenomena, HPSG is the only approach which covers the generalizations expressed in the *Head Movement Constraint*.

Before this treatment can be developed, however, it is necessary to introduce the framework in which our latest solution to verb order variants is embedded, Head Driven Phrase Structure Grammar.

4.5   Introduction to HPSG

In many respects, HPSG (Pollard, Sag 1987; Pollard 1989) is a further development out of GPSG (Gazdar et al. 1985). This is evidenced by, e.g., the feature structures that the former borrows from the latter as well as by a basic assumption which HPSG shares with GPSG, viz. that hierarchical relations and constraints on word order should be treated by different sets of rules. But apart from this, HPSG has been influenced by many other grammar theories and formalisms as well. Thus, for instance, HPSG includes as one of its components a further development of Chomsky's Binding theory (Chomsky 1981; Chomsky 1986b), based on grammatical functions.

With CG – as introduced in the previous sections – HPSG shares the assumption that lexemes – or signs in general – should be encoded as functors, in the sense that the combinatorial potential of a lexeme can be gleaned from its encoding in the lexicon. A further commonality between HPSG and CG concerns the number of grammar rules that both frameworks require. As established in Sect. 3, CG can manage with a handful of rules at most since it encodes most of the combinatorial information of the grammar directly in the lexicon. The same applies to HPSG.[19] In HPSG, many regularities are encoded into lexical heads, which renders superfluous a great number of specific rules that otherwise would be called for. Besides the lexicon, syntactic knowledge is distributed by two other components, a restricted set of rule schemata and a restricted set of general principles governing feature percolation and identity.

To explain the structure of the lexical entries and their intricate interactions with the other components of the grammar, the best strategy is to present a 'full blown' feature structure of a lexeme and then proceed to explain the substructures of this sign, thereby introducing rule schemata as well as principles.

(25)   Structure of 'unternahm' (undertook, did):

$$\begin{bmatrix} \text{SYNTAX} & : & \begin{bmatrix} \text{LOCAL} & : & \begin{bmatrix} \text{SUBCAT} & : & \langle \text{NP[AKK]}, \text{NP[NOM]} \rangle \\ \text{HEAD} & : & \begin{bmatrix} \text{VFORM} & : & \text{FIN} \\ \text{MAJOR} & : & \text{V} \end{bmatrix} \\ \text{LEX} & : & + \end{bmatrix} \\ \text{BINDING} & : & \begin{bmatrix} \text{SLASH} & : & \langle \rangle \\ \text{INDEX} & : & \begin{bmatrix} \text{NUM} & : & ... \\ \text{PERS} & : & ... \end{bmatrix} \end{bmatrix} \end{bmatrix} \end{bmatrix}$$

The first important distinction made in the structure of (25) is between the feature groups

---

[19] As will be explained in greater detail below, in distinction to CG, from the encoding of the combinatorial potential of a sign in HPSG the categoryhood of this sign cannot be predicted.

LOCAL and BINDING. In general, LOCAL features are features which have to be realized in a strict domain, notably, in the domain of the maximal projection of the head involved. This means that the categorial information of a sign as well as its combinatorial potential must be realized – in one way or another – inside this domain, or to put it the other way round: LOCAL information cannot influence other projections protected by a maximal constituent.

BINDING features on the other hand *can* percolate across the boundaries of a maximal projection. An example is given in (26). Here the reflexive pronoun *himself* is 'protected' by the PP but nevertheless agrees with the subject of the sentence.

(26)   He$_i$ muttered [$_{PP}$ to himself$_i$/*herself$_i$] that John was mad.

This explains, why in our variant of HPSG agreement features are not treated as HEAD (and ultimately as *LOCAL*) features. The other member of the BINDING group, SLASH, will be discussed in greater detail below, so it should not concern us here. However, it should be mentioned that – due to the fact that the sign described is a lexeme – SLASH has the empty list as its value. Naturally, in the course of derivation this list can be filled.

In the LOCAL attribute there is a threefold distinction between HEAD, SUBCAT and LEX attributes, respectively. The SUBCAT attribute, which is list-valued, stores the syntactic valency of a sign. The close connection to categorial approaches is obvious here. But – and this should be kept in mind – the SUBCAT attribute *only* stores the valency of a sign, and the valency does not make any predictions about the sign's categorial membership. Information pertaining to the categoryhood of a sign is encoded in the HEAD features.

The HEAD features given in (25) state that the object described belongs to the class of finite verbs (MAJOR: V, VFORM: FIN). Obviously, VFORM as a head feature is not attached to every lexeme – it would not be an appropriate desription for a nominal sign. Therefore, in nominal categories, indicated by (MAJOR: N), VFORM is replaced by NFORM, and CASE is used as an additional feature.[20]

Finally, the LEX feature states whether the object described is lexical, as in (25), or phrasal. Thus, the LEX feature can be viewed as a minimal integration of the well known X'-scheme into HPSG.

Except for mentioning the SUBCAT attribut, nothing about the actual combination of lexemes and phrases – the main task of a syntax – has been said. As mentioned before, with respect to the number of combination rules HPSG more resembles CG than GPSG, for it proposes only a few rule schemata, the most prominent of which are the COMPLEMENTATION (27) and ADJUNCTION (28) rule schemes.[21]

(27)   Complementation Rule:
         X[SUBCAT⟨M⟩, LEX −] → X[SUBCAT⟨N⟩], C

---

[20] The fact that different kinds of feature are appropriate to describe different types of objects is incorporated into 'pure' HPSG by the use of sortal information. In the LILOG grammar currently under development this step is not taken, so partiality has been given up in parts of the grammar. In future versions, however, feature structures will be fully typed through sortal information.

[21] Very similar rules have been proposed by Gunji (Gunji 1987) for Japanese – a fact we learned about after the basic tenets of our grammar architecture had been decided upon.

(28)   Adjunction Rule:
         X[SUBCAT⟨M⟩, LEX −] → X[SUBCAT⟨M⟩], ADJ

These rules are to be read as general constraints on feature structures.[22] In this respect, rule (27) can be construed as implying that a sign which has a non-empty SUBCAT attribute can combine with another sign which is an element of this list to become a phrasal sign with a SUBCAT list *different* from the original one. Rule (28) on the other hand states that a sign can combine with an adjunct, thereby yielding another sign with the *same* SUBCAT attribute.

These two rules are fairly general, and in fact they are *too* general as they stand. So – in their crude definition given above – nothing in (27) or (28) prohibits an NP becoming the mother of a V plus complement and nothing in (27) guarantees that the number and kind of realized complements unify with the number and kind of elements on the SUBCAT list, respectively.

Of course, encoding directly into the rules the information that mother and head in a given projection should be of the same category, as well as that a complement must be token-identical to an element of the SUBCAT list, would lead to a loss of generality.[23] Therefore, instead of proceeding like this, HPSG proposes so-called *principles*, which can be interpreted as general constraints on feature structures. One principle, the so-called *Head Feature Principle*, guarantees that mother and head daughter in a given projection belong to the same category. An informal but complete statement of this principle is the following:

(29)   *Head Feature Principle:*
         The head features of mother and daughter must agree.

A second principle, which requires matching between the complements and kind and number of the elements on the SUBCAT list, is the *Subcategorization Principle*:

(30)   *Subcategorization Principle*:
         A member of the subcat list of a daughter which does not belong to the subcat
         list of the mother must be realized as a sister of the daughter.

As mentioned earlier, apart from the LOCAL features, there are features that can percolate freely until they become bound via rule stipulation. For instance, the feature SLASH – which was actually taken over from GPSG[24] – indicates that a phrase contains a daughter that dominates an empty element or (as we prefer to call it) a trace.

(31) $\left[\text{SYNTAX} : \left[\begin{array}{ll} \text{LOCAL} & : [1] \\ \text{BINDING} & : [\text{SLASH} : [1]] \end{array} \right] \right]$

In HPSG, SLASH has as its values a set of LOCAL features. In the following, however, we shall restrict our attention to single-valued SLASH features. As a second major departure from

---

[22]Actually these rules are signs in themselves (cf. Pollard and Sag 1987, chap. 6).

[23]This would lead to a re-invention of the lexical Immediate Dominance rules utilized in GPSG, i.e., no real progress would be evidenced in HPSG.

[24]However, this feature in GPSG takes a syntactic category as its value, whereas in HPSG it takes a LOCAL structure as its value. This is so because we believe that any information which can be shared between a filler and a gap can be captured in the LOCAL attribute.

GPSG, HPSG does not treat gaps with the help of metarules. Instead, traces, which merely specify that their LOCAL value equals SLASH, are treated as lexical elements. The actual LOCAL value of a trace is then determined by unifying it (and, in consequence, its SLASH value) with an element in the SUBCAT list of a head. We cannot go into exact detail here on the introduction of SLASHes. It suffices to note here that the *Slash Inheritance Principle* sees to it that a SLASH percolates upwards until it is bound. For present purposes it can be assumed that SLASHes are introduced along the lines sketched in the section on gap treatment in Categorial Unification Grammar.[25]

The binding of SLASHes is accomplished by the rule (32), which fairly much resembles the complementation scheme except for the fact that the 'argument' is an element of the SLASH- and not of the SUBCAT-list of the mother.

(32)   Slash Binding Rule:
$$X[\text{SLASH}: \langle\rangle] \rightarrow Y, X[\text{SLASH}: \langle Y\rangle]$$

The derivation (36) – shown on the following page – of a verb-final sentence illustrates how the rule schemata and principles discussed control feature percolation and binding.

In addition to the SYNTAX attribute introduced in (25), HPSG establishes a special attribute called DTRS (daughters), which is split up into COMP-DTR and HEAD-DTR (33). Thereby, it is possible to encode the phrase structure representation of a given sign as part of the feature structure of this sign.

(33)
$$\begin{bmatrix} \text{SYNTAX} & : & \ldots \\ \text{DTRS} & : & \begin{bmatrix} \text{COMP} - \text{DTR} & : & \ldots \\ \text{HEAD} - \text{DTR} & : & \ldots \end{bmatrix} \end{bmatrix}$$

Another major advantage of this is that the principles sketched informally above can be formulated precisely via recourse to the DTRS-structures build up:

(34)   *Head Feature Principle*:
$$\begin{bmatrix} \text{SYNTAX} & : & \text{LOCAL|HEAD} : [1] \\ \text{DTRS} & : & \text{HEAD} - \text{DTR|SYNTAX|LOCAL|HEAD} : [1] \end{bmatrix}$$

(35)   *Subcategorization Principle*:
$$\begin{bmatrix} \text{SYNTAX} & : & \text{LOCAL|SUBCAT} : [2] \\ \text{DTRS} & : & \begin{bmatrix} \text{HEAD} - \text{DTR} & : & \text{SYN|LOC|SUBCAT} : \text{append}([1],[2]) \\ \text{COMP} - \text{DTR} & : & [1] \end{bmatrix} \end{bmatrix}$$

---

[25]It is obvious, however, that there must be some kind of constraint on the introduction of traces. In GPSG, this task is accomplished by the lexical head constraint, which states that metarules can only apply to ID-rules that introduce lexical heads. Therefore SLASHes (i.e., traces) which are introduced solely by metarules must always be sisters of lexical heads and are properly governed as such.

(36)

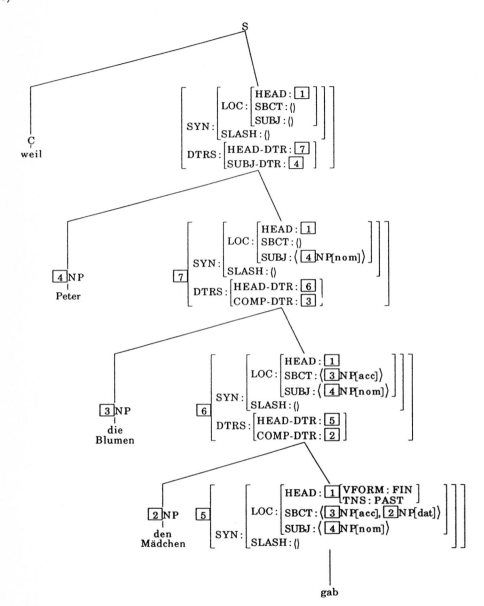

4.6 Deriving German Word Order

As in GPSG, hierarchical relations are encoded in HPSG by *Immediate Dominance* (ID) Rules, illustrated in (27), (28), and (32). The linear order of segments, on the other hand, is determined by *Linear Precedence* (LP) Rules. Following the proposals by Uszkoreit (Uszkoreit 1986b), German word order phenomena can be treated by the LP Rules in (37), the rule schema in (38)[26], and the topicalization rule in (32):

(37) a) $V[+INV] \prec X$
b) $X \prec V[- INV]$

(38) $V[SUBCAT\langle\rangle] \rightarrow V[SUBCAT\langle M\rangle], C*$

These rules make the correct predictions about possible verb positions in German:

(39) a. ..., weil Hans ein Boot kauft
..., because Hans a boat buys
b. Kauft Hans ein Boot?
Buys Hans a boat?
c. Hans kauft ein Boot
Hans buys a boat

However, as Uszkoreit notices, this description is not without its problems. For instance, under the assumption that all arguments and adjuncts to the verb are dominated by one and the same node, it is impossible to arrive at a principled description of complex-fronting phenomena.[27]

(40) a. Unbemerkt seine Brieftasche stehlen kannst Du Peter nur in der Oper.
Unnoticed his wallet steal can you Peter only in the opera.
b. Seine Brieftasche stehlen kannst du Peter nur in der Oper unbemerkt.
His wallet steal can you Peter only in the opera unnoticed.
c. Stehlen kannst Du Peter seine Brieftasche nur in der Oper unbemerkt
Steal can you Peter his wallet only in the opera unnoticed.
you can steal Peter's wallet unnoticed only in the opera.

(41) * nachher dem Peter die Schokolade geben kann ich
* later on to Peter the chocolate give can I

The topicalized constituents in (40a–c) could of course be accounted for by assuming that more than one constituent can be topicalized in German.[28] But then it remains to explain why the examples in (41), in which two constituents are fronted, are ungrammatical.

---

[26]It should be noted that (38) is just an extension of (27) in which the number of COMP-DTRs is not limited and the SUBCAT value of the mother is set to the empty list.

[27]Of course, one could stipulate that in German more than one phrase may be topicalized. But this only defers the problem, because we would have to explain why this is possible in one context only.

[28]Another solution suggests itself in terms of a general raising rule, in which arguments which are not realized inside the domain of the lower VP are 'raised' – in the sense used in transformational grammar, not in CG – into the SUBCAT list of a governing verb (cf. Hinrichs, Nakazawa 1990; Pollard 1990).

A more felicitous solution suggests itself in terms of a binary branching structure (e.g., as assumed by Nerbonne (Nerbonne 1985)). If we assume that the embedded VP in (40) has a binary branching structure, we obtain a nice explanation of the contrast between (40) and (41) without giving up the generalization that German allows for topicalizing a single element only.

However, if we follow this strategy, the method for regimenting verb order with the help of LP Rules collapses, because the arguments to the verb are no longer dominated exclusively by the direct projection of the verb.[29]

4.7 Verb Movement in HPSG

In the light of the results sketched in the previous section, a treatment of the variants of German verb order by a mechanism which simulates movement seems to be more fruitful than a treatment which focuses primarily on LP rules. At the same time, it should be kept in mind that head movement is constrained by principles differing from the ones usually at work in phrasal movement – especially, it must be ascertained that head movement, in contrast to phrasal movement, never crosses the boundaries of a sentence.

As we have seen in Sect. 2, this boundedness of head movement is a consequence of the *Head Movement Constraint* – a theorem following from the assumption that empty elements have to be licensed in appropriate ways. Therefore, we should attempt to capture the generalizations behind this phenomenon without taking recourse to additional stipulations.

The first unification-based approach to head movement that we are aware of stems from Jacobson (Jacobson 1987). She incorporates the notion of (bounded) head movement into the framework of GPSG to give a principled account of the notorious verb-particle construction in English as well as for the discontinuity of the transitive VP in a context-free grammar. To treat the differences between head and phrasal movement, Jacobson introduces a special feature called DOUBLE SLASH (DSL), which is used to describe all kinds of bounded dependency phenomena. That DSL-percolation (i.e., movement) is indeed bounded is accounted for by the following condition:[30]

(42)   *Bounding Condition*
         If A (the mother) has the feature DSL, then at most one daughter B_i has the
         same feature (with the same value), where B_i is not a bounding node and B_i is
         not [NULL].

In Jacobson's proposal, all categories which can serve as arguments – especially S' and VP' – are to be treated as bounding nodes. Although we cannot go into detail here, it should be noted that (42) is a kind of additional stipulation which does not follow automatically from the theoretical premises of GPSG. In this respect its status can be compared to, e.g., Gazdar's original *Left Branch Condition*, which in Gazdar's version of GPSG (Gazdar 1981) had to be stipulated. But it follows automatically from the treatment of SLASH as a HEAD as well as a FOOT feature in the GPSG version of 1985 (Gazdar et al. 1985).

---

[29]It should be noted in passing that the lexicalization of word order – as proposed, e.g., by Uszkoreit (Uszkoreit 1987) – does not avoid this problem either, because lexicalization in Uszkoreit's terms always implies that the elements regimented thereby are dependent on another lexical element. It is easy to see that this cannot be carried over to verbs.

[30]The additional clause for a possible [NULL]-value of the bounding node accounts for the fact that a node loses its bounding characteristics if it exclusively dominates the trace, viz. if it is the sole root of the DSL-dependency.

Towards this goal, a major improvement of Jacobson's analysis is presented by Borsley (Borsley 1989). Borsley tries to give an account of inverted sentences in English without resorting to a mechanism analogous to the *Subject Auxiliary Inversion Metarule* introduced by Pollard and Sag (1987), here shown in (43). This rule very much resembles Uszkoreit's rule of licensing a flat clause structure, the only difference in English being that the verb is initial in its (flat) phrase.

(43)   X[SUBCAT⟨⟩] → X[SUBCAT⟨...⟩, INV +], C*

In agreement with Jacobson, Borsley also bases his treatment of verb movement on a DSL feature. His main idea is that verb movement involves a kind of process comparable to type-raising in CG.[31] Adopting Borsley's assumptions for our LILOG grammar we propose a lexical rule, shown in (45), which changes finite verbs into (raised) finite verbs which take their verbal projections (modulo the double-slashed head) as arguments. This amounts to assuming that DSLs like SLASHes are special elements in the lexicon, as sketched in (44). The rule in (45), then, also accounts for the correct instantiation of the LOCAL features of the DSL.

(44) $\left[\text{SYNTAX} : \left[\begin{array}{ll} \text{LOCAL} & : [1] \\ \text{BINDING} & : \left[\text{DSL} : [1] \right] \end{array} \right] \right]$

(45)   V[LOCAL [1]] → V[SUBCAT⟨V[DSL [1]] ⟩]

As can be seen by (45), the only possibility to license a combination of a raised verb with a S[DSL: V][32] is actually by this rule, which demands that the raised verb and its subcategorized for 'headless' argument are token identical. So movement across the boundaries of a projection of a finite verb is blocked by the grammar without resorting to additional stipulations such as Jacobson's bounding condition, given in (42).

With the introduction of rule(45) we are in a position to explain the different sentence patterns occuring in German without any manipulation of the MF. To this end, we first propose the following LP-statement (46), which informally says that a category which has a non-null DSL attribute is preceded by all other phrasal categories. Thereby we are predicting that the verb (although sometimes realized as a trace) always stays in the final position.[33]

(46)   XP ≺ X[DSL: ⟨...⟩]

In a sense, rule (46) is a twofold generalization of Uszkoreit's pair of rules introduced in (37): First, no additional rules have to be stated to keep track of verbs in initial position (which are marked as [+ INV] in Uszkoreit's proposal), and second, the stipulation that all arguments of the main verb are dominated by the same node can be given up if we assume that DSL percolates just like SLASH through the mediation of the *Slash Inheritance Principle*. The necessity for another LP-statement which covers V-1 and V-2 occurences simply does not arise. The fact that the raised verb always precedes its verbal complement projection also can be subsumed under (46).

---

[31] The assumption that type-raising of verbs does not lead to the problematic aspects sketched in Sect. 2, has been taken up in recent work in CG as well (cf. Hepple 1990a).

[32] Where 'DSL: V' abbreviates X[DSL: some local structure].

[33] Naturally, an additional rule can be given which forces finite and non-finite verb to stay behind if the verb is not double-slashed.

V-F and V-1 sentences, then, are generated by the rules introduced so far without any additional stipulation. And obviously, due to the introduction of unbounded SLASHes and the necessity that these have to percolate from daughter to mother until they become bound, the derivation of V-2 sentences does not pose any problem for our framework, as can be seen in (49).[34] – shown on the following page.

Coming towards the end of this paper, some problematic aspects of this analysis should be pointed out. First, in its present version, it remains unexplained why finite verbs and subordinate complementizers like *dass* are distributed complementarily in German as shown in (47a,b).

(47) a. * kommt daß Peter nach Hause
          (* comes that Peter home)
      b. * daß kommt Peter nach Hause
          (* that comes Peter home)

In our model, the distribution exemplified above could be enforced if verbs which are raised by (45) are associated with a special HEAD feature which is incompatible with the subcategorization requirements of a complementizer, and if complementizers, just like raised verbs, were analyzed as elements that subcategorize for a sentence. Obviously, this would lead to a number of additional constraints and/or artificial HEAD features, which would altogether diminish the overall elegance of the theory. Moreover, incorporating such conditions on subcategorization would entail that complementizers must be marked as elements requiring that their complements do not inhibit a non-empty DSL attribute. This would go against one of the basic assumptions of HPSG, that information about gaps is irrelevant to subcategorization. If this position is given up, the elements in the SUBCAT attribute, which are now typed as LOCAL structures, have to be typed as full-fledged syntactic categories, thereby losing conceptual clarity as well (cf. Pollard 1989).

Another problem concerns the categorial classification of complementizers and finite verbs. Borsley proposes that complementizers and auxiliaries (in English) should be classified as belonging to the same categories; i.e., in terms of the *Barriers* framework of Chomsky (Chomsky 1986a) they should belong to the category C.[35] Arguments for carrying over this claim to German as well are not hard to find. For example, in German, V-F as well as V-2 sentences and VPs participate in the process of right-extraposition, as is exemplified in (48).

(48) a. Petra hatte versprochen [$_{V-F}$ daß sie den Mann nicht mehr treffen würde]
          (Petra has promised [that she the man not anymore meet would])
      b. Petra wünschte [$_{V-2}$ Klaus würde kommen]
          (Petra wished [Klaus would come])
      c. Petra hatte versucht [$_{VP}$ den Mann anzurufen]
          (Petra had tried [the man to call up])

---

[34]The derivation of V-2 sentences includes the gap mechanism for treating topicalized phrases as presented in Sect. 4.4.

[35]C is an abbreviation for the well known label COMP under which subordinate conjunctions and other categories are subsumed in the *Barriers* system.

237

(49)

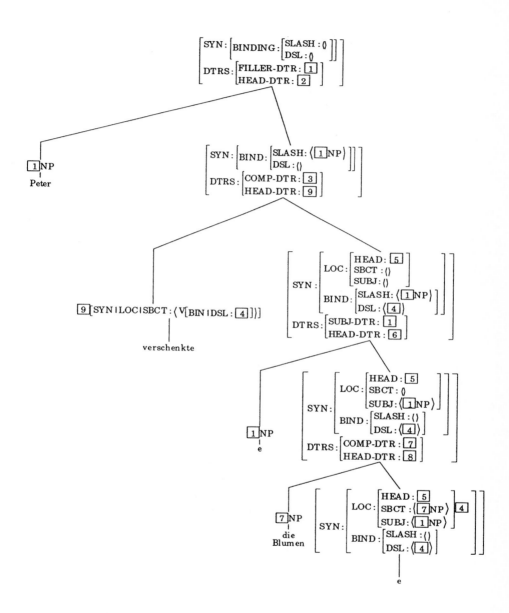

But if complementizers and finite verbs are mingled in the same category, it cannot be explained why right-extraposition is obligatory for V-2 (or in our framework, verb headed) sentences but only optional for (complementizer headed) V-F sentences, as exemplified by (50):

(50) a. * weil Petra [Peter würde kommen] wünschte
(* because Petra [Peter would come] wished)
   b. weil [daß Peter nicht kommen würde] jeder wußte
(because [that Peter not come would] everyone knew)

An explanation of this contrast, however, goes beyond the scope of this paper.

5 Summary

The crucial step in the treatment of the different finite verb positions in German is to give an adequate account for the change, or 'movement', from the final to the initial position. Within the first prototype we exploited the approach in terms of lexical rules changing the direction in which a functor category seeks its arguments. Thus, the order of the arguments in the functor category also has to be changed, which brings along unwanted implications on the structure of the MF. The effect of this restructuring is that appropriate scope and binding regularities across different clause types cannot be accounted for in an adequate way.

The approach favored subsequently explains the different verb patterns by stipulating an additional carrier of non-local information, the so-called DSL feature. From a linguistic viewpoint, this latter approach has clear advantages over the former, namely:

a) the structure of the MF is left intact, thereby leaving all options for scope determination open;

b) only a single rule for verb-fronting is needed to derive V-1 from V-F, accounting for arguments and adjuncts, as well as complex fronting constructions.

Thus we have shown that verb movement can well be accounted for in a unification-based approach to grammar, which does not involve explicit recourse to transformations, but captures all of the general insights gained within a transformational framework.

Acknowledgements

We would like to thank Bart Geurts and Esther König for valuable comments on this topic.

References

[Ades, Steedman 1982] Anthony E. Ades, Mark J. Steedman. On the Order of Words. *Linguistics and Philosophy*, 4:517–558, 1982.

[Ajdukiewicz 1935] Kazimierz Ajdukiewicz. Die syntaktische Konnexität. *Studia Philosophica*, 1:1–27, 1935. Translated as 'Syntactic connexion' in S. McCall (ed.) (1967): Polish Logic, Oxford, 207-231. Part I translated as 'On syntactical coherence', Review of Metaphysics 20 (1967), 635-647.

[Bach et al. 1988] Emmon Bach, Richard Oehrle, Deirdre Wheeler, eds. *Categorial Grammars and Natural Language Structures. Studies in Linguistics and Philosophy*, Reidel, Dordrecht, 1988. Proceedings of the Conference on Categorial Grammar, Tucson 1985.

[Baker 1988] Mark Baker. *Incorporation. – A Theory of Grammatical Function Changing.* Chicago University Press, Chicago, 1988.

[Bar-Hillel 1964] Yehoshua Bar-Hillel. On categorial and phrase structure grammars. In Yehoshua Bar-Hillel, ed., *Language and Information. Selected Essays on Their Theory and Application*, pages 99–115, Addison-Wesley, Reading, Mass., 1964.

[den Besten 1983] Hans den Besten. Root Transformations and Lexical Deletive Rules. In Werner Abraham, ed., *On the Formal Syntax of the Westgermania*, Benjamins, Amsterdam, 1983.

[Bierwisch 1963] Manfred Bierwisch. *Die Syntax des deutschen Verbs. Studia Grammatica*, Akademie Verlag, Berlin, 1963.

[Borsley 1989] Robert D. Borsley. Phrase-structure grammar and the *Barriers* conception of clause structure. *Linguistics*, 27:843–863, 1989.

[Bouma et al. 1988] Gosse Bouma, Esther König, Hans Uszkoreit. A Flexible Graph-Unification Formalism and its Application to Natural Language Processing. *IBM Journal Research and Development*, 32:170–184, 1988. Special Issue on Computational Linguistics.

[Chomsky 1981] Noam Chomsky. *Lectures on Government and Binding.* Foris, Dordrecht, 1981.

[Chomsky 1986a] Noam Chomsky. *Barriers. Linguistic Inquiry Monographs*, MIT Press, Cambridge, Mass., 1986.

[Chomsky 1986b] Noam Chomsky. *Knowledge of Language. – Its Nature, Origin and Use.* Praeger, New York, 1986.

[Curry et al. 1958] Haskell B. Curry, Robert Feys, William Craig. *Combinatory Logic.* Volume 1, North Holland, Amsterdam, 1958.

[Fukui 1986] Naomi Fukui. *A Theory of Category Projections and Its Applications.* PhD thesis, MIT, 1986.

[Gazdar 1981] Gerald Gazdar. Unbounded Dependencies and Coordinate Structures. *Linguistic Inquiry*, 12(2):155–184, 1981.

[Gazdar et al. 1985] Gerald Gazdar, Ewan Klein, G.K. Pullum, Ivan Sag. *Generalized Phrase Structure Grammar.* Blackwell, Oxford, UK, 1985.

[Gunji 1987] Takao Gunji. *Japanese Phrase Structure Grammar.* Reidel, Dordrecht, 1987.

[Hepple 1990a] Mark Hepple. Grammatical Relations and the Lambek Calculus. In *Proceedings of the Symposium on Discontinous Constituency*, pages 139–152, Tilburg, The Netherlands, Institute for Language Technology and Artificial Intelligence, 1990.

[Hepple 1990b] Mark Hepple. Verb Movement in Dutch and English. – A Categorial Grammar Analysis. In E. Engdahl, M. Reape, eds., *Parametric Variation in Germanic and Romance: Preliminary Investigations*, pages 41–72, 1990. DYANA Deliverable R1.1.A.

[Hinrichs, Nakazawa 1990] Erhard Hinrichs, Tsuneko Nakazawa. Subcategorization and VP Structure in German. In Shaun Hughes, ed., *Proceedings of the Third Symposium on Germanic Linguistics*, Amsterdam, John Benjamins, 1990.

[Hoeksema 1985] Jack Hoeksema. Wazdat? – Contracted Forms and Verb second in Dutch. In J.F. Faarlund, ed., *Germanic Linguistics*, pages 112–124, Indiana University Linguistics Club, Bloomington, Indiana, 1985.

[Jacobson 1987] Pauline Jacobson. Phrase Structure, Grammatical Relations, and Discontinuous Constituents. In *Discontinuous Constituency, Syntax and Semantics 20*, pages 27–69, Academic Press, 1987.

[König] Esther König. Gap-Handling Mechanisms in Categorial Grammars. this volume.

[Nerbonne 1985] John Nerbonne. *German Temporal Semantics: Three Dimensional Tense Logic and a GPSG Fragment*. Garland, New York, 1985.

[Pollard 1989] Carl Pollard. The Syntax-Semantics Interface in a Unification-Based Phrase Structure Grammar. In Stephan Busemann, Christa Hauenschild, Carla Umbach, eds., *Views of the Syntax-Semantics Interface*, pages 167–184, Berlin, KIT, Universitaet Berlin, July 1989. Proceedings of the Workshop 'GPSG and Semantics'.

[Pollard 1990] Carl Pollard. On Head Non-Movement. In *Proceedings of the Symposium on Discontinous Constituency*, Tilburg, The Netherlands, Institute for Language Technology and Artificial Intelligence, 1990.

[Pollard, Sag 1987] Carl Pollard, Ivan Sag. *An Information-Based Syntax and Semantics. Fundamentals*. Volume 1 of *Lecture Notes 13*, Center for Study of Language and Information, Stanford, Ca., 1987.

[Reinhart 1983] Tanya Reinhart. *Anaphora and Semantic Interpretation*. Croom Helm, London, 1983.

[Shieber 1986] Stuart M. Shieber. *An Introduction to Unification-Based Approaches to Grammar. Lecture Notes*, Center for the Study of Language and Information, Stanford, Ca., 1986.

[Thiersch 1978] Craig S. Thiersch. *Topics in German Syntax*. PhD thesis, MIT, 1978.

[Uszkoreit 1986a] Hans Uszkoreit. Categorial Unification Grammars. In *Proceedings of the 11th International Conference on Computational Linguistics*, pages 187–194, Bonn, 1986.

[Uszkoreit 1986b] Hans Uszkoreit. Constraints on Order. *Linguistics*, 24:883–906, 1986.

[Uszkoreit 1987] Hans Uszkoreit. Linear Precedence in Discontinuous Constituents: Complex Fronting in German. In *Discontinuous Constituency, Syntax and Semantics 20*, pages 405–425, Academic Press, 1987.

[Wesche 1989] Birgit Wesche. Spurious Ambiguities – On the Syntax-Semantics Relation in C(U)G. In Stephan Busemann, Christa Hauenschild, Carla Umbach, eds., *Views of the Syntax-Semantics Interface*, pages 184–193, Berlin, KIT, Universitaet Berlin, July 1989. Proceedings of the Workshop GPSG and Semantics.

[Wittenburg 1987] Kent Wittenburg. Predictive Combinators: A Method for Efficient Parsing of Combinatory Categorial Grammars. In *Proceedings of the 25th Annual Meeting of the Association for Computational Linguistics*, pages 73–80, Stanford, CA, 1987.

[Zeevat et al. 1987] Henk Zeevat, Ewan Klein, Jo Calder. *Unification Categorial Grammar*. Technical Report EUCCS/RP-21, Centre for Cognitive Science, University of Edinburgh, Edinburgh, Scotland, December 1987.

Chapter 1.4

Semantics

This is a surprisingly short chapter. One should have thought that semantics would play a very important and central role in a text understanding project like LILOG and that this should be reflected in the amount of scientific insights, and accordingly the number of papers contributed to this book on topics in natural language semantics.

In fact, however, this is not quite how things developed in the LILOG project. It turned out in the course of the project work that a large number of issues traditionally dealt with by natural language semantics wander off to the domain of knowledge representation and processing as soon as NL semantics is not practiced any more in the customary (und not necessarily splendid) isolation but in the context of a fully implemented system of natural language understanding. Instead the semantics researcher, in a sense already by education a Jack of all trades, slips into the role of a coordinating figure that has to see that things run smoothly in the place where practically all modules of the system meet: the traditional area of NL semantics.

Thus if it is right to say of the LILOG project as a whole that its main achievement is in the integration of a very large number of sophisticated modules into one fully implemented system of text understanding, rather than in particularly important results in isolated research questions, then this is probably even more applicable to the work on semantics.

The papers that follow in this chapter none the less have a number of interesting and important results to report, not all of them necessarily descriptions of the corresponding solutions that are implemented in the LEU/2 system. They report rather on the research that has accompanied the work on LEU/2 and that forms the environment from within which LEU/2 was conceived and constructed.

In this sense all of the papers take as their starting point issues that are relevant to the LILOG project, although not all the work has been or will be integrated into the LEU/2 system.

Peter Bosch

The Bermuda Triangle:
Natural Language Semantics Between Linguistics, Knowledge Representation, and Knowledge Processing.

Peter Bosch

Abstract

Linguistic parameters alone cannot determine the interpretation of natural language utterances. They can only constrain their interpretation and must leave the rest to other knowledge sources and other processes: language understanding is not just a matter of knowing the language, but also to a considerable degree a matter of logical inference and world knowledge. This is no news as far as the interpretation of referential expressions is concerned. Predicate expressions, however, tend to be treated as if they were functional or relational constants that are directly interpreted with respect to a model. In this paper an attempt is made to treat them too as referential. The only real difference is that the referents of predicate expressions are of a different type: concepts rather than first–order objects.

This generalized notion of reference gives us not only a natural way of understanding the interaction of knowledge representation and knowledge processing on the one hand and linguistic processing on the other, but also opens up a perspective for the modularization of Natural Language Understanding (NLU) systems that provides for a very high degree of independence of the more strictly linguistic component from the specific tasks and domains of a particular application. The overall result should be a less language–dependent knowledge representation and less domain–dependent linguistic components, i.e., overall improved portability of the modules.

> *Given that Knowledge Representation was principally driven by natural language concerns right up to the beginning of the decade, one would have expected substantial progress to have been made in the '80s on KR support for NL semantics. This seems not to have been the case.*
>
> *Ronald J. Brachman (Proceedings of AAAI 1990:1088)*

1   Introduction

It may seem that no substantial progress has been made in Knowledge Representation (KR) support for Natural Language (NL) semantics, and in view of the considerable amount of work that is actually carried out in this area, one may well get the impression that there is a kind of Bermuda Triangle where a good amount of this work simply disappears: the area between linguistics, knowledge representation, and knowledge processing.

A possible cause for this situation is that we have a serious problem with respect to the generality and portability of results. Even though logic and linguistics may interact smoothly in each individual research system that is built, there is probably too little attention for the question of how they ought to interact in general. Hence there are serious limitations to the portability of both the linguistics components and the knowledge representation modules, a "fresh start" is needed in just about every new project, researchers are overburdened with the essentially unnecessary repetition of work other have already done, and no time and resources are left to face the more fundamental questions and to make significant scientific progress. In other words: more work that mysteriously disappears in the Bermuda Triangle of natural language understanding.

LILOG, I believe, is one of the few projects in which some progress with respect to general solutions and portability has been made, as is visible from the contributions in this volume. A very important part of the progress is found in the tools that have been developed and that incorporate many of the general insights that have been gained. Another respect in which LILOG has advanced further than many other projects is the modularity of the system. But there is still a long way to go until we have the kind of principled division of modules that enables the full generality and portability that we are after. What is needed, in particular, is a better understanding of the division of labour of the AI and NL components in NLU.

When knowledge representation does part of the job of linguistic semantics, language–specific information tends to seep into knowledge representation, with the result that the knowledge representation becomes unnecessarily dependent on features peculiar to natural language, or even to a particular natural language, and NL components become unnecessarily dependent on the task and domain inherent to a particular knowledge base. Conversely, when linguistic semantics delivers linguistically insufficiently analyzed structures to knowledge processing components, the latter are burdened with tasks for which they are ill–equipped to provide principled solutions.

2 Inferential Instability

Let us assume for the sake of the argument that the core problem of linguistic analysis is disambiguation: the translation of natural language input strings into unambiguous representations on which inferential processes can operate, i.e., translation into inferentially stable representations.

Part of the problem of how linguistic and logical modules interact then turns on the nature of the inferential instability that characterizes natural languages.

For our purpose it will suffice to review just a few of the factors that lead to inferential instability or ambiguity. One is structural equivocation, such as the ambiguity of quantifier scope in (1):

(1)   Five companies sold two hundred installations.

(cf. also Link and Schütze, this volume, Section 1.4). Another is ambiguity of syntactic analysis, as with respect to the attachment of the prepositional phrase in

(2)   Fred saw the woman with the binoculars.

(cf. also Bosch and Geurts 1990). Further, the occurrence of word forms that are morphologically ambiguous in the sense that they could belong to different syntactic categories may cause different readings. For instance Chomsky's infamous *visiting* in

(3)   Visiting relatives can be boring.

Finally, the ambiguity of sentences may be due to the occurrence of ambiguous words, like the notorious *bank* in

(4)   Pete went to the bank this morning.

Some of these sources of equivocation are better under control than others. But what they have in common and what makes them look less threatening than the cases to come is that in each case there is, in principle, a finite disjunction of inferentially stable representations among which the linguistic analysis must make a choice.

This is no longer the case when we turn to indexical expressions, like the determiner *this* in the sentence

(5)   This paper is ten pages long.

This sentence may be true or false, depending on what paper *this paper* refers to. But then it is usually said that this case is a matter of referential ambiguity and is not due to an equivocation in linguistic analysis.

Usually the difference between (4), which is taken to depend on the lexical ambiguity of *bank*, and the case of indexicals in (5) is regarded as reasonably clear – which, unfortunately, it is not (cf. Bosch 1990). Take for instance the colour adjective *red*, which shows clear equivocation in the following contexts:

(6)   red tomato
        red apple
        red hair
        red wine
        red grapefruit
        red traffic lights

We are here not concerned with an ambiguity of the kind we find with lexical items like *bank*. There is good reason for the suspicion that there are not just the six variants of the concept of redness that we find under (6) but that this list can be extended ad libitum, and hence the equivocation of *red* would rather resemble the referential ambiguity we find with indexicals.

The equivocation we observe under (6) clearly leads to a difference in truth–conditions. If we assume compositionality, and the adjective *red* were to make the same contribution to the truth–conditions in all these cases, the conditions for calling a tomato, an apple, hair, wine, etc. *red* should be the same, which they are not, and one would surely want to avoid the system's conclusion that tomato, hair, grapefruit, etc., are, at some level of granularity, all of the same colour. However, there is no level of granularity at which these colours are the same, nor are the differences we find in (6) in any interesting sense related to vagueness.

But a treatment that postulates lexical ambiguity of *red*, possibly with suitable subcategorization restrictions that distinguish tomatoes from grapefruits, i.e., the postulation of competing lexical meanings, paraphrased as "red for a tomato" versus "red for a grapefruit", does not look like a good solution. The case bears much more similarity to the case of indexicals than to lexical ambiguity in the sense that the variation in the adjective's contribution to the truth–conditions depends on reference to objects of experience, i.e., on our empirical knowledge of tomatoes, grapefruits, etc. And such knowledge should certainly not be included in the dictionary, nor in any other representation of linguistic knowledge. It is strictly the business of the representation of knowledge of the world.

Thus the lexical semantics of *red* should be the same in all these cases – as it is for an indexical determiner like *this*. The variation in the contribution the adjective makes towards the truth–conditions can instead be explained by assuming that *red* (more precisely, its semantic specification) is a function which, depending on contextual factors, refers to different concepts, i.e., yields different concepts as its value – quite analogous to the reference of indexicals, with the difference that *this* refers to objects, while *red* refers to concepts. This at least looks like a reasonable approach at first blush (but compare Sections 6 and 7 below).

The point is not specific to adjectives or colour terms. Consider an example that may look quite different at the first glance. Rommetveit (1986) tells the story of a certain Smith who is mowing his lawn. His neighbour addresses him over the fence and asks "Are you not working today?". Smith's reply: "No,

I've taken the day off". At the same time Mrs Smith is on the phone to a friend telling her "My husband is working in the garden". Obviously, if *working* is taken at face value, our NLU system will derive a contradiction or ascribe contradictory beliefs to Mr and Mrs Smith.

But this does not mean that the English verb *to work* is lexically ambiguous. The verb means the same, but it is used in either case to refer to a different concept, again due to the different contextual parameters, in particular the available similarities and contrasts in the subject domain. In the question of Smith's neighbour, for whom Smith's physical activity is plain to see, a concept of work as physical activity cannot be at issue; hence other concepts of work are more plausible candidates, e.g. work in the sense of doing one's job. In the telephone conversation we have the more explicit formulation "working in the garden", which, ordinarily, suggests physical activity and is taken to exclude the concept of work in the sense of doing one's job. – As in the case of the colour adjectives, these distinctions reflect distinctions that are not of a linguistic nature, but are the business of knowledge about our particular social world and hence should be accommodated in the concepts we have about that social world rather than in the dictionary.

A point that is absent, or at most marginally relevant, in the colour example enters the scene in the case of Smith's garden work: communicative intentions that are understood among the interlocutors. They too influence the selection of relevant contrasting concepts from which the intended concept must be distinguished. This becomes even clearer in the following case, which is really a matter of different granularity of the concepts involved. The example is taken from Winograd and Flores (1986). Depending on whether an utterance of

(7)   There's water in the fridge.

is meant as a statement about where the addressee can find a cold drink or as a warning that moisture–sensitive chemicals should not be stored in the fridge, the truth of (7) may vary, while the fridge, its condition and contents remain the same.

If we want to get such cases of inferential instability under control we need to provide for a clear division of labour between intrinsically linguistic information and information from other sources. But before we progress in this direction, I want to make an attempt to weaken overdrawn expectations with respect to what linguistic meaning can do in processes of linguistic comprehension. I shall look at a simple example in the following section.

3   Dog biscuits and nut cake

No–one expects there to be a dog in a dog biscuit, but most people expect there to be a nut, and usually more than one, in a nut cake.

NLU systems may reasonably be expected to share this disposition of the majority of English speakers. Still, the disposition is not conditioned by any linguistic facts about English. It is a matter of our conceptual system, i.e., the knowledge representation. Concepts like those referred to by *dog biscuit* and *nut cake* play a role in the representation of those parts of the world where corresponding objects are relevant. They are means to represent beliefs like those expressed in English sentences like *Texans love dog biscuits* or *Dogs are usually fond of nut cake*, and the like.

But the English expressions *dog biscuit* and *nut cake* only hint at these concepts and do not determine them. If we do not already have those concepts, then there is no way of constructing them merely from the semantics of the English expressions – they would make your mind boggle and the result could be anything.

As already suggested, I want to regard the relation between English expressions and concepts as a relation of reference: literally in the same sense of a relation reference as between referentially used definite NPs and their objects of reference, e.g., between the English expression *The British Prime Minister* and, at the time of writing, a particular person of the name *John Major*. In neither case can the semantics of the English expression on its own make sure that the correct referent is identified. It can give some help in this respect by constraining the set of possible referents, but no more.

Whether or not the mechanisms of reference work to satisfaction is a matter of two kinds of factors: one is knowledge of English, the other is world knowledge (i.e., in particular knowledge of the domain from which the referents – concepts or first–order objects – are to be chosen, common–sense knowledge, and knowledge of the communication situation). The better we keep these factors apart, the more suitable our approach will be for unexpected cases and unintended applications, and hence the more generality and the more portability of both knowledge representation and linguistic components can be achieved.

4   Lexical Meaning

In order to sort out the contribution of linguistic factors to referent identification, i.e., the constraints imposed by the linguistic properties of an utterance, we require a full linguistic analysis of the relevant expressions, i.e., the exhibition and exploitation of all linguistic regularities (cf. also Lang, this volume, Section 2.2).

For instance we should not take two English expressions of the form

(8a)   x has been opened
(8b)   x is open

at face value and attempt to map them onto two concepts like HAS_BEEN_OPENED(x) and IS_OPEN(x) in the knowledge representation, even though it is straightforward enough to write suitable axioms that state the logical relationship between these concepts and model the usage of the English expressions.

Such an approach would ignore the fact that there is a linguistically regular semantic relation between the two expressions, which is a matter of English rather than of any particular conceptual representation. It is, in fact, not only a regular relation between the two expressions in (8), but between classes of English expressions. Relevant parameters are the aspectual classification (cf. Vendler 1967) of the verb *to open* as an accomplishment verb (or perhaps, more specifically, a causative verb), the relation between active and passive, a semantics of English tenses, a semantics for morphological derivation of causative verbs from adjectives (*to open* from *open*, *to clean* from *clean*, *to clear* from *clear*, or *to tighten* from *tight*, *to brighten* from *bright*, etc. – cf. Jespersen 1956, Vol. 6, Ch. 20.5), and perhaps others.

The latter regularity has been captured by Dowty (1979:206f) in a Montague–based approach by the following rules:

S23.   If $\alpha \varepsilon P_{ADJ}$, then $F_{23}(\alpha) \varepsilon P_{IV}$, where $F_{23}(\alpha)=\alpha$ **en** if α ends in a non–nasal obstruent, $F_{23}(\alpha)=\alpha$ otherwise.

T23. F_{23} translates into: $\lambda x[BECOME\ \alpha'(x)]$

Whether the regularity should actually be stated in this form is another question. We neither have the required generalization concerning the aspectual properties of the English perfect tense nor the generalization concerning the passive voice[1]. More importantly, however, the formulation still allows for the extraction of further, more general, regularities concerning the relationship between causative verbs, accomplishment verbs, and transitivity (cf. Bierwisch 1982:71–75 for proposals of the intended kind).

Such additions and amendments are not easily made in the format Dowty uses. The device of lexical templates, as used in the LILOG lexicon, would facilitate such generalizations. The point, to be sure, is not just economy of representation, but rather the extraction of linguistically relevant generalizations about notions like causativity, accomplishment, and transitivity – i.e., purely linguistic generalizations that not only define semantic relations among lexical items of English, but also constrain the set of concepts that can serve as the referents of the relevant classes of expressions.

5   Contextual Concepts

Thus the task of the linguistic analysis is to exhibit as much linguistic regularity as possible. And the role of linguistic regularities is to provide constraints that limit the class of concepts to which a linguistic expression can refer. This is what lexical semantic representation should do.

If this notion about the relation between linguistic expressions and concepts is to work, i.e., if lexical semantics is to constrain the class of potential referents of an expression, the following assumptions about concepts are required:

–   The language in which the semantic analysis is formulated must form a subset of the language in which concepts are represented. More specifically, the semantic language must be capable of describing classes of concepts. This need not mean that each of the constants of the semantic language refers to a concept. Concepts may be more complex than semantic constants and they may be more specific: they may contain attributes and attribute values that are not available in the semantic language.

–   Concepts must have structured representations so that it can be verified whether a concept satisfies constraints given in terms of semantic constants. The structure may be internal or external (in the sense that different concepts are logically related to each other)[2].

–   There must be concepts available from the knowledge base among which the linguistic expression can choose its referent, and there must be operations on concepts available that can build or modify concepts ad hoc to satisfy the constraints given in the semantic analysis of a linguistic expression.

When concepts from a more or less permanent knowledge base are used in a particular discourse, they are usually further constrained and modified by world knowledge of all varieties as it becomes available in the course of the text or discourse to yield the locally relevant inferentially stable representations. The result of such processes of modification are discourse–specific concepts or **contextual concepts**, for short

---

[1] This is not to be taken as a criticism of Dowty, who was not discussing the examples in (8) but only the relation between the adjective *open* and the verb *to open*.

[2] Note that we are here concerned with conceptual representations and not with semantic representations. In the latter case there is a long–standing controversy about the internal or external representation of the relevant structure (cf. Bierwisch 1982:63; Fodor et al. 1980), and I have to leave the question undecided here to what extent arguments carry over to the issue of conceptual representation.

CCs[3]. We have seen examples above in Sec. 2: the specific concepts related to *red*, *work*, and *water* that we discussed are CCs rather than unmodified abstract concepts that could be formed purely from the constraints that lexical semantic specifications impose.

In the following I want to demonstrate that CCs are of immediate relevance not only for knowledge representation but also already in the course of linguistic analysis. That regular (i.e. first order) objects of reference, as represented in discourse representations, play a role in the resolution of pronominal and full–NP anaphora is uncontroversial. But we can show analogously that concepts, CCs, are required for similar purposes, e.g., for VP anaphora, which is in English often expressed by the form *and so +* AUX + NP (e.g., *and so {does/has/is/will/...} Fred*). Consider the following cases:

(9a) John loves his mother and so does Fred. [... and Fred loves his mother]
(9b) John loves his mother and so does Mary. [... and Mary loves her mother]
(9c) John loves her and so does Fred. [... and Fred loves the same woman as John]

Early linguistic accounts used to assume that VP anaphora can be explained on the basis of a substitution of the VP anaphor for an underlying repeated VP. This could possibly be defended for cases like (9a). But already for (9b) the account must allow for variation in the form of the underlying expression (here the possessive pronoun, which in the antecedent is masculine and in the anaphoric repetition feminine). Cases like (9c) finally demonstrate that any account based on linguistic form is wrong. Here the interpretation of the anaphor contains a specific reference to a particular person and this person must be the same as the one referred to in the antecedent. If Fred loves another woman than John, the sentence is false. Hence the actual reference of *her* in the sentence token is relevant for the interpretation of the VP anaphor.

What the *and–so–do* expressions pick up anaphorically thus can be neither the linguistic expression nor the meaning of the linguistic expression of the antecedent (which could not contain specific references), but must be the interpretation of the antecedent expression with respect to a particular context, i.e., a CC. In (9a) and (9b) this may be the concept of loving ones own mother[4], which one may argue could be either compositionally derived or culturally entrenched. The concept required in (9c), however, can be neither; it is clearly formed for a purely ad hoc purpose and contains the reference to a specific woman, so that the same CC has obviously no value beyond the context immediately given.

A widespread misuse of the construction exemplified in (9) above is its use as an ambiguity test, the idea being that sentences like those in (9) are unmarked only in case the "meaning" of the antecedent VP is identical to the "meaning" of the anaphor. Hence if there is an ambiguous expression in the antecedent, then the reading that is intended in the antecedent must also be intended in the anaphor. If another reading is intended in the anaphor, we get a marked sentence, often a pun. Thus if we try to read (10) in a way that the first *port* is meant to be a harbour and the second fortified wine, we would get a marked interpretation and thereby proof of the fact that *port* is indeed ambiguous.

Similarly, if we wonder if *hit* is ambiguous between a specification as intentional and non–intentional action (an issue discussed in Lakoff 1970 and Catlin and Catlin 1973), the impossibility of

[3] In Bosch (1985) and other places I have used the term "contextual notions" in order to make a distinction between permanent "concepts" and the more fluctuating "notions". The fact that the structure and content of both is the same is a good reason, however, not to keep up an unnecessary terminological distinction and to speak simply of "concepts" in both cases. The adjective "contextual" can still be added occasionally, when it is important to emphasize that there is a process that leads from the permanent concept to the actual CC.

[4] Or the concept of loving John's mother – but let us ignore this complication for the moment, since it contributes nothing to the current argument.

reading sentence (11) with one interpretation in the antecedent and another in the anaphor should prove that this is indeed an ambiguity. Compare

(10)   The ship was steering for the port and so was the Captain.
(11)   Fred hit the wall and so did Pete.

We have seen already that meaning is not what is at issue in VP anaphora, and hence ambiguity is not at issue either. We are concerned with CCs, and since ambiguous lexical items would also ordinarily refer to different CCs, the assumption of CCs readily explains that ambiguous lexical items show the same effect.

Interestingly, in (11) we can observe that the acceptability of the sentence is subject to assumptions that are made about the context. And this is of course where the actually relevant CCs come from. If we assume that Fred trips over the carpet, hitting his head against the wall (unintentionally), and Pete furiously hits the wall with his fist (intentionally) then indeed the sentence is not a suitable description of the situation. The crucial difference, however, is not intentionality, but rather contextual standards for what may count as the same, i.e., what may in that context be subsumed under the CC which in that context is the referent of *hit*. Suppose Fred trips over the carpet as above and Pete imitates Fred's clumsiness, hence goes through the same moves, but quite intentionally[5]. In that situation the sentence is a true and unmarked description of the two events, despite the difference in intentionality. The difference is just that in this latter context the two events may count as tokens of the same type and hence fall under the same CC. – Thus if we want to have an intuitive test for the identity of CCs, VP anaphora will serve us fine[6].

6   Operations on Concepts

6.1   Bierwisch's proposal

A pioneering effort in the study of the role of concepts for natural language understanding and their interaction with linguistic semantic specifications was made in Bierwisch (1982). In particular, Bierwisch proposed an account for a set of metonymy phenomena to illustrate his more general points.

First, observe the variation in the interpretation of (12), depending on whether *Faulkner* is intended to refer to the man's pronunciation, his actions, or his literary work.

(12)   Faulkner is hard to understand.

Bierwisch says that we are concerned with a **conceptual shift** in the interpretation of the proper name; the interpretation is shifted to different conceptual domains: that of spoken utterances, of actions, or of literary works. Correspondingly, we get a **differentiation** in the respective concepts of understanding: auditory comprehension is another differentiation of the concept of understanding than the understanding of human action or the understanding of works of literature.

Neither shifting nor differentiation are a matter of linguistic semantics. In Bierwisch's formalization (cf. below) the lexical semantic representation in both cases only contains variables that are bound by one or the other operator (abstractor or existential quantifier respectively). The application of the abstract to an expression of a suitable category or the instantiation of the variable constitute the actual processes of

---

[5] The example is from Catlin and Catlin (1973); cf. also Lakoff (1970), Bosch (1979).

[6] There are a number of similar test constructions available (cf. Zwicky and Sadock 1975), which support the overall validity of the point (cf. also Bosch 1985).

shifting and differentiation and yield what I have called above the contextual concept, i.e., the inferentially relevant representation.

Another case of conceptual shift Bierwisch discusses is the interpretation variants that the word *school* exhibits in the following contexts[7]:

(13) a. The school made a major donation.
      b. The school has a flat roof.
      c. He enjoys school very much.
      d. School is one of the pillars of our civilization.

While in (a) we are concerned with an institution, in (b) it's a building, in (c) a certain totality of events, and in (d) the relevant concept is, as it were, a generic variant of the institution concept from (a), the "institution as a principle", as Bierwisch puts it.

The lexical semantic representation (SEM) of the word *school* is the same for all these cases; in Bierwisch's formulation:

(14) SEM ("school") = λX [PURPOSE X W]
      where W=PROCESSES_OF_LEARNING_AND_TEACHING

The conceptual shift is brought about by the application of certain functions that map SEM into a contextual concept (or, as Bierwisch calls it, an utterance meaning, *m*); in the case at hand these are the following functions:

(15) a. λX [INSTITUTION X & SEM X]
      b. λX [BUILDING X & SEM X]
      c. λX [PROCESS X & SEM X]
      d. λX [ENTITY X & SEM X]

Applying (15a) to (14), e.g., yields the contextual concept

(16) λX [INSTITUTION X & PURPOSE X W]
      where W=PROCESSES_OF_LEARNING_AND_TEACHING

This proposal shows a way of keeping the linguistic meaning constant and avoiding the postulation of any ambiguity, and still account for the differences in inferential potential between the different occurrences of the expressions in question.

6.2   Some elaborations

An aspect of the proposal I want to elaborate in this section is the role of the functions under (15). Bierwisch mentions the fact that words like *parliament, opera, university*, and many others allow for a very similar, if not identical, set of conceptual shifts. But it would be awkward if we had to explicitly state these functions in the representation of each of these concepts. A more plausible, and quite conventional way of representing these interpretation options in the knowledge representation is in terms of relational and functional attributes, i.e., roles and features, of the concept INSTITUTION (if this is what we call the

---

[7] Actually, Bierwisch discusses the German word *Schule*, not its English equivalent *school*, and the following sentences are my translations of his German examples. This must be mentioned because in German, unlike in English, all four sentences have *Schule* with a definite article. I cannot, however, discuss the implications of this difference in this paper.

concept under which all the relevant concepts fall – note that this is, of course, not the concept of "institution" that Bierwisch uses in (15a) and (16)). In other words: we have a general concept of institution and say that each of its sub–concepts or instances has an associated LOCATION, an associated SET_OF_EVENTS, and an idea or PRINCIPLE on which it rests. These three attributes are thus inherited by all concepts that fall under the INSTITUTION concept and allow for the predication that, at least by default, schools as well as parliaments or operas have these attributes in common.

In addition we must state that conceptual shifts from a concept to one of its attributes are regularly possible; very much in analogy to the rhetorical figure of *pars pro toto* we here get another metonymical shift: *concept for attribute*. The fact that there are differences between the shifts that *school* and *opera* allow, is again accounted for quite regularly by the device of multiple inheritance: the concept OPERA is not only subsumed by INSTITUTION, but also by WORK_OF_PERFORMING_ART, and hence has attributes that the school concept has not. This explains the additional shifts that *opera* shares with *symphony*, *drama*, *comedy*, etc. and which are not available for *school*.

Whether indeed the shifting–principle "concept for attribute" is correct is hard to say at the current stage of investigation, both for empirical and for conceptual reasons. We neither know enough about attributes in knowledge representation languages, nor have we looked at sufficiently many cases.

But let us consider some consequences. It may seem at first glance that there is an important difference between the *concept for attribute* and the *pars pro toto* shift: given a part, the corresponding whole of which it forms a part seems uniquely determined; but given a concept it is usually unclear which of its attributes the shift should go for. But the actual difference is smaller than it may look: also a part is not inherently a part of a particular whole and hence does not by itself determine a corresponding whole it is a part of. There is not significantly more determinacy in one case than in the other. If someone is called a "big mouth", the whole which the mouth is a part of could theoretically (but already limited to a 'natural' set of choices) be the face, the head, the body, or, as usually intended, the whole person.

Here as well as in the case of the school example we need additional information to solve what Bierwisch (1982:76, 92f) calls the "selection problem": How do we determine which of the available concepts is to be selected as the actual referent for a linguistic expression in a given context ? In the simplest case, we have already interpreted another linguistic expression whose selection restrictions solve the problem. If we read that "The new school is being built in Parks Road", the selection restrictions introduced by the concept of building would determine a concept of school in the sense of school building. But already here one may worry that compositionality of interpretation is endangered: we cannot first interpret each composite expression independently and then compute the interpretation of the whole sentence, but have to take the interpretation of some components into account while we interpret others. But this is nothing out of the ordinary. We may uphold compositionality by simply increasing ambiguity at the lower levels of analysis, i.e., first list all possible interpretations for each component and then see which can be eliminated in the course of their combination. Not a sensible strategy, and certainly not in the line of psychological realism, but it can preserve compositionality when this is important. The result of the combination may of course not always eliminate ambiguity entirely, and this is where things get more interesting. Because here the extra–sentential context comes into play and we require control strategies for the use of the various knowledge sources involved. In Sec. 7 below, we shall shall look at one part of this problem.

The selection problem, however, also crops up when several competing concepts are relevant to one interpretation. Formally, we may regard each entity as an instance of one or the other concept or of several concepts simultaneously. In the latter case we get multiple subsumption and multiple inheritance. This can be illustrated quite conveniently with Bierwisch's Faulkner example. The individual Faulkner may be classified in many, perhaps arbitrarily many ways: as an author, the speaker of a language, a rational agent (and, just to to please Plato, also as a featherless biped). Each of these concepts have attributes that their instance, Faulkner, may inherit. In particular the AUTHOR concept should provide a role WORKS_OF, the SPEAKER concept should provide an analogous role UTTERANCES_OF and a feature PRONUNCIATION_OF, and the rational AGENT should have associated ACTIONS.

If Faulkner as an instance of the concepts mentioned inherits these attributes, we have all the objects of understanding that are required for the suggested interpretations of sentence (12) above. Whether and to what extent it is possible to mix these variants of the interpretation of Faulkner is a matter also of the tolerance of the available concepts of understanding. A sentence like

(17)   His pronunciation as well as his stories are hard to understand.

sounds like a bad pun; but

(18)   He doesn't seem to care about others and whether or not they understand him. Nobody understands his stories, nor even his pronunciation.

already seems a good deal more acceptable.

This, I would like to suggest, is one of the points where context plays the major role in the business of the formation and modification of concepts in discourse: in determining what may and what may not count as the same from the point of view introduced by a particular discourse context. Specifically: is there a discourse perspective that allows for the construction of a CC for *understanding* that accepts both stories and pronunciation as arguments, i.e. a discourse perspective for which pronunciation and stories are both subsumed under one particular concept which characterizes the locally relevant objects of understanding ? See also Sec. 5 above and Bosch (1990). But it is well beyond the present paper to push these issues any further.

6.3   An extension

Let us now try and see how far we get with Bierwisch's proposal, slightly reformulated in terms of the theory of knowledge representation as above, when we apply it to the notorious case of the colour adjective *red* from Sec. 2.

Within Bierwisch's framework, we are, in (6), clearly not concerned with a conceptual shift in the interpretation of *red*, but rather with a differentiation, i.e., with the modification of a concept of redness that depends on the variation of the concepts of the various objects of which redness is predicated. But is this the correct approach ? Do we really want different concepts of red ? Are we not rather concerned with the same concept of redness, except that it applies to the various objects in a different manner ?

The point is, I believe, that concepts fundamentally do two things:

– they specify certain properties of the objects they comprise, either as inherent properties or as default properties
– they specify certain options for further specifications of these objects.

If we compare the concepts of a tomato and a grapefruit in this respect, we find that both have a default specification for the colour property: red and yellow respectively. Both concepts are supplemented by an axiom that the colour of the unripe fruit is green, otherwise as in the default specification (i.e. red or yellow). Apart from the actual values of the default colour parameter, this is not information one would explicitly represent for the specific cases of tomatoes or grapefruits, but rather higher up in the sort lattice, with the concept of fruit, from where the sorts tomato and grapefruit inherit this information.

The predication of redness of a tomato thus is only an explicit confirmation that the colour default holds, i.e., that the tomato is ripe. But what does the predication of redness do for the grapefruit ? It can either be interpreted in a conceptually incoherent manner that leads to the further question of how the grapefruit was turned red. Alternatively, there may be a richer concept of grapefruits that has a second colour attribute, for the colour of the pulp, with the disjunctive specification: either red or white, so that the predication of redness is related to the slot for the colour of the pulp.

If this is the structure according to which we arrive at the different interpretations for red tomato and red grapefruit, then the cause of the difference is exactly where it intuitively ought to be: in different structures of the concepts of tomato and grapefruit. Different empirical knowledge about the two kinds of fruit provides for different answers to the question: In what respect can this fruit be red and what follows from it ? Corresponding conceptual representations tell us that for hair, *red* articulates a choice between blonde, brown, black, and red, hence that the attribution of red excludes these alternatives; for wine the set of alternatives is rather red, white, and rosé.

In all these cases *red* articulates a particular choice from a set that is already given with the concept that is to be modified. If the concept is too poorly specified and leaves open what kind of modification is conceptually anticipated, then only a superficial interpretation is possible and inferences like those indicated cannot be drawn.

The type of interaction we have just observed between conceptual representation and explicit linguistic assertion is not restricted to the fairly permanent concepts in the example but can also be found with conceptual representations that are built up and vanish in the course of a discourse. The most general formulation of the phenomenon probably is that in the course of a discourse questions (and often also sets of potential answers) are built up to which subsequent portions of the discourse provide answers, i.e., the classical rhetorical notion of a *quaestio*. Properly worked out, this view leads to a significant reduction of the tasks of linguistic semantics. It makes clear that what is understood from an utterance (i.e., the inferentially stable representation that results from it) is not in the first instance determined by the semantics of the sentences uttered, but is rather the result of a modification the semantics of these sentences brings about with respect to concepts and assumptions that were already available in advance.

7 Semantic Composition and Reference to Concepts

Even if we take a declarative approach to lexical semantics and knowledge representation we still have to ask what information is used when, i.e., ask about the relevant control structures. This is particularly important in view of the fact that much of the relevant information needed in NLU is in principle available from more than one source, though often in a different form and with different consequences for the result. The point is that a robust system, as the human NLU system clearly is, cannot rely on just one source of information for one purpose nor can it rely on just one strategy of understanding. To put it bluntly: when logic fails or gets too complicated, experience can often help out, and conversely. But logic and experience do not always yield the same solutions for identical problems.

With respect to the problem of the interaction of linguistic knowledge and world knowledge we have been discussing, the question that matters is this: at what point in the course of processing an utterance is world knowledge and conceptual knowledge used ? On the assumption of strict compositionality, as briefly hinted above, we should first carry out the linguistic analysis in full and stand by and watch an explosion of spurious ambiguities. And only when the desaster is complete, we should use conceptual and world knowledge and start eliminating the irrelevant ambiguities. The opposite extreme is to first work out, on the basis of conceptual knowledge, domain knowledge, and knowledge of the communication situation, including discourse strategies, etc., what would be a likely thing to be said and then carry out some linguistic analysis for confirmation. Clearly, neither strategy is very attractive as it stands. In the following I want to look into the processing of some types of adjectives in order to show that the question of control strategies may well merit detailed investigation and that there may well be specialized standard control strategies for particular constructions.

Compare the interpretation options for the adjective *red* in the (a) and (b) variants of the following sentences:

(19a)   This is a red shirt.
(19b)   This shirt is red.

(20a)   This is a red tomato.
(20b)   This tomato is red.

(21a)   This is red hair.
(21b)   This hair is red.

(22a)   This is red wine.
(22b)   This wine is red.

The (a)-sentences straightforwardly subsume a particular object under a particular composite concept, referred to by the phase *red* φ. When such a concept is available in the knowledge base it would usually differ from the mere unification of the semantic specifications of the adjective and noun. The latter are only constraints on the referential process that selects the concept from the knowledge base and are not by themselves equivalent to a concept. This difference becomes obvious when we compare (19a) to the other (a)-sentences: red shirts don't seem to be anything over and above what one could predict from their redness and their shirtiness. *Red hair*, *red wine*, and to a possibly lesser degree, *red tomato*, seem to refer to concepts that are much more strongly influenced by our experience of their instances.

The (b)-sentences use the two concepts, red and φ, independently. *This* φ is a referential NP and refers to a particular object that is selected from the knowledge base by means of the semantic specifications of the noun φ. In a zero context such an object is simply an instance of a concept of φ taken from the knowledge base[8]. The representation of this referent is consequently modified by the predication of a concept of red, which, again, is selected independently from the knowledge base. The effect can be seen in the (b)-sentences and in how they differ from the (a)-sentences: in cases like (19) there is no clear difference, because there is no relevant composite concept of red shirts. In (20) – (22) however, the difference between the composite concepts and the independently interpreted expressions with their separate concepts is clearly visible.

When I point, say, to a clay tomato with red glazing, an utterance of (20b) is much more plausible than an utterance of (20a). And an utterance of (21a) in view of hair coloured in bright red is distinctly odd, while an utterance of (21b) would be fine.

Consider further

(23)   Red wine is not always red. Often its colour is much closer to brown.
(24)   Red hair is not usually red. It is rather very light brown with a touch of orange.

The first sentences in (23) and (24) are obviously not self-contradictory, which they would have to be if they were interpreted fully compositionally, i.e., without the control strategy just explained.

---

[8] This is probably the most plausible place where stereotypes could play a role: if no contextual specifications are available then such an object is represented as an instance of the stereotype shirt, tomato, etc.

The effects of this control strategy become even clearer in (non–intersective) relative adjectives that are used predicatively. For example,

(25a)   This is a good dentist.
(25b)   This dentist is good.

The second may be used to say that a particular dentist, one among several present, is a good dart player. The former cannot be used for that purpose, at least not in unmarked intonation[9]. The relative adjective *good* in (25b) can be interpreted relative to whatever you please in the context, but the same adjective attributively used, as in (25a), must be relative to the professional qualities of dentists. In other words: in (25a) we are concerned with the composite concept of a good dentist, which is not the case in (25b).

This hypothesis is further confirmed by non–subsective adjectives like *former, alleged, future, apparent*, etc., that is, adjectives for which it does not hold that

$$a(n)\ \alpha_{\alpha \in ADJ}\ \varphi_{\varphi \in N}\ \text{is a}\ \varphi$$

For these adjectives there is no equivalence between "This φ is α" and "This is an $\alpha\varphi$" for the plain reason that an $\alpha\varphi$ is not necessarily a φ.

Non–subsective adjectives cannot be used in predicative position. Compare

(26a)   [*]This police man is former.
(26b)   This is a former police man.

The reason is clear: if, according to our proposed control strategy, predicatively used adjectives are not directly (on the level of compositional semantic processes) applied to the relevant noun, but first refer to a concept, then non–subsective adjectives must fail in this position. They do not have concepts as their interpretation, but only modify concepts. They do not refer to functions from things into the truth–values, but to functions that take concepts as arguments and yield concepts as values. But such second order concepts cannot be the referents of predicate expressions, because they cannot be applied to the referents of subject terms. Non–subsective adjectives can however be used attributively, because in that position they can apply to concepts.

We may conclude from these observations that there is something like a **standard control structure** in the understanding of simple sentences, which provides for a referential interpretation, i.e., an anchoring in the discourse representation or knowledge representation, of the two major constituents, in the simplest case of the main functor and the main argument of the sentence, before any composition of semantic specifications between the two takes place, i.e., before the function is actually applied to the argument.

Below the sentential level however, i.e., in our examples within the NP, semantic composition takes place first and only then is there a referential interpretation, i.e., reference to a concept or object referent[10].

---

[9] The reading becomes possible when we assume that *good* is accented and there are several dart–playing dentists around, not all of them good dart players.

[10] Such control strategies are closely connected with syntax, in particular word order, but also with intonation. The data in the text about the interpretation of adjectives are further strengthened by data from French, which, by and large only allows postposed attributive adjectives, which are related to predicative adjectives pretty much the same way as in English. In cases however, where a separate interpretation of adjective and noun must be prevented, because the intended composite concept

For the mapping of lexical semantic specifications onto concepts these control facts have as their immediate consequence that lexical items that figure as independently referential, such as predicative adjectives, directly refer to concepts as they are available from the discourse representation or the more permanent knowledge representation. However, since non-subsective adjectives have no concepts as their interpretation, the interpretation of, say, (19a) must fail. For the same reason of independence of interpretation, the concepts of red in (19b), (21b), (22b), (23), (24), and (25b) are not influenced by their respective arguments, while the attributive adjectives have no independent interpretation but select a composite concept which they determine together with their noun. Hence there are no contradictions in (23) and (24), and there are different interpretation options for the (a) and (b)-sentences in (19)–(22) and (25).

8   Conclusion

The central point of this paper is to try to give a direction to work on the interaction of linguistic analysis and knowledge representation in knowledge-based NL Systems. I have tried to argue and to demonstrate that without a full linguistic analysis there is little hope that we shall ever have reasonably general and portable language modules in NL systems. It has also become clear, I hope, that this is not a trivial task but requires a decent amount of empirical research for many years to come. But the linguistic research required is not isolated research in pure linguistics, but close cooperation with work on knowledge representation and – although this is a point I have not argued for – psychological work on conceptual systems, is imperative.

The most difficult problem to overcome, I believe, is that the most generally held belief in the scientific community with respect to our problem is that the distinction between linguistic and conceptual facts is arbitrary and hence not a proper research question, but a matter of pragmatic decisions. It is this belief more than anything else that inhibits further progress of the kind Brachman found lacking.

---

cannot be regularly composed by a modification of the noun concept by the adjective concept, the attributive adjective is preposed. Often in these constructions the adjectives assume another meaning than they usually have. Compare, e.g., *ancien roi* vs *roi ancien*, *belle femme* vs *femme belle*, *brave homme* vs *homme brave*, etc. (cf. Chevalier et al., 1964). Also in accordance with our above observation there is no possibility of accenting preposed adjectives in French.

References

Bierwisch, M. (1982): Semantische und konzeptuelle Repräsentation lexikalischer Einheiten. In: R. Ružička and W. Motsch (eds.): Untersuchungen zur Semantik. Akademie–Verlag, Berlin, pp. 61–99

Bosch, P. (1979): Vagueness, ambiguity, and all the rest. In: M. van der Velde, W. Vandeweghe (eds.): Sprachstruktur. (= Akten des 13. Linguistischen Kolloquiums, Gent 1978). Niemeyer, Tübingen. pp. 9–19

Bosch, P. (1983): Agreement and Anaphora. Academic Press. London, New York

Bosch, P. (1985): Lexical meaning contextualized. In: G. Hoppenbrouwers, A. Weijters, P. Seuren (eds.): Meaning and the Lexicon. Foris, Dordrecht. pp. 251–258

Bosch, P. (1990): Indexicality and representation. In: R. Studer (ed.): Natural Language and Logic. Springer–Verlag, Berlin, Heidelberg, New York. pp. 50–61

Bosch, P. and Geurts, B. (1990): Processing definite NPs. Rivista di Linguistica 2:177–199

Brachman, R.J. (1990): The future of knowledge representation. In: Proceeding of the AAAI 1990. MIT Press, Cambridge, MA. pp. 1082–1092

Catlin, J.–C. and Catlin, J. (1973): Intentionality: a source of ambiguity in English? Linguistic Inquiry 3: 504–508

Chevalier, J.–C., et al. (1964): Grammaire Larousse du Francais Contemporain, Librairie Larousse, Paris

Dowty, D.R. (1979): Word Meaning in Montague Grammar. Reidel, Dordrecht

Fodor, J.A., Garrett, M.F., Walker, E.C.T., Parkes, C.H. (1980): Against definitions. Cognition 8:263–367

Jespersen, O. (1956): A Modern English Grammar on Historical Principles. Allen and Unwin, London / Munksgaard, Copenhagen

Lakoff, G. (1970): A note on vagueness and ambiguity. Linguistic Inquiry 1:357–359

Lang, E. (1990): Primary perceptual space and inherent proportion schema. Journal of Semantics 7:121–141

Rommetveit, R. (1986): Meaning, Context, and Control. Discussion Paper at the ESF Workhop in Zurich, Sept. 1986

Vendler, Z. (1967): Verbs and times. In: Z. Vendler: Linguistics in Philosophy. Cornell University Press, Ithaca, NY. pp. 97–121

Winograd, T. and Fernando, F. (1986): Understanding Computers and Cognition. Ablex, Norwood, NJ

Zwicky, A.M. and Sadock, J.M. (1975): Ambiguity tests and how to fail them. In: J.P. Kimball (ed.): Syntax and Semantics, Vol. 4. Academic Press, New York. pp. 1–36

Presupposition, Anaphora, and Lexical Content

Rob A. van der Sandt, Bart Geurts

1   Introduction

Presupposition and anaphora have always been regarded as distinct phenomena. However, an unprejudiced look at some data suggest that, at the very least, presupposition and anaphora have some common characteristics.

(1)   a.   Theo has a little rabbit and his rabbit is grey.

     b.   Theo has a little rabbit and it is grey.

(2)   a.   If Theo has a rabbit, his rabbit is grey.

     b.   If Theo has a rabbit, it is grey.

The (a) sentences are typically described as cases where the presupposition that Theo has a rabbit doesn't go through, for some reason or another. (1a) asserts that Theo has a rabbit, and therefore cannot presuppose it (assuming, as is common, that presupposition and assertion are mutually disjoint). The usual way of describing what is going on in the (b) sentences, on the other hand, is a quite different one. Here, one would say, the anaphoric pronoun *it* links up, or is bound, to its antecedent, *a (little) rabbit*.

At first glance, however, the phenomena that the (a) and (b) sentences exhibit do not seem to be radically different. In particular, we might suspect that the definite NPs in (1a) and (2a) work in precisely the same way as their pronominal counterparts in (1b) and (2b), respectively. Assuming this view, we might explain the fact that neither (1a) nor (2a) presupposes that Theo has a rabbit by pointing to the fact that in both cases the definite NP that induces this presupposition is bound to an antecedent.

We claim that these parallels between full definite NPs and pronominal anaphors extend to virtually all known cases of presupposition (this view was proposed for the first time by Van der Sandt 1989, to appear). If this claim can be upheld, presupposition is simply a species of anaphora, the main difference between presuppositional and anaphoric expressions (in the standard sense) being that the former are richer in semantic content, which accounts for the observation that anaphors must, in general, be bound to an antecedent, whereas presuppositions normally are but need not be bound. If they cannot be bound, they will be added—or, as we shall say, accommodated—to the context, in order to establish a suitable referent after all.

In this paper, then, we explore the idea of viewing presupposition as a kind of anaphora. The discussion is structured as follows. In Section 2 we introduce the notions of presupposition and presupposition projection, as they are known in the literature. We discuss semantic and, in Section 3, pragmatic conceptions of presupposition, and take the latter as a starting point for our own presupposition theory, which entails that we consider presupposition to be an essentially context-dependent phenomenon. Following Van der Sandt (1988), we demonstrate that the process of presupposition projection is subject to acceptability constraints, which we will take over into our theory of anaphora.

Our anaphora theory is an extension of Discourse Representation Theory (Kamp 1981), which is outlined in Section 4. Section 5 advances and defends the main claim of this paper, viz. that presupposition is simply a special kind of anaphora. In the remaining sections this theory is implemented in our extended version of DRT.

Our version of DRT deviates from the original theory in some, relatively minor, respects. First, in contradistinction to Kamp (1981) a discourse representation is constructed in two steps: in the first step an initial representation is derived compositionally, and it is only in the second step that anaphoric references are fixed. Secondly, these initial representations are derived in a bottom-up rather than in a top-down fashion. This is described in Section 6. In Section 7, finally, we discuss the process of anaphora resolution, focusing in particular on the role that constraints on binding and acceptability play in this part of the system.

2 Presupposition induction and presupposition projection

Most sentences we utter carry presuppositions, and the presuppositions they carry are conventionally marked. Definite descriptions are standard examples of presupposition inducers, but they represent only one of many cases where lexical items or syntactic constructions may be said to conventionally mark the presence of a presupposition. Since presuppositions came into focus in the philosophical and linguistic literature, many other presupposition inducers have been observed; the following lexical items and syntactic constructions are widely regarded as paradigm examples:

Factive verbs (*realize, regret, discover, ...*):

(3) a. Tom *regrets* that the goose has been killed.

    b. The goose has been killed.

Aspectual verbs (*begin, stop, continue, ...*):

(4) a. Jones has *stopped* beating his grandmother.

    b. Jones has been beating his grandmother.

Quantifiers (*all, most, ...*):

(5) a. *All* of John's children are asleep.

    b. John has children.

Cleft constructions:

(6) a. *It was* John *who* caught the thief.

    b. Someone caught the thief.

Presuppositional adverbs (*too, even, only, ...*):

(7) a. *Only* Muriel voted for Hubert.

    b. Muriel voted for Hubert.

The (a) sentences are said to have the (b) sentences as their presuppositions. Note first that all these presuppositions are encoded lexically or syntactically. In the example sentences above we indicated this by italicizing the relevant lexical items. These conventional signs which mark the presence of a presupposition are called presupposition inducers. The presuppositions they induce are found under a variety of names, like 'pre-suppositions' (Gazdar 1979), 'elementary presuppositions' (Van der Sandt 1988), 'conventional implicatures' (Karttunen and Peters 1979), etc. Note furthermore that presuppositions need not be independent of each other. Presuppositional constructions may embed further presuppositional constructions, as in (3a) or (6a). (8) constitutes a more dramatic example:

(8) James regrets that it was Jones who killed the butcher's goose. (He would rather have killed the animal himself.)

Here the complement of the factive, which is a conventional presupposition inducer, embeds a presupposition-inducing cleft, which contains a possessive construction, which in turn contains a definite description. This gives rise to the following hierarchy of elementary presuppositions, each member of which is a conventional presupposition of (8).

(9) a. It was Jones who killed the butcher's goose.
     b. Someone killed the butcher's goose.
     c. The butcher had a goose.
     d. There is a butcher.

Note finally that presuppositional inferences differ in their logical behaviour from standard semantic entailments. Semantic entailments are not normally preserved when their carrier sentence occurs as part of a disjunction or a conditional, when it is in the scope of negation or a modal operator, or when it is embedded in an attitude context. Presuppositions, in contrast, tend to survive any depth of embedding, independently of the logical properties of the embedding operators.

(10) a. John's wife will not join him to the cinema.
     b. If John booked for the second show, his wife will join him to the cinema.
     c. It is possible that John's wife will join him to the cinema.
     d. Mary probably thinks that John does not realize that his wife will join him to the cinema.
     e. John has a wife.

In the examples (10a) through (10d) the presuppositional expression John's wife is in the scope of one or more operators which do not preserve standard semantic entailments. But the inference that John has a wife which originates in this presuppositional expression turns out to be preserved in each of the above cases. Inferences emanating from presuppositional expressions thus do not enter into any scope relations with embedding operators, and tend to survive any depth of embedding. In this respect presuppositional expressions seem to be on a par with indexicals and other context-dependent expressions. They are different however in that presuppositional inferences may be blocked in some circumstances, as the following examples demonstrate:

(11) a. It is not true that John has a wife and that *his wife* will join him to the cinema.

    b. If John is married, *his wife* will join him to the cinema.

    c. It is possible that John has a wife and that *his wife* will join him to the cinema.

This phenomenon gives rise to the *projection problem* for presuppositions (this term was coined by Langendoen and Savin 1971): Which parameters are needed to compute the presuppositions of a complex sentence out of the presuppositional expressions of its components? And, given these parameters, how do we define a recursive procedure which, given the elementary presuppositions, yields the actual presuppositions of the compound sentence in a given context of utterance? This problem has been the major focus of research in presupposition theory since the early 1970s, and has given rise to many, often incompatible, 'solutions.'

Intuitively, presuppositional information is information which is taken for granted for the purposes of a discourse, and, as such, sentences which contain conventional presupposition markers impose certain requirements upon the contexts in which they may be uttered. The first task of a presupposition theory thus consists in determining which conventional means natural language has to indicate the existence of such presuppositional information, and specifying its function. The second task is to characterize the requirements the use of sentences containing conventional presupposition markers imposes upon the contexts in which they may be uttered. Once this has been done, we have to specify what happens to the presuppositional requirements of simple sentences under syntactical embedding, i.e. we have to give an account of presupposition projection.

Presupposition originally was conceived of as a semantic phenomenon, to be accounted for in terms of truth and reference. This view has its roots in Frege's philosophy of language. For Frege it is referring expressions that induce presuppositions. The proper use of a sentence containing such expressions requires that they have a denotation in order for the sentence to have a truth value. The solution to the projection problem then follows automatically from Frege's theory of meaning. For Frege the reference of a sentence is its truth value, and the reference of a complex expression is a function of the reference objects of its parts. Thus, if one of the component sentences of a complex sentence suffers from presupposition failure, and therefore has no reference, an extensional compound in which it figures as a part will have no reference either, and thus will suffer from presupposition failure as well. Hence, a purely Fregean theory of presupposition will predict that presuppositions are inherited under any extensional embedding. But, as (11a) and (11b) illustrate, this prediction is not borne out by the empirical data.

Strawson (1950) revived the Fregean theory with his attack on Russell's theory of descriptions. Strawson's basic thesis, which is very close to Frege's, is that a sentence that contains a conventional presupposition marker requires that the presupposition induced be true in order for the sentence to have a truth value. If we then take negation to be an operator which maps true onto false, false onto true, and preserves undefinedness, it follows that presuppositions are always preserved under negation. Strawson took this feature to be the defining characteristic of presupposition. Note that, once preservation under negation has been made the basis of the definition of presupposition, it immediately follows that presupposition should be construed as a binary relation between sentences or, alternatively, propositions. On this view it is sentences, or the propositions they express, which presuppose other sentences or propositions.

The main problem with this view on presupposition is brought out most easily if we adopt the standard way of defining it:

SEMANTIC PRESUPPOSITION:

φ presupposes ψ iff $\varphi \models \psi$ and $\neg\varphi \models \psi$.

On this definition, the presuppositions of a given carrier sentence are those, and only those, sentences that are entailed by both the carrier sentence and its negated counterpart. Although this way of defining presupposition actually requires a trivalent or other non-classical logic, the relevant notion of entailment is the classical one. This makes it easy to show that this strategy, like any attempt to define presupposition in terms of the classical notion of semantic entailment, cannot succeed in the general case. For, as the following examples demonstrate, presuppositional inferences behave in a *non-monotonic* way:

(12) a. It is possible that *John's horse* is in the stable.

    b. It is {not possible/impossible} that *John's horse* is in the stable.

    c. John has a horse.

    d. It is possible that John does not have a horse, but is is also possible that {*it/John's horse*} is in the stable.

    e. John does not have a horse. So {*it/John's horse*} cannot be in the stable.

The possessive constructions in (12a) and (12b) give rise to the presupposition that John has a horse, i.e. (12c), and from either sentence we would infer that (12c) is true. If we take this inference as an instance of semantic entailment and adopt the definition of semantic presupposition given above, it is predicted that (12c) is semantically presupposed by both (12a) and (12b). Now the classical entailment relation is a monotonic one, and hence the semantic stance on presuppositional inferences implies that presuppositions, being entailments, are always preserved under growth of information. This prediction is incorrect however. As (12d) and (12e) illustrate, adding the information that John may not have a horse, or that he does not have one, suffices to remove any inference to the truth of (12c). Consequently, in its standard formulation the semantic account is simply wrong.

In view of examples like (12d) and (12e) it has become customary in the presupposition literature to invoke the Gricean notion of cancellability or defeasibility (see, in particular, Gazdar 1979 and Soames 1979). Presuppositions are said to be cancellable, or defeasible, in the face of conflicting information. Note however that it need not be conflicting information which gives rise to the removal of a presuppositional inference. In (12d) the information that John may not have a horse suffices to remove the presuppositional inference that he has one. But, more importantly, the claim that presuppositional inferences can be cancelled by the addition of new information is just another way of saying that presuppositional inferences behave in a non-monotonic fashion. Cancellability just comes down to non-monotonicity, which is what prevents us from developing an adequate theory of semantic presupposition in terms of the classical notion of entailment.[1]

---

[1] This of course does not prove that one cannot develop and adequate theory of presupposition using some version of non-monotonic logic, but no such attempt to salvage the semantic notion of presupposition has been undertaken up to now. See, however, Mercer's (to appear) reinterpretation and elaboration of Gazdar's (1979) pragmatic theory in terms of Reiter's (1980) default logic.

Since the 1970s, a radically different view on presupposition has become prevalent. It was noted by several authors that contextual factors heavily influence presuppositional behaviour. Given the intuitive understanding of presupposition as information that is being taken for granted, this did not come as a surprise, but it deeply influenced the way presupposition phenomena were viewed, and gave rise to quite a number of theories of *utterance presupposition*. These approaches distinguish themselves in three important respects from previous logical-semantic accounts. First, presupposition is not conceived of anymore as a binary relation between sentences, but as a relation between utterances and propositions. According to this view it would be odd to say that a sentence presupposes another sentence. Rather, it is in *uttering* a sentence in a given context that a speaker takes certain propositions for granted, indicating that he does so by employing conventional presupposition markers.

Secondly, and equally important, presuppositional inferences are essentially independent of truth-conditional content. Only after the semantic content of a sentence has been determined are presuppositions computed. More precisely, they are computed on the basis of (i) the semantic content of the sentence with which they are conventionally, but not truth-conditionally, associated, and (ii) relevant contextual information and pragmatic principles. This view forces proponents of the pragmatic notion of presupposition to divorce semantic content, which attaches to the proposition expressed, from presuppositional content, which is pragmatic and non-truth-conditional in nature. Of course this picture does not rule out the possibility that some presuppositions are entailed by their carrier sentences, but if they are, this is never due to the presuppositional status of an inference. Such entailments, if they arise, should rather be traced back to the conventional meaning of specific lexical items, and will thus carry over to embedding constructions, in compliance with the standard rules of classical logic. In other words, since the presupposition-projection mechanism comes into play only after the propositional content has been computed, all standard entailments are preserved; presuppositional and other pragmatic information is computed only afterwards, and then added to the propositional information expressed. Thus presupposition is incorporated into a wider concept of utterance meaning.

A third characteristic of pragmatic accounts of presupposition is that presuppositional information is considered to be essentially context dependent. A sentence may presuppose a proposition in some contexts but not in others. (12d) and (12e) already demonstrated that this is in fact the case. We give one more example here; many others have been discussed in the literature (see, in particular, Karttunen 1973, Gazdar 1979, Soames 1982, and Van der Sandt 1988).

(13) If *John's girlfriend* sends him to the hairdresser's, he will look better afterwards.

(14) a. If John found a girlfriend, {*she/his girlfriend*} will send him to the hairdresser's.
     b. And if {*she/his girlfriend*} sends him to the hairdresser's, he will look better afterwards.

When confronted with an utterance of (13), we would normally infer that John has a girlfriend. However, if this sentence is uttered in a context in which her existence is merely hypothesized, as is the case in (14a), this presupposition disappears without a trace.

The upshot of these observations is that presupposition must be construed as a ternary relation between sentences, contexts and propositions, or otherwise we wouldn't be able to account for the fact that presuppositions vary with the context. And if we regard utterances, in the usual way, as context-sentence pairs, we can also do justice to the intuition that presuppositions are properties of utterances, not sentences. A context is then constructed as an n-tuple of coordinates, one of which is the context-set parameter. Intuitively, the context set is an information set comprising all propositions that are taken for granted at a given stage of the conversation. Formally this set may be defined as a set of propositions, or simply as their intersection, in which case it is a set of possible worlds that represent the alternatives open to the conversational participants for the remainder of the discourse. The primary function of assertions is to introduce new information. After an assertion has been made its content will be added to the current context set, thus yielding a new context set which will serve as the context for the next utterance. The informational status of the utterance changes in the process: unless retracted or denied, the information it conveys will be presupposed once it has been added to the context set.

Normally the context set will grow monotonically. The amount of information thus increases as the discourse or conversation progresses, and every piece of information which is introduced this way may act as a presupposition in the remainder of the discourse. By the same token, this information restricts the number of possible ways in which the discourse may be continued to those that are consistent with the context set. This is essentially the view Stalnaker presented in the early 1970s (see in particular Stalnaker 1973, 1974, and 1978).

3 Pragmatic theories of presupposition

3.1 PRESUPPOSITIONAL REQUIREMENTS: NEUTRALIZATION VS ACCOMMODATION

The pragmatic picture of presupposition outlined in the foregoing still leaves open the issue of the status concerning the conventional markers by means of which a speaker indicates which propositions he takes for granted. Of course it is not surprising that natural languages contain such markers. For normally the context set will not only include information that has been introduced explicitly, but also further information the speaker tacitly takes for granted. We do not convey the information that Mary is surprised that her cat has escaped by saying the there is a person named Mary, that she has a cat, that this animal escaped, that she did not expect this, but is aware of it now. A conversation in which all information that the speaker wanted to convey were introduced by explicit assertions would be exceedingly long-winded and tiresome. If the information that Mary's cat escaped is considered to be uncontroversial, (15) is a more efficient and straightforward way to convey it:

(15)   Mary is surprised that her cat escaped.

Among the conventional presupposition markers that this sentence contains are the possesive construction *her cat* and the factive complement, which together carry the information that Mary has a cat and that this animal escaped. These constructions allow a cooperative participant to first extend the current context to a richer context which does contain the information they convey, and subsequently evaluate the sentence against the enlarged context. Following Lewis (1979) the two presuppositions are then said to be *accommodated.*

As to the status of conventional presupposition markers, we pointed out that, according to theories of utterance presupposition, a presupposition imposes certain requirements upon the contexts in which its carrier sentence may be used. The strongest claim about these requirements is found in the work of Karttunen (1974), Stalnaker (1973, 1974) and Heim (1983). These authors all take as their point of departure the idea that the presuppositions of a carrier sentence must be *entailed* by the context of utterance in order for it to *admit* the sentence's presuppositions.

Since linguistic presuppositions are conventionally associated with lexical items and syntactic constructions, each simple sentence can be assigned a finite list of elementary presuppositions. The presuppositional requirement that simple sentences impose upon the context can then be characterized as follows:

ADMITTANCE:
A context c admits the presuppositions of a simple sentence φ iff c entails all of the elementary presuppositions of φ.

This means that a context will only admit a sentence φ if it already entails all of φ's elementary presuppositions, or, put otherwise, the utterance of a sentence φ in a context c can only be felicitous in case c entails all its elementary presuppositions. If φ is a complex sentence, presuppositional admittance can be defined recursively, by associating with each constituent sentence of φ its own, so-called 'local,' context, as follows:

ADMITTANCE (continued):
A context c admits a complex sentence φ iff the presuppositions of each of φ's constituent sentence are satisfied by their local contexts.

For an utterance $\langle \varphi, c \rangle$, where φ is of the form "ψ and χ" or "if ψ, then χ," c is the local context for ψ and $c + [\![\psi]\!]$ is the local context for χ.

These clauses are essentially Karttunen's (1974). As has been observed by McCawley (1979) the formulation given is completely neutral as to what happens semantically when a context does not admit the presuppositions of a given sentence. Does the resulting infelicity imply undefinedness—which would turn this into a semantic account? Or should we interpret infelicity simply as pragmatic unacceptability? This last interpretation would put Karttunen's theory on a par with the pragmatic accounts according to which presuppositional requirements may never affect the truth conditions of a sentence. Heim (1983), for instance, interprets Karttunen's felicity requirements as conditions on definedness, and thus reconstructs and elaborates Karttunen's ideas within the framework of her theory of file change semantics.[2]

---

[2]Heim's (1983) theory, though taking Karttunen's account as a starting point, is actually more sophisticated in that she tries to derive Karttunen's rules from her theory of context change, adding an accommodation mechanism and an account of quantified expressions. See Van der Sandt (1988, 1989), Soames (1989) and Zeevat (1991) for further discussion of this rather hermetic paper.

It is of course an overidealization to require that all the presuppositions of a sentence should already be present in the context for its utterance to be felicitous. We have seen above that normal conversation does not proceed in this inefficient and boring fashion. The absence of a 'required' presupposition normally does not result in infelicity. If possible, a cooperative participant will be prepared to simply adjust the context by *accommodating* the presupposition required, thus restoring felicity. It is by means of this notion of accommodation that Karttunen and Heim account for the fact that utterances may introduce new information simply by presupposing it. The definitions given above should therefore be interpreted as accounting for those cases where a presupposition is trivially satisfied, and is actually not felt to have a true presuppositional status anymore. The mechanism is thus essentially a specification of the circumstances under which presuppositions are *neutralized* because the context satisfies them trivially. If presuppositions are not neutralized, they must be accommodated so as to satisfy the presuppositional requirements after all, and it is only then that they emerge as 'real' presuppositions in the context of utterance.

The following examples provide some illustrations:

(16) a.   If John is married, *his wife* will be happy.

b.   If John is married, John has a wife.

(16a) contains the elementary presupposition that John has a wife. The clauses given above require that this presupposition should be entailed by the local context for its carrier sentence to be felicitous, i.e. it should be entailed by $c + [\![John\ is\ married]\!]$. Formally this comes down to saying that c should entail the implicative proposition (16b). Thus it is predicted that (16a) merely presupposes the noncommittal tautology (16b), and since tautologies give no new information whatsoever, the content of the presupposition is effectively neutralized. No accommodation of this presupposition need to be invoked in order to restore felicity.

Consider now:

(17)   If John made coffee, *his wife* will be happy.

Assuming that it is not known beforehand that John has a wife, the local context $c + [\![John\ made\ coffee]\!]$ does not entail that John has a wife. Again the requirement that the local context should entail this elementary presupposition comes down to the requirement that c should entail the implicative proposition *If John made coffee, he has a wife*. Since it does not, we have to accommodate this presupposition to the context in order to restore felicity. The prediction therefore is that an utterance of (17) presupposes that John has a wife, on the assumption that he made coffee. In other words it presupposes that:

(18)   If John made coffee, he has a wife.

It is of course rather curious and counterintuitive that (17) should merely presuppose (18) rather than the stronger *John has a wife*. In general, the Karttunnen/Heim theory predicts that presupposition triggers in the consequent of a conditional will surface, if at all, in a conditionalized form, as in the example given. This peculiar feature of the theory has given rise to quite a bit of discussion in the literature. We will not go into that here, but refer to the defenses by Karttunen and Peters (1979) and Heim (1983), and to the criticisms in Gazdar (1979) and Van der Sandt (1988).

While the Karttunen/Heim theory is basically a theory of neutralization, Van der Sandt's (1988) theory should be characterized as a theory of accommodation. The view on presuppositional requirements Van der Sandt advances is that a carrier sentence should be *acceptable* in a context that already contains its elementary presupposition, i.e. if an elementary presupposition does not yet belong to a context we should be able to accommodate it without violating certain, independently motivatable, constraints on informativeness and efficiency. Thus, while Karttunen and Heim require that presuppositions should already be there in order for the sentence to be felicitous, Van der Sandt merely requires that they can be accommodated without giving rise to infelicity.

Underlying Van der Sandt's approach are two simple assumptions concerning the notions of interpretation and presupposition. First, understanding of a sentence requires that we can interpret it in some context—that is, we must be able to construct a context in which the sentence is acceptable. Secondly, presuppositions belong to these contexts by default. Given these assumptions conventional presupposition markers, or elementary presuppositions, can be conceived of as lexico-syntactic indicators of context selection or context construction. Or in other words, the set of elementary presuppositions associated with a simple sentence determines a class of contexts, i.e. that class of contexts that allow the presuppositions of the sentence to be accommodated.

Context selection, of course, is not an arbitrary process, but is regulated by a number of restricting factors, of which constraints on informativeness and efficiency are the most important ones. Elementary presuppositions associated with a sentence are supposed to be part of the contexts in which their carrier sentences can be interpreted *unless* these acceptability principles prevent their inclusion. Elementary presuppositions thus function as indicators of context selection, and presupposition theory is conceived as a set of principles for selecting or constructing contexts in which the sentences that trigger these presuppositions are to be interpreted.

Speakers normally do not use presupposing sentences unless the presuppositions induced form part of the common background knowledge, or may at least be taken to be uncontroversial. This assumption remains in force unless overridden by stronger factors. One such factor is plain inconsistency, as in those cases that are often described as instances of presupposition cancellation. Another factor is violation of the principle of informativeness, which would happen with a presupposing interpretation of (14b) in a context which contains the implicative proposition expressed by (14a). If interpreted in a context that also contains the elementary presupposition, the violation of such constraints would result in unacceptability of the presupposition-inducing sentence, and consequently a non-presupposing reading is enforced. Contextual acceptability is thus taken to be the general constraint on presuppositional behaviour.

ACCEPTABILITY CONSTRAINT:

If a sentence contains an presupposition-inducing element, elementary presuppositions will be accommodated unless accommodation violates constraints on contextual acceptability.

So given an sentence of the form $\psi \to \chi_{\langle \xi \rangle}$ (where the subscripted $\langle \xi \rangle$ indicates the presence of an elementary presupposition), and a context c_n, we must check whether its utterance would be acceptable in the ξ-extension of c_n. Thus for an utterance of the following form,

Utterance: $\langle \psi \to \chi_{\langle \xi \rangle}, c_n \rangle$

we must check whether it preserves acceptability if uttered in $c_n + [\![\xi]\!]$:

Try: $\langle \psi \to \chi, c_n + [\![\xi]\!] \rangle$

If the utterance does remain acceptable in this enlarged context, c_n will be updated with both the presupposition and the propositional content of the utterance. That is to say, $c_{n+1} = c_n + [\![\xi]\!] + [\![\psi \to \chi]\!]$. The following examples illustrate this procedure.

(19) a. If John made coffee, *his wife* will be happy.

b. John has a wife.

b. John has a wife. If he made coffee, {*she/his wife*} will be happy.

In order to check whether (19a) has a presuppositional reading, we have to determine whether its utterance is acceptable in a context that already contains the elementary presupposition, i.e. a context that at least contains (19b). Accommodation is predicted to take place by default, unless the resulting structure, i.e. (19c), violates conditions on contextual acceptability. Since the addition of (19b) results in an acceptable text, (19a) is predicted to have a presupposing reading, which is correct. Note that this procedure does not yield a conditional presupposition, as on the Karttunen/Heim account, but the stonger presupposition corresponding to its trigger (which, we believe, is intuitively correct).

The following sentence, on the other hand, which is intuitively non-presupposing, resists interpretation in a context that contains the same elementary presupposition.

(20) a. If John is married, *his wife* will be happy.

b. *John has a wife. If he is married, *his wife* will be happy.

Once it is taken for granted that John has a wife, the utterance of a conditional that grants this fact a merely hypothetical status is unacceptable. Accommodation is therefore blocked. The sentence is predicted to have no presupposing reading, which, again, is intuitively correct.

The theory outlined gives rise to a general and relatively simple definition of utterance presupposition:

UTTERANCE PRESUPPOSITION:
An utterance $\langle \varphi, c \rangle$ presupposes a proposition $[\![\xi]\!]$ iff

- ξ belongs to the elementary presuppositions of φ, *and*
- φ is acceptable in $c + [\![\xi]\!]$

Constraints on contextual acceptability are defined in terms of efficiency, informativeness, and consistency. The whole predictive force of a theory like this of course depends upon an adequate definition of the constraints which govern contextual acceptability. We refer to Van der Sandt (1988) for a set of constraints which suffice to handle cases of presupposition projection. Although the proposal that we present in this paper goes beyond the theory of Van der Sandt (1988) in some quite fundamental respects, his acceptability constraints still constitute an important ingredient of the theory. We shall come back to this point later on.

Although empirically Van der Sandt's theory of utterance presupposition does rather well, and handles many examples that are known to present problems to alternative accounts (see Van der Sandt 1988 for details), it leaves us with a problem of explanatory adequacy: It remains unclear what happens to an elementary presupposition that cannot be accommodated. According to what we have said thus far, a presupposition that cannot be accommodated would seem to vanish without a trace. In our opinion the theory that we propose in this paper resolves this conceptual problem in a most natural way. But before we address this issue we first have to discuss a problem which is common to all theories which divorce semantic from presuppositional content.

3.2 A COMMON PROBLEM

In our discussion of the pragmatic notion of presupposition, we pointed out that in pragmatic presupposition theories presuppositional information is essentially independent of truth-conditional content. On a pragmatic account, semantic content is determined first, and presuppositions afterwards, on the basis of the semantic content of the sentence and relevant contextual information. Thus we obtain separate representations of assertoric and presuppositional content, which seems to have the initial advantage that each can be computed in different modes, so to speak. At the same time, however, this procedure gives rise to binding problems, when presuppositions enter into scope relations with quantified expressions.

This problem was first noticed by Karttunen an Peters (1979) and subsequently taken up by Heim (1983). Karttunen and Peters note that their rules predict that (21a) presupposes (21b).

(21)   a.   Someone *managed* to succeed George V on the throne of England.

       b.   It was difficult for someone to succeed George V on the throne of England.

This is unsatisfactory, for (21b) is true, and trivially so: There are many people for whom it would have been difficult to succeed George V on the throne of England. Whereas (21a) sounds odd precisely because it presupposes a falsehood, viz. that it was difficult *for George V's successor* to succeed him to the throne.

The problem is a direct consequence of the decision to represent presuppositional information independently of semantic content. For this decision forces us to bind the indefinite NP by different quantifiers in the presuppositional and the content expression. But what we would like to say is that the person who succeeded George V to the English throne is the *same* as the person who is presupposed to have had difficulties in doing so. And this is precisely what the use of two different quantifiers prevents.

It should be obvious that this problem is a general and fundamental one, and will crop up every time a quantifier binds some variable in a presuppositional expression. Consider (22a) and (22b).

(22) a. A boy beats his cat.

b. A boy has a cat.

The truth-conditional content of (22a) can be represented as (23).

(23) $\exists x \exists y [\text{boy}(x) \land \text{cat}(y) \land \text{poss}(x,y) \land \text{beat}(x,y)]$

We might try to represent the presuppositional expression as follows:

(24) $\exists x \exists y [\text{boy}(x) \land \text{cat}(y) \land \text{poss}(x,y)]$

However, the problem with this attempt, again, is that the resulting representation is too weak: If we evaluate (23) and (24) for their truth, we cannot rule out the possibility that two different boys make them come out true—which is precisely what we would like to avoid.

This problem can be solved in dynamic theories of discourse understanding, which allow us to extend the scope of quantifiers beyond sentence boundaries.[3] In this paper we will adopt a representational formalism in the style of Discourse Representation Theory (Kamp 1981). Another major consideration in favour of a representational account is that it allows us to see clearly that presuppositions can (and should) be construed as anaphors. But before turning to this issue, we must first discuss the general framework in some detail.

4   Discourse Representation Theory

In Discourse Representation Theory (DRT), an intermediate level of representation is postulated, consisting of Discourse Representation Structures, or DRSs. These DRSs are made up out of discourse markers, the objects that are introduced while a discourse proceeds, and predicates that are assigned to these entities. Discourse markers may thus store whatever information accrues on them in the course of a conversation.

A simple Discourse Representation Structure (DRS) K thus consists of a *universe* of variable-like discourse markers, U(K), and a set of *conditions*, Con(K), which ascribe properties to members of U(K). Indefinite NPs introduce discourse markers into the universe of a DRS. (25b), the DRS constructed for (25a), consists of a set of two markers, which will figure as the referents for de indefinite NPs in (25a) for the remainder of the discourse, and a set of conditions wich encode the descriptive content of the predicates. (25c) gives a pictorial representation:

---

[3]Many such theories have been developed over the last 15 years, by workers in artificial intelligence, linguistics and philosophy. Kamp (1981) presents a representational theory of discourse understanding; Fauconnier (1985) and Seuren (1985) propose representational theories of discourse semantics, too. Non-representational variants are Heim (1982) and Groenendijk and Stokhof (1991).

(25) a. A farmer bought a car.

b. $\langle$ {x, y}, { farmer(x), car(y), buy(x,y) } $\rangle$

c.
x y
farmer(x)
car(y)
buy(x, y)

d. $\exists x \exists y$[farmer(x) $\wedge$ car(y) $\wedge$ buy(x,y)]

The DRS in (25b) is true in a given model M if there is a function f that maps the discourse markers x and y onto individuals in M in such a way that f(x) is in the extension of *farmer* in M, f(y) is in the extension of *car*, and $\langle$f(x), f(y)$\rangle$ is in the extension of *buy*. We thus assign to (25b) exactly the same truth-conditions that we assign to (25d), the standard representation of (25a) in first order predicate logic. But note that the indefinite article is not represented as a quantifier. Instead, it is represented by a free variable, and it acquires its existential import from the truth definition, which requires that *there be* a function that verifies the DRS in the model.

Now, if the rudimentary discourse in (25a) is continued by the utterance in (26a), the DRS construction rules extend the DRS in (25b) to that in (26b):[4]

(26) a. It was pink.

b. $\langle$ {x, y}, { farmer(x), car(y), buy(x,y), pink(z), z=y } $\rangle$

c.
x y z
farmer(x)
car(y)
buy(x,y)
pink(z)
z = y

The pronoun requires some antecedent in the stucture established so far. Here it is is bound to the referent for the car in the previous sentence. This is represented by introducing a marker for the pronoun and identifying it with the marker already set up for the car. With respect to its semantic interpretation, (26b) is not dramatically different from (25); we only have obtained some additional restrictions on the form the embedding function can take. But if we think about this structure in standard logical terms, it becomes appararent wherein the interest of this approach lies. For, what this DRS means is that *there is* a farmer who has bought a car, which is pink. In other words, instead of binding separately the discourse markers corresponding to the car in the first sentence and the pronoun in the second, this way of setting up the interpretation procedure makes it possible to dynamically extend the 'scope' of indefinite NPs. It is herein that one of the main interests of DRT lies.

(25b) is a simple DRS, but not all DRSs are simple. In DRT many utterances give rise to DRSs that are embedded within other DRSs. This applies, among others, for utterances involving universal quantification and logical connectives, but also, in more

---

[4]Although we assume that discourse markers should be sorted according to either grammatical or natural gender, we will omit gender information from our representations.

recent versions of DRT, for, e.g., modals and the propositional attitudes (see e.g. Asher 1989).

Conditionals and universally quantified sentences are analysed as creating two structures: an antecedent representation and a consequent representation.

(27) a. Every farmer who owns a donkey beats it.

 b. If a farmer owns a donkey, he beats it.

 c.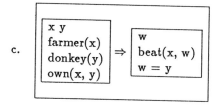

The DRS in (27c), which represents the content of both the universal sentence in (27a) and the conditional in (27b), thus involves the introduction of two subordinate DRS. The truth definition specifies that (27c) is true iff every function f that verifies the left-hand box of the conditional can be extended to a function g that also verifies the right-hand side box. In other words, every farmer-donkey pair in the extension of *own* that f hits upon must also be in the extension of *beat*. This yields, as before, the same truth conditions as would be assigned to their translations into first-order predicate logic. But the quantificational force derives again from the truth definition, which requires that every function which verifies the left-hand box can be extended to a function which verifies the right-hand side. And again we are able to extend the scope of the discourse markers introduced in the antecedent to the pronouns which pick them up in the consequent.

In (27c) the personal pronoun *it* occurring in (27a) and (27b) is initially represented by a discourse marker of it its own, w, which subsequently is equated with the discourse marker induced by the indefinite *a donkey*, y. This is only possible because y is *accessible* to w, in the sense that that w is introduced in a DRS that is subordinate to the DRS in which y is introduced (the right-hand side of a conditional is subordinate to its left-hand side). Somewhat metaphorically speaking: If a pronoun tries to find an antecedent, it must look up from its DRS, and it may not look down.

The notions of subordination and accessibility, which are at the heart of DRT, may be further clarified with the help of the following, schematic DRS:

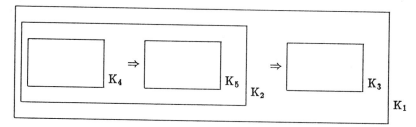

In this DRS, all DRSs are subordinate to K_1, including K_1 itself (we define subordination as a reflexive relation). K_5 is subordinate to K_4, which is subordinate to K_2, and since subordination is a transitive relation, K_5 is subordinate to K_2 as well. Furthermore, although K_3 is subordinate to K_2, and the latter contains K_4 and K_5, neither of these subordinates K_3. Hence, any discourse markers in K_2, but not in K_4 or K_5, will be accessible to discourse markers in the universe of K_3.

The following are definitions of the DRS language and the notions of subordination and accessibility:[5]

DRS DEFINITION:

The vocabulary out of which DRSs are built up consists of discourse markers: x, y, x_1,... ; unary predicates: walk, sleep,... ; and binary predicates: own, beat,...

A DRS K is a pair $\langle U(K), Con(K)\rangle$, where:

- $U(K)$ is a set of discourse markers,
- and $Con(K)$ is a set of DRS conditions.

A DRS condition is any expression of one of the following forms:

- $P(x)$, where P is a unary predicate
- $R(x,y)$, where R is a binary predicate
- $K \Rightarrow K'$, where K and K' are DRSs

SUBORDINATION:[6]

K subordinates K' iff one of the following holds:

- $K = K'$
- $Con(K)$ contains a condition of the form $K' \Rightarrow K''$, for some K''
- A condition of the form $K \Rightarrow K'$ is contained in $Con(K'')$, for some K''
- There is a K'' such that K subordinates K'' and K'' subordinates K'

ACCESSIBILITY

$x \in U(K)$, is accessible to $x' \in U(K')$, iff K' is subordinate to K.

Note that, because subordination is a reflexive relation, every two discourse markers that are in the same DRS are accessible to one another. The non-reflexive counterpart to subordination will be referred to as *strict subordination*.

The effects of the accessibility constraint on the interpretation of anaphoric pronouns— which is a crucial tenet of DRT—can be demonstrated with the help of the following example:

(28) a. Every farmer owns [a donkey]$_i$. *It$_i$ is grey.

b.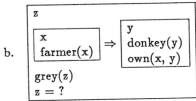

---

[5] The DRS language that we need for our present exposition is quite restricted. We will not need negation, for instance. We take it, of course, that the theory that we demonstrate with the help of this restricted language is extendable to languages that cover larger fragments of English.

[6] This standard notion of subordination will be extended below.

In this case, the discourse marker induced by *it*, z, cannot link up to y, because y is not accessible to z. Consequently, it is predicted that (28a), in the intended reading, is ill formed—which appears to be correct.

One way to view accessibility is as a configurational restriction on the construction of DRSs. Thus it serves to exclude discourses like the one above, which, without this constraint, would give rise to a configuration in which z and y are equal. Not only would this yield the incorrect empirical predictions with respect to well-formedness and anaphoric binding, but also would the resulting interpretation give the wrong result for the initial sentence: The DRS would only be true in models in which all farmers own the same donkey. Accessibility therefore is crucial to DRT, and it will turn out to be crucial to our notion of presuppositions as a anaphoric expressions as well.

What we have seen of DRT thus far offers explanations for two important types of data. First, it provides an explanation for the kind of anaphoric linking that we find in (27a). This is an important argument in favour of dynamic theories of discourse interpretation, like DRT. In some way or the other, the personal pronoun *it* that occurs in this example must be (semantically) bound by its antecedent. This being the case, we might expect that the pronoun would be syntactically bound by its antecedent as well. This however is not the case: Currently, there simply is no well-established notion of syntactic binding that could explain the semantic behaviour characteristic of 'donkey pronouns.' It is clear, and the data that we shall be discussing below shall make it even clearer, that the concepts of semantic and syntactic binding do not match perfectly. If anything, the latter applies in a more restricted domain than the former—and DRT promises to at least offer a plausible account of those cases where semantic binding applies while syntactic binding does not.[7]

The second, and in a sense complementary, set of data that DRT offers an explanation for is exemplified by (28a). These are the cases where semantic binding would have to apply but, somehow, cannot. The accessibility constraint serves to explain these data, in that it excludes anaphoric links between pronouns and antecedents that are not 'visible' to them.[8]

---

[7]Kamp (1981) even purports to offer a unified account of anaphora *simpliciter*, but thus far we have failed see how a theory of anaphora could dispense with the notion of syntactic binding altogether (for instance to account for the distribution of reflexives), although we do believe that the usefulness of this notion will turn out to be (even) more restricted than is widely assumed.

Finally, and perhaps most importantly, DRT is a dynamic theory of discourse, in the sense that it allows for the scope of certain NPs (in particular, of those that land at top level in the DRS) to be extended indefinitely. It is these features that make DRT an adequate point of departure for the kind of theory that we want to outline in the following.

5 Presupposition as anaphora

Up to now presupposition theory and theories of anaphora have developed along different lines. Presupposition projection and anaphora resolution have always been regarded as separate phenomena, each subject to a different set of rules. While presuppositions were originally analysed in terms of truth and entailment and were subsequently said to be required or satisfied by a context of utterance, anaphora theory centred around the analysis of pronouns which were analysed in terms of coreference and binding. It was only with respect to definite descriptions that it has been noted, by several authors, that they can be used anaphorically. But at the same time it was always taken for granted that the presuppositional properties of definite NPs had to be handled by a separate mechanism. McCawley (1979), for example, who presents an anaphoric account of definite descriptions, takes Karttunen's (1974) rules as a starting point for an account of their behaviour under embedding. In Heim's (1982) theory of file change semantics, to mention one other example, the analysis of definiteness simply comes down to a specification of the anaphoric properties of definite expressions. But still Heim (1983) presents a Karttunen-type account of presupposition projection, formulated in terms of context-change potentials.

In this paper we will follow van der Sandt (1989, to appear), and advance the claim that it is wrong to treat anaphora and presupposition separately. This claim does not just apply to definite descriptions, but to all paradigm cases of presuppositions. It generalizes to cleft constructions, factives, aspectual verbs, and presuppositional adverbs, by taking propositional and VP anaphora into account.[9] Presuppositions, we claim, just are

---

[8] As it turns out, however, the accessibility constraint excludes too much. DRT must predict that an embedded discourse marker is forever inaccessible after the sentence (or main clause) that introduces the marker has been processed. This prediction is corroborated by (28a), but makes false predictions in a number of other cases, as the following examples demonstrate:

(i)   Every rice farmer in Korea owns a wooden cart. Usually, *it* is a rickety old thing. (Sells 1985)

(ii) If John bought a book, he'll be home reading it by now. *It'll* be a murder mystery. (Roberts 1987)

(iii) Some farmers who own a donkey beat it, and some pamper *it*.

(iv) Many farmers in this town own a donkey, and they beat *it* every day.

All of these discourses present the same type of problem to DRT. In each case, the second sentence or main clause contains a 'donkey pronoun,' which must be bound by its antecedent. However, DRT predicts that anaphoric linking is impossible in cases like these. Each new processing unit that is added to the principal DRS K, which represents the previous discourse, has access only to the markers that are available at the top level of K. The italicized pronouns in (i)–(iv) must get at markers introduced in subordinate DRSs, and this is precisely what the accessibility constraint forbids. See, in particular, Roberts (1987) for further discussion.

[9] We may want to exclude the Fillmore-type lexical presuppositions that attach to lexical items such

anaphors. They can be handled in DRT by basically the same mechanism that handles the resolution of pronominal and other anaphora. They only differ from semantically less loaded anaphors, like pronouns, in that they have more descriptive content. This makes them, on the one hand, pre-eminently suited to control resolution in those cases where sorting for gender and number does not suffice to link a pronoun univocally to an antecedent. On the other hand, because they have substantial semantic content of their own, the information they contain may be accommodated in case no suitable antecedent can be found. Accommodation and anaphoric linking may thus be taken to be two sides of the same coin.

In order to see that there are quite a number of non-trivial correspondences between anaphora resolution on the one hand and presupposition projection on the other, it is instructive to compare Karttunen's initial paradigm cases of presupposition filtering with the donkey sentences that gave rise to the anaphora theory developed in DRT. Karttunen's (1973) examples are the following:

(29) a.   Jack has children and all of Jack's children are bald.

(30) a.   If Jack has children, then all of Jack's children are bald.

(31) a.   Either Jack has no children or all of Jack's children are bald.

And these are the well known donkey sentences:[10]

(29) b.   John owns a donkey. He beats it.

(30) b.   If John owns a donkey, he beats it.

(31) b.   Either John does not own a donkey or he beats it.

Now the problem as Karttunen formulated it for presupposition theory was how to account for the fact that none of the (a) sentences preserves the presupposition that Jack has children. The problem for a theory of discourse interpretation, on the other hand, was to find a mechanism that allows us to account in a uniform way for the anaphoric links between the pronouns and their antecedents in the (b) sentences.

It is obvious that the (a) sentences exactly parallel the (b) sentences. The only difference we find is that the (a) sentences contain full definite NPs where the (b) sentences contain pronouns. In fact we can easily pronominalize the presuppositional expression in the (a) sentences, and thus turn them into donkey sentences. It is equally simple to expand the pronouns in the (b) sentences into full definite descriptions, thus identifying the (b) sentences with cases of presupposition filtering. No difference in interpretation results in either case. Such observations suggests that there is something wrong in saying that

---

as *bachelor*. Zeevat (1991) claims that factive verbs should not be treated as anaphoric presuppositions either. A discussion of the anaphoric properties of different types of presupposition inducers is found in Van der Sandt (to appear).

[10]As it turns out, example (31b) presents a problem to DRT, because the donkey in the first disjunct is not accessible to the pronoun in the second. However, the accommodation mechanism that we propose easily handles the corresponding 'presuppositional' sentence in which the pronoun has been replaced by a full definite NP. This solution would carry over to the pronoun case, if we would treat the pronoun in the second disjunct as an E-type pronoun.

the presuppositions in the (a) sentences are suspended, cancelled or neutralized. Instead, we should say that they are linked to a previously established antecedent, just like the pronouns are.

We already remarked that pronouns are poorer in semantic content than definite NPs and other presupposition-inducing constructions. This is in fact an crucial observation, which accounts for some of differences in behaviour between anaphoric pronouns on the one hand and, e.g., definite NPs on the other. Since presupposing constructions may give rise to accommodation, whereas pronouns generally cannot, because they are very nearly empty semantically speaking, a presupposing sentence may get a determinate semantic value in cases where its pronominalized counterpart will not get an interpretation at all. Compare:

(32) a. All of Jack's children are bald.

(33) a. If baldness is hereditary, then all of Jack's children are bald.

(32) b. They are all bald.

(33) b. If baldness is hereditary, then they are all bald.

The (b) sentences are unintelligible in isolation, and the obvious explanation is that presuppositional expressions differ from pronouns, or other types of semantically less loaded anaphoric expressions, in that they contain enough descriptive content to establish a reference marker in case the discourse does not provide one. Accommodation may and in most cases will take place at top level. It then follows that the information contained in its trigger will be entailed by the DRS, and thus be preserved intuitively. However, certain principles that we will discuss below may force accommodation at some subordinate level. In these cases the presuppositional information will still be there, but remain invisible and not surface as an intuitive inference.

This picture allows a reinterpretion of the central theoretical notions of presupposition theory. To say that a sentence is presupposing (in a given discourse) simply means that its presupposition has been accommodated at top level. Projection comes down to contextual accommodation of the lexical information contained in the 'presuppositional anaphor,' which enables us to establish an anaphoric link after all. Neutralization or presuppositional satisfaction boils down to anaphoric binding at some level of representation. And the notion that presuppositions may be cancelled makes no sense anymore. We can do away with it as a misleading label which covered both cases where a presupposition is bound to some antecedent as well as cases where a presuppositon is is not accommodated at top level because otherwise a violation of acceptability would ensue.

Before implementing these claims in a formal framework we want to emphasize two points. First, the claim that presuppositional expressions are nothing but anaphors with the capacity to accommodate, is not confined to definite descriptions, but holds for presuppositional constructions generally. Here are two examples, one involving a cleft construction, the other a factive verb:

(34) a. If the problem was difficult to solve, it was Julius who solved it.

   b. If someone solved the problem, it was Julius who solved it.

(35) a.   If Mary made coffee, John is happy that she came home.

b.   If Mary came home, John is happy that she {came home/did}.

The (a) sentences are typical examples of accommodation. The information contained in the presuppositional expression cannot be bound and is projected to the top level of the discourse representation, which explains why they are intuitively perceived as presupposing. The (b) sentences do not for allow a presuppositional reading. They are instances of VP-anaphora and full propositional anaphora respectively. In both cases the presuppositional anaphor is bound in the antecedent.

Secondly, in a number of cases a presuppositional anaphor may but need not be bound. In the following sentences this gives rise to two interpretations. Binding absorbs the presuppositional expression in the antecedent, while accommodation at top level yields a presupposing reading.[11]

(36) a.   If someone at the conference solved the problem, it was Julius who solved it.

b.   If John murdered his wife, he will be glad that she is dead.

In these cases the antecedent entails the presupposition of the consequent but not vice versa. The presuppositional anaphor can either be resolved in the antecedent or accommodated at top level. The accommodating reading is most easily perceived in the following examples.

(37) a.   If someone at the conference solved the problem, it was Julius who solved it, but if it was solved at IWBS Stuttgart, it certainly wasn't Julius.

b.   If John murdered his wife, he will be glad that she is dead, but if she took those pills herself...

In the present account presupposing simply boils down to accommodation at top level. This means that a discourse marker is created which can function as an antecedent for the remainder of the discourse. Hence, we should expect that, on an accommodating reading, the presuppositions in the sentences above may be taken up anaphorically. The following continuations show that this prediction is borne out:

(38) a.   But whoever did, the solution was brilliant anyway.

b.   But whatever happened, her mother will be devastated by her death.

These discourses, therefore, provide additional support for our theory. Note again how the predictions of the present account contrast with the predictions of the Karttunen/Heim approach. For their prediction that an entailment relation between the the antecedent and a presupposition of the consequent effectively neutralizes this presupposition precludes an account of why the anaphora in (38) should be possible.

---

[11]Soames (1979) claims that such sentences were completely neutral with respect to survival of presuppositions. We refer to Van der Sandt (1988, 1989) for extensive argumentation that such sentences should not be analysed as presuppositionally neutral, but as pragmatically ambiguous between the two readings.

6 Lexical encoding of presuppositions

6.1 SENTENCE DRSs

We propose that an utterance φ is processed in (at least) two stages: In the first stage, the anaphoric elements that φ contains are collected; in the second stage, these anaphors are, in effect, processed, which means that they are either identified with a proper antecedent or that they are accommodated at some level of the DRS that represents the discourse. Our particular version of DRT mirrors this two-step process.

Kamp (1981) defines the DRS construction procedure as applying to a pair consisting of the main DRS, which represents the previous discourse, and the syntactic analysis of a given sentence. The syntactic tree is taken apart in a top-down fashion, and new discourse markers and conditions are added to the main DRS in the process. Also, anaphoric references are resolved against the current content of the main DRS. In our version of DRT, in contrast, we first construct a *sentence DRS* (SDRS; cf. Asher 1989). SDRSs will look much like DRSs, the main differences being that in an SDRS (i) anaphoric elements are, as yet, unresolved, and that (ii) an SDRS imposes a segmentation upon the the content of the sentence, in order to explicitly demarcate those parts of the sentence's content that are anaphoric. After an SDRS has been constructed (and we presently shall show how that can be done), it is first merged with the main DRS, and only then the anaphors that it contains are resolved.

In our version of DRT, SDRSs thus take the place that syntactic analyses occupy in Kamp's, but the correspondence is only a rough one, because the only thing that remains to be done, after an SDRS has been merged with the main DRS, is resolve any anaphoric elements that occur in the SDRS. A further difference is that, in contradistinction to Kamp's top-down approach, we shall construct SDRSs in a bottom-up fashion.[12]

We proceed to give a definition of the SDRS language. As said before, SDRSs look much like DRSs.—In fact, the SDRS definition just extends the DRS definition given above in a straightforward manner:

SDRS DEFINITION:
An SDRS K is a triple $\langle U(K), Con(K), A(K) \rangle$, where:

- $U(K)$ is a set of discourse markers,
- $Con(K)$ is a set of DRS conditions,
- and $A(K)$ is a (possibly empty) set of SDRSs.

This definition of an SDRS differs from the standard DRS definition only in that a third component is added to the DRS structure, viz. $A(K)$, which is a set of SDRSs. We shall refer to this component as the *A-structure* of K, and to its elements as *DRS-segments*. The function of the A-structure is to demarcate those parts of K that contain anaphoric material. Note that, since $A(K)$ is a set of SDRSs, which have A-structures themselves, we have a means for embedding chunks of anaphoric material into larger chunks.

An example will help to clarify what we want an A-structure to do. Officially the SDRS to be associated with (39a) will be the structure given in (39b):

---

[12]See Asher (1989), Reyle (1985), Zeevat et al. (1987), and Zeevat (1991) for alternative bottom-up versions of DRT.

(39) a. His dog sleeps.

b. ⟨ ∅, { sleep(x) }, ⟨ {x}, { dog(x), poss(y,x) }, ⟨ {y}, ∅, ∅ ⟩ ⟩ ⟩

In our pictorial representation of SDRSs, we indicate the A-structure of a SDRS by rendering anaphoric material in italics and enclosing it by boxes which are not prefixed by any operator. E.g. the SDRS in (39b) is represented thus:

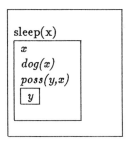

This representation visualizes that (39) contains two anaphors—one corresponding to the subject NP and one to the 'he' in *his*—and that one is contained in the other. The reason why we segment SDRSs in this way is that we want to be able to stipulate that, if an anaphor is embedded in another, the former has to be processed (i.e. linked to an antecedent or accommodated) before the latter. This ordering will be discussed below.

Since, on the one hand, SDRSs just contain more structure than DRSs do, and, on the other hand, we will need several notions that apply equally to DRSs and SDRSs, it will be convenient to have a single cover term for SDRSs and DRSs. We will use the standard term "DRS" for this purpose, and use the terms "main DRS" and "sentence DRS" only in those cases where the distinction is relevant.

The following definition extends the notion of subordination to apply to DRS-segments as well as to DRSs. We will need this extension to describe how anaphoric material (represented as DRS-segments) can be projected upwards to a higher DRS.

SUBORDINATION (final version):

A DRS K subordinates a DRS K′ iff one of the following holds:

- K = K′
- Con(K) contains a condition of the form K′ ⇒ K″, for some K″
- A condition of the form K ⇒ K′ is contained in Con(K″), for some K″
- K′ ∈ A(K)
- There is a K″ such that K subordinates K″ and K″ subordinates K′

The notion of a projection line will be needed to describe the path an anaphor must follow when it attempts to climb up to a higher position in a given DRS:

PROJECTION LINES:

The set of DRSs that a given DRS K is subordinate to is K's *projection line*.

A DRS K' is *lower* on K's projection line than K" iff both K' and K" subordinate K and K" strictly subordinates K'.

A DRS K' is *higher* on K's projection line than K" iff both K' and K" subordinate K and K' strictly subordinates K".

The basic idea that we want to put forward can now be summarized as follows: After a sentence DRS K has been merged with the main DRS, anaphoric material in the K will attempt to climb up along projection lines, starting with anaphors that contain no anaphors of their own, followed by anaphors that contain just a single anaphor, and so on. This process, which is subject to various constraints, will be discussed more thoroughly later on. But before we can go into that, we must first discuss the first phase of DRS construction, in which a sentence DRS is synthesized.

6.2 SDRS DESCRIPTIONS

We already said that we intend to construct sentence DRSs in a bottom-up fashion, i.e. in parallel with the syntactic analysis of the sentence. More in particular, we want to explore the idea of viewing this bottom-up procedure as a process of *collecting constraints* on possible SDRSs. The basic idea is the following: The lexicon associates with words partial descriptions of SDRSs. E.g. the adjective *bald* will be assigned the description $\{x \in U(K), bald(x) \in Con(K)\}$, which partially describes each SDRS whose universe contains a discourse marker x, and one of whose conditions is of the form "bald(x)," *or* which subordinates a SDRS that satisfies these two requirements. It is the task of the grammar to associate with each syntactic constituent X a partial description as a function of the descriptions associated with the constituents of X and the way in which these constituents are put together. So what we end up with is a partial SDRS description associated with the whole sentence. Let us call this description $\mathcal{D}$.

By definition $\mathcal{D}$ is a partial description of an infinitely large number of SDRSs. For instance, if $\mathcal{D}$ partially describes K, then it also partially describes all SDRSs that subordinate K. What we are interested in, intuitively, is the *simplest* SDRS that $\mathcal{D}$ partially describes—or put otherwise, we want to obtain an SDRS of which $\mathcal{D}$ is a *complete description*.[13]

In order to make these ideas a bit more precise, we first have to specify what an appropriate SDRS description looks like. The vocabulary for SDRS descriptions contains the same predicates as that for SDRSs (and DRSs). Apart from that we have: marker variables: x, y, x_1,... ; and SDRS variables: K, K_1,...

SDRS DESCRIPTIONS:

SDRS description $\mathcal{D}$ is a set of constraints, where a constraint is of either of the following forms:

- $x \in U(K)$

- $P(x) \in Con(K)$

---

[13]It will transpire that the set of SDRSs that $\mathcal{D}$ describes completely is infinitely large too (assuming that the inventory of discourse markers is indefinitely large). However, our definitions will guarantee that all members of this set are alphabetic variants.

- $R(x,y) \in \text{Con}(\mathbf{K})$
- $\mathbf{K} \Rightarrow \mathbf{K'} \in \text{Con}(\mathbf{K})$
- $\mathbf{K} \in A(\mathbf{K'})$
- $\mathbf{K} = \mathbf{K'}$
- $x = y$

It should be fairly obvious how SDRS descriptions, defined thus, can be employed to describe SDRSs. To give one simple example (more complicated ones will be offered later on), the following SDRS,

$$\boxed{\begin{array}{l} x \\ \text{man(x)} \\ \text{sleep(x)} \end{array}}$$

satisfies the description in (40):

(40) $x_1 \in U(\mathbf{K}_1)$, $\text{man}(x_1) \in \text{Con}(\mathbf{K}_1)$,
         $x_2 \in U(\mathbf{K}_2)$, $\text{sleep}(x_2 \in \text{Con}(\mathbf{K}_2)$,
         $x_1 = x_2$, $\mathbf{K}_1 = \mathbf{K}_2$

In the type of grammar that we shall outline presently, the equations that occur in descriptions like (40) are furnished, by and large, by the syntactic-semantic rules; the remaining conditions are projected up from the lexicon.

Without further provisions SDRS descriptions may be misused to describe structures that are not well-formed SDRSs. Of course, we wouldn't want our grammar to produce such descriptions, so we might as well ignore them. However, we must still define which SDRS actually satisfy a given SDRS description. And since we will need only a subset of SDRS-description language, as defined above, we may as well further restrict this notion of 'satisfaction' to the subset of SDRS descriptions that we need in practice. Apart from the fact that this is a reasonable move, it is also a convenient one, because it thus becomes possible to define the notion of satisfaction in a straightforward manner. Hence, we shall restrict our attention to a subset of SDRS descriptions, which we dub the *proper* ones. Roughly, a proper SDRS description is one in which all SDRS variables are linked into a graph structure. In order to be able to define what properness is, we first define the notion of embedding:

EMBEDDING IN $\mathcal{D}$:
$\mathbf{K}$ *embeds* $\mathbf{K'}$ in $\mathcal{D}$ iff either of the following hold:

- $\mathcal{D} \models \mathbf{K} = \mathbf{K'}$
- $\mathcal{D} \models \mathbf{K'} \Rightarrow \mathbf{K''} \in \text{Con}(\mathbf{K})$, for some $\mathbf{K''}$
- $\mathcal{D} \models \mathbf{K''} \Rightarrow \mathbf{K}_2 \in \text{Con}(\mathbf{K})$, for some $\mathbf{K''}$
- $\mathcal{D} \models \mathbf{K'} \in A(\mathbf{K})$
- There is some $\mathbf{K''}$ in $\mathcal{D}$ such that $\mathbf{K}_1$ embeds $\mathbf{K''}$ and $\mathbf{K''}$ embeds $\mathbf{K'}$ in $\mathcal{D}$

PROPER SDRS DESCRIPTIONS:

An SDRS description $\mathcal{D}$ is *proper* iff some $\mathbf{K}$ in $\mathcal{D}$ embeds all $\mathbf{K'}$ in $\mathcal{D}$; $\mathbf{K_1}$ is called *maximal* in $\mathcal{D}$.

Now we are all set to define what it means for a SDRS to satisfy a (proper) SDRS description:

COMPLETE SDRS DESCRIPTIONS:[14]

A proper SDRS description $\mathcal{D}$ is a complete description of an SDRS K iff there is a function σ such that, for some maximal $\mathbf{K}$ in $\mathcal{D}$, $\sigma(\mathbf{K}) = \mathbf{K}$.

σ may be any function, as long as it obeys the following constraints:[15]

   i. $\sigma(\mathbf{K}) = \langle \sigma(\mathrm{U}(\mathbf{K})), \sigma(\mathrm{Con}(\mathbf{K})), \sigma(\mathrm{A}(\mathbf{K})) \rangle$

  ii. $\sigma(\mathrm{U}(\mathbf{K})) = \{\sigma(x) \colon \mathcal{D} \models x \in \mathrm{U}(\mathbf{K})\}$

 iii. $\sigma(\mathrm{Con}(\mathbf{K})) = \{\sigma(\mathrm{C}) \colon \mathcal{D} \models \mathrm{C} \in \mathrm{Con}(\mathbf{K})\}$

 iv. $\sigma(\mathrm{A}(\mathbf{K})) = \{\sigma(\mathbf{K'}) \colon \mathcal{D} \models \mathbf{K'} \in \mathrm{A}(\mathbf{K})\}$

  v. $\sigma(\mathbf{K} \Rightarrow \mathbf{K'}) = \sigma(\mathbf{K}) \Rightarrow \sigma(\mathbf{K'})$

 vi. $\sigma(\mathrm{P}(x)) = \mathrm{P}(\sigma(x))$

 vii. $\sigma(\mathrm{R}(x,y)) = \mathrm{R}(\sigma(x),\sigma(y))$

viii. $\sigma(x) = \sigma(y)$ iff $\mathcal{D} \models x = y$

It should be obvious that in this definition it is the function σ that does the work. σ takes apart an SDRS description starting from the top, that is, from some maximal SDRS variable downwards, and then recursively pieces together SDRS universes, condition sets, conditions, and so on. σ maps SDRS variables that are equal onto the same SDRS, and equal pairs of marker variables to the same discourse marker (which is guaranteed by clause (viii) of the definition). But it is not restricted as to *which* discourse markers it should pick. Hence, assuming that the supply of discourse markers is indefinitely large, the set of SDRSs that satisfies any proper SDRS description is infinitely large as well—however, all SDRSs in this set will turn out to be identical under a systematic substitution of discourse markers.

6.3 PUTTING IT ALL TOGETHER

SDRS descriptions are the structures that our grammar will put together in deriving a sentence DRS. It remains to be seen, however, in what way the grammar puts together these structures. It is to this issue that we now turn. The notion of SDRS description is

---

[14] A convenient way of defining partial SDRS descriptions would be the following:

    A proper description $\mathcal{D}$ is a partial description of an SDRS K iff there is a function τ such that, for some maximal $\mathbf{K}$ in $\mathcal{D}$, $\tau(\mathbf{K}) = \mathbf{K}$ or $\tau(\mathbf{K}) = \mathbf{K'}$, where $\mathbf{K'}$ is subordinate to $\mathbf{K}$.

τ is defined exactly as σ is, except that, in the clauses (ii)–(iv), "=" is replaced by "$\supseteq$," which makes every complete description a partial description. Nor is it hard to see that the SDRS (but cf. note 13) that $\mathcal{D}$ describes completely is the simplest that $\mathcal{D}$ describes partially.

[15] In this definition, "C" stands for the counterpart of a DRS condition in a SDRS description, i.e. any expression of the form $\mathrm{P}(x)$, $\mathrm{R}(x,y)$, or $\mathbf{K} \Rightarrow \mathbf{K'}$. All other symbols have their expected meanings.

much in the spirit of a large body of research in syntactic theory, in which notions like 'unification' and 'constraint satisfaction' take pride of place, and we developed it with the explicit intention of combining it with a theory like CUG, LFG, or HPSG. The formalism as such really is indifferent as to which exact syntax it is combined with; here we want to embed it in a CUG-style grammar.[16]

Our lexicon assigns to words lexical entries that consist of three components. First, each word has a syntactic category, which may be either simple or a functor category. Secondly, each word comes with a set of constraints, CONS; this set is associated with the word itself. In contrast, the third component, a set of indices (INDs), is assigned to each element of a complex category. These indices are going to control the process of setting up equations of SDRS variables and marker variables. Thus an index is pair consisting of a SDRS variable and a marker variable, for which we write $K[x]$.[17]

The following is a list of lexical entries for a handful of words:

curate:
CAT: N
$\text{IND}(N) = K_1[x_1]$
CONS: $x_1 \in U(K_1)$, $\text{curate}(x_1) \in \text{Con}(K_1)$

queer:
CAT: N_1/N_2
$\text{IND}(N_1) = \text{IND}(N_2) = K_2[x_2]$
CONS: $x_2 \in U(K_2)$, $\text{queer}(x_2) \in \text{Con}(K_2)$

Theo:
CAT: NP
$\text{IND}(NP) = K_4[x_3]$
CONS: $x_3 \in U(K_3)$, $\text{Theo}(x_3) \in \text{Con}(K_3)$, $K_3 \in A(K_4)$

curses:
$S \backslash NP$
$\text{IND}(S) = K_5[.]$, $\text{IND}(NP) = K_5[x_5]$
CONS: $x_5 \in U(K_5)$, $\text{curse}(x_5) \in \text{Con}(K_5)$

the:
CAT: NP/N
$\text{IND}(NP) = K_7[x_6]$, $\text{IND}(N) = K_6[x_6]$
CONS: $x_6 \in U(K_6)$, $K_6 \in A(K_7)$

a:
CAT: NP/N
$\text{IND}(NP) = \text{IND}(N) = K_8[x_8]$
CONS: $\emptyset$

---

[16]This is really just a toy grammar, which however suffices for our present expository purposes. We use a categorial grammar mainly because categorial grammars are fairly well known, easy to formulate, and don't take up too much space. See Zeevat et al. (1987) for a more serious version of CUG.

[17]The second element of the index of a verb or sentence would involve something like an event marker. However, since our concern here is not with the semantics of events, we will simply leave this parameter out.

his:
CAT: NP/N
IND(NP) = $\mathbf{K}_{11}[x_{10}]$, IND(N) = $\mathbf{K}_{10}[x_{10}]$
CONS: $\begin{cases} x_9 \in \mathrm{U}(\mathbf{K}_9),\ x_{10} \in \mathrm{U}(\mathbf{K}_{10}), \\ \mathrm{poss}(x_9, x_{10}) \in \mathrm{Con}(\mathbf{K}_{10}),\ \mathbf{K}_9 \in \mathrm{A}(\mathbf{K}_{10}),\ \mathbf{K}_{10} \in \mathrm{A}(\mathbf{K}_{11}) \end{cases}$

's:
CAT: $(\mathrm{NP}_1/\mathrm{N})\backslash \mathrm{NP}_2$
IND(NP$_1$) = $\mathbf{K}_{13}[x_{13}]$, IND(NP$_2$) = $\mathbf{K}_{12}[x_{12}]$, IND(N) = $\mathbf{K}_{12}[x_{13}]$
CONS: $x_{12} \in \mathrm{U}(\mathbf{K}_{12})$, $\mathrm{poss}(x_{12}, x_{13}) \in \mathrm{Con}(\mathbf{K}_{12})$, $\mathbf{K}_{12} \in \mathrm{A}(\mathbf{K}_{13})$

The only two combination rules that we need can now be defined thus (in these definitions we use eq($\mathbf{K}_1[x_1]$,$\mathbf{K}_2[x_2]$) as a shorthand for the set $\{\mathbf{K}_1 = \mathbf{K}',\ x_1 = x_2\}$ if both x_1 and x_2 are defined, and for the set $\{\mathbf{K}_1 = \mathbf{K}'\}$ if either of them is not—in which case we are dealing with a verb; cf. note 17):

RIGHTWARD COMBINATION:
$X/Y_1 + Y_2 \ \Rightarrow\ X$, where:
CONS(X) = CONS(X/Y$_1$) $\cup$ CONS(Y$_2$) $\cup$ eq(IND(Y$_1$),IND(Y$_2$))

LEFTWARD COMBINATION:
$Y_2 + X\backslash Y_1 \ \Rightarrow\ X$, where:
CONS(X) = CONS(X/Y$_1$) $\cup$ CONS(Y$_2$) $\cup$ eq(IND(Y$_1$),IND(Y$_2$))

Now let us consider a few examples to see how the machinery that we have set up works, starting with a very simple case. Take the phrase *a queer curate*. In this phrase, *queer* combines to the right to take *curate*, and *queer curate* is taken as an argument by the indefinite article *a*. Taking the lexical entries as given above, and applying the rule of right combination, we obtain the following structure for *queer curate*:

queer curate:
CAT: N
IND(N) = $\mathbf{K}_1[x_1]$
CONS: $\begin{cases} x_1 \in \mathrm{U}(\mathbf{K}_1),\ \mathrm{curate}(x_1) \in \mathrm{Con}(\mathbf{K}_1), \\ x_2 \in \mathrm{U}(\mathbf{K}_2),\ \mathrm{queer}(x_2) \in \mathrm{Con}(\mathbf{K}_2), \\ \mathbf{K}_1 = \mathbf{K}_2,\ x_1 = x_2 \end{cases}$

Because the equations in these structures tend to become hard to read, we will henceforth substitute variables where possible, from left to right, noting in brackets which substitutions we have applied. This gives us the following:

queer curate: ($\mathbf{K}_1 = \mathbf{K}_2$, $x_1 = x_2$)
CAT: N
IND(N) = $\mathbf{K}_1[x_1]$
CONS: $x_1 \in \mathrm{U}(\mathbf{K}_1)$, $\mathrm{curate}(x_1) \in \mathrm{Con}(\mathbf{K}_1)$, $\mathrm{queer}(x_1) \in \mathrm{Con}(\mathbf{K}_1)$

When we combine this with *a*, the result is not particularly interesting, because the indefinite article contributes no constraints of its own, and simply passes on IND values. So, in effect, the content of *a queer curate* is the same as that of *queer curate*.

a queer curate: $(\mathbf{K}_8 = \mathbf{K}_1, x_8 = x_1)$
CAT: NP
IND(NP) $= \mathbf{K}_8[x_8]$
CONS: $x_8 \in \mathrm{U}(\mathbf{K}_8)$, curate$(x_8) \in \mathrm{Con}(\mathbf{K}_8)$, queer$(x_8) \in \mathrm{Con}(\mathbf{K}_8)$

If we combine *queer curate* with the definite article instead, however, things become slightly more interesting. For now we obtain:

the queer curate: $(\mathbf{K}_6 = \mathbf{K}_1, x_6 = x_1)$
CAT: NP
IND(NP) $= \mathbf{K}_7[x_6]$
CONS: $\left\{ \begin{array}{l} x_6 \in \mathrm{U}(\mathbf{K}_6), \text{curate}(x_6) \in \mathrm{Con}(\mathbf{K}_6), \\ \text{queer}(x_6) \in \mathrm{Con}(\mathbf{K}_6), \mathbf{K}_6 \in \mathrm{A}(\mathbf{K}_7) \end{array} \right.$

This structure is the same as the previous one, except that it features an additional constraint and the IND values are different. Formulated in procedural terms, the difference between the two structures can be described thus: The indefinite article simply takes the content of a nominal head and passes it on to the mother; no new structure is created. The definite article, in contrast, creates a new DRS K, shifts the DRS K' of its head into the A-structure of K, thereby effectively closing off K' (it cannot be extended anymore higher up in the tree), and passes on K as its value.

This 'shifting' of information into the A-structure of a DRS is obviously the crucial ingredient of our proposal, and it is always accounted for lexically: In most cases, as with *the*, the shift is triggered by lexical material; but occasionally, the result of a shift has already been performed in the lexicon, as with the possessive pronoun. The definition of *his* already contains a DRS (for the hidden 'he') that is closed off (the same applies for proper names). Or in other words, possessive pronouns are doubly anaphoric (cf. example (39)) in that they introduce two DRS-segments, one of which is contained in the A-structure of the other. Thus for *his queer curate*, we get:

his queer curate: $(\mathbf{K}_{10} = \mathbf{K}_1, x_{10} = x_1)$
CAT: NP
IND(NP) $= \mathbf{K}_{11}[x_{10}]$
CONS: $\left\{ \begin{array}{l} x_9 \in \mathrm{U}(\mathbf{K}_9), x_{10} \in \mathrm{U}(\mathbf{K}_{10}), \\ \text{poss}(x_9,x_{10}) \in \mathrm{Con}(\mathbf{K}_{10}), \mathbf{K}_9 \in \mathrm{A}(\mathbf{K}_{10}), \mathbf{K}_{10} \in \mathrm{A}(\mathbf{K}_{11}) \\ \text{curate}(x_{10}) \in \mathrm{Con}(\mathbf{K}_{10}), \text{queer}(x_{10}) \in \mathrm{Con}(\mathbf{K}_{10}) \end{array} \right.$

Of all the lexical entries that we have defined, the combinatorics of genitive *'s* are the most complex. Syntactically, *'s* combines with an NP to produce a determiner, which takes an N to produce an NP. Semantically, the result of applying *'s* to its first argument should yield the same type of structure that is directly associated with *his* in the lexicon. This is in fact what happens: If we analyze *the curate's cat*, we get the following structure:

the curate's cat:
CAT: NP
IND(NP) $= \mathbf{K}_{11}[x_{10}]$
CONS: $\left\{ \begin{array}{l} x_9 \in \mathrm{U}(\mathbf{K}_9), x_{10} \in \mathrm{U}(\mathbf{K}_{10}), \text{curate}(x_9) \in \mathrm{Con}(\mathbf{K}_9), \\ \text{poss}(x_9,x_{10}) \in \mathrm{Con}(\mathbf{K}_{10}), \mathbf{K}_9 \in \mathrm{A}(\mathbf{K}_{10}), \\ \mathbf{K}_{10} \in \mathrm{A}(\mathbf{K}_{11}) \text{ cat}(x_{10}) \in \mathrm{Con}(\mathbf{K}_{10}) \end{array} \right.$

Finally, if we combine this structure with the one-place verb *curses*, we get:

the curate's cat curses: $(\mathbf{K}_{11} = \mathbf{K}_5,\ x_{10} = x_5)$

CAT: S

IND(S) = $\mathbf{K}_{11}[x_{10}]$

CONS: $\left\{\begin{array}{l} x_9 \in U(\mathbf{K}_9),\ x_{10} \in U(\mathbf{K}_{10}),\ \text{curate}(x_9) \in \text{Con}(\mathbf{K}_9), \\ \text{poss}(x_9, x_{10}) \in \text{Con}(\mathbf{K}_{10}),\ \mathbf{K}_9 \in A(\mathbf{K}_{10}), \\ \mathbf{K}_{10} \in A(\mathbf{K}_{11})\ \text{cat}(x_{10}) \in \text{Con}(\mathbf{K}_{10}) \\ \text{curse}(x_{10}) \in \text{Con}(\mathbf{K}_{11}) \end{array}\right.$

According to the definitions given above, this completely describes the following SDRS, which has the same structure as the SDRS we associated with example (39):

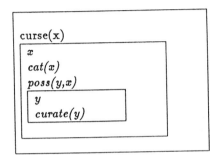

7 Presupposition projection

In section 6.1 we proposed to construct DRSs in two stages. In the first stage an SDRS is put together, which collects, but does not resolve, anaphoric elements in its A-structure. An SDRS thus is an intermediate structure, which is merged with the main DRS before anaphors are resolved. Actual processing of anaphoric elements takes place in the second phase of DRS construction. In this phase anaphors are either linked to some previously established antecedent or accommodated at some level of representation. This yields a proper DRS which is subject to the standard rules of semantic interpretation.

The mechanisms for representing anaphoric material and constructing SDRSs have been set out in detail in the previous section. Since on the current account presuppositions are taken to be anaphoric expressions this accomplishes the first task of presupposition theory (cf. Section 2): to provide an encoding for the conventional means a language has to indicate the existence of a presupposition and specifying its function. The second task, we said, consists in specifying what happens to these presuppositional anaphors under embedding, or put otherwise, giving an account of presupposition projection. In the proposal put forward here this simply comes down to giving an account of anaphoric binding and accommodation, or, formulated in the terminology introduced in the previous sections, in setting up a procedure for resolving the A-structure of an SDRS.

As we indicated already, the resolution of A-structures can come about in either of two ways. A presuppositional anaphor may either be bound to some accessible antecedent or be accommodated at some accessible position. Binding has priority over accommodation. In order to see whether a presuppositional anaphor can be bound to some pre-established antecedent we follow up its projection line and link it to the first marker that is a suitable antecedent. Technically this means that the marker of the A-structure will be identified with the antecedent marker which thus inherits all the descriptive information associated with the presuppositional anaphor. At this point we deviate slightly from alternative versions of DRT: we shall link anaphoric material in the boxes where its antecedent is rather than in the box where it originates, as is common in DRT. A moment's thought should suffice to see however that the final result will always be semantically equivalent. We proceed in this manner mainly for a technical reason: this procedure is easier to formulate, and carries over more smoothly to other cases of anaphora, than the alternatives we have considered.

If no suitable antecedent for an anaphor can be found, it will be accommodated. Accommodation generally will take place at the highest accessible level such that the resulting structure does not violate general constraints on (un)binding and acceptability. Technically accommodation simply consists in transferring the anaphoric marker plus its conditions to the level of accommodation, thereby establishing an accessible antecedent after all. Thus binding and accommodation can only take place at accessible positions. But binding involves a search upwards along the anaphor's projection line and will thus normally take place at the nearest accessible position. Accommodation on the other hand goes downwards. If accommodation at top level is blocked due to an imminent violation of well-formedness conditions on discourse stuctures, the next attempt at accommodation will be made one level lower. In the process of resolving a presuppositional anaphor we will thus describe a loop along the anaphor's projection line.

As we said, both binding and accommodation are constrained by restrictions on binding and acceptability. First, we should take care that the resolution of A-structures does not result in unbinding of variables which are contained in them. And, secondly, the resulting structure should respect constraints on contextual acceptability.

The binding constraint is dictated by the fact that presuppositional anaphors may embed further anaphoric expressions.

(41) a. If every man would love *John's wife*, she would be happier.

     b. If every man would love *his wife*, women would be happier.

The first sentence presupposes that John is married. This is correctly predicted by the rules given thus far. The information contained in the presuppositional expression cannot be bound in the antecedent of the conditional, and will thus be accommodated top level. Without further provisions, a similar prediction would be made for (41b). For, if we would assign it, analogous to the first sentence, the elementary presupposition that every man has a wife, this presupposition would again not be bound and therefore projected to top level. But this would give rise to a prediction which is blatantly wrong. Is certainly is not a prerequisite for the truth of (41b) that every man has a wife. Rather, (41b) means that women would be happier if every man who has a wife would love her. Thus, while the truth conditions of (41a) correspond to those of its paraphrase in (42a), (41b) appears to be equivalent to (42b):

(42) a. John has a wife, and if every man would love her, she would be happier.

     b. If every man who has a wife would love her, women would be happier.

The problem arises from the fact that the presuppositional anaphor *his wife* contains yet another anaphoric expression which depends on the quantified NP in the antecedent. Accommodation of the full expression at top level would thus result in creating a free variable for the pronoun instead of binding it properly. The solution that we propose involves the hierarchical structure of A-structures (which we devised precisely to this purpose). What we shall require is that, whenever an anaphoric DRS-segment in the A-structure contains further DRS-segments—that is, whenever an anaphor embeds another anaphor—the embedded material must be resolved first.

Secondly, there is a general restriction that the accommodation of presuppositional material K in some (sub-) DRS K' may not result in a configuration in which some discourse marker in Con(K) is no longer accessible from K'. Thus, in effect, embedded anaphors may intercept other anaphors as they are percolating up along their projection lines. Returning to the example in (41), in the (a) sentence the proper name *John* will be accommodated at top level.[18] And since no suitable antecedent for the presuppositional expression *John's wife* can be found it will be accommodated at top level as well. In (41b) however the situation is different. The embedded pronoun will be processed first and linked to the marker set up for the men in the antecent of the conditional. When processing the embedding expression *his wife* this anaphor will be intercepted in the antecedent. And since it cannot be bound there it will be accommodated, thus giving rise to the following structure:

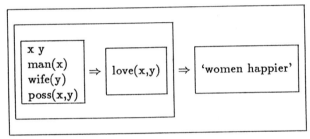

Together with the requirement that the most deeply embedded anaphors should be processed first, the binding constraint thus prevents accidental unbinding of variables, and accounts for the interception of presuppositions by quantified expressions, as in (41b).

The second factor constraining the resolution of anaphoric expressions is contextual acceptability, which we already discussed in Section 3. It was pointed out there that no sentence will ever have a presupposing reading if accommodation would violate conditions on contextual acceptability. The relevant principles here are: consistency, informativeness and efficiency. The requirement of consistency requires no further discussion, since it is a constraint on interpretation on any semantic theory. Constraints of informativeness and efficiency arise from independently motivated conversational principles. The main purpose of discourse is to convey information, and information is conveyed relative to

---

[18]It is common in DRT to introduce markers for proper names at the highest level of representation, thus accounting for the fact that proper names tend to escape from the scope of embedding operators. In our view however proper names are not rigid in this sense nor is there any need to stipulate that they should always be introduced at the highest structural level. Instead we take proper names to be presupposition inducers just like ordinary definite descriptions. Their tendency to accommodate at top level can readily be explained by their relative lack of informative content, which prevents constraints on accommodation to push them down to some deeper level of embedding.

a set of background information, which is already part of the current DRS. In DRT an assertion is thus incremental in the following sense. After an assertion has been made, its content will be added to the DRS under construction. The informational status of its content thereby changes. Unless retracted or denied the content will be part of the DRS from then on. Since the point of an assertion is to introduce new information, its utterance would be superfluous in a discourse which already contained or entailed its content. Processing such an utterance would result in a trivial mapping of the current DRS onto itself: no new information would be added. Thus informativeness constraints account, among other things, for the unacceptability resulting from iteration of sentences which have been uttered before or which contain information which has already been established in the current DRS.

Hence the the basic requirements informativeness and consistency impose upon the acceptability of sentences with respect to the current DRS are the following:

CONSISTENCY AND INFORMATIVENESS:

The utterance of a sentence φ against the background of the current DRS K is acceptable only if updating K with the content of φ results in a DRS K' such that

i. the set of models that embed K' is not empty (consistency), and

ii. the set of models that embed K' is a proper subset of the set of models that embed K (informativeness).

A further constraint on acceptability that is relevant for presupposition theory arises from efficiency principles. Efficiency demands that we should not convey information in a unnecessarily redundant and complex way, if language provides the means to achieve the same result in a more parsimonious fashion. This principle constrains, for instance, the use of the logical connectives. Suppose that the truth of φ has already been established. In that case, clearly, the utterance of χ is a more efficient and less redundant way of saying that χ than the utterance of "φ and χ" or "if φ then χ," although these more elaborate sentences would convey exactly the same information, in the context given. Or suppose that we want to convey the information that χ in case the falsity of φ has already been established. Given the contextual information that φ is false, we could do so in a number of equivalent ways. "φ or χ" or "if not φ then χ" are just two of many possibilities. But both would be more cumbersome and less efficient then the mere utterance of χ.

Note that efficiency and informativeness are distinct notions. If φ is contextually given, uttering "if φ then ψ" may be informative, in the sense that it conveys that ψ is the case. But this utterance would inefficient, and therefore inacceptable, because there is a simpler way of getting this message across, viz. by uttering ψ instead of the conditional.

In general, if a sentence contains clauses which do not contribute anything to the information conveyed, the resulting violation of the efficiency requirement yields sheer unacceptability. The following examples illustrate this phenomenon. The stretches of discourse in (43) violate the principle of informativeness. Those in (44) violate the efficiency principle, since they are particularly unfortunate attempts to convey the information that Mary has a dog.

(43) a. Mary has a cat. Mary has a cat. Mary has a cat...

   b. Mary managed to buy a cat. Mary has a cat.

   c.   Mary has a cat. Either she has a cat or she has a dog.

(44) a.   Mary has no cat. Either Mary has a cat or she has a dog.

       b.   Mary has a cat. If she has a cat, she has a dog.

Acceptability principles of consistency, informativeness and efficiency constrain the process of accommodation, and it is not hard to see why. Accommodation is a strategy of repair. If a presuppositional anaphor requires some antecedent for its carrier sentence to be processed, and no suitable antecedent can be found, then we will use the lexical material of the presupposition inducer for establishing an accessible antecedent after all. Of course, when revising the discourse representation in this manner, a cooperative hearer will take care that the resulting structure is interpretable and coherent. This explains why accommodation will take place at a lower level if accommodation at a higher accessible level would give rise to unacceptability of the resulting discourse structure.

Consider the following disjunction, for instance:

(45)   Either Jack has no donkey or *his donkey* is eating quietly in the stable.

The presuppositional expression *his donkey* in the second disjunct cannot access the donkey in the first disjunct, since it is not on its projection line. So we might try to create a marker for his donkey at top level, in order to establish an accessible antecent after all. This would not result in contradiction but the resulting structure would violate the efficiency principle. It would, in effect, represent the following unacceptable discourse:

(46)   Jack has a donkey. Either he has no donkey or his donkey is eating quitly in the stable.

The principles set out above thus force an attempt at accommodation one level lower on the anaphor's projection line. This yields (47), which *is* acceptable, and correctly represents the meaning of (45):

(47)   Either Jack has no donkey or he has a donkey and *his donkey* is eating quietly in the stable.

We want to note, finally, that Van der Sandt (1988) also discusses a principle of sequential interpretation. It stipulates that the interpretation of a conjunction or conditional takes place with respect to an temporarily enlarged set of background assumptions. As far as acceptability is concerned this means that the second conjunct of a conjunction or the consequent of the conditional should be acceptable with respect to this (temporarily) enlarged context. Since we implemented our current proposal in terms of discourse representation theory, this principle is already a proper part of the interpretation mechanism, so we do not need to account for it separately.

To conclude this paper, we want to demonstrate with the help of example how the theory that we have set up works.

(48)   If a curate works hard, his cat will be happy.

The initial representation that we get for this sentence is the following:

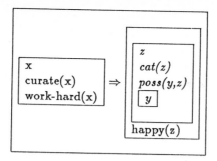

The most deeply embedded anaphor in this case is represented by the DRS-segment for y. If we try to bind this anaphor, we first check whether there is an appropriate antecedent for this anaphor in the consequent of the conditional, which there isn't. Then we move up to the left-hand box of the conditional, where we do find a suitable antecedent, viz. x. Hence we add the contents of the anaphor to this box, and add the appropriate equation, which yields the following structure:

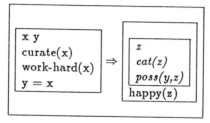

Now, if we try to bind the remaining anaphor, *his cat*, we do not get a match, simply because we do not have a cat yet. So we must try to accommodate the anaphor. We first try to accommodate the cat at top level, which gives the following structure:

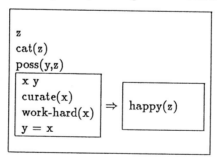

What this means, intuitively, is that there is someone who owns a cat, and if this person is a curate and works hard, then his cat his happy. This is not exactly what we want. What we want, rather, is that the presupposed material ends up being accommodated in the antecedent DRS. This is precisely what the binding restriction we formulated above will give us. For this restriction will rule out the structure above, because one of the conditions contains a discourse marker, y, which is not accessible. So we can't accommodate our cat at at top level, and therefore have to make another attempt, one level down. This gives us:

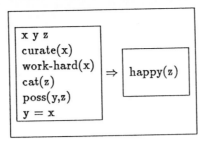

This structure is acceptable and well formed, and, as can easily be seen, it represents the meaning of (48) in an adequate manner.

Acknowledgment

We should like to thank Henk Zeevat for his comments on an earlier version of this paper.

References

Asher, N. 1989: Abstract Objects, Semantics and Anaphora. Ms., Department of Philosophy and Center for Cognitive Science, University of Texas, Austin.

Fauconnier, G. 1985: Mental Spaces. MIT Press, Cambridge, Mass.

Gazdar, G. 1979: Pragmatics. Implicature, Presupposition, and Logical Form. Academic Press, New York.

Groenendijk, J.A.G., and M.B.J. Stokhof 1991: Dynamic predicate logic. Linguistics and Philosophy 14: 39–101.

Heim, I. 1982: The Semantics of Definite and Indefinite Noun Phrases. Ph.D Thesis, University of Massachusetts, Amherst.

Heim, I. 1983: On the projection problem for presuppositions. In: Proceedings of the West Coast Conference on Formal Linguistics 2: 114–126.

Kamp, H. 1981: A theory of truth and semantic representation. In: J.A.G. Groenendijk, T.M.V. Janssen, and M.B.J. Stokhof (eds.) 1981: Formal Methods in the Study of Language. Mathematical Centre Tracts 135, Amsterdam. Pp. 277-322. Reprinted in: J.A.G. Groenendijk, T.M.V. Janssen, and M.B.J. Stokhof (eds.) 1984: Truth, Interpretation, and Information; Selected Papers from the Third Amsterdam Colloquium. Foris, Dordrecht. Pp. 1–41.

Karttunen, L. 1973: Presuppositions of compound sentences. Linguistic Inquiry 4: 167–193.

Karttunen, L. 1974: Presupposition and linguistic context. Theoretical Linguistics 1.1: 181–194.

Karttunen, L. and S. Peters, 1979: Conventional implicature. In: C.-K. Oh and D. Dinneen (eds.), Syntax and Semantics, vol. 11: Presupposition. Academic Press, New York. Pp. 1–56.

Langendoen, D.T., and H. Savin 1971: The projection problem for presuppositions. In: C. Fillmore and D.T. Langendoen (eds.), Studies in Linguistic Semantics. Holt, New York.

Lewis, D. 1979: Scorekeeping in a language game. Journal of Philosophical Logic 8:339–59.

McCawley, J.D. 1979: Presupposition and discourse structure. In: C.-K. Oh and D. Dinneen (eds.), Syntax and Semantics, vol. 11: Presupposition. Academic Press, New York. Pp. 371–88.

Mercer, R. to appear: Default logic and presuppositions: simple sentences and beyond.

Reiter, R. 1980: A logic for default reasoning. Artificial Intelligence 13: 81–132.

Reyle, U. 1985: Grammatical functions, quantification and discourse referents. IJCAI 9: 829–831.

Roberts, C. 1987: Modal Subordination, Anaphora and Distributivity. Ph.D Thesis, University of Massachusetts, Amherst.

Sells, P. 1985: Restrictive and non-restrictive modification. CSLI Report No. 85-28, Stanford.

Seuren, P.A.M..1985: Discourse Semantics. Blackwell, Oxford.

Soames, S. 1979: A projection problem for speaker presuppositions. Linguistic Inquiry 10: 623–666.

Soames, S. 1982: How presuppositions are inherited: a solution to the projection problem. Linguistic Inquiry 13: 483–545.

Stalnaker, R.C. 1973: Presuppositions. Journal of Philosophical Logic 2: 447–457.

Stalnaker, R.C. 1974: Pragmatic presuppositions. In: M.K. Munitz and P.K. Unger (eds.), Semantics and Philosophy. New York University Press, New York. Pp. 197–213.

Stalnaker, R.C. 1978: Assertion. In: P. Cole (ed.), Syntax and Semantics, vol. 9: Pragmatics. Academic Press, New York.

Strawson, P. 1950: On referring. Mind 59: 320–344.

Van der Sandt, R.A. 1988: Context and Presupposition. Routledge, London.

Van der Sandt, R.A. 1989: Presupposition and discourse structure. In: R. Bartsch, J. van Benthem, and P. van Emde Boas (eds.), Semantics and Contextual Expresssion. Foris, Dordrecht.

Van der Sandt, R.A. to appear: Presupposition projection as anaphora resolution.

Zeevat, H. 1991: Aspects of Discourse Semantics and Unification Grammar. Ph.D. Thesis, University of Amsterdam.

Zeevat, H., E. Klein, and J. Calder 1987: Unification categorial grammar. Edinburgh Research Papers in Cognitive Science, No. EUCCS/RP-21, Centre for Cognitive Science, University of Edinburgh.

Anaphora and Domain Restriction

Rolf Mayer

Abstract

The paper focuses on explicit and implicit domain restriction at the sentence and discourse level, and in particular looks at the behavior of (German) exception markers like 'außer' from a procedural point of view.

1 Introduction

The present article outlines a thread of research in the LILOG project that was meant to explore algorithmic aspects of domain restriction at the clausal and discourse level. For an in-depth analysis and extensive references to the literature, the reader is referred to (Mayer 1991). The focus is on domain restriction as exemplified by *explicit exception marking*, and *implicit domain restriction*. We also point out non-incremental aspects of information-packaging including what we call *constructional repair* and *perspectivization*. To round off the conceptual map, we also consider *complement formation without exception marking* (paradigmatic item 'd- anderen' ('the others')), and there will also be some remarks on semantic operations like *addition* and *domain set stabilization*.

Our usage of the notion 'anaphora' in the title is rather broad, ranging from items like 'd-anderen' – where a reference-set is calculated via subtraction of a 'complement anchor' from a context set – to 'ellipsis phenomena' where, for instance, an exception phrase may be linked to a universal NP in a preceding clause.

Let me give an informal understanding of the concepts via the text below.

We assume a scenario made up of a group of 12 objects a,...,l whose movement is to be described. A possible description is the following:

Explicit Exception Marking (at the sentence level):

(1)   a) Alle außer a fahren nach A.
           ("Everybody except a goes to A.")

        b) Außer b fahren dann alle nach B.
           ("Everybody goes to B, except for b.")

Explicit Exception Marking (at the discourse level):

(2)   a) Dann fahren alle nach C. Außer c.

      ("Then everybody goes to C. Except for c.")

    b) Von C fahren alle nach D. Nur d fährt nach E.

      ("From C everybody goes to D. Only d goes to E.")

Implicit Domain Restriction:

(3)   a) Von D fahren alle nach F. Keiner ist dort.

      ("From D everybody goes to F. Nobody is there.")

    b) Von F fahren sie nach G. Dort verlassen alle e.

      ("From F they go to G. There all of them leave e.")

Explicit Complement Formation without Explicit Exception Marking:

(4)   a) Von G fahren die einen nach H, die anderen fahren nach I.

      ("From G some go to H, the others to I.")

    b) Während dann der Rest von I nach J fährt, fahren f, g, h und i nach K.

      ("While the rest of them go from I to J, f, g, h, and i go to K.")

Addition and Domain Set Stabilization:

(5)   a) Von K fahren dann außer f auch g, h und i nach L.

      ("Apart from f, g, h, and i go from K to L.")

    b) Von L fahren alle einschließlich g nach M.

      ("From L everybody, including g, goes to M.")

2   Explicit Exception Marking

We will first consider German 'außer'. Note that 'außer' does not just behave as an exception marker but can also mean 'besides' and, in some fixed phrases, 'outside of' (cf. 'außer Haus'), or 'without' (cf. 'außer Atem'). It can be in construction with a dative NP, a prepositional phrase, or even a clause (where it may perform the function of 'unless'). As an exception marker, it occurs in connected exception phrases or in free exception phrases[1] (cf. (1a) versus (1b)). Connected exception phrases are syntactically linked to an NP or PP (via Chomsky-adjunction), while free exception phrases syntactically function as sentential operators. In logical structures 'Außer$(\alpha)(S'(\beta))$' where S' is the sentence radical without the exception phrase, we call α and β parallel sisters if α can be semantically linked to β. We also call β the target of α. Linkage (both in the case of restriction and addition) presupposes that α could structurally fill the slot of β in S'.

---

[1] This distinction goes back to (Hoeksema 1990).

In the paradigmatic case, exception phrases are related to universal NPs and have the semantic function of restricting a totality. What counts as a totality accessible to restriction can vary, though, and includes groups and spatial wholes (cf. (6) and (7)). Exception phrases single out subsets or functional/spatial parts from these totalities. In some cases the target can be reconstructed as an *implicit argument* (cf. (8)). Often – for instance in the context of a small group of what we may label 'completion' adjectives – there is no NP (or PP) target available nor can one be reconstructed (cf. (9)) – which points to the fact that in the general case restriction has to be construed as a relation between propositions.

(6) Etwa die Hälfte davon dürfte auf die Comecon-Staaten (außer Sowjetunion) entfallen, die andere Hälfte auf Westeuropa.

("About one half is due to the Comecon states (except the Soviet Union), the other half is due to Western Europe.")

(7) Die Partner müssen die Wohnung - außer Küche und Bad - getrennt benutzen.

("The partners must use the flat separately – except for the kitchen and the bathroom.")

(8) Außer z.B. in Manhattan ist der Kauf eines Hauses dem Mieten vorzuziehen.

("Other than, for instance, in Manhattan, purchasing a house is preferable to hiring it.")

(9) Die Sammlung ist komplett, außer der 'Bayernhochzeit'.

("The collection is complete, except for the 'Bavarian Wedding' ")

Restrict(p, q) can be said to obtain between p and q if p restricts q. As regards (9), p could be spelt out as "'The 'Bavarian Wedding' is missing in the collection", and q is identified with "The collection is complete". The relation could be stipulated in the sense of (Hoeksema 1990): Restrict(p, q) is true in a model M if q becomes true in any model M' resulting from M by minimally changing it such that p has changed its truth value in M'. For p to be a restriction ("exception") to q, the 'distance' between p and q should be "big" enough. With an implementation in mind, and relative to paradigmatic cases where an exception set can be linked to a target set from the residual clause, a (rough) maximal proportion would be a cardinality quotient of 1/3 (what we call the *proportionality constraint*).

From the implementational point of view, it would be nice if a link between an 'außer' phrase and a universal NP would always come along with an 'exception interpretation'. König and Kortmann (1987: p. 186f.) have, however, pointed out that this is an oversimplification. In an example like (10), an exception reading is only induced if Georg is a student. This piece of information may be triggered by an accent on 'alle' or just be part of a speaker's/hearer's knowledge base.

(10) Außer Georg waren alle Studenten im Garten.

("Apart from Georg, all the students were in the garden.")

There is an important cue, though: an "additive" interpretation is never possible when the 'außer'-phrase follows the target NP, which, for instance, is the case with connected exception phrases.

A few further remarks on the additive use of 'außer': Suppose we have an algorithm that allows us to verify that in structures 'Außer(α)($S'(\beta)$)' α and β are parallel sisters. For the sake of simplicity we also assume that α and β denote individuals or sum-objects (to be represented as sets). Then the truth definition of these structures relative to a model M may be stated as below. To point out the contrast, we also add a clause characterizing the additive use of 'neben' ('besides').

Def. 1 '*Außer*(α)($S'(\beta)$)' *is true in a model M iff* $S'(\alpha)$ *is true in M and* $S'(\beta)$ *is true in M.*

Def. 2 '*Neben*(α)($S'(\beta)$)' *is true in a model M iff* $S'(\beta)$ *is true in the submodel M' of M that does not contain* α, *and* $S'(\alpha)$ *is true in the submodel M'' of M that does not contain* β.

While these truth specifications clearly are no substitute for an exhaustive semantic analysis, they at least differentiate between cases like (11) and (12).

(11) Außer (Neben) John kam auch Jack zu meiner Party.

("Besides John Jack also came to my party.")

(12) Neben (*Außer) den USA ist die EG der größte Exportmarkt der Asean.

("Apart from the U.S., the EEC is the biggest export market of the Asean Company.")

In a number of additive uses, 'außer' embeds an NP with an argument structure such that the NP cannot find a target in the residual clause and has itself to be spelt out as a clause. Moreover, as is usual in the case of semantic coordination, the two clauses derivable from the original structure have to exhibit 'argumentative parallelism' along the lines of (Ducrot 1972).

(13) Außer der Erläuterung des außenpolitischen Leitantrages des Bundestages wird Kohl sich am Schlußtag zur Lage der CDU generell äußern.

("In addition to an explanation of the major motion of the 'Bundestag' concerning foreign policy, Kohl will make a general statement on the situation of the CDU.")

In order to determine the position of 'außer' on the map of German exception (and addition) markers, one should note the distinctions to markers with about the same semantic potential. We therefore include information on 'abgesehen_von', 'bis_auf', and 'sonst'. Let me emphasize once more that we are rather selective and do not, for instance, consider German 'nur' ('only') which alone would deserve plenty of space in a discussion of German exception markers.

Like 'außer', 'abgesehen_von' can be used as an exception marker and as an addition marker. However, there are a number of distinctions:

With 'abgesehen_von', there is a quantitative preference for sentence-initial and sentence-final position; the syntactic possibility of a clause-final position in its additive use sets it off against additive 'außer'.

Moreover, 'abgesehen_von' phrases in sentence-initial position license non-integrative word-order (in German: 'Adverbial - Topic - Finite Verb', cf. (König and van der Auwera 1988)), which is not possible with regard to 'außer' (and 'bis_auf').

Unlike 'außer', exception phrases constructed via 'abgesehen_von' induce the build-up of a semantic restriction with regard to the content of the target clause but generally do not impose the heavy structural constraints (syntactic parallelism) that in the majority of cases determine the behavior of 'außer'.

Let me now turn to a brief characterization of 'bis_auf'. Syntactically, it is a complex preposition governing accusative NPs. Semantically, it is productive as a restrictive particle. As such, it behaves much like 'abgesehen_von' in its restrictive use. However, it prefers clause-initial and clause-medial to clause-final word order. It also allows for inclusive interpretations ('bis auf den letzten Mann töten' ('kill to the last man')). However, then the NPs governed by 'bis_auf' have to designate something like a maximal element relative to a scale established by the clause.

The properties of the particle 'sonst' (roughly: 'otherwise'/'else') have been investigated in (Wunderlich 1979) and (Abraham 1980). As is correctly pointed out by both authors, the apparent multiplicity of uses results from the interaction of a core meaning with contextual parameters. Wunderlich (p. 373) singles out (i) modalized contexts (including conditional ones) and (ii) quantized contexts. (14) exemplifies (i), (15a) illustrates (ii). We here focus on contexts like (15a) where 'sonst' restricts the domain of universal quantifiers. The anaphoric status of 'sonst' allows for a converse information flow as against cases like (15b).

(14) Du mußt vorsichtig sein. Sonst fliegt der Safe in die Luft.

("You must be careful. Otherwise the safe will explode.")

(15)   a) John ist zu meinem Geburtstag gekommen. Sonst ist niemand erschienen.
        ("John has come to my birthday. Nobody else has appeared".)

    b) Niemand ist zu meinem Geburtstag gekommen. Außer John.
        ("Nobody has come to my birthday. Except for John.")

The clauses in (15a) exhibit what we call *restriction parallelism*. While biclausal restriction is not necessarily bound up with 'sonst', we will here explicate the notion with a structure like (15a) in mind. We assume a biclausal text T where the S(onst)-clause is anaphorically related to its P(redecessor)-clause. We assume that it has to be decided at the level of logical form whether the P-clause – here represented as '$\lambda x P_1(x)(N P_1')$' – and the S-clause (without 'sonst') – represented as '$\lambda x P_2(x)(N P_2')$' where $N P_2$ is a universal quantifier like 'alle $(\overline{N})$', 'niemand', and 'kein- $\overline{N}$'– exhibit *restriction parallelism*. For the sake of suggestiveness we have encoded the '$N P_i$' as arguments. Clearly, the reader may wish to interpret the $N P_i$ as Montagovian second-order predicates applied to the P_i.

We say that the predicates $P_i(x)$ have the same polarity if they are identical; they have different polarity if one is the negative counterpart of the other.

We also assume that the $N P_i$ can be categorized with regard to positive polarity (for instance, 'John', 'alle Franzosen' ('all Frenchmen')), or negative polarity (for instance, 'niemand' ('nobody'), 'kein Franzose' ('no Frenchman')).

The restriction parallelism check is performed as follows:

Rule 1 *(Restriction Parallelism) We first try to establish the existence of a predicate P_3 (that is either identical with P_2 or just has a different polarity) such that the following holds: '$\lambda x P_1(x)(N P_1')$' implies (or can be accomodated to imply) '$\lambda x P_3(x)(N P_1')$'.*
Suppose P_3 is identical with P_2. Then $N P_1$ must be a restriction of $N P_2$ in the following sense: both must have different polarity, and the corresponding sets are bound to meet the proportionality constraint.
Suppose P_3 and P_2 have different polarity. Then $N P_1$ and $N P_2$ must have the same polarity, and again the proportionality check relative to $N P_1$ and $N P_2$ must succeed.

3 Explicit Abstraction and Implicit Abstraction

Reference-sets of NPs may be explicitly adjusted via exception phrases or built up in a process of subtraction with the help of markers like 'die anderen' ('the others'). We call this linguistic process explicit abstraction. As is well known, abstraction can also be implicit. Let me provide the following examples:

(16) a) Everybody was looking at Emily Brent.

b) *Everybody except Emily Brent was looking at her.

(17) a) Nobody knows that my name is Rumpelstilzchen.

b) ?Nobody except myself knows that my name is Rumpelstilzchen.

(18) a) Nobody is as tall as Henrietta.

b) *Nobody except Henrietta is as tall as herself.

We assume that in a prototypical situation (i.e., against the empty context) the reference-set of the universal NP in (16a) does not contain Emily Brent; Emily Brent has been, so to speak, abstracted away.

The interesting and difficult question is when implicit abstraction is licensed. Examples like (17a) and (18a) are clear cases where implicit abstraction is enforced via the fact that without abstraction tautology or contradiction would ensue. In cases like these explicit abstraction is less appropriate (or completeley 'out').

The above examples suggest a rule along the following lines:

Rule 2 *Suppose that (in a first step) a clause S can be mapped onto a structure 'Det N Pred' with Det $\in \{all, no\}$ where 'Det' translates into 'D', 'N' into '$\lambda x\, Pred1(x)$' and 'Pred' into '$\lambda x\, Pred2(x)$'. We assume that S itself is neither a tautology nor a contradiction. Let $a = \{a_1 \ldots a_i \ldots a_n\}$ be the maximal set such that for each a_i 'Pred2(a_i)' is either a tautology or a contradiction[2]. Then S (in a second step) translates into 'D $(\lambda x(Pred1(x)\&\neg(x \in a)), \lambda x(Pred2(x)))$'.*

Rule 2 is situated at the clause level. It tells us when implicit abstraction has to be performed in order to avoid contradiction or tautology; in itself it is not sufficient to regulate the linguistic use of implicit abstraction: we would expect from Rule 2 that in (19) we are allowed to take away Henrietta from the domain of the universal quantifier via implicit abstraction. However, implicit abstraction does not license (19). Instead we need a separation marker like 'other', see (20).

(19) *Henrietta ist mindestens so schön wie alle Frauen.

("Henrietta is at least as beautiful as all women.")

(20) Henrietta ist mindestens so schön wie alle anderen Frauen.

("Henrietta is at least as beautiful as all other women.")

---

[2]Use of the classical concepts of tautology and contradiction certainly is too strong; more adequate are 'accepted (rejected) in an empty information state' and suchlike notions; for a formal elaboration of these ideas see (Veltman 1990).

So far it seems that constraints governing implicit abstraction have to be formulated in a construction-specific way. We would certainly prefer more general rules and algorithms with a large coverage. At present, though, topics like 'relevance' (including implicit abstraction) seem only tractable at a rather descriptive level.

The next illustration of implicit abstraction will follow this descriptive road, too. Unlike the phenomena feeding Rule 2, we will now look at a discourse-related pattern (with people being in or entering rooms).

(21) Tom entered. Nobody was in the room.

(22) Tom entered. Everybody was there.

In (21) and (22) there is implicit abstraction with regard to Tom. Explicit abstraction is again odd as (23) and (24) show. However, implicit abstraction in this type of construction only seems to be the default case: As A. Borillo pointed out with regard to (25) (personal communication), implicit abstraction may be blocked. Mediated by the temporal marker 'now', (25) allows for (but does not enforce) an interpretation where Tom's entering makes the group complete.

(23) *Tom entered. Except for him, nobody was there.

(24) *Tom entered. Only he (himself) was in the room.

(25) Tom entered. Now everybody was there.

The data roughly suggests something like the following rule:

Rule 3 *Let $T=S(1)+S(2)$ be a text such that $S(1)$ denotes an event $e:P(a)$ that implies the existence of a resultative state $s:Q(a)$ such that e temporally meets s. If $S(2)$ in isolation implies $\forall x_R(\neg Q(x))$ (or $\forall x_R(Q(x))$) where R is a sortal predicate, and if there are no linguistic or extralinguistic cues suggesting that $S(1)$ has to be interpreted as causally relevant for $S(2)$, then a is not in the quantifier's domain of quantification.*

4 Constructional Repair and Perspectivization

The authentic (26a) (taken from a story) is formulated against the contextual proviso that Emily Brent belongs to the quantifier reference-set of 'everyone' before abstraction takes place. Discourse-level restrictions of this kind have to be marked as such; cf. (26b). Note that a contrastive conjunction like 'but' will not suffice to perform the function of an exception marker; (26c) implies (under the contextual proviso) that Emily Brent also felt the need of a stimulant.

(26)   a) Everyone felt the need of a stimulant. Only Emily Brent demanded and obtained a glass of water.

   b) *Everyone felt the need of a stimulant. Emily Brent demanded and obtained a glass of water.

c) Everyone felt the need of a stimulant, but Emily Brent demanded (and obtained) a glass of water.

Restrictions are bound to be local in the sense that they should not be separated from the clause containing the corresponding quantifier phrase by intermediate clauses following it. This is in particular true with regard to anaphoric uses where a finite and well-established set gets restricted. Compare (27a) and (27b) with (28):

(27)   a) All my friends came to the party, except John, Mike, and David.

   b) All my friends came to the party. The only exception was David.

(28) ??Tom, Jim, Mike, and David are my best friends. All of them came to my party. So I was very pleased. It was only David who wasn't able to participate.

Examples like (27a) and (27b) represent constructional repair. In many cases the linguistic device of generalization and subsequent restriction offers a compact means of quantification. In biclausal structures, the price to be paid is some kind of *non-monotonicity*: the build-up of information is not just incremental but requires revision.

While it can be built into the semantics of exception markers that a clause like (29) just has models where David is the only exception to the generalization, this in itself does not exclude the possibility that (29) later turns out to be a case of *perspectivization* resulting in changes of the model that has previously been built up. We can illustrate this phenomenon with regard to (30).

(29) All my friends except David came to the party.

(30) I went on and checked some other things, which fit, and new things fit, and I was very excited. It was the first time, and the only time, in my career that I knew a law of nature that nobody else knew. (Of course it wasn't true, but finding out later that at least Murray Gellmann – and also Sudarshan and Marshak – had worked out the same theory didn't spoil my fun.)

According to what we formulated as a constraint on the iteration of exception marking, the restriction following the clause with the exception phrase 'nobody else' in (30) should be illegitimate. However, what is at stake here is perspectivization. What the speaker presents in the second sentence as a fact has to be reinterpreted as a belief.

Note that in cases of perspectivization, revision is not necessarily local and need not immediately follow the clause to be corrected.

Let me contrast the two notions of constructional repair and perspectivization by way of the following definitions where we assume (for the sake of simplicity) that a text T is a sequence of information units S(i), and a text fragment T*(k)=S(1)+ ... + S(k) comprises all the S(i) from T up to and including S(k). In the definitions below we assume that the texts T are formulated in the simple past.

Def. 3 *A (non-contradictory) text $T= S(1)...+ S(n-1)+ S(n)$ exhibits constructional repair relative to $S(n-1)$ iff T neither implies $S(n-1)$ nor $T'=S(1)...+...'It$ seemed that $S(n-1)'+S(n)$.*

Def. 4 *A (non-contradictory) text $T=S(1)...+S(n)$ exhibits weak perspectivization of p iff a text fragment $T^*(j)$ of T implies 'It seems that p' but T doesn't.*

Def. 5 *A (non-contradictory) text $T=S(1)...+S(n)$ exhibits strong perspectivization of p iff a text fragment $T^*(j)$ of T implies p but T doesn't.*

Let me finally note that it is an important research topic to investigate the conditions that *block* constructional repair or *constrain* perspectivization. To provide one clear example: Domain stabilization via 'inclusion operators' – a subcase of conceptual addition – cannot for pragmatic reasons be undone unless perspectivization is involved:

(31) *Alle einschließlich Tom sind wahre Gentlemen. Nur Tom ist ein Gauner.

("Everybody, including Tom, is a gentleman. Only Tom is a scoundrel.")

(32) Alle einschließlich Tom sind wahre Gentlemen. (...) Es stellt sich heraus, daß Tom in Wirklichkeit ein Gauner ist.

("Everybody, including Tom, is a true gentleman. (...) It turns out that Tom really is a scoundrel.")

5 Abstraction and 'While'-Parallelism

We will now illustrate the interaction of explicit and implicit abstraction, and complement formation with 'd- anderen' ('the others') as mirrored in while-parallelism.

(33a) is a typical example of what one may dub contrastive 'while'- parallelism; as the name already suggests, a paraphrase with 'while' is possible; this does not hold for restriction parallelism:

(33) a) Die Deutsche Bank hat 15 Berater, alle anderen weniger als 10.
   ("The German bank has 15 councillors, all the others less than 10.")
   b) Während die Deutsche Bank 15 Berater hat, haben alle anderen weniger als 10.
   ("While the German bank has 15 councillors, all the others have less than 10.")

(34) a) John ist gestern zu meiner Party gekommen. Sonst ist niemand erschienen.
   ("Yesterday John came to my party. Nobody else appeared.")
   b) *Während John gestern zu meiner Party gekommen ist, ist sonst niemand erschienen.
   ("While John came to my party yesterday, nobody else appeared.")

Contrastive 'while'-parallelism is induced by syntactic and semantic parameters. We can specify it in the following way:

Rule 4 *(Contrastive 'While'-Parallelism) '$\lambda x P_1(x)(NP_1')$' and '$\lambda x P_2(x))(NP_2')$' exhibit contrastive 'while'-parallelism iff (a) NP_1 and NP_2 are syntactically parallel (i.e., take the same position in the corresponding syntactic trees), (b) NP_1' and NP_2' (conceived of as denoting individuals or sets) are distinct (in the case of individuals) and non-overlapping (in the case of sets), and (c) the predicates P_1 and P_2 are conceptual opposites.*

A brief comment on condition (c) in the definition: In his discussion of adversative 'während' ('while'), Herweg (1990) correctly points out that logical contrariety (incompatibility) of the contrasting predicates would be too strong. Just consider (35) and (36). (35) and (36) only pragmatically (but not semantically) imply that Mary did not 'see a movie' yesterday and John did not 'visit a friend'.

(35) While John saw a movie yesterday, Mary visited a friend.

(36) Yesterday John saw a movie, and Mary visited a friend.

What we here call 'conceptual opposites' is meant as a label to refer to "predicates that in our everyday understanding are felt to be opposites because usually they cannot be simultaneously attributed to one object", see (Herweg 1990). Clearly, this characterization is far from algorithmically tractable but at least may serve as a starting-point for a more elaborate analysis[3].

Within contrastive parallel structures, acceptability of implicit abstraction relative to a pronominal use of 'alle' ('all') and a complement anchor is severely restricted. In the following texts we presuppose that the pronominals 'alle' and 'd- anderen' are related to appropriate context sets (groups) and that the individuals mentioned are already established as group members.

First, note the following linearization asymmetry in contrastive parallel structures: Implicit abstraction relative to the pronominal 'alle' and a complement anchor is only illicit if the clause with the complement anchor precedes the clause with 'alle' (cf. (37) versus (38)).

(37) Während Miss Brent ins Eßzimmer ging, gingen die andern (*alle) auf den Hof.
   ("While Miss Brent went into the dining room, the others (*all) went into the yard.")

(38) Während die andern (alle) auf den Hof gingen, ging Miss Brent ins Eßzimmer.
   ("While the others (all) went into the yard, Miss Brent went into the dining room.")

Let me briefly comment on the interaction of 'die anderen' with explicit exception marking. First, in contrastive parallel texts like (39) it sounds pragmatically odd to replace 'die anderen' ('the others') by an explicit exception phrase (cf. (40)). Note that the second clause of (40) implies that Rogers didn't go into the yard – something already conveyed in the first clause. With Fanselow (1989)[4] we may say that in the type of context under discussion 'd- ander-' pragmatically *wins the competition* against the exception phrase.

Moreover, it is impossible for 'die anderen' and explicit exception marking to access the same context set; (41) is unacceptable. Where they are licensed, cf. (42), the exception phrase induces subtraction from the set constructed via 'die anderen'.

[3] A definition of contrastive 'while' parallelism certainly has to consider the factors governing the various readings of 'während' ('while'). The subjunction 'während' can come along not only with a purely adversative but also with a purely temporal, or a mixed meaning, depending on the fulfilment of certain licensing conditions (cf. (Herweg 1990)): (i) Temporal 'während' imposes temporal congruence of the main and subordinate clause (including compatibility of temporal adverbials), and (ii) it only accepts temporary states in the subordinate clause. A purely adversative reading may be licensed if any of the above conditions is violated. 'Positive' conditions have been codified in clauses (b) and (c) in our definition of contrastive 'while' parallelism.
[4] Fanselow himself refers to the Proper Inclusion Principle and the Elsewhere Condition as known from phonology. These principles (roughly) require that from two competing linguistic expressions the one with the more restricted domain of application should be adopted.

(39) Emily Brent ging ins Eßzimmer. Die anderen gingen auf den Hof.

("Emily Brent went into the dining room. The others went into the yard.")

(40) ?Rogers ging ins Eßzimmer. Außer ihm gingen alle auf den Hof.

("Rogers went into the dining room. Everybody except him went into the yard.")

(41) *Rogers ging ins Eßzimmer. Außer ihm gingen die anderen auf den Hof.

("Rogers went into the dining room. Except for him, the others went into the yard.")

(42) Emily Brent ging ins Eßzimmer. Außer Rogers gingen die anderen auf den Hof.

(" Emily Brent went into the dining-room. Except for Rogers the others went into the yard.")

The subsequent example does not exhibit contrastive parallelism (note the impossiblity of linking the clauses with the subjunction 'während' ('while')). Implicit abstraction is not blocked:

(43) Noch immer etwas zweifelnd ließ sich Miss Brent ins Boot helfen. Alle (die andern) folgten ihr.

("Rather doubtfully, Miss Brent permitted herself to be helped into the boat. Everybody (the others) followed suit.")

6   A Procedural Set-up

In the following we will assume for the sake of simplicity that the universal quantifers in the small linguistic scenario that we will focus on do not occur generically. To make life easier, we will also assume that dependent NPs are anaphors and not cataphors. While we will not formulate the constraints relative to a specific scenario, the reader for the sake of visualization may wish to picture a situation where he mentally follows the genetic line of a group that is allowed to split and merge again, and where new members are allowed to join the group.

With regard to the major items that so far have played a role in this paper, we assume a grammar that in particular contains

- Dependent NPs: 'alle', 'niemand', 'keiner', 'alle $\overline{N}$', 'kein $\overline{N}$', 'die_anderen $\overline{N}$'
- Prepositions: 'außer', 'abgesehen von', 'bis_auf', 'einschließlich', 'neben'
- Particles: 'sonst', 'nur'

Dependent NPs are supposed to bear the feature [+dep(endent)]. We also assume that connected exception PPs are Chomsky-adjoined to NPs or PPs.

Prepositions like 'außer', 'abgesehen_von' and 'bis_auf' (and the corresponding PPs) may alternatively bear the feature [+restrictive] or [+additive]. This would correspond to two lexical entries. Instead one could also assume a disjunctive feature. 'Neben' is in this fragment assumed to be characterized via the feature [+additive]. In the case of connected exception PPs – that we, to repeat, assume to be Chomsky-adjoined to NP (or PP) – the complex NP (or PP) inherits the feature [+restrictive] and is additionally specified as [+con restrictive] to signal that the restriction comes NP (PP)-internally. If a free exception phrase is linked to a target NP (PP), the target NP (PP) is instantiated as [+restrictive] but does not bear the feature [+con_restrictive]. A free exception phrase can never be linked to an NP already marked as [+restrictive]. There is one exception, however: some NPs (PPs) like 'niemand-' allow modification via 'sonst' and can still be linked to a (free) exception phrase. A differentiation of the exception items – which we assume are all [+restrictive] – may be realized via a feature [+/-sonst]. Our modified procedure is then the following: a free exception phrase can never be linked to an NP[+restrictive;-sonst].

We also adopt a feature [+universal] to characterize universal NPs like 'alle $\overline{N}$' or 'niemand' but also plural NPs formed with the help of the definite article 'd-' ('the'); the latter receive the additional feature [+ddef]. We will assume that exception phrases can only be linked to universal NPs; as we have come to know, this assumption is justified on grounds of frequency (where NP[+universal;-ddef] are most privileged) but actually is too restrictive. In a large implementation that allows phrases like 'die Wohnung außer dem Badezimmer' ('the flat except the bathroom'), mereological subtraction has to be added to set-theoretical subtraction. An NP like 'die Wohnung außer dem Badezimmer' would be licensed if a procedure 'Functional_Part_Check' succeeds (that would try to relate the bathroom and the flat). Such a procedure has to check database information on the functional part structure of objects.

NPs like 'die anderen N' or 'alle anderen N' we call complementary; they are supposed to carry the corresponding feature [+compl]. The item 'alle anderen N' shows that the features [+universal] and [+compl] may co-occur.

In order to do justice to inclusion PPs like 'einschließlich X_{NP}' (that do not allow constructional repair with regard to X such that X is later 'subtracted' again), we assume that the embedded NP is passed on to the more inclusive complex NP and stored within a feature-structure 'Blocking(...)'.

We assume that a text $T=S(1)...+S(i-1)+S(i)...+S(n)$ is processed incrementally, with the proviso that a 'current' S(i) may cause revision of the structure built up by S(i-1).

We assume – along the LILOG set-up – a three-way interpretation of syntactic structure. First, a logical form LF1 is built up that, essentially, spells out the thematic relations between heads, their arguments, and adjuncts. At the next level, LF2, anaphora resolution takes place. A third level, LF3, is needed to take care of revision as a result of non-monotonicity.

The reader is best advised to think of logical forms as referring to discourse representation structures (cf. Kamp and Reyle (1991)).

Suppose a 'current' S(i) of a text T is being processed relative to LF2(T*(i-1)). What we want to get after processing S(i) is LF3(T*(i-1)) (that may differ from LF2(T*(i-1)) in case S(i) has caused some revision) and LF2(S(i)).

We will in the following use something like pseudo-Prolog jargon to describe the procedures that are invoked.

The procedural flow (at a 'point' S(i)) would be something like the following:

Input(LF2(T*(i-1)), S(i), LF3(T*(i-1)), LF2(S(i))) →
Syntactic_Processing(S(i), Syn(S(i)))
Compositional_Semantics(Syn(S(i)), LF1(S(i)))
Anaphora_Resolution(LF2(T*(i-1)), LF1(S(i)), LF3(T*(i-1)),LF2(S(i)))

The procedure 'Anaphora_Resolution' includes the subprocedure 'Resolve_Universal_NPs', which itself has the procedure '*Resolve_Complementary_NPs*' as a component; the latter has to care for NPs like 'die anderen N' ('the other N').

Within a system that principally allows for generic statements to occur, it would seem a sensible strategy to first try an anaphoric linking of an NP[+universal; -compl] and only then check whether a non-linking (for instance, generic) interpretation is licensed.

'Resolve_Universal_NPs' calls a routine that selects a proper domain set from the context LF. In the case of an NP[+compl], finding a proper domain has to go hand in hand with finding a complement anchor. These procedures are hard to realize algorithmically: one prerequisite is extensive codification of world knowledge. We also need more refined conceptual tools to analyze a text's thematic structure.

A minimal requirement is sortal compatibility of anaphor and antecedent. Sortal checks have to be performed even before anaphora resolution starts. One illustration is the following. We assume that in a structure like 'alle $\overline{N}$ außer NP' in a clause S(i) the logical form (LF1) is something like '$alle_{(\overline{N})} - X_{NP}$'. 'Alle' in the logical form is meant as a variable to be instantiated in the process of anaphora resolution, $\overline{N}$ and NP provide sortal and quantificational information (moreover, sortal restrictions come via subcategorization constraints as mediated, say, by the verb). A procedure 'Sortal_Check' tests whether the sortal information going with X (from LF1) is compatible with the sortal specification of $\overline{N}$ (with $\overline{N}$ again from LF1). If compatibility obtains but the sortal information going with X does not include the sortal specification provided by $\overline{N}$, this sortal specification has to be explicitly predicated of X in the text's database.

An analogous procedure may also add the inference that X is not P where P is the clausal predicate of S(i). Note that in the process of anphora resolution, finding the domain may be facilitated by the following constraint: with regard to the construction under discussion, the domain must contain the exception set X.

We assume that a structure like 'alle $\overline{N}$ außer NP' evokes subtraction on sets. In the case of a negative NP like 'niemand' ('nobody'), 'niemand - X_{NP}' (let it be the 'argument' of a clausal predicate P) also leads to subtraction – from the domain to which 'niemand' is linked. Obviously the spurious argument then has to be spelt out such that P does not hold of the elements of the reduced domain.

After spelling out the domain of the universal quantifier, the subprocedure 'Proportionality_Check' will be called and perform the function we have already described.

Free exception phrases are more difficult to process. Suppose that at LF1 we obtain structures like 'Außer $X_{NP}(LF1(S(i)'))$' where $S(i)'$ is S(i) minus 'Außer NP'. A procedure 'Find_Clausal - Link' tries to establish a link to an NP[+universal, -con_restrictive] from $S(i)'$. This NP may be an argument in the subcategorization list belonging to the major clause predicate of S(i); it can also function as an adjunct or be the "highest" NP contained in such an adjunct ("links" are not unrestrained but have to obey subjacency constraints). The procedure again includes a sortal check[5].

---

[5]In spoken language, "linking" is facilitated by focus information which itself is guided by stress. We have already mentioned that even the choice between an additive or restrictive reading may depend on the distribution of focus in the "linked" NP. We could easily simulate information on stress via features on constituents.

If Hoeksema (1990: p. 176) is right, a linkage procedure has to take scope into account. He argues, for instance, that a free exception phrase cannot be easily linked to a universal NP that is in the scope of an existential quantifier; cf. (i); as (ii) is supposed to show, a linearization constraint does not suffice.

As we remember, 'außer' may not only govern NPs but also PPs. In that case the link must go to a prepositional adjunct at the level of clause structure (for the sake of an easier implementation one may assume identity of prepositions). Again a proportionality check has to take place.

If a target *within the clause* cannot be found, a procedure 'Reconstruction' must be called.

This procedure is hard to make precise. Let me just say what it should perform: It tries to reconstruct LF1(NP) as *propositional* information LF2(NP) and checks whether the relation '$Restrict(LF2(NP), LF2(S(i)'))$' obtains. The latter kind of information may be accessed in a database[6].

Let me now look at the anaphoric use of 'sonst' as related to a NP[+universal;-ddet] and triggered by a sentence-initial position of 'sonst'. As is to be expected from our remarks on free exception phrases, we assume a logical form '$Sonst(LF1(S(i)'))$'. We will in the following represent logical forms, merely for compactness, in a lambda-categorial format $\lambda x P(x)(Y_{NP})$. A procedure 'Sonst_Resolution' calls the following routines: A subprocedure 'Create_Logical_Representation' builds up predicate-argument structures $\lambda x P1(x)(Y1_{NP})$ for the predecessor-clause. A routine 'Check_Restriction_Parallelism' tests whether $\lambda x P1(x)(Y1_{NP})$ exhibits restriction parallelism (as described above) with regard to $\lambda x P2(x)(Y2_{NP[+universal;-ddet]})$ as derived from the S(onst)-Clause. This procedure includes the build-up of the reduced domain $Y2 - Y1$, and a proportionality check.

With regard to implicit abstraction something like a 'general algorithm' is not available. What we can do is point to certain constructions where implicit abstraction is licensed. One of these constructions concerns relational patterns 'x R y' where abstraction has to remove x from y (or y from x), cf. examples like (18a): We take it that it is specified as lexical information on S(i)'s major predicate which elements of its subcategorization list (including the subject) may be affected. If there are two such arguments where one denotes a set (induced by a universal NP) and the other an item/set such that an inclusion relation obtains, subtraction takes place.

We now consider the procedure 'Constructional_Repair_Via_Nur': It is called when S(i) has an LF1 $\lambda x P1(x)(Nur(Y1_{NP1}))$; it should be clear that obtaining the focus of 'nur' is not algorithmically trivial. In case restriction parallelism holds with regard to the predecessor LF $\lambda x P2(x)(Y2_{NP2})$, Y2 is replaced by Y2-Y1. In all cases of constructional repair we assume that revision is not blocked. Blockage of $Y1_{NP1}$ (with regard to the above example) would, for instance, be encoded such that Y1 occurs within the feature-structure Blocking(...) going with NP2.

In our fragment, we allow a clause S(i) just to consist of a restrictive PP (possible heads: 'außer', 'abgesehen_von', 'bis_auf'). This case of constructional repair calls a procedure that tries to establish a link to an NP[+universal; -restrictive] from the preceding S(i-1). Again this NP may be an argument in the subcategorization list belonging to the main predicate of S(i-1)'s major clause; it can also be an adjunct or the "highest" NP of such an adjunct. The final step is revision of LF2(S(i-1)) via the replacement operation described above.

How to deal with complementary NPs? The anaphor 'die_andern $\overline{N}$' certainly need not have its complement anchor in the directly preceding clause. However, we may decide to restrict our

---

(i) *Except for this Cadillac, somebody damaged every car.
(ii) Except for Padua, there was a delegate for every Italian city.

[6]This procedural set-up first tries the 'special case', namely a link to an NP[+universal] within the residual clause. We call the link to such an NP the 'special case' because we think restriction is fundamentally a relation between propositions, and the 'special case' is an instance of such a relation. There is a clear analogy to sentence negation versus constituent negation.

language fragment to cases where 'die_andern' is just allowed to occur in parallel structures (as we do now).

Relative to an LF1-representation $\lambda x P1(x)(die\_anderen_{\overline{N}})$ (extracted from S(i)) and a logical representation $\lambda x P2(x)(Y2_{NP2})$ (from S(i-1)), a 'While_Parallelism_Check' has to be applied. In particular, Y2 must be possible as the complement anchor (the information carried by $\overline{N}$ must be compatible with the information carried by Y2 (via NP2)). There is a 'stylistic' constraint that could be integrated into the fragment discussed here: remember that there are NP[+compl; +restrictive]. In that case we should not allow the exception set to be identical to the complement anchor[7].

Let me now briefly look at the treatment of 'addition' phrases and paradigmatically consider 'außer'. Suppose we want to check whether relative to an LF1 'Außer $X_{NP}(LF1(S(i)'))$' an 'additive' use of 'außer' is licensed. We here just consider the linking procedure. Again the information going with X has to be compatible with the subcategorization information that comes along with a potential target slot. Unlike, say, 'abgesehen_von', the target of an additive 'außer X' must not precede the addition phrase. That is, the linking algorithm is syntactically constrained. We further need a disjointness constraint: If X is linked to Y as derived from the 'target', X and Y must be disjoint. If this piece of information is not already available via lexical information alone, it has to be added to the text's database. If an 'additive' interpretation is licensed, the information of the target clause is complemented by the information that we receive when X is replaced by Y. (Although additive 'neben' exhibits a different behaviour from the one displayed by additive 'außer', a 'flat' implementation may perhaps wish to neglect these differences.)

I will stop here. It should be obvious that this procedural presentation is incomplete in a number of respects. Plenty of implementational and linguistic problems are hidden behind the procedural schemata. Nevertheless, this toy model should at least have shown the road where to go. This brings me to my final remarks.

7 Outlook

This paper was meant to give an outline of what I think are major issues in the area under discussion. Clearly the subject matter is much more complicated and multifaceted. One of the most crucial problems is the interaction of grammatical knowledge and world knowledge. There are interesting links to the lingustics of time and space that deserve closer investigation.

We have here focused only on a few aspects concerning reference-set calculation. As is well known, reference-set calculation is embedded in the more inclusive question of how local contexts are determined. This in turn requires a deep and hitherto only partially available understanding of the interplay of syntax, semantics, and pragmatics (including world knowledge). In particular, there is so far no general procedure to calculate the salience and relevance of discourse referents. This implies that what we have called implicit abstraction still has to be spelt out relative to a restricted sample of construction types.

---

[7]This means we do not allow parallel structures like the following:

(i) *John worked in the garden. The others except John worked in the house.

References

Abraham, W. (1979): 'Außer'. In: Weydt H. (ed.): Die Partikeln der deutschen Sprache, de Gruyter, Berlin, pp. 239–255

Abraham, W. (1980): 'Sonst' und 'außer' als Folgerungskonnektoren. In: Brettschneider, G., Lehmann, Ch. (eds.): Wege zur Universalienforschung. Sprachwissenschaftliche Beiträge zum 60. Geburtstag von Hansjakob Sailer, Gunter Narr Verlag, Tübingen, pp. 406–418

Ducrot, O. (1972): Dire et ne pas dire. Hermann, Paris

Fanselow, G. (1989): Konkurrenzphänomene in der Syntax – eine nicht-pragmatische Reduktion der Prinzipien B und C der Bindungstheorie. In: Linguistische Berichte 123, pp. 385–414

Herweg, M. (1990): Zeitaspekte. Die Bedeutung von Tempus, Aspekt und temporalen Konjunktionen. Deutscher Uni-Verlag, Leverkusen

Hoeksema, J. (1990): Exploring exception phrases. In: Stokhof M., Torenvliet L. (eds.): Proceedings of the Seventh Amsterdam Colloquium, pp. 165–189

Kamp, H., Reyle, U. (1991): From Discourse to Logic. An introduction to modeltheoretic semantics of natural language, formal logic and discourse representation theory. To appear

König, E., van der Auwera, J. (1988): Clause integration in German and Dutch conditionals, concessive conditionals, and concessives. In: Haiman, J., Thompson, S.A. (eds.): Clause Combining in Grammar and Discourse, John Benjamins Pub Co, Amsterdam/Philadelphia, pp. 101–133

König, E., Kortmann, B. (1987): Absolute complementation in the lexical structure of English and German. In: Lörscher, W., Schulze, R. (eds.): Perspectives on Language in Performance. Studies in Linguistics, Literary Criticism, and Language Teaching and Learning To Honour Werner Hüllen on the Occasion of His Sixtieth Birthday, Günther Narr Verlag, Tübingen, pp. 170–198

Mayer, R. (1991): Domain Restriction and Other Kinds of Reference Set Operations. To appear as IWBS-Report, IBM Deutschland, Stuttgart

Veltman, F. (1990): Defaults in update semantics I. In: Kamp, H. (ed.): Conditionals, Defaults, and Belief Revision, Dyana Report, pp. 28–63

Wunderlich, D. (1979): Analyse einiger Funktionen von 'sonst' – ein Beitrag zur Klärung von Kontextabhängigkeit. In: Rosengren, I. (ed.): Sprache und Pragmatik. Lunder Symposium 1978, pp. 371–390

On Representing the Temporal Structure of Texts

Kurt Eberle

1 Introduction

Understanding a coherent natural language text, or to be more restrictive, a narrative, comprises the ability of the recipient to reconstruct the course of events the author or speaker had in mind when writing down or uttering the sequence of sentences (describing events and states) that makes up the text.

The main topic of the temporal subproject of LILOG is to model (parts of) this ability in order to automatize the representation of the temporal structure of texts.

Here, the first question to ask concerns the relevant parameters guiding the underlying algorithm which we intend to model. In particular, the question arises of the relevance of the temporal parameters which are provided by tense- and aspect-information.

Classical operator based tense logics of the Priorian style and most versions of Montague Grammar spell out the meaning of the tense forms from the viewpoint of single sentence discourses. If the essential meaning of the tense forms is grasped this way, their contribution to the just described task of understanding is highly restricted. However, in contrast to that, we think that the impact of the tenses reaches beyond the sentence level, so that spelling out the meaning of the tense forms is an important prerequisite for the understanding of the temporal coherence of texts.

French, in contrast to German, has a very elaborate tense system. So, to begin with, let us consider an example of a French text from Kamp und Rohrer together with the conclusions the authors draw from it:

> (1) Vite, docteur, dépechez-vous. Mon mari a pris deux cachets d'aspirine, il a avalé
> sa lotion contre les aigreurs d'estomac, il s'est mis un suppositoire contre la grippe,
> il a pris un comprimé à cause de son asthme, il s'est mis des gouttes dans le nez, et
> puis il a allumé une cigarette. Et alors, il y a eu une enorme explosion.

A succession of sentences whose main verb is in the passé simple or in the passé composé is normally understood as reporting events whose relative temporal order is isomorphic to the order in which the sentences reporting them follow each other in the text. Or, more simply, the order of the sentences corresponds to the order of the events.

```
------*-------*-------*-------*--------|----
    e1      e2      e3      en        to

    |       |       |       |
    S1      S2      S3      Sn
```

There is little that traditional model-theoretic semantics has to say about the truth value of a discourse consisting of several sentences. The implicit view appears to be that such sentence-sequence is true iff each of the sentences in it is true. According to this view (1) would be true provided there are past events $e_1, \ldots, e_n$ of the kind specified by $S_1, \ldots, S_n$, irrespective of how they are ordered in time... The only relevant temporal condition here is that each e_i lies before the speech point.

Clearly this is not right. The discourse conveys a definite temporal order among the events it reports and unless this was in fact the order in which these events actually occurred the discourse will not be countenanced as true. The only way out of this predicament is to incorporate the relevant intersentential temporal relations into whatever it is that determines the truth conditions of the discourse as a whole. In discourse representation theory the problem is solved in the following manner. The principle that a sentence in the passé simple introduces a new event, and that this event follows the last event already introduced, is incorporated into the rules for discourse representation construction.   (Kamp, Rohrer 1983), p.251f.

Beyond that, the meaning of the French tense form *passé simple* is twofold. It has the meaning that it places the thus described event before the speech time and it has, in addition, a certain kind of *anaphoric meaning* in placing its event after the existent reference event. Another regularity of the French tense system seems to be that *imparfait* introduces states which, in contrast to events introduced by *passé simple*, do not follow the reference event, but include it.

> *Pierre entra$_{e_1}$. Marie téléphonait$_{e_2}$.* $e_1 \subseteq e_2$

Of course, we do not want to present here a study about the French tense system. LILOG deals with German texts. But the phenomena illustrated by the contrast *passé simple :: imparfait* seem to depend on a difference which is much more general. Firstly, the meaning of the tense forms apparantly comprises an anaphoric part which is strongly suggestive of the case of nominal anaphora. Secondly, the aspect information influences the decision about the temporal relation to choose between the reference event and the new event or state. These observations are not new. Partee has discussed at length the parallelism between nominal and temporal anaphora (cf. (Partee 1973)). Beside this, the idea of tenses as anaphora underlies a long line of approaches, for instance the approaches of Dowty, Hinrichs, Moens/Steedman, Webber and, of course, Kamp and Rohrer (see, e.g., (Dowty 1986), (Hinrichs 1981), (Hinrichs 1986), (Moens 1987), (Moens, Steedman 1988), (Kamp, Rohrer 1983), (Kamp, Rohrer 1985), (Webber 1988)).

However, very often in such approaches, either one deals with very short discourses or the discussion of the phenomena observed leads to the conception of a number of principles which may locally drive the process of reconstructing the temporal structure, but which are not valid globally. This process of determining the temporal structure of the events the discourse is about, in the following, we call "temporal resolution". It should be clear that it would be too simple-minded a picture to take what we have illustrated above as the one and only principle directing temporal discourse understanding. It seems that there is a very subtle interplay between tense form, aspect, temporal adverbials, text structure of the preceding text and background information which directs the temporal resolution.

This problem of how to decide about the local principle of resolution directing the understanding of a particular text segment, and of how to determine the time(s) the context has to supply and to which the event of a new sentence has to be related according to the principle chosen, is largely neglected in theoretical discussions of the semantics of tenses. It will be the main topic of our discussion.

The LILOG system translates natural language texts into so-called E-DRSs which are extensions of *Discourse Representation Structures* (DRSs) (cf. (Geurts) in this volume).

In the framework of Discourse Representation Theory (DRT) (Kamp 1981) a DRS is a pair $< U, K >$ consisting of a set U of discourse referents (DRFs) and a set K of conditions. Conditions may take the following forms:

- $P(a_1, \ldots, a_n)$, where P is an n-ary predicate symbol and the a_i are discourse referents. Conditions of this form are also called atomic. For 2-place temporal relations we will also use infix notation. The relations used are $\prec, \subseteq$, *Meets* and *Finishes*.

- $f(a_1, \ldots, a_n) = a$, where f is an n-ary function symbol.

- $DRS_1 \implies DRS_2$; conditions of this form are also called duplex conditions. There are other duplex conditions, which are of no interest here.

DRT uses a variant of the Davidsonian method of talking about events: they are treated as a kind of object. Within LILOG we have adopted this. But we deviate from DRT in that we use a one-place event predicate and a number of thematic roles, i.e., functions, to describe what in DRT is expressed by a complex condition which consists of a DRS, containing the event description in terms of an n-ary event predicate, and of the DRF for the event put before the DRS. (Since we use this alternative notation, above, we have omitted to list the corresponding fourth type of DRS-condition.) Thus, for instance, we write:

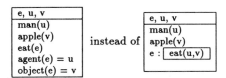

The LILOG inference component manipulates L_{LILOG}-formulas. It doesn't work with DRSs (cf. 2.1 of this volume). In order to make the knowledge base available for text processing and in order to introduce new information, which stems from a text, into the knowledge base, DRSs can be translated into L_{LILOG}-formulas. However, with regard to the subject of this paper there is no need to go into detail about the concrete LILOG-architecture and about the different formalisms used.

The component for the temporal resolution needs a number of prerequisites in order to behave intelligently. Mainly the work consisted here in

- contributions to the structuring of the knowledge base with regard to the temporal logic and ontology, and in
- implementing an aspect calculus.

We can say nothing here about the first point, on which refer to (Eberle 1990) and (Eberle 1989). In the next section, we briefly sketch the second point. Actually, the most elaborate description of the interplay between the background knowledge, the aspect calculus and the resolution component can be found in (Eberle 1991).

2 The Computation of the Aktionsart

Vendler distinguishes four classes of event descriptions (cf. (Vendler 1967)):

- *States* are temporally extended and homogeneous. They describe static situations, i.e., the validity of the statement is inherited by all subintervals t' of an intervall t for which the statement holds (even by points if they are allowed by the logic as is the case in LILOG).

- *Activities* are temporally extended and relatively homogeneous (modulo some pauses and inheritance onto points).

- *Accomplishments* are temporally extended and heterogeneous. That is, if an accomplishment holds at an interval t, it doesn't hold at any subinterval t' of t.

- *Achievements* are punctual.

The LILOG-system makes use of this classification. There are four sorts of events in the wider sense, namely states, activities and the events in the strict sense which are accomplishments and achievements. In the following, we call states and activities also *stative events* and accomplishments and achievements *non-stative events*. Originally, the Vendler classification was based upon the notion of *Aktionsart*. Often, a distinction is drawn between the Aktionsart and the (morphological) *aspect*, where the latter stands for things expressed by the *imparfait* :: *passé simple* opposition in French or the difference between *simple past* and *past progressive* in English. Notwithstanding such definitions, for simplicity, within this paper we do not distinguish between *aspect* and *Aktionsart*. Thus, on the basis of the Aktionsart (or the synonymous aspect) we get the following picture:

Events:

- *Paul speaks French*   state
  Paul is eating an apple $\rangle$ stative

- *Paul worked in the garden*   activity

- *Paul wrote a letter*   accomplishment
                          $\rangle$ non-stative

- *Paul reached the top*   achievement

In the following, we sometimes refer to these classes in turn by the abbreviations *state, act, acc* and *ach*.

It is well known that it is not the verb alone which decides about the Aktionsart of the event introduced by a new sentence. The different thematic roles influence the choice. Thus, for instance, bare plurals or mass terms often transform accomplishments and achievements into activities. The constituent

> *crossed the bridge*

refers to an accomplishment. However, if the subcategorized function, which is still missing, i.e., the subject, is instantiated by a bare plural like *cars* the resulting Aktionsart will be activity.

(1)   *Cars crossed the bridge.*

Notice, that from examples like these one cannot infer a general rule predicting the corresponding transition. Counterexamples are provided by sentences like the following:

(2)   *Students wrote a letter.*

Here, the preferred reading seems to refer to an accomplishment though the filler of the agent role similarly stems from a bare plural.

Carlson draws a distinction between *natural kinds, individuals* and *stages* which he uses to explain why cases like (1) are understood as states or activities: Firstly, bare plural phrases (like *cars*), very often, are representing natural kinds. Secondly, statements about natural kinds have to be generic statements which, of course, are stative (cf. (Carlson 1980)). Approaches like this do not explain, however, where the different preferences in cases like (1) and (2) come from. Instead of explaining the difference in such cases using different ontological types of DRFs (kinds and individuals), we have tried to show the difference extending an approach of Krifka ((Krifka 1987)). For Krifka the difference between the Aktionsarten relies on the different structural properties of the extensions of the event predicates in the model. Krifka's approach is an elaborate reformulation of Vendler's point of view within a framework with reified events. The details are of no interest here.

We think that in both cases (1) and (2) the bare plural phrase introduces a set or a sum of individuals. Now, in our opinion, the difference comes from the following.

With *crossed the bridge* in (1), the distribution over the set is preferred or, at least, is licensed, whereas with *wrote the letter*, the distribution over the set is not licensed or, at least, is not preferred.

The narrow scope reading for *a letter*, with regard to the distributive reading of the bare plural phrase, seems not acceptable. Similar examples have persuaded a number of researchers (like Carlson) that bare plurals do not introduce an existential quantifier (which, if introduced, should show the well known interaction patterns with regard to other quantifiers). We think that bare plurals introduce existential quantifiers, but that the interaction with other quantifiers is highly restricted. For lack of space, we cannot go further into detail with this. However, the wide scope reading for *a letter* seems unacceptable too in the distributive case, since this would mean that this letter had been written by each of the students.

Thus, the preferred readings seem to be the following:

(1) 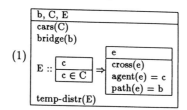 (2)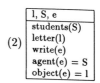

We cannot go into detail with the condition type DRF :: (DRS$_1$ ⇒ DRS$_2$). Informally, E stands for the set of events which can be abstracted from the duplex condition, i.e., E is the set of bridge-crossing events with regard to C. We think that, with regard to such distributive readings, the recipient is more inclined to think that the introduced events happened at different times, therefore *temp-distr(E)*, than to think that they happened at the same time.

These readings make the felt aspectual difference explicit in terms of the structural properties of the extensions of the event predicates in the model. In the first case the corresponding (complex) event predicate refers to sums of events which are "homogeneously distributed" whereas in the second case the (complex) event predicate refers to atomic events which are heterogeneous in the sense of Vendler and Krifka. In the second case there is no subevent of e which can take the place of e in the DRS for (2). In contrast to this, we can depict the characteristics of (1) as follows:

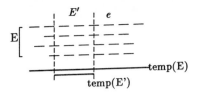

The sentence introduces the sum of events E consisting of an unspecified number of individual crossing events e. Since there are subsets of E, E', which are subsumed by the same event description, the sentence introduces an activity. Of course, with such cases, we have to make use of a formal definition of the different predicate types which is sensitive to event sums. (This goes beyond the approach of Krifka). In this paper, we cannot go further into detail either with this definition itself or with the aspect calculus based upon this definition. Here, with the sample texts of the introduction and the sample texts below, we just want to motivate that such a calculus is needed and that, in our opinion, it must be sensitive to quantificational phenomena.

The calculus used in the LILOG-system starts out with the aspect entry for the verb and computes step by step, accompanying the DRS construction algorithm, the aspect of the event of the sentence. Of course, this proceeds in dependence on the chosen reading of the roles to attach. The specification of the calculus is such that, conversely, the calculus can influence the choice of a specific reading of a particular role by means of specific role properties (which may depend on the verb in question) and by means of what has been processed so far. In addition, it is sensitive to *type coercion* in the sense of (Moens, Steedman 1988). However, this interdependence between DRS construction algorithm and aspect calculus is specified, as mentioned, but not implemented yet. With regard to (1) and (2) the specific role properties would suggest the (preference of the) distributive reading in the first case and the (preference of the) collective reading in the second case, i.e., these properties would give rise to a structural distinction which, to our opinion, is at the basis of the aspectual difference.

3 Temporal Resolution

3.1 Discourse Relations

As mentioned in the introduction, tense and aspect (or Aktionsart) must be understood as having an influence on the temporal relationship between the events of the preceding text and the event of the new sentence. To begin with, in order to sketch the influence of aspect, let us consider some examples with uniform tense form which meanwhile provide the common starting point of different approaches to the problem of temporal resolution.

(3) *The elderly gentleman wrote out the check, tore it from the book and handed it to Costain.*
((Hinrichs 1986), p.66)

(4) *John entered the president's office. The president walked over to him.* ((Dowty 1986), p.37)

(5) *He went to the window and pulled aside the soft drapes. It was a casement window and both panels were cranked out to let in the night air. The apartment was on the second floor. The window itself was a scant five feet above the roof.*   ((Hinrichs 1986), p.66)

(6)   *John entered the president's office. The clock on the wall ticked loudly.*
((Dowty 1986), p.38)

(3) and (4) are understood as describing events that follow each other in the order of their syntactical introduction. In contrast to that, in (5) the event of the first sentence appears to be included within the states of the second, third and fourth sentence and in (6), accordingly, the event of the first sentence appears to be included within the (equally stative) activity of the second sentence.

Examples like these are often used to conclude the informal rule:

(*) *Non-statives drive the action forward in time, statives do not.*[1]

In LILOG we use *discourse relations* to classify the different possibilities of the temporal incorporation of new events or states into the event structure of the preceding text. We call the non-stative part of (*) *continuation*, i.e., the case where the new sentence introduces an event which follows the last mentioned event, and we call the state part of (*) *background elaboration*, i.e., the case where the new sentence introduces a state or activity which includes the last mentioned event.

(*) is at best a local principle. Counterexamples are for instance the following (7) and (8) which, with respect to the aspectual stative/non-stative-distribution, are identical to (5) and (6), but which give rise to another temporal relation:

(7)   *Jameson entered the room, shut the door carefully and switched off the light. It was pitch-dark around him because the venetian blinds were closed.*   ((Hinrichs 1986), p.68)

(8)   *Jean trouva l'interrupteur à tâtons. Il appuya dessus. La lumière l'éblouissait.*
      (Kamp, Rohrer 1985)

Examples like these persuaded Hinrichs that the contextual temporal element in relation to which sentences must be interpreted is not the last mentioned event itself, but rather a time immediately following the event. If the new sentence describes an accomplishment or achievement, this event occurs within this time (introducing a new reference time immediately following the old one); if the sentence describes an activity or state, this activity or state is understood to obtain during a period including that time. (No new reference time is introduced in this case). Dowty takes the introduction of reference times even one step further. His *Temporal Discourse Interpretation Principle* (TDIP), formalized within the framework of Interval Semantics, predicts that, in all cases, the reference interval of a sentence S_i in a sequence of sentences $S_1, S_2, \ldots, S_n$ to be interpreted as a narrative discourse is a time which immediately follows the reference time of the previous sentence S_{i-1}, provided that there are no (definite) temporal adverbials in S_i. TDIP thus predicts that even in the case of a sequence of state descriptions there is a homomorphic chain of reference times such that the state of S_{i-1} holds (at least) at a time t_{i-2} immediately preceding t_{i-1} where the state of S_i holds. Dowty motivates TDIP with regard to states among other things by perceptional constraints. The perception of states of affairs in the world proceeds step by step, even if there is the expectation that the states overlap each other and/or the reference event. In (6) the protagonist first entered the office before perceiving the ticking of the clock even if one is led to assume that the ticking has begun long before the entering. In approaches using reified events, in order to express TDIP, reference times are not really necessary. Thus Bäuerle and Krifka for instance (cf. (Bäuerle 1988), (Krifka 1987)) simply map a sequence of stative or non-stative sentences of a narrative text onto a sequence of events (in the wide sense).

However, it seems to us that, with regard to phenomena described by examples like (3)–(8), both alternatives – that of Hinrichs and the different formalizations of TDIP – create at least as many problems as they solve. For in such approaches one is forced to explain the fact that in the majority

---

[1]Compare for instance the corresponding principle (P1) of Kamp and Rohrer for the French "event tense form" *passé simple* and "the state/activity tense form" *imparfait*:

(P1) *The passé simple drives the narrative's action forward, the imparfait is incapable of this.* (Kamp, Rohrer 1985)

of cases where there is no causal link between the last event and the new state, this state (and all following) is almost inevitably understood as surrounding this last event, as a matter of pragmatic inference: the extendedness of states is restricted only by positive knowledge about incompatibilities. This is the well known "negation as failure" applied to the extendedness of states. We do not find this very persuasive in this context. We think that it is just the other way arround. Only if there is positive knowledge allowing us to infer a causal link between the last event and the new state, is the state part of the rule (*) invalidated. We call this discourse relation *causal background elaboration*. It is only against this background that the state part of (*) appears to be a default rule. In the case of causality, incoherence may be avoided by applying (*) with reference to a temporal element which was not given explicitly by the antecedent text but can be inferred from what was explicitly given. In (7) and (8) this is the new state resulting from pressing the switch, or perhaps the onset of that state. Thus, at present, we see no need for explicit reference times which are introduced as successors of new events (or states). For us, on the basis of the three discourse relations mentioned, the temporal anchor for a subsequently introduced event or state is the last mentioned event itself or, in the case of consequent states as in (7) and (8), a (not yet qualified) event which has to be accommodated as a successor of this last mentioned event.

We do not want to pursue the subject of *discourse relations* and related specific uses of tense forms and aspect in great detail here. We just want to sketch the subject in such a way that it becomes clear what the principles are that guide the LILOG temporal resolution component and how this component works.

Therefore we briefly introduce two further discourse relations: *flashback* and *elaboration*.

(9) *Harry handed the book about giraffes to Jane (e_1). Two hours ago he had discovered it in Alfred's bookstore (e_2). He had bought it (e_3), had inserted a dedication (e_4) and had it wrapped up (e_5). Jane took the book with a smile (e_6).*

Here the relation between e_1 on the one hand and $e_2 - e_5$ on the other is that of *flashback*, i.e., $e_2 - e_5$ all precede e_1. In addition, e_2 precedes e_3 which precedes e_4 which precedes e_5 and e_1 precedes e_6: in both cases, within the set of flashback events and within the other, the discourse relation of continuation holds . The parallelism between the simple past line and the past perfect line as exemplified here can be observed in a majority of cases, so that extended flashbacks, i.e., flashbacks with more than one element, often can be understood as transposed simple past stories, where the vantage point is changed from the speech point to a point in the past. Thus, with regard to its anaphoric behavior, the meaning of past perfect should share certain properties with its non-analytic counterpart, i.e., with the meaning of simple past.

Reichenbach uses three time parameters and two relations to distinguish the different meanings of the tenses (Reichenbach 1947). The parameters are: the *time of the event* talked about, the *speech time* (time of utterance) and the *reference time*. The relations are temporal coincidence and precedence. On this structural analysis the difference between simple past and past progressive for instance consists in that in the past perfect case the event time precedes the reference time which itself precedes the speech time, whereas in the simple past case the reference time and the event time coincide and both precede the speech time. The refinement of coincidence into coincidence proper and inclusion allows for the distinction of progressive forms like past progressive from their non-progressive counterparts like simple past. On the assumption that the notion of reference time is given the textual flavor, as it is in the resolution rules of Hinrichs or Dowty, it should be clear how Reichenbach's analysis can be used in such systems. (Especially Hinrichs approach relies to a certain extent upon this analysis). In our system, if *reference time* has to be understood as the time of the actual reference event, we need a rather coarse-grained interpretation of coincidence to get things right. There is, however, also a deeper problem, which cannot be overcome by a liberal interpretation of coincidence. In (9), in keeping with Reichenbach's relational analysis for the past perfect, we must assume that each of the past perfect clauses has the time of Harry's handing the book to Jane for its reference time. In order to express the parallelism between sequences of simple past sentences and sequences of past perfect sentences with regard to (*), it is obvious that a parameter is missing. In addition, the role played by e_1 with respect to $e_2 - e_5$ is not the same as the one played by this event with respect to e_6. In the first case it is more the role that the speech point plays with regard to e_1 and e_6. Observations like these led Kamp and Rohrer to split the Reichenbachian reference time into two contextually given parameters: the *perspective time* and the *reference time* (in the narrow sense). The perspective time is the time, the vantage point, from which the event is seen (e_1 for $e_2 - e_5$, the speech point for e_1 and e_6), the reference time is something like the contextually given focus time, the local anchor for the ongoing of the story (e_2 for e_3, e_3 for e_4, ... and e_1 for e_6). The two-dimensional analysis of Reichenbach is overtaken, but now formulated using the perspective time instead of the Reichenbachian reference time. We do not want to go into detail spelling out the structural analysis of the English or French or German tense system along the lines of the criteria of Kamp and Rohrer. The point here is, first, to have explained the notion of perspective point, distinguishing it from pure reference times, and second, to sketch how it is used in the LILOG system: normally with sequences of simple past sentences the perspective is the speech time. If a past perfect sentence fires the rule for flashback interpretation, the perspective is shifted to the vantage point for the flashback events. All events of the flashback precede this perspective; internally they may be ordered along the lines of the possibilities of ordering which exist for the non-analytic case. We come back to this in a bit more detail when listing the resolution rules of the system.

Now let us consider an example for elaboration, taken from (Webber 1988).

(10)   *John bought Mary some flowers. He picked out three red roses, two white ones and one pale pink.*

Here, the picking out of roses has to be understood as an event elaborating the buying event on a more fine-grained level. Of course, on elaborating levels we can observe the same mechanisms at work as on "higher" levels. Compare for instance an example, which again stems from Kamp and Rohrer:

(11)   *Pierre dina chez 'Madame Gilbert'. D'abord il y eut un hors-d'oeuvre, puis une bouchée à la reine. Après cela le patron apporta une sole meunière. Le repas se termina par un dessert flambé, qui mit Pierre dans un état d'euphorie exceptionnelle.*

In (11) the meal is elaborated in four steps which follow each other, i.e., (*) is locally valid here, introducing events whose relative order is guided by the principle of continuation.

One of the LILOG texts which are used as test cases for the system illustrates the iterative use of the principle of elaboration:

(12)   *In der ersten Maiwoche fand der große LILOG-Workshop statt. Nach einer anstrengenden Projektsitzung am Montag, machten die Teilnehmer am Dienstag einen Ausflug in die Düsseldorfer Innenstadt. Der Bus brachte sie von ihrem Hotel zum Hofgarten. ... Um Mitternacht fuhren sie mit dem Bus wieder zurück zu ihrem Hotel.*

The meeting on Monday and the trip on Tuesday both elaborate the workshop event. In addition the trip on Tuesday is elaborated by a sequence of events starting and ending with a bus transfer event.

It is obvious that with regard to the events which elaborate the trip, all kinds of further expansions along the lines of the just sketched discourse relations (and others not yet mentioned) may be allowed. The restriction on the applicability of discourse relations will be more or less the same on "deeper"levels as on "higher" levels. We will come back to this point in more detail later. Informally, discourse levels and the depth of different such levels will be given by "embedding" discourse relations like elaboration and flashback. With elaborations we leave the main line of the story, and a "sub-story" is incorporated which tells us on a more fine-grained level how an event of the main story took place exactly. With flashbacks, sub-stories are inserted which describe earlier time slices with regard to the actual reference event of the main story. In both cases, while the sub-stories are told, the main story is stopped, so to speak. We do not call background elaboration an embedding discourse relation, since here the level of the sequence of reference events of the main story is not left.

At present it is important to note that especially with elaborations we encounter two serious problems. First, in general, aspectual and tense information is of no help when one is confronted with the question to decide whether a new event continues the reference event or whether it elaborates it. Webber contrasts (10) with the following (13):

(13) *John went into the florist shop. He picked out three red roses, two white ones and one pale pink.*

In both cases, in (10) and (13), a pair of non-stative events is introduced by simple past. However, whereas in (10) the second event is included within the first, in (13) the second follows the first, i.e., in the first case the right decision consists in choosing the rule for elaboration, in the second case it consists in choosing the rule for continuation. It is obvious that we need world knowledge here to get things right.

The second problem is that in the case of existing elaborations the last mentioned event is not necessarily the reference event for new events or states. Compare the following alternatives (10a) and (10b) which both can be regarded as plausible completions of the text segment (10):

(10) a. *Back on the street he met Gabi.*
     b. *Then he saw some very nice tulips. He put back the roses and took the tulips. He payed and left the shop.*

In (10a) the elaboration level is left. The meeting event follows the buying event, i.e., the buying event is the reference event with regard to the meeting event within the relation of continuation. Note that, at the time of incorporating the new event of (10a), the buying is not the last mentioned event. In contrast to that, in (10b), the last mentioned event, the picking out of the roses, serves as reference event for the seeing. With (10b) we arrive at a sequence of continuations on the level of the existing elaboration.

Thus, when going beyond the range of texts which are covered by the principle (*) we have to deal with more than one reference event.

It appears natural to think of the set of reference events which stems from an iterative use of elaboration as a hierachy of events which traces back the different (ordered) levels of elaborations such that leaving the local level, i.e., climbing up the hierarchy step by step decreases the prominence of the corresponding reference event.

(14) *Gegen drei Uhr verließ Peter die Bergstation e_1. Es schneite fürchterlich e_2. Trotzdem fuhr er recht flott hinunter zum Käsehüttli e_3.*

    a. *Er klopfte sich den Schnee aus den Kleidern e_{4a}. Dann trat er ein e_{5a} und bestellte sich einen Glühwein e_{6a}.*

    b. *Bei der Mittelstation legte er einen ordentlichen Sturz hin e_{4b}, rappelte sich aber schnell wieder auf e_{5b}.*
    Er klopfte sich den Schnee aus den Kleidern e_{6b}, wedelte weiter e_{7b} und war gegen halb vier Uhr unten e_{8b}.

(14a) and (14b) have identical beginnings. e_1, the leaving the mountain inn by Peter is the starting point of the story. The activity e_2, the snowing, supplies a background for (at least) e_1, so $e_1 \subseteq e_2$. The accomplishment e_3, the downhill running, continues the story: $e_1 \prec e_3$. Thus, till this point the text structure is completely directed by the complex principle (*) using exclusively the rules for continuation and background. In the case of (14a), (*) continues to govern the text structure till the end of the story. The cleaning, e_{4a}, follows the downhill run e_3 and also precedes e_{5a}, the entry of the Käsehüttli by Peter, and the final event e_{6a}, the ordering of hot wine. In the case of (14b), e_3 is elaborated by the sequence of events $e_{4b} - e_{8b}$, so that on this embedded elaborating level again the principle (*) is valid.

The point with this example is that the cleaning event that we rediscover in the alternative (14b) as e_{6b} chooses the event of standing up, e_{5b}, as reference event and not e_3. Note that this other variant, the continuation on the level of e_3, is not grammmatically excluded, i.e. by the tense and aspect information, as (14a) shows. In addition, world knowledge supplies nearly the same plausibility for both variants. It is nearly equally normal for a skier to clean his ski-suit after a fall or to clean it after a downhill run before entering a bar, especially if it snows heavily as is the case in the situation described by our sample text.

With regard to the earlier e_{4b} and e_{5b}, though grammatically licensed, the variant of continuation on the level of e_3 is ruled out by world knowledge. First, the fall must have happened *within* the downhill run and not afterwards, since it took place at the middle station, i.e., at a place with regard to which we have strong indications from the text and from common knowledge about ski-grounds that it is included in the path of the downhill run and not at the end of it. Second, the connection between an event of falling and one of standing up is highly conventionalized so that there is more plausibility to consider e_{5b} as a successor of e_{4b} than as a successor of e_3.

In contrast to that, we have seen that, even if world knowledge is available within the decision procedure, in the case of the cleaning event, the investigation remains undecided.

In such cases it seems to be the last mentioned event which is chosen as reference event proper from the set of possible reference events. Consequently, in a text which introduces step by step lower levels of elaborations, it is the reference event of the deepest level. Only if this choice is excluded for reasons of consistency or grammatical reasons or reasons of plausibility is this local level left. More than this, we think that the data justify the position that whenever the expansion of the deepest level seems possible at all, it is preferred to the expansion of higher levels even if there is some world knowledge plausibility motivating the expansion of some higher level.

For instance, think of an event of unbuckling the skis introduced immediately after the introduction of e_{6b} in (14b). Though it is not very convincing that Peter should unbuckle the skis after his fall – it would be mory convincing, having the ski-bindings opened after the fall, if he were to buckle the skis – and though the unbuckling of the skis is very plausible after a downhill-run to a bar, it seems to be more natural to read this event as one which follows e_{6b} than as one which immediately follows the downhill-run e_3.

If in such cases making reference to the embedded reference event appears to be completely out, for instance, because there is no possibility left to the recipient to get an idea of what the relevance is of the new event with regard to the reference event in terms of the logic of action, it seems to be the case that the recipient prefers to judge the text as incoherent rather than to make use of the possibility of referring to events of higher levels. Apparently, climbing up the hierarchy must be made explicit by positive linguistic information or at least by the fact that otherwise inconsistency would be the result.

There exists as yet no agreement on precisely what the set of discourse relations is. But it has been noted that it is a general feature of discourse and text understanding that each new sentence must be interpretable as related to its predecessor or predecessors in one of a fairly small number of different ways. In LILOG, in addition to the ones mentioned, we have investigated relations that we have called *projection*, *set* and *coset*. *Projection* is the opposite of flashback. If the reference event was introduced by simple past, normally, the corresponding rule is fired by the tense form *conditional*. *Set* and *coset* collect enumerations of events which, in the first case, are introduced in disregard of their relative order, and which, in the second case, are introduced with the intention to mark their relative temporal coincidence. Often, *set* appears as a specific use of elaboration, and *coset* as a specific use of continuation between two events where the second event, which is not explicitly introduced, is a complex event consisting of pairwise overlapping events which are enumerated as causal consequences of the first event.

When implementing the LILOG resolution component we have concentrated on the four discourse relations which we have described more extensively, i.e., we have concentrated on *continuation, elaboration, flashback* and on *background* with its specific use as *causally marked background*. In the following we will use therefore in turn the abbreviations **co, el, fb, bg, cbg**.

In the following we will continue to concentrate on these relations. In addition, sketching the resolution component we will restrict ourselves to the tense forms *simple past* and *past perfect* or, to be more precise, since the system was made for German texts, to the tense forms *Präteritum* and *Plusquamperfekt*. However, since the temporal discourse phenomena are more or less homomorphic with regard to German and English within the very restricted fragment which results from the restrictions mentioned, we continue to speak of *simple past* and *past perfect*. Though we can use only four discourse relations and two tense forms therefore, the range of texts we can arrive at by these means is not at all small. In addition, having a look at the rules of the system that are sketched below, it should be clear what some canonical extensions look like; for instance the extensions onto the case of projection with regard to the discourse relations, and onto the future tense system and explicit progressive aspect with regard to tense and aspect.

Considering the second embedding discourse relation of our system, flashback, we do not want to present the details of our reflections concerning the iterative use of flashback, the use of flashback and elaboration in turn, or the problem of prominence values for events within the set of reference events – which of course, in the presence of flashback, is richer and has more structure than in the case of elaboration alone.

We think that there are convincing examples which suggest licensing the iterative use of flashback[2] and the mixed use of flashback and elaboration. Elaborations of flashback events are governed by the same rules as elaborations of main story events, it seems to us. This conforms to our opinion that extended flashbacks are transposed pictures of simple past stories. However, we think that with multiply embedded (extended) flashbacks it is not so easy to climb up the hierarchy of flashbacks step by step on the basis of conditions corresponding to these of the elaboration case sketched above. The criterion for climbing up the hierarchy, that if otherwise we would encounter an inconsistency, is not as expressive in the flashback case as in the case of elaborations. For this reason the textual hints suggesting this alternative have to be based more extensively on positive world knowledge about the normal course of events. Since in our system we could only sketch a small part of relevant world knowledge of this kind, we have decided to postpone this alternative of stepwise climbing up a flashback hierarchy till a time in the future at which elaborated knowledge of this kind will be available. In our opinion, skipping the possiblity of stepwise climbing up a flashback hierarchy comes close to what a recipient does in the absence of world knowledge that can serve as specific background knowledge with regard to the story heard or read. This legitimizes our decision, we think.

Thus, flashbacks have to be locally expanded in the following sense. With regard to the reference event in the flashback a new flashback is established or a background is asserted or the reference event is elaborated or followed by the new event. If all this is not possible, since the tense form of the new event, simple past, indicates that we should understand the flashback story as terminated, we jump back to the point where the first flashback of the chain of iterated flashbacks (possibly consisting of just one element) starts. Of course, abstaining from more complicated types of tense resolution, we do not take into account texts where events are introduced by definite descriptions which have to be localized following the rules of the nominal anaphora resolution. In such texts there is more liberality to jump back and forth in the story, so, for instance, to jump right into the middle of such a chain of iterated flashbacks. For the same reason we do not deal with relative clauses, where a similar liberality can be observed. In addition, listing the restrictions, in the following we skip the perfective state reading of past perfect and all these kinds of type coercion in the sense of (Moens, Steedman 1988) which one should treat within the processing step of amalgamating the

---

[2]Rohrer presents an example from Voltaire's *Candide* which, it seems, makes an extensive use of iterated flashbacks (cf. (Rohrer 1986)). Moens presents a number of examples for English (cf. (Moens 1990)).

representation of the new sentence and the DRS of the preceding text, for instance, with German, the type coercion from "event in the narrow sense" to "progressive state" which may be made plausible only on the basis of the information of the preceding text.

To summarize, we conclude from the considerations above that with different embedding levels we arrive at a set of reference events, that these events are in focus to different degrees and that the most prominent reference event will be the last mentioned event. But the others are, with minor preference, also "accessible" as reference events. (Of course, with flashback iterations the restrictions mentioned are valid, i.e., here, practically only the events at both extremities are (latent) reference events, not those in the middle). It is clear that the kind of accessibility meant here is not accessibility in the sense of DRT. It is much closer to the notion of different focus spaces in the work of Grosz and Sidner (see, e.g., (Grosz, Sidner 1985)).

3.2 Reference Times

Take the following as an example for the textual structure of a narrative within the range of the dimensions outlined:

(15)

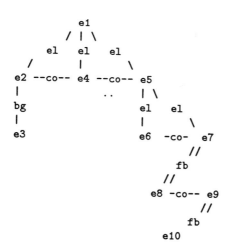

This list reflects the text structure in the following way (take the increasing number of the indices for the surface order in the text): e_2, e_4, e_5 elaborate e_1, which is the introductory event of the text. e_3 provides a background for e_2. e_5 is elaborated by e_6 and e_7. e_2, e_4, e_5 on the one hand and e_6 and e_7 on the other form chains of continuation. e_8 together with e_9 is an extended flashback with respect to the perspective e_7, where e_9 follows e_8. e_{10} opens a flashback within the existing flashback. Its vantage point is e_9. Knowing this structure, we have implicit information about what the hierarchically ordered set of reference events is for the next sentence to process. The reference events are the terminating nodes of the different text levels. Starting with the last mentioned or *actual* reference event we have in decreasing prominence: e_{10}, e_9, e_7, e_5 and e_1. (For e_9 we have to take into account the additional restrictions for iterated flashbacks which in the system design prevent this event from being accessible).

Doing temporal resolution presupposes the availablity of this set of reference events together with its internal structure in terms of the prominence of its members. Now, the strategy must be the following.

First, one has to try to expand the temporal structure of the preceding text at the position filled by the most prominent reference event along the lines of the rules provided by the different discourse relations. It is clear that the recipient will prefer consistent solutions to inconsistent ones. In addition, temporal and aspectual information can reject the one or the other alternative. If, at the end of this investigation, the recipient comes up with more than one alternative, in our opinion, he will prefer solutions recommended by world knowledge to others where such a suggestion is missing (compare to this heuristic the pair (10), (13)). If there is still more than one alternative left, since either more than one of the remaining alternatives is suggested by world knowledge or none of them is, we think that, in the restricted case that we have sketched up to now, the carrying-on of the story is preferred, i.e., we think that on each level the principle (*) is the default case. Note that our restricted system, in the case of a simple past reference event, boils the problem down to deciding just between continuation and elaboration.

Independently of this, it has been noticed that if there are no hints at all for the recipient to decide about the discourse relation, the text is felt to be infelicitous. This is stronger than what we have said above, that there must be at least one possibility to expand the structure, and it contradicts our default assumption.

However, a hint may be the textual structure of the preceding discourse itself. Ducrot, for instance, shows convincingly how an infelicitous text can be made felicitous by asserting a preceding text segment which indirectly, by the information from a surrounding discourse relation, makes clear the internal relations of the original, smaller text:

(16)   *Il y eut un tonnerre.* (preceding text)
        Jean se leva; Pierre s'assit. (original text)   (cf. (Ducrot 1979))

The original text of (16) is felt to be infelicitous. The preceding text alone makes clear what the relation between the standing up by Jean and the sitting down by Pierre is. In our terms it is the *coset*-relation of temporal coincidence which is called for by the surrounding context of causality where effects of the cause have to be listed. Once instantiated, there is a strong tendency to continue the enumeration till the moment we get a new hint that the enumeration is terminated. Of course, the changing of the agents intensifies the impression of being witness to an enumeration, and the identity of the agents of the different events would weaken this impression, perhaps till the turning-point where this becomes a hint for another discourse relation. But the point is here, that the changing of the agents alone is not specific enough to make the relation of enumeration more plausible than others. This is left to the surrounding discourse relation.

So, to be more precise with our default rule, we think that under the premise that the recipient has the impression that the rhythm of the segment leading up to the reference event is that of a sequence of continuations, it is licensed to claim that the default case for him is (*).

Since it is very hard to spell out the global rules which govern the discourse segmentation, the interplay between the textual structure of the preceding text and all the other kinds of information we have sketched (and others not mentioned and perhaps even not notified sufficiently – this is more or less unknown terrain) for the implementation, we have decided to skip such subtleties which could be dealt with in at best a rudimentary fashion. It seems to us that in a majority of cases, taking (*) as the default case without further assumptions is sufficient to arrive at the right results.

Now, assume that local expansion is not possible at all. Then, secondly, we have to try to expand the temporal structure of the preceding text at a less prominent position following the heuristic sketched for the most prominent reference event.

Since the idea of gradated accessibility which we use here is not the idea which underlies the notion of accessibility in DRT, the DRS-notation itself doesn't provide us with this information. Notice that the set of temporal relations between the events of the preceding text listed in the DRS representing this part of the text is less informative, with regard to the task in question, than our structured set of reference events. This is because with flashbacks – and, generalizing, with projections and non-past events – we can have several time slices with different (sub-) stories whose hierarchical order is reflected by the structured set of reference events. But, in terms of pure temporal order there is only a partially ordered event structure where the reference events are not highlighted. Notice that the last event of this structure, if it exists, or the "smallest event within the set of the latest events" is *not* necessarily the actual reference event. But, even if it is the actual reference event, it is not clear what the less prominent reference events are. (The actual reference event may be member of a projection so that there are less prominent reference events in its past.)

For this reason, we provide text DRSs with an index which reflects the textual structure of the discourse in exactly the same way as exemplified in the picture above. From this index the hierarchically ordered set of reference events can be deduced. We do not take this set as the index of the corresponding DRS, but the more general text structure itself, in order to allow for later extensions of the implementation with regard to generalizations alluded to above. We call this index the *list of reference times* or *times list* or *T-List*.

The syntax of the times list (T-List) is as follows.

Definition: T-List

T-List := [] ;
            [o(Z,D-List)|T-List]

where

o(Z,D-List): list item

with

Z: event-information (the event with its coordinates)
Z := z(DRF,TP,S,TL,DRF-Term)

DRF: the DRF of the event
TP: the temporal perspective (in general the speech time,
          with flashbacks the vantage point of the flashback)
S: the speech time
TL: the possibly empty list of hierarchically ordered location times
          (i.e. the hour, the day, the week etc. where the event took place)
DRF-Term information schema which stems from the sentence
          which introduces the event containing among other things
          a) the Aktionsart of the event
          (with values **ach**(ievement), **act**(ivity), **accomplishment**, and **state**
          with its sub-types lexical, progressive and perfective state)
          b) the tense form which introduces the event
          (with values **sp** for simple past, **ppf** for past perfect, ...)

D-List: list of the items depending on the event,

where
D-List := [];
           [bg([o(Z,[])|T-List'])|D-List];
           [el([o(Z,D-List)|T-List])|D-List];
           [el([closed|T-List])|D-List];
           [fb([o(Z,D-List)|T-List])|D-List];
           [pr([o(Z,D-List)|T-List])|D-List];
           [set([o(Z,D-List)|T-List])|D-List];
           [coset([o(Z,D-List)|T-List])|D-List]

It should be clear how these T-Lists are used to represent the textual structure of the discourse. In general, the neighborhood of T-List items signifies *continuation*. Thus, if we have a shallow T-List without embeddings the T-List enumerates the events of a sequence of continuations in such a way that the first element of the list normally is the last mentioned event, i.e., the actual reference event.

Of course, strictly speaking, it is not the actual reference event itself but the corresponding item in the sense of the definition. For reasons of simplicity, we continue to call list items events. If the event of the new sentence is understood as following this reference event it is put onto this stack, i.e., the update of the T-List after the incorporation of the DRS of the new sentence in the DRS of the preceding text consists of the new event in the first place and, in turn, of the elements of the old T-List in the following places. Now, each element of the T-List can give rise to the opening of one or more sub-stacks along the lines of the rhetorical dimensions given. Each sub-stack is marked by the (abbreviated) name of the discourse relation it corresponds to. For the sub-stacks the same holds as for the main stack with the following exceptions: *bg* collects the background information for a particular event, nothing else. Thus, we think that there is no need for further embeddings within such a list of stative events. Therefore, [] is the D-List of the corresponding items. (T-List' is a T-List exclusively consisting of items with an empty D-List). In addition, the assumption of continuation for list neighbors is suspended within lists which are in the scope of *bg*. Of course, this is equally true for items within *set-* and *coset*-lists. *closed* is used as a flag which is set when the corresponding level of elaboration is left in the upward direction. It indicates that it was decided to terminate this elaboration and that, at least within the fragment which is covered by the rules of our system, this elaboration level cannot be reopened.

With regard to such T-Lists, we use a number of access functions within the resolution component. Without going into detail with the definition, we only sketch some of them informally. We sketch those which are relevant for the illustration of the system.

akt-ref(T-List): This function gives us the most topicalized item in the list, the item of the actual referent. This is the first element of the main stack, i.e., the last element of a continuation chain, under the premise that this item contains no embeddings or that its first embedding is a *bg*-embedding or an embedding terminated by *closed*. Otherwise, we enter the first element of the D-List and investigate the first item that we find there in exactly the same way as just described and so on. Thus, in the sample text structure (15) above, we get the item of e_{10}.

el-embedder(T-List,Ref) This function gives us the (ordered) set of DRFs which include each other with regard to elaboration and which contain Ref in their first (and with regard to this system unique) *el*-embedding. That is, this function gives as the maximal sequence of event items $i_1, \ldots, i_n$, where e_1, the corresponding event of i_1, is elaborated directly by Ref, e_2 by e_1 and so on. Of course, if Ref is not an immediate member of an elaboration the function gives the empty list. With regard to e_7 in (15) we thus get: $[item(e_5), item(e_1)]$.

fb-embedder(T-List,Ref) This function gives us the highest vantage point which starts a chain of flashbacks leading back to Ref. (If there is no such chain, since Ref is not member of a flashback, of course, the value is the empty list again.) In (15) the value of this function is the item of e_7 with regard to both e_9 and e_{10}.

In addition to this, we use modification-functions for the updating of T-Lists. For instance,

lr_{el}(T-List,E,E1-Term): gives us the update of the T-List where the position E is elaborated by E1-Term, i.e., we add a new first element to the D-List of E which will be marked by *el* and which will contain the DRF-Term of E1. This function is only available, if the item of E doesn't already contain an elaboration sub-stack.

$lr_{DR}(T\text{-}List,E,E1\text{-}Term)$: the corresponding functions for the other dimensions. Therefore DR (DR = bg, fb, pr, co, set or $coset$). In the case of bg, set and coset a new sub-stack is created only if the first member of the D-List is of different type. If it is of the same type, we only extend this member by a new first item: the item for E1-Term.

$close(T\text{-}List,E)$: gives us the update of the T-List where all elaborations up to E are closed.

With all these functions, Ref and E are indeed discourse referents (and not items), i.e., we presuppose that (within our restricted case or, more generally, within the local domain which is inspected) each DRF of the T-List appears at just one position.

3.3   Rules for Resolution

To illustrate the system we now depict the rules which are relevant for our restricted case. We suppose that the new sentence introduces just one event and that it has no temporal adverbials. To render the amalgamation of a sentence DRS with a text DRS we use rewrite rules. In the following, to enhance readability, we do not distinguish between the DRF and the corresponding list-item within the T-List updates. In addition, within the rules we use access functions which are not yet specified. We now briefly specify them: drf, tp, tl, s and $drft$ in turn filter out the first, second, third, fourth and fifth place of the z-term of a T-List item, i.e., the discourse referent of the item, the perspective from which it is seen, its set of location times, the speech point and the drf-term of the DRF. Here, we only need drf, tp and $drft$. We have not made explicit what a drf-term looks like exactly. However, it suffices to repeat that, with regard to an event-DRF, it collects relevant information from the sentence which introduces the event. The additional access functions $tense$ and akt, applied to the drf-term of an event, allow for the retrieval of the tense form and the Aktionsart or aspect of this event. We assume that from this, together with the DRS of the new sentence (DRS_S), which is indexed by the DRF of the sentence event, and with the DRS of the preceding text (DRS_n), which is indexed by the corresponding T-List, we have all the information to do the integration of the new sentence against the background of world knowledge, provided that the drf-term of the sentence event is available. We note this term as a subscript of the sentence index. Of course, the rules depicted below deal with sentence integration in the absence of nominal resolution and other types of inter-sentential relations.

$Text_{n+1}$		$Text_n$	$Sentence_{n+1}$
$< T_{n+1}, DRS_{n+1} >$	$\Rightarrow$	$< T_n, DRS_n >$	$< e_{drft:Term}, DRS_S >$
$\downarrow$		$\downarrow$	$\downarrow$

1. Continuation:

(F1)
tense/aspect-
conditions:
$Tref = T$
$A = acc$ or ach

$Ref = drf(akt\text{-}ref(T_n))$
$Tref = tense(drft(akt\text{-}ref(T_n)))$
$TP = tp(akt\text{-}ref(T_n))$

$T = tense(Term)$
$A = akt(Term)$

....

a. (co1):
$DRS_{n+1} =$
$DRS_n \bigcup DRS_S$

e
$Ref \prec e$
$e \prec Tp$

T_{n+1}
$= lr_{co}(T_n, Ref, Term)$
$= .[e, Ref, .].$

(F2)
consistency-filter

(F3)$_{co1}$
evidence-filter

$[] = el\text{-}embedder(T_n, Ref)$

b. (co2):
$DRS_{n+1} =$
$DRS_n \bigcup DRS_S$

e
$Ref \prec e$
$eFinishesRef1$

T_{n+1}
$= lr_{co}(T_n, Ref, Term)$
$= .[e, Ref, .].$

(F2)
consistency-filter

(F3)$_{co2}$
evidence-filter

$[I \mid \_] = el\text{-}embedder(T_n, Ref)$
$Ref1 = drf(I)$

c. (co3):
$DRS_{n+1} =$
$DRS_n \bigcup DRS_S$

e
$Ref \prec e$
$e \subseteq Ref1$

T_{n+1}
$= lr_{co}(T_n, Ref, Term)$
$= .[e, Ref, .].$

(F2)
consistency-filter

(F3)$_{co3}$
evidence-filter

$[I \mid \_] = el\text{-}embedder(T_n, Ref)$
$Ref1 = drf(I)$

d. (co4):
$T'_n = close(T_n, Ref1)$
and
recursive call
of the system
with
T'_n instead of T_n

(F3)$_{co1}$
evidence-filter

$[I \mid \_] = el\text{-}embedder(T_n, Ref)$
$Ref1 = drf(I)$
$\{ Ref\ Finishes\ Ref1 \} \in DRS_n$

The applicability of the rules is restricted by three filters, the tense/aspect-filter, (F1), the filter which tests for consistency, (F2), and the filter which tests for evidence, (F3).

(co1)–(co4) list four particular cases of continuation. In each case, the new event must be non-stative and its tense form must be identical to the tense form of the actual reference event. Note that with this general formulation of the filter (F1), we allow for continuation not only with regard to the events of the main (simple past) story but also for others, in particular for events within a flashback.

(co1) is the easiest case. Here the reference event is not a member of an elaboration. The corresponding DRS conditions are canonical, if we see that, after what we have said about the two-dimensional meaning of the tenses, with simple past events the perspective is the speech point and with past perfect events within flashbacks it is the vantage point of the flashback. Thus, localizing the new event before the existing perspective is the right representation of one half of the tense meaning in both cases, simple past and past perfect. The other half, of course, with continuation consists in the relation $Ref \prec e$. It must be clear, however, that in the case of continuation, the perspective doesn't change. Thus, in order to show how this is guaranteed, for one time we render the relevant part of T_{n+1} fully expanded.

$$T_{n+1} = \ldots [e, Rpt, \ldots] \ldots$$

stands for:

$$T_{n+1} = \vdots [o(z(e, Tp, [], S, Term), []), o(z(Ref, Tp, Tl, S, drft(akt\text{-}ref(T_n)), D\text{-}List), \ldots] \vdots,$$

where
"$\ldots$" are the predecessors of Ref in T_n, and where
"$\vdots$" makes allusion to the possible existence of embeddings.

In the case of (co2)–(co4) the reference event is immediate member of an elaboration. If the new event follows the reference event *within the same textual level*, of course, there is no need for the relation $e \prec TP$, since e will be included within the event which is elaborated by Ref. From this event, Ref1, e inherits the ordering condition with regard to the perspective. However, in the presence of such an event Ref1, we arrive at different alternatives. e may be located somewhere "in the middle" of Ref1. Think of the event of eating a bouchée à la reine with regard to the dinner at 'Madame Gilbert' in (11). Also, it may be plausible to localize e at the end of Ref1. Think of the dessert in (11). (co2) represents the second alternative, (co3) the first.

But what about the case where Ref has already been treated along the lines of (co2) with regard to Ref1 and some earlier event Ref-old and where there is some plausibility that e is a continuation of Ref? For instance, think of the case of the concatenation of (10), (10b), (10a) with the event of buying some flowers (Ref1), which is elaborated in turn by the picking out of three roses, the seeing of some tulips, the putting back of the roses, the taking of the tulips, the paying (Ref-old) and the leaving of the florist shop (Ref). In this situation, the onset of being back on the street, e, is a plausible continuation with regard to Ref (even a consequence).

(co4) reflects such situations. The existing elaboration is terminated by means of the close-function. In addition, the system focuses the level of Ref1. Since closed elaborations cannot be reopened within the range of this system (compare the next rule for elaborations to this end), the alternative of elaboration doesn't arise with regard to the level of Ref1. Thus, within the recursive call of the rules the system will select for continuation between Ref1 and e, provided there is no plausibility for the other alternatives (flashback and background). Of course, in the case in question, background will be ruled out by filter (F1), since e is a non-stative event. However, flashback may be possible, since Ref1, Ref and e may be introduced by past perfect. Within the limits of consistency, however, the selection for continuation can be guaranteed if we make sure that in such cases the pair (Ref1,e) inherits the plausibility for continuation from the pair (Ref,e). We will come back to this in the next section.

Checking consistency, i.e., filter (F2), is not dependent on the rules. The general form of (F2) can be rendered as follows:

$$\forall_{WK, DRS_{n+1}} F$$

Here, *WK* stands for *world knowledge*. As mentioned in the introduction, the LILOG knowledge base comprises information about the standards of the temporal structures. In particular the knowledge base comprises a system of axioms for temporal relations in the style of (Allen 1983), a calendar, a sort hierarchy with different event sorts together with knowledge about some typical connections between events. We cannot go into detail with this here. It should be clear how all this directs the resolution system. For instance, if, with regard to e_1 and e_2, we test for continuation and if we know that the location time for e_1 is May 1987 and the one for e_2 is June 1986, this alternative is ruled out by the filter (F2) which serves as an interface to the knowledge base which in turn tells us that the calendar prescribes that all events within June 1986 have to be localized before the events which happened within May 1987. Similarly, continuation (on the elaborating level) can be ruled out with regard to the resolution problem posed before us with the pair (10):(10a), provided that the knowledge base excludes the overlapping of events of *agent x being in a shop* and *agent x being in a street*. To be precise, this information rules out the continuation between the picking out of roses and the (onset of) being on the street only if it is assumed that the consequence state of entering the florist shop, i.e., being in the shop, holds throughout the buying event. This problem is a specific instance of the well known frame problem which, among other things, has lead to the investigation of non-monotonic temporal reasoning systems. We have not yet outlined what, for the specific purposes of the LILOG scenario, such a system should look like. But we have projected to do this. Thus, at present, (F2) is a "hard" filter, so to speak. It excludes a solution only if otherwise F would be classically entailed. It doesn't exclude a solution which contradicts a default assumption. (F3) overtly has a "default flavor". It provides us with indications about the plausibility of discourse relations in specific contexts. We will come back to this filter in the next section.

Text_{n+1}		Text_n	Sentence_{n+1}
$< T_{n+1}, DRS_{n+1} >$	$\Rightarrow$	$< T_n, DRS_n >$	$< e_{drft:Term}, DRS_S >$

2. Elaboration:

$$DRS_{n+1} = DRS_n \bigcup DRS_S$$

(el) $\begin{array}{|c|} \hline e \\ \hline e \subseteq Ref \\ \hline \end{array}$

(fel) $\begin{array}{|c|} \hline e \\ \hline e \text{ Finishes } Ref \\ \hline \end{array}$

$$T_{n+1} = lr_{el}(T_n, Ref, Term) = .[Ref([el([e]).]),.].$$

(F1)
tense/aspect-
conditions:
$Tref = T$
$A = acc$ or ach

(F2)
consistency-filter

$\boxed{el}$: $(F3)_{el}$
$\boxed{fel}$: $(F3)_{fel}$
evidence-filter

$Ref = drf(akt\text{-}ref(T_n))$
$Tref = tense(drft(akt\text{-}ref(T_n)))$
there is no X with:
$akt\text{-}ref(T_n)$
$\in el\text{-}embedder(T_n,X)$

$T = tense(Term)$
$A = akt(Term)$

Of course, following (co2) and (co3), we have two rules for elaboration, the more general (el) and the more specific (fel). Here too, we will postpone the discussion about the filters deciding about the ordering to chose till the next section. Note, however, that the (new) elaboration of a reference event is possible only when an elaboration does not yet exist. In addition, note that the rules for elaboration are not restricted to the case of simple past events. They allow for the elaboration of flashback events.

Text_{n+1}		Text_n	Sentence_{n+1}
$< T_{n+1}, DRS_{n+1} >$	$\Rightarrow$	$< T_n, DRS_n >$	$< e_{drft:Term}, DRS_S >$

3. Flashback:

$$DRS_{n+1} = DRS_n \bigcup DRS_S$$

$\begin{array}{|c|} \hline e \\ \hline e \prec Ref \\ \hline \end{array}$

$$T_{n+1} = lr_{fb}(T_n, Ref, Term) = .[Ref([fb([e]).]),.].$$

(F1)
tense/aspect-
conditions:
$Tref = ppf$ or sp $T = ppf$
$A = acc$ or ach

(F2)
consistency-filter

$(F3)_{fb}$
evidence-filter

$Ref = drf(akt\text{-}ref(T_n))$
$Tref = tense(drft(akt\text{-}ref(T_n)))$

$T = tense(Term)$
$A = akt(Term)$

Notice here that the iteration of flashbacks is licensed, since the rule is not restricted to the case of simple past reference events.

Text_{n+1}		Text_n	Sentence_{n+1}
$< T_{n+1}, DRS_{n+1} >$	$\Rightarrow$	$< T_n, DRS_n >$	$< e_{drft:Term}, DRS_S >$
$\downarrow$		$\downarrow$	$\downarrow$

4. Background:

(F1)
tense/aspect-conditions:

$$\text{Tref} = T \qquad \text{Ref} = \text{drf}(\text{akt-ref}(T_n)) \qquad T = \text{tense(Term)}$$
$$A = \text{act or state} \qquad \text{Tref} = \text{tense}(\text{drft}(\text{akt-ref}(T_n))) \qquad A = \text{akt(Term)}$$

(F2)
consistency-filter

. . . .

a. (bg):

$DRS_{n+1} = DRS_n \bigcup DRS_S$

e
$Ref \subseteq e$

(F3)$_{bg}$
evidence-filter

T_{n+1}
$= lr_{bg}(T_n, Ref, Term)$
$= .[Ref([bg([e, .]).]), .].$

b. (cbg):

$DRS_{n+1} = DRS_n \bigcup DRS_S$

e
$e \in max\ e'\ (DRS_S[e/e'])$
$Ref\ Meets\ e$
$X \subseteq e$

(F3)$_{cbg}$
evidence-filter

T_{n+1}
$= lr_{cbg}(T_n, Ref, Term)$
$= .[X([bg([e]).]), Ref, .].$

With these rules, we can assert background information to simple past events as well as to flashback events introduced by past perfect. The essential criterion here is that the new event must be stative. In order to decide about the specific case of the assertion, the filters (F2) and (F3) are used. This is quite similar to the case of elaboration. Following the discussion in Sect. 3.1, *cbg* places its (stative) event immediately after the reference event (*Meets*).

Since stative events are not necessarily maximal phases with regard to the corresponding event description we must ensure that there is no such phase overlapping with the reference event, i.e., we must ensure that the new event is itself a maximal phase.

This is guaranteed by the (new) DRS-condition $e \in max\ e'\ (DRS_S[e/e'])$. $DRS_S[e/e']$ stands for the DRS which results from DRS_S by replacing e by e'.

max is a function from event descriptions onto sets of events which relates descriptions to its maximal events. We cannot go further into detail here by spelling out the model-theoretic impact of this definition.

Notice that with the rule for *cbg*, with regard to all dimensions considered, rules are missing which deal with reference events which are variables. For lack of space, we cannot go into detail with this either. It should be clear however, that within the function lr_{cbg} the variable inherits the tense information from the stative event of the new sentence and that elaboration of a variable will not be possible and that continuation (normally) will consist of unifying the new event with the reference event in this case.

Text_{n+1}	Text_n	Sentence_{n+1}
$< T_{n+1}, DRS_{n+1} >$ $\Rightarrow$	$< T_n, DRS_n >$	$< e_{drft:Term}, DRS_S >$
5. Return from Elaboration:		
$T'_n = \text{close}(T_n, \text{Ref1})$ recursive call with T'_n instead of T_n	$\text{Ref} = \text{drf}(\text{akt-ref}(T_n))$ $[I \mid \_] = \text{el-embedder}(T_n, \text{Ref})$ $\text{Ref1} = \text{drf}(I)$	
6. Return from Flashback:		
recursive call with I instead of akt-ref(T_n)	$\text{Ref} = \text{drf}(\text{akt-ref}(T_n))$ $I = \text{fb-embedder}(T_n, \text{Ref})$	$sp = \text{tense}(\text{Term})$

There is no need to further comment on these rules. They just follow the intentions sketched in Sect. 3.1 of this paper.

3.4 About Plausibility and Evidence

We now come back to discuss in a bit more detail what the impact of temporal defaults could be on the system outlined in the last section.

We think that investigations on linguistic data like those made by Moens and Steedman and by Herweg (cf. (Moens 1987), (Moens, Steedman 1988), (Herweg 1990)) suggest that there is more between neighbors within a sequence of continuations than temporal succession, something that convinces the recipient that nothing which could be relevant to the story has happened between. Of course, if this is true, it legitimizes approaches for non-monotonic temporal reasoning like the suggestions made by Kowalski/Sergot, Shoham or Sandewall (cf. (Kowalski, Sergot 1985), (Shoham 1988), (Sandewall 1988)) from the standpoint of discourse semantics. But there is another point. It seems that, for the recipient, from a pair of events (e_1, e_2) read as continuation, it develops something like an a posteriori felt causal connection.

It should be clear that the informational impact of a text describing a sequence of events which are connected in turn by a relation that reflects an a priori known causality is highly restricted. If the speaker makes excessive use of such chains, without using them as clues to the specific integration of other information, and if he knows that the hearer knows the regularity described, he violates Grice's maxims. Thus, such texts do not reflect the normal case.

However, if the normal course of events seldom is the subject of a discourse or text, there must be something within the scope of world knowledge which helps the recipient to disambiguate between different discourse relations and which is outside of filter (F2). Examples (10) and (11), for instance, are witness to this. Of course, one can pick out roses after having bought (other) flowers and of course, one can eat an hors d'oevre after a dinner, but this is not the normal case, this is not very plausible. Generalizing the idea that we have taken from the relation of continuation, we think that the knowledge which helps here to get the right ordering is knowledge which licenses the hearer to decide about the relation between reference and new event immediately *after* the introduction of the new event, but which doesn't license him to infer from the existence of the reference event the existence of an event of the same type as the new event and in the same position with regard to the reference event *before* the utterance of the new sentence. At least this knowledge does not license this type of inference in each and every case. We call this relational knowledge *evidence* to signify that it is knowledge that, after the utterance of a pair of event descriptions, makes the choice about the relation between the thus introduced events evident. Of course, we entail evidence from "hard" rules about event connections and from default assumptions, but, as discussed, not the other way around.

For further clarification of this point, let's have a look at some examples. With regard to some of our sample texts which are critical on this point, we assume that the knowledge base is equipped with rules which, simplified, we can render as follows:

(17) $evidence_{co}(E_1, E_2) \leftarrow E_1 \in FALL \wedge E_2 \in STAND\text{-}UP \wedge agent(E_1) = agent(E_2)$

(18) $evidence_{el}(E_1, E_2) \leftarrow E_1 \in BUY \wedge E_2 \in PICK\text{-}OUT \wedge agent(E_1) = agent(E_2) \wedge object(E_1) = object(E_2)$

(19) $evidence_{fel}(E_1, E_2) \leftarrow E_1 \in HAVE\text{-}DINNER \wedge E_2 \in EAT \wedge agent(E_1) = agent(E_2) \wedge object(E_2) \in DESSERT$

(20) $evidence_{fel}(E_1, E_2) \leftarrow E_1 \in MOVE \wedge E_2 \in ARRIVE \wedge agent(E_1) = agent(E_2) \wedge goal(E_1) = loc(E_2)$

(21) $evidence_{cbg}(E_1, E_2) \leftarrow E_1 \in TURN \wedge E_2 \in BEING\text{-}DARK \wedge object(E_1) \in SWITCH$

(22) $evidence_{cbg}(E_1, E_2) \leftarrow E_1 \in TURN \wedge E_2 \in BEING\text{-}LIGHTED \wedge object(E_1) \in SWITCH$

We have used in (19) and (20) the index *fel* to distinguish the specific case of *final elaboration* motivated by the discussion about (11) from the more general case of elaboration. The examples should be self-explaining, however. Of course, we assume that the event variables are universally quantified. (17)–(22) show that there is a wide range of differently legitimized evidences.

Obviously rules like (20) are grounded in "hard" world knowledge. We can sketch this kind of reasoning in general terms by the following schema:

$$evidence_{fel}(e_1, e_2) \leftarrow \vdash_{WK, DRS_n} \exists e \, [(DRS_S[e_2/e]) \wedge e \; Finishes \; e_1]$$

Assume here that DRS_S is a simple event description. Then evidence for final elaboration would be given if the knowledge base together with the DRS of the preceding text predicts the existence of an event finishing the reference event which is of the same type as the new event. Of course, here, $\vdash$ stands for the classical entailment relation and WK for a classical set of axioms.[3] Differently to that, rules like (17), (18) and (19) are grounded on canonical default assumptions. We can depict this connection as follows:

$$evidence_{co}(e_1, e_2) \leftarrow \vdash_{D(WK), DRS_n} \exists e \, [(DRS_S[e_2/e]) \wedge e_1 \prec e]$$

Here, we have rendered the schema for continuation. $\vdash$ stands for a not further specified default entailment relation. D(WK) stands for the extension of WK by default rules.

To make the difference clear, with regard to *fel*, think, for instance, of the following connections. Whereas each moving event leading to a particular local goal necessarily brings in the existence of an event of arriving at this goal, the corresponding statement about meals and desserts is not valid in each and every case. Examples like (17), (18) and (19) depict typical instances of connections between events which have motivated the introduction of *scripts* and (event-)*frames* into the discussion about the modelling of background knowledge (compare for instance (Schank, Abelson 1977)). Bartsch has worked with event frames in the context of DRT and recently, independent of our approach, Lascarides has tackled the problem of spelling out the logic which underlies the faculty for temporal resolution with regard to some critical cases (cf. (Bartsch 1987), (Lascarides 1990)). We cannot go into detail on discussing these different approaches here.

---

[3]For reasons of simplicity, we do not distinguish here between DRSs and other logical notations like L_{LILOG}, the language in which the LILOG knowledge base is written. Assume here that these different notations are made uniform by translation into the language of first order logic.

Here, we can only point to some complicating facts. To be explicit, the schemes, as they stand, are too restrictive. With more complicated sentence DRSs the idea cannot be that the whole DRS_S is entailed from the DRS of the preceding text on the basis of world knowledge, but that, from this, we can entail the existence of an event of a particular type P which, perhaps, is more general than the type represented by DRS_S, but which is selective enough to make the decision about the discourse relations in question clear. Thus, for instance, if we have to decide between continuation and elaboration, P is selective enough, if we can infer the existence of an event of type P which follows the reference event and if we cannot infer the existence of an event of type P which elaborates the reference event. Therefore, the first schema, for instance, should be represented as follows:

$$evidence_{fel}(e_1, e_2) \leftarrow \exists P[$$
$$\vdash_{WK,DRS_n} \exists e \ [P(e) \wedge \forall e'((DRS_S[e_2/e']) \rightarrow P(e')) \wedge e \ Finishes \ e_1]$$
$$\wedge$$
$$\not\vdash_{WK,DRS_n} \exists e \ [P(e) \wedge e_1 \prec e(+ \text{ further specifications})]]$$

For the purpose of dealing with examples underlying the rules (17)–(20) we can do with an inference component which makes use of a sort hierarchy together with simple defaults and simple classical implications entailing the existence of an event of type P, which is a simple event description. By simple implications we mean here $\forall\exists$-quantified implications, where the antecedent and the consequent are conjunctions of positive literals, and where the variables of the antecedent are the universally bound ones. Simple defaults stand for the corresponding formulas within a not-further-specified default logic. Note that, with regard to event descriptions, this comes very close to what normally is understood as an event-frame: with simple implications we can say things like "for all dinners there is an event of eating the hors d'oevre which starts the dinner and ... and there is an event of eating the dessert which ends the dinner". However, rules like (21) and (22) do not admit easy reduction to this case.

Of course, modelling default world knowledge, we will have a rule stating that the manipulation of an interrupter is the turning-point between a state of type BEING-DARK and a state of type BEING-LIGHTED and we will have a second rule for the opposite case. ((7), the venetian blinds, makes allusion to one of the reasons why this should be default knowledge and not hard knowledge.) Now assume variants of (7) and (8) where, from the preceding text including the manipulation of the switch, it is not clear what the quality of the initial state is, i.e., where it is not clear if it was dark or lighted before the switch-turning event. In this case the rules are not applicable and nothing is predicted. However, even in this case, with both variants, immediately after the utterance of the next sentence, it is clear what the right ordering conditions are.

It is obvious too, that, within the scope of reasoning with defaults, we can get rid of this problem if we combine both implications (together with other world knowledge) in order to build up a new implication which, without preconditions, states that an event of manipulating a light-switch normally marks the begin of a phase of being lighted or of a phase of being dark. Now, if we ground our interface-predicate *evidence* on the more precise rules written in the style of the improved schema which we have sketched above we get what we want to have, namely a predicate P (the disjunction of being lighted and being dark) which is selective enough to decide about the relations *bg* and *cbg*. However, in the case described, this is possible only if we allow for disjunctive frames with regard to events of a particular type.

What we wanted to show with this is, firstly, that at least some of the links established by temporal resolution introduce more than pure temporal relations, since these links are understood against a background which makes them plausible through the application of the regularities of the world. Secondly, we wanted to show that within the notion of (a posteriori) evidence, as we conceive it, lies more than what is established by the attitude of expectation associated with simple (default) implications for a particular event type.

It is not clear if all that we intend by evidence, and that we have tried to illustrate in the foregoing, is grounded completely on default reasoning or if there is some other kind of manipulating knowledge, like the use of associative links, that comes in.

Be that as it may. For the purposes of this paper there is no need to further spell out the foundations of the evidence-statements. Since a specific non-monotonic temporal reasoning component was not at our disposal at the time we implemented the resolution component (and, as mentioned, is not even now) we have worked with statements illustrated by (17)-(22), but using, of course, the possibilities made available by the sort hierarchy, i.e., inferring evidences for specific event types from more general ones. In addition, in order to solve the problems related to rules like (co4), we have rules which transfer evidence to higher levels:

$$evidence_{co}(E_1, E_2) \leftarrow \exists E_3 \ (E_3 \ Finishes \ E_1 \wedge evidence_{co}(E_3, E_2))$$

Filter (F3) relies heavily upon *evidence* and therefore, in contrast to filter (F2), it is rule-dependent. As discussed, also in contrast to filter (F2), we attribute a "flavor of default" to it. (F3) tests for positive indications in favor of a particular discourse relation. We think that this kind of plausibility is arrived at in two ways. Firstly, of course, this is arrived at if some evidence can be entailed for the discourse relation considered. However, secondly, we think it is also arrived at in the case of the absence of evidence, if each other alternative either is not possible, i.e., is ruled out by its filters (F1) and (F2), or is without evidence.

We can render this as follows. Assume that DR is the set of discourse relations including the specific cases *fel* and *cbg*:

$$DR = \{co, el, fel, bg, cbg, fb\}$$

Then, with regard to WK, DRS_n, DRS_S, Ref, e, the Filter (F3) accepts a particular relation $X \in DR$, that is, (F3)$_X$ goes through
$\leftrightarrow$
$[\vdash_{WK,DRS_n,DRS_S} evidence_X(Rpt, e)]$
$\vee$
$[\bigwedge_{Y \in DR, Y \neq X} \neg(Bpossible_Y(Ref, e) \wedge \vdash_{WK,DRS_n,DRS_S} evidence_Y(Rpt, e))]$

Here, $Bpossible_Y(Rpt, e)$ stands for something like "the recipient believes that it is possible that Ref and e are related by Y" in the sense that he is not able to prove the opposite. Considering the actual state of the "believer" which is marked, again, by WK, DRS_n, DRS_S, Ref and e, we can render this by the following:

$$B(possible_X (Ref, e) \leftrightarrow (\nvdash_{WK,DRS_{n+1}X} F \wedge (F1)_X(Ref, e))$$

Of course, here, $DRS_{n+1}X$ stands for the result of amalgamating DRS_n and DRS_S along the lines of the discourse relation X. (F1)$_X(Ref, e)$ means that the tense- and aspect-filter which is specific for X accepts the alternative X.

With this, we still have to explain what the particular filters (F3)$_{co1}$-(F3)$_{co3}$ stand for in the resolution rules for continuation. Of course, (F3)$_{co1}(Ref,e)$ is (F3)$_{co}(Ref,e)$. (F3)$_{co2}(Ref,e)$ is a combination of (F3)$_{co}(Ref,e)$ with $evidence_{fel}(Ref1,e)$, where Ref1 is the event of which Ref is an immediate elaboration. (F3)$_{co3}(Ref,e)$ is a combination of (F3)$_{co}(Ref,e)$ with $evidence_{el}(Ref1,e)$.

We have not yet given examples for $evidence_{bg}$ and $evidence_{fb}$. In the system, with the corresponding discourse relations we have completely relied on the filter (F1). Thus, we have not seen the necessity to spell out evidence-statements for these relations. Note that, in such cases where evidence cannot be proved, filter (F3) still can accept the relation in question, i.e., it can evaluate the relation as plausible, provided that for the competing relations, if possible at all, evidence cannot be proved.

3.5   Preferred Readings

The set of rules introduced in Sect. 3.3 sketch a Prolog implementation. Thus, the order of the rules is important. Local expansions are preferred to expansions which presuppose the changing of the level. The only exception to this strategy is the rule (co4). But, in a certain way, it is no exception, since here the actual reference event marks the end of an elaboration level so that it already points back to the initial level.

Within the local expansions, take for instance the case of a non-stative event on the past perfect tense line, then continuation is preferred to elaboration which is preferred to flashback, provided that no evidence statement can be entailed for one of these three dimensions.

Assume now that there is evidence for elaboration. Then continuation still is preferred to elaboration, provided that there is evidence for continuation too. However, if evidence cannot be entailed for continuation, the first disjunct of $(F3)_{co}$ is not valid and since the second also is not valid, because of the evidence for elaboration, the rule fails. So, in this case, elaboration is preferred to continuation.

In the case of flashback, however, even evidence would not suffice to prefer this relation to elaboration which, equally, is reinforced by evidence. This relation is preferred only if it is supported by evidence and if there is no evidence for continuation or elaboration.

Summarizing, if discourse relations A and B both are applicable then A is preferred to B, if it has evidence and B not, or if its rule comes before the rule of B and both A and B show evidence or both do not show evidence.

For this reason, with regard to stative events, the relation of background is preferred to the relation of causal background in the normal case, i.e., in the case where evidence for a causal link between the reference event and the new event cannot be entailed.

Thus, the system does what we required in Sects. 3.1 and 3.2. However, as it stands, there is a problem with alternative solutions. If a particular relation is reinforced by evidence the other alternatives are completely out. Thus, for instance, they are not arrived at by backtracking. Nevertheless it should be possible to get these solutions, having in mind the non-monotonic flavor of evidence (which in a certain way surrounds the possibility-statement, $B(possible_X (\_,\_))$, too). But it is clear how to remedy this shortcoming in Prolog. Within a corresponding Prolog specification we would copy the local rules, reject filter (F3) from each rule of the copy and insert the modified copy just after the original set of rules. The Prolog specification revised in this way provides us with the intended preference relation.

3.6   Extensions

In this paper, we cannot go further into detail and generalize the approach sketched to the case of sentences with more than one event and with temporal adverbs. However, we want to stress that the LILOG system is sensitive to all events and location times in the new sentence. This means that even in the case where we do not have a preference for a specific variant for relating the event of the main clause of the new sentence to the reference event, we can use the information available for the other events to arrive at a preferred discourse relation.

Consider for instance the following example taken from the LILOG scenario:

(23)   *The tourists went by bus from their hotel on the Rhine to the Hofgarten* e_1.
    a. After they had arrived e_2 , *it began to rain* e_3.
    b. After they had crossed the Oberkasselerbrücke e_2 , *it began to rain* e_3.

In this example, there is no obvious ordering between e_1 and e_3. However, since we know from the temporal conjunction *after* that e_3 follows e_2, in a), we can derive from the evidence that e_2 finishes e_1, that e_1 precedes e_3. In b), we can derive from the evidence that e_2 elaborates e_1, that e_3 also elaborates e_1. Here, we take as given that *after* in the normal case (without explicit reference to other times and without explicit distance information) establishes the relation of continuation between subclause- and mainclause-event. The choice about the $e_1 - e_2$-relation is recommended in the first case by the evidence (20), in the second case by the knowledge that the Oberkasselerbrücke is a part of the path from the Rhine to the Hofgarten. Remember that within the LILOG system we have knowledge available about the LILOG scenario. This includes the necessary knowledge about a map of Düsseldorf (with the Oberkasselerbrücke).

For lack of space we cannot depict the rules which deal with these more complicated cases. It should be clear, however, that the canonical way to arrive at such generalizations is to equip the DRS of the new sentence with an additional index which is a T-List. Note that the discourse relations considered and, with them, the possible T-List structure are wide enough to subsume all structural constraints which are expressible by the temporal conjunctions. Then, the T-List of a new sentence will contain a main level. Of course, the main level is the set of the events of the main stack, which is a sequence of events related in turn by continuation. (We repeat here that, in the normal case, the events of an *after*-clause are not processed as flashback events with regard to the event(s) of the main clause, but as events which precede the main clause event(s) on the continuation level.) Now, an attempt will be made to connect all the events of this main level to the actual reference event in a uniform way. (All the events of this level elaborate the reference event or, in turn, they follow the reference event, etc.). If this is not possible (or not plausible), one tries to partition this main level in order to arrive at uniform solutions for the events of each member of the partition. This, of course, has to be done in accordance with the structural constraints of the sentence T-List and, of course, in accordance with the strategy formulated for the simple case.

With regard to temporal locations, i.e., with regard to frame adverbials and punctual adverbials like *Thursday, last year, at 3 o'clock*, etc., we just mention that they are dealt with in the style of Lewis' *scorekeeping* (cf. (Lewis 1979)). Constraints are given by the fact that some adverbials refer to reference events which, in addition, have to be the bearers of the perspective. This is the case, for instance, for deictic adverbials like *yesterday* – here the perspective has to coincide with the speech point – but also for adverbials like *Thursday*.

Thus, *Thursday* introduces a temporal DRF, t, qualified as THURSDAY which is related to the actual perspective, *Per*, by a distance relation stating that the distance is at most one week.

Note that the meaning of *Thursday* doesn't make clear whether it holds $t \prec Per$ or whether it holds $Per \prec t$. The necessary disambiguation comes from the discourse relation chosen in order to relate the event, which takes t as location time, to the reference event. If the relation is flashback, for non-stative events e we get $e \subseteq t, t \prec Per$; if the relation is continuation, we get $e \subseteq t$, $Per \prec t$.

Of course, this presupposes the intelligent shifting of the perspective. We have skipped this point.

In addition, the system entails evidence for particular solutions from the granularity of the location times, i.e., if the granularity of the location time of the reference event is WEEK and the granularity of the location time of the new event is DAY, this is taken as an indication for elaboration with regard to reference and new event.

4   Conclusion

The implemented system computes the event structure of a discourse. Therefore it keeps track of the textual structure of the preceding text by means of the T-List. The T-List provides a structured set of possible reference events for the events of the new sentence. The integration of the new events proceeds along the lines of several discourse relations. In order to decide about the different possibilities of integration the system uses tense- and aspect-information. The aspect-information for the new sentence comes from the aspect calculus which accompanies the construction of the DRS of the new sentence. Since we think that the semantics of tense and aspect is not sufficient to establish the temporal discourse meaning, we use background knowledge to disambiguate between different readings.

The system is incomplete at present. The fragment it deals with does not allow for relative clauses. In addition the interaction between the NP-resolution and the temporal resolution is not available. The logic underlying the preference relation is only rudimentarily sketched. An elaborate nonmonotonic temporal reasoning system is missing. This is work in progress. We hope that therefore we can use suggestions for the design of a non-temporal nonmonotonic reasoning system which is going to be developed within LILOG for other components of the prototype.

References

Allen, J. (1983): Maintaining knowledge about temporal intervals. *Comm.ACM*, 26:832–843

Bartsch, R. (1987): Frame Representations and Discourse Representations. ITLI Prepublication Series 87-02, Univ. Amsterdam

Bäuerle, R. (1988): Ereignisse und Repräsentationen. LILOG Report 43, IBM Deutschland, WT LILOG, Stuttgart

Carlson, G. (1980): Reference to kinds in English. In: Hankamer, J. (ed.): *Outstanding Dissertations in Linguistics*. Harvard Univ.

Dowty, D. R. (1986): The effects of aspectual class on the temporal structure of discourse: semantics or pragmatics? *Linguistics and Philosophy*, 9(1):37–62

Ducrot, O. (1979): L'imparfait en Français. *Linguistische Berichte*, 60

Eberle, K. (1989): Eventualities in a natural language understanding system. In: Bläsius, K., Hedtstück, U., Rollinger, C. (eds.): *Sorts and Types for Artificial Intelligence*. Springer, Berlin

Eberle, K. (1990): Tenses in natural language processing. In: Borillo, A., Borillo, M. (eds.): *Semantics of Time, Space and Movement in N.L.* Edition Hermès, Paris

Eberle, K. (1991): *Ereignisse: Ihre Logik und Ontologie aus textsemantischer Sicht*. PhD thesis, Univ. Stuttgart

Grosz, B., Sidner, C. (1985): The Structure of Discourse Structure. Technical Note 369, SRI International

Herweg, M. (1990): *Zeitaspekte. Die Bedeutung von Tempus, Aspekt und temporalen Konjunktionen*. PhD thesis, Univ. Hamburg

Hinrichs, E. (1981): Temporale Anaphora im Englischen. Master's thesis, Univ. Tübingen

Hinrichs, E. (1986): Temporal anaphora in discourses of English. *Linguistics and Philosophy*, 9(1):63–82

Kamp, H. (1981): A theory of truth and semantic representation. In: Groenendijk, J., Janssen, T., Stokhof, M. (eds.): *Formal Methods in the Study of Language*. Mathematical Centre Tract, Amsterdam

Kamp, H., Rohrer, C. (1983): Tense in texts. In: Bäuerle, R., Schwarze, R., von Stechow, A. (eds.), *Meaning, Use and Interpretation of Language*. de Gruyter, Berlin

Kamp, H., Rohrer, C. (1985): Temporal reference in French. (ms.), IMS, Univ. Stuttgart

Kowalski, R., Sergot, M. (1985): A logic-based calculus of events. *New Generation Computing*, 4(1)

Krifka, M. (1987): *Nominalreferenz und Zeitkonstitution. Zur Semantik von Massentermen, Plural-termen und Aspektklassen.* PhD thesis, Univ. München

Lascarides, A. (1990): Knowledge, Causality and Temporal Representation. Research Paper HCRC/RP 8, Univ. Edinburgh

Lewis, D. (1979): Scorekeeping in a language game. In: Bäuerle, R., Egli, U., von Stechow, A. (eds.): *Semantics from Different Points of View.* pp. 172–187. Springer, Berlin

Moens, M. (1987): *Tense, Aspect and Temporal Reference.* PhD thesis, Centre for Cognitive Science, Univ. Edinburgh

Moens, M. (1990): Notes for R2.3.B. Univ. Edinburgh

Moens, M., Steedman, M. (1988): Temporal ontology and temporal reference. *Computational Linguistics*, 14.2 (Special Issue on Tense and Aspect):15–28

Partee, B. (1973): Some structural analogies between tenses and pronouns in English. *Journal of Philosophy*, 70:601–609

Reichenbach, H. (1947): *Elements of Symbolic Logic.* MacMillan, New York, London

Rohrer, C. (1986): Pour une sémantique du texte: La théorie des représentations discursives illustrés à l'aide du plusqueparfait et passé antérieur. In: *Linguistique générale et Linguistique Romane. Actes du XVIIe congrès international de linguistique et philologie romanes*

Sandewall, E. (1988): Non-Monotonic Entailment for Reasoning about Time and Action. LiTH-IDA R-88-27 - R-88-29, Linköping Univ., Department of Computer and Information Science, Linköping, Sweden

Schank, R., Abelson, R. (1977): *Scripts, Plans, Goals and Understanding.* LEA, Hillsdale

Shoham, Y. (1988): *Reasoning about Change, Time and Causation from the Standpoint of Artificial Intelligence.* MIT Press, Cambridge, MA

Vendler, Z. (1967): *Linguistics in Philosophy.* Cornell University Press, Ithaca, New York

Webber, B. L. (1988): Tense as discourse anaphora. *Computational Linguistics*, 14.2 (Special Issue on Tense and Aspect):61–73

The Treatment of Plurality in $L_{\textbf{LILOG}}$

Godehard Link and Hinrich Schütze

This paper summarizes research concerning the incorporation of plural constructions into the LILOG text understanding system. The treatment of plurality is based on the first order system LP, first presented in [Link 1983]. The paper consists of two parts. After a very short review of the system LP, a translation is given from a version of LILOG's discourse representation language L_{Dis}, containing plural constructions, into the formal language L_{LILOG}, which, in turn, is extended by LP. This shows how it is possible for LILOG's inference machine, modified along the lines indicated, to deal with pluralic bits of knowledge that are realistic representations of a wide array of plural constructions in language. Since in the field of plural phenomena there seems to be some danger of proliferation of readings, particular emphasis has been laid on questions of vagueness and ambiguity.

1 The Logic of Plurality, LP

LP is a first order theory with identity '$\doteq$' and λ-abstraction, together with the following special symbols: the binary functional symbol, '$\oplus$'; the general summing operator, 'σ'; the *plural operator* on one-place predicates, '$*$'; the *generalized quantifiers* **Q**: **MEIST, VIEL, WENIG, CARD** (= **1,2,3,...**); the one-place functional symbol, '$|\cdot|$' (= *cardinality of*).

Examples. The circled plus is used for combining names, e.g., $a \oplus b$ for *Hans und Maria*; the σ-operator generalizes the description operator 'ι'; thus, definite plural NPs like *die Kinder* are represented by σ-phrases, e.g., $\sigma x P x$; the star operator models pluralization of verb phrases, e.g., $*P(a \oplus b)$ for *Hans und Maria sind IBM-Mitarbeiter*. For details, see [Link 1983].

LP-expressions. In what follows 'SV' stands for "syntactical variable", and 'AcI' for "also used with accents and/or indices". SV for formulas are: 'ϕ', 'ψ', 'χ' (AcI); SV for variables over atomic individuals are: 'u', 'v', 'w', 'x', 'y', 'z' (AcI); SV for variables over plural individuals are: 'U', 'V', 'W', 'X', 'Y', 'Z' (AcI); SV for general individuals (atomic or proper sums) are: 'ξ', 'η', 'θ' (AcI). SV for predicates are: 'P', 'Q', (AcI); '$\vec{\xi}$' denotes a "vector" of variables.

Apart from the usual well-formed expressions of predicate logic the following schemata are also well-formed in LP:

1. $\lambda\vec{\xi}\phi$

2. $\xi \oplus \eta \doteq \theta$

3. $\eta \doteq \sigma\xi P\xi$

4. $*P\,\xi$

5. $\mathbf{Q}(\lambda\vec{x}\phi)(\lambda\vec{y}\psi)$

6. $|\,\xi\,| \doteq k$

Defined Symbols. The following symbols are defined symbols: '$\sqsubseteq_i$' stands for "*is an individual part of*" (*i-part*, for short); 'At' for "*is an atom*"; '$\cdot\sqsubseteq_i$' for "*is an atomic i-part of*"; '$Distr(P)$' for "*P is distributive*"; 'DP' for "*distributive version of P*"; '$\otimes P$' for the sort of the proper i-sums of atoms of sort P; '$\leq$' for the *subsumption relation* between sorts. (Sorts are not distinguished from regular predicates in the present context, but are assumed to be equipped with the the lattice structure of a concept hierarchy).

1. $\xi \sqsubseteq_i \eta \leftrightarrow \xi \oplus \eta \doteq \eta$

2. $At\,\eta \leftrightarrow \forall \xi(\xi \sqsubseteq_i \eta \rightarrow \xi \doteq \eta)$

3. $\xi \cdot \sqsubseteq_i \eta \leftrightarrow At\,\xi \wedge \xi \sqsubseteq_i \eta$

4. $Distr(P) \leftrightarrow \forall \xi(P\xi \rightarrow At\,\xi)$

5. $DP\,\xi \leftrightarrow \forall u(u \cdot \sqsubseteq_i \xi \rightarrow Pu)$

6. $\otimes P = *P \sqcap \neg P$

7. $Q \leq P \leftrightarrow \forall \xi(P\xi \rightarrow Q\xi)$

Axioms for LP

1. $(\lambda \vec{\xi} \phi[\vec{\xi}])\vec{\eta} \leftrightarrow \phi[\vec{\eta}]$

2. $\forall \xi \forall \eta[\xi \oplus \eta \doteq \eta \oplus \xi]$

3. $\forall \xi \forall \eta \forall \theta[(\xi \oplus \eta) \oplus \theta \doteq \xi \oplus (\eta \oplus \theta)]$

4. $\forall \xi[\xi \oplus \xi \doteq \xi]$

5. $\forall \xi \exists \eta \neg \xi \oplus \eta \doteq \eta$

6. $\forall \xi \forall \eta[\neg \xi \sqsubseteq_i \eta \rightarrow \exists u[At\,u \wedge u \sqsubseteq_i \xi \wedge \neg u \sqsubseteq_i \eta]]$

7. $\exists \xi P\xi \rightarrow \exists \eta[\eta \doteq \sigma \xi P\xi \wedge *P\,\eta]$

8. $\exists \xi P\xi \rightarrow \forall \eta[*P\eta \rightarrow \eta \sqsubseteq_i \sigma \xi P\xi]$

9. $\exists \xi P\xi \rightarrow \forall \eta[\forall \xi[*P\xi \rightarrow \xi \sqsubseteq_i \eta] \rightarrow \sigma \xi P\xi \sqsubseteq_i \eta]$

10. $\forall \xi[At\,\xi \wedge \xi \sqsubseteq_i \sigma \eta P\eta \rightarrow \exists \eta[P\eta \wedge \xi \sqsubseteq_i \eta]]$

11. $P \leq *P$

12. $P \leq Q \rightarrow *P \leq *Q$

13. $*\neg P \leq \neg *P$

14. $*(P \sqcap Q) = *P \sqcap *Q$

15. $*P \sqcup *Q \leq *(P \sqcup Q)$

16. $\mathbf{Q}PQ \leftrightarrow \mathbf{Q}P(P \sqcap Q)$ for all $\mathbf{Q}$

17. $\mathbf{Q}PQ \wedge Q \leq Q' \rightarrow \mathbf{Q}PQ'$ for $\mathbf{Q} = $ **MEIST, VIEL, CARD**

18. $\mathbf{WENIG}PQ \wedge Q' \leq Q \rightarrow \mathbf{WENIG}PQ'$

19. $\mathbf{CARD}PQ \wedge P \leq P' \rightarrow \mathbf{CARD}P'Q$

Axiom 1 is usual λ-conversion. Axioms 2–4 say that the collection of i-sums form a *(join) semilattice*. These axioms also entail that the i-part relation is a partial order. Axiom 5 means that plural domains do not contain a zero element. Furthermore, plural domains are *atomic* (Axiom 6); they are *definably complete*, i.e., non-empty definable subsets have a supremum (Axioms 7–9); and they are *free* in the sense of Axiom 10. Axioms 11–15 specify the star operation, and Axioms 16–19 give postulates for the generalized quantifiers. For logical questions of LP, see [Lønning 1989, Schütze 1989, Link 1991a].

2   A Formulation of the Language L_{Dis}

L_{Dis} is a sorted DRT-language. A DRS K is an ordered pair $\langle U, Con \rangle$ such that the following holds: $U = \{\xi_1 : se_1, \ldots, \xi_n : se_n\}$ is a set of sorted discourse referents, and $Con = \{C_1, \ldots, C_m\}$ is a set of DRS-conditions.

Simultaneous inductive definition of DRS-conditions und DRSs:

1.1 $\xi \doteq \eta$ is a DRS-condition;

1.2 $\xi \oplus \eta \doteq \theta$ is a DRS-condition;

1.3 $|\xi| \doteq k$ is a DRS-condition;

1.4   If R is an l-place DRS-relation then $R(\eta_1, \ldots, \eta_l)$ is a DRS-condition;

2. $K = \langle U, Con \rangle$ is a DRS if U, Con as above, and the C_i are DRS-conditions ($1 \leq i \leq m$);

3.   If K is a DRS then $\neg K$ is a DRS condition;

4.   If K_i are DRSs ($i = 1, 2$) then $K_1 \vee K_2$ and $K_1 \Rightarrow K_2$ are DRS-conditions;

5.   If K_i are DRSs ($i = 1, 2$), $\vec{x} : \vec{se}$ in U_{K_1}, and $Q = $ *jeder, kein, die meisten, viele, wenige, CARD*, then $K_1 \left\langle \!\!\! \begin{array}{c} Q \\ \vec{x} \end{array} \!\!\! \right\rangle K_2$ is a DRS-condition;

6.   If $K = \langle U, Con \rangle$ is a DRS, $\eta \in U$, and $\vec{x}$ is a vector of length l consisting of variables in U, then $\xi \doteq \Sigma \eta\, K$ is a DRS-condition and $\lambda \vec{x} K$ is an l-place DRS-relation.

3   A Translation of L_{Dis} into L_{LILOG}

We assume that L_{LILOG} is extended by the logic of plurality, LP. Let '$\vec{\xi} : \vec{se}$' stand for $(\xi_1 : se_1, \ldots, \xi_n : se_n)$; '$K_1 + K_2$' for $\langle U_{K_1} \cup U_{K_2}, Con_{K_1} \cup Con_{K_2} \rangle$; and '$KE[]$' for "knowledge-engineered version of".[1]

Inductive definition of the translation relation **U**:

1.1   Let $C = \xi \doteq \eta$, $\xi \oplus \eta \doteq \theta$, $|\xi| \doteq k$; then C **U** C;

1.2   Let $C = R(\eta_1, \ldots, \eta_l)$; then C **U** $KE[R(\eta_1, \ldots, \eta_l)]$;

2.   If $K = \langle U, Con \rangle$ with $Con = \{C_1, \ldots, C_m\}$ and C_i **U** C_i' ($1 \leq i \leq m$), then K **U** $(C_1' \wedge \ldots \wedge C_m')$;

3. $\neg K$ **U** $\neg (\exists \vec{\xi} : \vec{se})\, K'$, if $\xi_i : se_i \in U_K$ and K **U** K';

4.   Let K_i **U** K_i' ($i = 1, 2$); then, with the stipulations under 5., the following holds:

4.1 $K_1 \vee K_2$ **U** $K_1' \vee K_2'$;

4.2 $K_1 \Rightarrow K_2$ **U** $(\forall \vec{\eta_1} : \vec{se})[\, K_1' \rightarrow (\exists \vec{\eta_2} : \vec{se})\, K_2'\,]$;

---

[1]We use the operator 'KE' to remind the reader that it is a non-trivial task to transform the close-to-language relations of L_{Dis} into the KL-ONE inspired format of L_{LILOG}.

5. Let $C = K_1 \left\langle\!\!\!\begin{array}{c} Q \\ \diamondsuit \\ \vec{x} \end{array}\!\!\!\right\rangle K_2$;

suppose K_i **U** K_i' $(i = 1, 2)$; furthermore, let $\vec{\eta_1} : \vec{se}$ be the vector formed from the sorted variables in U_{K_1} (comprising $\vec{x} : \vec{se}$); let $\vec{\eta_2} : \vec{se}$ be the vector formed from the sorted variables in $U_{K_2} \setminus U_{K_1}$; let $\vec{\eta_{12}} : \vec{se}$ be the vector formed from the sorted variables in $U_{K_1+K_2}$; let $\vec{\xi} : \vec{se}$ be the vector formed from the sorted variables in U_{K_1} not occurring in $\vec{x}$; and let $\vec{\theta} : \vec{se}$ be the vector formed from the sorted variables in $U_{K_1+K_2}$ not occurring in $\vec{x}$;

5.1 $Q = \underline{jeder}$; then: C **U** $(\forall\vec{\eta_1} : \vec{se})[\, K_1' \rightarrow (\exists\vec{\eta_2} : \vec{se})\, K_2'\,]$;

5.2 $Q = \underline{kein}$; then: C **U** $\neg(\exists\vec{\eta_{12}} : \vec{se})\,[K_1' \wedge K_2']$;

5.3 $Q = \underline{die\,meisten}$, $\underline{viele}$, $\underline{wenige}$, $\underline{CARD}$, and let **Q** be the corresponding generalized quantifier; then: C **U**
Q $[(\lambda\vec{x} : \vec{se})(\exists\vec{\xi} : \vec{se})K_1'] \, [(\lambda\vec{x} : \vec{se})(\exists\vec{\theta} : \vec{se})K_1' \wedge K_2']$;

6.1 $C = \xi \doteq \Sigma\eta\, K$, and K **U** K'; let $\vec{\xi}$ be the vector formed from the variables in $U_K \setminus \{\eta\}$; then: C **U** $\xi \doteq \sigma\eta\, \exists\vec{\xi}K'$;

6.2 $C = \lambda\vec{x}K$, and K **U** K'; then: C **U** $\lambda\vec{x}K'$.

Let K' be the translation of the DRS K, and let $Fr(K') = \{\xi_1 : se_1, \ldots, \xi_n : se_n\}$ be the set of free variables in K'. Let $r_0, \ldots, r_m$ be the already existing referents; then $K'' = K'[\xi_1/r_{m+1}, \ldots, \xi_n/r_{m+n}]$ is the discourse knowledge, represented in L_{LILOG}, that is gained from K.

4 Types of Involvement of Plural Noun Phrases[2]

In this section, we apply the logic of plurality to the problem of how to interpret plural noun phrases. We first address the question whether the variation in the construal of plural NPs is ambiguous or indeterminate in nature for a number of constructions.[3] We will then investigate what the proper truth conditions for both the ambiguous and the indeterminate readings are.

Based on Roberts' theory of distributivity [1987a, 1987b], we give an analysis of sentences with indefinite singular NPs (Sect. 4.1) and bare plurals (Sect. 4.2). Section 4.3 extends the results to individual-denoting determiners in general and concludes that the truth conditions of collective readings cannot be reduced to something more specific than group involvement.

4.1 Singular Indefinite NPs

Roberts shows in her 1987 dissertation that verb phrases as in (1a) are ambiguous between a distributive and a collective reading. Her key evidence is the anaphoric potential of the noun phrase *a salad*. (1a) can be continued with (1b) in the collective reading (*Kim and Pat brought it* together), but not in the distributive reading (*they each brought a salad*).

(1) a. Kim and Pat brought a salad.

    b. It tasted great.

---

[2]We are grateful to Stanley Peters and Ivan Sag for comments and criticism of an earlier version of this section. We alone are responsible for errors that remain.

[3]See Gillon's 1987 article for a definition of the terms *indeterminate* and *ambiguous*.

In her analysis, Roberts assumes that there is an implicit adverbial quantifier, the D operator, in the distributive reading. The absence of the D operator results in the collective reading. The different anaphoric potential of the two readings then follows from the fact the the D operator masks the singular indefinite NP *a salad* under its scope, thus making it impossible for a pronoun to refer to it. But in the collective reading, *a salad* is available for anaphora.

Roberts' basic assumption is that the D operator behaves like a floated quantifier. The masking of noun phrases from anaphora alone would be relatively weak evidence for this hypothesis; but there are two other arguments for the D operator. First, if D is an adverbial quantifier, it should interact with the scope of other quantifiers. As (2) shows this is indeed the case. The D operator and floated *all* both allow a narrow scope interpretation of *at least*.

(2) a. Applicants have to know at least one foreign language.

   b. Applicants all have to know at least one foreign language.

The common reading of (2a) is that the applicants have to know one language, but that it can be different for each of them. If we don't assume a D operator and leave the subject noun phrase undistributed, *at least*'s scope may or may not include *applicants*, but in either case we don't get the intended reading. In DRT, we have the following straightforward interpretation of the distributed reading of (2a):[4]

(3)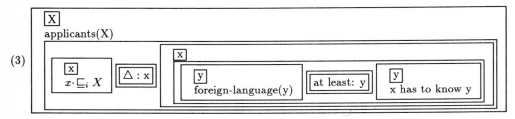

The second piece of evidence for the quantificational character of distribution is based on an observation by John Nerbonne [1987]. He notes that donkey sentences like (4a) could be a problem for Roberts' analysis, since the distribution operator within the relative clause would have to scope out to cover *reported*. However, we can derive the intended reading of (4a) from the implicit quantifier analysis by assuming a D operator in the main clause. An interpretation rule for floated quantifiers as in (4b), which would be similar to that for standard donkey sentences like (4c), will also apply to (4a) leaving us with the DRS (4d). Again, this reading would not be available without the D operator.

(4) a. The scouts who saw an army reported it to General Stuart.

   b. The scouts who saw an army all reported it to General Stuart.

   c. All scouts who saw an army reported it to General Stuart.

---

[4]We use a small box in the upper left corner of a DRS for the discourse referents, and a doubly framed box instead of a diamond for the quantifier of a duplex. Lower case letters stand for singular referents and upper case letters for plural referents. $\triangle$ symbolizes the distribution operator. Recall that $\cdot \sqsubseteq_i$ stands for *is atomic part of*.

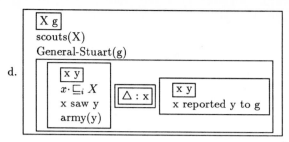

d.

Given the evidence from anaphora, quantifier scope and donkey sentences, we have to conclude that verb phrases with singular indefinite NPs are ambiguous between a distributive reading (with the implicit D operator) and a collective reading (without the D operator). All three tests show that the two readings have incompatible discourse representations, a fact that would be hard to explain if the two readings were different construals of an indeterminate phrase.

4.2   Dependent Plurals

Let us now investigate whether the construal of dependent plurals, i.e., plural indefinite NPs in the scope of (usually) a plural subject NP, is ambiguous or indeterminate. Chomsky opts for ambiguity [1975]. According to him, dependent plurals as in (5a) are ambiguous between a singular reading (*every unicycle has one wheel*) and a plural reading (*every unicycle has several wheels*). He claims that (5a) is ambiguously the plural of (5b) or (5c) and that plurality thus is "a semantic property of the sentence", not of a single NP.

(5) a. Unicycles have wheels.

   b. A unicycle has a wheel.

   c. A unicycle has wheels.

However, the standard ambiguity tests fail for (5a): (6a) can mean that every unicycle has one wheel and that every bicycle has more than one. (6b) denies both that any unicycle has one wheel and that any unicycle has more than one. The outcome of both tests therefore suggests that dependent plurals give rise to indeterminacy, not ambiguity. If we examine the range of possible readings of (5a) more closely, we realize that there are many cases in between the two extremes that every unicycle has exactly one wheel and that every unicycle has more than one wheel. These cases are those in which some unicycles have one wheel and the rest of them more than one. We cannot naturally construe (5a) in such a way, but the intermediate readings are available for sentences like (6c). To account for the continuum between the extreme cases, we follow Kamp and Reyle [1990] and use *general* discourse referents. Recall that greek letters and starred predicates stand for general individuals and predicates holding of plural as well as singular individuals, respectively. The DRS for (6c) is then (6d). (6d) roughly stands for (6e) in plain English.

(6) a. Unicycles have wheels, and bicycles do, too.

   b. Unicycles don't have wheels.

   c. The students bought books.

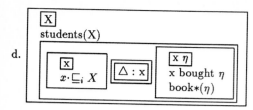

d.

e. All students bought one or more books.

The indeterminacy of the dependent plurals is an important means of efficiency in languages like English or German. If we want to describe a situation in which either some students bought several books and some only one; or in which it isn't important whether the number of books is equal to or greater than one; or if we simply don't know enough about the event, we can use dependent plurals to express exactly the amount of information appropriate or known.

One could even go one step further, as DeMey and Roberts do [Roberts 1987a], and classify sentences with dependent plurals as a subtype of the completely indeterminate collective-collective readings that we will deal with shortly. On that view, the bare plural introduces only one plural individual into the discourse, which interacts collectively with the subject NP. In order to prevent bare plurals from taking narrow scope and introducing several individuals in (6c), one would then have to stipulate that the existentially quantified NP *books* is not masked by the D operator whereas *book* in (7a) is, clearly an undesirable stipulation.

Moreover, notice that there is independent evidence for the generality of bare plurals from occurrences within the scope of a quantifier as in (7b) and (7c): the narrow scope reading of *books* is general in both sentences.

(7) a. The students bought a book.

   b. The students all bought books.

   c. Few students bought books.

   d. Those men who had bought books in the morning were reading them now.

Finally, donkey sentences like (7d) only have a narrow scope reading for the bare plural: Every man was reading his own books. A collective-collective reading would allow for some men to read books that others had bought.

We conclude that the general analysis of bare plurals provides a better account for the facts.

It is worth mentioning that *non-dependent* bare plurals, i.e., plurals that are not in the "scope" of a plural NP, also have an general meaning in certain contexts [Krifka 1989]. The answer in (8a) is perfectly natural, indicating that singular as well as plural individuals are in the denotation of *apples*. If plurality is the focus of the utterance, it has to be expressed using special linguistic devices such as the adjective *multiple* in (8b). This is further support for the general analysis of bare plurals.

(8) a. Did you buy apples? – Yes, one.

   b. We apologize if you receive multiple copies of this announcement.

4.3 Types of Involvement of Plural NP's

We will now generalize the results of Sects. 4.1 and 4.2 on the basis of Roberts' DRT classification of plural determiners [1987b]. She classifies indefinites, *some*, numbers, *the*, *these* and *those* as *individual-denoting*, and *most*, *few*, *many*, etc., as *quantificational*. Extending our findings about definite plural subjects to the other individual-denoting determiners, we can put forward the following hypothesis:

Hypothesis 1. A sentence with an individual-denoting plural subject and a VP containing an indefinite object is ambiguous between a collective reading and a distributive reading that predicates the denotation of the VP of each of the atomic parts of the denotation of the subject.

Let us now turn to cases that involve plural subjects and *definite* objects. Gillon claims in his 1987 article that subject noun phrases are ambiguous and that their readings "bijectively correspond with the minimal covers of the set denoted by the subject plural noun phrase." [Gillon 1987] He bases his theory on the following ambiguity test:

(9) A sentence is ambiguous iff, with respect to a given state of affairs, the sentence can be both truly affirmed and truly denied.

and the two types of examples illustrated in (10a) and (10b).

(10) a. The men wrote songs.

b. The buses in this town consume more gasoline than the cars.

Gillon constructs the following example situation: *the men* denotes two persons who have written songs individually, but have never cooperated on a song. He claims that in such a situation (10a) can be truly affirmed when the hearer is thinking of the men's separate involvement with song writing; and truly denied if the hearer is thinking of the men's common involvement with song writing. We think this judgement is not correct. In response to (10a), one might say: "Yes, but they have never written a song *together*.", but an outright denial is not possible.

(10b) really is ambiguous. Under the distributive-distributive reading it will be correct in a typical town, and it would be affirmed. Under the collective-collective reading it is false under normal circumstances, and one would deny it. But from this one cannot infer that plural noun phrases are ambiguous in general. (10b) can be plausibly viewed as a short form of (11). We see that the sentence (10b) semantically consists of two subparts, each of them with a definite plural subject and an indefinite NP. So (10b) is just an example of the ambiguity of sentences of the type examined in Sect. 4.1, and by no means evidence for the indeterminacy of definite plural noun phrases in general.

(11) The buses in this town consume more gasoline than the cars consume gasoline.

Gillon therefore hasn't given any evidence bearing on sentences with definite plural objects. (12a) is an example for such a sentence:

(12) a. The students were reading the newspapers.

b. The students didn't read the newspapers.

c. The students were reading the newspapers, and so were they.

Note that the ambiguity test (9) fails here. One cannot truly deny and affirm (12a) for different readings. For instance, if the students are reading newspapers separately, one cannot deny (12a) in the collective-collective construal. The ambiguity tests in (12b) and (12c) also fail, providing further evidence for the indeterminacy of (12a): in (12b) all possible readings are negated and in (12c) the verb anaphor can be construed in a different way than the antecedent. In general, we propose the following two hypotheses for readings involving two individual-denoting NPs:

Hypothesis 2. A sentence with an individual-denoting plural subject and a VP containing a non-indefinite individual-denoting plural object has only a collective-collective reading.

Hypothesis 3. Collective readings are indeterminate as to how the atomic individuals in the denotation of the NP are involved in the relation denoted by the rest of the sentence.

There are several "dimensions" of indeterminacy for collective readings:

Separate vs. Common Involvement. *Examples.* In (12a), groups of several students may read a newspaper together, others may read one on their own. Similarly, a group of newspapers may be read at the same time by some student(s) (for the purpose of comparing their coverage, etc.), and the other newspapers may each be read by only one student. (13a) has a marginal partitional reading, in which there are three events of two boys gathering.

Singular vs. Multiple Involvement. *Example.* (13b) is appropriate if some of the individuals were involved in many song writing events. A given individual may have written songs on his own, some songs together with individual A, other songs together with another individual B. It is this dimension that Gillon drew attention to in his 1987 article about set covers. He pointed out that there is no restriction imposing singular involvement on the interpretation of plural noun phrases, as examples like (13b) show.

Few vs. Many Involvements. (for relations of an arity greater than 1) How many of the $|A| \cdot |B|$ pairs in $R \subseteq A \times B$ are involved in the action or state R denoted by the verb? *Example.* In (13c) the most likely interpretation is that there each guard is holding (at least) one prisoner, i.e., that there are at most as many involvements as guards. In (13d), it is entirely possible that each guard is watching each prisoner, a state of affairs, in which all possible involvements are realized. Langendoen [1978] thinks that readings like those for (13c) and (13d) are the basis for weak and strong reciprocity, respectively.

Finally, Scha has dubbed as "cumulative" those readings that are completely chaotic in that they are not at one end of the spectrum on any of the dimensions. (13e), for instance, can be true of a state of affairs where some, but not all computers are jointly owned (separate vs. common involvement); some but not all companies have common property with several distinct groups of other companies (singular vs. multiple involvement); many, but not all of the possible owner-ownee involvement pairs are contained in the denotation of *have* (few vs. many involvements).

(13) a. Six boys gather. [Scha 1984]

　　b. The men wrote songs. [Gillon 1987]

　　c. The guards were holding the prisoners. (cf. [Langendoen 1978])

　　d. The guards were watching the prisoners. (cf. [Langendoen 1978])

　　e. 600 Dutch firms have 5000 American computers. [Scha 1984]

In our view, it depends entirely on the context and on world knowledge whether a collective sentence will be interpreted cumulatively, in a manner corresponding to weak or strong reciprocity, or by a model that realizes a set cover or a partition. There are no facts whatsoever that support the *linguistic* relevance of any of these interpretations. Linguistically, the collectively interpreted NP forms a unit that cannot be broken up. But there is sufficient semantic evidence for the linguistic status of the distributivity phenomena dealt with in Sects. 4.1 and 4.2. We therefore regard the types of involvement of individuals in *collective* sentences as an extralinguistic matter, whereas linguistics can give clear truth conditions for the involvement of individuals in *distributive* sentences.

4.4　Conclusion

The distinction between indeterminacy and ambiguity is important for natural language processing systems. Ambiguous sentences are usually used only when context rules out all but one reading.

On the contrary, indeterminate sentences are a powerful tool to express just the information that is appropriate or known in a given situation. In the case of ambiguity, the sentence should be disambiguated as soon as possible. In the case of indeterminacy, a representation has to be found that captures all possible readings in a unified way, conforming with the intention of the speaker to leave unanswered any unimportant questions about the state of affair described.

Using LP and DRT as a framework, we have shown how to develop guidelines for the kind of processing that sentences with plural noun phrases require.

References

[Bäuerle, Schwarze, von Stechow 1983] Bäuerle, R., Schwarze, C., von Stechow, A. (eds.) (1983): *Meaning, Use, and Interpretation of Language.* De Gruyter, Berlin

[Chomsky 1975] Chomsky, N. (1975): Questions of form and interpretation. In Austerlitz, R. P. (ed.) (1975): *The Scope of American Linguistics.* Peter de Ridder Press, Lisse

[Dowty 1986] Dowty, D. (1986): Collective Predicates, Distributive Predicates and ALL. ESCOL '86

[Gärdenfors 1987] Gärdenfors, P. (ed.) (1987): *Generalized Quantifiers. Linguistic and Logical Approaches.* Reidel, Dordrecht

[Gillon 1987] Gillon, B. S. (1987): The readings of plural noun phrases in English. Linguistics and Philosophy 10, pp. 199-219

[Groenendijk, Janssen, Stokhof 1981] Groenendijk, J., Janssen, T. M. V., Stokhof, M. (eds.) (1981): *Formal Methods in the Study of Language.* Mathematical Centre, Amsterdam

[Groenendijk, Janssen, Stokhof 1984] Groenendijk, J., Janssen, T. M. V., Stokhof, M. (eds.) (1984): *Truth, Interpretation and Information.* Foris, Dordrecht

[Kamp 1981] Kamp, H. (1981): A theory of truth and semantic representation. In [Groenendijk, Janssen, Stokhof 1981]

[Kamp, Reyle 1989] Kamp, H., Reyle, U. (1989): *Vom Diskurs zur Logik III.* Lecture notes, Institut für maschinelle Sprachverarbeitung, Universität Stuttgart

[Kamp, Reyle 1990] Kamp, H., Reyle, U. (1990): *From Discourse to Logic. Volume I.* Manuscript, Institut für maschinelle Sprachverarbeitung, Universität Stuttgart

[Krifka 1989] Krifka, M. (1989): *Nominalreferenz und Zeitkonstitution. Zur Semantik von Massentermen, Pluraltermen und Aspektklassen.* Fink, München

[Landman, Veltman 1984] Landman, F., Veltman, F. (1984): *Varieties of Formal Semantics. Proceedings of the Fourth Amsterdam Colloquium.* GRASS Series No. 3, Foris, Dordrecht

[Langendoen 1978] Langendoen, D. T. (1978): The logic of reciprocity. Linguistic Inquiry 9, pp. 177-197

[Link 1983] Link, G. (1983): The logical analysis of plurals and mass terms: A lattice-theoretical approach. In [Bäuerle, Schwarze, von Stechow 1983], pp. 302-323

[Link 1984] Link, G. (1984): Hydras: On the logic of relative constructions with multiple heads. In [Landman, Veltman 1984], pp. 245-257

[Link 1987] Link, G. (1987): Generalized quantifiers and plurals. In [Gärdenfors 1987], pp. 151-180

[Link 1991a] Link, G. (1991): First order axioms for the logic of plurality. In Allgayer, J. (ed.) (1991): *Processing Plurals and Quantification.* CSLI Lecture Notes, Stanford

[Link 1991b] Link, G. (1991): Plural. In von Stechow, A., Wunderlich, D. (eds.) (1991): *Handbuch Semantik.* De Gruyter, Berlin

[Lønning 1989] Lønning, J. T. (1989): *Some Aspects of the Logic of Plural Noun Phrases.* COSMOS-Report No. 11, Department of Mathematics, University of Oslo

[Nerbonne 1987] Nerbonne, J. (1987): *Anaphora and Distributivity: A Discussion of C. Roberts's Dissertation.* Manuscript, HP Labs and CSLI

[Roberts 1987a] Roberts, C. (1987): *Modal Subordination, Anaphora, and Distributivity.* Ph.D. dissertation, University of Massachusetts, Amherst

[Roberts 1987b] Roberts, C. (1987): *Distributivity.* Paper presented at the Sixth Amsterdam Colloquium

[Scha 1984] Scha, R. (1984): *Distributive, Collective and Cumulative Quantification.* In [Groenendijk, Janssen, Stokhof 1984]

[Schütze 1989] Schütze, H. (1989): *Pluralbehandlung in natürlichsprachlichen Wissensverarbeitungssystemen.* IWBS Report 73. IBM Deutschland, Stuttgart

Chapter 2

Knowledge Representation and Processing

The LILOG approach to natural language understanding can be considered as the the translation of German texts into a logical representation. This translation is performed on the background of some semantic knowledge about the domain to which the natural language texts refer. Thus, the purpose of our knowledge representation language L_{LILOG} is twofold: on the one hand it is used to represent the semantic background knowledge of our natural language understanding system LEU/2; on the other hand, it is the target language for the translation of information provided in natural language. In order not to make the translation process from natural texts into a processable logical form too complicated, the knowledge representation language should be abstract enough to avoid what are known as 'implementational details' as far as possible. On the other hand, the knowledge representation language has to offer a rich reservoir of language constructs if it is to be used within the framework of understanding natural language texts. This argument for abstractness and expressiveness holds for the aspect of modeling the semantic background knowledge as well.

According to the scenario set up above, L_{LILOG} as it is used within LEU/2 integrates different streams of knowledge representation on the basis of first-order predicate logic. This 'naked' logic has been enriched by a type concept having its origin in the KL-ONE world and in the world of attribute-based feature structures known from computational linguistics. Thus, the kernel of L_{LILOG} can be characterized as an advanced order-sorted predicate logic and the inference engine we have implemented processes this kernel language.

Besides these fundamental features of L_{LILOG}, other aspects of knowledge representation have been addressed within the project as well. This has lead to theoretical investigations of non-monotonic reasoning, attributive description formalisms, structuring mechanisms for knowledge bases, control of the LILOG inference engine, and multiple-valued logic. Some of the results achieved there have already made their way into L_{LILOG} and the inference engine interpreting the language.

Udo Pletat

Chapter 2.1

Representing Semantic Knowledge

The LILOG activities as summarized here under the title 'Knowledge Representation and Processing' comprise all activities of handling world knowledge underlying a natural language understanding system.

This starts, of course, with the language to be used for representing the semantic knowledge of our natural language understanding system LEU/2: L_{LILOG}. The knowledge of LEU/2 being represented in L_{LILOG} stems from two sources: (1) the semantic background knowledge developed by our knowledge engineers, and (2) the knowledge extracted from German texts. These two kinds of knowledge have to be made available to all componets of LEU/2 that need to have accessto semantic information. In order to store this knowledge adequately, an advanced deductive database system has been developed for our natural language undrstanding system and is used for the permanent storage of knowledge. Finally, the knowledge available to LEU/2 needs to be processed: this task is solved by our inference engine for L_{LILOG}.

On the background of this rough sketch of the requirements for handling semantic knowledge within a natural language understanding system the following subjects are addressed in this part of the book:

1. The knowledge representation language L_{LILOG} itself plus several approaches to potential enhancements,

2. The inference engine for processing L_{LILOG},

3. The knowledge engineering activities for developing the semantic background knowledge of our natural language understanding system,

4. The enhanced deductive database system satisfying the special requirements set up by the knowledge based systems framework.

Udo Pletat

The Knowledge Representation Language L$_{\text{LILOG}}$

Udo Pletat

The development of a language for representing the semantic knowledge underlying the natural language understanding system LEU/2 has been one of the central activities of the LILOG project since its very beginnings. Creating a new language was necessary because we could not find a suitable formalism in the scientific literature that satisfied our multiple requirements for a knowledge representation language:

- To offer a rich expressiveness for capturing a wide range of natural language phenomena,

- To be a communication medium between the linguistic and the logic part of the project, and

- To be provided with a formal semantics as the basis for the LILOG inference engine.

Considering these requirements and taking a look at the knowledge representation literature (see [Brachman and Levesque 1985] for a compact overview), we found that most formalisms that have been suggested address specific aspects of knowledge representation. This reflects a situation where formalisms emerge from investigations of particular problems in order to get the right understanding of the various concepts being necessary for the representation of knowledge.

Looking for an adequate knowledge representation formalism for a wide-spectrum natural language understanding project like LILOG, the well-established approaches dealing with specific aspects of knowledge representation did not cover the range of features we expected for our purposes. What seemed to be necessary was to integrate various of the specific approaches to knowledge representation within one language. To achieve such an integration has been the major impetus for the development of our knowledge representation language L$_{\text{LILOG}}$. In the long run only the integration of various research directions can lead to the knowledge representation formalisms that are required in the framework of natural language understanding and other applications of realistic size of knowledge based systems.

On the background of the above discussion of the state of the art in knowledge representation, the definition of L$_{\text{LILOG}}$ can be seen as one of the first attempts to integrate different streams of knowledge representation language within one formalism. This integration has been achieved in terms of a formal language that can be processed on a computer, not just a description of such an integrated language in prose.

1 The Basic Ideas Behind L$_{\text{LILOG}}$

The starting point for the enterprise of developing L$_{\text{LILOG}}$ was the decision to create a logic based knowledge representation formalism because this seemed the most promising way to fulfill our requirement to define a language in terms of both a formal syntax and a formal semantics.

To be more specific, we have considered order-sorted predicate logic as the basis for the development of L$_{\text{LILOG}}$ since it offers a type concept, and type systems are an essential part of modern programming languages, see [Jensen and Wirth 1975], [Wirth 1985], [Gordon *et al.* 1978]. Also in the area of formal software specification, type concepts play an important role (see [Goguen *et al.* 1978] or [Björner and Jones 1978]). Last but not least, types have also made their way into a particular class of AI languages: the attributive set description languages we know for example from computational linguistics ([Pereira and Shieber 1984]) or from the KL-ONE family of languages ([Brachman and Schmolze 1985a]).

The role of type systems is to describe the object classes of a program, or - as in our setting - a knowledge base. Since we are using the attribute-based set description language STUF (cf. [Bouma et al. 1988] and [Dörre and Seiffert this volume]) in the linguistic part of the LILOG project we have decided to develop a type system in the STUF or KL-ONE style for L$_{\text{LILOG}}$. These approaches to type definitions fit nicely into the framework of an order-sorted predicate logic (cf. [Oberschelp 1962] and q [Walther 1987]) since they also deal with a set of sorts together with a partial ordering between them reflecting the subset relationship between the sets interpreting the sorts.

The common idea of speaking about sets ordered by inclusion both in the semantic and linguistic knowledge representation formalism was the reason for using (parts of) STUF as the type system of the first version of L$_{\text{LILOG}}$, see [C. Beierle and J. Dörre and U. Pletat and C.-R. Rollinger and R. Studer]. In the meantime we have obtained an improved understanding of the feature term description languages and how to combine them with predicate logic. This enabled us to integrate concepts of languages like KL-ONE [Brachman and Schmolze 1985b] and Feature Logic [Smolka 1988] into the sort descriptions offered by L$_{\text{LILOG}}$ (cf. [Pletat and v. Luck 1990]).

This integration of attribute-based set descriptions into the framework of order-sorted predicate logic has to be seen as a contribution towards integrating two philosophies of knowledge representation: classical logic-based approaches and typical object-oriented approaches having their roots in artificial intelligence (see also [Brachman et al. 1985]).

The discipline of logic has not only created formalisms for pure mathematical patterns of reasoning (of which order-sorted predicate logic is a representative), but also, during the last 10 years, put the more flexible patterns of human reasoning onto formal foundations. One of the more elaborate of these enrichments of logic providing better models of human reasoning is nonmonotonic reasoning, cf. [Ginsberg 1987]. The basic idea of nonmonotonic reasoning may be characterized as a logical framework which offers less rigid quantifications than the usual universal ones, with the aim of arriving at a logic which still works well in situations where exceptions to general rules occur. Especially in the framework of natural language understanding the required reasoning mechanisms are strongly influenced by the common sense humans apply. In this situation, standard logics show inadequacies since they have been introduced to describe reasoning processes in the precise, and even formalized, world of mathematics. In contrast to that, formal reasoning about information provided in natural language has to mimic the imprecise reasoning humans apply in everyday situations. Thus the results that have been achieved in the field of nonmonotonic reasoning should be made available to a project like LILOG and have found their place in our knowledge representation language.

The features of L$_{\text{LILOG}}$ discussed so far have emphasized the improved facilities for representing knowledge. But knowledge is not only of the static nature suggested by the term 'representation'. Knowledge that is only representable but not processable is of little practical use (at least from a computer scientist's point of view). Processing knowledge formulated within a certain logic is still a complex task and often touches the limits of the available computational power. This is due to the fact that the inferential processes we use for putting knowledge into operation are still search procedures traversing immense search spaces in a rather uncontrolled way. The efficiency advantages of conventional programming languages over most knowledge representation languages stem mainly from the efforts we have to expend on the explicit control of the execution of a program.

In L$_{\text{LILOG}}$ we have made some first attempts to provide control information for the theorem prover implementing the language. This comprises facilities to select logical axioms for forward chaining, backward chaining, or both reasoning modes in order to exclude certain rules of a knowledge base from the reasoning process. Moreover we are able to delegate deductive tasks to external inference systems which are assumed to process certain requests in a more efficient way than the main theorem prover interpreting L$_{\text{LILOG}}$. In the context of LEU/2 the depictional reasoner (see [Habel this volume]) for processing spatial information can be activated for performing reasoning tasks on the basis of analog representations of spatial knowledge.

Besides these basic concepts for expressing knowledge we have developed a concept for structuring knowledge into modules that can interact on the basis of export and import interfaces. This allows us to separate large knowledge bases into different components, each of which deals with specific aspects of the domain of discourse to be modeled.

After this general overview of L$_\text{LILOG}$ we will provide a more detailed discussion of the particular language constructs in the next section. The style of the discussion will remain informal, since formal definitions of the concepts available in L$_\text{LILOG}$ may be found elsewhere (e.g., [Schlechta 1989], [Pletat and v. Luck 1990], and [Pletat 1991]).

2 Representing Knowledge in L$_\text{LILOG}$

An L$_\text{LILOG}$ knowledge base is the formalization of a particular application domain over which a knowledge based system is supposed to reason. Within the LILOG project we use L$_\text{LILOG}$ for modeling the semantic background knowledge of the natural language understanding system LEU/2. The knowledge developed for LEU/2 deals with tourist information about the city of Düsseldorf one would expect from a tourist guide, plus general knowledge about places of interest to a visitor to a city. A particular description of the knowledge that has bee modeled for LEU/2 can be found in [Klose and von Luck this volume].

In this section we want to provide an informal description of the language constructs offered by L$_\text{LILOG}$. The discussion proceeds along the lines of introducing the concrete syntax of the language by means of examples. We explain what can be described by the various constructs of L$_\text{LILOG}$ for which a formal definition of the semantics has been developed. The corresponding formalizations are provided elsewhere and we will refer to the respective background papers whenever further information on the language could be of interest to the reader.

2.1 Knowledge Items

As L$_\text{LILOG}$ is a knowledge representation language based on typed logic, type definitions and logical axioms play the major role in an L$_\text{LILOG}$ knowledge base. Axioms state the logical properties of functions and predicates; thus the declarations of these predicate and function symbols occurring in the logical formulas of a knowledge base are further knowledge entities.

2.1.1 Sort Declarations

Sort declarations introduce tne object classes of a knowledge base. In order-sorted predicate logic the sort declarations are of a very simple nature: they consist just of the name of the sort to be declared plus the embedding of the sort into the hierarchy of sorts of a knowledge base.

As an example we may have the following sort declarations recalling what can be expressed in order-sorted logic:

> **sort** *person*.
> **sort** *woman* < *person*.
> **sort** *man* < *person*.

These sort declarations introduce the data domains *person*, *woman*, and *man* and state that *woman* and *man* are contained in *person*.

L$_\text{LILOG}$ offers a richer sort concept than the one we are used to from order-sorted predicate logic. This results from integrating concepts of feature term description languages like STUF, Feature Logic, and KL-ONE into L$_\text{LILOG}$. Since all these languages pursue the paradigm of modeling semantic knowledge by defining sets, they offer sophisticated means for describing object classes. Thus, in contrast to order-sorted logic, where sets can only be described in terms of sort names, L$_\text{LILOG}$ allows for complex set descriptions by means of sort expressions. These sort expressions are constructed over a collection of operators defining, for example, the intersection, the union or the complement of object classes.

Besides splitting the data domain of a knowledge base into several different object classes (generalizing one-sorted logic to many-sorted logic) it was realized very soon that stating subset relationships between object classes is an expressive means for modeling knowledge about the world (generalizing many-sorted logic to order-sorted logic). Thus, a modern knowledge representation language should support the explicit positioning of sorts within the lattice of sort expressions (with respect to the subsumption ordering, see below) of a knowledge base. In L$_\text{LILOG}$ this is achieved by means of so-called sort constraints that may be part of a sort declaration.

Requiring the subset relationship to hold between two sorts (*woman* and *person* as well as *man* and *persom* in the above example) is not the only way of constraining the interpretation of sorts: we may also express that one sort is disjoint from another. A sort declaration like

> **sort** *man < person;*
> **disjoint** *woman.*

in our L$_\text{LILOG}$ knowledge base introduces the sort *man* in such a way that *man* and *woman* are disjoint subsets of *person*. The disjointness of the sorts *man* and *woman* could also be expressed by a declaration of the sort *man* by

> **sort** *man* = **and***(person,* **not***(woman)).*

where the sort expression **and***(person,* **not***(woman))* stands for the intersection of *person* with the complement of the sort *woman*. (Note that the two ways of introducing the sort *man* lead to sort hierarchies which are not completely equivalent.) A third alternative for defining these three sorts is the following collection of sort declarations using the union operator:

> **sort** *woman.*
> **sort** *man;*
> **disjoint** *woman*
> **sort** *person* = **or***(man, woman).*

In L$_\text{LILOG}$ we call the equations, the inequations, and the disjointness conditions between a sort name and a sort expression *sort constraints*, since they constrain the interpretation of the sort name being declared to the same set, a subset, or a set disjoint from the set interpreting the sort expression, respectively. For the first example above this means that both *man* and *woman* are contained in *person*. Moreover, *man* and *woman* don't have any object in common.

The sort constraints are a means for influencing the structure of the sort hierarchy induced by the subsumption relation ≪ between the sort expressions of a knowledge base:

> se ≪ se′ *iff in any interpretation the denotation of* se *is*
> *a subset of the set interpreting* se′.

This subsumption relation has been studied for various feature term languages, see [Brachman and Schmolze 1985b], [Kasper and Rounds 1986], [Smolka 1988].

Besides positioning a sort within the lattice of sort expressions we can also introduce attributes, i.e., features and roles, for a sort as part of its declaration. In the more detailed declaration of the sort *person* below we introduce the two features *age* and *sex* with their corresponding ranges *integer* and *sexes*.

> **sort** *person;*
> **features** *age : integer,*
>   *sex : sexes.*

These attributes allow us to speak about the age and the sex of a person. Features are functional attributes, i.e., they have a unique value for each object they can be applied to. In certain situations it is convenient to have relational attributes available as well. This holds, e.g., for the parenthood of a man or a woman, respectively, since a person can be the father/mother of several (may be no) children.

> **sort** *man < person;*
>   **roles** *father_of :: person.*

> **sort** *woman < person;*
>   **roles** *mother_of :: person.*

Semantically, features stand for one-place total functions while the roles are interpreted as two-place relations, see [Pletat and v. Luck 1990].

In many situations we want to introduce some specific objects of a sort when declaring it. The objects that can be introduced as part of a sort declaration are called *atoms*. Referring back to our sort *person*, we still have to declare the target sort *sexes* of the feature *sex*. A reasonable definition could be the following one:

> **sort** *sexes*
>   **atoms** *female, male.*

The atoms which can be declared for a sort are objects of that sort for which we impose a unique names assumption. For the sort *sexes* this means that it contains (at least) the two different elements *male* and *female*.

Atoms can be used to form a further kind of sort expression: intervals of integers and enumerations which appear in the definition of the sort vehicle below. Let us first say what kinds of vehicles we might want to consider:

> **sort** *vehicle-type;*
>   **atoms** *bike, boat, car, plane, train.*

Then we define vehicles as

> **sort** *vehicle;*
>   **features** *wheels : [0 .. 256],*
>   *doors : [0 .. 256],*
>   *type : vehicle-type,*
>   *driver : person*
>   *owner : person.*
>   **roles** *user :: person.*

The declaration of the sort *vehicle* makes use of intervals of integers, i.e. sort expressions like

> *[0 .. 256].*

Such an interval is a short form for enumerating a set of integers. In general, enumerations have the form

> $\{ a_1, ..., a_n \}$

where the a_i are atoms and define the set consisting exactly of those elements interpreting the atoms mentioned in the enumeration.

Sort expressions of the form $f : se$ where f is a feature and se is some sort expression define the subset of all those elements in the domain of the feature f which are mapped to the data domain defined by se. This mechanism is typically called feature value restriction, cf. [Brachman and Schmolze 1985a]. An expression like

> *type : { car }*

stands for all vehicles for which the *type*-feature has the value *car* and we could use this expression to define the sort of *cars* by

> **sort** *car* = **and***(wheels* : {4}, *doors* : {2, 3, 4, 5}, *type* : { *car* }*);*
> **features** *body* : *body-type.*

where the body types of a car may be defined as follows:

> **sort** *body-type;*
> **atoms** *cabrio, coupe, hatchback, sedan.*

According to this definition, cars are vehicles having 4 wheels and 2 to 5 doors, depending on the body type. Intuitively, any car should be a vehicle, and that's exactly what the formal semantics of L$_{\text{LILOG}}$ establishes, see [Pletat and v. Luck 1990]. That is, the subsumption relationship *car* ≪ *vehicle* holds for these two sorts.

Value restrictions involving roles may also be formulated: here L$_{\text{LILOG}}$ offers two variants. The sort expression

> **all** *user teenager*

describes all vehicles the user of which is a teenager provided that the vehicle is in use, i.e., that there is a person driving the vehicle.

In many modeling situations we wanted to express that, referring to the above example, there is indeed a user of the vehicle. In order to avoid notational overhead for describing this using the **some** operator discussed below, we have introduced the following useful syntactic sugar into the sort description features of L$_{\text{LILOG}}$: the sort expression

> *driver* :: *teenager*

is a shorthand for

> **and***(***all** *driver teenager,* **some** *driver).*

The sort declarations

> **sort** *father* = **some** *father_of.*
> **sort** *mother* = **some** *mother_of.*

define *fathers* and *mothers* by stating that a *father* or a *mother* is a *man* or a *woman*, respectively, such that there is at least one person of whom he/she is a parent. That is to say: the sort expression **some** *mother_of* stands for all objects m of sort *person* such that there is an object c of sort *person* for which *mother_of(m, c)* holds.

The operator **agree** allows us to form the set of all objects for which two feature paths (i.e., sequences of features) have the same value. Thus, the sort expression

> **and***(vehicle,* **agree***(owner, driver))*

characterizes vehicles which are owned by people who don't allow others to drive their vehicle. The counterpart of the agreement operator is the disagreement operator **disagree**. It defines the set of all objects such that the two feature paths involved in the sort expression have different values.

Last but not least, we want to introduce sort expressions which allow us to speak about sets containing finite subsets over some base set as their elements. The sort declaration

> **sort** *group-of-tourists* < *person*⁺.

defines the sort *group-of-tourists* as a set containing finite sets of *persons* as elements. In several modeling situations it is convenient to consider a base set and finite subsets within one set. Such classes of objects could be described by the union **or***(person, person+)*, if we take the sort *person* as the base set. This union will be abbreviated by another operator *; thus for the sort *person* we obtain *person** = **or***(person, person+)*.

Summarizing, the sort descriptions of L$_{\text{LILOG}}$ have integrated concepts from order-sorted predicate logic and KL-ONE like languages. This supports an object-oriented description of the data domain of a knowledge base in the sense that we are able to speak about objects and their attributes. The formal semantics of these language constructs interprets sort expressions as sets (of a certain structure according to the set-forming operators used in the expression), features as total functions, and roles as relations, see [Pletat and v. Luck 1990]. This allows us to handle subsumption relationships between sort expressions in a natural way. An interesting, although only too natural, phenomenon of the semantics for the sort descriptions of L$_{\text{LILOG}}$ is that we get an important concept of object-oriented languages for free: the concept of multiple inheritance. The inheritance mechanism works in two directions: features and attributes are inherited downwards in the lattice of sort expressions while objects of a sort are inherited upwards. This results from two simple mathematical properties. A function $F : D \longrightarrow R$ can also be applied to any subset $D' \subseteq D$ of its domain, thus we say that F is inherited down to any subset D' of D. Referring to our L$_{\text{LILOG}}$ knowledge items introduced so far this means, e.g., that the *age*-feature of a *person* may also be evaluated for any *mother*, since *mother* $\ll$ *person*, i.e., *mother* is subsumed by *person* formalizing that any mother is (of course) also a person. On the other hand, the subset relation between the sets interpreting the sorts causes any object of a sort s to be also an element of the sort s', if s is subsumed by s'. In this sense we obtain the upward inheritance of the atoms (and also any other objects we will become acquainted with below) of a sort. All this is no magic: we simply exploit the natural properties of the subset relation between sets and the element relation between objects and sets.

2.1.2 Function Declarations

The sort declarations of a knowledge base introduce its sort hierarchy or, to use a different terminology, the taxonomy of its data domains. The formulation of the logical axioms of a knowledge base requires further declarations: we need to know the relations which the axioms are speaking about. To introduce these relations between the data classes of the knowledge base is the purpose of the function and predicate declarations to be discussed next.

We have already seen simple kinds of function and predicate declarations: the features and roles attached to a sort. Their simplicity results from the fact that they can relate only two sorts. In general, both functions and predicates of arbitrary arity are desirable.

A function declaration

function F *(argname$_1$: se$_1$, ..., argname$_n$: se$_n$)* $\rightarrow$ *se.*

in L$_{\text{LILOG}}$ states that within the world modeled by the knowledge base the object classes represented by the sort expressions *se$_i$* are functionally related to the set *se* and that this relationship bears the name *F*.

Within the domain of traveling functions is a convenient means for modeling knowledge. A typical functional relationship is the seat allocation assigning a seat to each of the passengers within a vehicle. Assuming for simplicity that any seat can be identified by an integer number, we may obtain the following function declaration as part of our knowledge base:

function *seat-allocation (passenger : person, carrier : vehicle)* $\rightarrow$ *integer.*

The above declaration exhibits another feature of the concrete syntax of L$_{\text{LILOG}}$: the arguments of a function (and also those of a predicate) need not be identified by their position in the argument list; instead we support the more flexible way of explicit naming of argument positions.

Choosing a function for representing the seat allocation is a good means for expressing that each passenger in a vehicle has a unique seat. Unfortunately, seats may be overbooked; this can also be captured adequately by modeling the seat allocation with a function, since functions are in general not injective. So it may happen that both Mr Miller and Mr Smith are allotted to the same seat No. 15 in a Boeing 737, i.e., we have logical formulas expressing the function values

    seat-allocation(passenger : Mr Miller, carrier : Boeing 737) = 15.

and

    seat-allocation(carrier : Boeing 737, passenger : Mr Smith) = 15.

in a knowledge base.

Functions may have no arguments. Such functions are considered as elements of their target sort. The syntax of L_{LILOG} offers such nullary functions as *constants* or *reference objects*. So we may have further declarations like

    constant *Mr Miller : man.*

    refo *Mr Smith : man.*

    refo *Boeing 737 : type : { plane }.*

as part of a knowledge base. Logically, there is no difference between constants and reference objects. However, in the natural language understanding context of the LILOG project, which is currently the major application area of L_{LILOG}, reference objects (refos, for short) are distinguished constants. The type of a constant or a reference object may be given by an arbitrary sort expression, for example we want to speak about two distinguished sportscars:

    constant *porsche_911 :* **and***(car, doors : { 2 }), body-type : { cabrio }).*

and

    refo *ferrari_dino :* **and***(car, doors : { 2 }), body-type : { coupe }).*

L_{LILOG} offers several built-in functions for the arithmetic operations. Thus the following functions are part of any knowledge base:

    function *(integer + integer) → integer.*
    function *(integer − integer) → integer.*
    function *(integer * integer) → integer.*
    function *(integer / integer) → integer.*
    function *− (integer) → integer.*

Since in L_{LILOG} we may have data domains containing sets over a certain base set as elements, we would like to be able to form unions of these sets or to create the set containing two elements of the base set. This is the idea behind the following built-in function:

    function *(top* & top*) → top⁺.*

The sort expression *top** abbreviates the union **or***(top, top⁺)* which is the top element of the entire lattice of sort expressions over a knowledge base. For example, the function & can be used to form the set *john & mary*, which is a set-object of the type *person* ⁺ and contains the two elements *john* and *mary*.

2.1.3 Predicate Declarations

A predicate declaration

> **predicate** R *(argname$_1$: se$_1$, ..., argname$_n$: se$_n$).*

appearing in a L$_{\text{LILOG}}$ knowledge base tells us that we have an arbitrary relation named R between the sets interpreting the sort expressions se_i, where there is no functional dependency between the arguments of the predicates.

An important predicate that should occur in any knowledge base on traveling is the following:

> **predicate** *travel (who : person*, fr : location, to : location, with : vehicle).*

The declaration of the predicate *travel* states that a relation *travel* exists between the sorts *person**, *location*, and *vehicle* which can tell us who is traveling from where to where using which vehicle. By choosing the sort expression *person** we express that we want to speak about groups of traveling people as well as individual travelers in a uniform way.

Other candidates for relations are time schedules for planes, buses or trains relating the origin and destination of a transport vehicle plus the respective departure and arrival times.

> **predicate** *schedule (fr : location, departure : time, to : location,*
> *arrival : time, carrier : vehicle).*

Further built-in predicates available in any knowledge base are the comparison predicates between integers and an equality predicate.

In order to test the subset or membership relation between objects of the sort *top** we have the predicate

> **predicate** *(top** **in** *top*).*

made available as a built-in of L$_{\text{LILOG}}$. Using the constants *john* and *mary* of sort *person* and the union operator & we obtain that

> *mary* **in** *john* & *mary*

is true since *mary* is an element of the set *john* & *mary*. Also

> *mary* & *john* **in** *john* & *mary*

holds, because *john* & *mary* and *mary* & *john* denote the same set-object.

Finally we have a further collection of useful predicates which are available as built-ins of L$_{\text{LILOG}}$: the so-called sort-predicates. They could be declared as follows for each sort expression *se*:

> **predicate** { *se* } *(top*).*

Thus, we may use an arbitrary sort expression as a unary predicate. Using sort expressions as predicates we are able to state sort memberships that cannot be expressed in the declaration of constants, refos, or functions. This holds for example for conditional memberships like: "if somebody travels more than 50 000 miles per year he is a globetrotter", where *globetrotter* is a subsort of *person*.

> **sort** *globetrotter* < *person.*
> **sort** *year.*
> **predicate** *travels (who : person, distance : int, period : year).*
> **axiom** *globetrotters*
>   **forall** D *: distance,* P *: person,* Y *: year;*
>   *travels(period :* Y*, distance :* D*, who :* P*)*
>   **and** $D \geq$ *50 000*
> $\rightarrow$
>   { *globetrotter* } *(P).*

expressing that somebody is traveling from San Francisco to Los Angeles.

Introducing the first logical axioms is a good indicator for having completed the discussion of function and predicate declarations and for taking a more detailed look at the logical axioms that may occur in a knowledge base.

2.1.4   The Axioms of a Knowledge Base

The declarations of sorts, functions, and predicates we have discussed so far introduce the basic building blocks for formulating the logical axioms of a L$_{\text{LILOG}}$ knowledge base. As in any logic, the logical axioms express which objects of which sort are related by the relations (i.e., functions and predicates) declared within the knowledge base.

The expressive power of the axioms that may occur within a L$_{\text{LILOG}}$ knowledge base is that of full first-order predicate logic. Due to the knowledge based systems context for which L$_{\text{LILOG}}$ has been designed we have chosen a rule-oriented notation for the logical axioms of the following form:

axiom ⟨ *axiom-id* ⟩
⟨ *quantifications* ⟩;
⟨ *premise* ⟩
→
⟨ *conlusion* ⟩.

Thus every axiom has a name; next we have the quantifications introducing the variables occurring in the axiom together with the quantifiers to which the respective variables are bound. Both universal and existential quantifiers are offered; moreover default quantifiers are possible as well; see below for the discussion of how to handle defaults in L$_{\text{LILOG}}$. Then we have the body of an axiom which is basically an implication where the premise may be a conjunction of disjunctions of literals while the conclusion may be a disjunction of conjunctions of literals. Compared to the clausal form often used for logical formulas this is a moderate generalization which has the following advantages: (1) various quantifiers are available to the knowledge engineer, (2) writing the axioms as implications supports the 'what follows from what' intuition which is often used in the framework of operational logic, and (3) no normalizations (except skolemization) are necessary for processing these formulas as long as we use the model elimination calculus for generalized clauses, which is described in more detail in [Bollinger 1991] and [Bollinger *et al.* this volume].

This general structure of the logical axioms allows us to formulate ground facts like

axiom *john-and-mary-travel*
travel(who : john & mary, fr : los angeles, to : san francisco, with : porsche).

expressing that both John and Mary travel from Los Angeles to San Francisco with their Porsche, and rules like

axiom *group-member*
forall *M : person, G : person*, F, T : location, V : vehicle;*
travel(who : G, from : F, to : T, with : V) **and**
M **in** *G*
→
travel(who : M, from : F, to : T, with : V).

expressing that if a group of people travels with some vehicle any member of the group uses the same vehicle.

While the above two rules involved either no or only universal quantification, the concrete syntax of L$_{\text{LILOG}}$ also supports the use of the existential quantifier to formulate axioms like

axiom *lonely-traveler*
exists *P : person;*
travel(who : P, from : san francisco, to : los angeles, with : porsche).

Defaults in L$_{\text{LILOG}}$

The quantifications appearing in the axioms of a knowledge base are also the means to formulate default knowledge. The basic idea behind this approach is that a default proposition can be seen as a special form of universally quantified formula stating that the proposition doesn't hold strictly for every object of the sort of the quantified variable but rather permits exceptions.

Assuming a predicate

   predicate *uses (who : person, which : road).*

and reference objects

   refo *highway-1 : road.*
   refo *highway-101 : road.*

we can state that people typically use either Highway 1 or Highway 101 when going from San Francisco to Los Angeles by the following axiom involving a default quantification:

   axiom *typical-route*
      o_**default** *P : person,* **forall** *V : vehicle;*
      travel(who : P, from : san francisco, to : los angeles, with : V)
      →
      uses(who : P, which : highway-1) **or**
      uses(who : P, which : highway-101).

The quantification o_**default** *P : person* states that the axiom *typical-route* involves what we call an optimistic default. Applying an axiom containing optimistic default quantification does not trigger consistency checking (of the conclusions of the applied rules involving a default) immediately after the actual inference process. The more standard situation of performing the consistency check before the application of a rule can be specified by the so-called pessimistic defaults for which we foresee quantifications like p_**default** *P : person.* The effect of this differentiation is that the LILOG inference engine will use rules involving an optimistic default as if the corresponding variable had been universally quantified. Only when it becomes necessary to revise knowledge relying on default information, may formulas that have been derived using optimistic defaults be withdrawn, whereas this is not the case for formulas relying on hard information only. In [Lorenz 1990] the truth maintenance system which has been realized for handling this default reasoning approach in the LILOG inference engine is described. The pessimistic defaults behave like normal defaults where a default rule may only be applied in situations causing no contradictions (see, e.g., [Reiter 1980]). From an operational point of view this means that we have to verify that no contradiction occurs when performing an inference step involving a pessimistic default.

Furthermore, the default mechanism of L$_{\text{LILOG}}$ offers the concept of graded qualities of default knowledge, see [Lorenz 1990] and [Schlechta 1989]. While in the early approaches to nonmonotonic reasoning, the quality of knowledge relying on default information consisted only of the two degrees *hard* and *default* (cf. [McCarthy 1980], [Reiter 1980]) more recent approaches have implicitly suggested using an arbitrary partial ordering as the quality scale for the default knowledge (see, e.g., [Horty et al. 1987]). In our setting of an order-sorted logic it seems quite natural to use the partial ordering of the sort expressions as the scale for measuring the quality of default information described in L$_{\text{LILOG}}$ knowledge bases. The basic idea is that information involving smaller sorts is of higher quality than information stated for larger sorts.

The default reasoning concepts of L$_{\text{LILOG}}$ allow for elegant formulations of some typical puzzles which have become rather famous in the meantime: the question whether *tweety* can fly, and the question whether *nixon* is a pacifist.

Let us treat *tweety* first and assume we have the following knowledge entities in our knowledge base:

> **sort** *bird*.
> **sort** *large-bird* < *bird*.
> **predicate** *fly (bird)*.
> **refo** *tweety : large-bird*.
> **axiom** *flying-birds*
>   **p-default** *B : bird;*
>   *fly(B)*.
> **axiom** *non-flying-birds*
>   **p-default** *LB : large-bird;*
>   **not** *fly(LB)*.

Then our knowledge implies both

> *fly(tweety)*

and

> ¬ *fly(tweety)*,

but since we have *large-bird* < *bird*, the information that *tweety* doesn't fly is of better quality than the information asserting that *tweety* flies. Such analyses of the quality of default information are performed by our truth maintenance system ([Lorenz 1990]). Therefore we don't run into an inconsistency because the TMS discards the worse information that tweety flies.

Of course, life is not always that easy since the sort hierarchy of a L_{LILOG} knowledge base is not a total but a partial ordering. Taking a partial ordering as the quality scale for default information faces us with the problem of what to do with inconsistent statements, the quality of which is incomparable with respect to the underlying sort hierarchy. This is discussed in the framework of the Nixon diamond formulated in L_{LILOG} below.

> **sort** *quaker*.
> **sort** *republican*.
> **sort** *pacifist*.
> **refo** *nixon : **and**(quaker, republican)*.
> **axiom** *peaceful quakers*
>   **p-default** *Q : quaker;*
>   *pacifist(Q)*.
> **axiom** *brave republicans*
>   **p-default** *Q : republican;*
>   **not** *pacifist(Q)*.

Since *nixon* is both a *quaker* and a *republican* we obtain both *pacifist(nixon)* and ¬ *pacifist(nixon)*. Because the default information leading to this contradiction is of incomparable quality we will take a sceptical approach and believe neither in *nixon* being a pacifist nor in *nixon* not being a pacifist. For a more detailed discussion of the concepts of nonmonotonicity be(com)ing part of L_{LILOG} see [Lorenz 1990] and [Schlechta 1989].

Controlling Inferences in L_{LILOG}

As L_{LILOG} is implemented by an inference engine interpreting the language (see [Bollinger and Pletat 1991] and [Bollinger *et al.* this volume]), we, like any other theorem prover, face the problem of having to traverse large search spaces. In the natural language understanding context of LEU/2 the size of these search spaces results not so much from the depth of the proofs to be performed, but instead from the fact that we have to deal with large knowledge bases: the background knowledge base of LEU/2 consists for example of about 600 sort declarations together with about 300 facts and rules. Thus, means for excluding parts of the axiomatic knowledge for certain inference tasks are welcome.

The application of L$_{\text{LILOG}}$ in the natural language understanding framework suggests performing both forward and backward chaining tasks over a knowledge base. This is due to the two operation modes of the LEU/2 system: when texts have to be understood by the system, we want to draw conclusions from the information contained in the texts with respect to the background knowledge provided to LEU/2. This is a typical situation where the forward chaining mode of the inference engine is the main inference task to be used. In many situations we know in advance that only specific axioms of the knowledge base will/should be used for these forward chaining tasks.

Analogously, we can say the same about the backward chaining reasoning mode, i.e., there are certain axioms in the knowledge base of which the knowledge engineer knows in advance that they will/should only be used in the problem solving mode, which is the basic inference task when questions about the contents of texts have to be answered by LEU/2.

This gives us two classes of axioms within a knowledge base:

1. Axioms to be applied for knowledge base extension, i.e., in the forward chaining mode of the inference engine;

2. Axioms to be applied for problem solving, i.e., in the backward chaining mode of the inference engine.

Of course, these two classes of axioms need not be disjoint. The technical concept for qualifying axioms to be relevant for backward or forward inferences are the *entrypoints* which may be attached to the literals occurring in an axiom. In order to make an axiom available to forward chaining tasks one of the literals in the premise of the axiom must be tagged with an entrypoint. The backward chaining tasks may use all axioms in which either no entrypoint occurs or where an entrypoint is provided for one of the literals in the conclusion. Axioms that may be used both for forward and backward chaining tasks have to have literals tagged with entrypoints both in their premise and their conclusion.

To illustrate the effect of marking literals by entrypoints we want to return to our axiom *group-member* from above.

> **axiom** *group-member-bwc*
> **forall** *M : person, G : person*, F, T : location, V : vehicle;*
> *travel(who : G, from : F, to : T, with : V)* **and**
> *M* in *G*
> $\rightarrow$
> *EP travel(who : M, from : F, to : T, with : V).*

The entrypoint specified for the literal

> *travel(who : M, from : F, to : T, with : V)*

qualifies the axiom *group-member-bwc* as one to be used for backward inferences only.

By placing an entrypoint on a literal in the premise of the axiom we can qualify it to be usable in forward inferences.

> **axiom** *group-member-fwc*
> **forall** *M : person, G : person*, F, T : location, V : vehicle;*
> *EP travel(who : G, from : F, to : T, with : V)* **and**
> *M* in *G*
> $\rightarrow$
> *travel(who : M, from : F, to : T, with : V).*

The entrypoint specified for the literal

travel(who : G, from : F, to : T, with : V)

makes the axiom available for forward inferences which have been triggered by a formula containing a literal that unifies with the labeled literal. Thus we may use the axiom

axiom *john-and-mary-travel*
  travel(who : john & mary, fr : los angeles, to : san francisco, with : porsche).

as a trigger formula and derive that both John and Mary travel from Los Angeles to San Francisco by means of forward inferences. Note that the formula *group-member-fwc* is blocked for application in forward chaining mode.

The second means for controlling the inference engine is to delegate inference steps to an external deductive component. In particular this means that in L$_{\text{LILOG}}$ we are able to state that certain literals shall be evaluated outside the theorem prover interpreting L$_{\text{LILOG}}$. Currently there is only one such external reasoner being supported: the depiction module for processing spatial information on the basis of cell matrices, see [Khenkhar 1989] and [Habel this volume]. The depiction module is a special evaluator for predicates (appearing in literals) like *close-to...* defining when some object is located close to another one. Typical invocations of the depiction module look like

depic *close-to(what-is : church, close-to-what : bicycle)*

and indicate a switch from the theorem prover to the depiction module to have the above literal processed there. A literal can be processed externally in two ways, corresponding to the basic inference modes of knowledge base extension and problem solving:

1. In the imagination mode the depiction module is provided with some literal and extends its internal knowledge base with the information given by the literal. This corresponds to knowledge base extension, and whenever a depic-literal like the one above appears in the conclusion of an axiom the imagination mode of the depiction module is triggered with this literal.
   This general idea behind the imagination mode of the depictional reasoner is illustrated by the axiom below:

   axiom *bike-and-church*
     forall *B : bicycle, C : church;*
     EP distance(between-object1 : B, and-object2 : C) ≤ 1m
       →
     depic *close-to(what-is : B, close-to-what : C).*

   When the axiom will be processed by the inference engine, it causes the depiction module to store the fact that a bicycle is close to a church whenever it is possible to prove that the distance between the bicycle and the church is less than one meter. What we can see from this axiom is that its application only makes sense in a forward reasoning mode, which is why we qualify the rule to be only applicable in forward chaining tasks by placing an entrypoint on the premise of the axiom.

2. The inspection mode of the depiction module corresponds to the problem solving inference task. Whenever the inference engine has to process a depic literal in backward chaining mode it does not search the set of axioms for a complementary literal in order to make a 'classical' resolution step over that literal. Instead of this, the literal is passed to the depiction module in order to verify it and to return substitutions as the solution for that literal to the theorem prover.
   For the goal formula below this means that the inference engine will delegate the finding of a solution to the depictional reasoner and not try to solve the goal according to the knowledge in the propositional knowledge base.

goal *what-is-close-to-what*
  exists *OB1 : object, OB2 : object;*
  ?- **depic** *close-to(what-is : OB1, close-to-what : OB2).*

Summarizing, the axiomatic part of a L$_{\text{LILOG}}$ knowledge base allows us to formulate the logical relationships between the objects of a knowledge base in a rather sophisticated way. The generalized clausal form in which axioms may be presented supports the 'what follows from what' intuition that has proven very sucsessful in languages like PROLOG and other rule-based programming languages for knowledge based systems. Moreover, the default logic as well as the means of controlling the inference processes can be used with little notational overhead and should have a clear intuition behind it.

3 Modularizing Knowledge in L$_{\text{LILOG}}$

The L$_{\text{LILOG}}$ knowledge base containing the background knowledge of LEU/2 has reached a size where it becomes reasonable to separate it into several modules dealing with specific aspects of the encoded knowledge. This experience has arisen from the development of LEU/2. Other projects emphasizing the handling of large scale knowledge bases like CYC (see [Lenat 1990]) or MYCIN (cf. [Buchanan and Shortliffe 1985]) have not developed structuring for their knowledge bases, although the amount of knowledge compiled within the corresponding systems would strongly suggest they should have done.

Thus, concepts for modularizing knowledge bases should become part of today's knowledge representation languages and should reach a level of indispensability that is common in modern procedural programming languages like Ada ([Manual 1981]) or Modula ([Wirth 1985]).

The purpose of this final section about L$_{\text{LILOG}}$ is to give a rough sketch of the module concept we have proposed for L$_{\text{LILOG}}$. A detailed description of this approach to modularizing knowledge has been provided in [Pletat 1991] where we define the formal semantics of the module concept employing techniques known from the area of formal software specification, cf. [Goguen *et al.* 1978], [Ehrig and Mahr 1985], or [Goguen and Burstall 1984].

The basic idea behind the module concept we suggest for L$_{\text{LILOG}}$ is to consider a knowledge base as a collection of modules which communicate their knowledge via export and import interfaces. Thus, each such module consists of three parts:

1. Its import interface, stating which knowledge is imported from other modules,

2. Its export interface, stating which knowledge is offered to other modules, and

3. Its body, defining the local knowledge of the module where knowledge imported from other modules may be reused.

To give an idea what the module concept looks like we will present some small modules which contain knowledge described in the examples of the previous section. This will lead to a knowledge base consisting of three modules:

TRAVELING = { PERSON, VEHICLE, TRAVEL }.

In the module PERSON we collect the knowledge items concerning people. The sort *sexes* has become a **local sort** of the module because it is not exported. It serves only for deriving the sorts *man* and *woman* from the sort *person* via the internal feature *sex* and the atoms *female* and *male*.

```
module PERSON
exports
    sort person.
    sort man.
    sort woman.
    feature age : person → integer.
    constant mary : woman.
    constant john : man.
body
    sort sexes < top;
        atoms female, male.
    sort person < top;
        features age : → integer;
                sex : → sexes.
    sort woman = sex : { female }.
    sort man = sex : { male }.
    constant mary : woman.
    constant john : man.

end module
```

The exported *declarative knowledge items* of a module (the three sorts, the feature, and the two constants in the above case) are a module's contribution to the *public knowledge* within a modularized knowledge base.

All the inferencing that may be performed with respect to a modularized knowledge base must refer to the public knowledge of its modules. To be more precise, this means that any logical inference task (as such we consider subsumption checks between sort expressions, and deductions of goal queries having the form of conjunctions of literals) submitted to some module must contain only symbols of the public knowledge exported by some module. If substitutions of terms for variables have been computed as answers to a goal query, these substitutions are only acceptable as solutions if they contain only symbols exported by the module with respect to which the query has been posed.

Thus we have to take into account that *inference tasks* that can be submitted to a module, and *solutions* which can be returned from it may not be *well-formed with respect to the interface* of the module. Such ill-formed queries will simply be rejected, while we have to be a bit more inventive for handling hidden solutions that don't fit the interface (see below).

The above restriction reflects a trivial principle of communication: I can only talk to someone if we use a language common to both of us; and the common language of a module and its users is determined by the symbols of the export interface of the module.

The knowledge formulated within a module can be accessed by submitting a logical inference task (as such we consider subsumption checks for sort expressions or proving a goal formula) to the module. The query submitted to a module must be formed using only symbols exported by that module.

Considering the module PERSON we know so far, we could submit a subsumption checking inference task to it such as

$$woman \sqcap man \ll_{PERSON} \bot$$

and we obtain the answer *yes* because the definitions of the sorts *man* and *woman* in the module body make them disjoint and the L$_{LILOG}$ semantics for modules reflects all the semantic properties of knowledge items defined in the body at the export interface of a module, see [Pletat 1991].

The goal query

$$?\text{-}_{PERSON}\ \textbf{exists}\ X : sexes;\ sex(John) = X$$

will be rejected by the module PERSON since it refers to the knowledge items *sexes* and *sex* which are only available inside the module body and do not belong to the public knowledge contributed by the module.

However, we may query the age of Mary by

$$\text{?-}_{PERSON} \textbf{ exists} : integer; \ age(mary) = X$$

which would be answered by $X \leftarrow 27$ because we consider the sort integer and all its atoms (which are the numbers) as built-in and thus as part of any module interface.

The module VEHICLE below imports the sort *person* from the module PERSON in order to define the role *driver* for the sort *vehicle*. Because we want to export the constant *ferrari_dino*, the sort *vehicle* and its features *wheels* and *doors* have to be exported as well because otherwise **and***(car, doors : { 2 }), body : { coupe }* is not a valid sort expression of the export interface. In general this means that the following closure property has to hold for the export interface of a module: we have to export as many knowledge items as we need to make the export interface an (unstructured) knowledge base. Thus the sort *vehicle* has to be exported together with the features *body* and *doors* due to this closure condition. (A sophisticated concrete syntax should of course require to export only the *ferrari_dino* explicitly, even without the type information attached to it; completing the information about the exported knowledge items could be the job of a clever compiler.)

```
module VEHICLE
imports from PERSON :
    sort person.
exports
    sort vehicle.
    sort body-type.
    atom coupe : body-type.
    feature body : vehicle → body-type.
    feature doors : vehicle → integer.
        role driver :: person.
    sort car.
    sort plane.
    refo ferrari_dino : and(car, doors : { 2 }), body : { coupe }).
    constant boeing_747 : plane.
body
    sort vehicle < top;
        features wheels : → [ 0 .. 256 ],
                 doors : → [ 0 .. 256 ],
                 type : → vehicle-type,
                 body : → body-type;
        roles driver :: person.
    sort vehicle-type < top;
        atoms bike, boat, car, plane, train.
    sort body-type;
        atoms cabrio, coupe, hatchback, sedan.
    sort plane = type : { plane }.
    sort car = and(wheels : {4}, doors : {2, 3, 4, 5}, type : { car });
        features body : body-type.
    constant porsche_911 : and(car, doors : { 2 }), body : { cabrio }).
    refo ferrari_dino : and(car, doors : { 2 }), body : { coupe }).
    constant boeing_747 : plane.

end module
```

According to the export interface of our module *VEHICLE* we may submit the query

?- *VEHICLE* **exists** *V : vehicle;doors(V) = 2*

to the module VEHICLE asking it about all vehicles having 2 doors. The only answer we obtain is the *ferrari_dino* because the *porsche_911* has not been exported and no term equivalent to the *porsche_911* can be formed using only symbols exported by the module VEHICLE. That is, the module is not allowed to communicate the other vehicle it knows to have two doors because this Porsche is what we would like to call a *hidden solution*.

The last module TRAVEL uses both the modules we have introduced above and we thus obtain the following module hierarchy reflecting the export/import relationship between the three modules:

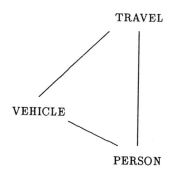

Figure 1: The hierachy of knowledge base modules TRAVELING

module TRAVEL
imports from PERSON :
    sort *person.*
    sort *man.*
    sort *woman.*
    constant *mary : woman.*
imports from VEHICLE :
    sort *vehicle.*
    sort *plane.*
    sort *car.*
    feature *wheels :* → [*0 .. 256*].
    feature *doors :* → [*0 .. 256*].
    role *driver :: person.*
    refo *ferrari_dino :* **and***(car, doors : { 2 }), body : { coupe }.*
exports
    sort *location.*
    sort *plane.*
    predicate *travel : (who : person, fr : location, to : location, with : vehicle).*
    constant *berlin : location.*
    constant *brussels : location.*

constant *milano : location.*
constant *paris : location.*
constant *boeing_747 : plane.*
constant *john : man.*
role *driver :: person.*
body
    sort *location.*
    predicate *travel : (who : person, fr : location, to : location, with : vehicle).*
    function *distance : (between : location, and : location) → integer.*
    constant *berlin : location.*
    constant *brussels : location.*
    constant *milano : location.*
    constant *paris : location.*
    axiom *long-distance-trips*
      forall *P : Person, F, T : Location, V : Vehicle;*
      travel(who : P, fr : F, to : T, with : V) **and**
      distance(between : F, and : T) > 1000
       →
      plane (V).
    axiom *short-distance-trips*
      forall *P : person, F, T : location, V : vehicle;*
      travel(who : P, fr : F, to : T, with : V) **and**
      distance(between : F, and : T) < 500
       →
      car(V).
    axiom *medium-distance-trips*
      forall *P : person, F, T : location, V : vehicle, D : int;*
      travel(who : P, fr : F, to : T, with : V) **and**
      distance(between : F, and : T) = D **and**
      $D \geq 500$ **and** $D \leq 1000$
       →
      plane(V) **or** *car(V).*
    axiom *mary-goes-by-car*
      forall *F, T : Location, V : Vehicle;*
      travel(who : mary, fr : F, to : T, with : V) **and**
      distance(between : F, and : T) ≤ 1000
       →
      car(V).
    axiom *mary's-vehicles*
      exists *V1, V2 : Vehicle;*
      travel(who : mary, fr : paris, to : brussels, with : V1) **and**
      travel(who : mary, fr : paris, to : milano, with : ferrari_dino) **and**
      travel(who : mary, fr : paris, to : berlin, with : V2).
    axiom *distances*
      distance(between : paris, and : brussels) = 300 **and**
      distance(between : paris, and : milano) = 800 **and**
      distance(between : paris, and : berlin) = 1100.
end module

The axioms tell us that small trips of less than 500 kilometers are made by car, planes are used for long distance trips of more than 1000 kilometers, while medium distance trips can either be made by car or by plane. The literals *car(V)* and *plane(V)* used for expressing this are further applications of the sort literals in which sort expressions may be used to express that the argument term belongs to the set described by the sort expression.

Mary is a passionate car driver and she uses cars unless she has to make a big trip. Moreover, she uses her favourite *ferrari_dino* when going from Paris to Milano while for other trips she doesn't care which vehicle she uses. These ideas have been modeled in the axiom telling us about Mary's trips. The last axioms just state some distances and that John is the pilot of the Boeing 747.

To process the module the existentially quantified variables of the axiom *mary's-vehicles* will be skolemized and the Skolem functions will become local functions of the module. For our example this means that we obtain two Skolem constants *sc1* and *sc2* of the sort *vehicle* replacing the variables *V1* and *V2*, respectively.
Querying the module TRAVEL

> ?- TRAVEL **exists** *V : vehicle; travel(who : mary, fr : paris, to : berlin, with : V).*

we obtain *yes* as the answer, because there is a vehicle taking Mary from Paris to Berlin, but this vehicle (represented by a Skolem constant) is only locally known inside the module and may not be communicated to the outside world. Here we have the effect that the solution (a substitution) is not well-formed with respect to the export interface of the module TRAVEL although the validity of the goal formula is not affected.

In contrast to the above query the following goal

> ?- TRAVEL **exists** *V : vehicle; travel(who : mary, fr : paris, to : milano, with : V).*

has the solution *V ← ferrari_dino*, because the constant has been exported.

The last aspect of the module concept to be discussed here is the autonomy of modules. In the module VEHICLE we introduced and exported the sort *plane*; due to our sort literals, we may submit the following query to the module:

> ?- VEHICLE **exists** *P : person, V : vehicle; driver(V, P).*

and ask it who is the driver of which vehicle. The answer will, of course, be *No solution found* since no such information is provided in the module *VEHICLE*.
If we submit the same query to the module TRAVEL

> ?- TRAVEL **exists** *P : person, V : vehicle; driver(V, P).*

we obtain the answer *P ← john, V ← boeing_747* because a corresponding ground fact is available in the module TRAVEL while it is unknown in the module VEHICLE.

The autonomy of the modules is given according to the phenomenon that different modules may produce different answers to identical queries. This may be desirable in certain situations, while in others it may not be what one wants. The module concept should offer a mechanism allowing us to specify (and assure) that certain pieces of knowledge which are imported by a module should not be modified in its body. In the world of formal software specification, such *import protections* can be formulated by means of so-called constraints (cf. [Goguen and Burstall 1984], [Ehrig and Mahr 1990]. In [Pletat 1991] we have introduced such a concept allowing us to specify that the knowledge imported from some module must not be modified by the importing module.

4   Conclusion

The knowledge representation language L$_{\text{LILOG}}$ can be characterized as a typed predicate logic offering a rich sort concept, defaults, and the possibility to control inference processes. Although the current major application of L$_{\text{LILOG}}$ is the natural language understanding framework of the LILOG project, the concepts of the language are general enough to use it also for other applications of knowledge based systems.

The current stage of development the knowledge representation language L_{LILOG} should not be considered as a final state. We are thinking of several enhancements: the module concept for L_{LILOG} as described here and formally defined in [Pletat 1991] will become part of the implementation of L_{LILOG}. Thus well-established ideas known from languages like Modula ([Wirth 1985]) or Ada ([Manual 1981]) will become available for knowledge representation based on L_{LILOG}. Moreover, it has turned out during the development of the LEU/2 knowledge base that a polymorphic type concept (cf. [Gordon et al. 1978] or [Cardelli and Wegner 1985]) can be useful for several modeling situations.

The concepts underlying L_{LILOG} have enough potential to make the language the logical basis of a general purpose knowledge representation system. The inference engine for L_{LILOG} together with the other components that have to be considered as part of the implementation of L_{LILOG} (the L_{LILOG} compiler generating the internal representations on which the inference engine operates, the LILOG data base system we use for storing the compiled code of our knowledge bases, and the knowledge engineering tools supporting the development of L_{LILOG} knowledge bases) could then form an advanced programming environment for knowledge based systems.

References

[Björner and Jones 1978] Björner, D. and Jones, C. B., editors. *The Vienna Development Method: The Meta-Language*, volume 61 of *Lecture Notes in Computer Science*. Springer Verlag, Berlin, Heidelberg, New York, 1978.

[Bollinger and Pletat 1991] Bollinger, T. and Pletat, U. Knowledge in Operation. IWBS Report 165, IBM Deutschland, 1991.

[Bollinger et al. this volume] Bollinger, T., Lorenz, S., and Pletat, U. The LILOG inference engine. In *Text Understanding in LILOG: Integrating Computational Linguistics and Artificial Intelligence*, Lecture Notes in Artificial Intelligence. Springer-Verlag, Berlin, Heidelberg, New York, this volume.

[Bollinger 1991] Bollinger, T. A Model Elimination Calculus for Generalized Clauses. In *Proceedings IJCAI 91*, 1991.

[Bouma et al. 1988] Bouma, G., Koenig, E., and Uszkoreit, H. A flexible graph-unification formalism and its application to natural-language processing. *IBM Journal of Research and Development*, 32(2):170–184, March 1988.

[Brachman and Levesque 1985] Brachman, R. J. and Levesque, H. J., editors. *Readings in Knowledge Representation*. Morgan Kaufmann, Los Altos, Cal., 1985.

[Brachman and Schmolze 1985a] Brachman, R. J. and Schmolze, J. G. An overview of the KL-ONE knowledge representation system. *Cognitive Science*, 9(2):171–216, April 1985.

[Brachman and Schmolze 1985b] Brachman, R. J. and Schmolze, J. G. An overview of the KL-ONE knowledge representation system. *Cognitive Science*, 9(2):171–216, April 1985.

[Brachman et al. 1985] Brachman, R. J., Gilbert, V. P., and Levesque, H. J. An Essential Hybrid Reasoning, System: Knowledge and Symbol Level Accounts of KRYPTON. In *Proceedings IJCAI-85*, pages 532–539, 1985.

[Buchanan and Shortliffe 1985] Buchanan, B. G. and Shortliffe, E. H., editors. *Rule-Based Expert Systems*. Addison-Wesley, Reading, Massachusetts, 1985.

[C. Beierle and J. Dörre and U. Pletat and C.-R. Rollinger and R. Studer] C. Beierle and J. Dörre and U. Pletat and C.-R. Rollinger and R. Studer. The knowledge representation language L-LILOG. In E. Börger and H. Kleine Büning and M. M. Richter, editor, *CSL'88 - 2nd Workshop on Computer Science Logic. Lecture Notes in Computer Science, Volume 385*, volume 385 of *Lecture Notes in Computer Science*, pages 14–51. Springer-Verlag, Berlin, Heidelberg, New York, 1989.

[Cardelli and Wegner 1985] Cardelli, L. and Wegner, P. On Understanding Types, Data Abstraction and Polymorphism. *Computing Surveys*, 17(4):471–522, December 1985.

[Dörre and Seiffert this volume] Dörre, J. and Seiffert, R. STUF - A formalizm for natural language. In *Text Understanding in LILOG: Integrating Computational Linguistics and Artificial Intelligence*, Lecture Notes in Artificial Intelligence. Springer-Verlag, Berlin, Heidelberg, New York, this volume.

[Ehrig and Mahr 1985] Ehrig, H. and Mahr, B. *Fundamentals of Algebraic Specification 1 - Equations and Initial Semantics*. EATCS Monographs on Theoretical Computer Science. Volume 6, Springer-Verlag, Berlin, Heidelberg, New York, 1985.

[Ehrig and Mahr 1990] Ehrig, H. and Mahr, B. *Fundamentals of Algebraic Specification 2 - Module Specifications and Constraints*. EATCS Monographs on Theoretical Computer Science. Volume 21, Springer-Verlag, Berlin, Heidelberg, New York, 1990.

[Ginsberg 1987] Ginsberg, M. L., editor. *Readings in Nonmonotonic Reasoning*. Morgan Kaufmann, Los Altos, Cal., 1987.

[Goguen and Burstall 1984] Goguen, J. and Burstall, R. Introducing institutions. In Clarke, E. and Kozen, D., editors, *Proceedings, Logics of Programming Workshop*, volume 164 of *Lectures Notes in Computer Science*, pages 221–256, Berlin, Heidelberg, New York, 1984. Springer-Verlag.

[Goguen *et al.* 1978] Goguen, Joseph A., Thatcher, James W., and Wagner, Eric G. An initial algebra approach to the specification, correctness and implementation of abstract data types. In Yeh, R., editor, *Current Trends in Programming Methodology IV: Data and Structuring*, pages 80–144. Prentice Hall, 1978.

[Gordon *et al.* 1978] Gordon, M., Milner, R., and Wadsworth, C. *Edinburgh LCF*, volume 78 of *Lecture Notes in COmputer Science*. Springer Verlag, Heidelberg, 1978.

[Habel this volume] Habel, C. Processing of spatial expressions in LILOG. In *Text Understanding in LILOG: Integrating Computational Linguistics and Artificial Intelligence*, Lecture Notes in Artificial Intelligence. Springer-Verlag, Berlin, Heidelberg, New York, this volume.

[Horty *et al.* 1987] Horty, J. F., Thomason, R. H., and Touretzky, D. S. A sceptical theory of onheritance in semantic networks. In *Proceedings of the 6th National Conference of the American Association for Artificial Intelligence*, 1987.

[Jensen and Wirth 1975] Jensen, K. and Wirth, N. *PASCAL : User Manual and Report*. Springer Verlag, Heidelberg, 1975.

[Kasper and Rounds 1986] Kasper, R. T. and Rounds, W. C. A logical semantics for feature structures. In *Proceedings of the 24th Annual Meeting of the Association for Computational Linguistics*, pages 257–265, Columbia University, New York, 1986.

[Khenkhar 1989] Khenkhar, M. N. DEPIC-2D: Eine Komponente zur depiktionalen Repräsentation und Verarbeitung räumlichen Wissens. In Metzing, D., editor, *GWAI-89. 13th German Workshop on Artificial Intelligence*, pages 318–322. Springer, Berlin, West Germany, 1989.

[Klose and von Luck this volume] Klose, G. and Luck, K. von. The representation of knowledge in LILOG. In *Text Understanding in LILOG: Integrating Computational Linguistics and Artificial Intelligence*, Lecture Notes in Artificial Intelligence. Springer-Verlag, Berlin, Heidelberg, New York, this volume.

[Lenat 1990] Lenat, D. CYC : Toward Programs with Common Sense. *Communications of The ACM*, 33, 1990.

[Lorenz 1990] Lorenz, S. Nichtmonotones Schließen mit ordnungssortierten Defaults. IWBS-Report 100, IBM Deutschland, Scientific Center, January 1990.

[Manual 1981] Manual, ADA Reference. *The Programming Language ADA*. Springer Verlag, Berlin, Heidelberg, New York, 1981.

[McCarthy 1980] McCarthy, J. Circumscription—a form of non-monotonic reasoning. *Artificial Intelligence*, 13(1–2):27–39, 1980.

[Oberschelp 1962] Oberschelp, A. Untersuchungen zur mehrsortigen Quantorenlogik. *Mathematische Annalen*, 145:297–333, 1962.

[Pereira and Shieber 1984] Pereira, F. and Shieber, S. M. The Semantics of Grammar Formalisms seen as Computer Languages. In *Proceedings of 10th International Conference on Computational Linguistics*, pages 123–129, Stanford, 1984.

[Pletat and v. Luck 1990] Pletat, U. and Luck, K. v. Knowledge Representation in LILOG. In K. H. Bläsius and U. Hedtstück and C.-R. Rollinger, editor, *Sorts and Types for Artificial Intelligence*, volume 449 of *Lecture Notes in Artificial Intelligence*. Springer-Verlag, Berlin, Heidelberg, New York, 1990.

[Pletat 1991] Pletat, U. Modularizing knowledge in L$_{LILOG}$. IWBS Report 173, IBM Deutschland, 1991.

[Reiter 1980] Reiter, Raymond. A logic for default reasoning. *Artificial Intelligence*, 13(1):81–132, April 1980.

[Schlechta 1989] Schlechta, K. Defeasible Inheritance: Coherence Properties and Semantics. In Morreau, Michael, editor, *SNS-Bericht 89-47*. Seminar für natürlich-sprachliche Systeme, Univertsität Tübingen, 1989.

[Smolka 1988] Smolka, G. A Feature Logic with Subsorts. Lilog-report 33, IBM Deutschland GmbH, Stuttgart, 1988.

[Walther 1987] Walther, C. *A Many-Sorted Calculus Based on Resolution and Paramodulation*. Research Notes in Artificial Intelligence. Pitman, London, and Morgan Kaufmann, Los Altos, Calif., 1987.

[Wirth 1985] Wirth, N. *Programming in Modula 2*. Springer Verlag, Heidelberg, 1985.

Knowledge Packets and Knowledge Packet Structures

Ipke Wachsmuth, Barbara Gängler

1 Introduction

One of the most challenging tasks in knowledge representation for text-understanding systems is the development of large-scale knowledge bases containing semantic background knowledge. Many current knowledge-based systems restrict their applicational scope to narrow world domains, that is, they are equipped to handle domain-specific tasks by using domain-specific facts and rules. However, for the domain of text understanding this restriction appears to be unacceptable since the understanding of natural-language texts draws on a large background of diverse world knowledge and belief. Even if a knowledge-based system could be provided with a large body of world knowledge sufficiently rich to cover a broader domain of discourse, the problem of *using* this knowledge to build and utilize representations for natural language inputs might prove a serious one with respect to computational resources.

The experiences gained in the development of a LILOG text understanding system led to the conclusion that large-scale knowledge bases are unavoidable when more realistic application domains are modeled. In particular, the authors were involved in constructing the background rule knowledge base for the Düsseldorf tourist guide domain realized in the second LILOG experimental environment, LEU/2. Building upon about 600 sort declarations, this knowledge base incorporates about 300 axioms (rules) serving for different purposes. On the one hand, the information extracted from a natural language text by means of parsing and constructing a semantic representation (explicit text knowledge) needs to be elaborated and enriched by read-time inferences. On the other hand, question-time inferences are necessary in order to generate answers to queries by which the success of text understanding is demonstrated (Gängler, Wachsmuth 1991).

Some of the rules in the background knowledge base are *performance rules* which achieve the re-representation of situation-(verb-)centered semantic text representations by object-centered representations so that information about objects of interest can be more readily retrieved. Further performance rules were incorporated to give rise to a more flexible choice of wordings in queries. For example, it should be equally possible to ask at which date the construction of a church was "finished" or when it was "completed." Other rules are *elaborative rules* which make implicit text information explicit by enriching it through commonsense or specific domain knowledge. While in some cases longer chains of inference are necessary to achieve a coherent text representation, elaborative rules often bridge very short gaps. For example, when the text mentions that a particular church has a crooked spire, then the system should be able to infer that this church in fact has a spire (which is not true for all churches).

Since performance and elaborative rules in many cases perform tiny inference steps, the background knowledge base must include a quite enormous number of rules even when the scenario is relatively restricted. It was observed that the size of search spaces to be managed by the system results not so much from the depth of proofs to be performed, but results rather from the amount of memory search necessary when deeper text representations are constructed or when a query is answered. Even though an attempt was made to enhance the efficiency of the system by tailoring the rules, costly memory search often could not be avoided. More significantly, the more rules are incorporated, i.e. the more "knowledgeable" the system becomes, the larger becomes the body of knowledge elements to be screened.

The question arises whether there is a means for excluding parts of the axiomatic knowledge for certain inference tasks *by way of principle*. The experiences in furnishing domain-specific rules for the Düsseldorf domain showed that in many cases it was clear for which specific subaspect of the domain the particular rule was invented. In turn, it was clear in many cases which domain segment was relevant for finding an answer to a given query. Hence the set of possible rules of inference could be restricted if the relevant domain segment could be identified when processing a piece of text or a query. As a prerequisite for such a selective memory search procedure, the rule inventory needs to be structured in a modular fashion. It should be possible to build up and use portions of a knowledge base that pertain to subareas or subaspects of the general discourse domain. As far as possible these portions should be independent units which are organized in a way making access possible according to actual needs. That is, besides being concerned about the content of a background knowledge base, its *structure* needs particular attention as well as the *conditions for using* its knowledge.

This paper presents the general ideas which gave rise to our proposing modules of knowledge called *knowledge packets* and for specifying *knowledge packet structures* which establish usability conditions. To avoid any confusion it is noted that "module" is meant to refer to a component of a knowledge base, and it should not be confused with the notion of specialized systems dedicated to sensory and linguistic input analysis and to linguistic and motor output as in (Fodor 1983) and (Garfield 1987). Further it should be understood that "module" does not refer to a single propositional statement (fact or rule) but rather to a set of statements that "belong together" in a certain respect. The basic idea of knowledge packets was first introduced in (Wachsmuth 1987). It is grounded on findings from empirical research which suggest that the domain knowledge accumulated by humans is grouped in such a way that subbodies perceived to be relevant in a given situation can be separated out. These findings were elaborated toward an abstract specification for a modular knowledge representation scheme that provides a clear and formal basis for handling problems of consistency and accessibility of domain-specific knowledge (Wachsmuth 1989b).

In the following section we discuss a number of demands to be recognized for the conception of modular knowledge bases. In the third section a brief summary of an empirical study is given from which basic ideas of human knowledge organization can be drawn. As the main part of this paper, the fourth section presents principles of domain-oriented knowledge structuring (the "DOKS principles") which were elaborated from the empirical findings. The core ideas of how these principles can be related to modular knowledge base development and some implications are discussed in the final section.

2 Modular Knowledge Bases

The need for explicit consideration of large and diverse knowledge bases and the question of how to modularize them is finding increasing attention (Wachsmuth 1989a; Prerau et al. 1990; Wachsmuth, Meyer-Fujara 1990; Pletat 1991). The question of how to grasp a module concept for a knowledge representation language is rather straightforward, though a number of technical questions remain to be dealt with (cf. Pletat, in this volume). Principles from the area of formal software specification suggest that each knowledge base module consist of an export and an import interface and a module body. A mathematically precise definition of the syntax and semantics of L_{LILOG} which includes the basis for such module definitions is given in (Pletat 1991). As will be motivated below, the semantics of these module definitions should imply that the modules of a modular knowledge base are basically autonomous knowledge bases which may even deliver different answers to the same logical query, depending on the actual context or view.

While categories of classical software engineering do seem relevant in constructing a large knowledge-based software system, fundamental questions need to be answered that concern the question of how knowledge (not programs) can be perceived in a modular fashion. There are many possible ways in which particular modules may be interrelated in terms of exporting and importing knowledge among each other, and the question has not been solved on principle in which way a knowledge base in a given application domain is to be structured in modules. The modularity of a domain knowledge base cannot be defined solely in a way that is convenient for software development. The question is whether principles can be found, on the knowledge level, which give rise to a modular conception of a body of knowledge and which can guide the construction of modular knowledge bases. Such principles should account for quite a diverse set of demands as listed below:

- **(Alternative) views on a knowledge base:** It should be possible to consider partitions of a background knowledge base that can be asserted selectively and by this support context-dependent answers (e.g., Hendrix 1979);

- **Elaboration tolerance:** When a knowledge base is elaborated through adding facts, formal reasoning gets slower because more axioms need to be screened. In contrast, human reasoning does not seem to undergo significant decrease in speed by the accumulation of more knowledge. John McCarthy made the point that, ideally, a reasoning process should not be altered or grow in length much when facts that should not affect that process are added to a knowledge base (cf. Lifschitz 1989);

- **Toleration of inconsistencies:** Deductive problem solving requires knowledge bases to be logically consistent. However, humans can successfully deal with their knowledge even though inconsistencies are possible and probably unavoidable (Minsky 1981);

- **Restriction of consistency proofs:** The question has been raised whether for broad knowledge bases the requirement of global consistency can be weakened such that consistency proofs are restricted to portions of a knowledge base that potentially interact during a problem-solving process (Lenat, Feigenbaum 1987);

- **Locality of reasoning:** When formalizing commonsense reasoning by including default information, McCarthy recommends that as much of the reasoning as possible should involve small numbers of facts, i.e., be kept "local" (cf. Lifschitz 1989);

- **Reduction of memory search:** With domain knowledge bases becoming richer, the problem of retrieving relevant facts from an excessive variety can hardly be ignored, for it involves the need to prevent the search from a possible combinatorial explosion (Minsky 1981);

- **Restricted reason maintenance:** When the validity of a conclusion can be traced to a limited set of facts, the expense of reason maintenance could possibly be reduced by recording dependencies with respect to that limited set instead of to the particular facts (to the authors' knowledge no such proposal has yet been made);

- **Transparency and maintainability:** An important aim is to make large knowledge bases more easily comprehensible and maintainable, in particular, when several developers are involved or when maintenance is to be carried out by users (e.g., Prerau et al. 1990). The point is especially relevant when different knowledge sources are incorporated in a knowledge base.

Thus, beside increasing efficiency by controlling inferences, there are a number of further reasons why a modular knowledge base design seems desirable. While the above points are not in all cases independent from one another, they illustrate different aspects to be kept in mind when thinking about design principles for modular knowledge bases.

3   The Empirical Basis

The ideas presented in this paper are grounded on findings from empirical research which gave rise to a basic understanding of how the knowledge that human beings possess is structured. As human beings have proven to take good advantage of quite an impressive body of knowledge, it seems well-motivated to observe findings from cognitive research. For example, Newell and Simon (1972) have used protocol analysis in order to elucidate general heuristics of intelligent problem solving. Rosch (1978) and Dahlgren (1985) have done empirical analyses of cognitive categories that can help to design ontologies for natural language understanding. The rationale for the research exploited here is that the observation of human intelligent behavior can help to find cognitive principles of knowledge organization. The study and its findings are described in detail in (Wachsmuth 1989b). Here we just give a rough sketch of what was done.

In a one-year clinical teaching experiment on the acquisition of mathematical knowledge (Post et al. 1985), a large body of interview data was acquired and analyzed to observe the genesis of domain-specific knowledge structures. During the whole period, the gradual development of selected students' ability to answer questions and deal with problems involving fractions was recorded. No propositional "products" such as rules were taught to the students. Instead, there was ample occasion for them to make observations and gain experience about how concepts in the chosen domain are interrelated. In the course of the study, students showed a strong tendency to abstract observations about the interrelation of concepts in conditional statements (rules). These were accumulated to the repertoire of things students know about, and know how to perform with, the conceptual entities in the field. Such rules were considered as representing belief particles making up the competence of individual subjects, as a potential for generating action (cp. Newell 1982).

For selected topics, the repertoire of rules subjects possessed by the end of the teaching experiment was identified from the interview data. As was evident from subjects' verbal explanations, they would recognize the applicability of a rule by matching rule conditions with task information. With respect to the questions addressed in this paper, the following issues were of interest: How is such a repertoire of domain-specific knowledge utilized in applied situations? Are all rules always attempted? Is full use of all resources always made? If there are any restrictions, what are their features and characteristics? Can they serve to extract general principles comprising a model of a modular representation of domain-specific knowledge? Of course, there is no way to observe structure in human knowledge other than through inferring it from subjects' behavior. To this end, several complex problem-solving tasks were presented toward the end of the teaching experiment. For success with these tasks, a coordinated use of rules from the repertoire the subjects had acquired was necessary.

In summary, evaluation of behavioral data from task-based interviews gave a strong indication that performance differences across subjects depended not only on the soundness of their rules but also on the way their rules appeared to be accessible. The crucial observation is that such pieces of domain-specific knowledge are not assembled as an unstructured collection but that larger structures evolve that reflect the context in which these rules are abstracted. Rules appear to be grouped in a way enabling subjects to separate out subbodies of domain-specific knowledge they perceive as relevant for use in a given task situation. By way of extrapolation, this observation could contribute to understanding the general problem-solving ability of human beings, namely, from their ability to access appropriate subbodies of knowledge based on clues from a task situation. It may also explain how one can act on the basis of an enormous repertoire of knowledge without getting confused by having to face all of it most of the time.

The findings of the study suggest that a critical feature of human intelligence lies in a dynamic partitioning of the total knowledge into "visible" and "invisible" parts such that the visible part is normally small enough to be tractable. Further findings show that the presence of certain concept words in a situation seems to trigger access to domain knowledge and further vocabulary associated with this knowledge. In turn, domain- and situation-specific word meanings seem to be mediated by association of concept words with portions of domain-specific knowledge.

Without going into details, the next section elaborates general principles characterizing those observations that seem relevant for structuring domain-specific knowledge. These principles aim at devising a way that allows large amounts of domain-dependent knowledge to be used by a knowledge-based system while keeping the system manageable. Each of the nine principles is motivated by certain empirical observations. Altogether, the principles are understood as an abstract specification rather than a symbol-level description for a representation scheme.

4 Domain-Oriented Knowledge Structuring

The central point in our proposal is that knowledge be structured in a way oriented at the domain. More precisely, admitting that much and important intellectual capability can be credited to domain-specific knowledge (Feigenbaum 1977), domain specificity is made the explicit target of structuring. This refers to different degrees of specificity as well as to different aspects in which a specific body of knowledge may branch to extend into specific subbodies. The principles of domain-oriented knowledge structuring, for short, the *DOKS principles* discussed in this section, are of a wider scope than solely for the area of natural language systems. However, for the reasons mentioned in the introduction, they are particularly relevant for natural language understanding and processing, and throughout this section we have chosen examples from this application area for illustration.

Adopting Newell's slogan equation, REPRESENTATION = KNOWLEDGE+ACCESS (Newell 1982) we will have to concern ourselves with (1) the organization of a body of knowledge "in a form that can be used to make selections of actions in the service of goals" and (2) the way particular parts of a structured body of knowledge are accessed such that they "can be used by the larger system that represents the knowledge about goals, actions etc." (all quotes see Newell 1982, p.114). We assume the knowledge base (KB) of a knowledge-based system (KBS) to be constituted by a set of identifiable statements each of which interrelates domain-specific concepts and asserts something held for true in a modeled world. Thus, we consider a collection of entities like logical sentences or production rules or any means-ends relations as givens which hereafter will be referred to by the term *knowledge elements*. A knowledge element could also be a structured term (e.g., a sort declaration with features and roles) describing an entity or a class of entities to which statements in a KB refer.

Overall, the DOKS principles specify a representational scheme for a KBS *abstractly*, without any commitment to particular programs. Additional structuring features of a syntactic nature might be brought in by a particular implementation, e.g., when representing a KB as a connection graph of first-order logical sentences (Kowalski 1975) or when using a restriction strategy like set-of-support for efficient theorem proving (Wos et al. 1984). As pointed out by Levesque and Brachman (1986) in elaborating on Newell's (1982) recommendations, such decisions concern an entirely separate issue that has been widely investigated in automated theorem proving.

The first three principles pertain to the way the knowledge elements are *organized* in a static knowledge base. This arrangement is viewed as permanent until an explicit change of the KB takes place. The other principles concern the way in which structured knowledge is *accessed* and made available to the knowledge-based system.

4.1 Organization of Knowledge

Principle of packing knowledge elements. Collections of knowledge elements that pertain to a specific domain of knowledge are comprised in a *packet*. We say the packet *owns* these knowledge elements. A packet may properly contain further packets of knowledge elements that constitute identifiable subbodies of more specific knowledge within the outer packet.

Principle of competitive knowledge. Collections of knowledge elements that concern alternative methods or views in a given domain of knowledge are packed separately within the surrounding packet. Such packets are referred to as *competitive*.

Principle of local consistency. The collection of knowledge elements in one packet must not permit conclusions that are contradictory (or actions that are incompatible). A packet P may only contain contradictory (or incompatible) knowledge elements if they are packed separately within P. A collection of knowledge elements satisfying this principle is called *locally consistent*.

The principle of packing knowledge elements is visualized in Figure 1. Within the most general packet P1, the packet P3 (or likewise P2) comprises more specific knowledge contained in P1 (thus, owned by both P3 and P1), with P4 being still more specific than P3. Consider for example P3 containing general knowledge about restaurants such as attributed features, opening-hours or date-of-origin. P4 might then contain specific knowledge about a special kind of restaurant, say, taverns. In general, the decision about what knowledge is considered more specific is a separate issue that involves domain modeling heuristics. A criterion for a knowledge element k to be "more specific" than those in a collection of knowledge elements $k_1,..., k_n$ could be that a reasonable body of problems can be dealt with without using k. "More specific" knowledge might also concern the question of how the more general knowledge around it is adapted to certain contexts.

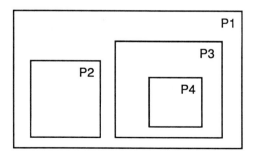

Figure 1

The intent of the principle of competitive knowledge is to make only one alternative, at a given time, available for use by the KBS as will be provided for by further principles describing static access conditions. In Figure 1, P2 and P3 (but not P3 and P4) depict competitive knowledge packets. For example, P2 may contain knowledge about sights and objects of interest whereas P3 could contain some information about restaurants.

The principle of local consistency reflects the fact that a method devised to guarantee global consistency can prove computationally intractable. The intent is to restrict consistency checks to packed subcollections of knowledge elements to be performed at any incremental augmentation of a KB. It would also allow "alternative worlds" to be modeled within a KB. According to this principle, P2 and P3 in Figure 1 may include inconsistent knowledge elements among them, but not so P3 and P4.

Imagine that P3 contains some knowledge about traffic, including information about streetcars as moving objects on which people are conveyed to a certain schedule, etc. In contrast, P2 might contain knowledge about objects of interest, including information about a streetcar as a *non-moving* object of historical and technical interest that could be seen in a museum. Conflicting implications would be possible depending on whether a streetcar is considered in Packet P2 or P3. The principle of local consistency tolerates such global inconsistencies as long as they are captured in separate knowledge packets.

The three principles of knowledge organization describe how a collection of knowledge elements can be structured by way of set containment. Though such a structure cannot be directly observed from the empirical findings, the structural principles are compatible with what was gleaned from the empirical data. We now proceed to describe how knowledge in a KB satisfying the above structuring principles is accessed. There will be static and dynamic access conditions.

4.2 Static Access Conditions

Principle of eligibility of knowledge elements. The knowledge elements owned by a packet P are conjointly eligible for use by the knowledge-based system when their packet P, or a packet within P, is tagged ACCESSED, *but only as far as they are not also owned by a packet contained within the one tagged* ACCESSED. We say a knowledge element (or a set of knowledge elements) eligible for use is VISIBLE. No knowledge elements packed separately from the packet tagged ACCESSED are eligible.

Principle of single access to packed knowledge. Only one packet at any given time may be tagged ACCESSED.

Principle of reachability of knowledge. When a knowledge packet P tagged ACCESSED owns knowledge elements that are also owned by a packet Q within P, then the set of knowledge elements in Q (or for simplicity, the packet Q) is REACHABLE. A collection of knowledge elements packed separately from the one tagged ACCESSED is NOT REACHABLE.

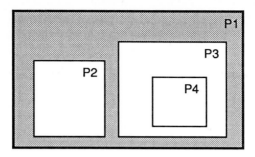

Figure 2a

In Figure 2a, the bold shading of P1 is used to depict that P1 is currently tagged ACCESSED. That is, the collection of knowledge elements that are in P1, but not in P2 or P3, are VISIBLE. In Figure 2b, P3 is tagged ACCESSED, that is, the knowledge elements in P3 and in the surrounding packet P1 are VISIBLE. The knowledge elements in P2 and P4 are not eligible for use by the KBS in the access condition shown.

For illustration, consider P1 containing some general knowledge stating that institutions are localized in buildings. In the access condition shown in Figure 2a only such general information about institutions is VISIBLE. Now think of P3 containing knowledge about restaurants. When P3 is tagged ACCESSED (as in Figure 2b) knowledge about restaurants in P3 is VISIBLE as well as more general knowledge about institutions in the surrounding packet P1.

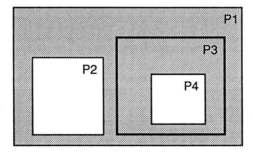

Figure 2b

The principle of single access seems restrictive but it is only posited here to keep things straight for the basic model. The meaning of "multi-access" needs separate discussion which is postponed to the end of this paper. Multiple access would allow reasoning with competitive knowledge at one time which would make it possible to obtain (or detect!) contradictory statements among VISIBLE knowledge.

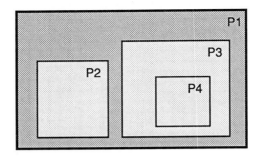

Figure 3a

In Figure 3a, P1 is tagged ACCESSED and thus P2, P3, and P4 are REACHABLE. In Figure 3b, P3 is tagged ACCESSED, hence only P4 is REACHABLE while P2 is not (and neither it is VISIBLE). If P2, for example, contains knowledge about museums, P3 about restaurants, and P4 about Japanese restaurants, then all this information is REACHABLE in the access condition shown in Figure 3a. In Figure 3b, restaurant information (P3) is tagged ACCESSED, hence only information about Japanese restaurants is REACHABLE. The principle of reachability of knowledge attributes a special role to knowledge elements packed within the packet tagged ACCESSED which is reflected in a principle describing a dynamic access condition (structure-dependent access) given further below.

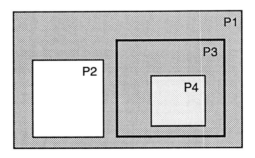

Figure 3b

Overall, static access conditions are characterized in these three principles by splitting the notion of accessed knowledge into VISIBLE and REACHABLE knowledge.

4.3 Dynamic Access Conditions

Dynamic access conditions concern the way the movement of the ACCESSED tag in the structured KB is controlled by some strategy. There may be global control having to do with domain-independent problem-solving strategies, agenda setting, goal selection, etc. These may bring about a KBS's ultimate decisions to act (which may include the need to use certain knowledge from the KB), whereas a KB, by itself, can only support different potential ways of acting (possibly competitive ones). However, the way a KB is structured and what sorts of knowledge elements are packed together does embody some sort of local control in that it constrains the succession in which access to knowledge is attempted.

In general, the empirical observations called upon here say much about human cognitive functioning in terms of how one is able to act on the basis of an enormous repertoire of knowledge elements without getting confused. The findings suggest that a critical feature of human intelligence lies in a dynamic partitioning of the total knowledge into "visible" and "invisible" parts such that the visible part is normally small enough to be computationally tractable. To prepare the ground for exploiting this feature in a KBS, an attempt is made here to capture some observations on principles of dynamic access conditions.

Principle of structure-dependent access. When dealing with a task situation on the basis of knowledge currently VISIBLE turns out unsuccessful, the ACCESSED tag is moved to *one* of those knowledge packets REACHABLE next.

Principle of keyword-dependent access. A means to tag a packet of domain-specific knowledge ACCESSED is the finding of certain concept words (or combinations of concept words) directly associated with knowledge elements in this packet. We refer to such words as *keywords*.

Principle of persistence of access conditions. Upon completion of a goal, the current ACCESSED tag persists as a start-off condition for the partitioning state of the knowledge base when the next goal is issued.

The principle of structure-dependent access reflects the empirical observation that "zooming in" or "focusing" within a packet of domain-specific knowledge is given preference over "wandering." It suggests that, given that a certain domain was found relevant, more specific knowledge (if available) in that domain is accessed next. Thereby, while the VISIBLE part of a KB gets larger, the REACHABLE part gets progressively smaller (see Figures 3a,b). For motivation, imagine that a query about some specialty in a restaurant is issued. If no suitable information is found in the restaurant packet, it seems reasonable to look into the Japanese-restaurant packet. It may come to the point that the resources of a packet are exhausted with no knowledge found applicable but competitive knowledge still available. The question what is to happen then is left open for treatment in a particular implementation. If desired, some form of backtracking would allow a KB to be traversed totally. In this case, the advantage of a well-structured KB over an unstructured one might lie in a higher chance to find the "right" piece of knowledge soon.

The principle of keyword-dependent access suggests the inclusion of vocabulary terms (concept signifiers) among knowledge elements associated with those concepts within a packet. This reflects the empirical observation that rapid access to certain knowledge is often triggered by wordings or technical terms in the context or in a question or a problem statement conveyed. For example, when in a piece of touring guide text the words "museum" and "ceramics collection" are mentioned, one can be pretty definite in many cases that it is about objects of interest (and not about Japanese restaurants). It might even be the case that this interaction, or association, between term words and knowledge elements constitutes a primary means of access that may also be involved in choice making among competitive knowledge packets.

Again, the principle of persistence of access conditions is suggested by empirical observations. As further task-descriptive data (or queries, or sentences in a discourse) are issued to an individual, the recent history (previous discourse) may influence the way these data are processed, at least when there is no break in coherency. This feature reflects what one might call a "mind set."

5 Discussion

The proposal presented in this paper characterizes domain-specific knowledge as an organized repertoire of knowledge elements. The notion of structure is based on cognitive principles and is independent of particular representation languages. Static and dynamic access conditions give rise to a finite set of knowledge base partitions each of which can be considered as an autonomous knowledge base which characterizes a certain segment of the modeled domain. While the completeness and consistency of a so-structured knowledge base cannot be guaranteed in general, the notion of local consistency restricts consistency proofs to the domain of VISIBLE knowledge and might prove tractable and sufficient most of the time. Since knowledge pertaining to different (sub)domains is kept separate by packing, global inconsistencies seem less likely. Even when inconsistencies exist they might not come to bear. However, a mechanism should be provided for which gives notice of the discovery of inconsistencies at run time so that corrective action can be taken.

The principles are not claimed to be comprehensive. There might be additional ones yet to be formulated. In turn, only some of the principles might be realized in an actual implementation, depending on the particular problem domain or purpose of a KBS. It should be understood that the principles are intended for improving the manageability of *large* knowledge bases containing *diverse* knowledge. A conclusion near at hand is that knowledge packets might be encapsulated as modules from the aspect of a "responsibility assignment" (Parnas 1972).

One of the experiences in software engineering is that in order to obtain a transparent module structure, the use conditions among modules should be hierarchic to the greatest extent possible (Nagl 1990). If a knowledge base is to be conceived in a hierarchical fashion then the question arises under which aspect a hierarchical structure should be established. The DOKS principles presented in the fourth section take *specificity* as an aspect of hierarchic subordination. A lot of the background knowledge in a knowledge base is domain-specific, and it is often possible to distinguish different degrees of specificity. The more specific a piece of knowledge is, the more restricted is its use with respect to the number of situations it can come to bear on. That is, more general knowledge should be exported more "generously" than more specific knowledge, and the more general knowledge should not import very specific knowledge which could be of very local impact and even be unqualified to be applied. On the other hand, very specific knowledge should import a lot of general knowledge that covers a broad range of situations including the ones that the very specific knowledge is good for.

While the point of view in the preceding sections was directed toward increasingly specific knowledge, one can easily imagine larger knowledge bases to be built by integrating existing knowledge bases from different origin. Each knowledge base can be regarded as a large knowledge packet that may have an internal knowledge packet structure. Where different knowledge sources were used to construct self-contained knowledge bases, these could be viewed as separate packets which are made competitive knowledge packets and by this become integrated in a larger knowledge packet structure. In this way, ever larger bodies of diverse background knowledge can be assembled to cover growing domains of discourse. It has been the subject of debate whether domain-specific inference rules should be part of the LILOG inference engine or should be kept in the domain knowledge base. It should be one aspect of further research to clarify which kind of rules should be globally available (i.e., part of the inference engine) and which rules should be kept separate in knowledge packets as repositories for local reasoning.

Several issues have been excluded in this paper. The technical questions and implications of an *overlap of knowledge packets* have been discussed extensively in (Wachsmuth 1989b). More research is needed to see when this feature should actually be used in structuring a knowledge base. While knowledge packet structures as presented here have a tree-structured access graph (concerning visibility and reachability of knowledge packets), general knowledge packet structures may have access graphs that allow competitive knowledge packets to become VISIBLE. There are two main issues that need to be considered: the sharing of partitions of a knowledge base in certain access states, and the requirements arising from local consistency. If the VISIBLE knowledge of competitive knowledge packets needs to be included for handling specific situations, it may be motivated to subordinate a new and more specific knowledge packet coined for this situation to these competitive packets. Then at this point the consistency of the comparatively large partition of the whole knowledge base that can become eligible for inferences needs to be scrutinized for consistency.

The notion of *multi-access* mentioned in discussing the principle of single-access has to be further researched. It might be motivated to make competitive knowledge packets simultaneously available for inferencing when their knowledge needs to be drawn on in one task. However, simply unifying the corresponding partitions of the knowledge base would conflict with the conditions of local consistency. Rather, it seems sensible to accumulate the results of inferences drawn on different KB partitions in a KB workspace and record their origin (i.e., the focus under which they were derived). Then the conclusions generated from different foci can be used by the system while further inferences that draw on background knowledge still submit to the principle of single access. Early experimental implementations have taken first steps to make use of these ideas (Wachsmuth 1985, Gust 1986) but they are not fully worked out yet. Apparently, reason maintenance would have to be related to the different partitions that are used at run time.

While the principles characterizing knowledge organization and static access conditions are addressed to the idea of modular knowledge bases in general, particularly interesting ideas for dynamic access control arise for natural language systems. With respect to task-oriented dialogue systems, Grosz and Sidner (1986) have formalized similar ideas to those presented above by means of a "focus space stack." They define a focus space to capture "an abstraction of the participants' focus of attention as their discourse unfolds" by including information about objects, properties, relations, and intentions that are most salient. The focus space of the task under consideration is pushed onto a stack and remains there until the task is completed. That is, it is VISIBLE regardless of whether or not other focus spaces of subtasks are considered at intermediate inference steps.

Furthermore, components of linguistic analysis and a focus space stack could take mutual advantage of each other. The focus space of the discourse segment under consideration may constrain the search for possible referents of definite noun phrases and pronouns and help to resolve ellipsis (cf. Scha, Bruce, Polanyi 1987). In the interpretation of an incoming definite noun phrase (or pronoun or ellipsis) possible referents are first searched in the most recent focus space before going back to less recent ones. In turn, information about the attentional state of the unfolding discourse can be gained from linguistic structure (e.g., functional words and word order). The principles of keyword-dependent access and of the persistence of access conditions are particularly keyed to the use of knowledge-based systems in natural language interaction. Further insight into selective knowledge use might be gained by more subtle analysis of the general interaction of linguistic structure and knowledge access. It would be an interesting research question to analyse the interaction of linguistic structure and domain-focusing and exploit it for elaborating dynamic access control in modular knowledge bases.

References

Dahlgren, K. (1985): The cognitive structure of social categories. Cognitive Science 9(3), 379-398

Feigenbaum, E.A. (1977): The art of artificial intelligence: themes and case studies of knowledge engineering. Proc. 5th Int. Joint Conf. on Artificial Intelligence (IJCAI-77), Cambridge, MA

Fodor, J.A. (1983): The Modularity of Mind. MIT Press, Cambridge, MA

Gängler, B., Wachsmuth, I. (1991): Antwortgenerierung, flexible Wortwahl und elaborative Inferenzen - ein Regelinventar für LEU/2. In: Klose, G., Lang, E., Pirlein, T. (eds.): Die Ontologie und Axiomatik der Wissensbasis von LEU/2. IWBS-Report 171, IBM Deutschland, Stuttgart/ Heidelberg

Garfield, J.L. (ed.) (1987): Modularity in Knowledge Representation and Natural Language Understanding. MIT Press, Cambridge, MA

Grosz, B., Sidner, C. (1986): Attention, intentions and the structure of discourse. Computational Linguistics 12, 175-204

Gust, H. (1986): Strukturiertes Wissen als Grundlage für Sprachverstehensprozesse. LDV-Forum 4(2), 9-14

Hendrix, G.G. (1979): Encoding knowledge in partitioned networks. In: Findler, N.V. (ed.): Associative Networks - Representation and Use of Knowledge by Computers. Academic Press, New York, pp. 51-92

Kowalski, R. (1975): A proof procedure using connection graphs. Journal of the ACM 22(4), 572-595

Lenat, D.B., Feigenbaum, E.A. (1987): On the thresholds of knowledge. Proc. 10th Int. Joint Conf. on Artificial Intelligence (IJCAI-87), Milano, pp. 1173-1182

Levesque, H.J., Brachman, R.J. (1986): Knowledge level interfaces to information systems. In: Brodie, M.L., Mylopoulus, J. (eds.): On Knowledge Base Management Systems. Springer-Verlag, New York, Berlin, Heidelberg, pp. 13-54

Lifschitz, V. (1989): Benchmark problems for formal nonmonotonic reasoning, version 2.00. In: Reinfrank, M., deKleer, J., Ginsberg, M.L., Sandevall, E. (eds.): Non-Monotonic Reasoning. Proc. 2nd Int. Workshop, Springer-Verlag, Berlin, Heidelberg, New York, pp. 202-219

Minsky, M. (1981): A framework for representing knowledge. In: Haugeland, J. (ed.): Mind Design, MIT Press, Cambridge, MA, pp. 95-128

Nagl, M. (1990): Softwaretechnik: Methodisches Programmieren im Großen. Springer-Verlag, Berlin, Heidelberg, New York

Newell, A., Simon, H.A. (1972): Human Problem Solving. Prentice Hall, Englewood Cliffs, NJ

Newell, A. (1982): The knowledge level. Artificial Intelligence 18(1), 1-20

Parnas, D.L. (1972): On the criteria to be used in decomposing systems into modules. Communications of the ACM 15(12), 1053-1058

Pletat, U. (1991): Modularizing Knowledge in L$_{LILOG}$. IWBS-Report 173, IBM Deutschland, Stuttgart/ Heidelberg

Post, T.R., Behr, M.J., Lesh, R., Wachsmuth, I. (1985): Selected results from the rational number project. Proc. 9th Int. Conf. for the Psychology of Mathematics Education, Utrecht, pp. 342-351

Prerau, D.S., Gunderson, A.S., Reinke, R.E., Adler, M.R. (1990): Maintainability techniques in developing large expert systems. IEEE Expert June 1990, 71-79

Rosch, E. (1978): Principles of categorization. In: Rosch, E., Lloyd, B.B. (eds.): Cognition and Categorization. Erlbaum, Hillsdale, NJ

Scha, R.J.H., Bruce, W.C., Polanyi, C. (1987): Discourse understanding. In: Shapiro, S.C., Eckroth, D., Vallasi, G.A. (eds.): Encyclopedia of Artificial Intelligence, Vol. 1. John Wiley and Sons, New York, pp. 233-245

Wachsmuth, I. (1985): LAKOS - Ein Modell der Wissensrepräsentation zur Erklärung kognitiven Verhaltens. In: Mandl, H., Fischer, P.M. (eds.): Lernen im Dialog mit dem Computer. Urban and Schwarzenberg, München

Wachsmuth, I. (1987): On Structuring Domain-Specific Knowledge. LILOG-Report 12, IBM Deutschland, Stuttgart

Wachsmuth, I. (1989a): Modularisierung wissensbasierter Systeme - Rahmenentwurf für ein Forschungsprogramm im Bereich Wissensbasierte Systeme/Künstliche Intelligenz. University of Bielefeld (MOSYS-Report 1), Bielefeld

Wachsmuth, I. (1989b): Zur intelligenten Organisation von Wissensbeständen in künstlichen Systemen. IWBS-Report 91, IBM Deutschland, Stuttgart/Heidelberg

Wachsmuth, I., Meyer-Fujara, J. (1990): Addressing the retrieval problem in large knowledge bases. Proc. 3rd Conf. Computational Intelligence (CI-90), Milano (Summary). Full paper: University of Bielefeld (MOSYS-Report 3), Bielefeld

Wos, L., Overbeek, R., Lusk, E., Boyle, J. (1984): Automated Reasoning - Introduction and Applications. Prentice Hall, Englewood Cliffs, NJ

Deductive Aspects of Three-Valued Logic

Introduction

In the Detailed Project Description of the LILOG project [Herzog et al. 1986] we find in subproject B.2.2 on knowledge manipulation the objective:

> ... inference mechanisms will be developed meeting the requirements set up ... by the different types of knowledge, which are held in the knowledge base, e.g., inconsistent knowledge and/or partial knowledge, i.e., vague, uncertain or incomplete knowledge.

This deliberately left open which approach, maybe along different lines, should be taken and, indeed, several methods were persued later on. Among these were the method of uncertainty factors and the introduction of defaults, which led to the implementation of a sophisticated truth maintenance system based on a special version of non-monotonic logic, see [Lorenz 1990]. The potential of using three-valued logic to make progress towards the mentioned objective were first staked out in [Schmitt 1987]. Parallel to these conceptual considerations, the question of possible inference system for three-valued logic was raised. The first idea was to extend the resolution method by allowing more than one pair of complementary literals. One such resolution system for a three-valued logic with two negation symbols has been described in [Schmitt 1986], where also references to related work may be found. Though the system has its merits, it was felt that the transformation of formulas into clausal normal form, which now is of course three-valued clausal normal form, results in expressions that are hard to interpret and bear no resemblance to the untransformed formulas. The second thought was to use a variation of the tableau calculus. This approach has been taken up in a project, called TCG, between IBM's Institute for Knowledge Based Systems in Heidelberg and the Institute for Logic, Complexity and Deduction Systems at the University of Karlsruhe and is still being continued. We will give in the first section a short description of the basic novelty of the three-valued tableau system developed in TCG. Further details may be found in [Hähnle 1990] and [Hähnle 1991a]. In the second section we present an application of three-valued logic recently found by D. Mundici [Mundici 1991]. In the last section we present some evidence that deduction in three-valued logic is more efficient than reduction into two-valued logic.

A Three-Valued Tableau System

We will use the three truth values 0 (= false) , 1 (= true) and u (= unknown). Sometimes we will think of these three values as being ordered as $0 < u < 1$. The problem of what the third truth value u stands for has been the topic of many debates. Among others the following points of view have been proposed:

- In [Rosser Turquette 1952] it is proposed to use u as the truth value of statements like *It will rain in Karlsruhe on New Year's Eve of the year 2000*, that refer to future events.

- Consider a Turing machine that computes yes/no answers to the query whether a number n has some given property P. On some inputs n the Turing machine may not terminate. This situation has been dealt with in [Kleene 1938] by viewing P as a three-valued predicate: P(n) is assigned the truth value u if the Turing machine on input n loops for ever.

∧	0	u	1
0	0	0	0
1	0	u	u
2	0	u	1

∨	0	u	1
0	0	u	1
1	u	u	1
2	1	1	1

Table 1: Truth tables for cautious conjunction and disjunction

- In assigning truth values to natural language sentences one occasionally encounters the problem of presuppositions, as in *The east pole is surrounded by water*. The use of the definite article *The* presuposes the existence of something it refers to. For the example *east pole* this is not the case (at least not in the model of the world I am using to interpret this sentence). It has been proposed to evaluate sentences like this neither to false nor to true but to some third truth value u. One may consult [Blau 1978] for more examples on this issue. For a more recent and critical account of the subject, see [Kreiser et al.], Chap. 9.

- Very similar to the previous item is a problem described in [Gries 1981] in the context of formal verification methods for computer programs. The basic idea is to define formally the effect of a construct C of the programming language by two logical formulas P and Q. Then P C Q is to be read as *if P is true and C is executed, then Q will be true*. One such precondition P may involve a list L = $< a_1, \ldots, a_k >$ and a number i and read : i = k+2 and $a_i > 0$. The formula P is certainly not true, but it is also not outright false. It refers to an item a_i, where i falls outside the scope of the list L. To distinguish scoping errors like this from deeper logical mistakes David Gries proposed a three-valued logic for program construction and verification. In this logic the formula P would receive truth-value u.

- Two-valued propositional logic is used to compute two-valued circuits. With the study and realisation of three-valued circuits the third truth value has become a physical reality, see, e.g., [Smith 1988]

Our position in this dispute is a very pragmatic one. We want to build a deductive system that is flexible enough to be useful independently of the meaning that is associated with the third truth value. One way this intended meaning enters into a formal system is through the truth tables for the propositional connectives, or even before that in the choice of what connectives will be used. The most common definition for logical conjunction and disjunction is

$$truthvalue(A \wedge B) = min(truthvalue(A), truthvalue(B))$$

$$truthvalue(A \vee B) = max(truthvalue(A), truthvalue(B))$$

The truth tables for these conectives are given in Table 1.

These truth tables arise in a situation where we reason about partial knowledge. Some facts may be known to be true, others may be known to be false, while for still others no information is available. The principle now is to be cautious: an expression $x \wedge y$, where x, y are truth values 0, u or 1, is evaluated to a definite truth value $z=1$, or $z=0$ only if all possibilities to replace u by 0 or 1 yield in classical logic the same result z. For example, the expression $u \wedge 0$ is evaluated following this principle to 0, since no matter how u is replaced by 0 or 1 the result in classical logic evaluation will be 0. On the other hand $u \wedge 1$ yields 0 when u is replaced by 0, and yields 1 when u is replaced by 1. Thus the principle forces us to evaluate $u \wedge 1$ in three-valued logic to u.

There is also a choice about what the negation of the third truth value should be, whether it should be 1 or remain u. We introduce two negation symbols, one for each of these possibilities. The second version satisfies the cautiousness principle and is called *strong negation* , denoted by ¬, while the first alternative, denoted by ∼, is called *weak negation*. If you believe that negation should send u to 0 you can use the combination ∼∼ ¬, see Table 2.

¬	
0	1
u	u
1	0

~	
0	1
u	1
1	0

~~ ¬	
0	1
u	0
1	0

Table 2: Truth tables for strong negations

⊙	0	u	1
0	0	0	0
u	0	0	u
1	0	u	1

⊕	0	u	1
0	0	u	1
u	u	1	1
1	1	1	1

Table 3: Truth tables for Ulam's game

Other truth tables for disjunction and conjunction are possible, like the ones given in Table 3. These can be defined by

$$truthvalue(A \oplus B) = min(1, truthvalue(A) + truthvalue(B))$$

$$truthvalue(A \odot B) = max(0, truthvalue(A) + truthvalue(B) - 1)$$

where u is identified with the rational number $\frac{1}{2}$ and + , - have their usual meaning. These truth tables will be used later in the formalization of Ulam's game.

Our approach, already mentioned above, can now be explained more precisely. Given any set of propositional connectives, like $\odot$, $\oplus$, ¬, ~, ∧ and ∨, by their truth tables we construct a sound and complete tableau calculus for the first-order predicate logic using the given connectives and of course also existential and universal quantifiers. There is no restriction on the number of arguments, as the examples may suggest. The general framework of the calculus and the quantifier rules remains fixed. We only have to design for each propositional connective corresponding tableau rules. There is an algorithm that computes these tableau rules, such that a complete and sound calculus results. This approach was first described in [Carnielli 1987]. But the computed rules tend to be more complicated than necessary, so it is advisable to consider each rule separately, which is not a major problem, since changes of the set of connectives do not occur very often.

Let us have a look at Carniellis system. Like all proof systems using the tableau calculus it is a refutation proof system. To prove that a formula A is a two-valued logical consequence of a set of formulas Σ one assumes that all formulas in Σ are true and A is false. Using the tableau rules one tries to derive a contradiction from these assumptions. If this succeeds then A is indeed a logical consequence of Σ. In the three-valued case two contradictions have to be obtained: first it has to be refuted that all formulas in Σ can be true and A false, and in addition it has to be shown that it is impossible to have all formulas in Σ be true and A have the truth value u. We give an example where $\Sigma = \emptyset$ and the formula to be proved is $A = A_1 \vee A_2 \vee \ldots A_n \vee \sim A_1$. This is not a particularly interesting statement, but it will serve us well in demonstrating some typical features of Carniellis system. For easy readability we have omitted parentheses. Putting them back would make A look like $(A_1 \vee (A_2 \vee \ldots (A_n \vee \sim A_1) \ldots))$. The assumption that formula A is false will be expressed by the prefix F leading to the notation FA, similarly the assumption that A has truth value u will be denoted by UA. The tableau rules we will use are given in Tables 4, 5, 6. The proof procedure starts with a tableau containing only the formula FA or UA. Using the tableau rules the tableau is successively extended. This may involve a branching of the original tableau. The goal is to prove all branches to be contradictory. This may be done in many ways. We restrict ourselves to the simplest case and call a branch B contradictory (or equivalently closed), if there are formulas $S_1 A_1$ and $S_2 A_2$ in B, such that $S_1 \neq S_2$ and A_1 and A_2 are unifiable. Our examples deal only with propositional

$$\frac{F(A \vee B)}{\begin{array}{c} FA \\ FB \end{array}} \qquad \frac{T(A \vee B)}{TA \mid TB} \qquad \frac{U(A \vee B)}{\begin{array}{c|c|c} UA & UB & UA \\ FB & FA & UB \end{array}}$$

Table 4: Carnielli's tableau rules for disjunction

$$\frac{F \neg A}{TA} \qquad \frac{T \neg A}{FA} \qquad \frac{U \neg A}{UA}$$

Table 5: Carnielli's tableau rules for strong negation

logic, so A_1 and A_2 are unifiable if and only if $A_1 = A_2$. Note that there is no tableau rule with premisse $U \sim A$, this is because $\sim A$ can never attain the truth value u. If $U \sim A$ appears on a branch B it is immediately declared "closed".

The tableau for the refutation of FA is shown in Figure 1.

The tableau for the refutation of UA whose beginning is shown in Figure 2 contains $2^{n+1} - 1$ branches. A similar exponential growth in the size of the tableau can be observed for many formulas. It can also be observed that there are many repetitions of the same or almost the same formulas on different branches.

We have discovered that a very efficient way to reduce the complexity of the tableaux is to use as prefixes not only truth values but sets of truth values. Signed formulas now are of the form WA where W is an arbitrary nonempty subset of the set of all truth values $\{T, U, F\}$, e.g., $\{U, F\}A$. A signed formula $\{U, F\}A$ is interpreted as the assumption that the formula A has truth value U or F. To prove that A is a three-valued tautology it suffices to consider one tableau with root $\{U, F\}A$. As an example the tableau rules for disjunction with prefix sets is shown in Table 7. Note that none of these rules yields a branching into three branches, as was the case before. It turns out that for the standard set of propositional connectives, $\sim, \neg, \vee, \wedge$ plus both quantifiers only the sets $\{T\}$, $\{U\}$, $\{F\}$ and $\{U, F\}$ are needed. This may change when other connectives are used. It may then be a problem to choose the needed collection of prefix sets to be minimal; this and related issues are investigated in [Hähnle 1991b]. As a very spectacular example for the reduction of the tableau size look at the proof of the formula in Figure 3, which consists of just one branch.

Ulam's Game

In this section we present an application of three-valued logic that has been found recently by D. Mundici [Mundici 1991].

As an introduction remember the game played between two players Q and A, the questioner and the answerer. They both agree first on a range of objects, e.g. ,the natural numbers between 0 and 6. Player A chooses a number X in this range without disclosing it to Q. It is now Q's task to ask as few yes/no questions as possible to find X. We know of course that three questions suffice in this case. In Ulam's variation of the game, A is allowed to lie, but at most once (see [Ulam 1976], p. 281). In fact Ulam proposed more generally that k lies be allowed, and Mundici showed how to translate

$$\frac{F \sim A}{TA} \qquad \frac{T \sim A}{FA \mid UA}$$

Table 6: Carnielli's tableau rules for weak negation

$\{U,F\}(A \vee B)$	$T(A \vee B)$		$U(A \vee B)$		$F(A \vee B)$
$\{U,F\}A$	TA	TB	$\{U,F\}A$	UA	FA
$\{U,F\}B$			UB	$\{U,F\}B$	FB

Table 7: Tableau rules for disjunction using prefix sets

$$FA_1 \vee \ldots \vee A_n \vee \sim A_1$$
$$FA_1$$
$$FA_2 \vee \ldots \vee A_n \vee \sim A_1$$
$$\vdots\vdots\vdots$$
$$FA_n$$
$$F \sim A_1$$
$$TA_1$$
closed

Figure 1: The tableau for refuting FA

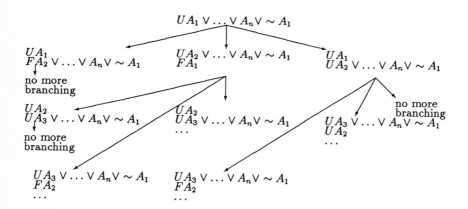

Figure 2: The tableau for refuting UA

$$\{U,F\}A_1 \vee \ldots \vee A_n \vee \sim A_1$$
$$\{U,F\}A_1$$
$$\{U,F\}A_2 \vee \ldots \vee A_n \vee \sim A_1$$
$$\vdots\vdots\vdots$$
$$\{U,F\} \sim A_1$$
$$\{T\}A_1$$
closed

Figure 3: The tableau proving A using prefix sets

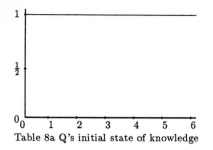

Table 8a Q's initial state of knowledge

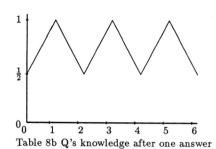

Table 8b Q's knowledge after one answer

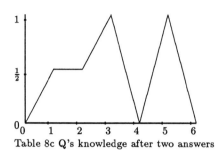

Table 8c Q's knowledge after two answers

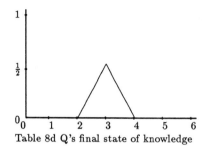

Table 8d Q's final state of knowledge

Table 8: Q's knowledge as Ulam's game progresses

this into a problem in (k+2)-valued logic. We will stick to the case k=1.

Mundici's idea goes like this: Before the first question the information that Q has about number X may be represented as shown in Table 8a.

All numbers are equally possible. Let $q_1(x)$ be the first question, e.g., $q_1(x)$ could be "is x an odd number ?", and A's answer to it is "yes". Then the possibility level of every even number n is decreased by $\frac{1}{2}$. If the possibility level is already 0 then no further subtraction is possible and the result remains 0. This gives the picture shown in Table 8b.

Let $q_2(x)$ be the second question, e.g., "is x a prime number ?" and A's answer again "yes". A similar decreasing operation now yields the result shown in Table 8c

We may for this analysis assume that A's answers are always "yes", replacing $q_i(x)$ by $\neg q_i(x)$ if necessary. After the further questions

- $q_3(x)$: "is x even ?"

- $q_4(x)$: "is $x \geq 3$?"

- $q_5(x)$: "is $6 - x \geq 2$?"

the information obtained by Q looks like the curve represented in Table 8d.

From this Q concludes that X = 3.

In general a sequence of question $q_1, \ldots, q_n$, all answered positively, yields the solution X = k if:

$$truthvalue(1 \odot q_1(k) \odot \ldots \odot q_n(k)) \neq 0$$

and there is only one number k with this property. We can say a little bit more. When truth value$(1 \odot q_1(k) \odot \ldots \odot q_n(k)) = 0$ for all k, then A has lied too much. If k is the only number with truth value$(1 \odot q_1(k) \odot \ldots \odot q_n(k)) \neq 0$ and truth value$(1 \odot q_1(k) \odot \ldots \odot q_n(k)) = \frac{1}{2}$ then A has lied exactly once, otherwise he has always answered truthfully.

Reduction to Two-Valued Logic

One critisism that is raised against theorem proving in three-valued logic is to point out that there is a simple transformation from three-valued formulas to two-valued formulas. The basic idea of this transformation is to replace one three-valued predicate symbol P (see Figure 4) by two two-valued predicate symbols P_0 and P_1 (Figure 5). The elements e in a model of three-valued logic

$$P(x) = 0 \qquad P(x) = u \qquad P(x) = 1$$

Figure 4: A three-valued predicate P

Figure 5: Two-valued predicates replacing three-valued P

satisfying "truth value$(P(e)) = u$" are then those elements e in the corresponding two-valued model, for which $\sim P_1(e) \land \sim P_1(e)$ is true. The complete description of the transformation requires some more details, such as forming a three-valued negation normal form before the described replacements can be performed and making sure that P_0 and P_1 are disjoint (see, e.g., [Fenstad et al. 1985]).

Our standard reply to this critisism has been that the description of three-valued problems can best be done in three-valued logic. The transformation leads to less intelligible formulas. This is certainly true, but we had always hoped to find that three-valued theorem provers are also faster on three-valued formulas than two-valued provers on the transformed formulas. It is still too early to endorse this statement in full generality, but in special cases we found that the three-valued prover outperformed the two-valued version by a factor of 4, not counting the time needed for the transformation. To give a concrete example consider the formula:

$$((K_0 \lor K_1 \lor K_2) \land (\neg K_0 \lor \neg K_1 \lor \neg K_2)) \qquad \Rightarrow$$
$$((\neg K_0 \land K_1) \lor (\neg K_1 \land K_0) \lor (\neg K_0 \land K_2) \lor (\neg K_2 \land K_0) \lor (\neg K_1 \land K_2) \lor (\neg K_2 \land K_1))$$

The transformed formula looks like this, where K_{i1} replaces the 0-part of K_i and K_{i0} replaces the 1-part of K_i:

$$(\sim K_{00} \land \sim K_{10} \land \sim K_{20}) \quad \lor \quad (\sim K_{01} \land \sim K_{11} \land \sim K_{21}) \quad \lor \quad (K_{01} \land K_{10}) \lor (K_{11} \land K_{00}) \quad \lor$$
$$(K_{01} \land K_{20}) \lor (K_{21} \land K_{00}) \quad \lor \quad (K_{11} \land K_{20}) \lor (K_{21} \land K_{10})$$

Table 9 gives the time and the number of tableau branches that had to be considered by the three-valued prover 3TAP and its two-valued version 2TAP.

	sec	branches
3TAP	2.550	619
2TAP	9.084	2 368

Table 9: Comparison of resources

References

[Blau 1978] U. Blau: *Die dreiwertige Logik der Sprache.* Walter de Gruyter, 1978

[Carnielli 1987] W.A. Carnielli: Systematization of finte many-valued logics through the method of tableau. *J. of Symbolic Logic,* 52:473–493, 1987

[Fenstad et al. 1985] J.E. Fenstad, P.-K. Halvorsen, T. Langholm, J. van Benthem: Equations, schemata and situations: A framework for linguistic semantics. Report CSLI-85-29, CSLI, Stanford, CA, 1985

[Gries 1981] D. Gries: *The Science of Programming.* Text and Monographs in Computer Science. Springer-Verlag, Berlin, Heidelberg, New York,1981

[Hähnle 1990] R. Hähnle: Spezifikation eines Theorembeweisers für dreiwertige First-Order Logik. IWBS Report 136, IBM Deutschland, Stuttgart, September 1990

[Hähnle 1991a] R. Hähnle: Towards an efficient tableau proof procedure for multiple-valued logics. In W. Schönfeld (ed.): *Proc. Computer Science Logic,* page to appear. Springer-Verlag, 1991

[Hähnle 1991b] R. Hähnle: Uniform notation of tableau rules for multiple-valued logics. In *Proc. The Twenty-First Int. Symposium Multiple-Valued, Victoria,* 238 – 245, IEEE Computer Soc. Press, Los Alamitos, CA, 1991

[Herzog et al. 1986] Herzog et al.: Lilog - linguistic and logic methods for the computational understanding of German detailed project description. LILOG-REPORT 1b, IBM Deutschland GmbH, Stuttgart, February 1986

[Kleene 1938] S.C. Kleene: On a notation for ordinal numbers. *J.Symb. Logic,* 3:150–155, 1938

[Kreiser et al.] L. Kreiser, S. Gottwald, W. Stelzner (eds.): *Nichtklassische Logik.* Berlin, Akademie-Verlag, 1990

[Lorenz 1990] S. Lorenz: Nicht Monotones Schließen mit ordnungssortierten Defaults. IWBS Report 100, IBM Deutschland, Stuttgart, January 1990

[Mundici 1991] D. Mundici: The logic of Ulam's game with lies. *Cambridge Studies in Probability, Induction and Decision Theory.* to appear, 1991

[Rosser Turquette 1952] J.B. Rosser, A.R. Turquette: *Many-Valued Logics.* North-Holland, Amsterdam, 1952

[Schmitt 1986] P.H. Schmitt: Computational aspects of three-valued logic. In J. Siekmann (ed.): *Proceedings of the 8th Int. Conference on Automated Deduction.* Lecture Notes in Comp Science, Vol. 230, p. 190–198, Berlin, Heidelberg, New York,1986

[Schmitt 1987] P.H. Schmitt: Eine dreiwertige Logik zur Verarbeitung partieller Information. *Informatik, Forschung und Entwicklung,* 2:182–190, 1987

[Smith 1988] K.C. Smith: Multiple-valued logic: A tutorial and appreciation. *IEEE Computer Society,* p. 17–27, April 1988

[Ulam 1976] S.M. Ulam: *Adventures of a Mathematician.* Sribner's, New York, 1976

The LILOG Inference Engine

Toni Bollinger, Sven Lorenz, Udo Pletat

The development of an inference engine implementing our knowledge representation language L_{LILOG} has been strongly influenced by the natural language understanding context of the LILOG project. However, in the architecture of the inference engine we have anticipated using its logical kernel also for a wider spectrum of applications.

1 Design Objectives for the Inference Engine

In the framework of the natural language understanding system LEU/2, knowledge represented in L_{LILOG} may stem from two sources:

- Our knowledge engineers have developed the background knowledge of LEU/2 in the context of touring through a city in which we find streets, museums, restaurants and other things of interest. This background knowledge contains specific information about the city of Düsseldorf.

- The LEU/2 system interprets German texts describing, for example, specific museums, or the location of department stores in Düsseldorf by constructing L_{LILOG} representations of the information provided in such texts.

The natural language understanding capabilities of LEU/2 require that the knowledge provided to the system be made operational via an inference engine for various purposes. Knowledge extracted from German texts needs to be combined with the background knowledge by means of forward inferences (this corresponds to the text input mode of LEU/2). Of course, we would also like to query the knowledge available to LEU/2 in natural language and obtain natural language answers to our questions (this corresponds to the query mode of LEU/2).

Apart from these two overall requirements, the linguistic capabilities of a natural language understanding system can be improved by supporting, e.g., the linguistic analysis with background knowledge about the application domain. Typical tasks that benefit from the evaluation of background knowledge are the disambiguation of different readings of a natural language sentence, or the resolution of anaphoric references between a pronoun and the explicitly mentioned referent it refers to. Another component which can benefit from the services of the inference engine is the generation component of the LEU/2 system. Here the inference engine supports the generation of natural language answers to queries posed against the knowledge of LEU/2.

The above discussion shows that in the natural language understanding framework of LEU/2 the inference engine has to offer a variety of *application-dependent inference tasks*.

On the other hand, L_{LILOG} is a typed logic that doesn't know the applications it is being used for. However, any logic suggests certain inference tasks that can be performed over the knowledge represented in this logic. Let us call these inference tasks *application-independent*. Since L_{LILOG} is a typed logic, the following three logical inference tasks are realized by the inference engine no matter what application it is supposed to support:

1. The classical logical inference task of solving the problem of whether a goal formula follows from the formulas given in a knowledge base.

2. Besides the classical backward chaining inference task, a forward chainer (with consistency checking capabilities) is of considerable interest for combining new pieces of knowledge with existing knowledge.

3. The sort language of L_{LILOG} constitutes a (sub)logic in itself, suggesting inference tasks like testing the validity of the subsumption relation for two sort expressions or computing their greatest lower bound. Thus special sort processing capabilities are available as a logical inference task.

These application-independent inference tasks can be considered as a second level of inferential capabilities – realizing the application-dependent inference tasks – offered by the inference engine of LEU/2.

Logics are typically made operational by means of theorem provers. Classical theorem provers implement pure first-order predicate logic in terms of a proof procedure for testing whether a set of clauses is inconsistent. Very often they are optimized towards performing this basic inference task efficiently. Looking at the variety of tasks the LEU/2 inference engine has to deal with, it is clear that the functionality of such basic theorem provers is not sufficient for our purposes. Of course, also the inference tasks we have in mind require the basic theorem proving functionality of showing that a set of clauses is inconsistent. According to the application context given by the LEU/2 natural language understanding system, these tasks are executed in specific contexts and may require different settings for the basic proof procedure. Therefore, we should have a parametrizable theorem prover as the basic inference algorithm which is adaptable to the various specific inference tasks it is supposed to solve. The *general proof procedure* meets these requirements and can be considered as the "heart" of the inference engine. The second basic reasoning algorithm we have is an *inconsistency checker* for sort expressions which processes the sort information of a L_{LILOG} knowledge base.

The following diagram may illustrate the vertical structure of the LILOG inference engine outlined so far:

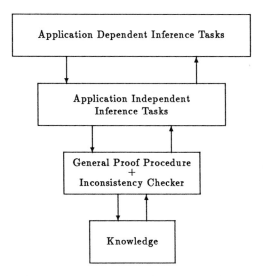

Figure 1: The vertical structure of the LILOG inference engine

The discussion above has illustrated the different levels of abstraction at which knowledge formulated in L_{LILOG} should be made operational within LEU/2. The basic idea of introducing the vertical structuring of the inference engine is to make a clear distinction between application-dependent inference tasks and the logical inference tasks that are supported independently of the application. These logical inference tasks themselves form a higher level of inferential capability than the basic inference algorithms represented by the general proof procedure and the inconsistency checker.

Besides the vertical structure of the LILOG inference engine we have imposed a horizontal structure of the logical level of the inference engine, which has been strongly influenced by further overall objectives for LEU/2.

One objective for the development of LEU/2 was to create an experimental environment offering basic processing modules needed for natural language understanding in such a way that extensions of these modules or the integration of new components into LEU/2 are easily possible. This decision has been taken in order to provide an experimental system for testing the feasibility of theoretical solutions in a given software environment. Of course, this overall objective for LEU/2 applies to the knowledge representation and processing activities of the LILOG project as well.

In the context of processing L$_{LILOG}$ (and knowledge processing in general), several interesting questions require practical experience based on an implementation of the knowledge representation language:

- To what extent does the inference behavior of the various logical inference tasks depend on the inference calculus being used for the inference task?

- Can specialized external reasoners improve the inferential capacities of the inference engine?

- How do inference calculi and strategies for traversing the search space interact; which search strategy fits best to which calculus?

- Does one inference calculus fit better to some specific knowledge base than another?

- Can we tailor the behavior of the inference engine by setting certain parameters and options so that the inference behavior improves for a specific knowledge base?

In order to make experiments with the inference behavior of our inference engine to answer such general questions, we had to establish a very clean module structure for the inference engine as a whole and the general proof procedure in particular. This led to an architecture where, for example, the general proof procedure is able to make explicit reference to the inference calculus and the search strategy it is supposed to use. Thus the inference calculus and the search strategy became separate modules of which different realizations can be interchanged easily in order to impose different inference behaviors on the general proof procedure. The high degree of flexibility that can be achieved by such an architecture has its price in terms of lower efficiency. But for a system serving as an enviromnent for experimenting with inference calculi, search strategies et cetera we are willing to pay this price.

The above list of questions, which we are now able to tackle with the inference machinery developed so far, has not been answered yet; this will be the subject of future (and longer term) work. However, the implementation of LEU/2 has already shown the practical usefulness of the modular architecture of the logical level of the inference engine. The user is already able to choose among several search strategies. The reasoning capacities can be enhanced by adding specialized calculus rules (e.g., for processing sort literals).

The rest of this paper will discuss the three layers of the inference engine. First we address the application-dependent layer: the user interface. Then the logic interface, representing the application-independent inference tasks, is discussed, where we give also a more detailed view of the low-level inference mechanisms represented by the general proof procedure and the sort processing algorithm. Finally, we explain the underlying basic logical mechanisms (including calculus rules) of our inference engine.

2 The User Interface

The user interface level of the inference engine offers the application-dependent inference tasks. Since also some of logical inference tasks provided by the inference engine are of interest to some of its users within LEU/2, the user interface is also the point at which to access those. Below we describe typical situations in which various modules of the LEU/2 system will access the inference engine.

Inference Tasks Supporting Text Understanding

Having constructed the semantic representation of a sentence, the new knowledge has to be integrated into the previously acquired text knowledge and the background knowledge available to LEU/2. This is done by checking whether the new knowledge is consistent with the existing knowledge and by performing forward inferences in order to make implicit knowledge explicit. Consistency checks and the execution of forward inferences are part of the functionality offered by the logic machine and will be described in more detail in Sect. 3 of this paper.

The resolution of anaphoric references is one part of the interpretation process in constructing Lᴌɪʟᴏɢ representations for German texts. It has to determine whether there is an antecedent in the text to which a pronoun may refer. One possibility of supporting this decision is to compare the sort of the object representing the antecedent with the sort attached to the object representing the pronoun. The linguistic algorithms will discard any of the candidate antecedents the sort of which is incompatible with the sort of the pronoun, i.e., if the greatest lower bound of the sort of the antecedent and that of the pronoun is the empty set. Computing the greatest lower bound is an inference task the logic machine offers to its users within LEU/2.

Inference Tasks Supporting Question Answering

In the question answering mode of LEU/2 we are able to have a natural language dialogue with the system about the knowledge it has acquired during previous text understanding phases. One objective here is to achieve a dialogue behavior which can be called *cooperative*. That is to say, instead of verbalizing the logical answers to the questions posed to the system in a straightforward way, LEU/2 is expected to provide more informative natural language answers.

Basically there are two question types the logical representations of which have to be handled by the inference engine: *yes/no-* and *wh-questions*[1]. For yes/no-questions it suffices to try to prove the goal formula representing the question and, if the proof doesn't succeed, the negated goal as well in order to provide the natural language answers *Yes*, *No*, or, *I don't know*, instead of being only able to say *Yes* or *I don't know*. For wh-questions like *"Which museum is open at 11 o'clock?"* the logical answer has to provide instantiations of specific variables in the goal formula representing the question.

To achieve a cooperative dialogue behavior, concepts like over-answering and presupposition handling have to be realized as part of the generation component to avoid simple *"Yes"* or *"No"* answers to a question. For example, the answer *"No"* to the question *"Does the museum open at 9 o'clock?"* is not very cooperative; a better answer would be *"No, the museum opens at 10 o'clock"*.

In order to support such features by the inference engine some extensions of the general proof procedure have been made, leading to more elegant solutions than ad hoc ideas based on standard approaches. The standard solution for producing the answer *"No, the museum opens at 10 o'clock"* is first to submit the original goal representing the yes/no-question. Then, if this proof fails, the "9 o'clock term" in the question goal could be replaced by a variable and the more general goal resubmitted to the inference engine.

We are able to realize this within one query by immediately replacing the "9 o'clock term" by a variable in the question goal and by telling the inference engine that it shall prefer solutions instantiating the variable with terms that are compatible with the "9 o'clock term". In case the

---

[1] These are questions beginning with *who, what, which and where.*

compatibility constraint set up by the "9 o'clock term" cannot be satisfied we just drop it and search for further solutions to our modified goal; if we find the "10 o'clock term" it becomes the result of the inference process. We give a more detailed description of this method in Sect. 3.2 about the general proof procedure.

Detecting violated presuppositions is another means for generating cooperative answers. Assuming that no Picasso museum exists in Düsseldorf, a good answer to the question *"Is the Picasso museum open on Monday?"* would be *"There is no Picasso museum"* instead of replying simply *"No"* or *"I don't know"*. This is because the latter answers presuppose that there is a Picasso Museum which, however, is closed on Mondays. The semantic representation of the original question may be split into a conjunction of two subgoals corresponding to the questions *Q1: "Is there a Picasso Museum?"* and *Q2: "Is it open on Monday?"*. This conjunction of subgoals is submitted to the inference engine and it is asked to prove first Q1 and then Q2. The inference engine can't find a proof of Q1 and reports this to the generation component, which is now able to give the desired cooperative answer. In general, for producing the logical answers to such questions the subgoals of the question goal have to be processed in a given order, the presupposition order. If the proof of the entire question fails, those subgoals that could be proved as well as the first non-proven subgoal are returned to the generation component, enabling it to give its cooperative answer.

From an abstract logical point of view, the answers to wh-questions are terms instantiating a variable of the question goal. One task of natural language generation is to verbalize these terms by finding an appropriate succinct description distinguishing it from other objects of the same category (i.e., sort). Thus the inference engine may be asked to compute all attributes for which a certain object has distinct values compared to other objects of the same sort.

For example, if we intend to speak about a specific pencil among a number of others, it may happen that the one we are interested in is the only red one. If there is a *color*-feature, then its value is *red* for the red pencil and different from red for the other pencils, i.e., *color* is a discriminative attribute for the red pencil and *"red pencil"* is an appropriate verbalization of it.

3   The Logic Machine

The logic machine of the LILOG inference engine performs the logical tasks, i.e., the application-independent inference tasks, on top of which the more complex, application-dependent inference tasks of the user interface are realized. So, here we find the inference services one would expect from an implementation of L_{LILOG} as a stand-alone knowledge representation language.

The general structure of the logic machine is outlined in Figure 2 below.

The three subcomponents for the execution of logical inference tasks are

- the problem solver,
- the knowledge base extender, and
- the sort processor.

The first two subcomponents use the general proof procedure since their major concern is to process the knowledge provided in terms of the axioms of a L_{LILOG} knowledge base. The general proof procedure contains the inference calculus (together with the search strategy) as a fundamental submodule. Since the truth maintenance system as well as the external deductive component (a reasoner performing special deductions) are triggered by special calculus rules, the general proof procedure is also the point where these components are attached to the inference engine.

The sort processor offers inference tasks evaluating the knowledge represented in the sort declarations of a knowledge base. These inference tasks are realized in terms of an inconsistency checker for sort expressions.

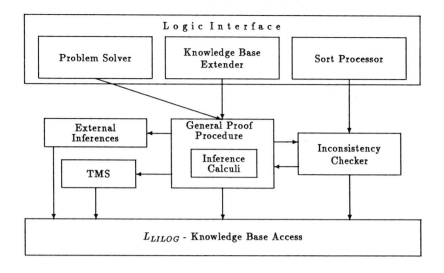

Figure 2: Architecture of the LILOG logic machine

The access to the knowledge bases is realized by a special interface module connecting the inference engine with the data base system storing the compiled L_{LILOG} code on which the inference engine operates.

3.1 The Logic Interface

The logic interface is, so to speak, the entrance through which one can access the logical inference tasks offered by the inference engine. Let us now describe its three doors.

Problem Solver

The problem solver can be considered as a generalized theorem prover whose essential task is to prove L_{LILOG} goal formulas, given in terms of conjunctions of disjunctions of literals.

The problem solver itself performs essentially some initialization tasks comprising the negation of the goal formula and the setting of various parameters directing the search within the general proof procedure. The negated goal is then passed to the general proof procedure for finding a proof of the goal.

Some features distinguish the problem solver (with the general proof procedure) from ordinary theorem provers. First of all there is a bunch of options available allowing us to set various parameters for the execution of an inference task. Besides some options for specifying the search depth, the number of results (like 1 for yes/no-question or "all" for wh-questions), we may, for example, specify how to represent the result of an inference process: the simplest form is to return just a success or fail message. Alternatively, one may request the inference result to be presented as the instantiations of the goal formula, or in terms of the valid substitutions for the variables in the goal. An option more specific to the LILOG inference engine allows us to focus the search on particular instantiations of certain variables; this is useful for realizing some kind of over-answering (cf. Sect. 2). Another special option deals with handling the implicit presuppositions when asking natural language questions. For this, the problem solver gets a list of L_{LILOG} formulas, which is interpreted as a conjunction and represents the presupposition order. The task is to prove a maximal number of these L_{LILOG} formulas in the given (presupposition) order. The formulas for which the proof failed represent the violated presuppositions.

Knowledge Base Extender

The knowledge base extender offers the inference tasks of executing forward inferences in connection with performing consistency checks. For checking the consistency of a formula with respect to a given knowledge base it suffices to pass the formula itself to the general proof procedure, which – being a refutation procedure – detects an inconsistency by deducing the empty clause.

The execution of forward inferences is triggered by the input facts provided to the knowledge base extender. These facts are applied to forward(-chaining) rules by trying to resolve them with the premises that are marked by an entrypoint. The resulting resolvents are passed to the general proof procedure for "resolving away" the remaining premise literals. If this succeeds, the instances of the conclusions constitute valid facts deduced by a forward inference step. In the axiom

axiom *fw-axiom1*
   forall *x, y, z : top*
   EP P(x,y) **and** *Q(y,z)*
   $\rightarrow$
   R(x,z)

the first premise is marked by an entrypoint. Thus, a forward inference step can be initiated by the fact *P(a,b)*; if the second literal of the forward rule can be proven by *Q(b,c)*, the literal *R(a,c)* has been deduced by a forward inference step. This fact can be the input of another forward inferencing cycle.

Since the inferential closure is infinite in general, the forward search depth, i.e., the number of iterations for using deduced facts as new triggering formulas for further forward inference steps, needs to be limited by a special parameter of the knowledge base extender.

Sort Processor

The sort processor solves logical inference tasks which refer to the sort hierarchy defined in terms of the sort declarations of a L_{LILOG} knowledge base. Typical such inference tasks that can be submitted to the sort processor are to test whether the subsumption relationship holds between two L_{LILOG} sort expressions, to compute the greatest lower bound for two sort expressions, or to ask whether a sort expression stands for the empty set.

This kind of inferencing is on the one hand offered to users of the inference engine. On the other hand we use the sort processor also within the inference engine, e.g., during the unification process when the compatibility between the sort of a variable and the sort of a term that shall be substituted for the variable has to be checked. Processing the sort literals, i.e., those literals where the predicate is a sort expression, also requires us to invoke the sort processor for checking whether a sort literal can be eliminated (see also Sect. 4 and [Beierle *et al.* 1989]).

The sort processor is realized in terms of an inconsistency checker for sort expressions since all the inference tasks concerning sort expressions can be reduced to the question whether a sort expression is inconsistent, i.e., whether it stands for the empty set. If we have to test whether a subsumption relation *se* $\ll$ *se'* holds, this is equivalent to the question whether **and***(se,* **not***(se'))* stands for the empty set. The computation of the greatest lower bound of two sort expressions can be represented in terms of subsumption tests and an inconsistency test.

3.2   The General Proof Procedure

The General Proof Procedure (GPP) can be considered as the heart of the inference engine. It is the basic inference algorithm on top of which the Problem Solver and the Knowledge Base Extender offered at the Logic Interface are realized through special calls of the GPP.

From an abstract point of view the GPP can be viewed as a theorem prover, as its essential task is to prove goals formulated in L$_{\text{LILOG}}$. Typical theorem provers that have been developed in the recent past like the Prolog Technology Theorem Prover (see [Stickel 1984]) or SETHEO (see [Letz et al., to appear 1991]) focus on the efficient implementation of pure predicate logic. Their efficiency results from choosing one specific inference calculus as the basis of the prover and then implementing it in "lower"-level languages like C by using special implementation techniques such as abstract machines.

All these provers have been designed as stand-alone implementations of predicate logic and efficiency has often been their major design objective. In contrast to that, the inference engine for L$_{\text{LILOG}}$ has been designed with a concrete application in mind: to be the processor of the semantic knowledge of a natural language understanding system. Moreover, the idea of being able to experiment with inference calculi and search strategies has had a major influence on the architecture of our proof procedure as well. Thus, our main objective was to have an inference engine that was able to deal with a quite broad range of different tasks and was easily adaptable to new applications. In order to achieve these objectives efficiency had to be sacrificed.

Considering the spectrum of possible objectives one may set up for developing a theorem prover, the LILOG inference engine stands a bit off the mainstream, where efficiency seems to be the major concern. Thus, making direct comparisons between rigid high-speed provers for pure predicate logic and a flexible prover for a powerful sorted logic gets a bit difficult.

Characteristics of the General Proof Procedure

The General Proof Procedure is realized as a search procedure for traversing/constructing proof graphs. Comparing it to standard theorem provers, there are several special features distinguishing it from them:

- *Generalized clauses* are used instead of normal clauses. These generalized clauses are disjunctions of *complex literals* consisting themselves of a conjunction of (simple) literals (cf. [Pletat, this volume]).

  This representation avoids certain disadvantages of the classical clausal normal form. In particular, rules with conjunctive conclusions or disjunctive premises need not to be split into several clauses. Also for representing the negation of L$_{\text{LILOG}}$-goals one generalized clause is sufficient, since the negation of the goal formula yields a disjunction of conjunctions, i.e. again a clause in our generalized normal form.

  Using generalized clauses the proofs become shorter in general. Furthermore, due to a method for generating lemmas, multiple proofs of identical subgoals can be avoided.

- The GPP can run under different *inference calculi* as well as different *search strategies*. Therefore the "naked" GPP, i.e., without a calculus and search strategy plugged in, can be considered as a theorem prover shell.

  For the GPP an inference calculus is a set of calculus rules. In the current implementation the following rules are realized; they are described (except the last two ones) in Sect. 4.

  - The *model elimination extension* rule (see [Loveland 1978]) adapted to our generalized clauses.

  - The *model elimination reduction* rule adapted to the generalized clauses.

  - The *sort-elimination* rule for proving sort formulas.

  - The *execute-builtin* rule for evaluating built-in predicates and functions, features and built-in arithmetic operators that occur in equations and inequations.

  - The *tms-lookup* rule for consulting the Truth Maintenance System (see Sect. 3.3.1),

  - The *depic-inspection* rule for letting a subgoal be proven by the depictional component (see Sect. 3.4), the only external reasoning component connected to the GPP at the moment.

The GPP can run with any subset of these rules. Thus it is easy to configure the inference engine. If, for example, one is not interested in using the TMS or the depictional component, one only has to delete the corresponding inference rule from the calculus. Adding a new rule is also not too complicated. One has to write the Prolog code that implements the rule without having to modify existing code.

- A part of the search space can be temporarily disregarded during a proof. This is realized by introducing a new kind of nodes in the search tree or graph, the *suspended* nodes, which will be explained in more detail below.

- The conditions for terminating the search of a proof can be quite complex. In particular, it is rarely enough to deduce the empty clause as in classical theorem proving applications, as the GPP has to support the realization of a variety of other inference tasks.

Finding a Proof as a General Search Problem

The task of finding a proof of a logical formula can be formulated in terms of a tree/graph-search-problem (cf. [Nilsson 1980]); i.e., given a set of nodes with some specific initial and terminal nodes plus a relation that determines the successors for each node, the problem is to find a path from an initial node to a terminal node.

For resolution-based calculi the nodes in such a tree represent clauses from the initial clause set (also called the input set) as well as clauses created during the proof. The set of initial nodes depends on the resolution refinement[2] used. Considering the set-of-support strategy, for example, the initial nodes of the proof graph are the clauses of the support set; for the linear resolution and model elimination one has to choose one of the input clauses, such that the set of the remaining clauses is satisfiable.

The expansion of a node, i.e., the calculation of its successor clauses, consists of applying the calculus rules with possibly additional arguments to this selected node. For the resolution rule, expanding the selected node means performing all the resolution steps which are valid according to the resolution refinement used. In case of the set-of-support strategy, all clauses in the current search tree and the initial clause can be used, as due to the choice of the initial nodes the proof tree contains only descendants of clauses from the support set, such that resolution steps of clauses not belonging to the support set are excluded. If linear resolution or model elimination are used, the relevant clauses for performing resolution steps with the selected node are those of the input set, in case of linear resolution, the predecessors of the clause to be expanded have to be considered as well.

A terminal node in a normal theorem-proving application corresponds to the empty clause. But as we use the inference engine for a variety of user-specified inference tasks, the conditions for a terminal node can be more complex, and only in few situations does the empty clause happen to be a terminal clause. For example, when the GPP is used for executing forward inferences any clause containing only literals originating from the conclusion of an applied forward inference rule qualifies as a terminal clause. This is due to the fact that in forward chaining mode we resolve away the premises of some L$_{\text{LILOG}}$ axioms and take the instances of the conclusions as inferred formulas.

The search space is traversed according to a certain strategy. In the context of tree/graph-search there are two kinds of nodes: the open and closed nodes. Open nodes have not yet been expanded, whereas for closed nodes the successors have been determined already. The role of the strategy is therefore to select the next open node to be expanded; in the depth-first search this is the latest created open node, for an apparently more intelligent strategy this could be the node with the shortest clause.

---

[2] We assume here that different refinements of the resolution rule constitute different resolution calculi. For the most common resolution refinements see [Chang and Lee 1973] or [Loveland 1978].

The distinction between closed and open nodes is the simplest one. For our proof procedure we have introduced a third class of node, called suspended nodes, in order to realize more complex search strategies. Suspended nodes are nodes which are temporarily disregarded by the search procedure. In situations where no terminal node could be reached, suspended nodes are "reactivated" for the search. Various search strategies can be modeled using the concept of suspended nodes: for example iterative deepening, where a node is suspended, if its depth is equal to the current maximal search depth, or a combination of an efficient, incomplete search strategy with a less efficient, but complete one, where the suspended nodes play the role of a reserve to be used when the efficient search strategy fails. This technique also allows the focusing of the search to particular solutions, as nodes that lead to incompatible solutions are simply suspended. We explain this in more detail in the section about the proof graph analyzer.

After this general overview we describe the proof procedure in more detail by walking through one inference cycle of the inference engine. Figure 3 shows the main parts of the general proof procedure. The indices in the boxes indicate for the corresponding subprocedures whether they are parametrized by the inference calculi (C) or by the search strategies (S):

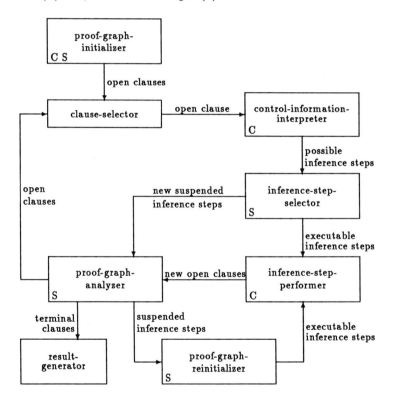

Figure 3: The general proof procedure

Proof Graph Initializer

Due to our model elimination calculus for generalized clauses, the initialization of the proof graph becomes trivial. We suppose that background and text knowledge bases, from which the goal shall be derived, are consistent. According to the model elimination calculus the goal is a logical consequence of these knowledge bases if the proof search leads to a terminal clause when starting from one of the clauses in the negated goal. The usual choice of the starting clause can be avoided for our generalized clauses, since the negated goal can always be represented by exactly one generalized clause. This choice would be necessary if we had used the classical clausal normal form; e.g., the negation of the goal $P \lor Q$ yields $\neg P \land \neg Q$, which is a single clause (with one complex literal) in our normal form, but has to be represented by two clauses in the classical normal form.

Additionally, a temporary proof knowledge base for the clauses of the proof graph is created where the initial goal clause is stored. Including this clause in the input clause set is necessary for obtaining indefinite solutions.

Clause Selector

When entering a new inference cycle, the first activity is to select a clause to be expanded next. The set of open clauses in the proof graph is always ordered according to the criteria imposed by the search strategy. Therefore the clause selector has just the trivial task of taking the first open clause as the clause to be expanded.

Control Information Interpreter

Given the selected clause, the control information interpreter determines the possible inference steps that can be applied to this selected open clause. In some sense, the actual calculus rules themselves make this choice because a calculus rule not only performs the actions for its execution, but determines also its potential inference steps. In this way, a resolution-like calculus rule selects those clauses to which it can be applied. This allows us to conceive different calculus rules that perform the same actions but interpret the control knowledge in different ways, e.g., one rule may consider only L_{LILOG}-rules whose conclusion is marked by an entrypoint, whereas another calculus rule may look at all clauses in the knowledge bases.

For resolution-like inference steps, the unifier can be determined already when computing the possible inference steps. This means that we select only such clauses for the possible inference steps which pass the "full unification filter". Due to the complex sort information which has to be considered during the unification process as well, computing the unifiers as part of the clause selection may be too costly. As an alternative, one may specify special calculus rules for which the cheaper unsorted unification is done by the control information interpreter and the more expensive sort checks are executed by the inference step performer.

This shows that we interpret the term "calculus rule" in a very broad sense and also that a part of the inference strategy is transferred into the calculus rules. However, as one of our main goals is to be able to have an experimental environment for testing different calculi with different strategies, this general concept of calculus rules is an important means to achieve the amount of flexibility we are aiming at.

Calculus rules may require specific control operators in order to be applied. The switch to the external reasoners is realized by such an operator. If a literal of the goal should be proven by such a component it has to be marked by the corresponding control information. The calculus rule for invoking an external reasoner checks whether the respective control information is attached to the goal literal, and only if this is the case does it generate the corresponding inference step specification consisting of the calculus rule with its arguments.

The same holds for the rules processing literals that involve specific predicates. The execute-builtin rule, for instance, checks if the literal to be proven is an equation or has a built-in predicate. Analogously, the sort-elimination rule tests whether the literal to be processed is a sort literal.

Inference Step Selector

The output of the control information interpreter is a set of inference step specifications, containing the necessary information for the execution of an inference step. This set of possible resolution steps is divided according to a strategy which is a part of the search strategy by the inference step selector into two disjoint subsets: the set of executable inference steps and the set of the suspended inference steps.

Inference Step Performer

The inference step performer executes the selected inference steps. For resolution steps this means in general that the two parent clauses, instantiated by the calculated unifier, are concatenated without the resolved literals. Other inference steps need more processing, e.g., if an external reasoner is consulted.

Proof Graph Analyzer

The result of the inference step performer is a set of new open clauses. This set has to be integrated into the existing proof graph which consists of the actual sets of open, suspended, closed and terminal nodes. More precisely, the new terminal clauses are determined. The remaining new open clauses are integrated into the set of open clauses according to the search strategy, e.g., if we have breadth-first search, the set of open clauses is reperesented by a list and the new open clauses are added at the end of that list.

It may happen that the set of the open clauses and the set of the terminal clauses are not disjoint. This is useful for realizing certain options in an elegant way. According to one option, one may request to deduce the most specific facts by forward inferences, i.e., if a disjunction $D_1 \vee D_2$ can be deduced and $\neg D_1$ can be proven (or in other words the literals in D_1 can be "resolved away") then D_2 should be inferred by forward inferences. $D_1 \vee D_2$ already represents a terminal clause. To specialize this disjunction it is necessary to try additional inference steps so that $D_1 \vee D_2$ also has to remain in the set of the open clauses.

This possibility of allowing a clause to be both a terminal and as an open clause is also exploited for handling the presupposition order of the subgoals in the representation of a question. According to this option the subgoals have to be processed in a certain order until the proof of one subgoal fails. The result of this process is either the list of proven or the list of nonproven subgoals of the original question representation. A simple way to achieve this is to include open clauses whose literals originate from the initial question representation into the set of terminal clauses as well. After the proof search, the literals in the shortest terminal clause represent the minimal set of nonproven subgoals.

The proof graph analyzer is also the part of the GPP responsible for focusing the search on specific solutions. How is that achieved? Suppose that for a query

> **goal** *goal-1*
> **exists** $X{:}S_X$, $Y{:}S_Y$;
> ?- $Q(X,Y)$.

the preferred solutions for X are a_1 or a_2 and those for Y are b_1, b_2 or b_3. The proof graph analyzer determines for every new open clause if the instantiations of the variables X and Y are still compatible with the preferred solutions. If X is replaced by a term t_X this means that t_X has to be unifiable with either a_1 or a_2; thus, if t_X is a variable, the sort of t_X has to be a supersort of sort of a_1 or a_2. In case t_X is a ground term, it has to be either a_1 or a_2. Open clauses whose instantiations of X and Y are incompatible with the preferred solutions are suspended, i.e., in our search tree we have two classes of suspended nodes: *suspended inference steps* determined according to a search strategy and *suspend clauses* for realizing the preferred solutions option. If no open clauses are left in the search tree, the proof graph analyzer has to drop one of the constraints for the instantiations of the variables. In our example these may be the constraints on the variable X. Then all suspended clauses are reactivated, i.e., reconsidered as open clauses which don't violate the remaining constraints, and the proof search continues as usual.

Having determined the new sets of open, suspended and terminal clauses, the proof graph analyzer has to decide whether the proof is finished. This depends on the option specifying the number of desired solutions. If only one solution shall be computed, the proof terminates when the first (real) terminal clause has been generated. If all solutions are desired, then the search continues until the set of open clauses becomes empty.

Result Generator

The result generator has to select the relevant terminal clauses that contribute to the results. As the example of the most special facts deduced by forward inferences shows, there may be terminal clauses that can be subsumed by other terminal clauses. From the selected terminal clauses the results are determined according to the "kind-of-result" options. With these options one can specify whether valid instantiations of the goal, the valid substitutions, or simply success/fail should be the inference result reported by the GPP.

Proof Graph Re-Initializer

If the set of open clauses is empty and there are still some suspended nodes not satisfying the termination conditions, we can reactivate such suspended inference steps as possible ones and select one of them according to the search strategy for the re-inititialization of the search. The selected inference steps are executed and the generated clauses constitute the new set of open clauses.

3.3   Inconsistency Checker for Sort Expressions

The basic inference algorithm for processing the knowledge given in terms of the sort declarations of a L$_{\text{LILOG}}$ knowledge base is an inconsistency checker for sort expressions. Its task is to decide whether a sort expression stands for the empty set. Due to the richness of our sort description language, other inference tasks concerning the sort information of a knowledge base can be reduced to the question of whether a sort expression is inconsistent (see also Sect. 3.1).

The basic steps of the inconsistency checking algorithm are the ones described below:

1. Fully expand the given sort expression according to the sort constraints in the knowledge base. This replaces every occurrence of a sort name by a sort expression corresponding to the constraints for that sort name. Apply this expansion process recursively until no further expansion of user defined sort names is possible.

   The recursive nature of the expansion process requires that the sorts of a knowledge base must not be defined cyclically. This is checked by an algorithm for detecting cyclic sorts within a knowledge base.

2. Normalize the expanded sort expression by transforming it according to the following rules:

   - Push the negation symbols inward as far as possible; after this only sort names and enumerations can be negated.
   - Apply the law of associativity by flattening nested intersections and nested unions.
   - Contract sort expressions $f{:}se$ and $f{:}se'$ appearing in an intersection to $f{:}\mathbf{and}(se,\ se')$ until there is at most one such expression per feature within an intersection.
   - Contract sort expressions $r{::}se$ and $r{::}se'$ appearing in an intersection to $r{::}\mathbf{and}(se,\ se')$ until there is at most one such expression per role within an intersection.
   - Contract the enumerations (and negated enumerations) in intersections until there remains exactly one enumeration per intersection or the intersection is replaced by the empty set.

3. Test whether the consistency of the normalized sort expression can be assured, i.e., the sort expression cannot be inconsistent.
This is the termination condition for delivering a negative result.

4. Test whether the inconsistency of the normalized sort expression can be assured.
This is the termination condition for delivering a positive result.

5. If the termination conditions are not satisfied, reduce the question whether the given sort expression is inconsistent to certain subgoals, i.e., to the inconsistency of other sort expressions, according to the inconsistency checking calculus for L_{LILOG} sort expressions to be described in [Pletat, to appear 1991].

Besides computing whether a sort expression stands for the empty set, the sort processor stores the results it has once computed by filling a table of greatest lower bounds of sort expressions in order to avoid repeated computations during the lifetime of a knowledge base.

3.3.1 Truth Maintenance System

The truth maintenance system (TMS) is a subsystem of the inference engine. It maintains the assumptions and conclusions generated by the general proof procedure, and protocols the dependencies between them. Thus it is able to determine the current set of valid conclusions (*beliefs*) and to name the assumptions supporting those conclusions. If an inconsistency arises, the TMS follows the dependencies back to the assumptions which caused the inconsistency. It can remove these assumptions and all dependent conclusions from the set of current beliefs. In other words, it propagates validity changes (of assumptions and conclusions) through some kind of dependency network. So a TMS is a practical tool for the revision of inconsistent sets of beliefs.

Besides its main purpose of supporting belief revision, a TMS can serve as a *cache* for inferred problem solver data. Since it protocols the inference process it can also generate simple explanations. Some types of TMS also control the inference process of the problem solver, e.g., by supporting intelligent search strategies such as dependency-directed backtracking. The best-known TMSs are those of [Doyle 1979] and [de Kleer 1986].

Default Reasoning in LILOG

In [Pletat, this volume] the basic ideas of default reasoning in LILOG have been described. The use of a default in an inference process can be viewed as introducing an assumption, that is, the assumption that there is no information to the contrary. The defaults in L_{LILOG} are partially ordered according to the underlying sort hierarchy, so we have different levels of default information (defaults of different *quality*). "Information to the contrary" means that a default can be overwritten by "hard" information or by a stronger default. According to a skeptical approach, contradictory defaults of the same or incomparable quality cancel each other.

Since defaults are only generalized axioms (with the generalized quantifiers **p-default** and **o-default**), they can be used just like other axioms during proof search. The resulting proof is of a certain quality depending on the defaults used in it. Thus proofs are defeasible, i.e., they can be invalidated by contradictory proofs of higher quality[3]. Defeasible proofs are called *arguments*, and an *argument-based TMS (ArgTMS)* maintains sets of such arguments, compares their qualities, computes a validity, and propagates any changes in the validity of arguments.

---

[3]The way contradictory defeasible proofs influence each other is similar to skeptical inheritance [Horty *et al.* 1987]. It is described in full detail in [Lorenz 1989].

The Argument-Based TMS

The validity of an argument is determined within a given set of arguments. Of course, a realistic problem solver will be restricted to finite sets of arguments. Validity of an argument for a statement φ means that the current information level supports the conclusion φ. New information leading to new arguments can invalidate φ. A problem solver will incrementally build up a set of arguments. An adequate representation for this set of arguments has to be found, which keeps track of the interdependencies between arguments and is able to reflect the current set of supported statements. This task is performed by the argument-based TMS (ArgTMS).

The ArgTMS receives arguments (proofs) from the general proof procedure of the inference engine. It computes their quality, integrates them into the current set of arguments, and evaluates their validity along with a re-evaluation of all arguments somehow affected by the new ones. On the other hand the ArgTMS answers questions on the validity of statements according to the current set of arguments.

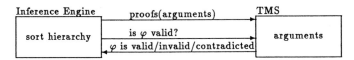

Figure 4: Inference engine / TMS interface

The Components and Operations of the ArgTMS

The central components of the ArgTMS are *argument nodes* and *data nodes*. An argument node represents the usage of one formula or default in a proof. The entire proof is represented by a tree of argument nodes whose leaves are the facts (default or "hard") the proof is based upon. Inner nodes represent hard or default rules, whose premises are supported by subproofs. The entire tree of argument nodes is called an *argument*. Every subtree of an argument is itself a (sub-)argument. Each argument has a certain *quality* which depends on the sorts of the defaults of its argument nodes. Furthermore an argument has a *validity* label which is either 'valid', 'invalid', or 'contradicted'[4].

Arguments for or against a statement (*positive* or *negative* arguments) are connected via a data node. A data node represents a statement *along with its complement*. This is important, since during validity evaluation positive and negative arguments for a statement have to be compared. Data nodes can have *positive support* if one or more positive arguments are valid, *negative support* if one or more negative arguments are valid, or no support at all, e.g., if there are only contradicted arguments for the statement represented by the data node. A data node cannot have positive and negative support at the same time. If a data node has positive support then the statement it represents is said to be valid. If it has negative support then the negated statement is valid.

The main operations the ArgTMS has to perform are the evaluation of the argument validity and the propagation of validity changes to superarguments of an argument which changed its validity label. The construction of arguments ensures that the resulting graph is acyclic (which was already implied by use of the word *argument tree*), so that the propagation is guaranteed to terminate. Furthermore, some preservation properties of argument sets restrict the propagation process to certain subargument-argument validity constellations.

To give a rough idea how the ArgTMS works let us consider the following part of an L_{LILOG} knowledge base:

---

[4]'contradicted' means that the argument is not 'valid', but it might (in contrast to 'invalid' arguments) still invalidate other arguments. Both arguments in the Nixon-diamond example of [Pletat, this volume] are 'contradicted' in this sense.

sort *circus-performer.*
sort *elephant.*
sort *circus-elephant* = **and**(*circus-performer,elephant*).
sort *young-circus-elephant* < *circus-elephant.*
refo *clyde : young-circus-elephant.*
axiom *trained-elephants-are-not-shy*
   p-default X *: circus-performer*
   trained(X)
      →
   not *shy(X).*
axiom *elephants-are-shy*
   p-default X *: elephant*
   shy(X).
axiom *circus-elephants-are-trained*
   p-default X *: circus-elephant*
   trained(X).
axiom *young-circus-elephants-are-not-trained*
   p-default X *: young-circus-elephant*
   not *trained(X).*

There are two arguments concerning the shyness of *clyde*:

$$A1 = \langle\ trained(clyde),\ trained(clyde) \rightarrow \neg\ shy(clyde)\ \rangle$$

supports ¬ *shy(clyde)* while

$$A2 = \langle\ shy(clyde)\ \rangle$$

supports *shy(clyde)*. Of course, *A1* and *A2* are contradictory and their respective qualities are incomparable since the sorts *circus-performer* and *elephant* are incomparable with respect to subsumption. But argument *A1* is invalidated by argument

$$A3 = \langle\ \neg\ trained(clyde)\ \rangle$$

which is of higher quality than the subargument

$$A1' = \langle\ trained(clyde)\ \rangle$$

of *A1*. Hence, argument *A2* "wins" although contradicted by the invalidated argument *A1*.

The corresponding ArgTMS structure is shown in Figure 5. The two data nodes *trained(clyde)* and *shy(clyde)* each have one positive and one negative argument.

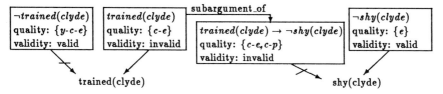

Figure 5: An example of an ArgTMS structure

3.4 External Reasoners

In the current implementation there is one external reasoner attached to the inference engine: the depictional component ([Khenkhar 1989], [Habel, this volume]), which reasons over spatial information on the basis of analog representations. The two main processes of this component are

- imagination, and

- inspection.

The *imagination* process generates the analog representation for a certain spatial relationship within the internal knowledge base of the depictional reasoner. It is activated when the knowledge base extender derives a literal which is marked to be processed by the depiction module. Instead of adding the literal to the propositional knowledge base it is handed to the depiction module to be memorized there. The *inspection* is the dual process. It determines if a certain spatial relationship holds. The *depic-inspection* calculus rule transfers a literal that shall be processed outside the theorem prover to the depiction component. In case the depiction module is able to prove this subgoal it returns an answer substitution to the general proof procedure which can then resolve away this literal.

3.5 Access to the Knowledge

The knowledge base access system allows us to retrieve the knowledge entities of a L_{LILOG} knowledge base we need for the inferential processes. In the corresponding queries, syntactic properties can be specified as search patterns. Thus we may search for the declarations of certain predicates, the roles and features of specific sorts, or axioms of a certain type (like facts or backward chaining rules) containing certain literals (e.g., with a specific predicate and polarity).

This knowledge base access system is realized in terms of an interface module to the LILOG data base system ([Ludwig 1990], [Gehlen *et al.*, this volume]) that has been developed as an advanced background storage mechanism satisfying special requirements from the knowledge based systems context.

4 Logical Basis

In this section we want to describe the basic logical mechanisms, in particular the calculus rules, that make the inference engine work.

Basically, L_{LILOG} can be considered as an enhanced order-sorted predicate logic. For processing the axiomatic part of L_{LILOG} knowledge bases we have developed an extension of Loveland's model elimination method [Loveland 1969], where order-sorted unification is used for taking into account the type restrictions of terms. There are, however, some features of L_{LILOG} that go beyond pure order-sorted predicate logic and require special calculus rules for their appropriate treatment. Sort literals, i.e., literals where sort expressions are used as unary predicates, can be used in any axiom. They are processed by the *sort-elimination* rule. Due to the close coupling between the taxonomic and the axiomatic part of L_{LILOG} terms may be of a more specific sort than their declared sort. To take this possibility into account we need an extension of order-sorted unification as part of our calculus.

A specific treatment is also required for built-in predicates as well as for handling equality. The *execute-builtin* rule realizes this in a pragmatic, but still incomplete way.

Model Elimination for Generalized Clauses

L_{LILOG}-axioms are internally represented by *generalized clauses* which are disjunctions of conjunctions of literals. We refer to conjunctions of literals also as *complex literals*. This representation has in particular the advantage that every L_{LILOG}-axiom can be represented by one generalized clause.

In this section we present the unsorted version of an extension of the model elimination calculus to generalized clauses. To adapt it to order-sorted predicate logic one has only to use order-sorted unification instead of standard unsorted term unification.

The standard model elimination calculus[5] for ordinary clauses, i.e., disjunctions of simple literals, can be considered as a refinement of linear resolution where resolution steps are restricted to input clauses. Resolution steps with predecessor clauses in the proof tree are simulated by the reduction rule. For this it is necessary to mark resolved literals instead of deleting them.

More precisely, instead of clauses, we have *chains* which are ordered sequences of ordinary literals, called *O-literals*, and resolved literals, *R-literals*. R-literals are enclosed in brackets ([L]) to distinguish them from O-literals. Chains containing only O-literals are *elementary* chains. A chain is called *admissible* if the rightmost literal is an O-literal. The *contraction operation* transforms a chain into an admissible one by removing all R-literals to the right of the rightmost O-literal.

The model elimination method consists of two inference operations:

- the *extension rule* corresponding to the resolution rule, and

- the *reduction rule*.

To define them we use the notion of *complementarity of literals* and say that two literals L_1 and L_2 can be made complementary with a most general unifier Θ iff L_1 and the complement of L_2 are unifiable with a most general unifier Θ.

The extension and reduction rules are defined as follows:

ME Extension: Let $c_1 = c_1' L_1$ and $c_2 = c_2' L_2 c_2''$ be two admissible chains, L_1 and L_2 be O-literals and α be a renaming of the variables in c_2 such that c_1 and $c_2\alpha$ have no variables in common. If L_1 and $L_2\alpha$ can be made complementary with a most general unifier Θ, then the contraction of $(c_1'[L_1]c_2'\alpha c_2''\alpha)\Theta$ is called the *ME extension* of c_1 with c_2.

ME Reduction: Let $c = c'[L_1]c''L_2$ be an admissible chain. If L_1 and L_2 can be made complementary with a most general unifier Θ then the contraction of $(c'[L_1]c'')\Theta$ is a result of the *ME reduction* of c.

The rationale behind the reduction rule is that in a chain $c'[L]c''$ the subchain $c'L$ is always an instance of a chain used for an extension step. Therefore the reduction of a chain corresponds to an extension step eventually followed by a factorization.

Example 1 *We will use the following example to illustrate our modifications of the standard model elimination calculus.*
Given the following axioms:
ax_1: $\forall x G(x) \lor Y(x) \rightarrow C(x) \land S(x)$,
ax_2: $G(p) \lor Y(p)$,
where $G(x)$ may stand for "x is a gourmet", $Y(x)$ for "x is a yuppy", $C(x)$ for "x likes to drink champagne", $S(x)$ for "x likes to eat snails" and p can be interpreted as "Peter", we would like to prove the goal
g: $\exists x C(x) \land S(x)$.

After building a clausal normal form of the axioms and the negated goal we get the following deduction of the empty chain $\Box$:

---

[5]To be more precise it is Loveland's *weak* model elimination method [Loveland 1978] that we will present in the following.

(a_{11}) $\neg G(x)C(x)$
(a_{12}) $\neg G(x)S(x)$
(a_{13}) $\neg Y(x)C(x)$
(a_{14}) $\neg Y(x)S(x)$
(a_2) $G(p)Y(p)$
(1) $\neg C(x)\neg S(x)$ *negation of the goal*
(2) $\neg C(x)[\neg S(x)]\neg G(x)$ *extension with a_{12}*
(3) $\neg C(p)[\neg S(p)][\neg G(p)]Y(p)$ *extension with a_2*
(4) $\neg C(p)[\neg S(p)][\neg G(p)][Y(p)]S(p)$ *extension with a_{14}*
(5) $\neg C(p)$ *reduction*
(6) $[\neg C(p)]\neg G(p)$ *extension with a_{11}*
(7) $[\neg C(p)][\neg G(p)]Y(p)$ *extension with a_2*
(8) $[\neg C(p)][\neg G(p)][Y(p)]C(p)$ *extension with a_{13}*
(9) $\square$ *reduction*

Extension and reduction are sound inference rules. Moreover, they form a (refutationally) complete calculus.

Extending this basic model elimination calculus to generalized clauses is very easy. One just has to modify the conditions on the complementarity of literals. Making two (simple) literals complementary is equivalent to finding a substitution such that the conjunction of these two literals is inconsistent. If one takes complex literals instead of simple literals, it is easy to see that it suffices to find one simple literal in each of the two complex literals and make them complementary. This is due to the fact that a complex literal is a conjunction of simple literals.

Therefore we may extend the notion of *complementarity of literals* introduced above to complex literals in the following way: Let $\mathcal{L}_1 = L_{11} \wedge ... \wedge L_{1m}$ and $\mathcal{L}_2 = L_{21} \wedge ... \wedge L_{2n}$ be two complex literals. $\mathcal{L}_1$ and $\mathcal{L}_2$ can be made *complementary*, with a *most general unifier* Θ, iff a simple literal L_{1i} from $\mathcal{L}_1$ and the complement of a simple literal L_{2j} from $\mathcal{L}_2$ are unifiable with most general unifier Θ.

To adapt the ME-extension and ME-reduction rules to generalized clauses (or better chains) it suffices to use this notion of complementarity. We call these modified rules *GME-extension* and *GME-reduction*.

Example 2 *Having built generalized chains for the axioms and the negated goal of Example 1 we get the following GME-refutation:*

(a_1) $(\neg G(x) \wedge \neg Y(x))(C(x) \wedge S(x))$
(a_2) $G(p)Y(p)$
(1) $\neg C(x)\neg S(x)$ *negation of the goal*
(2) $\neg C(x)[\neg S(x)](\neg G(x) \wedge \neg Y(x))$ *extension with (a_1)*
(3) $\neg C(p)[\neg S(p)][\neg G(p) \wedge \neg Y(p)]G(p)$ *extension with (a_2)*
(4) $\neg C(p)$ *reduction*
(5) $[\neg C(p)](\neg G(p) \wedge \neg Y(p))$ *extension with (a_1)*
(6) $[\neg C(p)][\neg G(p) \wedge \neg Y(p)]G(p)$ *extension with (a_2)*
(7) $\square$ *reduction*

GME extension and GME reduction are sound inference rules. Together they form a complete calculus (see [Bollinger 1991]).

Although GME-refutations are in general shorter than the corresponding ME-refutations, we still have the problem of redundant proofs of premises whose rules have conjunctive conclusions. In Example 2 we see that the chain a_1 is applied twice, whereas one application should suffice. In chain (2) the "premise" literal $\neg G(x) \wedge \neg Y(x)$ of a_1 stands to the right of the resolved literal. If this literal is proven one can deduce the conclusion. This is done by the two subsequent inference steps, i.e. at that moment $C(p) \wedge S(p)$ should have been deduced as a lemma. How can we achieve this?

We introduce a third type of literal called *lemma candidates* or *L-literals*. When extending a chain $\mathcal{C}$ with an auxiliary chain $\mathcal{C}_a$ the resolved literal in $\mathcal{C}_a$ is declared as a lemma candidate and is put besides the bracketed literal, the resolved (complex) literal of C, in the resulting chain. Lemma candidates are put into braces, such that, in Example 2 above, the extension step of chain (1) with chain a_1 yields:

(2') $\neg C(x)[\neg S(x)]\{C(x) \wedge S(x)\}(\neg G(x) \wedge \neg Y(x))$

If it is possible to deduce the empty chain from the subchain to the right of an L-literal, the corresponding instantiation of the L-literal becomes a valid lemma.

Example 3 *The refutation of Example 2 becomes shorter if lemmas are generated:*

(a_1)	$(\neg G(x) \wedge \neg Y(x))(C(x) \wedge S(x))$	
(a_2)	$G(p)Y(p)$	
(1)	$\neg C(x)\neg S(x)$	negation of the goal
(2)	$\neg C(x)[\neg S(x)]\{C(x) \wedge S(x)\}(\neg G(x) \wedge \neg Y(x))$	extension with (a_1)
(3)	$\neg C(p)[\neg S(p)]\{C(p) \wedge S(p)\}[\neg G(p) \wedge \neg Y(p)]G(p)$	extension with (a_2)
(4)	$\neg C(p)$	reduction and
		generation of lemma
		$(l)\ C(p) \wedge S(p)$
(5)	$\square$	extension with (l)

A more detailed presentation of our generalized model elimination calculus can be found in [Bollinger 1991].

Proving Sort Literals

In the axiomatic part of L_{LILOG} the sort membership relation can be explicitly referred to by sort literals. To process them appropriately, the GME-rules described above have to be generalized. This is necessary as sort literals can be made complementary even though they do not have the same sort at the predicate position; e.g., if the sort *car* is a subsort of *vehicle* the sort literals $\neg\{vehicle\}(t)$ $\{car\}(t)$ are complementary, i.e., the conjunction $\neg\{vehicle\}(t) \wedge \{car\}(t)$ is inconsistent, as there is no car that is not a vehicle, or in other words, as the sort expression $and(not(vehicle), car)$ denotes the empty set.

For (simple) sort literals we therefore define the notion of complementarity as follows: Let $S_1(t_1)$ and $\neg S_2(t_2)$ be two sort literals. They can be made complementary, iff t_1 and t_2 are unifiable with a most general unifier Θ and the sort expression $and(not(S_1), S_2)$ is inconsistent.

However, with the GME-rules using this extended notion of complementarity not all possible cases are covered. Sort literals can also be proven just by comparing the sort in the predicate position with the sort of the argument. For these cases we have developed the *sort-elimination* rule. First it tries to prove (or better refute) the sort literal subgoal directly by exploiting the following conditions under which a sort literal holds (or its negation is inconsistent):

Let SE be a sort expression and t a term with the sort S_t. We have
$\{SE\}(t) \Longleftrightarrow TRUE$ (or equivalently $\neg\{SE\}(t) \Longleftrightarrow FALSE$)

- if t is a variable, SE and S_t must have common elements,
  i.e., the intersection $and(SE, S_t)$ must not be the empty set, or

- if t is a non-variable term, t has to belong to SE too,
  for which it is sufficent that S_t is a subsort of SE.

The above conditions can also be applied analogously to sort literals with negative polarity due to $\neg\{SE\}(t) \Longleftrightarrow \{not(SE)\}(t)$.

For determining the most specific sort of a term, it may be necessary to derive it from the axioms of a knowledge base. Therefore, if a sort literal cannot be proven according to the above description, the following equivalences are exploited by the sort-elimination rule, thus performing a theory resolution operation where the residues, i.e., the literals to be proven additionally, correspond to their right-hand sides. These equivalences can be considered also as a kind of second-order axioms being applied by the sort-elimination rule. If they cannot be applied directly to the sort-expression SE an attempt is made to expand it by replacing atomic sorts by their equivalent defining sort-expression.

$$
\begin{array}{lll}
(\text{se1}) & \{and(SE_1,\ SE_2)\}(x) & \Longleftrightarrow & \{SE_1\}(x) \land \{SE_2\}(x) \\
(\text{se2}) & \{or(SE_1,\ SE_2)\}(x) & \Longleftrightarrow & \{SE_1\}(x) \lor \{SE_2\}(x) \\
(\text{se3}) & \{not(SE)\}(x) & \Longleftrightarrow & \neg\{SE\}(x) \\
(\text{se4}) & \{\{a_1,...,a_n\}\}(x) & \Longleftrightarrow & a_1 = x \lor ... \lor a_n = x \\
(\text{se5}) & \{f:SE\}(x) & \Longleftrightarrow & \{SE\}(f(x)) \\
(\text{se6}) & \{ro::SE\}(x) & \Longleftrightarrow & \exists z : and(range(ro), SE)\ ro(x, z) \\
(\text{se7}) & \{some\ ro\}(x) & \Longleftrightarrow & \exists y : range(ro)\ ro(x, y) \\
(\text{se8}) & \{all\ ro\ SE\}(x) & \Longleftrightarrow & \forall y : range(ro)\ ro(x, y) \rightarrow \{SE\}(y) \\
(\text{se9}) & \{agree\ f_p\ f_{p'}\}(x) & \Longleftrightarrow & term(f_p, x) = term(f_{p'}, x) \\
(\text{se10}) & \{disagree\ f_p\ f_{p'}\}(x) & \Longleftrightarrow & term(f_p, x) \neq term(f_{p'}, x)
\end{array}
$$

where $term(f, x) = f(x)$ and $term(f \circ f_p, x) = term(f_p, f(x))$.

Example 4 *Given the following knowledge base containing information about one of the authors' favorite soccer club:*

    sort sort sports_club;

       roles champion_in :: int .

    sort soccer_club < sports_club.

    sort top_soccer_club = and(soccer_club, some champion_in).

    refo FC_Kaiserslautern : soccer_club.

    axiom FCKs_championships

       champion_in(FC_Kaiserslautern, 1951) **and**

       champion_in(FC_Kaiserslautern, 1953) **and**

       champion_in(FC_Kaiserslautern, 1991).

the query

?- { top_soccer_club }(FC_Kaiserslautern)

is solved by the following proof (to save space we omit here the R-literals):

    negated goal:

    (1) $\neg\{top\_soccer\_club\}(FC\_Kaiserslautern)$

    replacing top_soccer_club by defining sort expression:

    (2) $\neg\{and(soccer\_club, some\ champion\_in\}(FC\_Kaiserslautern)$

    application of (se1):

    (3) $\neg\{soccer\_club\}(FC\_Kaiserslautern)\ \neg\{some\ champion\_in\}\}(FC\_Kaiserslautern)$

    application of (se7):

    (4) $\neg\{soccer\_club\}(FC\_Kaiserslautern)\ \neg champion\_in(FC\_Kaiserslautern, y:int)$

    extension with FCKs_championships:

    (5) $\neg\{soccer\_club\}(FC\_Kaiserslautern)$

    soccer_club is the sort of FC_Kaiserslautern

    (6) $\square$

A presentation of similar calculus rules for processing sort literals can be found in [Hedtstück and Schmitt 1990].

Extending Order Sorted Unification

In the previous section we have seen that terms may be of a more specific sort (which can be deduced from L$_{\text{LILOG}}$-axioms) than their declared sort. This affects order-sorted unification, as one cannot always be sure that the declared sort of a term is the most specific one. In order-sorted unification a variable can be replaced by a non-variable term if the sort of the term is subsumed by the sort of the variable. If the corresponding subsumption check fails, it may still be possible that the required subsumption relation holds due to the axiomatic sort information about a term.

For example, given the knowledge base of Example 4, if one tries to prove the following goal

    goal *who_was_champion_in_1953*
        exists *X : top_soccer_club;*
        ?- champion_in(X, 1953).

the unification of the negated goal with the second conjunct of the axiom *FCKs_championships* fails. This is because *soccer_club*, the declared sort of *FC_Kaiserslautern*, is not a subsort of *top_soccer_club*. However, as we have seen in Example 4, one can prove that *FC_Kaiserslautern* belongs to *top_soccer_club*.

To remedy this situation we let the unification succeed conditionally. The (negated) conditions under which the unification should succeed are represented by new subgoal literals. According to our example the unification should succeed if $\{top\_soccer\_club\}(FC\_Kaiserslautern)$ can be proven, which is why its negation is added as a new subgoal. Or, more formally, the proof of *who_was_champion_in_1953* begins as follows:

    Negation of the goal who_was_champion_in_1953
    (1) $\neg champion\_in(X : top\_soccer\_club, 1953)$.
    extension with 2nd conjunct of FCKs_championships
    (2) $[\neg champion\_in(X : top\_soccer\_club, 1953)] \neg\{top\_soccer\_club\}(FC\_Kaiserslautern\}$
    ...

New subgoals should not be generated without restrictions. One of the big advantages of order-sorted unification is that it reduces the search space considerably, simply because terms to be unified have to pass the "sort check filter". If this filter is made more permeable we are sacrificing this advantage.

What may such restrictions look like? The most obvious restriction is to generate a new subgoal $\neg\{SE\}(t)$ only if the sort S_t and SE have a non-empty common subsort, i.e., $and(S_t, SE) \neq \perp$. The most restrictive version would be just to renounce the generation of new subgoals, which means that we accept a certain incompleteness of the calculus. To counterbalance this one may think of changing the declaration of a term dynamically if a more specific sort has been deduced by forward inferences. An additional measure would be to use a classifier which determines the most specific sort for each declared reference object during the compilation of a knowledge base.

For our system we have adopted the most restrictive solution with the counterbalancing measure. We are considering however realizing the generation of subgoals as an option of order-sorted unification, so that we can conduct experiments on how it influences the inferential behavior.

Axiomatizing Sort Expressions

The sort-elimination rule allows us to access axiomatic knowledge for determining taxomatic relationships, like the validity of a sort membership relation. We have also the inverse phenomenon.

Roles and features can be used as binary predicates and unary predicates respectively in L$_{\text{LILOG}}$-axioms, but their values may also be specified by sort expressions. To prove, for instance, a literal with a role as a predicate, it may be necessary to access this taxonomic knowledge.

One could think of considering literals with roles and features as sort literals and of extending the sort-elimination rule appropriately. For roles this could work. But for features this is more difficult, as they may appear arbitrarily nested in any term.

Therefore we have chosen another approach: Instead of "going " from the axiomatic to the taxonomic part, we do the inverse. We generate axioms for sort expressions according to the sort equivalences (se1) – (se10) above. This is done for every sort expression in the declaration of a sort and a reference object. However, as we are only interested in axioms with features and roles, we (pragmatically) restrict the generation of axioms to those containing no sort literals.

Example 5 *Given the following reference object declaration:*

> refo FC_Kaiserslautern : and(soccer_club ,
> > champion_in :: {1951},
> > champion_in :: {1953},
> > champion_in :: {1991},
> > city :{ Kaiserslautern})

the following axioms are generated:
> **axiom** sort_ax_1
> > champion_in(FC_Kaiserslautern, 1951).
>
> **axiom** sort_ax_2
> > champion_in(FC_Kaiserslautern, 1953).
>
> **axiom** sort_ax_3
> > champion_in(FC_Kaiserslautern, 1991).
>
> **axiom** sort_ax_4
> > city(FC_Kaiserslautern) = Kaiserslautern.

Executing Built-in Predicates and Functions

The *execute-builtin* rule evaluates built-in predicates and functions. We distinguish two classes of built-in predicates:

- predicates defined entirely by an external Prolog predicate,

- predicates like "=" or the arithmetic comparators needing some additional processing.

For the first class of built-in predicates we take into account that Prolog is able to compute only positive instances. "Negation by failure" is not considered here because of our "open world assumption", i.e., negative information has to be deducible explicitly and is not identified with the absence of positive information. Therefore only negative literals with such built-in predicates are treated by the execute-builtin rule, which passes the atomic formula to Prolog and asks it to compute all solutions. These solutions can be considered as a (virtual) set of unit chains. All of them are applied the actual goal clause by an operation equivalent to GME-extension which tests also whether the instantiations of the variables are compatible with the sort restrictions.

The treatment of the second class of built-in predicates, i.e., of equality and arithmetic comparators, is more complicated. Independently, if the literal to be processed has negative or positive polarity, first one tries to simplify as much as possible the terms on the left-hand and right-hand side. Up to now this is done only for ground subterms, i.e., subterms containing no variables, by

- evaluating built-in functions, like arithmetic operators;

- evaluating features, which is done by applying facts $f(t_1) = t_2$ (where f is a feature and t_1, t_2 are arbitrary terms) as rewrite rules $f(t_1) \rightarrow t_2$;

- evaluating functions analogously to features.

The actual evaluation of the predicate is performed on the simplified arguments:

- for an equation with negative polarity the left-hand side is unified with the term on the right-hand side;

- an equation with positive polarity (i.e., an inequation has to be proven) is refuted, if left-hand side and right-hand side are different L_{LILOG}-atoms, for which the "unique name assumption" holds; it can also be refuted, if the sorts of the terms on the left-hand and right-hand side have no common subsort;

- for evaluating the arithmetic comparators $<, >, =<, >=$ the simplified left-hand side and right-hand side must either be a variable or an integer. If both are an integer, it simply checks if the relation holds or not. If one of them is a variable its sort is restricted such for all of its possible instances the relation must hold; e.g., for the negative literal $\neg(5 < X : [0..1000])$ the sort of X is restricted to $[6..1000]$.

It is clear that our treatment of equality is still incomplete. No L_{LILOG}-rules are applied by execute-builtin for proving an equation. The GME-extension does this, but only for the top function symbol of the term on the left-hand side of an equation. Another source of incompleteness is the restriction of our term simplification to ground subterms.

We are currently working on integrating an e-unification algorithm [Goltz 1991] that is complete for a class of equations satisfying certain syntactic properties.

5   Conclusion

The LILOG inference engine has been implemented in Quintus Prolog[6] and is running on PS/2, RISC/6000 systems under AIX[7].

The original design objectives have been achieved. The inference engine offers the required functionality to its users. The modular design guarantees the flexibility required for an experimental system.

In the framework of LEU/2 the inference engine is used for processing the background knowledge of the system together with those knowledge bases containing the L_{LILOG} representations of natural language texts. The background knowledge base of LEU/2 with 600 sort declarations and some 300 logical axioms comprises knowledge about the city of Düsseldorf as well as specifications of numerous temporal and spatial relationships.

The current stage of development of the inference engine is not considered as a final state. We are thinking of several enhancements like implementing an alternative version of General Proof Procedure on the basis of an abstract machine [Warren 1977]. Users would then have two options for executing their L_{LILOG}-code: to let it be interpreted by the actual GPP or to let it run compiled on the abstract machine.

Acknowledgements

Karl Hans Bläsius, Uli Hedtstück and Karl Schlechta contributed with their ideas and suggestions to the development of the inference engine. Karin Neuhold, Josef Gemander, Thomas Link, Martin Müller and Gerd Kortüm did a part of the implementation work.

---

[6] Quintus Prolog is a trademark of Quintus Computer Systems, Incorporated.
[7] AIX is a trademark of International Business Machines, Incorporated.

References

[Beierle *et al.* 1989] Beierle, C., Hedtstück, U., Pletat, U., and Siekmann, J. An order-sorted predicate logic with closely coupled taxonomic information. IWBS Report 86, IBM Deutschland, Stuttgart, 1989.

[Bollinger 1991] Bollinger, T. A model elimination calculus for generalized clauses. In *Proceedings of the 12th International Joint Conference on Artificial Intelligence*, Sydney, Australia, 1991. Morgan Kaufmann.

[Chang and Lee 1973] Chang, C.-L. and Lee, R.C.-T. *Symbolic Logic and Mechanical Theorem Proving*. Computer Science and Applied Mathematics Series. Academic Press, New York, 1973.

[de Kleer 1986] de Kleer, J. An assumption-based truth maintenance system. *Artificial Intelligence*, (28):127–162, 1986.

[Doyle 1979] Doyle, J. A truth maintenance system. *Artificial Intelligence*, (12):231–272, 1979.

[Gehlen *et al.*, this volume] Gehlen, E., Ley, M., Ludwig, T., Maier, A., and Walter, B. DB support for KB systems. In *Text Understanding in LILOG: Integrating Computational Linguistics and Artificial Intelligence*, Lecture Notes in Artificial Intelligence. Springer-Verlag, Berlin, Heidelberg, New York, this volume.

[Goltz 1991] Goltz, H.J. Ein praktischer Algorithmus für die E-Unifikation. IWBS Report 166, IBM Deutschland, Stuttgart, 1991.

[Habel, this volume] Habel, C. Processing of spatial expressions in LILOG. In *Text Understanding in LILOG: Integrating Computational Linguistics and Artificial Intelligence*, Lecture Notes in Artificial Intelligence. Springer-Verlag, Berlin, Heidelberg, New York, this volume.

[Hedtstück and Schmitt 1990] Hedtstück, U. and Schmitt, P. H. A calculus for order-sorted predicate logic with sort literals. In Bläsius, K.H., Hedtück, U., and Rollinger, C.-R., editors, *Sorts and Types for Artificial Intelligence*, Lecture Notes in Computer Science. Springer-Verlag, Berlin, 1990.

[Horty *et al.* 1987] Horty, J.F., Thomason, R.H., and Touretzky, D.S. A skeptical theory of inheritance in nonmontonic semantic networks. CMU-CS-87-175, Carnegie Mellon University, 1987.

[Khenkhar 1989] Khenkhar, M. N. DEPIC-2D: Eine Komponente zur depiktionalen Repräsentation und Verarbeitung räumlichen Wissens. In Metzing, D., editor, *GWAI-89. 13th German Workshop on Artificial Intelligence*, pages 318–322. Springer-Verlag, Berlin, 1989.

[Letz *et al.*, to appear 1991] Letz, R., Schumann, J., Bayerl, S., and Bibel, W. SETHEO: A high-performance theorem prover. *Journal of Automated Reasoning*, to appear 1991.

[Lorenz 1989] Lorenz, S. Nichtmonotones Schließen mit ordungssortierten Defaults. Master's thesis, University of Karlsruhe, 1989.

[Loveland 1969] Loveland, D. A simplified format for the model elimination theorem-proving procedure. *Journal of the Association for Computing Machinery*, 16(3):349–363, 1969. Also published in [Siekmann and Wrightson 1983 pages 233-248].

[Loveland 1978] Loveland, D. *Automated Theorem Proving: A Logical Basis*, volume 6 of *Fundamental Studies in Computer Science*. North-Holland, New York, 1978.

[Ludwig 1990] Ludwig, Th. A brief overview of LILOG-DB. In Liu, M., editor, *Proceedings of the 1990 Conference on Data Engineering*. Los Angeles, 1990.

[Nilsson 1980] Nilsson, N. J. *Principles of Artificial Intelligence.* Tioga, Palo Alto, CA, 1980.

[Pletat, this volume] Pletat, U. The knowledge representation language L$_{LILOG}$. In *Text Understanding in LILOG: Integrating Computational Linguistics and Artificial Intelligence,* Lecture Notes in Artificial Intelligence. Springer-Verlag, Berlin, Heidelberg, New York, this volume.

[Pletat, to appear 1991] Pletat, U. Inconsistency checking of L$_{LILOG}$ sort expressions. IWBS Report, IBM Deutschland, Stuttgart, to appear 1991.

[Siekmann and Wrightson 1983] Siekmann, Jörg and Wrightson, Graham, editors. *Automation of Reasoning 2.* Springer-Verlag, Berlin, 1983.

[Stickel 1984] Stickel, M. E. A Prolog technology theorem prover. *New Generation Computing,* 2:371–383, 1984.

[Warren 1977] Warren, D. Compiling predicate logic programs. DAI research report, University of Edinburgh, 1977.

Knowledge Based Control of the LILOG Inference Engine: Kinds of Metaknowledge

K.H. Bläsius

Abstract

Investigations in the context of the LILOG project have shown that a knowledge based control of the inference engine may lead to significant improvements in efficiency. The object is to allow the specification of knowledge (metaknowledge) about the intended use of the real knowledge (object knowledge). For that purpose a special control language has been designed allowing the specification of metaknowledge, which is used by the inference engine for an immediate control of its inference steps. By that, a partial control of the knowledge processing is possible. The basis for the development of the actual control language was an analysis of different kinds of metaknowledge which have turned out to be important within the LILOG context. These different kinds of metaknowledge also demand different procedures for interpretation. In this paper the different kinds of metaknowledge are presented by means of several examples, from which we derive certain elements of the control language for the inference engine.

1 Introduction

Knowledge based systems (KBS) usually have large knowledge bases, consisting of problem-specific, domain-specific and general world knowledge. In this paper, these kinds of knowledge are called "object knowledge". An uncontrolled use of this object knowledge may lead to a large search space during the problem solving process, since many different inference operations may be applicable in each step, without its being clear which operation might be the best one with respect to the given goal. Consequently many given goals may not be solvable, at least in an acceptable period of time. Short response times are especially necessary in systems processing natural language, which are often used in a dialog mode with a human user who does not want to wait for minutes or hours to get an answer.

LEU/2 is the prototype of a text understanding system developed within the LILOG project. The system understands German texts and answers questions within the scope of a tourist guide of Düsseldorf. Since LEU/2 is used in dialogs with a human user, short response times are required. Therefore the LILOG inference engine contains a lot of heuristics and strategies in order to restrict the search space (Bollinger, Lorenz, Pletat, this volume, Sect. 2.1). These domain-independent heuristics and strategies are necessary, but not always sufficient for efficient inference processing.

For example the simple question "Which museums are open at 11 o'clock" (originally given in German: "Welche Museen haben um 11 Uhr geöffnet") could be answered, but the system took about one hour to find the solution. Many questions concerning reasoning about time and space couldn't be solved at all. For these examples a domain (or knowledge) dependent control of inferences is necessary. For parts of the (object) knowledge, (control) knowledge is necessary to specify how the object knowledge is to be used during inference. This kind of control knowledge is called metaknowledge, since it is knowledge about the use of knowledge.

A simple form of knowledge based control of reasoning has been used in LEU/1 (Bollinger, Hedtstück, Rollinger 1989) as well as in LEU/2 (Bollinger, Lorenz, Pletat, this volume, Sect. 2.1). The knowledge engineer could mark literals in the input clauses by so-called "entrypoints" (see also Emde, Schmiedel 1983 and Schmiedel 1984). Entrypoints trigger the application of a rule. If a premise literal of a rule is marked by an entrypoint, then this rule may be used for forward chaining, and if the literal of the consequent is marked by an entrypoint, then this rule may be used for backward chaining. A rule may have entrypoints for each literal, i.e., it might be used for forward and backward chaining. The absence of an entrypoint means that some inference steps, which would be possible otherwise, are prohibited. A rule without any entrypoint could never be used within the deduction process.

Extending the concept of entrypoints, a special control language has been designed within the LILOG project allowing the user to activate, prefer, delay or prohibit certain inference operations (Klabunde 1989 and Bläsius, Rollinger, Siekmann 1990). The experience with LEU/2 has shown that these concepts still do not suffice, since they only allow the specification of metaknowledge concerning the inference operations of the underlying calculus. In addition, more problem-specific concepts are necessary. This experience has led to a further extension of the control language (Müller 1990), which is partially presented in Sects. 3-6.

The control language we propose is based on predicate logic and contains a lot of special predicate and function symbols allowing the user to specify the effects to be gained. The knowledge representation language L-LILOG (Pletat, von Luck 1990 and Pletat, this volume, Sect. 2.1), which has been developed to represent the object knowledge, could have been used to represent control knowledge as well. However, with regard to an efficient interpretation of control knowledge, predicate logic, or even Horn logic, seems to be sufficient for the present.

In this paper we do not give a detailed description of the designed control language, but present an analysis of the different kinds of metaknowledge required to enable a "knowledge based control" of the LILOG inference engine. The aspects of control of reasoning are restricted to the logical part of L-LILOG, i.e., metaknowledge describes how clauses, which mostly are Horn clauses and therefore often named "rules", are to be used.

2 Kinds of Metaknowledge

The experience gained with LEU/2 has shown that there are different kinds of metaknowledge allowing an efficient control of the LILOG inference engine. A classification of metaknowledge is necessary, since different kinds of metaknowledge have different effects and require different procedures for interpretation. We do not expect that the classification given in this paper is in any sense complete, but only describe the analysis of the most important instances from LEU/2. The information to be specified as metaknowledge may be classified by the intended effects and by the possible reference points.

Metaknowledge might refer to

- the representation language (e.g., clause, generalized clause)
- an element of the knowledge base (e.g., a fact, a certain rule or a literal)
- the given problem (i.e., the actual goal)
- the signature of the knowledge base (e.g., a sort, a function or a predicate symbol)
- operations of the calculus (e.g., resolution, factorisation)

Metaknowledge might effect

- an immediate control of the inference engine, by the
    - evaluation of certain inference operations
    - creation of sequences of inference operations
    - introduction of additional inference operations
    - creation of macro operations

- a modification of the representation of formulas of
    - the object knowledge base
    - the given goal

This paper deals with the effects of metaknowledge rather than the possible reference points.

The immediate control of the inference engine refers to the operations of the underlying calculus. Depending on certain formulas or predicates, for example, the knowledge engineer might evaluate the potentially applicable inference operations by specifying priorities or stating that some operations are to be activated or are prohibited. Entrypoints belong to this class of metaknowledge, since they are used to prohibit certain inference steps. Priorities set by the knowledge engineer can be used by the inference engine to select one operation from the set of applicable ones.

Another kind of immediate control of the inference engine is the creation of sequences of operations. In some cases knowledge engineers know that after using a certain formula, another particular formula should be used, or more generally: after the execution of a certain operation another operation should be executed next.

Metaknowledge effecting the control of the inference engine by evaluating operations or creating sequences of operations has mainly been treated in the past and also has been investigated within the LILOG project on the basis of LEU/1. In (Klabunde 1989) and (Bläsius, Rollinger, Siekmann 1990) concepts are described to represent and interpret these kinds of metaknowledge.

The experience with LEU/2 has led to new kinds of metaknowledge effecting the control of the inference engine or modifying the representation of formulas. Modifying the representation of formulas in this paper only concerns the reordering of literals. However, there also may exist other operations to modify a given formula, such as comprising literals or constructing other levels of abstraction. In the following sections different kinds of metaknowledge are described.

3 Reordering of Goals Generated Automatically

In LEU/2 goals for the inference engine stem from natural language questions offered to the system. These questions are transformed into a logical formula which is treated as the goal in the inference process. In general, such goals are conjunctions of literals each of which is to be solved in order to reach the overall goal. As an example we consider the following question

"Which museums are open at 11 a.m.?"

(originally given in German: "Welche Museen haben um 11 Uhr geöffnet"). The LILOG system automatically generates a goal containing six literals. A simplified version (not restricting the effect to be shown) of the generated goal is

G1: exist x such that

   is_open_at (x, 11)   and
   is_a_museum (x).

This goal is logically equivalent to the following goal

G2: exist x such that

   is_a_museum (x)   and
   is_open_at (x, 11).

However, as far as the search space is concerned, there is a big difference between them, since the inference system treats the subgoals in the given order. In the second case, all objects that are museums are searched for first, and then for each museum (i.e., each solution found), the inference engine tests whether it is open at 11 o'clock. In the first case (i.e., the goal G1) first all objects are searched for which are open at 11 o'clock. However, in general, there may exist many objects fulfilling this goal, such as any restaurant, shop, office, and so on. Then for each solution found, the system has to test whether it is a museum.

Whereas the treatment of the goal G2 corresponds to the behavior of a human problem solver, a huge search space arises for goal G1, leading to unacceptable response times.

Appropriate heuristics to reduce the search space might be to treat literals having a small solution space or containing the fewest variables first. However, a heuristic for reordering literals based on the degree of instantiation doesn't work in the example above. In the original goal containing six literals, the first one which concerns the sort "time" has two arguments, one variable and one constant, whereas the literal which should be solved first contains two variables, i.e., is less instantiated.

Besides the reordering of literals there also may exist other operations to modify a given formula, such as comprising literals or constructing another level of abstraction. In general, the representation of a formula, especially the order of literals, determines the strategy for solving a given problem, and therefore is a certain kind of procedural knowledge. It seems to be difficult to find a general method for an optimal modification of conjunctive goals with respect to the problem solving process.

Hence metaknowledge is required, in order to specify a desirable modification of the given goal. The appropriate metaknowledge for the example above might state that in conjunctive goals, literals concerning "institutions" are to be treated before literals concerning "time".

The metaknowledge to be specified has to effect a reordering of the goal. Since the reordering of a generated goal seems to be a fundamental meta-operation, a separate meta-predicate "goal-position" will be used. This predicate needs a list, containing specifications of the literals to be reordered, as argument. There are different ways to specify literals, for example by predicates or sorts of variables (see Müller 1990). With a second argument the user can fix a reference point for the reorganization of subgoals. The reference point might be "front", "behind" or one of the specified literals. For example the meta-formula

goal-position(front, (predicate(is_a_museum), predicate(is_open_at)))

means that if the actual goal contains two literals with predicates is_a_museum and is_open_at, then the literal with predicate is_a_museum is to be solved first and the literal with predicate is_open_at is to be solved second.

In LEU/2 more general predicates are used. Therefore such formulas need not be restricted to museums, but could refer to institutions. In general, literals to be reordered may be specified by any sort or literal pattern (see Müller 1990).

4 Ordering the Premise Literals of Rules

In LEU/2 object knowledge may be specified by implications which need not be Horn clauses (PROLOG-clauses). Nevertheless, these more general implications are called "rules" too. Defining such rules, the knowledge engineer determines a specific order of the premise literals. This order often corresponds to an intended specific problem solving process. However, in some cases, it is not possible to determine the appropriate order in advance, because it depends on the kind of instantiation (most general unifier) which is to be applied, when the rule is used. In LEU/2 many rules belonging to the model of "time" are of this kind as for example (Eberle 1989):

meets(I1, I3) and meets(I3, I2) and meets(I1, I4) and meets(I4, I2) implies I3 = I4

This rule describes situations in which time intervals are identical. I1, I2, I3, I4 are variables of the sort "interval_of_time". The literal meets(I,J) is fulfilled, if and only if the final point of the interval I is equal to the start point of the interval J. If the rule is applied in a backward chaining process, then the premise literals are to be reordered, depending on the kind of instantiation. Suppose the rule is applied to the goal

G: I = a

where "I" is a variable and "a" is a constant. Then the new goal

meets(I1, I) and meets(I, I2) and meets(I1, a) and meets(a, I2)

is created. Since the third and forth subgoals are instantiated, they should be solved first. Unfortunately it isn't always as easy as in this example to determine the degree of instantiation for the literals of a new goal. Suppose the goal to be solved is

G: a = b

where a and b are both constants of the sort "interval_of_time". The sort "interval_of_time" is defined to have certain features, among these a feature "start_point" and a feature "end_point". The values of these features may be fixed time points or "UNKNOWN". If the values of the start_point and the end_point of a constant a are both UNKNOWN, then this constant is not more strongly instantiated than a variable of this sort. Hence for time intervals the kind of instantiation also depends on the values of certain features.

From the above example we learn that metaknowledge is required to describe that literals of formulas are to be reordered depending on the kind of instantiation to be applied (variable bindings) when using the rule. Furthermore the kind of instantiation cannot be determined by a general procedure, but depends for example on the sorts concerned. Hence metaknowledge is required to compute the level of instantiation for a term of a specific sort.

The metaknowledge to be specified has to effect a reordering of the premise literals of a rule. Since such a reordering seems to be a fundamental meta-operation, a separate meta-predicate "premise-order" will be used. Similar to the predicate "goal-position" described in the previous section, the literals to be ordered are to be specified in the arguments of this predicate. But now an additional argument is required to specify the formula concerned. Furthermore, premise literals are required to be able to compute the degree of instantiation. Metaknowledge for the example above might be specified as follows:

    is_premise_literal_of(X,axiom1) and
    is_premise_literal_of(Y,axiom1) and
    instlevel(X) > instlevel(Y)
impl
    premise_order(axiom1,front,[X, Y])

This formula means that if X and Y are premise literals of axiom1 and the instantiation level of X is larger than the instantiation level of Y then the literal X should be solved before Y. Additional meta-formulas are necessary to compute the instantion level (instlevel) of time intervals (see Müller 1990).

5 User Guided Instantiation

Using unification as the basis of the resolution calculus makes a separate instantiation rule superfluous (Robinson 1965). This has led to progress in controlling inference processes, since a general instantiation rule as used in traditional calculi is hardly manageable automatically. On the other hand, to find an appropriate instance which specializes the given problem is often the essential step for human problem solving. Some examples from LEU/2 show that well-aimed instantiation is necessary for automatic problem solving too. But besides the local guidance of instantiation by unification, no general methods are known to perform well-aimed instantiation automatically. However, depending on the object knowledge or the given task, the knowledge engineer is sometimes able to specify instances to be applied in certain cases.

Let's consider the following example from LEU/2. In order to be able to describe a renaming of a road or a place of a city, the concept "renaming" has been defined. Furthermore, objects may have several names, which are valid at different periods of time. Each name is specified by a "name_time_unit" consisting of the name itself and the time interval for which the name is valid. The following rules concerning the renaming of objects have been defined:

Rule 1: forall u:renaming, n:object, nz1:name_time_unit
                  exists nz2:name_time_unit

                  name_of(n, nz1)
         and   name(nz1)=old_name(u)

         implies

                  end_point(time(nz1)) = rentime(u)
         and   start_point(time(nz2) = rentime(u)
         and   name(nz2) = new_name(u)
         and   name_of(n, nz2)

Rule 2: forall n1,n2: object, nz1,nz2:name_time_unit

                  name_of(n1, nz1)
         and   name_of(n2, nz2)
         and   name(nz1) = name(nz2)

         implies   equal(n1, n2)

The first rule should be applied in a forward reasoning step immediately after creating an object of sort "renaming". This rule restricts the period for which the old name was valid, creates an instance of the sort "name_time_unit" for the new name and relates it to the object.

After a successful application of rule 1, the second rule should be applied in order to detect whether there is another object having the same name. If this is true, it can be concluded that the objects regarded as different until now are equal.

However, the application of the second rule has to be controlled carefully. The premise literals contain only variables which are universally quantified. One of the premise literals selecting a name_time_unit from an object is to be applied first. However, both literals have huge numbers of solutions, regardless which one is tried first. Hence a modification of the order of the literals as explained in Sect. 4 doesn't help. This rule should only be used together with an instantiation step specified by metaknowledge.

The concept of renaming has been represented descriptively in LEU/2. However, a certain algorithm has been kept in mind to perform the process of renaming when suitable information is given. The rules stated above can be regarded as logical specification of the algorithm. However the algorithmic information was lost when specifying the concept of renaming. This algorithmic information should now be introduced again using metaknowledge.

The metaknowledge to be specified for the second rule is: After applying rule 1 to an object n rule 2 should be instantiated with the same object n and then checked for applicability.

The effect to be achieved is to instantiate and possibly apply the second rule. The precondition for applying this meta-rule is the successful application of the first rule. In order to specify this metaknowledge a predicate "activatewi" (activate with instance) is used, which has two arguments: one specifying the inference operation to be performed and a second specifying the substitution which is to be applied first. The inference operation may be specified by a term like "resolution(literal(rule2,1),y)", which denotes a resolution step between the first literal of rule 2 and an arbitrary literal of another clause. To specify the desired precondition a predicate "executed" is used, having two arguments: one for specifying the inference operation and the second to determine the substitution (most general unifier) used within this inference step. Furthermore a function "subst" is necessary having two arguments, a list of variables and a substitution. The value of this function is the substitution resulting from a restriction of the second argument to the variables specified in the first argument. The respective meta-formula may be

if   executed(resolution(literal(rule1,x), y), s')   and   s = subst([n], s'))
then activatewi(resolution(literal(rule2,1), z), s)

which means that if any resolution with rule 1 has been executed with unifier s' and the restriction of s' to the variable n is s, then a resolution with rule 2 is to be executed if possible after instantiating rule 2 with s. The example above also illustrates how sequences of inference operations may be created.

6 Macro Operations

Comprising rules with equivalent premises and using them within a macro operation may have a similar effect of instantiation, as explained in the previous section. Such a macro operation corresponds to a sequence of single inference operations followed by an instantiation or factorization step.

The possibility to specify such macro operations has been demanded by the knowledge engineers of LEU/2. Especially spatial reasoning requires such operations, as is shown in the following example (Röhrig 1991). The actual goal may be

G: exists SB,RR

      thema(SB) = hetjensmuseum and
      anlocspec(RR, hetjensmuseum) and
      lokal(SB, RR)

The rule to be applied may be

R: forall SB, RR, LE

      lokal(LE, RR) implies lokal(SB,RR) and thema(SB) = LE

This rule would usually be normalized into the rules

R1:   forall SB,RR,LE lokal(LE, RR) implies lokal(SB,RR) and
R2:   forall SB,RR,LE lokal(LE, RR) implies thema(SB) = LE

The rule R2 would be applied to the first literal of the goal yielding the new goal:

G1:   lokal(hetjensmuseum, RR) and
      anlocspec(RR1, hetjensmuseum) and
      lokal(SB, RR1)

However if the rule R were applied to the goal G such that both literals of the conclusion were unified concurrently with the corresponding literals of the goal, then the following new goal would be created:

G2:   lokal(hetjensmuseum, RR1) and
      anlokspec(RR1, hetjensmuseum)

Whereas in G1 the variables RR and RR1 are independent, a dependence is given in G2. The macro operation which is a resolution between conjunctions of literals leads to stronger instantiations reducing the search space drastically. In G2 the second literal "anlokspec(RR1, hetjensmuseum)" need only be solved for the solutions (instances) found for the first literal "lokal(hetjensmuseum,RR1)". In G1, however, there are no restrictions to this subgoal, leading to a huge set of partial solutions, most of which are withdrawn when one tries to solve the third literal of G1.

This example demonstrates the disadvantage of the normalization of first-order predicate formulas with respect to the resulting search spaces. In LEU/2, formulas like the rule R are not normalized, but handled separately as generalized clauses. However, using only macro operations with such clauses as explained above would prevent the system from finding all solutions and therefore would lead to incompleteness.

The experience has shown that metaknowledge is required specifying whether generalized clauses are to be used in macro operations. Generalized clauses are a major concept in LEU/2 to reduce search spaces, consequently a special predicate "macro operation" is defined to enable the knowledge engineers to describe how generalized clauses are to be handled. The predicate "macro operation" has three arguments, one specifying the clause concerned, a second which is the list of literals to be treated as conjunction, and a third argument to specify whether a macro operation should be preferred or used exclusively for the formula specified in the first argument. As an example, the formula

macro operation(R, [2, 3], exclusive)

means that the rule R must only be used if the second and the third literal are applicable as a conjunction in one step.

7 Conclusion

The examples presented in this paper show that the use of metaknowledge may lead to a significant improvement in efficiency. The metaknowledge required can be classified based on the desired effects. This classification leads to different kinds of metaknowledge, which are to be interpreted by different procedures. An appropriate treatment of metaknowledge requires essential modifications of the inference engine and the underlying calculus. Additional inference rules for the calculus, such as an instantiation rule and macro operations, are necessary.

The concepts for knowledge based control of reasoning presented in this paper are not completely integrated into the LILOG inference engine. Procedures directing the selection of inference operations based on the priorities assigned by the knowledge engineers are implemented and integrated. The creation of chains of inference operations is possible as well. However, practical results have not been available until now.

Based on the actual inference engine, we are currently developing a clause graph procedure (Kowalski 1975). Using clause graphs it will be possible to interpret metaknowledge at phases of development, and to inherit the control information constructed at run time. In this way, we hope for further improvements of the response times when the system is used during a dialog with a human user.

References

Bläsius K.H., Rollinger C.-R., Siekmann J.-H. (1990): Structure and control of the L-LILOG inference system. In: Bläsius K.H., Hedtstück U., Rollinger C.-R.(eds): Sorts and Types in Artificial Intelligence. Lecture Notes in Artificial Intelligence, Vol. 418, Springer-Verlag, Berlin, Heidelberg, pp. 165 – 182

Bollinger T., Hedtstück U., Rollinger C.-R. (1989): Reasoning for text understanding - Knowledge processing in the 1st LILOG prototype. In: Metzing (ed): GWAI-89 13th German Workshop on Artificial Intelligence, Informatik Fachberichte 216, Springer-Verlag, Berlin, Heidelberg, pp. 203 – 212

Eberle K.(1989): Quantifikation, Plural, Ereignisse und ihre Argumente in einer mehrsortigen Sprache der Prädikatenlogik erster Stufe. IWBS Report 67, IBM Deutschland, Stuttgart

Emde W., Schmiedel A. (1983): Aspekte der Verarbeitung unsicheren Wissens. KIT-Report 6, TU Berlin, FB Informatik, Berlin

Klabunde K. (1989): Erweiterung der Wissensrepräsentationssprache L-LILOG um Konstrukte zur Spezifikation von Kontrollinformation. IWBS Report 92, IBM Deutschland, Stuttgart

Kowalski R. (1975): A proof procedure using connection graphs. Journal of ACM, 22 (4)

Müller M. (1990): Implementierung und Integration von Verfahren zur wissensbasierten Steuerung der LILOG-Inferenzmaschine. Diplomarbeit, Fachhochschule Dortmund

Pletat U., v. Luck K. (1990): Knowledge representation in LILOG. In: Bläsius K.H., Hedtstück U., Rollinger C.-R.(eds): Sorts and Types in Artificial Intelligence. Lecture Notes in Artificial Intelligence, Vol. 418, Springer-Verlag, Berlin, Heidelberg, pp. 140 - 164

Robinson J.A. (1965): A machine oriented logic based on the resolution principle. Journal of ACM, 12(1): pp. 23 – 41

Röhrig R. (1991): Kommentar zu Verarbeitung von L-LILOG – Theorie und Praxis. In: Klose G., Lang E., Pirlein T.(eds.): Die Ontologie und Axiomatik der Wissensbank von LEU/2. IWBS Report 171, IBM Deutschland, Stuttgart, pp. IX-11 – IX-14

Schmiedel A. (1984): Eine Inferenzmaschine zur Verarbeitung unsicheren Wissens. In: Rollinger C. (eds.): Probleme des (Text-) Verstehens. Niemeyer-Verlag, Tübingen

Attributive Description Formalisms
...and the Rest of the World

Bernhard Nebel and Gert Smolka*

Abstract

Research in knowledge representation has led to the development of so-called terminological logics, the purpose of which is to support the representation of the conceptual and terminological part of Artificial Intelligence applications. Independently, in computational linguistics, so-called feature logics have been developed which are aimed at representing the semantic and syntactic information natural language sentences convey. Since both of these logics rely mainly on attributes as the primary notational primitives for representing knowledge, they can be jointly characterized as attributive description formalisms.

Although the intended applications for terminological logics and feature logics are not identical, and the computational services of systems based on the respective formalisms are quite different for this reason, the logical foundations turn out to be very similar – as we pointed out elsewhere. In this paper, we will show how attributive description formalisms relate to "the rest of the world." Recently, a number of formal results in the area of attributive description formalisms have been obtained by exploiting other research fields, such as formal language theory, automata theory, and modal logics. This connection between these different fields of formal research will be highlighted in the sequel.

1 Introduction

Terminological logics, which have their roots in the knowledge representation formalism KL-ONE (Brachman 1979; Brachman, Schmolze 1985), have been developed to support the representation of the conceptual and terminological part of Artificial Intelligence applications.

Starting with *primitive concepts* and *attributes* (in this context usually called *roles*), new concepts are defined by employing attributive descriptions. For instance, given the *concept* Human and the *attribute* child, the concept of a Parent can be defined by the description

a Human who has at least one child who in turn is a Human,

or, more formally,

$$\text{Parent} = \text{Human} \sqcap \exists \text{child}: \text{Human}.$$

The main computational services provided by terminological representation systems are the computation of the *concept hierarchy* according to the *subsumption* relation between concepts and the computation of *instance relationships* between concepts and objects of the application domain.

---

*Address for correspondence: DFKI GmbH, Stuhlsatzenhausweg 3, D-6600 Saarbrücken 11, Germany; e-mail: nebel@dfki.uni-sb.de, smolka@dfki.uni-sb.de.

Feature logics grew out of research in computational linguistics. They form the constraint logic underlying the family of *unification grammars* that originated with Lexical Functional Grammar (LFG) (Kaplan, Bresnan 1982) and Functional Unification Grammar (FUG) (Kay 1979; Kay 1985). In unification grammars, syntactic and semantic objects are described by employing attributive descriptions. For instance, the class of linguistic objects that are

third-person singular noun phrases

can be described formally as follows (Shieber 1986):

$$\begin{bmatrix} \text{cat:} & \text{NP} \\ \text{agreement:} & \begin{bmatrix} \text{number:} & \text{singular} \\ \text{person:} & \text{third} \end{bmatrix} \end{bmatrix}$$

or, in a linear notation as:

cat: NP ⊓ agreement: (number: singular ⊓ person: third).

While parsing a sentence, such descriptions are combined by "unification," and, in the end, the combined descriptions provide the syntactic and semantic structure of the sentence. One main step during this process is the test whether a newly formed description is *satisfiable*, i.e., describes any linguistic structure at all.

As we pointed out in (Nebel, Smolka 1990), terminological logics and feature logics are closely related. Although the intended applications are not identical, and for this reason, the computational services of systems based on the respective logics are quite different, the logical foundations turn out to be the same. Both logics employ restrictions on attributes as the primary notational primitives and are best formalized using a Tarski-style model theory. The main difference between terminological logics and feature logics is that the former permit set-valued attributes (called *roles*), while the latter permit only single-valued attributes (called *features*). This seemingly minor difference has drastic consequences as it amounts to computational complexity. Nevertheless, for a large range of problems, formal results apply to both kinds of logics.

In the the LILOG project, there two applications of attributive descriptions. The STUF formalism (Bouma, König, Uszkoreit 1988; Dörre, Seiffert in this volume) is based on feature logic and is employed in the linguistic components. The knowledge representation language L-LILOG (Pletat, von Luck 1990; Pletat in this volume) is a hybrid formalism combining predicate logic and attributive descriptions.

The remainder of the paper is organized as follows. In the next section, we will briefly introduce the logical foundations of terminological and feature logics. Sect. 3 shows the applicability of results from *automata theory* to attributive description languages in terms of computational complexity results and algorithms. Sect. 4 summarizes a number of undecidability results which have been obtained by reductions using the *word problem for Thue systems*. In fact, for some proofs a slightly stronger condition is necessary, namely, that the semigroup generated by the Thue system is a group. In particular, we consider the problem of determining satisfiability for feature terms containing *functional uncertainty* in the case that the feature logic is propositionally complete. In Sect. 5, a correspondence between a certain terminological logic and the *propositional polymodal logic* $K_{(m)}$ is considered, which leads to quite a number of interesting applications of results from modal and dynamic logic to attributive description formalisms. Finally, in the conclusion we will sketch some applications of results achieved in the area of attribute descriptions to other research fields. A summary of the relations discussed in the paper is shown in Figure 1.

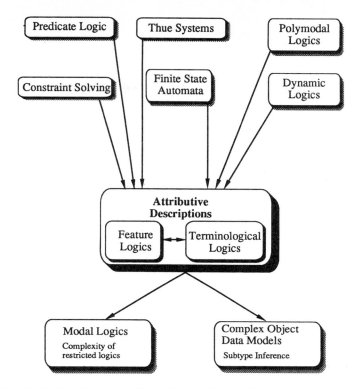

Figure 1: Attributive description formalisms and the relation to the rest of the world

2   Logical Foundations

While terminological logics were introduced originally with an informal semantics only, it quickly became obvious that a formal semantics is necessary to describe the intended meaning – and the obvious candidate, first-order predicate calculus and its associated model theory, was used for this purpose (Schmolze, Israel 1983; Brachman, Levesque 1984). A similar process took place in the area of unification grammars (Kasper, Rounds 1986; Johnson 1987; Smolka 1988).

This logical reconstruction revealed in both cases that the formalisms correspond to subsets of ordinary first-order predicate logic. Although this correspondence is very helpful for understanding the meaning of the formalism and yields a firm base for extensions, it does not help much in determining the computational properties. Nevertheless, a logical foundation is a necessary prerequisite for an analysis of computational properties. In the following, the logical foundations of attributive description formalisms are briefly recalled.

In terminological logics, we start with an alphabet **C** of *concept symbols* (denoted by C) and an alphabet **R** of *role symbols* (denoted by R), which are disjoint. Concept symbols are intended to denote some subset of a domain, and role symbols are intended to denote unary, set-valued functions or, equivalently, two-place relations on the domain.[1] From concept and role symbols, complex *concept descriptions* (denoted by D) are composed using a variety of description-forming

---

[1]We will use both notations interchangeably.

operations. In order to give an example, the language $\mathcal{ALC}$ will be specified, originally introduced by Schmidt-Schauß and Smolka (1991):

$$D \longrightarrow C \mid \top \mid \bot \mid D \sqcap D' \mid D \sqcup D' \mid \neg D \mid \forall R\colon D \mid \exists R\colon D.$$

The formal meaning of concept descriptions built according to the above rule is given by an interpretation $\mathcal{I} = (\mathbf{D}^{\mathcal{I}}, \cdot^{\mathcal{I}})$, where $\mathbf{D}^{\mathcal{I}}$ (the *domain*) is an arbitrary nonempty set and $\cdot^{\mathcal{I}}$ (the *interpretation function*) is a function such that:

$$C^{\mathcal{I}} \subseteq \mathbf{D}^{\mathcal{I}}$$
$$R^{\mathcal{I}} \subseteq \mathbf{D}^{\mathcal{I}} \times \mathbf{D}^{\mathcal{I}}.$$

The denotation of complex concept descriptions is given inductively by:

$$\top^{\mathcal{I}} = \mathbf{D}^{\mathcal{I}}$$
$$\bot^{\mathcal{I}} = \emptyset$$
$$(D \sqcap D')^{\mathcal{I}} = D^{\mathcal{I}} \cap D'^{\mathcal{I}}$$
$$(D \sqcup D')^{\mathcal{I}} = D^{\mathcal{I}} \cup D'^{\mathcal{I}}$$
$$(\neg D)^{\mathcal{I}} = \mathbf{D}^{\mathcal{I}} - D^{\mathcal{I}}$$
$$(\forall R\colon D)^{\mathcal{I}} = \{d \in \mathbf{D}^{\mathcal{I}} \mid R^{\mathcal{I}}(d) \subseteq D^{\mathcal{I}}\}$$
$$(\exists R\colon D)^{\mathcal{I}} = \{d \in \mathbf{D}^{\mathcal{I}} \mid R^{\mathcal{I}}(d) \cap D^{\mathcal{I}} \neq \emptyset\}.$$

Based on this semantics, the notion of *subsumption* mentioned above is defined as set-inclusion. A concept D is *subsumed* by another concept D', written $D \preceq D'$, iff $(D)^{\mathcal{I}} \subseteq (D')^{\mathcal{I}}$ for every interpretation $\mathcal{I}$. From this relation, a concept hierarchy can be computed. If the logic is extended to describe single objects by using role and concept symbols, then the notion of *instance relationship* can be formalized as set-membership in concepts.

Note that one can think of quite different terminological logics employing, for instance, role-forming operators, cardinality restrictions on roles, and so on. Indeed, quite a number of different representation systems have been built using a variety of terminological logics (for a survey, see (Nebel 1990a)).

Turning now to feature logic, we notice that the formalization of so-called *feature terms* resembles the formalization of concept descriptions. In feature logics, we start with three pairwise disoint alphabets, namely, a set $\mathbf{S}$ of *sort symbols* (denoted by S), a set $\mathbf{F}$ of *feature symbols* (denoted by f), and a set $\mathbf{A}$ of *atoms* (denoted by a). Based on that, the following rule (see, e.g., (Smolka 1988)) specifies how to built complex *feature terms* (denoted by F):

$$F \longrightarrow a \mid S \mid \top \mid \bot \mid F \sqcap F' \mid F \sqcup F' \mid \neg F \mid (f_1 \dots f_n)\colon F \mid (f_{1,1} \dots f_{1,m}) \downarrow (f_{2,1} \dots f_{2,n}).$$

The formal meaning is provided by interpretations $\mathcal{I} = (\mathbf{D}^{\mathcal{I}}, \cdot^{\mathcal{I}})$, also called *feature algebras* in this context, where $\mathbf{D}^{\mathcal{I}}$ is a nonempty set and $\cdot^{\mathcal{I}}$ is a function such that:

$$a^{\mathcal{I}} \in \mathbf{D}^{\mathcal{I}}$$
$$S^{\mathcal{I}} \subseteq \mathbf{D}^{\mathcal{I}}$$
$$f^{\mathcal{I}} \subseteq \mathbf{D}^{\mathcal{I}} \times \mathbf{D}^{\mathcal{I}}.$$

Additionally, the restrictions

$$(d, e), (d, e') \in f^{\mathcal{I}} \implies e = e'$$
$$a \neq b \implies a^{\mathcal{I}} \neq b^{\mathcal{I}}$$
$$a \in \mathbf{A}, f \in \mathbf{F}, d \in \mathbf{D}^{\mathcal{I}} \implies (a^{\mathcal{I}}, d) \notin f^{\mathcal{I}},$$

have to be satisfied formalizing that features are functional, that different atoms denote different elements in the domain, and that atoms are never in the domain of a feature.

The meaning of chains of features $f_1 \ldots f_n$, also called *feature paths*, is the composition of functional relations:

$$(d, e) \in f_1 \ldots f_n^{\mathcal{I}} \iff \exists d_0, \ldots, d_n : d_0 = d \wedge d_n = e \wedge \bigwedge_{i=1}^{n} (d_{i-1}, d_i) \in f_i^{\mathcal{I}}$$

Feature paths will also be denoted by the letters p and q. Using these definitions, the denotation of complex feature terms is given inductively by:

$$\begin{aligned}
(a)^{\mathcal{I}} &= \{a^{\mathcal{I}}\} \\
\top^{\mathcal{I}} &= \mathbf{D}^{\mathcal{I}} \\
\bot^{\mathcal{I}} &= \emptyset \\
(F \sqcap F)^{\mathcal{I}} &= F^{\mathcal{I}} \cap F^{\mathcal{I}} \\
(F \sqcup F)^{\mathcal{I}} &= F^{\mathcal{I}} \cup F^{\mathcal{I}} \\
(\neg F)^{\mathcal{I}} &= \mathbf{D}^{\mathcal{I}} - F^{\mathcal{I}} \\
(p \colon F)^{\mathcal{I}} &= \{d \in \mathbf{D}^{\mathcal{I}} \mid \emptyset \neq p^{\mathcal{I}}(d) \subseteq F^{\mathcal{I}}\} \\
(p \downarrow q)^{\mathcal{I}} &= \{d \in \mathbf{D}^{\mathcal{I}} \mid p^{\mathcal{I}}(d) = q^{\mathcal{I}}(d) \neq \emptyset\}.
\end{aligned}$$

A feature term F is *satisfiable* iff there exists an interpretation such that $F^{\mathcal{I}} \neq \emptyset$.

If attributive description formalisms contain *intersection* "$\sqcap$" and *complement* "$\neg$," they are called *propositionally complete*. In such formalisms, the notions of satisfiability and subsumption are obviously closely related. More precisely, subsumption and unsatisfiability are linear time reducible to each other (see, e.g., (Nebel, Smolka 1990)).

3 Regular Languages and Finite State Automata

As mentioned in the previous section, the logical semantics for attributive description formalisms proved to be quite useful in understanding the expressive power of these formalisms. Terminological logics as well as feature logics are obviously subsets of ordinary first-order logic. These subsets, however, were unexplored previously with respect to their computational properties. For instance, it was not known until 1988 whether there are undecidable terminological logics (Schild 1988) and only in 1989 was it shown that subsumption in KL-ONE (Brachman, Schmolze 1985; Schmidt-Schauß 1989) and NIKL (Moser 1983; Patel-Schneider 1989b) is undecidable – a point we return to in the next section.

Since in knowledge representation and computational linguistics, efficiency is an important issue, decidability of a formalism is not the only concern. *Tractability*, i.e, solvability in polynomial time, is also relevant. As a matter of fact, Brachman and Levesque (1984) requested that knowledge representation formalisms should always permit polynomial time computations. They started an inquiry concerning the trade-off between expressiveness and tractability of representation formalisms, which led to a number of analyses of different terminological logics (Nebel 1988; Patel-Schneider 1989a; Schmidt-Schauß, Smolka 1991). However, only recently, terminological logics that are maximally expressive and still tractable have been identified (Donini et al. 1991a) using the *constraint solving* technique introduced in (Schmidt-Schauß, Smolka 1991).

Another open problem was whether the computational complexity of subsumption for tractable terminological logics is preserved under the introduction of *terminological axioms*. This problem was solved by discovering a correspondence between *nondeterministic finite state automata* and a particular, simple terminological logic. Exploiting complexity results from the theory of finite state automata, it was possible to show that the addition of terminological axioms increases the computational complexity considerably (Nebel 1990b). Further, the mentioned correspondence proved to be useful for characterizing the semantics of so-called *terminological cycles* (Baader 1990; Nebel 1991).

3.1 Terminological Axioms and the Lexicon

Investigations of the computational complexity of terminological logics are usually based on the semantics given in Sect. 2. They analyze what resources are necessary for checking subsumption between two concept descriptions. In particular, it is assumed that all concept symbols appearing in the descriptions are undefined. In existing systems, however, it is possible to assign a *name* to a concept description and to use this new name in other expressions instead of the original description. This aspect of the use of terminological logics can be straightforwardly formalized by the notion of *terminological axioms*, which have the following form:

$$C \doteq D$$

Usually, it is assumed that sets of such axioms, also called *terminologies* (denoted by T), satisfy two restrictions, namely,

1. a concept symbol C appears at most once on the left hand side of a terminological axiom, and

2. the terminology is cycle-free, i.e., there is a partial order on the set of concepts $\mathbf{C}$ such that for every terminological axiom $C \doteq D$, every concept symbol in D is strictly less than C.

Given such a terminology T, subsumption is relativized to this terminology, written as $D \preceq_T D'$, by considering set-inclusion of concept denotations only in interpretations that are *models* of the terminology. An interpretation $\mathcal{I}$ is a *model* of a set of terminological axioms iff for all axioms $C \doteq D$ the interpretation satisfies $C^{\mathcal{I}} = D^{\mathcal{I}}$.

If the restrictions spelled out above are satisfied, subsumption relative to a terminology can easily be reduced to subsumption over concept descriptions relative to "the empty terminology" by *expanding* all defined concepts by their definitions. However, in the worst case, this can lead to an exponential increase of the size of a concept description (Nebel 1990b). Thus, even when subsumption determination for a particular terminological logic is tractable, this does not mean that subsumption determination relative to terminologies is also tractable. On the other hand, all results on the complexity of subsumption seem to have assumed that the reduction from $\preceq_T$ to $\preceq$ can be done in polynomial time – and in applications this reduction did not seem to be a source of computational problems, provided some caching is performed (Lipkis 1982).

Finally, it turned out that there is indeed a "hidden computational cliff." The minimal terminological language abstract syntax rule

$$D \longrightarrow C \mid D \sqcap D' \mid \forall R\colon D$$

is closely related to nondeterministic finite state automata and, by this, to regular expressions – provided terminological axioms are permitted.

Suppose we are given two *nondeterministic finite state automata* $\mathcal{A}_1, \mathcal{A}_2$ with $\mathcal{A}_i = (\Sigma, \mathcal{Q}^i, \delta^i, q_0^i, \mathcal{F}^i)$, where Σ is the alphabet, $\mathcal{Q}^i$ are the sets of states, where we assume without loss of generality that $\mathcal{Q}^1 \cap \mathcal{Q}^2 = \emptyset$, $\delta^i \subseteq \mathcal{Q}^i \times (\Sigma \cup \{\epsilon\}) \times \mathcal{Q}^i$ are the transition functions, $q_0{}^i \in \mathcal{Q}^i$ are the initial states, and $\mathcal{F}^i \subseteq \mathcal{Q}^i$ are the sets of accepting states. The *language accepted by these automata* is denoted by $\mathcal{L}(\mathcal{A}_i)$. If such automata are *cycle-free*, a cycle-free terminology can be specified such that language inclusion corresponds to subsumption relative to the terminology (Nebel 1990b):

Automata	Terminology
$\mathcal{A}_1,\ \mathcal{A}_2$	T
Σ	$\mathbf{R} = \Sigma$
$(\mathcal{Q}^1 \cup \mathcal{Q}^2)$	$\mathbf{C} = (\mathcal{Q}^1 \cup \mathcal{Q}^2) \uplus \{F\}$
$q \in \mathcal{F}^1 \cup \mathcal{F}^2$	$q \doteq \ldots \sqcap F \sqcap \ldots$
ϵ-transition from q to q'	$q \doteq \ldots \sqcap q' \sqcap \ldots$
s-transition from q to q'	$q \doteq \ldots \sqcap \forall s\colon q' \sqcap \ldots$
$\mathcal{L}(\mathcal{A}_1) \supseteq \mathcal{L}(\mathcal{A}_2)$	$q_0^1 \preceq_T q_0^2$

Since inclusion of languages accepted by cycle-free automata is known to be co-NP-complete (Garey, Johnson 1979), it follows that $\preceq_T$ is co-NP-hard.

Interestingly, this correspondence also works the other way around. Given a terminology and two concepts, we can construct two automata such that subsumption coincides with language inclusion, which gives us co-NP-completeness for $\preceq_T$ in the language considered.

Note that for the proof of this correspondence the set-valued nature of attributes in terminological logics is inessential. The same arguments are valid for functional attributes, which gives us an interesting corollary in the area of unification grammars. Satisfiability of feature terms relative to a lexicon – which is nothing else than a cycle-free terminology for a feature logic (Nebel, Smolka 1990) – is also NP-hard, even if satisfiability for the underlying feature logic is polynomial. For instance, adopting the ψ-terms introduced in (Aït-Kaci 1984), for which satisfiability can be decided in quasi-linear time, leads to an NP-complete satisfiability problem if a lexicon is added.

This intractability result does not seem to show up in practical applications very often, however. As a matter of fact, it is not easy to construct a terminology that exhibits exponential time behavior when an efficient algorithm is used that resembles the language inclusion algorithm for finite automata, such as the one described in (Lipkis 1982). Nevertheless, it shows us that provable tractability is hardly achievable in the area of attributive description formalisms.

3.2 Terminological Cycles

The correspondence between automata and terminologies not only helped to solve the problem concerning the complexity of subsumption relative to a terminology, but also provides a good tool to analyze so-called *terminological cycles*. Such cycles appear when the second restriction on terminologies mentioned above is dropped. In this case, the definition of a concept refers, either directly or indirectly, to the concept itself. Such constructions present problems because neither the right semantics nor the computational properties are obvious.

Based on the correspondence spelled above, Baader (1990) shows that the three possible styles of semantics, namely, *descriptive, least fixpoint, and greatest fixpoint semantics* (Nebel 1990a; Nebel 1991), can be characterized by finite state automata. In particular, the greatest fixpoint semantics has an elegant characterization, because it corresponds to automata isomorphic to the terminology.

Besides confirming the conjecture in (Nebel 1990b) that subsumption becomes PSPACE-complete for least and greatest fixpoint semantics, this characterization also led directly to sound and complete subsumption algorithms for these cases. In addition, this result gave rise to the idea of extending the expressive power of terminological logics by adding regular expressions over roles (Baader 1991).

4 Thue Systems

For feature logics, the computational complexity was analyzed quite early. The feature logic described in Sect. 2 without union "⊔" and complement "¬," which give essentially the ψ-terms mentioned above, was shown to have a quasi-linear satisfiability problem (Aït-Kaci 1984). The addition of union or complement leads to NP-completeness, as shown in (Kasper 1987; Johnson 1987; Smolka 1988).

The situation in terminological logics was more problematical because of the variety of possible concept- and role-forming operators. As mentioned above, for a long time it remained an open problem whether there are terminological logics such that subsumption is undecidable. The first undecidability result (Schild 1988) considered a language containing role complements – which do not have practical relevance. Subsequently, Schmidt-Schauß (1989) proved a small subset of KL-ONE to be undecidable using a reduction from the word problem in *invertible Thue systems* to subsumption. Since this result proved to be quite fruitful for solving other related problems, we will briefly describe the correspondence.

4.1 Feature Agreement and Role-Value-Maps

In the presentation of the logical foundations of attributive descriptions, we mentioned already that other terminological logics than $\mathcal{ALC}$ are conceivable. The reader might have noticed already that *feature-path agreement* $p \downarrow q$ has no counterpart in the presented terminological logic. As a matter of fact, some terminological logics support such an operator, for instance, KL-ONE and NIKL. Let us consider a subset of those formalisms as specified below:

$$D \longrightarrow C \mid D \sqcap D' \mid \forall R{:}D \mid (R_{1,1} \ldots R_{1,m}) \downarrow (R_{2,1} \ldots R_{2,n}),$$

where the denotation of role chains is identical to the denotation of feature chains, i.e., relational composition, and role chains are denoted by P and Q. The agreement of such role chains, often called *role-value-map* is defined by:

$$(P \downarrow Q)^{\mathcal{I}} = \{d \in \mathbf{D}^{\mathcal{I}} \mid P^{\mathcal{I}}(d) = Q^{\mathcal{I}}(d)\}.$$

Such a construct could be used, for instance, to define the concept of a father such that all his children have the same surname as the father:

$$\text{Father} \sqcap (\text{surname}) \downarrow (\text{child surname}).$$

Although a very useful construct, it leads unfortunately to undecidability of subsumption. This means that as long as our attributes are functional, subsumption stays decidable (NP-complete for the feature logic considered in this paper or even quasi-linear for the more restricted ψ-terms). If we allow for set-valued attributes, subsumption becomes undecidable. This result follows from a reduction from the word problems for a special class of Thue systems. A *Thue system* $\mathcal{T}$ over an alphabet Σ is a finite set of pairs of words $u_i, v_i \in \Sigma^*$: $\mathcal{T} = \{\{u_i, v_i\}\}$. Such a Thue system defines a binary relation $\overset{\mathcal{T}}{\leftrightarrow}$ on Σ^* by:

$$u \overset{\mathcal{T}}{\leftrightarrow} v \iff \exists w_1, w_2 \in \Sigma^* \ \exists \{u_i, v_i\} \in \mathcal{T}{:}\ u = w_1 u_i w_2 \wedge v = w_1 v_i w_2.$$

The symbol $\overset{\mathcal{T}}{\sim}$ is used to denote the transitive and reflexive closure of $\overset{\mathcal{T}}{\leftrightarrow}$. The *word problem* is the problem to decide $u \overset{\mathcal{T}}{\sim} v$ for given $\mathcal{T}$ and words $u, v \in \Sigma^*$.

An *invertible Thue system* is a Thue system such that for each $s \in \Sigma$ there exists $r \in \Sigma$ such that $sr \overset{\mathcal{T}}{\sim} \epsilon$, where ϵ is the empty word. In other words, the quotient $\mathcal{T}/\overset{\mathcal{T}}{\sim}$ is a group under concatenation. It is known that there exist invertible Thue systems such that the word problem is undecidable (Boone 1959). Undecidability of subsumption in the above mentioned terminological logic can now be shown by using the following correspondence:

Invertible Thue system	Terminological logic
Σ	$\mathbf{R} = \Sigma \uplus \{R\}$
$\mathcal{T} = \big\{\{u_i, v_i\}\big\}$	$D = \prod_{s \in \Sigma}(R\ s) \downarrow (R) \sqcap \prod_i \forall R\colon (u_i \downarrow v_i)$
$u \overset{\mathcal{T}}{\sim} v$	$D \preceq \forall R\colon (u \downarrow v)$

4.2 Arbitrary Axioms

Since, on one hand, agreements of role-chains are a very useful construction, and on the other hand, they lead to undecidability in case of set-valued attributes, it seems to be a good idea to restrict agreements to chains of functional attributes. Indeed, the terminological logic employed in the CLASSIC system (Borgida et al. 1989; Brachman et al. 1991) is based on this insight. Beside ordinary roles also functional attributes are supported and agreements are only permitted on the latter kind of attribute.

While such a move preserves decidability for the terminological logic (Hollunder, Nutt 1990), it leads to problems if terminologies containing cycles are allowed. Using a similar reduction as above, Smolka (1989) shows that ψ-terms plus cyclic terminological axioms result in undecidability of satisfiability of feature terms w.r.t. terminological axioms. This result can be easily reformulated for the corresponding terminological logics, and it turns out that subsumption for descriptive and greatest fixpoint semantics becomes undecidable (Nebel 1991). For this reason, CLASSIC does not support terminological cycles.

Nevertheless, in the CLASSIC system, *implicational rules* are supported. These rules are interpreted procedurally, and they act on a database of objects that are described using concept and role symbols. Given such a rule of the form

$$C(x) \Rightarrow C'(x),$$

any object which the system has classified to belong to the denotation of the concept C will be asserted to belong also to the denotation of C'. If this assertion leads to an inconsistency, i.e., to a situation where an object is interpreted to belong to the denotation of $\perp$, the system signals this contradiction. Although these rules are not identical to axioms, we have the following restriction. A CLASSIC database can be consistently "completed," i.e., allow to be mentioned explicitly all objects that have to exist because of terminological axioms, only if the database plus the terminology have a model. This in turn, however, is equivalent to satisfiability of the terminological axioms plus the implicational rules, which is undecidable in the general case by the above result. This means it is undecidable whether a CLASSIC database has a consistent completion.

4.3 Functional Uncertainty

Another interesting application of the undecidability of the word problem in Thue systems is a reduction from the word problem to satisfiability of feature terms that contain *functional uncertainty* (Kaplan, Maxwell 1988). This term-forming operator was invented for the concise description of so-called long-distance dependencies in LFG (Kaplan, Bresnan 1982). It has the form

$$\exists(L)F,$$

where L is some finitely represented regular set of words over $\mathbf{F}$. It denotes all individuals $d \in \mathbf{D}^{\mathcal{I}}$ such that there is some feature path $p \in L$ and an element $e \in F^{\mathcal{I}}$, where $e \in p^{\mathcal{I}}(d)$. One can think of $\exists(L)F$ as an infinite union: $p_1\colon F \sqcup p_2\colon F \sqcup \ldots \sqcup p_i\colon F \sqcup \ldots$, where all p_i are elements of L. Formally, the denotation of functional uncertainty is defined as

$$(\exists(L)F)^{\mathcal{I}} = \{d \in \mathbf{D}^{\mathcal{I}} \mid \exists p \in L\colon \emptyset \neq p^{\mathcal{I}}(d) \subseteq F^{\mathcal{I}}\}$$

Decidability of the satisfiability of feature terms containing functional uncertainty has been an open problem. A restricted version of the problem was addressed in (Kaplan, Maxwell 1988), where a partial solution involving an acyclicity condition is given.

Recalling from Sect. 3.2 the fact that terminological cycles under the greatest fixpoint semantics are closely related to terminological logics that permit regular expressions over roles, one would expect that undecidability would show up again in this case. In fact, if the feature logic specified in Sect. 2 is extended by functional uncertainty, then satisfiability of feature terms is undecidable (Baader et al. 1991).[2] An even stronger result can be shown. Satisfiability of a feature term relative to a set of arbitrary axioms can be reduced to satisfiability of a feature term without axioms (Baader et al. 1991).[3] However, these results strongly depend on the presence of the complement operator. Thus, decidability for functional uncertainty in weaker feature logics – feature logics that are not propositionally complete – is still an open problem.

5 Modal Logics

The most surprising connection between attributive description formalisms and other research areas was recently discovered by Schild (1991). He showed that a large number of possible terminological logics are notational variants of different propositional modal and dynamic logics. Exploiting this correspondence, a number of interesting properties for the latter logics, such as finite model properties, complexity results, and algorithms, can be straightforwardly applied to the corresponding terminological logics. In order to demonstrate the connection between the different fields, we will focus on the correspondence between the terminological logic $\mathcal{ALC}$ (Schmidt-Schauß, Smolka 1991) introduced in Sect. 2 and the *propositional polymodal logic* $K_{(m)}$ (Halpern, Moses 1985).

Given a set of *atomic propositions* $\Psi = \{a, b, c, \ldots\}$, the constants $\top$ and $\bot$ denoting the truth-values **true** and **false**, a set of m operators $K_1, \ldots, K_m$, the set of well-formed $K_{(m)}$-formulas (denoted by ϕ) is defined by

$$\phi \longrightarrow a \mid \top \mid \bot \mid \phi \wedge \phi' \mid \phi \vee \phi' \mid \neg\phi \mid K_i\phi.$$

Satisfiability of such formulas is defined with respect to *Kripke structures*

$$M = (S, \pi, \kappa_1, \ldots, \kappa_m),$$

where S is a set of states, $\pi(s)$ is a truth-assignment for all atomic propositions in Ψ at the state $s \in S$, and $\kappa_i \subseteq S \times S$ are the accessibility relations. A formula ϕ is said to be *satisfied at a world* (M, s), written $(M, s) \models \phi$, under the following conditions:

$$
\begin{aligned}
(M, s) &\models a &&\iff \pi(s)(a) = \text{true} \\
(M, s) &\models \top \\
(M, s) &\not\models \bot \\
(M, s) &\models \phi \wedge \phi' &&\iff (M, s) \models \phi \text{ and } (M, s) \models \phi' \\
(M, s) &\models \phi \vee \phi' &&\iff (M, s) \models \phi \text{ or } (M, s) \models \phi' \\
(M, s) &\models \neg\phi &&\iff (M, s) \not\models \phi \\
(M, s) &\models K_i\phi &&\iff \forall t \in \kappa_i(s)\colon (M, t) \models \phi
\end{aligned}
$$

[2]Note that no terminological axioms are involved here!
[3]A similar result for terminological logics is shown in (Schild 1991).

A $K_{(m)}$-formula ϕ is *satisfiable*, iff there exists a world (M, s) that satisfies ϕ. ϕ is *valid*, written $\models \phi$, iff all worlds satisfy ϕ.

This notion of satisfiability is obviously closely related to satisfiability of $\mathcal{ALC}$-concepts. Indeed, there is a one-to-one correspondence between $\mathcal{ALC}$ and $K_{(m)}$, as can be seen from the following table:

Polymodal logic $K_{(m)}$	Terminological logic $\mathcal{ALC}$
Ψ	$\mathbf{C} = \Psi$
$\{1, \ldots, m\}$	$\mathbf{R} = \{R_1, \ldots, R_m\}$
$\top$	$\top$
$\bot$	$\bot$
$\phi \wedge \phi'$	$\phi \sqcap \phi'$
$\phi \vee \phi'$	$\phi \sqcup \phi'$
$\neg\phi$	$\neg\phi$
$K_i\phi$	$\forall R_i : \phi$
$\neg K_i \neg\phi$	$\exists R_i : \neg\phi$
ϕ satisfiable	ϕ is a satisfiable $\mathcal{ALC}$-concept
$\models \neg\phi \vee \phi'$	$\phi \preceq \phi'$

PSPACE-completeness of subsumption in $\mathcal{ALC}$ follows immediately, because satisfiability in $K_{(m)}$ is known to be PSPACE-complete (Halpern, Moses 1985). Hence, we have an alternative proof of the complexity of subsumption to the one presented in (Schmidt-Schauß, Smolka 1991). The most interesting aspect of this close correspondence is that it also works for other variants of propositional modal and dynamic logics (Schild 1991), giving us a large number of complexity results and algorithms for free. This correspondence also applies to feature logics. In this context, deterministic dynamic logics are the right kind of logics to establish the correspondence. However, although these correspondences can be used to solve a number of open problems, there are aspects which have not been considered in modal and dynamic logics. For instance, agreements of feature paths do not have a counterpart in modal or dynamic logics.

6 Conclusion

We have demonstrated that the study of formal properties of attributive description formalisms, which jointly characterize terminological and feature logics, is quite closely connected to other areas of formal research. In particular, we have shown how the theory of finite state automata helps in solving some open problems in terminological logics, and how the word problem for Thue systems is applied to a number of problems to prove undecidability. Finally, we have examined the close correspondence between attributive description formalisms on one side and modal and dynamic logics on the other.

Interestingly, the study of attributive description formalisms is not only a sink for results in other areas, but also provides insights which can be applied elsewhere. For instance, complex object data models, such as O_2 (Lécluse, Richard, Velez 1989), are closely related to attributive description formalisms, so that the techniques are applicable. Such an application reveals that the subtype-inference algorithm specified in (Lécluse, Richard, Velez 1989) is incomplete, and that the subtype-inference problem is PSPACE-complete (Bergamaschi, Nebel 1990). Further, the study of sublanguages of $\mathcal{ALC}$ (Donini et al. 1991b; Donini et al. 1991a) can be directly applied to sublogics of $K_{(m)}$. For example, if only negation of propositional atoms is allowed and there is no disjunction, then satisfiability of a $K_{(m)}$-formula is co-NP-complete. Finally, the undecidability result for subsumption constraints in feature logics yields the undecidability of semi-unification over rational trees (Dörre, Rounds 1990).

Acknowledgement

We would like to thank Franz Baader and Werner Nutt for a number of helpful comments on an earlier version of this paper.

References

Aït-Kaci, H. (1984): A Lattice-Theoretic Approach to Computations Based on a Calculus of Partially Ordered Type Structures. PhD thesis, University of Pennsylvania, Philadelphia, PA

Baader, F., Bürckert, H.-J., Nebel, B., Nutt, W., Smolka, G. (1991): On the expressivity of feature logics with negation, functional uncertainty, and sort equations. DFKI Report RR-91-01, German Research Center for Artificial Intelligence (DFKI), Saarbrücken

Baader, F. (1990): Terminological cycles in KL-ONE-based knowledge representation languages. In: Proceedings of the 8th National Conference of the American Association for Artificial Intelligence, Boston, MA, pp. 621–626

Baader, F. (1991): Augmenting concept languages by transitive closure of roles: an alternative to terminological cycles. In: Proceedings of the 12th International Joint Conference on Artificial Intelligence, Sydney, Australia. To appear

Bergamaschi, S., Nebel, B. (1990): Theoretical foundations of complex object data models. Technical Report 74, CIOC-CNR, Bologna, Italy

Boone, W. W. (1959): The word problem. Ann. of Math. 70(2), 207–265

Borgida, A., Brachman, R. J., McGuinness, D. L., Resnick, L. A. (1989): CLASSIC: a structural data model for objects. In: Proceedings of the 1989 ACM SIGMOD International Conference on Mangement of Data, Portland, OR, pp. 59–67

Bouma, G., König, E., Uszkoreit, H. (1988): A flexible graph-unification formalism and its application to natural-language processing. IBM Journal of Research and Development 32(2), 170–184

Brachman, R. J., McGuinness, D. L., Patel-Schneider, P. F., Resnick, L. A., Borgida, A. (1991): Living with CLASSIC: when and how to use a KL-ONE-like language. In: Sowa, J. (ed.): Principles of Semantic Networks. Morgan Kaufmann, San Mateo, CA

Brachman, R. J., Levesque, H. J. (1984): The tractability of subsumption in frame-based description languages. In: Proceedings of the 4th National Conference of the American Association for Artificial Intelligence, Austin, TX, pp. 34–37

Brachman, R. J., Schmolze, J. G. (1985): An overview of the KL-ONE knowledge representation system. Cognitive Science 9(2), 171–216

Brachman, R. J. (1979): On the epistemological status of semantic networks. In: Findler, N. V. (ed.): Associative Networks: Representation and Use of Knowledge by Computers. Academic Press, New York, NY, pp. 3–50

Donini, F. M., Lenzerini, M., Nardi, D., Nutt, W. (1991a): Tractable concept languages. In: Proceedings of the 12th International Joint Conference on Artificial Intelligence, Sydney, Australia. To appear

Donini, F. M., Lenzerini, M., Nardi, D., Nutt, W. (1991b): The complexity of concept languages. In: Allen, J. A., Fikes, R., Sandewall, E. (eds.): Principles of Knowledge Representation and Reasoning: Proceedings of the 2nd International Conference, Cambridge, MA, pp. 151–162

Dörre, J., Rounds, W. C. (1990): On subsumption and semi-unification in feature algebras. In: Proceedings of the 5th IEEE Symposium on Logic in Computer Science, Philadelphia, PA, pp. 301–310. Also available as IWBS Report 97, IWBS, IBM Germany, Stuttgart, December 1989

Garey, M. R., Johnson, D. S. (1979): Computers and Intractability—A Guide to the Theory of NP-Completeness. Freeman, San Francisco, CA

Halpern, J. Y., Moses, Y. (1985): A guide to the modal logics of knowledge and belief: Preliminary draft. In: Proceedings of the 9th International Joint Conference on Artificial Intelligence, Los Angeles, CA, pp. 480–490

Hollunder, B., Nutt, W. (1990): Subsumption algorithms for concept languages. DFKI Report RR-90-04, German Research Center for Artificial Intelligence (DFKI), Kaiserslautern

Johnson, M. (1987): Attribute-Value Logic and the Theory of Grammar. CSLI Lecture Notes 16, Center for the Study of Language and Information, Stanford University, Stanford, CA

Kaplan, R. M., Bresnan, J. (1982): Lexical-functional grammar: a formal system for grammatical representation. In: Bresnan, J. (ed.): The Mental Representation of Grammatical Relations. MIT Press, Cambridge, MA, pp. 173–381

Kaplan, R. M., Maxwell, J. T. III (1988): An algorithm for functional uncertainty. In: Proceedings of the 12th International Conference on Computational Linguistics, Budapest, Hungary, pp. 297–302

Kasper, R. T., Rounds, W. C. (1986): A logical semantics for feature structures. In: Proceedings of the 24th Annual Meeting of the ACL, New York, NY, pp. 257–265

Kasper, R. T. (1987): Feature Structures: A Logical Theory with Applications to Language Analysis. PhD thesis, University of Michigan, Ann Arbor, MI

Kay, M. (1979): Functional grammar. In: Proceedings of the Fifth Annual Meeting of the Berkeley Linguistics Society, Berkeley, CA, Berkeley Linguistics Society

Kay, M. (1985): Parsing in functional unification grammars. In: Dowty, D., Karttunen, L. (eds.): Natural Language Parsing. Cambridge University Press, Cambridge, UK

Lécluse, C., Richard, P., Velez, F. (1989): Modeling complex structures in object-oriented databases. In: Proceedings of the 8th ACM SIGACT-SIGMOD-SIGART Symposium on Principles of Database-Systems, pp. 360–367

Lipkis, T. (1982): A KL-ONE classifier. In: Schmolze, J. G., Brachman, R. J. (eds.): Proceedings of the 1981 KL-ONE Workshop, Cambridge, MA, pp. 128–145. The proceedings have been published as BBN Report No. 4842 and Fairchild Technical Report No. 618

Moser, M. G. (1983): An overview of NIKL, the new implementation of KL-ONE. In: Research in Knowledge Representation and Natural Language Understanding, BBN Report No. 5421. Bolt, Beranek, and Newman Inc., Cambridge, MA, pp. 7–26

Nebel, B., Smolka, G. (1990): Representation and reasoning with attributive descriptions. In: Bläsius, K.-H., Hedtstück, U., Rollinger, C.-R. (eds.): Sorts and Types in Artificial Intelligence. Lecture Notes in Artificial Intelligence, Vol. 418, Springer-Verlag, Berlin, Heidelberg, New York, pp. 112–139. Also available as IWBS Report 81, IWBS, IBM Germany, Stuttgart, September 1989

Nebel, B. (1988): Computational complexity of terminological reasoning in BACK. Artificial Intelligence 34(3), 371–383

Nebel, B. (1990a): Reasoning and Revision in Hybrid Representation Systems. Lecture Notes in Artificial Intelligence, Vol. 422, Springer-Verlag, Berlin, Heidelberg, New York

Nebel, B. (1990b): Terminological reasoning is inherently intractable. Artificial Intelligence 43, 235–249. Also available as IWBS Report 82, IWBS, IBM Germany, Stuttgart, October 1989

Nebel, B. (1991): Terminological cycles: Semantics and computational properties. In: Sowa, J. (ed.): Principles of Semantic Networks. Morgan Kaufmann, San Mateo, CA

Patel-Schneider, P. F. (1989a): A four-valued semantics for terminological logics. Artificial Intelligence 38(3), 319–351

Patel-Schneider, P. F. (1989b): Undecidability of subsumption in NIKL. Artificial Intelligence 39(2), 263–272

Pletat, U., von Luck, K. (1990): Knowledge representation in LILOG. In: Bläsius, K.-H., Hedtstück, U., Rollinger, C. (eds.): Sorts and Types in Artificial Intelligence. Lecture Notes in Artificial Intelligence, Vol. 418, Springer-Verlag, Berlin, Heidelberg, New York, pp. 140–164

Schild, K. (1988): Undecidability of $\mathcal{U}$. KIT Report 67, Department of Computer Science, Technische Universität Berlin, Berlin, Germany

Schild, K. (1991): A correspondence theory for terminological logics: Preliminary report. In: Proceedings of the 12th International Joint Conference on Artificial Intelligence, Sydney, Australia. To appear

Schmidt-Schauß, M., Smolka, G. (1991): Attributive concept descriptions with complements. Artificial Intelligence 48, 1–26. Also available as IWBS Report 68, IWBS, IBM Germany, Stuttgart, June 1989

Schmidt-Schauß, M. (1989): Subsumption in KL-ONE is undecidable. In: Brachman, R. J., Levesque, H. J., Reiter, R. (eds.): Principles of Knowledge Representation and Reasoning: Proceedings of the 1st International Conference, Toronto, ON, pp. 421–431

Schmolze, J. G., Israel, D. J. (1983): KL-ONE: Semantics and classification. In: Research in Knowledge Representation and Natural Language Understanding, BBN Technical Report, No. 5421. Bolt, Beranek, and Newman Inc., Cambridge, MA, pp. 27–39

Shieber, S. M. (1986): An Introduction to Unification-Based Approaches to Grammar. CSLI Lecture Notes 4, Center for the Study of Language and Information, Stanford University, Stanford, CA

Smolka, G. (1988): A feature logic with subsorts. LILOG Report 33, IWBS, IBM Germany, Stuttgart. To appear in: J. Wedekind, C. Rohrer (eds.), Unification in Grammar. MIT Press, 1991

Smolka, G. (1989): Feature constraint logics for unification grammars. IWBS Report 93, IWBS, IBM Germany, Stuttgart. To appear in the Journal of Logic Programming

Chapter 2.2

Knowledge Engineering and Database Support

Within knowledge based text understanding systems a lot of background knowledge is needed for being able to capture the meaning of the given texts. Since the LILOG system is oriented towards understanding non-technical texts of travel guide books the required background knowledge is primarily common-sense knowledge. It is wellknown that a large amount of such background knowledge has to be provided for ending up with text understanding systems offering adequate text understanding capabilities.

In "The Background Knowledge of the LILOG System" G. Klose and K. v. Luck investigate some of the problems which have to be solved when building up common-sense knowledge bases. They especially discuss how the domain of discourse, the set of texts at hand, and the kind of questions to be answered by the system have influenced the structure and granularity of the LILOG common-sense model.

E. Lang provides in his paper "The LILOG-Ontology from a Linguistic Point of View" a thorough analysis of the ontology having been built up as part of the LILOG background knowledge. He discusses various design criteria for introducing sorts and proposes a distinction between linguistic and conceptual categorizations. Furthermore, a precise notion of domain of knowledge is provided and contrasted with the partitioning of the LILOG ontology.

In contrast to the first two papers of this chapter M. Börkel and P. Gerstl address in their paper "A Knowledge Engineering Enviroment for LILOG" the more technical knowledge engineering aspects by specifying requirements a knowledge engineering tool has to meet. Based on this requirements analyis the logical design of such a tool is outlined introducing four kinds of views of knowlegde: a conceptual view, a physical view, a tools view, and an operational view.

The paper "Knowledge Engineering in the Context of Related Fields of Research" by J. Angele et al. investigates what kind of concepts and methods being known in software engineering and information systems design may be used for knowledge engineering as well. Furthermore, it is shown that the model-based approach to knowledge engineering as used for developing expert systems is not directly applicable to the development of common-sense based systems.

"LILOG-DB: Database Support for Knowledge Based Systems" by St. Benzschawel et al. addresses the problem of how to store, access, and manipulate the large of amount of linguistic and background knowledge, being required within a text understanding system, in an efficient way. In essence, LILOG-DB may be characterized as a next generation database system supporting knowledge based systems by handling complex objects, incomplete and variant schemas, deductive query-answering, and taxonomies. LILOG-DB is based on a powerful data model, the Feature Term Data Model, and related database languages.

Rudi Studer

The Background Knowledge of the LILOG System

G. Klose, K. von Luck

Abstract

The LILOG system under development at IBM Germany is a text understanding system with a question/answering component for proving successful text processing. The texts under investigation are non-technical texts understandable for 'normal people' with commonsense knowledge. As well known in AI, text understanding systems require background knowledge for dealing with tacit and implicit textual information; in our case, this background knowledge has to be a kind of commonsense knowledge. The LILOG project works with the logical paradigm for reconstructing models of the world as the relevant domain of discourse. The modeling itself is oriented towards both the linguistic requirements and the demands resulting from tractability aspects of inference.

In this paper we characterize the texts under investigation and sketch the relevant features of the logical language for the modeling task. We will present examples of linguistic requirements and discuss some features of the model already implemented. The lesson learned from these works is that 'classical' knowledge acquisition techniques and methodologies developed for so-called expert systems are not suitable for commonsense modeling with underspecified tasks in mind, as in text understanding systems for nontechnical texts.

On the basis of these experiences a new methodology is sketched and discussed. Examples of tools for supporting this undertaking are given.

1 Introduction

The LILOG system under development at IBM Germany is a text understanding system with a question/answering component for proving successful text processing. The texts under investigation are non-technical texts understandable for 'normal people' with commonsense knowledge. It is well known in AI that text understanding systems require background knowledge for dealing with tacit and implicit textual information. In our case, this background knowledge has to be a kind of common sense knowledge.

A typical cookbook for building expert systems includes most of the following steps:

- · Get one or more experts motivated.
- Get some ideas of the problems tackled by these experts.
- Reconstruct the problem solving process of these experts in a generalized way.
- Extract the relevant knowledge for these problem solving processes.
- Implement and test a knowledge base out of this knowledge.
- Sell the resulting program to the management.

Obviously most of these points do not meet our concerns. For example, we have no problems for a typical domain expert – instead, native speakers are the people we have to compete with – and there are no obvious problem solving processes in a 'shallow' understanding of everyday texts. Most of the common proposals for knowledge acquisition tools and methodologies reflect the procedure sketched above. Consequently, a straightforward strategy of transferring this procedure in order to reconstruct commonsense knowledge is inappropriate. Thus another kind of methodology has to be developed for acquiring the background knowledge necessary for a text understanding system for everyday texts.

In our case, the LILOG project works with the logical paradigm for reconstructing models of the world as the relevant domain of discourse. The modeling itself is oriented towards both linguistic requirements and the demands resulting from tractability aspects of inference. So linguistic and logical approaches have to be the backbone for this methodology.

In the following we will present the task in a more detailed way, show the solutions worked out so far and extract a first idea of a methodology suitable for such an approach.

2   The Domain Under Investigation

A *general* text understanding system without any limits for the possible domain of discourse is – at least until now – far from any chance of realization. One of the first tasks within the design process is the selection of a *domain* under investigation and its detailed analysis.

As in the area of expert systems, the domain can be chosen from a wide range of possibilities. The first decision in the selection process is the determination of the scope of the model, or, as Pat Hayes in [Hayes 79] posed it, the detection of the relevant items of the domain you want to reconstruct. So for example, computer technology will be a broader domain than IBM personal computer technology, if you do the reconstruction on the same level of granularity (see below).

In the next step, a set of *tasks* has to be selected to delimit the depth of the model, its *granularity*, and *problem solving capabilities*. So for the domain IBM personal computer technology, you will have to decide whether you are interested in the different types or models of IBM PC, or if you have to represent additional information about parts or software packages. This type of design decision depends on the kind of problem solving tasks you are intended to run on the basis of the model. This example illustrates the strong interrelationship between domain and task in the area of expert systems you have to deal with as soon as you start to analyze the domain under investigation.

For text understanding systems this type of direct coupling seems to be less adequate. Similarly to Pat Hayes, Doug Lenat claimed in [Lenat et al. 86] that a huge amount of knowledge, closely intertwined, can serve as the basis for a broad coverage of text understanding systems with this model as a knowledge base. For example, the decision whether you have to reconstruct the political, social or architectural aspects of the concept church, inducing the distinction between aspects of institution and those of building, determines the granularity of the model. This decision can be taken without having a specific task in mind. The inferences you will deliver on the basis of a sentence like 'The highest building in town, located directly in the city center, is the Catholic church' reflect basically the problem solving capabilities of the model. Following this argument, you find on the one hand 'puzzle mode' inferences (as a typical trait of expert system performance), such as in

John and Paul drink five glasses of beer together. John drinks one more glass of beer than

Paul. How many glasses of beer does John drink ?

For text understanding systems on the other hand, you tend to expect obvious inferences like

Ron entered the saloon yesterday at high noon. Where was Ron yesterday at high noon ?

This qualitative distinction only seems true at first glance. At a deeper look, as we try to show below, you have to decide along a *continuous scale* of 'obvious' inferences on the one hand and 'puzzle mode' on the other. Consequently, text understanding systems like expert systems require decisions on the inferential services the knowledge base is supposed to deliver in a given domain. But these decisions have to be taken – in the average case – on the basis of broader task settings.

At least three dimensions can be seen as determining factors for a modeling process, as shown in Figure 1. In the field of commonsense knowledge the position within these dimensions is quite different from typical expert system settings. This evaluation constitutes one part of the modeling process.

In what follows, some of the modeling decisions in LEU/2 along these dimensions will be discussed, with special focus on the realization in the logical formalism L_{LILOG}.

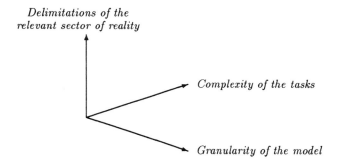

Figure 1: Three dimensions determining the model

For the system referred to in this paper, the LEU/2 system (**LILOG E**xperimental **E**nvironment 2), travel guide information about the city center of Düsseldorf was chosen as the domain under investigation. In a first phase, some written information about that domain was selected and – partly – constructed on the basis of information obtained from travel guides, travel agencies and an examination of Düsseldorf city center. This process was guided by the intention of receiving prototypical textual information with a broad coverage of linguistic phenomena to be handled by the linguistic parts of the system (i.e., parsing and generating components). On the other hand, the set of different entities mentioned in the texts had to be large enough for an appropriately sized knowledge base, interconnected enough to support interesting inferences but small enough to be handled within a prototypical implementation.[1]

We decided to work with short texts (frequently found in travel guides) describing single sightseeing items, and with a one-page story about a group of people on a prototypical sightseeing tour. In the next step, the chosen texts were classified according to linguistic criteria and analyzed for their propositional contents. Native speakers were asked to pose questions and give acceptable

---

[1]In the final section we will give some quantitative and qualitative characteristics of the actual knowledge base.

answers concerning the content of the texts in order to obtain a first hint of the kind of overall behavior to be expected LEU/2.

This behaviour is determined by the capabilities of the ensemble of system components. So the relevant tasks of the knowledge base had to be isolated from the tasks of the lexical, syntactic, semantic analysis components and the generation module. The result of this investigation was the identification of a couple of obvious inference tasks as well as a first set of decisions on the granularity of the model. This material was the basis for starting the modeling process described in the next section.

3 Modeling in LEU/2

In the field of logic-based formalisms for coding background knowledge in natural language processing systems there are controversial debates concerning the design and use of formal constructs. Topics in these debates include the function of axioms compared to recent expert system technology, the function of structured concept hierarchies [Monarch, Nirenburg 87], the quality and number of additional attributes (roles in KL-ONE lookalikes) or syntactic validation criteria [Horacek 89]. Our approach aims at finding useful selection criteria for different expressive means for the formalism L_{LILOG} in order to bridge the actual gap between *problem-driven* and *technology-driven*[2] research.

In our case, we can make use of two different kinds of structuring constructs:

- A frame-description language similar to KL-ONE (cf., e.g., [Brachman, Schmolze 85]) serves as a formalism for structuring the terminology of the domain and consists of
  - sort expressions for classes of entities, organized hierarchically as sets and subsets (i.e., the logical subsumption relation), and
  - two-place predicates and functions (i.e., features and roles), attached to specific sorts and constituting functional and relational connections between sorts, and
- axioms of first order predicate logic, expressing inferential dependencies between domain terms in the form of axiomatic semantics for those terms.

So the formalism used here[3] is comparable to, say KRYPTON (see, e.g., [Brachman et al. 85]).

Sort expressions are used to represent the categories of our domain model. The *upper structure* of the resulting ontology portrays some generalized schemes of organization of relative domain-independence. When descending through the model towards the *lower structure*, the categories are defined much closer to the word level and are therefore domain-specific in the sense of *explicit* text knowledge. [4]

In the following, we will illustrate some decisions concerning the scope and granularity of our model with the corresponding parts of our upper structure.

A basic decision about our model is due to J. Hobbs [Hobbs et al. 87] and results in a reification of predicates. In our model, all events, states, etc. have concept status on their own. For example, instead of having

---

[2]See [Lehnert 88] for that distinction.
[3]For a detailed description of the formalism L_{LILOG} see [Pletat, von Luck 90].
[4]This differentiation between *upper* and *lower* structure of the model is introduced by [Mann et al. 85].

driving(John, N.Y., S.F.)

for the utterance 'John drives from New York to San Francisco' we have

driving(c_1) $\wedge$ agent(c_1,c_2) $\wedge$ source(c_1,c_3) $\wedge$ goal(c_1,c_4) $\wedge$
human(c_2) $\wedge$ name(c_2)=John $\wedge$
city(c_3) $\wedge$ name(c_3)=N.Y. $\wedge$
city(c_4) $\wedge$ name(c_4)=S.F.

This technique enables us to model the case frames for verbs in a manner analogic to the lexical entries of the analyzing component as well as to incorporate the structures for events, etc., within the categories like the schemata for objects.[5]

Given the fact that our model has to capture domain knowledge from tourist guides, we decided to discriminate between ENTITIES and ABSTRACTCONCEPTS. This differentiation allows us to separate the ontological definitions which are most likely to be the goals of questioning from those (abstract) concepts which are necessary for the definition of spatial, temporal or other qualitative specifications (measures, units, names, etc.). As we mentioned in Sect. 2, we want to simulate understanding of basically two different types of texts, i.e., short texts describing single sightseeing items and narrative texts dealing with fictive sequential events. This leads us to the requirement for both an object-oriented and an event-oriented part of the conceptual hierarchy. So ENTITIES can be further divided into OBJECTENTITIES and EVENTS, with several types of semantic connections between them. It makes sense to think about objects as well as about events in terms of their spatial and temporal environment, although these knowledge specifications will obviously be quite different.

Among the most important criteria for introducing new subconcepts are selection criteria for the attachment of additional attributes. Spatial specifications of physical objects on the one hand and thematic roles for events on the other may serve as examples.

As to the field of spatial relations, we decided to follow Ewald Lang's detailed analysis of the interaction between linguistic and conceptual knowledge (see, e.g., [Lang 87], [Lang, Carstensen 89]). One part of the modeling consists in associating explicit *object schemata* to those sorts which can be talked about in terms of spatial localizations. The different elements of the object schemata are implemented as roles and features within sort definitions. One of these elements fulfills the task of selecting relevant *parameters of dimension* out of a limited number of alternatives. They carry two main kinds of information: the number of axes (or dimensions) involved in the description of a certain object, and whether or not two of these axes are integrated. A "normal" round cup and a house both have to be described by using three dimensions, but due to the shape of the cup's base (with two integrated axes) it has no length or breadth. Thus the parameters can be explained as parts of an abstract, three-dimensional model of space on the one hand, and as selection constraints for the use of adjectives on the other.

When looking at the representation of EVENTS, we can make use of two-place relations in correspondence with thematic roles in the linguistic sense and thus determine a useful set of parts of the same sentence when generating an answer. In our context we tried to isolate different groups of events, according to their typical thematic roles, and to formulate constraints about these roles on the conceptual level. Two important dichotomies are

- states vs. events (in the narrow sense, i.e., inducing changes in the object part of the ontology)

---

[5] A similar technique can be found, for example in [Mann et al. 85].

1. The museum is located next to the church.

2. The facade was renovated in 1956.

- movements vs. "indirect" events

1. A bus took the conference participants to the city center.

2. The academy was founded in 1831.

It is obvious that decisions in the EVENT-part of the ontology will have an important impact on the structure of the OBJECT-part. For example, it is useful to have groups of entities which can be AGENTS of events, like HUMANS or INSTITUTIONS, and others which – for conceptual reasons – are involved in states, like HOUSES, STREETS and STATUES.[6] In addition, we need the distinction between those ENTITIES which can be agents or patients in MOVEMENTS and those which are conceptualized in a static way, and so on.

In the field of temporal relations, we attempted to cover a broad range of phenomena in the texts by implementing Allens's interval logic[7] into our formalism L$_{\text{LILOG}}$. This approach led us into three types of difficulties. In order to answer questions about the sequential order of intervals, one has to take a look at what happens in these intervals. In the ideal case, plausible groups of EVENTS will be selected which can reasonably be associated with one another. These relations, though, are far beyond the analytical scope of purely temporal interval properties.

A second problem arose in the OBJECT part of the ontology as to facts like opening times associated with institutions. A sentence like

The museum opens daily (except Monday) from 10 a.m. to 17 p.m.

requires the representation of regularities and involved periods, whereas Allen's temporal relations are mainly defined on sets of two intervals of the same kind, without the possibility to distinguish calendar times from vague labels like *winter* or *morning*.

The third kind of difficulty can be found in the connection between logical relations of succession on the one hand and the language surface level on the other. Sequences are – among other things – introduced by prepositions or conjunctions and have to be mapped onto (in Allen's case: 13) types of relations, and it turned out to be even more complicated to find an adequate way back: the use of prepositions, for example, depends largely upon the position of the deictic center (in our context identical with speech time) on the conceptualized time line. *From ... on* tends to be used for intervals which ended before speech time, whereas *since* requires continuation until the present, and so on.

The upper structure sketched here is – of course – an idealization of the real domain model of LEU/2, as Fig. 2 shows. In addition to the systematic attachment of roles and features, we will give some examples of decisions about clusters of axioms resulting from the conceptual structure in the next section.

---

[6]The decision to exclude houses from the set of possible agents of an event depends on the kind of texts we consider and does not cover, say, fairy tales or metaphorical readings.

[7]See [Allen, Kautz 85].

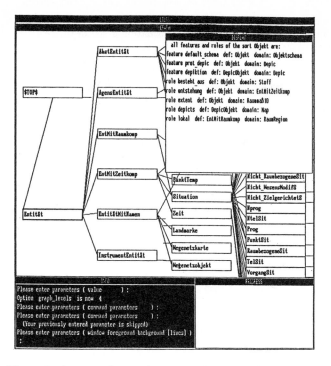

Figure 2: A screen dump of a sector of the LEU/2 ontology

4 What About Shallow Inferences in Text Understanding ?

The example below shows typical shallow inferences induced by the sentence processed:

Text:

(T1): Mrs. Smith constructed the Catholic church at the market place in 1835.

Questions:

(Q1): What did Mrs. Smith do in 1835 ?

(Q2): Where is the Catholic church located ?

(Q3): When was the Catholic church constructed ?

In order to produce the answers for the questions, the following steps have to be taken: In question (Q1) simply the activity reported in (T1) is asked for and has to be generated (indexed by the person) as the answer[8], e.g., 'She constructed the church'. In question (Q2) one has to find the instantiation of the location-role associated with the event of constructing.

---

[8]Sometimes the answer may have an elliptical form and use anaphorical references.

Question (Q3) demonstrates a qualitatively different case, because in order to give an adequate answer one has to attach the temporal information given in the text not only to the event but also to the building constructed, which is modeled in the object part.

The implications of a woman being an architect of Catholic churches in the nineteenth century belong to a class of inferences far outside the inferential competence of LEU/2 and can be characterized as deep reasoning. But if we had defined this type of conclusion as the *task* of our system, the meaning of deep and shallow inferences might have been different.

The example above shows that systematic groupings for axioms include both clusters for specific parts of the ontology and clusters representing connections between those parts, like temporal information in different kinds of events, but concerning the same object.

It should be noted here that selectional decisions about the kind of questions the system is expected to answer introduce an additional task level compared to decisions about inferential capacities. From the perspective of other system components (see Sect. 2), the same types of question may pose totally different problems or topics of interest.

5   Further Aspects and Conclusion

The work reported was undertaken for the text understanding system LEU/2, which is under development at IBM Germany in cooperation with some university partners. LEU/2 is fully implemented in Prolog under AIX and runs within the LILOG context. The knowledge base for the domain under investigation consists of more than 600 concept definitions, among these some 100 belonging to the upper structure. The average number of attributes for each of these concepts is some 20. At the moment the number of axioms for our domain is some 300. This quantitative characterization of the LEU/2 knowledge base gives – of course – only a first hint of the complexity of the model represented as a part of the overall system, because a sensible measure for the adequacy of a model cannot be defined without the class of tasks in mind.

The upper structure especially seems to be quite stable for the system and seems, after careful analysis of different models for text understanding systems, to have a more domain-independent status than, e.g., the JANUS knowledge base (see [Mann et al. 85]). Due to the highly structured model it was possible to minimize the number of axioms necessary (as the basis for inferencing) and to group these axioms close to the domain clusters. The interrelationships between different clusters could be handled mostly by stating the interrelationships of very abstract concepts.

The tension between linguistic and inferential demands on the modeling is still alive and forces compromises on both sides, but reification techniques as proposed by J. Hobbs in [Hobbs et al. 87], fulfilled a couple of demands for both sides. The adaption of the axiomatization of time of [Allen, Kautz 85] failed in many respects, as remarked above, but seems to be at least a starting point for formalizing the time cluster.

The challenge of the next phase of LEU/2 will be the anticipation of other, different domains. Especially the knowledge base has to be proven to be relative stable at least within the upper structure for this venture. But knowledge representation for a text understanding system is an ongoing affair for the next decade at least.

References

[Allen, Kautz 85] James F. Allen, Henry A. Kautz: A model of naive temporal reasoning. In J. R. Hobbs, R. C. Moore (eds.): *Formal Theories of the Commonsense World*, p. 251–268, Ablex, Norwood, NJ, 1985

[Brachman, Schmolze 85] Ronald J. Brachman, James G. Schmolze: An overview of the KL-ONE knowledge representation system. *Cognitive Science*, 9(2):171–216, April 1985

[Brachman et al. 85] Ronald J. Brachman, Victoria Pigman Gilbert, Hector J. Levesque: An essential hybrid reasoning system: knowledge and symbol level accounts in KRYPTON. In *Proceedings of the 9th International Joint Conference on Artificial Intelligence*, p. 532–539, Los Angeles, Cal., August 1985

[Hayes 79] Patrick J. Hayes: The naive physics manifesto. In D. Michie (ed.) *Expert Systems in the Microelectronic Age*. Edinburgh Univ. Press, 1979

[Hobbs et al. 87] Jerry R. Hobbs, William Croft, Todd Davies, Douglas Edwards, Kenneth Laws: Commonsense metaphysics and lexical semantics. *Computational Linguistics*, 13(3-4):241–250, December 1987

[Horacek 89] Helmut Horacek: Towards principles of ontology. In D. Metzing (ed.) *Proc. GWAI-89*, p. 323–330, Springer-Verlag, Berlin, Heidelberg, New York, 1989

[Lang 87] Ewald Lang: Semantik der Dimensionsauszeichnung räumlicher Adjektive. In Manfred Bierwisch, Ewald Lang (eds.): *Grammatische und konzeptuelle Aspekte von Dimensionsadjektiven*, p. 287–458, Akademie Verlag, Berlin, 1987

[Lang, Carstensen 89] Ewald Lang, Kai-Uwe Carstensen: OSKAR-Ein Prolog-Programm zur Modellierung der Struktur und der Verarbeitung räumlichen Wissens. In D. Metzing (ed.): *Proc. GWAI-89*, p. 234–243, Springer-Verlag, Berlin, Heidelberg, New York, 1989

[Lehnert 88] Wendy G. Lehnert: Knowledge-based natural language understanding. In Howard Shrobe (ed.): *Exploring Artificial Intelligence*, p. 83–131, Morgan Kaufmann, San Mateo, CA, 1988

[Lenat et al. 86] Douglas Lenat, Mayank Prakash, Mary Shepherd: Cyc: using common sense knowledge to overcome brittleness and knowledge acquisition bottlenecks. *The AI Magazine*, 6(4):65–85, 1986

[Mann et al. 85] William C. Mann, Yigal Arens, Christian M. I. M. Matthiessen, Shari Naberschnig, Norman K. Sondheimer: Janus abstraction structure — draft 2. Draft paper, University of Southern California, Information Science Institute, Marina del Rey, CA, October 1985

[Monarch, Nirenburg 87] Ira Monarch, Sergei Nirenburg: The role of ontology in concept acquisition for knowledge-based systems. In John Boose, Tom Addis, Brian Gaines (eds.): *Proc. EKAW-87*, Reading University, 1987

[Pletat, von Luck 90] Udo Pletat, Kai von Luck: Knowledge Representation in LILOG. In Karl-Hans Bläsius, Uli Hedtstück, Claus Rollinger (eds.): *Sorts and Types in Artificial Intelligence*, Lecture Notes in Artificial Intelligence, Vol. 418, p. 140–164, Springer-Verlag, Berlin, Heidelberg, New York, 1990

The LILOG Ontology from a Linguistic Point of View

Ewald Lang

Introduction

The most crucial problem any natural language understanding system such as LEU/2 has to cope with is this: *How to interrelate word knowledge and world knowledge* ? To put the question this way is as simple as it is difficult to spell out the answer. As a matter of fact, almost all problems that emerge in the course of modeling the system's knowledge base are somehow related to this one, and the solutions found to settle them have eventually to be assessed on their contribution to mastering this central task. In this perspective, the knowledge base of LEU/2 (its history and its present make-up) deserves attention on the part of theoretical linguists in several respects:

(1)   As a proposal for how to model knowledge in an implemented system. That is, as a means of model formation under conditions which – unlike familiar customs practised in linguistic theorising – require formal consistency and thorough explicitness. How linguistic theorizing can be tested, refined, and supplemented by implementation has been shown, within the LILOG framework, in (Lang, Carstensen 1989; 1990), (Lang, Carstensen, Simmons 1991), (Simmons 1991), and (Carstensen, Simmons, in Chap.3 of this volume), so we need not delve into this here.

(2)   As a concrete moulding of hypothetical assumptions on the structure of knowledge and the modes of its processing. That is, as a KE account of modelling knowledge which is possibly alternative to, but hopefully compatible with, the sort of account that linguistic semanticists have always sought for in their own interests. As linguists have specific "grammatically" determined views on the requirements of knowledge representation, the ontology (sort hierarchy and axioms) presented by LEU/2 invites for an interdisciplinary debate on types and structures of knowledge and principles of knowledge representation.

(3)   As a suitable landing-site for theoretical insights and testing ground for methods and heuristic procedures developed in recent linguistic research. In view of the fact that a text understanding system, of necessity, involves the integration of language and knowledge processing, it is up to the linguist to prevent that in designing the system "things are mistaken for their names" (as Jean-Paul Sarte put it in *Les mots*).

In everday life we are well aware of the fact that the structure of language (as we are used to using it) and the structure of the world (as we usually conceive of it) do not coincide. But the situation is different when we are faced with the task of creating a text comprehension system that is to cover the underlying structures of both domains, i.e., of word knowledge and world knowledge, or, more generally: of linguistic knowledge and non-linguistic conceptual knowledge.

Under these circumstances, the structure of language plays a dual role. It is, properly allocated to the parsing and generating components, a constitutive part of the object to be modeled (that is, the system which is to integrate linguistic and non-linguistic knowledge). But at the same time it is also part of the device by means of which this object is accessed, that is, the categorization of lexical items into nouns, verbs, etc., provides an apparently natural grid for establishing corresponding sorts of entities in the ontology, which, by definition, is to represent non-linguistic common sense knowledge. Given this, the risk of confusing linguistic and non-linguistic categories is latent; moreover, it is practically unavoidable as long as we are confined (or confine ourselves) to looking at common sense knowledge through the window of language only, i.e., without a chance to draw on independent evidence from non-linguistic (say, visual or kinesthetic) ways of accessing the structure and contents of common sense knowledge.

This is the background against which I will venture some methodological considerations and suggest a couple of evaluation criteria based on which we may eventually arrive at some theory-led principles of "ontological engineering" – I owe this useful term to (Simmons 1991). The discussion will center on providing arguments in favour of the following proposal:

(P)   In the knowledge base of a text comprehension system like LEU/2, grammatically determined linguistic knowledge and conceptually anchored world knowledge should be kept distinct as regards structure and representation, but should be interrelated by a many-to-many mapping between linguistic categories and ontological entities (sorts).

The two-level approach advocated here has been proposed by (Bierwisch, Lang 1989) and has been worked out since then in a series of related works – see (Carstensen, Simmons, in this volume), (Habel, in this volume), (Herweg 1989, 1990), (Lang, Carstensen, Simmons 1991), (Maienborn 1990 a, b, 1991, and in this volume), (Simmons 1991) and further references cited therein. Instead of recounting the pros and cons of the two-level distinction in an abstract way, I will exemplify its main tenets by discussing some of the design decisions taken in LEU/2. This opens the way for gaining new insights by exploiting the rich experience that has been gathered by now in the course of creating and utilizing the LILOG ontology. Note that there are several aspects of modeling according to which a knowledge base is validated. At issue are the degree of lexical faithfulness ("Wortnähe"), the granularity, and the task orientation of the given knowledge base. We will touch them all in the discussion that follows.

1   Where do Sorts in LEU/2 Come from ?

From a linguistic point of view, the ontology of LEU/2 seems to be rather heterogeneous with respect to the motivation of particular sorts and the relations that are supposed to hold between them. Before discussing examples, let us recall what we might rightly expect of a sort definition. An ontological sort should not merely be a labelled node within a lattice-theoretical structure but should stand for a systematically justified element of a specific knowledge base which (a) is to represent extra-linguistic common sense knowledge, and (b) is to represent it in such a way that this knowledge is accessible both to the analysis of (German) input texts and to the generation of (German) output texts. If this is granted, then for any sort X to be included in the ontology, the following question has to be answered:

(D)   (a)   Is X included in the ontology as representing a conceptual (i.e. extra-linguistically founded) category, whose relations to lexical units are regular but arbitrary and cross-linguistically varying? Or
      (b)   Is X included in the ontology due to (frequent) occurrences of a lexical item X with the same name in the underlying (German) texts which the knowledge base is to account for ?

Seen in the light of the alternatives in (D), the inventory and structure of sorts in the ontology of LEU/2 turn out to come from a variety of different sources. On closer inspection, we may delimit the following sorts of sorts (as LEU/2 is designed for German, I will henceforth stick to the original sort labels):

(1)   **Conceptually based sorts** – e.g., Entitaet, Zustand, Ereignis, Situation ['entity','state', 'event', 'situation'] and the entire branch of virtual entities under TOP with the (somewhat misleading) label ' --- Konzept '. These are sorts the inclusion of which in the LEU/2 ontology is more or less determined by the criterion given in (D)(a) above.

(2) **Lexically based sorts** come in two variants which differ as to their origin but also as to the impact they have on the architecture of the entire ontology. We may thus distinguish (2)(a) and (b):

(2a) **Text base specific sorts.** These are sorts representing special vocabulary items like `Altbier-kneipe, Tritonengruppe, Flanierstrasse,` etc., which were collected from the Düsseldorf city tourist guide texts and transferred straight into the 'Lower Structure' of the LEU/2 ontology.

Due to the specificity of the items at issue and quite in line with the demand for lexical faithfulness, these sorts almost unavoidably suggest a rather direct mapping between items of the text base and entities of the knowledge base. However, the apparently close correspondence between word and world knowledge in these cases may not obscure the fact that linguistic and conceptual categorizations are actually distinct.

(2b) **Sorts projected from grammar.** The paragon case of this way of establishing ontological entities is provided by the decision to include a sort `Praeposition` as a subsort of `Raumkonzept`. Though this is perhaps the most obvious case of confusing linguistic and conceptual categories by equating them with one another, it is by no means the only one in the LEU/2 ontology. The decision taken for prepositions is indicative of a prevailing tendency in the way the ontology was designed.

On closer inspection we observe that the sort hierarchy in (what might be called) the 'Middle Structure' of the LEU/2 ontology is essentially designed according to patterns provided by the major lexical categories nouns, verbs, and adjectives. As a matter of fact, the availability of pertinent nouns has determined the structure assigned to the hierarchy of `Objekt` entities whereas the taxonomy of `Ereignis` entities [events, situations] is based on a classification of underlying verbs. As adjectives proved to be resistant to such treatment, one had to make compromises: the subset of so-called referential adjectives like *gotisch, blau* is accounted for by adding corresponding sorts of carrier objects like `GotischesObjekt < ObjektAusEpoche; BlauesObjekt < FarbigesObjekt;` for a careful discussion of how to treat dimensional adjectives see (Simmons 1991) and (Carstensen, Simmons, in this volume).

So the solution chosen for prepositions is especially instructive: (a) it reveals what has been a major pattern for creating sorts in the LEU/2 ontology, i.e., the tacit projection of grammatical categories into ontological entities; (b) it yields striking evidence for the claim that an adequate sorting of ontological entities cannot simply be paralleled to the grammatical categorization of their linguistic labels.

(3) **Sorts of mixed origin.** These include the majority of subsorts of the supersort `Entitaet` in the 'Middle Structure' of the LEU/2 ontology. They can be said to be of 'mixed origin' because both of the criteria formulated in (D) are – simultaneously but without strict allocation of roles – involved in the decision to include them in the ontology. What we are left with here is a difference of motivation in the vertical versus the horizontal organization of the sort hierarchy, which, roughly, amounts to the following picture.

The vertical structure of the sort hierarchy, which is based on the subsumption relation, draws mainly on the availability of corresponding linguistic labels categorized as nouns (cf. the subsorts of `Entitaet-MitNamen` or of `RaumEntitaet`) or as verbs (cf. the various subsorts of `BewegungsZustand, LokalisZustand,` or `LokalisEreignis`). Actually, the subsumption hierarchy assumed here is linguistically based as it mirrors the hierarchy of lexical hyponyms in the sense of (Lyons 1977). So, for instance, the sortal subsumption chain `Terrassencafé < Café < GastronomBetrieb < Geschaeftsbetrieb < Institution` echoes the transitive lexical hyponymy relation "an x is a (kind of) z", the applicability of which to pairs of lexical items forms part of our lexical knowledge.

However, the horizontal dimension of the sort hierarchy, that is, the selection of subsorts to be assigned to a common supersort, is mainly determined by features that emerge from our extra-linguistic conceptual knowledge of objects and spatio-temporally specifiable events or situations – examples are discussed in Sect. 2.2 below.

The brief review of design decisions presented in (1) – (3) of this section should suffice to show that, in the LEU/2 ontology, the question of how to interrelate word knowledge and world knowledge has been answered in a rather unsystematic manner, to say the least. Despite this objection, I hasten to add that this situation can be improved only gradually. Given the conditions imposed by implementability, on the one hand, and our poor understanding of the distinction between word knowledge and world knowledge, on the other, ontological engineering will not do without ad hoc solutions and compromises for a long time yet. But all this does not release us from the methodological commitment to realize what it actually means to construct the knowledge base of a text comprehension system, namely, to represent what we know and to know what we represent. Thus, the proposal suggested in (P) is in fact a full-fledged research program. In the sequel, I will clarify its background and point out some consequences.

2 Categorizing Entities

2.1 Linguistic Categories ≠ Conceptual Categories

In order to assess and possibly remedy the problem of mixed sorts mentioned above, we should first of all recall the following facts concerning the knowledge base:

(a) a taxonomy of entities can be designed on the basis of linguistic and non-linguistic (i.e., conceptual) categorizations (as shown by the mixture we find in LEU/2),

(b) these two categorizations, however, do not coincide (as I will show in Sect. 2.2),

(c) thus, a sort hierarchy that claims to be designed consistently should follow either the linguistic or the conceptual grid, which, in consequence, will lead us to setting up two distinct though systematically interrelatable taxonomies.

This is what I will provide arguments for by starting with the following consideration: the proper ontology of the knowledge base, viz. that subset which is designed to represent so-called common sense knowledge, should reflect all and only conceptual categorizations. However, in order to be able to account for the lexicon-based access to, and for the linguistic output derived from, this conceptual knowledge base we need an intermediary categorization grid that reflects linguistic categorizations. If this is accepted, the knowledge engineer should be able to decide whether a given sort or sort distinction is motivated by linguistic or by conceptual categories. Although differentiation between linguistic and conceptual categories is anything but obvious, we will get further by applying the criteria listed in (I) and (II) below.

(I) **Linguistically based categorization** into K-entities and non-K-entitites (where K is a variable for a sort criterion) can be justified by showing that the distinction at issue is overtly reflected in the grammatical system. The phenomena that count as reflexes in this sense include the following:

(a) **Grammaticalization** – the distinction K/non-K is explicitly coded in the morpho-syntactic and/or lexical organization of language (e.g., by overt marking of category features, subcategorisation restrictions, accessibility of referents, etc.).

(b) **Semantic selectional restrictions** – the distinction K/non-K is linked with the satisfaction or violation of certain conditions on combinability that emerge from the internal semantic (not conceptual) structure of the expressions involved. Just one example: conceptually, the entities "the family" and "all the members of the family" should be categorized as mutually substitutable salva veritate; linguistically, however, the German expressions for these concepts, viz. *die Familie* and *die Familienmitglieder*, are categorized as collective noun (K) and count noun (non-K), respectively. The semantic selection restriction

linked with this distinction concerns distributivity of predication; compare *Die Familie haßt einander* with *Die Familienmitglieder hassen einander* [*'The family hates/ The members of the family hate each other'].
(c) **Sortal restrictions** – if the distinction K/non-K is linked with making or avoiding category mistakes (or type crossings) on the logical level. Sortal restrictions are wellformedness conditions on conceptual complex formation. They are not anchored in the structure of language (as are (I)(a,b)), but they become apparent in the impossibility of assigning a regular interpretation to sentences like *Einstein's theory is blue* or *The ball saw the accident* – cf. (Maienborn 1991a).

(II) **Extra-linguistic categorization** into K-entities and non-K-entitites draws on features that have to be justified in terms of their relevance to certain domains of common sense knowledge. Cues for categorization are provided by the following dimensions of relevance:
(a) **Saliency features** as regards physical properties (shape, size, substance), functional properties (instrument, artifact), and/or attributes assigned by social convention (private versus public matter, biological versus legal status, temporary or permanent state, etc.).
(b) **Task-oriented specification and combination** of features listed in (II)(a). This is what knowledge engineers usually conceive of as 'knowledge clusters' in a KR system. No doubt, there is something in the much-discussed 'cluster formation' as suggested by some seminal papers like, say, (Hayes 1985), though I fear the notion is still lacking a sound basis for definition.

To sum up, entities which are categorized according to (II) represent more or less complex concepts, that is, elements of our everyday knowledge supposedly stored in long-term memory and ready to be instantiated and processed in actual contexts of use. Entities that are determined according to (I), however, represent elements of our linguistic knowledge, which, when combined into more complex expressions, may be used to refer to entities of the first-mentioned type. The interrelation between these two sets of entities is not a one-to-one mapping, but rather a partially restricted many-to-many mapping. Some of the differences are hinted at in the next subsection.

2.2 Examining Some Sort Distinctions in LEU/2

Applying the criteria in (I) and (II) above to the subsorts within the supersort Objekt, we observe that the distinctions of

(1) Lebewesen vs. UnbelebtesObjekt ['living (animate) creature' vs. 'inanimate object']
(2) Mensch, Tier, Pflanze < Lebewesen ['man, animal, plant' < 'living creature']

are not linguistically motivated but conceptually based in that they reflect common sense categorizations. While (1) at least imposes sortal restrictions on verbs like *heranwachsen, eingehen* [to grow up, to die], (2) has no linguistically traceable effects whatsoever. If the corresponding distinctions were to be put on a proper linguistic basis, the relevant categorical distinction would have to be narrowed down to something like

(3) BeseeltesObjekt vs. Nicht-beseeltesObjekt [≈'person-like' vs. 'non person-like']

As natural languages are organized anthropocentrically, this distinction is grammaticalized in the sense of (I)(a). Consider the semantic selection of *wer /was* within the German pronominal system (*Wer /*Was* *lacht denn da* ? and *Was /*Wer nistet / blüht / fließt denn da* ?), the distribution of *it* and *he / she* in English, or the systematic alternation of genitive and accusative case for direct objects of transitive verbs in most slavonic languages, from where the term 'Beseeltheit' ['odushevlënnost', ≈'animacy'] is borrowed.

As there is also no inner-linguistic motivation for splitting up the subsorts of the sort Objekt into

(4) ErschaffenesObjekt vs. EntstandenesObjekt [≈ 'artifact' vs. 'natural kind' ?]

we may conclude that in LEU/2 this distinction is meant as a conceptual one, which is rooted in common sense knowledge. Given this, however, we might ask: why are the sorts Nahrungsmittel ['food stuff'] and Messing ['brass'] regarded as subsorts of EntstandenesObjekt instead of being subsumed under ErschaffenesObjekt ? We might surmise that (4) was meant to capture something like "artifact" vs. "natural kind" (or, perhaps, "organic" vs. "synthetic"). If so, then brass just fails to be a natural kind (as opposed to gold or water); brass is an artifact. Likewise, it is not so clear that in our everday experience, foods should rank among natural kinds. Rather, in our industrialized society even guaranteed organic E-free health food, say, fruits and vegetables, are primarily conceptualized as goods, that is, as objects produced and worked on to flood the market with.

The example shows that even apparently obvious common sense distinctions cannot be reconstructed in the ontology without a theoretical basis. What is required in the case of (4) is a suitable theory on the role of needs and purposes on which to define the extension of the concept "artifact". That such a theory is badly needed can also be seen from the following distinction made in LEU/2:

(5) Nutzgegenstand vs. Nicht-Nutzgegenstand
[≈ 'article for practical use' vs. others objects]

What articles may serve what functions (actually or potentially, constantly or changeably) can only be fixed in terms of a "naive theory" of means and ends in our highly developed society. Though there is no direct linguistic evidence for (5) in the sense of criterion (I), I should mention a revealing semantic fact.

When nouns that designate objects (artifacts) with a genuine instrumental function are combined with modal verbs, we observe an interesting selectional restriction. In German, sentences like *dieser Ofen heizt, dieses Fahrzeug fährt, dieses Boot schwimmt* are okay, but their modalized counterparts sound pretty weird: *?dieser Ofen kann heizen, ?das Fahrzeug kann fahren, ?dieses Boot kann schwimmen*, while, say, *dieses Fahrzeug kann schwimmen* is okay again. In English, this point could perhaps be illustrated by examples like *this motor runs/ ?can run; this program works/ ?can work*, etc. What's going on here?

The lexical-semantic representations of nouns such as *Ofen, Fahrzeug, Boot* [stove, vehicle, boat] obviously do contain an obligatory component PURPOSE (specified by the attributes "heating", "driving","floating", respectively). Now, this semantic component seems to produce the following effects: (a) it excludes explicit modalization, if the nouns at issue are combined with pertinent main verbs; (b) it restricts the interpretation of, say, *der Ofen heizt* to the so-called habitual reading ("the stove works as it should"); (c) it admits as informative, however, sentences like *das Fahrzeug kann schwimmen* or *das Boot kann fliegen* , because "floating" or "flying" are not constitutive PURPOSE features of the artifacts designated by *Fahrzeug* and *Boot*, respectively.

The lesson to be learnt from this thus reads: the representation of nouns like *Ofen, Fahrzeug, Boot* in the lexicon contains a specific component PURPOSE (hence, an element of our linguistic knowledge) by means of which the sort `Nutzgegenstand` in the knowledge base is being accessed. This is but one example of how linguistic aspects of lexical representation can be made use of in defining ontological sorts in the knowledge base.

This leads us to the question whether or not there are genuine linguistic features based on which sort distinctions in the ontology might be justified. I think there are such features. Thus, I would consider the following distinctions (disregarded in LEU/2) to be relevant to the middle structure of the ontology:

(6) "bounded object"   vs.   "non-bounded object"

(7) "concrete object"   vs.   "abstract object"

The distinction in (6), no matter whether coded as sorts or attributes, provides the lexical basis for categorizing entities into delimitable units (by means of count nouns) or masses/substances (by means of mass nouns). (6) cross-classified with (7) provides the lexical basis for the pertinent types of plural formation. Thus, "bounded object" correlates with regular plural formation of concrete or abstract nouns (cf. *Haus – Häuser* [house – houses], *Gedanke – Gedanken* [thought – thoughts]), whereas "non-bounded object" allows plural formation with concrete nouns only as so-called sort plurals (*Wasser – Wässer* [= sorts of water], *Stoff - Stoffe* [= sorts of fabrics]) but excludes plurals of abstract nouns altogether (*Mitleid – *Mitleide* [pity – *pities], *Glück – *Glücke* [luck – *lucks]).

The categorizations listed in (6) and (7) are anchored in the lexicon and thus clearly grammaticalized in the sense of criterion (I) above. So they suggest themselves as useful information in modeling the word-to-world interrelation, that is, the linguistic access to ontological sorts in the knowledge base. Against this background, then, one might ask what subsumption relations like `Stoff < AbstrakteEntitaet` or `Material < Stoff` (as assumed in LEU/2) were actually meant to capture.

2.3 Merological Relations

The unsystematic way in which sorts are established in the LEU/2 ontology sometimes leads to unsatisfying compromises as regards central aspects of knowledge structure. A case in point is:

(8) `TeilObjekt   <   Objekt`   ['partial object ' < 'object ']

In view of (a) the underdeterminedness of the sort `Objekt`, and of (b) the crucial role merological relations (part-whole relations) play in determining the structure of what is to be represented in the knowledge base and of the inferences supposed to operate on it, (8) is simply underspecified as a subsumption relation between sorts. That is, merology should not be confined to just one detail in the ontology, instead, merological relations (and their calculi) should be recognized and utilized as decisive factors in designing the knowledge base. Next to subsumption, part-whole relations (which come in various guises) form the most important source of inferences involved in text understanding. This makes them extremely relevant to design decisions on the architecture and granularity of the ontology at issue. Let us look at just two aspects of how to improve the decision taken in (8).

2.3.1   Decomposition of complex objects. In addition and, in a sense, orthogonal to the subsumption hierarchy, which is based on the "x is a (kind of) y" relation, there is a logical grid of conditions according to which complex objects or events can be decomposed into suitable parts. What we are faced with are networks of part-whole relations that determine the specific structure of what are usually called 'clusters' or 'domains' of everyday knowledge. So, contrary to what is suggested by (8), we will not do with just one general "x is (a) part-of z" relation. Depending on the domain from which the instances replacing "x" and "z" are taken, part-whole relations embody different specifications and display distinct inferential properties. Here is an example.

Suppose our German text basis contains a selection of reference objects (RefOs) of the sorts Kühl-schrank, Küche, Wohnung, and Haus [fridge, kitchen, flat, house], respectively, and we are interested in finding out what merologically based inferences can be drawn on this sample. There are several possibilities to be taken into consideration. We may take the RefOs as complex objects that form part of a domain "standard items of housing environment" or we may construe them as belonging to the domain of spatial objects. The valid inferences will vary accordingly. In the first case, the "x is (a) part-of z" relation has to be specified as "x **is-a-component-of** z", where this relation holds for certain pairs of x, z, but is not really transitive, as the examples in (9) show:

(9)	Der Kühlschrank ist Bestandteil	der Küche.	[The fridge is a component of the kitchen]
	Die Küche ist Bestandteil	der Wohnung.	[The kitchen is a component of the flat]
	Die Wohnung ist Bestandteil	des Hauses.	[The flat is a component of the house]
↛	Der Kühlschrank ist Bestandteil	des Hauses.	[The fridge is a component of the house]

In the second case, if we take the RefOs to belong to the domain of spatial objects, the "x is (a) part-of z" relation has to be specified as **spatial inclusion**, say, as "x **is-in** z", which is a clearly transitive relation:

(10)	Der Kühlschrank	ist in	der Küche.	[The fridge is in the kitchen]
	Die Küche	ist in	der Wohnung.	[The kitchen is in the flat]
	Die Wohnung	ist in	dem Haus.	[The flat is in the house]
→	Der Kühlschrank	ist in	dem Haus.	[The fridge is in the house]

Thus, the decomposition of complex objects into parts is domain specific. In the domain we tentatively dubbed "standard items of the housing environment" (though poorly understood as yet, this *is* an important area of common sense knowledge), the relation between components and integral objects is defined by functional conditions, hence the non-transitivity of "x **is-a-component-of** z". In the domain of spatial objects, however, the part-whole relation is conceived as topological inclusion, which is basically transitive. For details on the transitivity of "x **is-in** z" see (Pribbenow 1989,1990), (Lang 1990).

2.3.2   Part-whole inheritability. Ontological engineering can also profit greatly from merology by taking inheritability of properties into account. Thus, interacting with the conditions on decomposing complex entities into parts, the properties these entities can be assigned to are classified according to their part-whole and/or whole-part inheritability, which, in turn, determines the kind of inferences that can be drawn on this basis. Part-whole inheritability thus provides important clues to deciding on the granularity of the knowledge base. Consider the following sample of valid and invalid inferences associated with the properties assigned to some complex object x :

(11) (a)   All parts of x are   oily/rusty/warm/radioactive
        $\longrightarrow$ x is   oily/rusty/warm/radioactive
      (b)   All parts of x are   round/flexible/pivoted
        $\nrightarrow$ x is   round/flexible/pivoted

(12) (a)   x is   underground/airborne/waterproof/frost-resistant
        $\longrightarrow$ All parts of x are   underground/airborne/waterproof/frost-resistant
      (b)   x is   heavy/expensive/novel
        $\nrightarrow$ All parts of x are   heavy/expensive/novel

This should be sufficient to show that merological inheritability of properties is related to specific domains. Thus, properties that apply to an object's substance are part-whole inheritable – cf. (11a), properties that apply to an object's shape or function are not – cf. (11b); properties referring to an object's location in large-scale space are whole-part inheritable – cf. (12a), whereas norm-related gradable properties of objects are not – cf. (12b). If we replace "x" with, say, *the machine* in (11,12), it becomes clear that the knowledge base is not only structured by means of subsumption relations (such as `Maschine < HergestelltesObjekt < Nutzgegenstand < UnbelebtesObjekt` in the LEU/2 ontology), but also by means of merological relations of the type illustrated above. In order to come to grips with the various domains that can be discerned within the realm of common sense knowledge, a careful merological analysis thus seems to be indispensable.

Of course, the difference between linguistic and conceptual categories marked out by (I) and (II) in Sect. 2.1 above applies to merological relations too. As regards the structure of knowledge according to (II), we should take notice of the following facts:

(13) (a)   In a natural conceptual system C it holds: for any predicate p occurring in C it has to be fixed whether or not p is part-whole inheritable and/or whole-part inheritable.
      (b)   The merological relation "x is (a) part-of z" covers a certain range of more specific conceptual relations with corresponding inferential properties.

A linguistic approach to merology along the lines of (I) has been proposed in studies on meronymy, i.e., on lexicalized part-whole relations, by (Lyons 1977, Cruse 1986) or (Winston, Chaffin, Herrmann 1987). The latter show that the ordinary English-speaker's use of the term *x is part of z* covers six different types of merological relations (1. Component – Integral Object; 2. Member – Collection; 3. Portion – Mass; 4. Stuff – Object; 5. Feature – Activity; 6. Place – Area) on the conceptual level. To illustrate the fertility of this approach let us add two more merological relations that are grammaticalized. Note the equivalence of genitive constructions (14a) to so-called pertinence constructions (14b) in German:

(14) (a) Annas Gesicht/Arm/Brille/Mantel/Flur/Auto ist schmutzig.

[Anna's face/arm/specs/coat/corridor/car is dirty]

Peter streichelte/säuberte Annas Gesicht/Arm/Brille/Mantel/Flur/Auto

[Peter caressed/cleaned Anna's face/arm/specs/corridor/car]

(b) Anna ist schmutzig im Gesicht/am Arm/an der Brille/ *am Mantel/*am Flur/*am Auto

[≈ 'Anna is dirty in her face/on her arm/on her specs/*on her coat/*on her corridor/*on her car']

Peter streichelte/säuberte A. im Gesicht/am Arm/an der Brille/ *am Mantel/*am Flur/*am Auto

[≈ 'Peter caressed/cleaned A. on her face/on her arm/ ... /?on her coat/ ... /*on her car']

While the genitive constructions in (14a) leave the relation of z to x completely unspecified, the adverbial constructions in (14b) show clearly that in German the relation "z **pertains-to** x" is grammaticalized in such a way that if x refers to the human body, then the range of z includes not only the anatomic body parts but also prostheses in the broader sense, whereas separable belongings or property (clothing, car, corridor) are excluded from instantiating z in this relation.

Similarly we can sort out the "z is **(non-)alienable-to** x" relation from the genitive constructions in (15a). Non-alienablity is linked with semantic selectional restrictions which, inter alia, rule out the verb *besitzen* [own, possess] in (15b) or change-related copula verbs like *werden/bleiben* [become, stay] in (15c) for non-alienable z. The latter case shows, in addition, that within kinship relations there is a linguistically marked distinction between relation by blood (unchangeable, transitive) and relation by marriage (changeable, non-transitive).

(15) (a) Annas Sohn/Vater/Schwiegersohn/Schwiegervater/Freund/Hund ist krank

[Anna's son/father/son-in-law/father-in-law/boy friend/pet dog is sick]

(b) Der Freund/Hund/*Sohn/*Vater/*Schwiegersohn/*Schwiegervater, den Anna besitzt, ist krank

(c) Rudi wird/bleibt Annas Freund/Hund/Schwiegersohn/Schwiegervater

[Rudi becomes/stays Anna's friend/pet dog/son-in-law/father-in-law]

Rudi wird/bleibt Annas *Sohn/*Vater

[Rudi becomes/stays Anna's *son/*father]

In sum, the various aspects of ontological engineering discussed in the subsections of this section, namely the need to justify sort distinctions and the relevance of merology, are all meant to back up the main thesis forwarded in (P). The proposal that grammatically determined linguistic knowledge and conceptually anchored world knowledge should be kept distinct in the knowledge base may also shed some light on the following crucial problem.

3 How to Specify Domains of Knowledge ?

3.1 What's specific to a conceptual domain ?

It needn't be emphasized that the notion "domain" (just like "level", "phenomenon", "scope", or "frame of reference") is of a purely instrumental nature, that is, its formal definition and substantial interpretation will eventually depend on the purpose this notion is to serve within a given theory or model. This applies also to the way the notion "domain" has been, is being, and will be treated in the course of developing the LEU/2 ontology. In a sense, the definition of "domain of knowledge" is a definition in progress. To get a clearer picture of how far we have come in LEU/2 in this respect, I will first propose a somewhat rigorous working definition of "conceptual domain" and then contrast it with the various partitions of the LEU/2 ontology.

Starting from the basic assumptions (discussed in (Bierwisch 1988), (Bierwisch, Lang 1989)) that our conceptual knowledge comprises a (potentially open, though actually limited) set of domains $D = D_1$, $D_2, ..., D_n$, and that these domains are constituted by sorted entities, we get, as a first approximation, the following connection between concept formation and domain formation:

(16) (a) The structure of (what we call) knowledge is determined by a system of conceptual conditions $C = C_1, C_2, C_3, ...$, which act as restrictions on admissible entities and as constraints on their combinability to form complex entities.

(b) A domain D_i is a (potentially infinite, internally structured) set of entities E, whose specific properties in D_i are defined by a set of conceptual conditions C_i (= intrinsic restrictions) and whose relations to entities of other domains are defined by a set of conceptual conditions C_j (= extrinsic restrictions).

The crucial point here is the rigorous attempt to define an ontological domain in terms of specific intrinsic conditions on the entities that are supposed to fill it. Most ontologies proposed so far (LEU/2 included) have proceeded the other way round: they start with a collection of entities (subsumable under a certain supersort, say, AbstrEntität, AbstrRaumkonzept, EntitaetMitNamen) and make domains of what spreads out around them – I will come back to this in Sect. 3.2 below.

In view of (16) we are expected to keep the number of domains as small as possible. Semantic research done along the lines of (16) has confirmed that D should contain at least the following domains:

(17) D_1: objects; D_2: substances; D_3: locations;
     D_4: time intervals; D_5: events; D_6: attitudes.

There are, of course, further candidates to be considered, among them domains that represent the norms and purposes that manifest themselves in social institutions (law, administration, marriage, education) and in communicative behaviour (etiquette, conversation, group dynamics) – an admittedly uncharted territory so far. But the sample given in (17) is sufficient for illustrating the intrinsic and extrinsic restrictions imposed on the entities of the corresponding domains.

D_1, the domain of objects, is populated by entities $o_1, o_2, o_3, ...$ which are defined by intrinsic conditions like boundedness, discernibility, dimensionality, and specific part-whole relations (e.g., over-summativity, where the whole is more than the sum of its parts, as shown by (9) in Sect. 2.3.1 above).

D_2, the domain of substances, is set up by entitites $s_1, s_2, s_3, ...$ which are defined by intrinsic conditions like non-boundedness, non-discernibility, and part-whole homogeneity (all parts of an extrinsically delimited quantity of water are again water, etc.).

D_3, the domain of locations, is defined by the elements l_1, l_2, l_3, ...which occur in the scope and range of a topological function 'loc', where 'loc' assigns an entity x a location l on the basis of two intrinsic conditions (a) $loc(x) = l_i$ (" l_i is the place of x in D_3"), and (b) $loc(l_i) = l_i$ ("l_i is defined by the place it occupies in D_3").

D_4, the domain of time intervals, is defined by a linear ordering relation on entities t_1, t_2, t_3, ... which are intrinsically one-dimensional.

D_5, the domain of events, is set up by entities which we usually conceive of as states of affairs (extensionally) or as propositions (intensionally). The specific feature of events as ontological entities is that events form intrinsically determined configurations of elements from other domains. Based on this, events can be mapped onto the domains D_3, D_4, and D_6, that is, events are the kind of entities that can be localized, temporally specified, or attitudinally evaluated.

D_6, the domain of attitudes, comprises the various epistemic and emotive moods in which we evaluate a proposition as factual, probable, possible, counterfactual, etc.

In the rigorous approach I am advocating here, domains like D_1, D_2, D_3 are construed in a more abstract way than in other proposals concerning ontological domains. This implies that e.g., D_1, the domain of objects, comprises both concrete (physically manifest) objects and abstract (propositionally represented) objects as subdomains whose entities differ as to dimensionality. Likewise, D_3, the domain of locations, is not confined to physical or geographic space only; rather, D_3 conceives of space as of the domain where localization takes place – in the most general sense of the word. The rationale for defining conceptual domains as abstractly as possible lies in the advantages this approach may offer to ontological engineering. Let us briefly outline some of the favorable consequences of this approach.

• **Mapping relations between domains.** The distinction between intrinsic and extrinsic conditions on entities in the sense of (16) provides us with the appropriate means to determine the entities of which domains may be mapped onto which other domains. Thus, it is due to extrinsic conditions that the entities of D_1, D_2, D_3, D_5 can be mapped onto D_3, while those of D_4 or D_6 cannot (that is, objects, substances, places, and events can be localized, while time intervals or attitudes cannot); that the entities of D_4, D_5, or D_6 can be mapped onto D_4, while those of D_1, D_2, D_3 cannot (that is, time intervals, events, and attitudes are subject to temporal specification, while objects, substances, or places are not); that the entities of some of the subdomains of D_1, D_2, D_3, D_5 can be mapped onto D_6, but not vice versa (propositions that are meant to identify objects, substances, places, or events can be in the scope of attitudes, but not vice versa).

• **Preservation of properties.** When entities of some domain D_i are mapped onto a domain D_j, their intrinsic D_i properties are preserved and integrated into the structure determined by D_j. This explains why, as shown in (10), mapping objects of the sorts `Fridge`, `Kitchen`, `House` by means of "x is-in z" from D_1 onto D_3 results in spatial inclusion – the objects carry their spatial dimensions with them, whereas mapping objects of the sorts `Syllable`, `Word`, `Text` by means of "x is-in z" from D_1 onto D_3 will result in a part-whole relation of the type 'component – integral object'; in this case, the objects carry their non-spatial compositional properties with them. Likewise, it becomes clear this way why events can be mapped by means of "x is-in z" from D_5 onto D_3 and/or D_4 (cf. *the workshop is in Berlin ; the workshop is in the fall*) without losing their event characteristics.

- **Setting up sorts and axioms together.** Modeling the knowledge base along the lines of (16) implies that the ontology be partitioned into domains in such a way that the entities at issue and their inferential properties – or, put more technically: sorts and axioms – are set up correlatively. In the course of designing LEU/2, these two components of the knowledge base were developed in a sequential order which roughly comes out as 'first have the sorts, then write the axioms'– see (Klose, Pirlein 1991). The requirement to bring axioms into line with sorts from the very beginning, however, is but a consequence of the more general point that comes next.

- **Linguistic versus conceptual structure.** The assumptions in (16), though formulated from a linguistic point of view, are supposed to hold for domains of conceptual knowledge; they are not meant to apply to the level of linguistic structure by means of which conceptual knowledge is being accessed. The rigorous approach to domains of knowledge proposed here thus presupposes that the distinction of linguistic versus extra-linguistic knowledge be taken into account for both sorts and axioms. What effects the differentiation of linguistic from non-linguistic categories may have on the definition of ontological sorts has been discussed in Sects. 2.1 – 2.3 already. We should now add the point that regarding inferences there is a corresponding distinction to be observed. In other words, we have to distinguish linguistically based inferences (which draw on grammaticalized relations of equivalence, conversion, presupposition, etc.) from conceptually based inferences (which draw on relations of (in-)compatibility, containment, cause–effect, etc., that are anchored in our world knowledge) — for details see (Lang, Carstensen, Simmons 1991), (Simmons 1991) and (Carstensen, Simmons, in Chap. 3 of this volume).

To sum up: the rigorous approach to conceptual domains as outlined in (16) requires the kind of systematization and scrutiny that ideally should guide the process of designing the knowledge base of a text comprehension system. So much for the advantages. It should be admitted, however, that there are disadvantages as well. These are more or less due to the fact that we are just at the beginning of getting a deeper understanding of conceptual structure. Though the two-level approach advocated here has been backed up in a series of studies (see, inter alia, the contributions on spatial knowledge in Chap. 3 of this volume), quite a lot of research work remains to be done to spell out the guidelines of (16) in sufficient detail.

But there is reason for optimism. Approaching conceptual structure along these lines seems to be a rewarding issue for opening a new field in basic research, where computational linguistics and knowledge engineering may closely co-operate with each other and at the same time attempt to integrate the results and methods of other cognitive sciences. Moreover, additional evidence in support of the rigorous approach to domains of knowledge can be gained from reviewing the experience gathered in the course of designing the LEU/2 ontology. The attempt to partition the ontology into 'clusters', 'Upper Structure' versus 'Lower Structure', 'concepts' and 'entities' is indicative of the fact that the problem of grasping domain specificity was always present for the creators of LEU/2. Whether or not the solutions they have found are the best ones remains to be seen. Thus, to get an idea of what has actually been achieved in working out the notion 'domain of knowledge' so far, we will have another look at the LEU/2 ontology.

3.2   The Partitions of the LEU/2 Ontology Revisited

• **Clusters**. Following the KE work report presented by (Klose, Pirlein 1991), 'clusters' are conceived of in LEU/2 as "relativ eigenständige Konzeptbereiche" [relatively autonomous conceptual domains] such as **Space; Objects; Quality, Quantity, and Measurability** etc., which are supposed to be somehow associated with corresponding sets of inferences. What this rather vague definition of 'cluster' is actually meant to cover turns out to be a certain part of the scenario-based area which is preferably accessed by a certain subset of text-base-specific vocabulary (cf. Sect. 1.2). Thus, at this stage, the notion of a 'cluster' is merely a compromise between text-based sort declaration and subsequent rule writing. Nevertheless, the notion of a 'cluster' should be regarded as a pre-theoretic but indispensable vehicle on the way that will eventually lead us to a satisfying definition of 'domain of knowledge'.

• **'Upper Structure' versus 'Lower Structure'**. As regards the area of Entitaeten < TOP in LEU/2, this distinction is taken to be a gradual one rather than a strict one. What it actually amounts to is a three-layered hierarchy, the top of which is formed by sorts that are designated by rather general linguistic labels (hyperonyms like *object, event*), while the bottom is determined by factual details that require sorts with a high number of attributes. This, too, is a kind of compromise. Why ? The distinction of 'Upper' and 'Lower' in the hierarchy certainly does suggest a scaling of the sorts thus allocated from "very general" to "highly specific", but the presumed end-points are not on the same scale. Note that between the sort Objektentitaet in the 'Upper Structure' and the sort Altbierkneipe in the 'Lower Structure' there is, as discussed in Sect. 1.2, a large area set up by sorts of mixed foundation. To make the 'Upper'–'Lower' distinction reflect a specificity gradation (as it is obviously intended to do) thus presupposes the availability of a common scale base.

• Entitaeten **versus** Konzepte **under** TOP . The decision to partition the sort hierarchy into Entitaeten < TOP and Konzepte < TOP shows most clearly that the creators of LEU/2 were well aware of the problems posed by the non-correspondence of linguistic and conceptual categorizations, but somehow did not quite succeed in finding the right way out. The Entitaeten were meant to represent the genuine ontological entities, which "can vary in space and time", to quote (Klose, Pirlein 1991) again, in other words: entities that can be instantiated as discourse referents. The Konzepte, being stop-gap pseudo-entities from an ontological point of view, were meant to serve as a purely technical aid to provide the proper entities with local, temporal and other specifications. Instead of pointing out in detail why this partition cannot be the whole story yet, I will conclude with some remarks on how we could get rid of it.

4   Concluding Remarks

This paper has been an attempt to plea for the distinction of (grammatically coded) linguistic knowledge from (conceptually anchored) extra-linguistic knowledge as a prerequisite for designing the knowledge base of a text comprehension system. The two-level approach proposed in (P) has been substantiated by examining the sort hierarchy assumed in the LEU/2 ontology from a methodological perspective. I hope to have shown that the distinction I am advocating has been implicitly present in many modeling decisions taken there, but so far has not been carried out in a systematic way.

Having pointed out what levels of knowledge representation have to be distinguished, what notions need to be sharpened, and what sort of relations structuring the knowledge base must be accounted for, I should drop some hints about the prospects of working out the proposals forwarded here. Much relevant discussion on related aspects can be found in (Klose, Lang, Pirlein 1991), a collection of papers devoted exclusively to the knowledge base of LEU/2. From a linguistic point of view, the next steps to improve ontological engineering might consist in settling the following issues:

• **Structure and substance of the knowledge base.** The artificial bi-partition of ontological basic elements into `Entitaeten` and `Konzepte`, which, though formally linked by being subsorts of TOP, are actually meant to reflect the essential difference between proper entities and pseudo-entities, should be replaced with an architecture that embodies two distinct levels of knowledge representation and an appropriate device for mapping entities of one level onto those of the other. There are several technical solutions available to do this. However, within the notional framework advocated here, the crucial point is to clarify what distinction is to be captured in substance.

Knowledge comprises all and only conceptual knowledge. Even that subset of knowledge which we call "linguistic knowledge" is but a special brand of conceptual knowledge which is determined by an autonomous module called "grammar". From this it follows that, by their very nature, any elements to be included in the ontology of a knowledge base have to be construed as concepts. This also holds for the knowledge base of a text comprehension system. However, the structure of this knowledge base should be designed in such a way that the concepts and conceptual relations it is meant to reflect are accessible to grammatically coded knowledge representation with respect to input, processing, and output. In other words, the knowledge base of a text comprehension system has to be equipped with a representation level of regular lexicon-based access, which serves as interface between linguistically and extra-linguistically categorized entities. This claim is just the methodological translation of a well-known fact: there are concepts that have more or less direct linguistic labels, there are other concepts that are addressable only by means of complex linguistic expressions, and there is a large area in between in which the conceptual interpretation of morphological markings and lexically anchored semantic roles has to be spelled out. It goes without saying that the interface thus conceived has to account for a complex many-to-many mapping between linguistic and conceptual categories.

The arguments presented in favor of the linguistic versus conceptual distinction hence should not be misunderstood as a plea for ontological inflationism, but should be taken as a proposal on how to revise the LEU/2 architecture in order to remedy some of the shortcomings it shows. This revision will involve two representationally separate but theoretically intertwined procedures: (a) re-structuring the sort hierarchy on the basis of the criteria discussed in sections 2.1 – 2.3 ; (b) extending and stocking up the lexicon entries by adding categorial information in the sense of (I) and thereby improving the lexicon architecture as a whole.

In the long run, we might thus do away with the pseudo-ontological partition of entitites into `Enti-taeten` and `Konzepte` and let the job it was meant to do be taken over by a complex mapping between proper entities of the ontology and linguistically motivated categories for accessing these entities.

To spell out the details of the many-to-many mapping between lexicon-based (morphosyntactic and semantic) categories and conceptual entities remains a central task for years to come yet, but there is interesting work in progress, e.g., (Croft 1990) and (Schwarze, in press).

• **Domains of knowledge.** In Sect. 3.2 I have attempted to show how the various partitions assumed in the LEU/2 ontology can be interpreted as provisional measures to pin down the notion 'domain of knowledge'. To clarify what has been achieved so far and what has yet to be done, I have contrasted these partitions with a rigorous approach to defining domains of knowledge. Here, too, much has yet to be invested to get a more reliable picture of what is specific to a domain. However, within the LILOG project and in closely adjacent research areas we find a number of case studies that treat conceptual domains as being determined by intrinsic and extrinsic conditions in the spirit of (16). Let me briefly outline how these studies might be continued.

First, a paragon of an ontological domain defined by intrinsic conceptual conditions is provided by the domain of objects, and the inventory of object schemata as proposed and justified in detail by (Lang, Carstensen, Simmons 1991), (Simmons 1991) and (Carstensen, Simmons, in this volume) seems to be a suitable format to represent the entities of this domain in the ontology. Now it is not at all far-fetched to surmise that the entities of the domain of events (or situations) should be representable in a similar format. Of course, event schemata will differ from object schemata in being based on a different set of dimensional parameters and values, but they will be similar to the latter in representing the fact that (admissible) event concepts are the result of restrictions imposed on event formation by *intrinsic* conditions in the sense of (16). Since the appearance of Vendler's classic work of 1967, there has been a vast number of studies that offer slightly varying lists of event features again and again. Maybe the time has come to make a step forward by arranging a set of more or less undebated event parameters into schemata.

Second, setting up event schemata in the way suggested above would also have an impact on making the distinction of 'Upper Structure' versus 'Lower Structure' more precise. Suppose the entire Konzepte branch of the LEU/2 ontology could be eliminated along the lines suggested above. On this approach, the 'Upper' – 'Lower' distinction is reserved to apply to the proper ontology only, that is, to a hierarchy of conceptually justified sorts. Within this hierarchy, then, object schemata and event schemata would clearly belong to the primary sorts Objekt and Ereignis, respectively, and hence to the 'Upper Structure', whereas the 'Lower Structure' would comprise sorts that account for more specific or complex object and event concepts, the representation of which draws on the same inventory of object or event schemata but with the necessary specifications added. This suggestion is a slight modification of the proposal made by (Simmons 1991). If it should prove to be feasible, it would render the Konzepte branch under TOP superfluous. Within the rigorous approach, the task assigned within the LEU/2 framework to stop-gap sorts like AbstrEntitaet, AbstrRaumkonzept, BegriffsKonzept, etc. would then be performed by mappings of entities between domains on the basis of *extrinsic* conditions in the sense of (16).

Yeah, doing the everyday work of ontological engineering means creating the world anew — every day !

480

Acknowledgements

Thanks to Geoff Simmons for his valuable comments on this paper and for checking my English. – This work was supported by a guest scientist grant of IBM Germany in 1990. Thanks also to the colleagues in the LILOG project for their cooperation and engagement in the discussion of ontological problems; for a state-of-the-art report, see especially (Klose, G.; Lang, E., Pirlein, T. (eds) 1991).

References

Bierwisch, M. (1988): On the Grammar of Local Prepositions, in: Bierwisch, M. et al. (eds.), Syntax, Semantik und Lexikon, Akademie-Verlag, Berlin, 1–65

Bierwisch, M., Lang, E. (eds.)(1989): Dimensional Adjectives: Grammatical Structure and Conceptual Interpretation, Springer-Verlag, Berlin, Heidelberg, New York

Carstensen, K.-U., Simmons, G. (1991): Why a Hill can't be a Valley: Representing Gestalt and Position Properties of Objects with Object Schemata. (In this volume)

Croft, W. (1991): A Conceptual Framework for Grammatical Categories, Journal of Semantics 7, 245–280

Cruse, D. (1986): Lexical semantics. Cambridge University Press, Cambridge, UK

Freksa, C., Habel, C. (eds.)(1990): Repräsentation und Verarbeitung räumlichen Wissens, Informatik-Fachberichte 245, Springer-Verlag, Berlin, Heidelberg, New York

Gerstl, P. (1991): Praxisgerechte Verwaltung der Ontologie: Erfahrungen und Vorschläge, in: Klose, G., Lang, E., Pirlein, T. (eds.): Die Ontologie und Axiomatik der Wissensbasis von LEU/2: Erfahrungen – Probleme – Ausblicke, IWBS Report 171, IBM Deutschland, Stuttgart, X.1–14

Habel, C. (1991): Processing of Spatial Expressions in LILOG. (In this volume)

Habel, C., Herweg, M, Rehkämper, K. (eds)(1989): Raumkonzepte in Verstehensprozessen. Interdiszipli-näre Beiträge zu Sprache und Raum, Linguistische Arbeiten 233, Max Niemeyer Verlag, Tübingen

Hayes, P. J. (1985): Naive Physics I: Ontology for Liquids, in: Hobbs, J. R. et al. (eds.): Formal Theories of the Commonsense World, Ablex Publishing Corporation, Norwood, NJ, 71–107

Hobbs, J. R., Moore, R. C. (eds.)(1985): Formal Theories of the Commonsense World, Ablex Publishing Corporation, Norwood, NJ

Herweg, M. (1989): Ansätze zu einer semantischen Beschreibung topologischer Präpositionen, in: Habel, C. et al. (eds.): Raumkonzepte in Verstehensprozessen. Interdisziplinäre Beiträge zu Sprache und Raum, Max Niemeyer Verlag, Tübingen, 99–127

Herweg, M. (1990): Zeitaspekte. Die Bedeutung von Tempus, Aspekt und temporalen Konjunktionen, Deutscher Universitätsverlag, Wiesbaden

Klose, G., Lang, E., Pirlein, T. (eds.)(1991): Die Ontologie und Axiomatik der Wissensbasis von LEU/2: Erfahrungen – Probleme – Ausblicke, IWBS Report 171, IBM Deutschland, Stuttgart

Klose, G. & Pirlein, T. (1991): Methodologie der Modellierung in LEU/2, in: Klose, G., Lang, E., Pirlein, T. (eds.): Die Ontologie und Axiomatik der Wissensbasis von LEU/2: Erfahrungen – Probleme – Ausblicke, IWBS Report 171, IBM Deutschland, Stuttgart, III.1–20

Lang, E. (1989): The Semantics of Dimensional Designation of Spatial Objects, in: Bierwisch, M., Lang, E. (eds.): Dimensional Adjectives: Grammatical Structure and Conceptual Interpretation, Springer-Verlag, Berlin, Heidelberg, New York, 263–417.

Lang, E. (1990): Sprachkenntnis, Objektwissen und räumliches Schließen, Zeitschrift für Linguistik und Literaturwissenschaft 78, 59–97

Lang, E., Carstensen, K.-U. (1989): OSKAR - ein Prolog-Programm zur Modellierung der Struktur und Verarbeitung räumlichen Wissens, in: Metzing, D. (ed.): GWAI-89. 13th German Workshop on Artificial Intelligence, Informatik-Fachberichte 216, Springer-Verlag, Berlin, Heidelberg, New York, 234–243

Lang, E., Carstensen, K.-U. (1990): OSKAR – A Prolog Program for Modelling Dimensional Designation and Positional Variation of Objects in Space, IWBS Report 109, IBM Deutschland, Stuttgart

Lang, E., Carstensen, K.-U., Simmons, G. (1991): Modelling Spatial Knowledge on a Linguistic Basis. Theory – Prototype – Integration, Lecture Notes in Artificial Intelligence 481, Springer-Verlag, Berlin, Heidelberg, New York

Lyons, J. (1977): Semantics. Vols. 1, 2. Cambridge University Press, Cambridge, UK

Maienborn, C. (1990a): Lokale Verben und Präpositionen: Semantische und konzeptuelle Verarbeitung in LEU II, IWBS Report 119, IBM Deutschland, Stuttgart

Maienborn, C. (1990b): Position und Bewegung: Zur Semantik lokaler Verben, IWBS-Report 138, IBM Deutschland, Stuttgart

Maienborn, C. (1991a): Motivation einer Ontologie aus linguistischer Perspektive – 3 Fallstudien aus LEU/2, in: Klose, G., Lang, E., Pirlein, T. (eds.): Die Ontologie und Axiomatik der Wissensbasis von LEU/2: Erfahrungen – Probleme – Ausblicke, IWBS Report 171, IBM Deutschland, Stuttgart, V.1–20

Maienborn, C. (1991b): Verbs of Motion and Position: On the Optionality of the Local Argument. (In this volume)

Metzing, D. (ed.)(1989): GWAI-89. 13th German Workshop on Artificial Intelligence. Eringerfeld, September 1989, Informatik-Fachberichte 216, Springer-Verlag, Berlin, Heidelberg, New York

Pirlein, T. (1990): Rekonstruktion von Hintergrundwissen für ein wissensbasiertes textverstehendes System, IWBS Report 129, IBM Deutschland, Stuttgart

Pribbenow, S. (1989): Regelbasierte Interpretation lokaler Präpositionen am Beispiel von IN und BEI, in: Habel, C. et al. (eds.): Raumkonzepte in Verstehensprozessen. Interdisziplinäre Beiträge zu Sprache und Raum, Max Niemeyer Verlag, Tübingen, 202–227

Pribbenow, S. (1990): Interaktion von propositionalen und bildhaften Repräsentationen, in: Freksa, C., Habel, C. (eds..): Repräsentation und Verarbeitung räumlichen Wissens, Informatik-Fachberichte 245, Springer-Verlag, Berlin, Heidelberg, New York, 156–174

Schwarze, C. (in press): Concept Types and Parts of Speech. Journal of Semantics

Simmons, G. (1991): Empirical Methods for Ontological Engineering, in: Klose, G., Lang, E., Pirlein, T. (eds.): Die Ontologie und Axiomatik der Wissensbasis von LEU/2: Erfahrungen – Probleme – Ausblicke, IWBS Report 171, IBM Deutschland, Stuttgart, VI.1–38

Vendler, Z. (1967): Philosophy in Linguistics, Cornell University Press, Ithaca, NY

Winston, M. E., Chaffin, R., Herrmann, D. (1987): A Taxonomy of Part-Whole Relations, Cognitive Science 11, 417–444

A Knowledge Engineering Environment for LILOG

M. Börkel, P. Gerstl

Abstract

An important aspect of knowledge engineering (in short: KE) is the management and maintenance of entries in the knowledge base and of KE activity in general. Little attention has been given to this task in the history of artificial intelligence. Since powerful knowledge representation formalisms are available, the creation of big knowledge bases causes problems of its own. These problems are well known in the traditional business of software design where they have led to the development of a whole range of software engineering methods. We outline the influence of some of these methods on the organization of the KE subproject of LILOG[1] and focus on the development of a KE environment especially tailored to the requirements of the domain at issue.

1 Introduction

Knowledge engineering in LILOG differs from typical industrial projects in many respects. However, seen from the viewpoint of project organization one may find parallelisms that make it worthwhile to draw a methodological comparison. The main efforts in the area of knowledge representation have so far mainly focused on the development of adequate languages coupled with powerful reasoning mechanisms. The applications were mostly restricted to miniature worlds. The problems noted above of course did not arise in those simple cases. But when developing the knowledge base for a large natural language processing system a systematic methodology for the management and maintenance of KE data becomes as important as the formulation of the data itself. LILOG as a basic research project combines the development of components for a text understanding system with considerations about adequate organization and support strategies for the corresponding activities. The KE subproject of LILOG accordingly integrates two fields of activity: the development of the knowledge base on the one hand and the development of guidelines and tools for the management and maintenance of KE activity on the other.

Knowledge engineering for NLP systems differs from knowledge engineering for expert systems in many respects. Expert systems are specialized pragmatic systems intended to solve problems in narrow, limited domains. They are designed for a specific task using the relevant expert knowledge together with inference methods tailored to the properties of the domain under consideration. Feigenbaum proposed to call this task "expertise modeling" [Karbach 1988]. Expert systems, as the first commercially available results of research in artificial intelligence, turned out to cause the same problems of development and maintenance as "ordinary" software products. Anyway, approaches to a software engineering methodology appropriate for the demands of expert system design are not easily transferable to knowledge engineering for NLP systems. The knowledge base of an NLP system

---

[1]The KE subproject of the LILOG project will henceforth simply be called LILOG-KE.

requires deep, well-organized and mostly task-independent knowledge on the level of common sense. In expert systems one can use specific assumptions, abstractions and simplifications. That is not the case for NLP systems. There seems to be a growing tendency to diverge that lead to two branches of engineering techniques according to the area of application [Schefe 1985]: one branch concerns technically-oriented conceptual systems (expertise modeling). The other concentrates on common sense models of knowledge (ontological engineering). The task of LILOG-KE belongs to the second category.

We will further elucidate two aspects of a KE-specific methodology for the maintenance and administration of KE data: the management of the knowledge base and the user interface. Both aspects profit from results in the area of software engineering with respect to the specific requirements of LILOG-KE. The first section below describes these requirements from a rather general point of view. The subsequent sections concentrate on the specification of an environment that provides a set of tools on the basis of a uniform and easily manageable user interface.

2 Knowledge Engineering in LILOG

In order to develop a design and maintenance methodology specifically tailored to the requirements of LILOG-KE the first step is a careful analysis of the relevant characteristics. We will restrict this step to an examination of the task under the following perspectives: the *formalism*, the *domain*, the *knowledge engineers* and the *process* of knowledge engineering.

The knowledge representation formalism L_{LILOG} as a formal basis of the common sense model is the most important means for the representation of KE data. In addition to its logical status and criteria of algorithmic tractablility it should fit epistemological and ergonomical requirements. Epistemological adequacy is defined in terms of the possibility to reconstruct certain phenomena. Ergonomical adequacy on the other hand characterizes user friendliness and suitability. According to its experimental status, the syntax and semantics of the language should be easily extendable thereby supporting the introduction of new constructs without unintended 'side-effects' on existing code. Another requirement calls for a careful arrangement of the L_{LILOG} syntax. The expressions of the language should intelligibly reflect the underlying semantics in order to make their meaning as transparent as possible, thereby improving the readability of code.

The paper by vonLuck and Pirlein in this volume describes the *domain* and the scenario of the LILOG system in detail. Here we shall concentrate on the consequences of its characteristics for the development of a KE environment. The quite narrow application scenario determines the breadth of the model. It is more difficult to establish its depth. In fact there are neither empirical nor theoretical guidelines for the selection of relevant pieces of knowledge and for the choice of a lower bound on the degree of detail (the *granularity* of the model). This again points to the experimental charactacter of LILOG-KE. Design decisions which the knowledge engineers have to make for lack of a well-founded methodology tend to be uncertain and ad hoc [Klose et al. 1991]. It is one objective of our project to analyze the experience made in this area in order to develop a set of guidelines for a systematic KE methodology.

The coordination of results in LILOG-KE suffers from its status as a cooperative project between groups in different and quite remote locations (Stuttgart, Hamburg, Bielefeld). The permanent exchange of design decisions is crucial under these conditions. Apart from that, the groups bring together people with different skills and backgrounds. It is therefore very important to minimize the amount of time needed for introducing new group-members to the relevant material by means of a thorough and well organized documentation. This is particularly the case for students doing a period of practical training since they typically spend only a couple of weeks in the project. Likewise it is desirable to have design decisions available as fast as possible in order to avoid messing around with obsolete knowledge base entries. The knowledge base as a whole should be designed according to a set of formal and organizational criteria in order to provide the necessary documentation hand in hand with the respective database entries.

We emphasized already that our way of doing KE has a rather experimental status. This imposes specific requirements on the *process* of knowledge engineering. Typical subtasks of this process are the determination of relevant 'pieces' of knowledge, the formulation of knowledge base entries in L$_{\text{LILOG}}$ and the maintenance of different types of KE data. Each of these tasks imposes specific demands on the design of an adequate KE environment. Because of the experimental status of the project it is important to have a set of diagnosis tools at hand which provide statistical data about the use of knowledge elements, about the interaction with various modules of the system and other types of relevant information[2].

We will base our argument in favour of a management and maintenance methodology for KE activity on two aspects that strongly correspond to related topics in the area of computer science: *database management* and *software engineering*. Both of these aspects offer theoretical as well as practical implications for the development of a KE environment specifically tailored to the characteristics mentioned.

Table 1. A history of the frequency of L$_{\text{LILOG}}$ constructs in sort definitions[3]

Version No	Date	Size	Sorts	Features		Roles		Atoms
	(1989/90)	*(kBytes)*		*def.*	*restr.*	*def.*	*restr.*	
2.1	27.10	37	261	0	111	0	25	0
2.2	7.11	40	282	0	122	0	25	0
2.3	15.11	42	297	0	264	0	54	0
2.4	23.11	45	309	0	167	0	28	0
2.6	14.12	44	313	0	195	0	37	0
2.9	20.12	50	320	76	194	16	40	44
3.2	10.1	63	346	79	430	19	78	72
4.0	27.2	61	352	99	334	0	80	87
4.3	23.3	48	298	109	268	33	21	196
4.5	4.4	64	385	116	288	44	21	196
4.8	20.4	84	423	118	430	46	9	250
4.9	21.4	86	435	124	472	47	9	260
5.1	6.5	153	665	167	609	86	29	255
5.2	10.5	156	656	180	631	84	39	255
6.0	29.6	170	678	187	844	124	39	257

Regarding the treatment of a huge amount of data with different properties (Table 1), the task of dealing with knowledge elements calls for the application of an appropriate database management

---

[2]A package of convenient statistical tools for the evaluation of various knowledge elements was developed in LILOG-KE by a student during his period of practical training.

[3]*def.* stands for declarations of sorts, features, roles and atoms. *restr.* represents restrictions constraining the domain and range of roles and features.

methodology. Seen from the viewpoint of documenting and maintaining results from the work of several people in different locations, the demands are similar to those traditionally faced by software engineering techniques. The exact choice depends on a couple of requirements that arise on the one hand from the task and on the other hand from the domain under consideration.

3 Some Requirements an Environment Should Meet

In the past few years the first attempts have appeared that try to identify at least some fundamental principles a knowledge engineering environment has to provide in order to support the diversity of KE activities ([Alexander et al. 1986], [Horacek 1989], [Lenat, Guha 1988], [Hobbs et al. 1987], ...). The following list shows five fundamental criteria that illustrate the basic functionality a knowledge engineer might expect from a set of KE tools [Börkel 1989]:

presentation The knowledge engineer must be able to choose the way in which contents of the knowledge base are presented. That helps to unravel underlying design principles despite the heterogeneity of their origin.

navigation An important requirement is the capability to locate specific elements in the knowledge base and to skip from an element to a related one by exploiting the regularities expressed by the use of roles, features and the subsumption relation.

interaction The tools must support the application of update operations on the knowledge base, basically the addition, modification and deletion of elements. It is (at least partially) the system's job to supervize these operations in order to keep the knowledge base consistent.

integration The tools which manage presentation, navigation and interaction should be integrated into a homogeneous environment on the basis of a uniform and simple user interface.

documentation The system must support an adequate documentation methodology that renders the process of knowledge engineering and its results transparent and comprehensible.

Different working groups in LILOG-KE dealing with the realization of tools for the management and maintenance of KE data assign different weights to these criteria. One line of activity which focuses on the aspect of interaction treats the addition, modification and deletion of knowledge elements as operations on a single knowledge base. These operations might be carried out concurrently by different persons in different locations. This problem calls for a solution similar to strategies for access and version control in the area of database management. The situation looks roughly as follows: The content of the knowledge base is determined by a collection of L$_{LILOG}$ source files. These files in turn are composed of L$_{LILOG}$ constructs defining single knowledge elements. This is the level where update operations come into play. Update operations are used for adding, modifying or deleting the source code of single knowledge elements. In order to keep track of the actual set of definitions the system must distinguish private copies from a commonly accessible pool of public and universally accepted definitions belonging to a specific *version* of the knowledge base. The private copies might themselves be subject to update operations which a sort of modification history must keep track of. Hence the private copies can be tested and modified locally without influencing the currently available set of public definitions. After successfully passing the test procedure some updated private definitions might be selected for integration into the pool, thereby creating a new commonly available version of knowledge base definitions [Müller 1991].

The most problematic aspect of this procedure is the way in which new releases of private copies are to be integrated into the set of public definitions without violating integrity and consistency constraints. Since a couple of private copies of the same definitions might be held on different local workstations by different people at the same time, another problem arises if these copies are to be *merged* in order to build a new public version. This task cannot be performed automatically since the decision on how to resolve cases of inconsistency cannot be made on the basis of formal criteria alone. This is a very intriguing situation where interaction between knowledge engineers is crucial for the creation of a homogeneous and universally accepted set of knowledge element definitions.

Another aspect where the interaction plays an important role for the uniformity of KE results is the documentation of design decisions. It turned out to be useful to have at hand a simple and easily comprehensible set of guidelines which specify standards and strategies for documentation. Depending on the purpose of a document its content may be determined by a set of formal conditions which standardize its style and its layout. The fixed format of L$_{\text{LILOG}}$ *source files* containing expressions of a precisely defined formal language makes them formally the most restricted type of KE documents. Even the freedom of commenting on source files is limited by a set of formal criteria in order to avoid the unrestricted accumulation of different sorts of specifications, hints, reviews or any other kind of notes. This rather informal but nonetheless important information is kept in *interaction protocols* which help to point out problematic aspects of definitions with respect to certain versions. These protocols, which are not subject to any conventional constraints[4], can be exchanged by means of electronic mail, simplifying the interaction of knowledge engineers even in remote locations. The third type of files, the so-called *design decisions*, belong neither to the strictly formatted source file type, nor to the format-free type of interaction protocols. In fact they are intermediate in flexibility according to conventions about form and layout. Design decisions contain L$_{\text{LILOG}}$ source code together with detailed comments about the status of these definitions (whether they are obsolete, why they have to be integrated, etc.). The purpose of design decisions is to provide a semi-formal representation of a set of definitions the acceptance of which has to be negotiated by the knowledge engineers. In case of an agreement about the status of these decisions the content of the respective file can be split into the formal part to be (automatically) integrated into the current version of the knowledge base definitions and the corresponding comments to be appended to the currently active interaction protocol.

One aspect we postponed in the preceding considerations is the technical view of KE tools which support the management, maintenance and documentation of KE data. The main task of a knowledge engineering environment was specified to be to provide the basic functionality listed at the beginning of this section. It therefore has to support the operations of the knowledge engineering process and at the same time must abstract from (low-level) considerations about database management and about the (linear) structure of definitions in a source file. This architectural subdivision into two levels of abstraction makes the tools-oriented work in LILOG-KE an interesting case for exploiting the client-server architecture provided by the X Window System[5]. The main goal of this line of activity is to shift a great deal of off-line functionality from the host to a front-end workstation. An illustrative example for this kind of distributed architecture is a syntax checker for L$_{\text{LILOG}}$ which provides a maximum of user friendliness (information about possible sources of an error, a pointer to the relevant piece of source text, etc.) in an early stage of the development process. The L$_{\text{LILOG}}$-compiler may then reside on the host and be specifically optimized for speed and quality of code generation. In this kind of distributed architecture the host can be configured as a Prolog-server which operates on the actual version of the (compiled) knowledge base. The knowledge engineer can then visualize and modify the source of knowledge base entries on the basis of his local environment, independently of the actual configuration of the network. The L$_{\text{LILOG}}$ sources of knowledge elements might be kept in a relational database located on any machine in the network, thus making the individual elements accessible not as a couple of lines of code but as logical *objects* uniquely determined by means of

---

[4]Of course there may be technical constraints implied by the communciation mechanism but the choice of an individual style and layout is entirely the responsibility of the users.

[5]X Window is a well established standard in the world of local area networks. It provides the basic elements of modern user interfaces by establishing a well defined protocol which may be implemented on any computer system [Scheifler et al. 1988].

individual identifiers. The local environment should be designed according to the criteria of user friendliness and ease of treatment by exploiting the full functionality of X Window without regularly falling back on the resources of the host machine. This kind of modular structure might well prove to be a good basis for a non-prototypical implementation of the LEU/2 architecture even outside the world of LILOG-KE[6].

4 Design of a KE Environment for LILOG

In this section we shall discuss the design of an environment for knowledge engineering in the context of LEU/2. Parts of this design have been implemented in an environment called LIKE-ET which manages the following subtasks:

- Maintenance of the formal definitions of knowledge elements.

- Supervision of the security and consistency conditions for the accumulated data.

- Preparation of an appropriate user interface for the knowledge engineers.

For such an environment we shall distinguish four kinds of view of knowledge. Figure 1 illustrates these together with their relations.

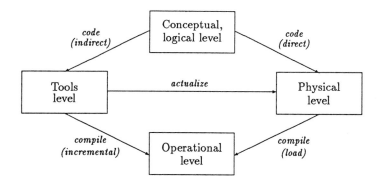

Figure 1: Views of knowledge

In the *conceptual, logical view* we locate the concepts and ideas of knowledge elements in the mind of the knowledge engineer. The translation of these ideas into L_{LILOG} code is the task of the knowledge engineer. He should do this by coding them either directly into the files of the physical view using an adapted text editor or indirectly using the user interface. In the *physical view* we locate the textual, persistent definitions of knowledge elements in L_{LILOG}. These definitions are the input of a knowledge integrator, which integrates the knowledge elements into the knowledge bases of the *operational view* by using a compiler. The operational view contains the knowledge in the form of structures which can be processed by the inference engine. Finally the *tool-oriented view* is the view of the knowledge engineer using the interface. Here the knowledge elements are presented to the user in different ways.

---

[6]It should be emphasized that considerations about this kind of distributed architecture at the moment are at an experimental stage and are being evaluated with respect to a demonstrator implementation [Mezger 1991].

The job of the *knowledge integrator* is the supervision of the knowledge bases and the co-ordination of the physical, operational and tool-oriented views. Problems during the integration of certain knowledge elements occurring either because of syntactic reasons detected by the compiler or because of logical reasons detected by the inference engine should be reported in a cooperative, constructive and comprehensible way. If a knowledge element is successfully integrated into the knowledge base the corresponding entries in the other views have to be updated. Especially the potentially different presentations in the tools-oriented view have to be renewed in order to meet the requirement of direct feedback.

The user interface has to fulfill some general requirements. We will just list them here in the form of headwords[7]: task appropriateness, comprehensibility, reliability, tolerance and transparency of errors, multiple representation, passive and active adaptability, direct feedback, capability of quick construction, extension and ease of change. To fulfill all of these requirements wouldn't be a realistic aim, but they should be kept in mind.

An appropriate user interface for knowledge engineering in LILOG should offer some features which allow for easy interactive retrieval of information during the editing process. One very important feature is a sort graph showing the subsort/supersort relation. In this graph the user is able to scroll and to select certain sorts in order to get more information. This information includes the features and roles of this sort together with the information whether they are locally defined or inherited from one of its supersorts and which value those features and roles can take. If the desired feature has not yet been introduced, another mouse click will open the sort definition in the editor to make the appropriate changes.

Another feature is an adapted editor. This editor should be integrated with the graphical presentation, thus making it possible for the knowledge engineer to toggle between the two kinds of presentation.

For quick reference to certain knowledge elements we propose two lists: the agenda and the stack. The *agenda* is a list of knowledge element names which have to be defined in order to get a consistent knowledge base. A knowledge element name becomes a member of the agenda list if it is used in another definition but isn't defined so far or if it is defined inconsistently. The *stack* is a list of knowledge element names which have been in use recently. The user has the option to select names from these two lists in order to see or modify their definitions in other parts of the interface.

The selection of interesting knowledge elements is the task of a *selector window*. This window contains an alphabetical list of knowledge element names, a field for direct input of a name and one field for a description. In the input field it is possible to type in a knowledge element name. The list will be adjusted in such a way that the string in the input field corresponds to the left substring of one member of the presented part of the list. This list is scrollable and contains knowledge elements according to the description in the description field. This description consists of a list of knowledge element names. The alphabetic list contains only those knowledge elements which are defined using the knowledge elements in the description field.

5   Conclusion

At first glance it might not seem a reasonable and creative strategy to develop tools and applications which make use of the tools at the same time. One would prefer to have a complete and reliable set

---

[7]A detailed discussion of these requirements is contained in [Herczeg 1986].

of tools at his disposal that ease the management and maintenance of his activity. Why should these tools at the same time be subject to research activities?

The answer is straightforward: Most of the requirements actually arose in the course of developing the knowledge base, and it was not obvious from the start which kind of functionality would prove practicable for the work in LILOG-KE. Giventhat the organizational line of KE activity developed tools and guidelines in strong interaction with the "traditional" tasks of knowledge engineering, the limitations and demands could be coordinated in a more flexible and cooperative way than a simple adaption of existing tools would allow. The management and maintenance of KE activity is therefore an important subtask of LILOG-KE which integrates theoretical and practical aspects of knowledge base design for a natural language understanding system in order to provide a set of tools and guidelines specifically tailored to the demands of the application.

References

Alexander et al. 1986: James H. Alexander, Michael J. Freiling, Sheryl J. Shulman: Knowledge level engineering: ontological analysis. In *Proc. of AAAI-86, Philadelphia, PA*, pp. 963–968

Börkel 1989: Manfred Börkel: *Knowledge Engineering für ein natürlichsprachliches wissensbasiertes System*. Master's thesis, Universität Stuttgart, Diplomarbeit Nr. 747, also available as IWBS Report 116, IBM Deutschland, Stuttgart

Herczeg 1986: Michael Herczeg: *Eine objektorientierte Architektur für wissensbasierte Benutzerschnitstellen*. PhD thesis, Universität Stuttgart

Hobbs et al. 1987: Jerry R. Hobbs, William Croft, Todd Davis: Commonsense metaphysics and lexical semantics. *Computational Linguistics*, (13):pp.241–250

Horacek 1989: Helmut Horacek: Towards principles of ontology. In D. Metzing (ed.): *GWAI-89, 13th German Workshop on Artificial Intelligence. Eringerfeld, September 1989*, pp. 323–330

Karbach 1988: Werner Karbach: Methoden und Techniken des Knowledge Engineering. *Arbeitspapiere der GMD, Bonn*, (338)

Klose et al. 1991: Gudrun Klose, Ewald Lang, Thomas Pirlein: *Die Ontologie und Axiomatik der Wissensbasis von LEU und 2: Erfahrungen, Probleme, Ausblicke*. IWBS Report 171, IBM Deutschland, Stuttgart

Lenat, Guha 1988: Doug Lenat, R.V. Guha: *The World According to CYC: MCC Technical Report No. ACA-AI-300-88*. Microelectronics and Computer Technology Corporation, Austin, TX

Mezger 1991: Martin Mezger: *Eine netzwerktransparente Dialogschnittstelle für natürlichsprachliche Systeme*. Master's thesis, Universität Stuttgart, Studienarbeit

Müller 1991: Adrian Müller: *Konzeption und Implementierung einer formalen Sprache zur Integritätskontrolle von Wissensbasen - ICL (Integrity Control Language)*. Master's thesis, Universität Stuttgart, Diplomarbeit

Schefe 1985: Peter Schefe: Zur Rekonstruktion von Wissen in neueren Repräsentationssprachen der Künstlichen Intelligenz. In H. Stoyan (ed.): *GWAI-85, 9th German Workshop on Artificial Intelligence, Dassel/Solling, September 1985*, pp. 230–244

Scheifler et al. 1988: Robert W. Scheifler, James Gettys, Ron Newman: X Window System. Massachusetts Institute of Technology and Digital Equipment Corporation. Digital Press

Knowledge Engineering in the Context of Related Fields of Research

J. Angele, D. Fensel, D. Landes, S. Neubert, R. Studer

1   Introduction

For developing knowledge based systems (KBS) systematic methods and corresponding tools are required in the same way as for the development of "conventional" software systems. One very important aspect in that context is the knowledge engineering area, addressing the problem of how to build up, evaluate, and maintain the knowledge bases within KBS. Obviously, the method used for building up the knowledge base immediately determines the way in which the knowledge base may be evaluated and maintained later on. This problem is crucial for the development of all the different types of KBS, including, e.g., common-sense based natural language understanding systems or expert systems.

When considering the problems which have to be solved within the knowledge engineering area one can easily recognize that similar problems exist in the software engineering area as well as in the area of information systems design. However, as we shall discuss subsequently, there do exist differences, especially in the requirements analysis phase. Nevertheless, the question arises rather naturally whether wellknown methods which have been developed in these related fields of research may be applied for the knowledge engineering process as well.

The fact that one has to manage a lot of different types of information and documents and that one has to define and maintain a large number of different types of relationships between the information and the document types is a common characteristic of all the development methods encountered in the different fields mentioned above.

For developing expert systems, model based approaches have become rather popular, see, e.g., (Breuker, Wielinga 1989). These approaches are characterized by first building up an abstract model of the expertise which is then used for further guiding the knowledge acquisition process.

The rest of this paper is organized as follows: we start by discussing the common characteristics as well as the differences between the knowledge engineering area on the one hand and the software engineering and information system design area on the other hand. In Sect. 4 we investigate to what extent model based approaches may be applied for developing common-sense based systems as well. Finally, the role hypertext techniques may play in supporting the knowledge engineering process is analyzed. A more detailed discussion of all these aspects may be found in (Angele et al. 1990).

2   Knowledge Engineering and Software Engineering

In the 1960s the "software crises" arose. This was due to the fact that the techniques which were used for developing small programs for special applications were inappropriate for developing large software systems with wide application areas which are used for a long period of time. Thus incalculable costs, production times, error rates, and maintenance problems evolved. One of the reactions which aimed at tackling these problems was the development of software engineering techniques transforming the programming of software systems from an art to an engineering discipline.

The field of KBS has now reached a similar point. The production of small prototypes has changed to the development of large KBS used for commercial applications. However, we think that the development of KBS will fail if the process of building KBS doesn´t change. Thus we propose that the development of KBS should learn from the field of software engineering.

To answer the question whether concepts of software engineering are usable in the development of AI software, you have to answer the question about the difference between traditional and AI software, and why this difference exists. (Partridge 1989) uses the concept of "incompletely specified functions" to describe the features of problems only solvable by using AI software.

In the domain of traditional software it is assumed that one is able to specify the problem and the functionality of the system in a correct and complete manner. With the use of such a correct and complete specification, a system developer is able to design and implement the system without any interaction with the system user about his domain. So the question of what the system has to do is independent from the question of how the system works. For an AI problem this method is not applicable. Here we will give two kinds of reasons.

First, the algorithmic complexity of the problem is a serious barrier for all general problem solvers. For many problems which are completely specifiable (e.g., chess) it is not possible to find an algorithmic solution. The task is easy to specify (e.g., choose the best move) but it is not possible to derive an efficient algorithm from the specification. For the design and implementation of a solution, domain-specific heuristics or domain-specific inference knowledge is needed. So the design of the solution is not independent from the domain.

Second, the context sensitivity of AI problems is extremely high. This means that they have a high qualitative complexity. The calculation of "sin(x)" is a context-free problem. So it is easily solvable by a context-free standard software module. For problems like the understanding of natural language sentences, this is not possible. Natural language sentences are only comprehensible with a large amount of common-sense knowledge and knowledge about the specific context of a dialog situation. The high degree of context sensitivity prevents a correct and complete specification of the task. For example, for comprehending natural language, it is not possible to specify for each input sentence a complete set of adequate output sentences. As a result, this means that analysis is not simply interested in *what* happens, as in conventional systems, but also in *how* and *why*.

But we do not think that this is really an argument for applying the rapid prototyping approach to building KBS, as, e.g., (Partridge 1989) proposes. The work of, e.g., (Newell 1982), (Clancey1985) or (Schreiber, Akkermans, Wielinga 1990) which introduced the knowledge level and gave descriptions of problem solving methods at a level which is independent from their realization at the symbol level, allows us to separate knowledge which is inherent to the problem solving method from knowledge which deals with the specific implementation techniques to realize it. These two kinds of knowledge are mixed if one uses the rapid prototyping approach. Therefore we think that
- a well structured building process (life cycle) with clearly defined milestones;
- the separation of analysis, design, and implementation;

- a general description of the problem and its solution without knowledge about the symbol level during the analysis phase;
- a modularization of the knowledge into separate parts with defined interaction during the design phase;
- and structured programming

are subjects which AI can and must learn from software engineering, compare (Angele, Fensel, Studer 1990).

We do not argue against prototyping in general. In fact we propose the integration of prototyping into a well structured development process. In general there are two possible ways:

(1) A prototype is built to support the analysis phase. As soon as the problem and its solution has been specified it is thrown away; compare, e.g., (Angele et al. 1991) and (Fensel, Angele, Landes 1991).

(2) A system is built by using several well structured life cycle iterations, e.g., the spiral model (Boehm 1986) offers a general framework for this kind of development process.

By applying such a life-cycle oriented development methodology including a welldefined prototyping phase, the development of KBS can be transformed into an engineering discipline as well.

3   Knowledge Engineering and Information Systems Design

The goal in developing an information system is very similar to that in developing a KBS. In both areas models have to be built up: in KBS models of expertise or of other cognitive human skills, in information systems models of processes and data of the real world. Therefore it is promising to take methods or techniques from information system design and change them in an appropriate manner in order to use them in the building process of a KBS.

Up to now, the very important phase of knowledge acquisition has the weakest methodological foundation within the building process. So it seems worthwhile to look into the related area of information system design, the requirements analysis, in order to learn from the experience gathered over a long time in this area. There are essentially four topics of interest when investigating the relationship between information systems design and knowledge engineering:
- formalization of natural language,
- integration of different views,
- bottom-up vs. top-down strategies,
- integration of the whole system into a larger environment.

In the following we shall discuss the common characteristics and differences between knowledge engineering and information system design with respect to these four aspects.

3.1   Formalization of Natural Language Texts

In general, a lot of knowledge is available as natural language texts. Thus it would be very useful to have a method to systematically extract knowledge from this extensive data material and to transfer this knowledge into an information system. This would minimize the time-expensive interviews of experts and thus would make both knowledge acquisition and requirements analysis much more efficient.

However, most methods in information system design do not consider the problem of extracting knowledge from natural language texts. We only know of two methods covering this early phase of analysis.

The NIAM method (Twine 1988) is based on examples and counterexamples about the domain. Starting with these a conceptual model about the domain is built up using several steps. The reason for using examples – as it is described in the articles – is that the expert may better express his knowledge in the form of examples and that examples represent the knowledge in an objective manner. The difficulty is that the examples used must be representative and complete for the domain.

The AISCHYLOS tool (Eick, Lockemann 1985) aimes at supporting nearly automatically the analysis of natural language texts and represents the semantics of these texts in a formalism of so-called S-Diagrams. However it is not precisely defined which syntactic or semantic restrictions must be met by the input text such that the tool is able to analyse these texts.

Nevertheless, it is necessary to have tools available providing (automatic) support for this phase. A future upgrade of a system like LILOG that is able to read texts with unknown words and unknown concepts would be a powerful tool for building a model representing the semantics of such texts. This would be a useful aid for both areas of concern.

3.2   Integration of Different Views

Different persons and groups of persons use different terminology to describe a domain of concern, and they look on the domain from different individual points of view. So the acquisition of knowledge leads to different, perhaps inconsistent conceptual models, containing different terminology, different concepts to model similar affairs and so on. The problem is now, starting from these different models, to integrate them into one single model, by removing the conflicts and inconsistencies between the different individual models. From the integrated model the different individual views and terminologies have to be reproducable in order to meet the requirements of the persons who delivered the original models.

Though there are a lot of problems involved in this integration of views, the acquisition of knowledge from different experts makes the acquired knowledge within the system more complete and objective. So this may lead to more adequate KBS.

While there is much awareness of these problems within the methodologies of information system design (Battini, Lenzerini, Navathe 1986) these problems have had very little influence on the discussion about methodologies to build KBS. For the KBS area this situation has changed rather recently. On the one hand there is a lot one can learn from information system design in this area, especially for the structured part of knowledge bases. On the other hand totally new aspects such as non-monotonicity have to be considered for the capability to handle the rule part of knowledge bases as well.

3.3   Bottom-up vs. Top-down strategies

In information system design both strategies are established. The NIAM method (Twine 1988) starts with examples for building up a conceptual model using different steps. So

NIAM represents a bottom-up approach for modeling a conceptual model. The INCOME method (Nemeth, Schönthaler, Stucky 1988) proposes to describe a system on a high level with extended predicate/transition nets. These nets are refined in successive steps leading to hierarchical nets on different levels of detail.

For both approaches – bottom-up and top-down – there exist problems: Within the top-down approach it is difficult, e.g., to decide which parts should be refined in which subparts or when to stop the refinement. Whereas within the bottom-up approach one has, e.g., the problem of deciding which concepts have to be generalized to superconcepts.

Some methods in information system design propose to mix both approaches (Eder, Mittermeir, Wernhart 1987). This means that the domain is analysed both bottom-up and top-down. The results of both approaches are integrated to a – hopefully – optimal solution. By thus integrating both approaches, many of the discussed problems may be weakened or even avoided .

For building KBS there exist also both approaches. Obviously, combining both approaches, e.g., a model based approach with case based reasoning, is also very promising in the KBS area.

3.4 Integration of the Whole System into a Larger Environment

In information system design an additional goal within the phase of requirements analysis is the specification of how the resulting information system should be integrated into a larger environment. This includes the integration into the organizational structure as well as into a larger technical system (Essink 1986) (Nissen 1983). Up to now this aspect has found only slight consideration within knowledge engineering. In most cases KBS are only designed as isolated systems. However, in order to put KBS into commercial use, KBS have to be integrated into the existing technical and organizational environment, too. Thus these aspects have to be considered in the requirements analysis phase of KBS as well.

4 Model-Based Knowledge Representation

During the last decade, a lot of research has been done in the area of developing model-based approaches for building expert systems (cf., e.g., Generic Tasks (Chandrasekaran 1986) or KADS (Breuker, Wielinga 1989)). In (Karbach, Linster, Voß 1990) a model is defined as a "purposeful abstraction that allows us to reduce complexity by focusing on certain aspects". The development of expert systems can be supported if there are models of expertise which describe how certain types of problems can be solved. Most of the model-based approaches for building expert systems assume that the solution for a task can be constructed by combining several generic building blocks which describe elementary problem-solving methods. As the models which are made up from these building blocks also include information about the types of knowledge needed for problem-solving, they can be used to guide the acquisition of knowledge. In addition to this guidance, these models also impose a structure on the domain knowledge which allows us to group knowledge elements into classes. Often models of expertise provide some kind of documentation, as they describe the knowledge at hand not only in terms of the chosen representation formalism, but also in terms which are more familiar and easier to understand for an expert. Furthermore, structuring a knowledge base and providing an appropriate documentation leads to easier maintenance later on.

Model-based approaches have been quite successful for building expert systems. Therefore the question arises whether a similar approach can be taken for other types of KBS, namely common-sense based and natural language systems. It is impossible to simply transfer the approach taken for expert systems to these other types of systems. All the model-based approaches in the expert system area rely on the assumption that it is possible to describe how a certain task can be solved by the expert system. Contrary to that, in common-sense based systems the task which the system should carry out cannot be specified exactly. For example, in CYC (Lenat, Guha 1989) the knowledge base is intended to be used by many different application systems. Thus, no single task can be specified in advance. Similarly, the task of understanding natural language is too complex to be described exactly. Therefore, no models which focus on the problem-solving method can be used for these types of systems. Instead, the existing proposals try to provide means for an abstract and task-independent description of the domain.

Such a description, a so-called model schema, is used in the natural language system EVAR as the basis for partially automating knowledge acquisition (Landes 1988, Rieck 1988). The model schema explicitly describes the structure of the domain and can thus be used to control how new knowledge is transferred into the knowledge base. This mechanism simplifies modifications of the knowledge base. This approach, however, cannot be used for common-sense knowledge bases because in this case the model schema would be too complex to be manageable.

Abstract information about the contents of a knowledge base can be provided implicitly by structuring it. (Hobbs 1984) describes a method for constructing the knowledge base of a natural language system where the knowledge is organized into clusters. A similar approach is taken by (Dahlgren, McDowell 1986, Dahlgren 1988). They propose an ontology for structuring knowledge. This ontology has been developed on the basis of representative empirical studies. The problem with these approaches lies in the fact that it is not clear which criteria and which grain size should be used for forming clusters.

Another approach is taken by (Moeller 1988). He uses interpretation models from KADS (i.e., generic descriptions of a problem solving method) in order to automatically identify and extract classes of relevant knowledge elements from written texts. However, this approach seems to work only if it is possible to use a suitable interpretation model, i.e., there must be knowledge about the task to be fulfilled, and the domain must be restricted in order to avoid ambiguity.

A proposal for a semi-formal mediating representation is made in (Johnson 1989). Such a representation may be useful as an intermediate step in gradually transforming informal knowledge into a formal represention. Additionally, a mediating representation may serve as a documentation of the contents of the knowledge base derived from it. The Systemic Grammar Networks, however, which are proposed by (Johnson 1989) are not appropriate because it is not clear how they can be mapped to a formal representation of knowledge.

All these approaches are only first steps on the way to support the development and maintenance of natural language or common-sense based systems by providing abstract models. They address only single aspects which are relevant in this context, and propose initial solutions which are based on more or less simplifying assumptions. So a lot of further research has still to be done before there are methods and tools available for building natural language and common-sense based systems that are similar to those for expert systems.

5   Hypertext and Knowledge Engineering

In this chapter the usage of concepts of hypertext systems in the context of knowledge engineering is discussed.

Hypertext is a form of non-linear text organisation that is used to represent relationships (links) between text elements. Therefore hypertext is useful for types of texts that contain a lot of cross-references such as scientific papers, technical manuals, guidelines, catalogs, etc. Conventional texts also contain a lot of meta-information such as footnotes, references, or tables of contents, which can be adequately represented with hypertext techniques. The reader of a hypertext is able to take any one of the existing paths through the text by following the links between elements (navigating), i.e., there is no predefined way of reading the text.

Currently, there exists a great conceptual distance between an expert and the representation formalisms offered by expert systems. This gap can be narrowed by using hypertext techniques. An informal structuring of knowledge protocols in a hypertext network provides support in constructing knowledge bases, cf., e.g., (Anjewierden, Wielemaker, Toussaint 1990, Motta et al. 1990), or in documenting and explaining knowledge bases, cf., e.g., (Rada, Barlow 1988, Taylor et al. 1990), as well as in offering teaching facilities for new users, cf., e.g., (Delfs 1988, Moia 1990). Up to now, two main aspects of using hypertext techniques in knowledge engineering have been discussed:

- Hypertext for documentation:

Most proposals for offering a documentation with hypertext techniques assume an isomorphism between the network structure of the knowledge base and of the hypertext network, cf., e.g., (Moia 1990, Wells 1989). This means that every knowledge base element, e.g., a concept or a rule, is connected with a corresponding hypertext documentation node.

A better basis for maintaining a knowledge base can be achieved by associating it with such a hypertext documentation. Furthermore, such an informal, yet structured documentation may be used for partially evaluating the developed knowledge base by experts who are not familiar with the underlying knowledge representation formalism. Finally, by navigating in the hypertext network and exploiting the available links between the documentation and the knowlege elements, new users may become acquainted with the contents of the KBS in an incremental and rather comfortable way.

- Hypertext for knowledge acquisition:

Most of the present approaches applying hypertext in the context of KBS are concerned with the technical support for developing a knowledge base (Motta et al. 1988, Motta et. al. 1990, Motta, Rajan, Eisenstadt 1990, Anjewierden 1987, Anjewierden, Wielemaker, Toussaint 1990).

A first informal structuring of the elicited knowlege in a hypertext network (see Wells 1989) can also support the further acquisition of knowlege which has to be interpreted and formalized by the knowledge engineer. In addition, a hypertext approach provides means for directly involving experts in the structuring of knowledge as well as in the informal evaluation of the acquired knowledge.

- Hypertext and LILOG:

For LILOG all the described aspects of using hypertext techniques in the context of knowledge engineering are important. To build a very large and complex knowledge base with a frequently changing team, good documentation is absolutely necessary. Thus, it is desirable to extend LILOG's existing knowledge engineering tools with hypertext components to offer means for associating an informal documentation with the knowledge base.

Similarly, the support provided for knowledge acquisition has to be improved. In particular, because no knowledge protocols or text books about common sense knowledge exist, a first informal modeling and structuring of knowledge is of high importance. Hypertext would be a useful technique for supporting the first phase of knowledge acquisition.

6 Conclusion

It should have been become clear that there exist a lot of relationships between knowledge engineering, software engineering, and information systems design. Furthermore, a more detailed analysis of the knowledge engineering process shows that knowledge engineering methods for the development of expert systems have to meet partially different requirements compared to these for common-sense based natural language understanding systems. This is due to the task and domain dependency of expert systems which does not apply to natural language understanding systems.

The main results of our analysis of knowledge engineering aspects from the point of view of a common-sense based natural language understanding system may be summarized as follows:

(i) The spiral model (Boehm 1986) is an appropriate general methodology for developing common-sense based systems by supporting a systematic development of several system versions and by offering a framework for integrating specification-oriented methods with evolutionary prototyping.

(ii) When developing large knowledge bases, concepts for structuring a knowledge base are mandatory in order to be able to handle partial inconsistencies, to define different views, and to maintain such a knowledge base. Without such structuring principles the complexity of large knowledge bases soon becomes unmanageable.

(iii) When building up large knowledge bases, knowledge from different sources has to be integrated. Furthermore, such knowledge bases are usually developed in a decentralized way. As a consequence, methods for integrating different views in a systematic way have to be developed. Of course, by being forced to handle rules and thus non-monotonic integration operations, such methods are much more complicated compared to the view integration methods known in the database area.

(iv) Model based approaches to knowledge engineering, which are currently the most promising approaches to develop expert systems, are not directly applicable to develop common-sense based systems since the notion of task and domain dependent models does not fit to the characteristics of common-sense based systems.

(v) Hypertext techniques are well suited to support the early phases of knowledge acquisition and to integrate a knowledge base with a corresponding documentation in a very flexible way.

In general, we can say that there exists still a big lack of appropriate methods for the development of KBS. Comparing the available methods for developing expert systems with those which are available for developing common-sense based systems, we can

easily see that the situation in the common-sense area is much more worse than that in
the area of expert systems.

References

Angele, J., Fensel, D., Studer, R. (1990): What could the knowledge engineer learn from
the software engineer? In: Ehrenberg, D. et al. (eds.): Wissensbasierte Systeme in
der Betriebswirtschaft. Reihe betriebliche Informations- und Kommunikations-
systeme, Nr. 15, Erich Schmidt Verlag, Berlin, pp. 285-303

Angele, J., Fensel, D., Landes, D., Neubert, S., Studer, R. (1990): Knowledge
Engineering und verwandte Fachdisziplinen: Eine Literaturstudie. Universität
Karlsruhe, Institut für Angewandte Informatik und Formale Beschreibungs-
verfahren, Research Report No. 210

Angele, J., Fensel, D., Landes, D., Studer, R., Messing, B. (1991): Explorative prototyping
in KADS. Universität Karlsruhe, Institut für Angewandte Informatik und
Formale Beschreibungsverfahren, Research Report No. 214

Anjewierden, A. (1987): The KADS System. In: Proceedings of EKAW, Reading, UK, E2/1
- E2/12

Anjewierden, A., Wielemaker, J., Toussaint, C. (1990): Shelley - Computer aided
knowledge engineering. In: Wielinga, B. et al. (eds.): Current Trends in
Knowledge Acquisition, IOS Press, Amsterdam, pp. 41-59

Battini, C., Lenzerini M., Navathe S.B. (1986): A Comparative Analysis of Methodologies
for Database Schema Integration. ACM Computing Surveys 18, 323 - 364

Boehm, B.W. (1986): A spiral model of software development and enhancement. ACM
SIGSOFT Software Engineering Notes 11, 4, August 1986

Breuker, J., Wielinga, B. (1989): Models of Expertise in Knowledge Acquisition. In:
Guida, G., Tasso, C. (eds.): Topics in Expert Systems Design. North-Holland,
Amsterdam, pp. 265-295

Chandrasekaran, B. (1986): Generic tasks in knowledge-based reasoning: high level
building blocks for expert system design. IEEE Expert 1, 23-30

Clancey, W.J. (1985): Heuristic classification. Artificial Intelligence 27, 289-350

Dahlgren, K. (1988): Naive Semantics for Natural Language Understanding. Kluwer
Academic Publishers, Boston

Dahlgren, K., McDowell, J. (1986): Kind Types in Knowledge Representation. In:
Proceedings of COLING, Bonn, Germany, pp. 216-221

Delfs, H. (1988): Diagnose-Expertensysteme brauchen Hypertext - Das Beispiel MAX. In:
Gbor, P., Streitz, N. (eds.): Hypertext und Hypermedien: Von theoretischen
Konzepten zur praktischen Anwendung. Springer-Verlag, Berlin, Heidelberg,
New York

Eder, J., Mittermeir, R., Wernhart H. (1987): Induktive und deduktive Ermittlung des
Informationsbedarfs. In: Informationsbedarfsentwicklung und -analyse für den

Entwurf von Informationssystemen. Informatik Fachberichte, Nr. 143, Springer-Verlag, Berlin, Heidelberg, New York

Eick, F., Lockemann P.C. (1985): Acquisition of terminological knowledge using database design techniques. In: Proceedings of ACM SIGMOD, International Conference on Management of Data, Austin, TX

Essink, L.J.B. (1986): A modelling approach to information system development. In: Olle, T.W. et al. (eds.): Information Systems Design Methodologies: Improving the Practice. Proceedings of the IFIP WG 8.1 Working Conference, North-Holland, Amsterdam

Fensel, D., Angele, J., Landes, D. (1991) : Knowledge representation and acquisition language (KARL). In: Proceedings of 11th International Conference Expert Systems and their Applications, Avignon, France, pp. 513-525

Hobbs, J. (1984): Building a large knowledge base for a natural language system. In: Proceedings of COLING, Stanford, CA, pp. 283-286

Johnson, N.E. (1989): Mediating representations in knowledge elicitation. In: Diaper, D. (ed.): Knowledge Elicitation: Principles, Techniques and Applications. Ellis Horwood, Chichester, UK, pp. 179-193

Karbach, W., Linster, M., Voß, A. (1990): Models of problem-solving: one label - one idea? In: Wielinga, B. et al. (eds.): Current Trends in Knowledge Acquisition, IOS Press, Amsterdam, pp. 173-189

Landes, D. (1988): Wissenserwerb für ein sprachverstehendes System auf der Basis einer ATN-Grammatik (Syntax). Master's Thesis, University of Erlangen-Nuremberg

Lenat, D., Guha, R. (1989): Building Large Knowledge-Based Systems - Representation and Inference in the CYC Project. Addison-Wesley, Reading, MA

Moeller, J.-U. (1988): Knowledge acquisition from texts. In: Boose, J., Gaines, B., Linster, M. (eds.): Proceedings of EKAW, Bonn, Germany, pp. 25/1-25/16

Moia, M. (1990): Expert systems and hypertext: a promising integration for training. In: F. Gardin, F., Mauri, G. (eds.): Computational Intelligence II, North-Holland, Amsterdam

Motta, E. et al. (1988): Support for knowledge acquisition in the knowledge engineer's assistant (KEATS). Expert Systems, 5:1, 6-28

Motta, E. et al. (1990): Methodological foundations of KEATS, the knowledge engineer's assistant. In: Wielinga, B. et.al. (eds.): Current Trends in Knowledge Acquisition, IOS Press, Amsterdam, pp. 257-275

Motta, E., Rajan, T., Eisenstadt, M. (1990): Knowledge acquisition as a process of model refinement. Knowledge Acquisition, 2:1, 21-49

Nemeth, T., Schönthaler F., Stucky W. (1988): Formale Spezifikation und Rapid Prototyping - Flexible Systementwicklung mit INCOME. Universität Karlsruhe, Institut für Angewandte Informatik und Formale Beschreibungsverfahren, Research Report No. 191

Newell, A. (1982): The knowledge level. Artificial Intelligence 18, 87-127

Nissen, H.-E. (1983): Subject matter separability in information systems design methods. In: Olle T.W. et al. (eds.): Information System Design Methodogies. North-Holland, Amsterdam

Partridge, D. (1989): KI und das Software Engineering der Zukunft, McGraw-Hill, Hamburg

Rada, R., Barlow, J. (1988): Expert systems and hypertext. The Knowledge Engineering Review 3, 285-301

Rieck, S. (1988): Wissenserwerb für ein sprachverstehendes System auf der Basis eines Lexikons (Semantik/Pragmatik). Master's Thesis, University of Erlangen-Nuremberg

Schreiber, G., Akkermans, H., Wielinga, B. (1990): On problems with the knowledge level perspective. In: Proceedings of the 5th Knowledge Acquisition for Knowledge-Based Systems Workshop, Banff, Canada

Taylor, G. et al. (1990): Techniques for capturing expert knowledge: an expert systems / hypertext approach. In: Proceedings of the 3rd Florida AI Research Symposium

Twine, S. (1988): From information analysis towards knowledge analysis. In: Proceedings of EKAW, Bonn, Germany, pp. 6/1-6/15

Wells, T. (1989): Hypertext as a means for knowledge acquisition. SIGART Newsletter, No. 108, Knowledge Acquisition Special Issue, 136-138

LILOG-DB: Database Support for Knowledge Based Systems

Stefan Benzschawel, Erich Gehlen, Michael Ley,
Thomas Ludwig, Albert Maier, Bernd Walter

1   Introduction

A logic-based natural language understanding system like LEU2 is very data-intensive.

For example, inference and discourse representation require the administration of very large amounts of runtime data, and at each stage of computation large linguistic and/or conceptual background knowledge bases need to be accessed. Efficiency in the administration of runtime data and background knowledge bases will thus be crucial for the performance of the whole system. Therefore database technology is needed to ensure an effective administration of knowledge bases.

In this paper, we describe the subproject LILOG-DB, dedicated to database support for LEU2. We will show that adequate database support cannot be achieved by straight application of standard techniques from the development of traditional database systems: in the context of logic-based knowledge processing several new problems arise which require the development of new technology.

In fact, existing standard database systems are well suited only for a very limited range of applications, which is by far exceeded by the requirements of (e.g.) LEU2.

Therefore the work presented here can be seen in a more general perspective. We understand it as a part of the large field of ongoing research in non-standard database systems. The mainstream of this work is dedicated to new applications in engineering, such as CAD/CAM, while our direction is the support of knowledge-based systems.

It is widely accepted that the state of the art, as far as practically available systems are concerned, is given by relational database systems, which are theoretically founded in first-order logic. So, what are the problems which inhibit the direct use of relational technology for knowledge based applications such as LEU2?

The most important problem is the restriction that relational systems impose on the *format* of their data: their so-called first-normal-form enforces all data to be normalized to flat tables, i.e., relations of the relational model are sets of attribute-value pairs (tuples), where the values can only be atomic objects such as character-strings or numbers. In other words: no attribute can have a complex term as its value.

That means for example, that if we want to construct a relation containing the restaurants in the streets of a city, we cannot encode this as

street	restaurant
a-street	{ a-restaurant, b-restaurant }
b-street	{ c-restaurant , d-restaurant , e-restaurant }

Instead, we have to "flatten" this table to

street	restaurant
a-street	a-restaurant
a-street	b-restaurant
b-street	c-restaurant
b-street	d-restaurant
b-street	e-restaurant

This necessity to decompose relations with inherently complex attributes into flat tables is not only cognitively inadequate, but the overhead in space resulting from the decomposition is exponential in the worst case.

This deficiency can be tolerated when a database system is applied to worlds that can be encoded on filing cards, such as the classical example of the *employee - security number - manager - salary* database. However, this restriction cannot be accepted in an environment where complex object descriptions have to be stored. For effective support of knowledge based systems, it has to be overcome.

Another restriction that stems from the "filing card paradigm" of traditional database systems is that they force the user to completely specify the *schema* of the database, i.e., in the design phase of the database (before any tuple can be inserted), the user has to specify exactly which relations contain which attributes. No data can be entered into the database that do not satisfy the format described by the schema. In particular, no additional attributes can be stored.

As we will show by example later on, this is too restrictive in a natural language processing environment: the descriptions of objects that occur in a text can contain items that simply cannot be completely known beforehand, and thus the terms encoding these descriptions cannot be restricted by a normal form forbidding the storage of additional information.

Besides the first normal form restriction and the requirement for completely specified schemas, there is a third problem with the application of traditional databases for knowledge based applications. From our point of view, possibly the most important enhancement of knowledge based systems with respect to database systems is that the latter only facilitate the retrieval of extensional knowledge while the former additionally allow for deduction of intensional knowledge.

We can state this fundamental difference from another point of view: while queries in traditional database systems can only be answered by *combination* of extensional knowledge stored in different database relations, knowledge based systems additionally use mechanisms of *derivation* to deduce answers which are intensional, i.e., cannot be achieved by simply combining extensional knowledge.

The resulting challenge to database technology is the effective support of, in our case: logic-based, deduction and inference mechanisms. The more technical sections of this chapter will discuss some of the problems arising: the implementation of recursive queries or the support of multiple inference mechanisms.

For the discussion of another fundamental problem, let's return to the "filing card paradigm" of traditional databases again. If we apply databases to mini-worlds that can be encoded on filing cards, we can suppose a "flat" structure of the world: all concepts are equally ranked, and only limited means of classification are needed. In contrast, a system supporting natural language discourse about a structured mini-world, as given by the LEU2 scenario, has to incorporate knowledge about that structure to answer queries adequately.

We can assume that any known object of the mini-world of interest has a representation in the database. However, if we administered a table for each object-class of the real world (e.g., restaurants, pubs, bars, grill-rooms, drive-in-restaurants, pizzerias,...), we would have to keep too many very small tables and to store the same object in multiple tables. Since too many tables and too much redundancy in the tables are severe sources of inefficiency, such behavior has to be avoided. Therefore, our database system has to provide effective support of taxonomies. For example, if we ask for all pizzerias where the cheapest pizza costs less than 10 marks and we have no table for pizzerias, the system has to know by itself that it has to look up the restaurant table.

We have now isolated four basic challenges to database technology that determine our research activities. These are support of:

1. complex objects,

2. variant and incomplete schemas,

3. deductive query-answering and inferencing,

4. taxonomies.

Especially the first and third of these challenges have been partially accepted by the database community since the early 1980s. Many solutions were offered which used the principle of building a deductive complex-object interface on top of an existing standard database system. However, such "loosely coupled" systems were of striking inefficiency since:

- the conversion costs between the complex object data-model of the application and the flat data-model of the database were too high;

- too much data transfer between application and database was needed because every query had to be decomposed into many tasks that could be handled only by either database or application but which had to exchange data.

This problem was often addressed as "impedance mismatch" between application and database. We ourselves made this experience with our contribution to the first LILOG prototype. The conclusion that has to be drawn is that the new requirements cannot be satisfied by building an interface on top of a standard database; new "tightly coupled" database systems are needed which offer a *built-in* treatment of the phenomena described above.

We can now summarize the aim of the subproject LILOG-DB in one sentence: *a next generation database system with built-in support of complex objects, incomplete and variant schemas, inferencing and taxonomies has to be built.*

Our approach to capturing this goal was to first develop a data-model that covers the expressive needs specified above and a hierarchy of languages which are suited for encoding inferencing and database querying on the data of our model. Both model and languages are designed for support of general knowledge based systems. This formal part of our work is briefly reviewed in Sect. 2.

Knowledge about a mini-world can be given in forms not foreseen by the implementors of the database management system, and thus not covered by the operations and data types of the DBMS. So, it is generally agreed upon by the database community that database systems of the future have to be *extensible*, i.e., they have to allow the database programmer to include application-specific data types and operations. In Sect. 3, we discuss the principle of extensibility and its realization in LILOG-DB.

Our discussion of data modeling, languages, and extensibility is resumed in Sect. 4, where some practical aspects of database programming within the previously exhibited framework are discussed.

We then work out what principles an implementation of the model and the languages will have to follow in order to provide effective database support for knowledge based systems, with all their requirements for efficiency, robustness, extensibility and ease of use in mind. These are discussed in Sect. 5.

Section 6 exhibits the architecture we have developed based on these principles. We show which problems have to be handled where in the system, and present some of the techniques we employ to solve them.

In Sect. 7 we relate our work to the LEU2 system, focusing on how the services of LILOG-DB will be made feasible for the system as a whole. The conclusion in Sect. 8 discusses some related work, reviews the basic steps of our argument and gives some perspectives for further work.

Since we cannot assume the reader to be closely familiar with the state of the art with theory and technology of databases, we will be informal in style and keep our presentation of techniques on an intuitive level wherever possible. Often the answers to the "why" and "what" questions will dominate the deep treatment of the "how" question. Readers interested in more technical material are referred to (Gehlen 1989), (Ley, Walter 1990), (Ley 1991), (Ludwig 1988a-c), (Ludwig 1989), (Ludwig et.al. 1989), (Ludwig 1990a-b), (Ludwig, Walter 1991), (Ludwig 1991a-b), (Maier 1989), (Maier, Ley, Gehlen 1991), (Maier 1991).

The presentation will be continuous in that we aim to give a guided tour through the whole system. However, it will not be balanced, since we will highlight some aspects which we feel to be well suited for a prototypical demonstration of theoretical bases, architectural principles or techniques employed in our system.

We hope that this will enable readers with little or no experience in databases to develop an understanding of the role of database technology in a knowledge based system like LEU2.

2 LILOG-DB: The Data-Model and the Languages

The LILOG-DB system contains a hierarchy of three fully developed programming languages, which shall be presented in this section. The highest level of this hierarchy is given by the extended Prolog-implementation *TLPROLOG*, intended as a tool for writing inference engines with access to the LILOG-DB database.

The interface to the database is embedded in TLPROLOG via the purely declarative first-order based deductive database language *FLL*, which constitutes the second level of the language hierarchy.

Considering the state of the art of deductive database technology, it appears impossible to write an interpreter that efficiently evaluates database queries stated in FLL. Therefore a third language level had to be introduced: the database algebra *EFTA*, which is much better suited for interpretative query processing. In LILOG-DB, FLL queries are compiled to EFTA, and the resulting EFTA queries are interpreted by the query processor.

An essential of LILOG-DB, which is treated to more detailed discussion later on, is that these different levels of languages work on the same data-model, the so-called *Feature-Term Data-Model* (*FTDM*).

The following presentation will start by introducing the FTDM and then discuss the languages based on it, in decreasing hierarchical order: first TLPROLOG, then FLL and EFTA.

2.1 The Feature Term Data Model

A data-model describes what kind of objects can be processed by a programming system, what notion the system has of their structure and values and how this universe is structured with respect to comparability and compatibility of its objects.

The term universe of the FTDM consists of atomic terms (integers, reals, symbols), complex terms (functors and lists, sets and feature-tuples) and variables. Examples of FTDM terms are

2	an integer	2.0	a real
two	a symbol	$f(2)$	a functor
$[2, two]$	a list	$\{1, 2, 3\}$	a set
$\langle one : 1, two : 2 \rangle$	a feature-tuple	*TWO*	a variable

Functors and lists of the FTDM can be understood as in Prolog, so that only feature-tuples and sets remain for further discussion.

The introduction of sets $\{t_1, \ldots, t_n\}$ of terms is simply motivated by the fact that we need an unordered data-structure for the description of (the results of) set-oriented database-queries. They are sets in the mathematical sense, i.e., not multi-sets.

The origin of the feature-tuples of our data-model can be settled somewhere between the categorial unification grammars (CUGs) of computational linguistics (Shieber 1986), the record-structures of type-theory (Aït-Kaci 1986), the frames of AI (Minski 1975) and the tuples of relational algebra (Codd 1972). A feature-tuple is a term of the form

$$\langle label_1 : term_1, \ldots, label_n : term_n \rangle .$$

Let us use the example

$$\langle name : george, age : 35 \rangle$$

to explain the basic properties of feature-tuples. Feature-tuples can be seen as aggregations of attribute-value pairs (so-called *features*) with open-world semantics, given by a unification-schema. **Example:** The feature-tuple above describes the *35*-year old *george* and can thus be unified with

$$\langle name : X, salary : 30000 \rangle ,$$

yielding the *most general unifier (mgu)*

$$\langle name : george, age : 35, salary : 30000 \rangle ,$$

instantiating the variable X to *george*.

Equality of two feature-tuples depends neither on the order of the features nor on the values of features which are not common to both tuples, e.g.,

$$\langle name : george, age : 35 \rangle = \langle age : 35, name : george, husband : georgina \rangle .$$

One can see feature-tuples as object-descriptions which can be unified if they are compatible in all features with identical names, the unification yielding a refined object-description (the *mgu*).

2.1.1 Unification as a Means of Structuring the Universe

Note that this notion of unifiability describes the relation between each two terms of the FTDM universe and thus belongs to the data-model: the *unification imposes the structure on our universe*. The semantics of our data-model are given by a unification schema. So, when can two terms be unified?

While the standard unification algorithm of (Robinson 1965) is retained for terms of pure first-order predicate logic, we have to define unification for sets and feature-tuples too.

Sets can be unified if and only if they are ground and equal, i.e., set-unification fails in the presence of variables. That is because it seems impossible to assign adequate semantics and pragmatics to a formula like $\{W, X, Y, 3\} = \{1, 2, Z\}$.

As can be seen in the example above, unification of feature-tuples is defined as elementwise unification of the features whose names are equal.

2.1.2 The Open-World Assumption on Knowledge-Elements

The example shows that we treat feature-tuples as *open structures* in the sense that we consider missing features as *not specified* instead of seeing them as *not present*.

Applied to the treatment of feature-tuples in knowledge-bases, our view is an open-world assumption (OWA) on knowledge elements since feature-tuples do not specify all information about an object, but only that which is known (to the system). We feel that our assumption of the incompleteness of descriptions of knowledge elements is the only realistic one in a natural language processing environment. Other examples in later sections will (hopefully) clarify that point.

Note that the OWA on knowledge elements has to be carefully distinguished from the OWA on knowledge bases themselves. To oversimplify slightly, the first one says that our knowledge elements are incomplete descriptions of entities of the world; the latter one states that the knowledge-base itself is incomplete in that it does not contain all propositions that are true for the entities.

2.1.3 Collecting Information in Open Structures

With the introduction of feature-tuples we can directly model incomplete information, simply leaving some features open. This allows us to describe the collection of information about objects during the process of computation by successive unification, i.e., by successive refinement of the object description. For example, suppose a database about crime fiction is given by

> *writer*(⟨ *authorname* : *agatha_christie*,   *book*(⟨ *title* : *'TheRedKimono'*,
> *nationality* : *british*   ⟩).   *authorname* : *agatha_christie*   ⟩).
> ...   ...

We can now define the TLPROLOG predicate

> *bookinfo*(W) :- *writer*(W), *book*(W).

and the TLPROLOG query

> ?- *bookinfo*(X).

which yields the output

$$X = \langle\, title :\, 'TheRedKimono',\, authorname : agatha\_christie,\, nationality : british\,\rangle$$

i.e., we have collected the information of *writer* and *book* in the variable X.

2.1.4 Sorts in the FTDM

Since LILOG-DB is designed for the support of inference engines working on large knowledge bases, we need a means of structuring our (possibly very complex) universe of discourse.

So we replace the untyped first-order unification by a unification procedure relying on strong typing given by a powerful, yet simple sort concept.

This allows us to comprise the entities of knowledge processing into different classes according to their intended role in the mini-worlds modeled by our programs.

A sort specification is of the form

> *sort* SORTNAME = SORTDESCRIPTION
> *with* CONSTRAINT
> *isa* SORTNAMELIST.

It introduces a sort named SORTNAME. The syntax of the introduced sort is given by SORTDE-SCRIPTION; semantic constraints can be specified in the CONSTRAINT-part and supersorts of SORTNAME are enumerated in the SORTNAMELIST. The proper and efficient incorporation of semantic constraints can be considered one of the main contributions of the LILOG-DB sort concept. A self-explanatory example is the sort specification

> *sort person* = *tuple* $\langle$ *name* : *symbol*, *age* : *integer* $\rangle$
> *with* *age*.$\square$ < 150 *and age*.$\square$ > 0
> *isa being*.

It specifies *persons* as tuples which have a feature *name* of the built-in sort *symbol* (the built-in sorts are *symbol, real, integer, term* and *nil*, the latter ones denoting the complete universe and the empty set respectively) and a feature *age* of sort *integer*. The *age*-feature is constrained to values between 0 and 150, and it is stated that *persons* are *beings*, which are not further specified here.

As can be seen above, *paths* are used in constraints. A *path* is a sequence of integers and feature-names ended by a $\square$-symbol, addressing a subterm of a term. For example, $[\langle name :$ *john, age* : 35$\rangle]$ has the subterm 35 at path 1.*age*.$\square$.

Note that sort specifications can be recursive, so that

> *sort person* = *tuple* $\langle$ *name* : *symbol, age* : *integer, father* : *person* $\rangle$
> *with* *age*.$\square$ < 150 *and age*.$\square$ > 0
> *isa being*.

is a valid sort specification, too.

A constraint is basically a boolean formula built from simple binary conditional expressions of paths and terms (relative to the *SORTDESCRIPTION*). An important application of constraints is the description of coreferences as illustrated in another example extending our description of *persons*:

$$\begin{aligned}
sort\ person\quad =\quad tuple\,\langle\quad &name : symbol,\\
&firstname : symbol,\\
&children : setof\ person,\\
&sex : \{\,male, female\,\},\\
&hobbies : hobbyset,\\
&age : integer\,\rangle\\
with\quad &age.\square > 0\ and\ age.\square < 150\ and\\
&(\,forall\ V\ in\ children.\square : V.name.\square = name.\square)\\
isa\ being\quad &
\end{aligned}$$

This coreference description makes use of the *QUANTIFIED-CONSTRAINT* which allows existential and universal quantification of constraints by using the *in*-operator denoting membership in a set.

We follow the convention of omitting trivial parts of sort specifications, so that the (somehow silly) sort specification *sort term$_2$ = term with true isa term* would be abbreviated to *sort term$_2$*. The syntax of sort specifications is given in Fig. 1.

2.1.5   Restructuring the Universe: Order-Sorted Unification

For our crime fiction example above, we can introduce the sorts

$$\begin{aligned}
sort\ nationality\quad &=\quad \{\,us, british, german, \ldots\}\quad &&isa\ symbol.\\
sort\ european\quad &=\quad \{\,dutch, french, \ldots\}\quad &&isa\ nationality.\\
sort\ asian\quad &=\quad \{\,chinese, turkish, \ldots\}\quad &&isa\ nationality.\\
sort\ eurasian\quad &=\quad \{turkish, russian\}\quad &&isa\ european, asian.
\end{aligned}$$

and can then define

$$european\_fiction\,(X) :\text{-}\ bookinfo\,(X), X = \langle\,nationality : \_.\,european\,\rangle.$$

This example illustrates how every (sub-)term can be assigned a sort restriction by the dot-operator ("."").

We stated above that these sort restrictions are a means of structuring possibly very complex universes of discourse in knowledge base applications. Since the structure of our data-model is given by unification, we have to incorporate order-sorting in our unification schema. This works as follows.

We require our sorts to form a *sort lattice*. That means that the *greatest lower bound* of two sorts s_1 and s_2 (*glb* = the greatest common subsort of s_1 and s_2) and the *least upper bound* (*lub* = the smallest common supersort of s_1 and s_2) are always uniquely defined. The built-in sorts form a *default lattice* depicted in Fig. 2a, and the user's sort declarations are then embedded into this lattice (see Fig. 2b).

Suppose two well-sorted terms $t_1.s_1$ and $t_2.s_2$ are given. They can be unified iff

1. all of their arguments can be unified according to their positions and feature names respectively,

2. the *glb* of s_1 and s_2 is a sort $s \neq nil$ (i.e., s_1 and s_2 have a non-empty intersection), and

3. the *mgu* t of t_1 and t_2 satisfies the sort specification of s.

For example, we can unify *X.european* and *turkish.asian*, yielding the *mgu turkish.eurasian*, but cannot unify *X.european* and *chinese.asian* since the third condition is violated.

```
SORTSPECIFICATION
  ::=  sort SORTNAME
       = SORTDESCRIPTION
       with CONSTRAINT
       isa SORTNAME* .

SORTNAME
  ::=  SYMBOL – DEFAULTSORT

DEFAULTSORT
  ::=  nil | term | real | integer | symbol

SORTDESCRIPTION
  ::=  SORTNAME
     |  DEFAULTSORT
     |  ENUMERATION
     |  setof SORTDESCRIPTION
     |  listof SORTDESCRIPTION
     |  functor SYMBOL ( SORTDESCRIPTION+ )
     |  tuple ⟨ FEATUREDESCRIPTION* ⟩
     |  SORTDESCRIPTION and SORTDESCRIPTION
     |  SORTDESCRIPTION or SORTDESCRIPTION
     |  not SORTDESCRIPTION

ENUMERATION
  ::=  {TERM*}

FEATUREDESCRIPTION
  ::=  SYMBOL : SORTDESCRIPTION

PATH
  ::=  □ | POSITIVE-INTEGER.PATH | SYMBOL.PATH

ITEM
  ::=  TERM | PATH | VARIABLE.PATH

CONSTRAINT-OPERATOR
  ::=  = | < | > | ≥ | ≤ | in | has | hassort | hasarity

CONSTRAINT
  ::=  ITEM CONSTRAINT-OPERATOR ITEM
     |  TRUE
     |  FALSE
     |  CONSTRAINT and CONSTRAINT
     |  CONSTRAINT or CONSTRAINT
     |  not CONSTRAINT
     |  QUANTIFIED-CONSTRAINT

QUANTIFIED-CONSTRAINT
  ::=  forall VARIABLE in ITEM : CONSTRAINT
     |  forsome VARIABLE in ITEM : CONSTRAINT
```

Figure 1: Syntax of sort-specifications

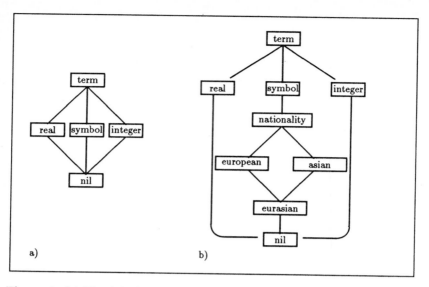

Figure 2: (a) The default sort-lattice, (b) the embedding of user-defined sorts

2.1.6 Multiple Inheritance

We stated above that two terms $t_1.s_1$ and $t_2.s_2$ can be unified if all their arguments can be unified, s_1 and s_2 have a *glb* $s \neq nil$ and $mgu(t_1, t_2)$ is in the denotation of s.

We omit giving complete formal semantics for the denotations of sorts (see (Ludwig 1988a)). Nevertheless, it should be mentioned that each sort in the lattice inherits the properties of all its supersorts.

This *multiple inheritance* guarantees that the denotation of each sort is a subset of the denotations of all its supersorts. More formally, if for a sort specification

$$sort\ sn = sd\ with\ constraint\ isa\ sn_1, \ldots, sn_m$$

$desc(sd)$ is the set of all terms satisfying the sort description sd and $con(constraint)$ is the set of all terms satisfying the constraint *constraint*, then the denotation $den(sn)$ of the sort named sn is given by

$$den(sn) = desc(sd) \cap con(constraint) \cap \bigcap\nolimits_{i=1..m} den(sn_i)$$

As will be shown below, this sort concept not only provides a means of incorporating a powerful, yet computationally tractable theory to unification, but additionally yields a notion of a database schema – in LILOG-DB database schemas are given by sorts – covering the new requirements stemming from the new application domain we try to open for databases.

2.2 The Language Levels Working on the FTDM

With this presentation of the data-model in mind, we can now describe the three languages TLPRO-LOG, FLL and EFTA, each employing the data-model on a different level.

While TLPROLOG as a language for the description of inferencing tasks uses the whole term-universe

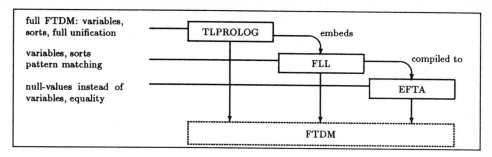

Figure 3: Language levels of LILOG-DB

and the full bidirectional unification, the deductive database language FLL uses the unification only in one direction, i.e., as pattern matching (one of the terms to be unified is always ground!), but works on the full universe too.

TLPROLOG serves as a host language for embedded database operations formulated in FLL. The relation between FLL and EFTA is different: For reasons of efficient query processing, FLL queries are compiled to the database algebra EFTA. EFTA works on a restricted FTDM in that it cannot process variables. The FLL Compiler (Ludwig 1990b) maps them to null-values.

While FLL employs the unification of the FTDM only in one direction (as pattern matching), EFTA – in the absence of variables – further restricts this to semantics based on equality (see Fig. 3 for a more illustrative description of the language levels).

2.2.1 TLPROLOG

TLPROLOG can be easily described as

> Prolog's SLDNF-Resolution
> on the FTDM
> with an embedded FLL interface
> $= \overline{\textit{TLPROLOG}}$

That means that TLPROLOG is an upward compatible extension of Edinburgh-Prolog. This is the case since in the absence of sets, feature-tuples and sorts, our order-sorted glb-unification of the FTDM reduces to Prolog's ordinary first-order unification.

TLPROLOG itself shall not be further discussed here, except for the embedding of sort declarations and FLL programs. Assuming *streets* to be a set of feature-terms in the database (an *FT-set*), the TLPROLOG program[1]

> *sort location = ...*
> *sort big_city = ... isa location.*
>
> *fll_section*
> *street(X.location, Y.location) :- ⟨ source : X, target : Y ⟩ in_ft_set streets.*
>
> *big_route(X.big_city, X.big_city).*
> *big_route(X, Y) :- street(X.big_city, Z.big_city), big_route(Z, Y).*
> *end_of_fll_section*

---

[1]The sort specifications are only sketched in this example.

$$big\_routes(X,Y) :- fll\ big\_route(X, SET\_Y),\ Y\ in\ SET\_Y.$$

shows how the embedding of FLL database calls in TLPROLOG works. TLPROLOG programs can include *fll-sections* that describe FLL programs working on the database. These can be called by TLPROLOG clauses using the prefix-operator *fll*.

Some things have to be remarked:

1. From the previous considerations, it should have become clear that TLPROLOG programs can contain sort declarations, as in the upper two lines of the example above.

2. As the declaration of the predicate *street* in the *fll-section* shows, the link of predicates to the database is done via the *in_ft_set*-operator. The example shows that this allows the linkage to arbitrarily structured FT-sets of the database; they do not have to be of "predicate-style" form.

3. The *big_routes*-predicate is a typical example for the conversion of a set of results delivered by the set-oriented FLL query processing to a stream of terms that can be accessed via backtracking. But note that TLPROLOG is able to work directly with the resulting set too.

2.2.2   FLL

Starting with the first-order based DATALOG that is well known in the deductive database community, FLL can be described by the following schema:

	DATALOG
+	complex objects of the FTDM
+	order-sorting
+	negation
+	set-grouping
=	FLL

The semantics of FLL are set-oriented. For example, suppose we have a binary relation

$$way(X,Y)$$

on terms given by the table

way	
X	Y
a	b
b	c
c	d

and a predicate

$$directly\_reachable(X,Y) :- way(X,Y).$$

We can now ask

$$?- directly\_reachable(a,Y).$$

and get the set of all towns reachable from *a*. We can also enter

$$?- directly\_reachable(X,Y).$$

and receive the set of all pairs (X, Y) of towns where Y can be directly reached from X. The answer-table looks like this:

directly_reachable	
X	Y
a	b
b	c
c	d

The most important aspects of FLL shall now be briefly overviewed, mainly in comparison with DATALOG.

Recursion: The need for recursion in first-order databases has often been stressed in the literature (see (Bancilhon, Ramakrishnan 1986), (Tsur, Zaniolo 1986)). In our example above, we may want to compute the set of all cities reachable from each other, using the predicate

$$reachable(X, Y) :- way(X, Y).$$
$$reachable(X, Y) :- way(X, Z), reachable(Z, Y).$$

The answer to

$$?- reachable(X, Y).$$

then is the table

reachable	
X	Y
a	b
a	c
a	d
b	c
b	d
c	d

In FLL, as in DATALOG, we have the possibility to write arbitrary recursive programs, i.e., there are no restrictions to linear recursion or whatever else.

Set-Grouping: What can we do if we want a list like

reachable	
X	Y
a	b,c,d
b	c,d
c	d

instead of the answer above? So far our language does not enable us to get such an answer since we are unable to explicitly (dis-)aggregate sets. DATALOG does not distinguish different levels of *set-grouping* (Tsur, Zaniolo 1986). Thus we augment FLL by a set-grouping operator and state the query

$$?- reachable(X, < Y >).$$

which means that our answers are to be grouped by Y. Our result is the intended table shown above.

In contrast to the lists, feature-tuples and functors introduced above, sets have no internal structure. They are the appropriate representation for large collections of entities which do not fit into the more or less tree-like structure of lists, feature-tuples and functors.

Negation: Another aspect of the missing expressive power of DATALOG for our purposes of "knowledge processing" is that we cannot handle negation. We are not able to state predicates like

$unmarried(X) :- person(X), not(married(X)).$

Thus we introduce *stratified negation* (Przymusinski 1988), (Tsur, Zaniolo 1986) into FLL. That means that we allow predicates like the one defined above with negated literals on the right-hand side of a rule if this negation is not part of a recursive cycle as in the following case:

$even(0).$
$even(I) :- not(odd(I)).$
$odd(succ(I)) :- even(I).$

This is because such an unstratified program might not have a unique minimal model, i.e., it has no proper declarative semantics (this is oversimplified, see (Przymusinski 1988) for a discussion).

Sorts as filters: If we reconsider the embedded FLL program

$street(X.location, Y.location) :-$
$\langle source : X, target : Y \rangle in\_ft\_set streets.$

$big\_route(X.big\_city, X.big\_city).$
$big\_route(X, Y) :-$
$street(X.big\_city, Z.big\_city),$
$big\_route(Z, Y).$

from above, we see that in FLL sorts act as a filter: Only those *streets* are included in the result that connect *big_cities*.

Besides the inclusion of the complex objects of the FTDM, stratified negation and set-grouping, this concept of filtering data via order-sorting is the main extension of FLL with respect to DATALOG.

Compared with the language LDL (Tsur, Zaniolo 1986), which has received much attention in recent years, this kind of filtering by sorts is one of the two basic improvements. The other is the possibility of coping with open structures without needing to employ full unification, as in (Beeri, Nasr, Tsur 1988). In (Ludwig 1988a), Ludwig has shown that the model-theoretic semantics of these languages can be extended to our model in a natural way.

2.2.3 EFTA

Almost every fully developed database system can be divided into an implementational kernel and peripheral modules that provide a user interface working on the database kernel. The kernel normally implements the operations that can be performed on sets of data, while the peripheral modules parse queries, submit them to the kernel, or present the results to the user. The kernel has to have a language in which it is told what operations it is to perform on data. Because the way of describing database operations is commonly an algebraic one, such languages are often called *database algebras*.

While the abstract language of the currently available commercial systems is mostly *relational algebra (RA)*, we had to introduce the more expressive EFTA (*Extended Feature Term Algebra*) to satisfy the needs of our domain of work. What follows is a brief overview of EFTA, containing some comparison with the classic relational algebra, summarized in Fig. 4.

Relational Algebra	EFTA
Relational Model	**FTDM**
constants: integers, reals, symbols	constants: integers, reals, symbols
aggregations: tuple, relation	aggregations: list, set, functor, feature-tuple
outer aggregation: relation	outer aggregation: set
inner aggregation: tuple	inner aggregation: arbitrary
depth of aggregation: 1	depth of aggregation: arbitrary
Relational Schema	**Feature Term Schema**
fix	variant, incomplete, recursive
Basic Level	**Basic Level**
attributes (paths of length 1)	paths (of length $0 .. \infty$)
conditions (without type- and	conditions (including type- and
structure-inspection)	structure-inspection)
tuple-aggregation	constructors
	conditional constructors
Operator Level	**Operator Level**
$\cup$	$\cup$
$\times$	$\times$
$-$	$-$
π_p	$\gamma_{if\ true\ then\ p.\square}$
σ_c	$\gamma_{if\ c\ then\ \square}$
	$\gamma_{if\ c\ then\ cc_1\ else\ cc_2}$
	$nest_p$
	$unnest_p$
	Φ
corresponds to	**corresponds to**
DATALOG^{nr}	FLL

Figure 4: Comparison of EFTA and Relational Algebra

(1) Basic Operations on Terms

We see the *basic level* of a database algebra as the level describing operations on individual terms, the *operator level* as the operations on relations/sets of tuples/terms.

Since RA relies on first normal-form while EFTA allows arbitrarily complex objects, we have to generalize the concept of an attribute a_i of a "flat" tuple $\langle a_1 : t_1, \ldots, a_n : t_n \rangle$ by the concept of the application t/p of *paths* p (of arbitrary length) to terms t. A path is a (possibly empty) sequence of feature-names and position-numbers, finished by a $\square$. For example,

$$f(\langle age : 20 \rangle) \ /\ 1.age.\square\ =\ 20$$

The *conditions* that can be checked for terms in EFTA extend RA in that they allow type- and structure-inspection of terms (see (Ludwig, Walter 1991)).

To compose arbitrary complex objects, we have to replace the tuple-aggregation by the application $cons(c, t)$ of *constructors* c to terms t. For example,

$$cons(f(\langle age : \square \rangle),\ 20)$$

constructs the term $f(\langle age : 20 \rangle)$.

In addition, we allow the application $apply(cc, t)$ of *conditional constructors* cc which perform construction-operations dependent on the evaluation of conditions, so that, e.g., the application of

$$if\ 2.\square < 30\ then\ person(1.\square, young)\ else\ person(1.\square, middle\text{-}aged)$$

to $person(john, 20)$ yields $person(john, young)$.

RA has no equivalent for this. We will now discuss the basic differences between EFTA and RA on operator-level.

(2) Sets instead of Relations

Feature-term sets (*FT-sets*), the data-containers of EFTA, are (potentially heterogeneous) sets of (arbitrary) terms instead of relations structured by columns as in RA. Because EFTA is designed for (deductive) *retrieval* of feature-terms, we disallow the occurrence of variables. The decision for sets instead of relations is based on the insight that in the general case of knowledge bases with incomplete information, it is not appropriate to force the information into relations by flattening since this requires too much effort for decomposition and produces too many small "intermediate" and "secondary" relations which are expensive to update.

(3) Databases as Collections of Named Sets

We then regard the database as a collection of named sets too. However, if more about the structure of the elements is known, it can be encoded in the schema of this set (see below).

(4) Cross Product, Union and Difference

The cross-product $A \times B$ of two sets $A = \{a_1, \ldots, a_n\}$ and $B = \{b_1, \ldots, b_m\}$ in EFTA is the set of all binary tuples $\{\langle '1' : a_1, '2' : b_1\rangle, \ldots, \langle '1' : a_n, '2' : b_m\rangle\}$. Note that it is neither commutative nor associative. That is the bad news. The good news is that, in contrast to the union-compatibility-restrictions of RA, we can define union $A \cup B$ and difference $A - B$ in a purely set-theoretic manner.

(5) The γ-Operator

The γ-operator $\gamma_{cc}\ S$ allows the application of the basic term-level operators of EFTA as described above to sets of terms. It comprises the capabilities of EFTA for single scans of sets: a conditional constructor cc can be applied to each element of a given set S, and the set of resulting terms is the result of the γ-application.

We can now write "selections" and "projections" informally as

(i) $\sigma_c\ R\ =\ \gamma_{if\ c\ then\ \square}\ R$
(ii) $\pi_p\ R\ =\ \gamma_{if\ true\ then\ p}\ R$

Thus the γ-operator is an abstraction of selection and projection in *relational algebra* including constructive capabilities as they are needed for deductive retrieval. For instance, the evaluation of

$$\gamma_{if\ 1.\square>5\ then\ f(1.\square,2.\square)\ else\ f(5,2.\square)}\ \{g(3,4), g(4,5), g(9,6), g(7,2)\}$$

yields the result

$$\{f(5,4), f(5,5), f(9,6), f(7,2)\}.$$

Another example might illustrate how EFTA supports the open-world-assumption on feature-tuples. If we got the "relation"

$$R = \{\langle name : john, job : waiter, age : 20\rangle, \langle name : peter, age : 30\rangle\},$$

the query

$$\gamma_{if\ job=waiter\ then\ \Box}\ R \qquad (1)$$

will have the answer R since we do not suppose R to contain all information (closed world assumption), but suppose it to contain all *known* information (open world assumption). The query should be read as *"Give me all the people who may be waiters !"* instead of *"Give me all the people who are (positively known to be) waiters !"*.

The possibility to state *has*-conditions in the γ-operator allows the closed-world query too:

$$\gamma_{if\ \Box\ has\ job\ and\ job=waiter\ then\ \Box}\ R \qquad (2)$$

While the query (1) assumes the second tuple of R to possibly be an underspecified waiter and lets it pass, the second query checks whether the feature *job* is really specified in the tuple, and the result is

$$\{\langle name : john, job : waiter, age : 20\rangle\}.$$

Note that (2) is a typical example for *structure inspection* within a condition, since it checks whether a feature-tuple contains the feature *job*.

(6) Nesting and Unnesting

nest and *unnest* are needed for (dis-)aggregation of FT-sets. The *unnest*-operator $unnest_p F$ decomposes an element of F with a set-valued attribute s at path p into a set of terms with the elements of s at position p:

$$unnest_{1.\Box}\ \{\ f(\{1,2\}),\ f(\{2,3\})\ \} = \{\ f(1), f(2), f(3)\ \}$$

nest works in the opposite direction:

$$nest_{1.\Box}\ \{\ f(1), f(2), f(3)\ \} = \{\ f(\{1,2,3\})\ \}$$

As can be seen in the example, *nest* and *unnest* are not inverse to each other!

(7) The Closure-Operator

With the operators given so far, we do not yet have enough power to cope with recursive queries. Thus we include a *closure-operator* Φ. This enables us to process an arbitrary (recursive) query in our data model (if it has been proved safe by our safety checker!).

For space reasons, the closure-operator will not be discussed in detail here, and only an example will be given. Nevertheless, it should be mentioned that – seen from an operational point of view – the closure-operator mimics what is called in the literature a *naive machine* (Bancilhon 1986), (Bancilhon, Ramakrishnan 1986): When evaluating $\Phi_{\langle e_1,...,e_n\rangle}\ \langle I_1,\ldots,I_n\rangle$, a vector (syntactically represented as a tuple) $\langle e_1,\ldots,e_n\rangle$ of n EFTA expressions is iteratively applied to a vector $\langle I_1,\ldots,I_n\rangle$ of n initializing arguments until no more terms are generated. The terms generated in each iteration are added to the intermediate result. The example

$$\Phi_{\langle \gamma_{if\ (1.2.\Box=2.1.\Box)\ then\ anc(1.1.\Box,2.2.\Box)}\ (1\times 1)\rangle}\ \langle R\rangle \qquad (3)$$

with $n = 1$ shows that the intermediate results can be accessed via *position-numbers*, as in the cross-product 1×1. The evaluation-schema for $\Phi_{\langle e_1,...,e_n\rangle}\ \langle I_1,\ldots,I_n\rangle$ is the following (*imr* stands for "intermediate result"):

```
/* initialize imr[0] to I */
for j = 1 to n
   imr[0,j] := I_j
i := 1
repeat
   /* for all positions j */
   for j = 1 to n
      /* apply expression e_j to the vector imr[i-1] */
      /* of last generation intermediate results */
      imr[i,j] := e_j(imr[i − 1])
      /* if imr[i] = imr[i-1], nothing has changed */
   nothing_changed :=
      (∀j = 1...n : imr[i,j] = imr[i − 1,j])
   i := i + 1
until nothing_changed
```

For

$$R = \{ \ anc(peter, george), anc(george, harry), anc(george, paul), anc(paul, david) \ \}$$

the sample query (3) yields

$$imr_0 = \langle\{anc(peter,george), anc(george,harry), anc(george,paul), anc(paul,david)\}\rangle$$
$$imr_1 = \langle\{anc(peter,harry), anc(peter,paul), anc(george,david)\} \cup imr_0 \rangle$$
$$imr_2 = \langle\{anc(peter,david)\} \cup imr_1 \rangle$$
$$RES = \{ imr_2 \}$$

(8) Non-Ground Operators

For simplicity and convenience, we define three important operators which are non-ground in the sense that they are specializations/compositions of ground *FTA* operators.

Extended Projection: Let p be a path. We define the *extended projection* on p by

$$\pi_p R :\Leftrightarrow \gamma_{if\ true\ then\ p}\ R$$

Extended Selection: Let c be a condition. We define the *extended selection* via c by

$$\sigma_c R :\Leftrightarrow \gamma_{if\ c\ then\ \Box}R$$

θ-Joins: Let p, q be paths, $\theta \in \{=, \neq, <, >, \geq, \leq, in\}$. We define the *$\theta$-Joins* by

$$A \underset{p\theta q}{\bowtie} B \ :\Leftrightarrow \sigma_{1.p\ \theta\ 2.q}\ (A \times B)$$

These operators are called "non-ground" since they can be expressed using ground EFTA expressions. However, they are implemented in the database kernel by specialized algorithms. This is because they represent database operations frequently needed in query processing. Their specialized implementations are much more efficient than a composition of the standard ones would be. The interested reader is referred to the paragraph about join processing below in this paper.

A final remark on the comparison of EFTA and RA. While *RA* can serve as a target language for compilers of non-recursive DATALOG (DATALOG^{nr}), EFTA has exactly the expressive power of FLL. However, the next section will argue that this expressive power is not always sufficient from the point of view of practical database programming, and that extensibility of database languages is required to bridge the gap between the abstract "expressive power" of a database language and its concrete usability in a specific, especially non-standard, application domain.

3 Extensibility

EFTA is an extensible algebra, i.e., there is a regime of augmenting the algebra by user-defined operators without any need to touch the LILOG-DB source code. This satisfies an important requirement for next generation database management systems, which – in a world of more and more widespread and specialized database applications – have to be adaptable to the different operational characteristics of different application contexts.

As will become clear below, an important aspect of our work on extensibility is that since we map queries of our top levels to EFTA, EFTA extensibility automatically buys extensibility of our top levels, too.

Our approach to extensibility is to include *evaluable functions* into EFTA. These functions accept 0 or more terms as a parameter and return a term as a result.

The proper place to include these evaluable functions is the apparatus of *constructors*. Syntactically, we do not need to extend EFTA at all. The only step from EFTA to XFTA (eXtensible FTA) is that we *interpret* certain function symbols, i.e., we do the same as we do for the function symbols $+,-$, etc.

The semantics for this interpretation is given by the semantics of the function supplied by the user (in the language C_{FTA}), formally:

$$f(t_1,\ldots,t_n) = f_{C_{FTA}}(t_1,\ldots,t_n)$$

For example, if we define operations

$$\begin{aligned} intersect(X,Y) &= \text{intersection of sets } X \text{ and } Y \\ max(X) &= \text{maximal element of set } X \end{aligned}$$

the γ-operator

$$\gamma_{max(intersect(1.\square,2.\square))} \; F$$

applied to the set

$$F = \{ \, pair(\{1,2,3\},\{0,2,3,4\}), \, pair(\{5,6\},\{5\}) \, \}$$

returns the set $\{3,5\}$.

3.1 Extension Functions: C_{FTA}

Extension functions are described in C_{FTA}, which is an extension of C. The introductory description of *simple* C_{FTA} functions assumes a little knowledge of C; the *composite* functions discussed below don't require such knowledge at all.

3.1.1 Simple Functions

Simple functions are needed to allow the user to directly extend the kernel of EFTA, which is written in C. So, C_{FTA} programs basically are C-programs, but with a few differences which are needed for our preprocessor to recognize extension functions:

- C_{FTA} functions are declared by the following syntax:

  efta_function name : Name *arity* : Arity

  One can use the ordinary function-syntax of C, too. But in this case, the function can only be an auxiliary one (which can then be called from C_{FTA} functions). It will not be implanted into EFTA.

- the return-statement always has to be of the form

  return(Term)

  which returns *Term* as a result. In case of failure, one must always use

  return(NULL)

- The end of a function is not indicated by a "}" as in C, but by the keyword

  end_of_efta_function

- C_{FTA} has a fixed parameter passing convention, which is adapted to the parameter passing conventions of the EFTA Query Processor. So, for access to the n-th parameter, one uses

  argterm(n)

All other statements of C can also be freely used in C_{FTA} without causing any trouble. To give a flavor of how a C_{FTA} program looks like, we give the following source code:

```
-----------------------------------------------------

efta_function name:list_element arity:2

        TERM            t1 = argterm(1);
        TERM            t2 = argterm(2);
        TERM            t3;

    if (!is_integer(t1)) return (NULL);
    term_list_element(term_integer_value(t1), t2, &t3);
    return (copy_term(t3));

end_of_efta_function

-----------------------------------------------------
```

The function *list_element(I, List)* described by this piece of code retrieves the I-th element of list *List*, so that we can now state the EFTA query

$$\gamma_{list\_element(1.\square,2.\square)}\ F$$

which, applied to

$$F = \{f(1,[a_1,a_2,a_3]), f(2,[b_1,b_2,b_3], f(3,[c_1,c_2,c_3])\}$$

will yield the result $\{a_1, b_2, c_3\}$.

3.1.2 Composite Functions

As will occur in the following case studies, we have a large library of already implemented and tested XFTA functions, so that most new functions could be expressed in terms of these functions. For example, the *gradient* (in degrees) of a line between two points (x_1, x_2) and (y_1, y_2) can be computed as

$$arctan((y_2 - x_2)/(y_1 - x_1)).$$

We now suppose a given set *Lines* of lines given by pairs

$$\langle source : Point, \ target : Point \rangle$$

of points

$$\langle xcor : Integer, \ ycor : Integer \rangle.$$

To retrieve the inclination of these lines, we would have to write the query

$$\gamma_{arctan}\left(\begin{array}{c}(target.ycor.\square - source.ycor.\square)\\ /\quad (target.xcor.\square - source.xcor.\square)\end{array}\right)\ Lines.$$

Even in EFTA's surface syntax, which is not presented here, this is unreadable: if it occured in a larger query, nobody would be able to decipher that it means the gradients of the lines.

In XFTA, we have the possibility of functional abstraction over conditional constructors. The user can define *composite functions* in the following general syntax:

$$composite\_function\ f(A_1, \ldots, A_n) := Conditional\_Constructor$$

so that we could write

$$composite\_function\ gradient(Source, Target) :=$$
$$arctan\left(\begin{array}{c}(Target.ycor.\square - Source.ycor.\square)\\ /\quad (Target.xcor.\square - Source.xcor.\square)\end{array}\right)$$

and modify our query to

$$\gamma_{gradient(source.\square,target.\square)}\ Lines.$$

This form of functional abstraction is not only more adequate from a cognitive point of view. As early performance considerations show, it is more efficient, too. The reason is that these composite functions are not simply macro-expanded, but are completely translated to C functions and included into the LILOG-DB code the same way simple functions are.

The same holds for aggregate functions, i.e., functions that "aggregate" a set of objects to a single objects, e.g., the *count* function that for a set returns the number of its elements. An aggregate function is described by an *initialization*, a *transition function* and a *return function*. For the *count* function, these are given by

$$aggregate\ count\ :=\ \langle\ init : Count := 0,$$
$$transition : Count := Count + 1,$$
$$return : Count$$
$$\rangle.$$

In the definitions of composite functions, other functions can be freely and even recursively used, even if they are to be defined later. The loader of XFTA functions into LILOG-DB can handle that.

So, our approach allows us to incorporate new functions "written in C" into XFTA without writing C-programs at all, by using the machinery of composite functions with its very simple syntax together with the powerful library of already implemented XFTA functions. This makes the writing of extension functions possible for users without notable programming skills[2].

3.2   Some Case Studies on Extensibility

3.2.1   String- and List-Operations

In the context of real-world database applications, format conversions and the computation of key fields are frequently performed operations.

For example, in Germany, one can compute the *social security number* of an employee from his or her initials, birthday and some other personal data. It is our belief that a database system should have a way to learn and perform such operations, since the alternatives are not very attractive.

The solution that is mostly applied in current DBMS is that the data manipulation language of the database system is *embedded* into a procedural programming language such as COBOL or C, and the user has to perform operations like the one described above on the level of the host language, and then "push" the result into the DBMS through a *call interface*.

Besides the notorious impedance mismatch often observed for such embedded systems, such a way of proceeding forces the user to keep and maintain programs written in two different languages: the programming language and the database query language. Additionally, for example when certain format requirements have to be met, this enforces a separate post-processing of the result of a query, which could have been avoided if the DBMS had learned the appropriate format conversions. And, most important, no way is provided to make the "new" operations available from an ad-hoc query interface. That means that inexperienced, non-programming users cannot benefit from the flexibility of such a solution.

To solve this problem for LILOG-DB, we implemented a collection of libraries that can be easily accessed by every user. For example, in the *strings_and_lists* library, we have implemented some functions for the processing of lists and strings, each of which has 5-20 lines of C_{FTA} code (see Fig. 5).

This library solution provides us with the necessary tools to encode format operations. Suppose, for example, that our output format required names of persons to be represented with initials only, we could now write the query

$$\gamma_{strconcat(firstchar(1.\Box),strconcat('.',last(\Box)))}\ \gamma_{split('\ ',\Box)}\ R$$

which, applied to

$$R = \{'Peter\ Pan','Rudolf\ the\ Red\ Nosed\ Reindeer'\}$$

---

[2]Additionally, to our very best knowledge our preprocessor for composite functions guarantees that no runtime errors can occur, i.e., the C_{FTA} compiler generates code that avoids infinite loops, system crashes, etc.

Function	Semantics	Example
$firstchar(X)$	first character of a symbol X	$firstchar('Peter\ Pan') =' P'$
$restchars(X)$	X with the first character cut off	$restchars('Peter\ Pan') =' eter\ Pan'$
$strconcat(X,Y)$	concatenation of the strings X and Y	$strconcat('Peter','Pan') =' Peter Pan'$
$strlen(X)$	length of string X	$strlen('Peter\ Pan') = 9$
$split(X,Y)$	substrings of Y separated by X	$split('\ ','Peter\ Pan') = ['Peter','Pan']$
$concat(X,Y)$	concatenation of lists X and Y	$concat([1,2,3],[4,5]) = [1,2,3,4,5]$
$head(L)$	head of list L	$head([1,2,3]) = 1$
$tail(L)$	the tail of list L	$tail([1,2,3]) = [2,3]$
$last(L)$	last element of list L	$last([1,2,3]) = 3$
$n\_th(N,L)$	Nth element of list L	$n\_th(3,[a,b,c,d,e,f]) = c$
$length(L)$	length of list L	$length([a,b,c,d,e,f]) = 6$

Figure 5: A set of XFTA operations for strings and lists

$$
\begin{aligned}
min\ R &= R - \gamma_{if\ 1.\square<2.\square\ then\ 2.\square}\ R \times R \\
max\ R &= R - \gamma_{if\ 1.\square>2.\square\ then\ 2.\square}\ R \times R \\
count\ R &= max\,(\gamma_{1.\square}\,(\Phi_{\{\gamma_{if\ (1.1.\square=2.1.\square\ and\ 1.2.\square<2.2.\square)\ then\ (2.1.\square+1,2.2.\square)}\ 1\times1\}}\ \langle\gamma_{\{1,\square\}}\ R\rangle\,)) \\
sum\ R &= max\,(\gamma_{3.\square}\,(\Phi_{\{\gamma_{if\ 1.2.\square<2.1.\square\ then\ (1.1.\square,2.2.\square,1.3.\square+2.3.\square,1.4.\square\cup2.4.\square)}\ 1\times1\}}\ \langle\gamma_{\{\square,\square,\square,\{\square\}\}}\ R\rangle\,)) \\
avg\ R &= \gamma_{1.\square/2.\square}\,(sum\ R \times count\ R)
\end{aligned}
$$

Figure 6: EFTA encodings of aggregate functions for sets of integers

yields

$$\{'P.\ Pan','R.\ Reindeer'\}.$$

However, if we frequently needed a name formatting operation like this, it would be better to write a composite XFTA function

$$composite\_function\ name\_format(String) :=$$
$$strconcat(\ firstchar(head(split('\ ',String))), strconcat('.',last(split('\ ',String)))\ )$$

for that and simply call

$$\gamma_{name\_format\square}\ R$$

which, as a side effect, saves a scan.

In general, we can keep the result that an important function of our extensibility regime is the provision of a simple means to adapt the DBMS to different format requirements of different applications and front-ends.

3.2.2 Aggregate Functions

EFTA is computationally complete (Ludwig, Walter 1991). However, it is very inconvenient to express aggregate functions in EFTA. As the examples in Fig. 6 suggest, the results are neither readable nor efficient, and some of them employ expensive joins or even a closure-operator where a naive user would suppose that a simple scan with a sort of "memory" would be sufficient.

For instance, to encode the maximum function max in C_{FTA}, we write

Our setting is the comparison of the application of the XFTA expression

$$\gamma_{max(\square)}\, F$$

to ft-sets

$$F = \{\, \{1,2,\ldots,n\}, \{n+1,\ldots,2n\}, \ldots, \{(m-1)*n+1,\ldots,n*m\}\,\}$$

with the equivalent EFTA expression, which is given by

$$
\begin{aligned}
F_1 &= unnest_{2.\square}\, \gamma_{f(\square,\square)}\, F \\
F_2 &= F_1 - \gamma_{if\ 1.2.\square > 2.2.\square\ then\ 2.\square}\, (F_1 \times F_1) \\
F_3 &= \gamma_{2.\square}\, nest_{2.\square}\, F_2
\end{aligned}
$$

The times are measured in milliseconds, the system worked with 1 MB of available main-memory. (*) in a column indicates that the computation cannot be performed with this restriction since the intermediate results require more memory. Varying the parameters n and m, we obtain the following tables:

XFTA: n / m	5	10	20	50
5	3	5	6	12
10	5	5	14	16
20	8	13	17	21
50	14	16	20	24

EFTA: n / m	5	10	20	50
5	3195	7002	(*)	(*)
10	7643	(*)	(*)	(*)
20	(*)	(*)	(*)	(*)
50	(*)	(*)	(*)	(*)

Figure 7: A performance experiment with XFTA aggregates

$$
\begin{aligned}
aggregate\ max := \langle\ & init: Max := Null, \\
& transition: if\ Current > Max \\
& \qquad\qquad Max := Current, \\
& return: Max \\
& \rangle
\end{aligned}
$$

The memory we need is provided by the variable Max, which is initialized to the null term $Null$. The *transition* feature describes how Max is changed by each step of the scan of the parameter set of max: if the currently considered term $Current$[3] is greater than Max, Max is set to the value of $Current$. The *return* feature describes that after the scan is completed, the value of Max is returned as a result of the aggregate function.

A little performance experiment[4] shows how much efficiency we have gained by replacing the above EFTA solutions by XFTA code. As Fig. 7 shows, applying $\gamma_{max\ (\square)}$ instead of the standard EFTA version to a sample collection of ft-sets yields significant performance increases, which grow tremendous when larger inputs are processed. So, besides a simple and proper treatment of aggregate functions, we have gained a lot of speed-up for query processing.

---

[3]$Current$ is a built-in variable (the only one!).

[4]The process of systematically benchmarking LILOG-DB is still on its way. In this paper, we can only give results of isolated small-scale experiments which we consider representative.

3.2.3 Recursive Algebra

From our current point of view, as stated in (Ludwig 1991a), the non-recursiveness of EFTA is a major design error: An algebra for complex objects has to be able to apply its operators at each nesting level of sets (Colby 1989).

In (Ludwig, Walter 1991), we sketched what a recursive variant of EFTA could look like, and proved that this would not increase its expressive power. Thus, recursive algebra is a question of efficiency and cognitive adequacy only, but this is important enough. From the point of view of efficiency, recursive algebra can avoid a lot of superfluous nesting and unnesting of sets; and there is no question that the admissibility of sub-queries is an improvement with respect to intuitiveness.

We therefore implemented an XFTA function

$subquery(Query)$

which returns the result of *Query*. Supposing a set *Tutors* given by $Tutors =$

$$
\begin{aligned}
\{ \\
\langle \quad name : \quad & tim, \\
profs : \quad & \left\{ \begin{array}{l} \langle name : pete, sex : male \rangle, \\ \langle name : paula, sex : female \rangle \end{array} \right\}, \\
students : \quad & \left\{ \begin{array}{l} \langle name : stan, sex : male \rangle, \\ \langle name : sam, sex : male \rangle \end{array} \right\}, \\
\langle \quad name : \quad & tom, \\
profs : \quad & \left\{ \begin{array}{l} \langle name : pete, sex : male \rangle, \\ \langle name : petula, sex : female \rangle \end{array} \right\}, \\
students : \quad & \left\{ \begin{array}{l} \langle name : sarah, sex : female \rangle, \\ \langle name : stan, sex : male \rangle \end{array} \right\} \\
\rangle \; , \\
\dots \\
\}
\end{aligned}
$$

we can now express the query for all men in direct professional contact with a tutor as

$$
\gamma_{subquery} \left(\begin{array}{l} \gamma_{if\,sex.\square=male\,then\square}\; profs.\square \\ \cup \quad \gamma_{if\,sex.\square=male\,then\square}\; students.\square \end{array} \right)^{Tutors}
$$

The implementation of the *subquery* function turns out to be simple:

1. we first save the state of the query processor (about 100 bytes),

2. then reinitialize the query processor with the new query,

3. let it evaluate it and fetch the result,

4. shutdown the new instance of the query processor,

5. restore the old state, and

6. deliver the result.

The whole function requires about 40 lines of C-code, and these buy a lot of expressive power in database programming practice. This sheds a light on an important aspect of our work: making EFTA recursive by introducing *subquerying* overcomes an operational weakness of the algebra and

Function	Functionality
$pic\_and(T_1, T_2)$	creates a picture that has a black point exactly where both T_1 and T_2 have a black point
$pic\_or(T_1, T_2)$	creates a picture that has a black point exactly where one of T_1 and T_2 has a black point
$pic\_neg(T_1)$	creates a picture that has a black point exactly where T_1 has a white point
$pic\_lr(T_1, T_2)$	appends T_1 to the right of T_2
$pic\_hd(T_1, T_2)$	appends T_1 below T_2

Figure 8: Some XFTA functions operating on bitmaps

thereby shows that algebra extensibility is not only a means of incorporating application-specific functionality, but can help to adapt the algebra to specific query profiles.

In this case study, we have shown this for recursive subquerying, but it also holds for other tasks such as the support for existential queries or approximation queries.

3.2.4 Including New Data Structures

On the previous pages, we studied cases where extension functions worked inside the FTDM, the data model of EFTA. We now want to discuss the handling of pictorial objects by XFTA functions which operate on a bitmap encoding of pictures, i.e., a representation outside the scope of the FTDM.

The rationale behind this example is our belief that no new database algebra should be designed for each new application – most share similar algebraic structures on different kinds of objects, anyway – but the framework of universal database algebras should be made applicable to different classes of objects, e.g., pictures.

Our approach to modeling pictures is truly object oriented. We don't let users manipulate the bitmaps representing pictures directly, but only provide a handle on them.

The starting point of our mechanism are bitmaps stored on external files. The function $pic(Name)$ asserts that a bitmap object *Name* is known. When first called, it retrieves a bitmap from the file *Name*, stores it in an internal *picture store* under the ID $pic(name)$, and returns the term $pic(Name)$ as a result. When called again, it finds the object identified by $pic(Name)$ in the picture store and does nothing (except returning $pic(Name)$).

Other functions working on pictures are described in Fig. 8. All these functions behave as if they were uninterpreted, but as a side effect do their work on the bitmap objects.

As an example, we give a query which computes complex labyrinths from simple ones. We describe a labyrinth by a tuple

$$\langle id: \ldots, hsize: \ldots, vsize: \ldots, in: yx(\ldots, \ldots), out: yx(\ldots, \ldots)\rangle$$

so that the labyrinth could be described by the tuple

$$\langle id : lab1, hsize : 14, vsize : 7, in : yx(1,11), out : yx(6,14)\rangle$$

since it is of size 14×7 and has a path through it, a way, with in-coordinates $(1,11)$ and out-coordinates $(6,14)$[5].

The query

$$\Phi_{(Change\_ways \bowtie_{J\_expr} Change\_ways)} \langle Labyrinths\rangle$$

with $Change\_ways =$

$$1 \cup \gamma_{(id:pic(id.\Box),hsize:hsize.\Box,vsize:vsize.\Box,out:in.\Box,in:out.\Box)} 1$$

and the join expression J_expr given by

$$
\begin{aligned}
&if \quad '1'.out.2.\Box =' 2'.in.2.\Box \\
&\qquad and \; '1'.out.2.\Box =' 1'.hsize.\Box \\
&\qquad and \; '2'.in.2.\Box = 1 \\
&then \quad \langle id : pic\_lr('1'.id.\Box,'2'.id.\Box), \\
&\qquad\qquad hsize :' 1'.hsize.\Box +' 2'.hsize.\Box, \\
&\qquad\qquad vsize :' 1'.vsize.\Box, \\
&\qquad\qquad in :' 1'.in.\Box, \\
&\qquad\qquad out :' 2'.out.\Box \\
&\qquad\qquad \rangle \\
&else \quad \left\{
\begin{aligned}
&if \quad '1'.out.2.\Box =' 2'.in.2.\Box \\
&\qquad and \; '1'.out.1.\Box =' 1'.vsize.\Box \\
&\qquad and \; '2'.in.1.\Box = 1 \\
&then \quad \langle id : pic\_hd('1'.id.\Box,'2'.id.\Box), \\
&\qquad\qquad hsize :' 1'.hsize.\Box, \\
&\qquad\qquad vsize :' 1'.vsize.\Box +' 2'.vsize.\Box, \\
&\qquad\qquad in :' 1'.in.\Box, \\
&\qquad\qquad out :' 2'.out.\Box \\
&\qquad\qquad \rangle
\end{aligned}
\right.
\end{aligned}
$$

computes all labyrinths that can be composed from a given set of labyrinths.

For example, applied to the labyrinths

the query produces a result ft-set containing the description of

$$\begin{pmatrix} 5 & 6 & 4 \\ 3 & 1 & 2 \end{pmatrix}$$

Our little toy example shows how very complex retrieval operations on non-FTDM objects can be easily performed in the framework of XFTA, once the atomic operations on these objects (in this case: bitmap operations) are made known to the query processor by C_{FTA} functions. The framework of the database algebra does the rest.

---

[5]Note that if there were multiple paths through this labyrinth, we would need multiple tuples to describe it.

The technique employed here has also been successfully applied to implement access to external file systems and machine-readable natural language dictionaries.

The implementation of the bitmap operations and the labyrinth example for this case study took one day; and what we created can be very well considered as an algebra of bitmap pictures. So, we can state the result that XFTA provides a powerful tool for the implementation of query processors for non-standard database applications.

3.2.5 Extensibility: A Summary

There are some important achievements of our work on extensibility with respect to previous work as reported in (Batory et.al. 1988), (Carey, Dewitt 1987), (Schek, Weikum 1991), (Schwarz 1986), (Stonebraker 1987):

- The same extension functions are available at each nesting level of complex object algebra: they can be applied as operators on the top level as well as on deeper levels of arbitrary complex objects.

- Composite XFTA functions can be expressed in a very simple language, which is compiled to C by an extensibility preprocessor. This allows the writing of object level functions without knowing the object level, and makes extensibility a useful feature not only for the database implementor, but for the ordinary user.

- XFTA functions can be expressed in terms of other XFTA functions; they can even be mutually recursive. This allows the building and use of libraries, and the incremental building of large application specific query processors.

The implementation of XFTA can rely on a powerful library that makes the encoding of extension functions a simple task. Additionally, composite and aggregate functions can be described in a simple manner and are translated to evaluable C-functions, too. This, in combination with the large set of already implemented functions, allows for the quick and bug-free specification of new extension functions.

Our concept of algebra extensibility proved to be of significant use for query simplification, for speeding up query processing, for extending the basic operational capabilities of the query processor, and for quickly writing query processors for non-standard data models. Using XFTA, too, makes it rather easy to provide useful "higher-level" features of knowledge based environments, e.g., *methods*, directly on database level.

A final remark shall be made on the embedding of our results in the context of LILOG-DB: As will be discussed below, our logic-based front-end language FLL is compiled to XFTA in a way that function symbols of FLL are directly mapped to function symbols of XFTA. As a consequence, extensibility is propagated upwards to the logic level without more ado. For example, suppose we wrote the FLL rule

$$maximal\_common(X, Y, max(intersect(X, Y))).$$

For the query $?-maximal\_common(\{1, 2, 3\}, \{2, 3, 4\}, Z).$ we now obtain $Z = 3$. That shows that by interpreting function symbols on the algebra level, we obtain interpreted function symbols on all higher level of LILOG-DB automatically, i.e., an extensible kernel induces extensible front-ends. This is a very important aspect for LILOG-DB as an open deductive database system designed for database support of higher-level knowledge based systems.

4 Some Discussion of Database Programming in LILOG-DB

4.1 Feature Tuples as Open Attributed Structures

The main criticism with respect to relational algebra as a language for advanced database systems has been on its first normal form restriction disallowing the use of complex structures.

This is not only because of the cognitive inadequacy of decomposing relations between inherently complex objects into flat tables, but also because of the inefficiency of this way of proceeding. So, the main problem for the development of a next-generation data model appears to be: *what kind of complex objects, and why?*

Since Prolog is the most frequently used logic programming language and the language of our embedding project LILOG, we decided to make our data model compatible to Prolog by incorporating functors and lists.

From the point of view of TLPROLOG, our decision for the incorporation of sets stems from the need to model the results of set-oriented database queries.

From the database point of view, general sets are our equivalent to the relations of RA, and so an *arbitrary* nesting of sets is necessary to really overcome the first normal form restriction of RA.

The introduction of feature-tuples as open structures is likely to be the most crucial point in our argument, at least for the database community: *Wouldn't optional fields in tuples be sufficient?* The answer, especially in the context of natural language based knowledge processing is: no.

Suppose we want to store all cars referred to in a text in an ft-set *cars*. We may introduce a sort

$$sort\ car = tuple\ \langle type : symbol, colour : symbol, speed : integer \ldots \rangle.$$

and then create an ft-set in the database by

$$create\_ft\_set(\langle name : cars, schema : car \rangle).$$

But what do we do with a piece of text like:

A red car with a dent in the right fender came around the corner.

This example illustrates the following general statement: In a natural language processing context, one cannot foresee all possible characterizations of *cars* and describe them as optional fields in a database schema. If the universe of a natural language discourse cannot be restricted to a limited set of entities and their characterizations, optional fields in closed tuples are not sufficient for the supporting database system.

Some consequences of this argument for the processing of the database schemas in LILOG-DB, given by sort restrictions, are discussed on the following pages.

4.2 Conceptual Modeling

Let us consider the rule

$$single(X) :\!- person(X), not(\ married(X)\ ).$$

describing *singles* by means of a deductive rule. We could as well have modeled *persons* and *singles* by the sort specifications[6]

$$
\begin{aligned}
sort\ person\ =\ tuple\ \langle\ &name : symbol,\\
&firstname : symbol,\\
&husband : person\ or\ \{\ none\ \},\\
&children : setof\ person,\\
&sex : \{\ male,\ female\ \},\\
&age : integer\ \rangle
\end{aligned}
$$

$$
\begin{aligned}
with\quad &age.\Box\ >\ 0\ and\ age.\Box\ <\ 150\ and\\
&\Box\ has\ name\ and\ \Box\ has\ firstname\ and\\
&(\ forall\ V\ in\ children.\Box\ :\ V.name.\Box\ =\ name.\Box)\\
isa\ term
\end{aligned}
$$

$$
sort\ single
$$

$$
\begin{aligned}
with\quad &husband.\Box\ =\ none\\
isa\ person
\end{aligned}
$$

This example suggests some discussion of the power of sorts as an instrument for conceptual modeling:

1.) The example exhibits some more of the modeling cababilities of our sort concept.

1. Note that *person* is a recursively defined sort since the feature specifications for *husband* and *children* refer to other *persons*.

2. In the declaration of the feature *children*, the sort constructor *setof* has been used: *children : setof person* denotes that the value of the feature *children* has to be a (possibly empty) set of *persons*.

3. The specification { *male, female* } for the *sex* of *persons* restricts the admissible values of the feature *sex* to one of the constants *male* or *female*. It shows that finite sets of terms can serve as sort constants.

4. The constraint for *person* is a boolean conjunction of five simple constraints. Not only conjunction, but also boolean negation and disjunction are allowed for the combination of constraints and sort descriptions. Another example is the limitation of *husbands* to either *persons* or the constant *none*.

5. The constraint $\Box$ *has name and* $\Box$ *has firstname* enforces that all terms of sort *person* have to have at least the features *name* and *firstname* specified. This restricts openness of feature-tuples by specifying which information is at least required for proper processing. For example, ⟨ *firstname : jim, age : 35*⟩ is not a member of this version of sort *person* since no *name* is specified.

6. In contrast, the term ⟨ *name : jones, firstname : jim, job : waiter*⟩ is a member of the sort *person* since the sort specification specifies *persons* as (open!) feature-tuples, and no restriction on a possible feature *job* is imposed. This shows that sorts allow for the description of incomplete as well as of additional information.

7. Finally, observe that we have made use of universal quantification by stating that all *children* of a *person* have to have the same *name* as the *person* itself.

---

[6] $\Box$ stands for the root term considered.

So, our little example exhibits most of the relevant constructs for the description of sorts in the FTDM. They provide a convenient and powerful means for the description of the structure of a mini-world.

2.) Sorts are a concept for describing *properties* of terms. Unlike most object-oriented systems, LILOG-DB does not administer extensions of sorts. Sorts cannot be queried, but only be used as filters during query processing.

In general, sorts express the conceptual structure of a mini-world, while rules work on the concrete database, i.e., the stored extensions.

Sorts free the user from expressing the taxonomic structure of a mini-world by hand, and leave only the "hard" deduction tasks – the derivation of new knowledge from existing knowledge – to rules.

In the above example, encoding of the *single* property in a rule requires an unnecessary join which is inefficient and inadequate since the *single* property is a specialization of the *person* property that can be checked by filtering.

So, replacing filtering with predicates by filtering with sort restrictions can significantly speed up query processing: unnecessary joins are replaced by on-the-fly filtering.

4.3 Incomplete and Variant Schemas

In the LILOG-DB environment, sets stored in the database are called *ft-sets*. They are created by statements like

$$create\_ft\_set(\langle\, name : ftsetname, schema : sortname\,\rangle).$$

That means that sorts serve as conceptual schemas of *ftsets*.

The facilities for the declaration of sorts include the possibility to express incomplete or variant sort information. Incompleteness is used in the specification of feature-tuple sorts. For example, the sort declaration

> *sort person* = *tuple* ⟨ *name* : *symbol*,
> *age* : *integer* ⟩
> *isa term*

is incomplete since the OWA allows terms of the sort *person* to have more than the two features *name* and *age*, e.g., the term ⟨ *name* : *john, age* : *32, job* : *waiter* ⟩ is of the sort *person*. In contrast, a "closed" sort *person* would look like this:

> *sort person* = *tuple* ⟨ *name* : *symbol*,
> *age* : *integer* ⟩
> *with* □ *hasarity* 2
> *and* □ *has name*
> *and* □ *has age*
> *isa term*

This can be abbreviated to

> *sort person* = *closed tuple* ⟨ *name* : *symbol, age* : *integer* ⟩
> *isa term*

Sort declarations may be variant too, i.e., disjunction can be expressed. The sort

$$sort\ person\ =\ tuple\ \langle\ \ name : symbol,$$
$$age : integer\ or\ symbol\ \rangle$$
$$isa\ term$$

allows the expression of *age* by a number or a textstring.

A more convincing example, returning to the objects of geometry, is the following: it is well known that triangles are completely described by two sides and an angle or by two angles and a side. This can be captured by a variant sort specification looking like this:

$$sort\ triangle = tuple\ \langle$$
$$side\_a : real,$$
$$side\_b : real,$$
$$angle\_ab : degree\ \rangle$$
$$or\ \ tuple\ \langle$$
$$side\_a : real,$$
$$angle\_ab : degree,$$
$$angle\_ac : degree\ \rangle$$
$$with\ \Box\ hasarity\ 3$$

The above examples show that the modeling power offered by LILOG-DB stems from three important design characteristics:

1. Free use of arbitrarily nested complex objects,

2. The inclusion of open attributed structures ("feature-tuples"), and

3. A powerful typing regime allowing incompleteness, variants, quantified constraints, etc.

In the following section, we will discuss the techniques required to implement such powerful modeling capabilities in a database management system.

5 Architecture and Basic Principles of the Implementation

5.1 The Architecture of the LILOG-DB Toolkit

The implementation of LILOG-DB has five major components, depicted in Fig. 9. The *Query Processor* (QP) as the kernel module basically evaluates database queries in main memory, relying on the *Term Manager* (TM), which provides the interface to secondary storage, i.e., updates, and retrieves ft-sets stored on disk.

The *Sort Lattice Manager* (SLM) and the *Rule System Manager* (RSM) use special techniques for the administration of sort lattices and rule systems. They require Term Manager services for the secondary storage of their data. The SLM provides operations such as checking whether a term is in a sort or computing the internal representation of a schema given by a sort. These are needed by QP and TM.

At the current stage of our work, the link between RSM and QP is rather weak, but in the near future the RSM will use QP-operations for the retrieval of rules.

The *Logic Programming System* (LPS) provides the interface of LILOG-DB to first-order based applications, such as the LEU2 inference engine. It uses the SLM to manage taxonomies, the RSM to administer large rule systems, and the QP to evaluate embedded database queries.

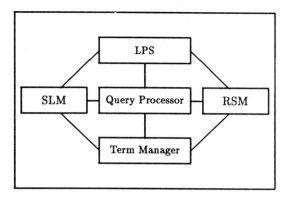

Figure 9: Overall architecture of LILOG-DB

Some of our previous discussion of the data-model and languages suggests that LILOG-DB is not primarily intended as a closed database management system with fixed functionality which can be run standalone by an imaginary user. The credo of our work is database support for knowledge based systems, and we have designed an extensible toolkit for the fast and secure implementation of efficient specially tuned database components for knowledge based systems.

Therefore, one may see the five major subsystems of LILOG-DB as programmable tools for what we consider the dominant database tasks underlying knowledge based systems: storage management (TM), query processing (QP), typing (SLM), management of large rule systems (RSM), and interfacing to the logic levels of the knowledge-based systems (LPS).

These functionalities are orthogonal, and to be useful as a toolkit, the implementations of the subsystems have to be orthogonal, too. This is the dominant principle induced by our toolkit approach.

Orthogonality gives us a great deal of flexibility in configuring a DBMS for a special application. For example, the query processor can run standalone as a pure main memory database system, or we can run a programming language such as TLPROLOG as a standalone environment without any access to the database. The TM can be used as a simple object store in any environment, and its use is not limited to LILOG-DB. And so on.

In case of two or more modules being coupled, there are standard interfaces between these modules. For example, EFTA can express a condition

if □ hassort person ...

which on the implementation level makes the query processor ask the SLM whether the term addressed by the path □ is a member of sort *person*. We claim that our approach using tools with standard interfaces provides a flexible, powerful, and convenient way to quickly construct database components for KBMS.

5.2 Principles

This section provides a little bridge between the exposition of the formal apparatus of LILOG-DB and the following discussion of architectural and technological issues. We will elaborate five basic principles underlying the implementation of our system:

1. Tight coupling,

2. Intelligent memory management,

3. Specially tuned management for rule systems and sort lattices,

4. Sophisticated optimization,

5. Extensibility.

We discuss these principles before going into technical details in the next section. The reason is that they are guidelines for design and implementation of the entire system, which have to be followed by the architecture as a whole as well as by the implementation of each of its components. The next section will then contain some prototypical descriptions of the techniques we use to implement these principles.

5.2.1 Tight Coupling

One of the main problems in the interaction of applications written on an existing database management system is the *impedance mismatch* between front-end and the database back-end, stemming from the high interaction costs at an interprocess interface realized via pipes (or even files) and the high conversion costs between the data model of the implementation language and the one of the database system.

This argument has been especially elaborated by several authors for the loosely coupled interaction between logic programming front-ends and relational database systems, most of whom have come to the conclusion that an efficient implementation of an integrated logic programming/deductive database system has to be tightly coupled.

For us, tight coupling has two major aspects. On the one hand, the whole system has to have an integrated memory management that facilitates the communication between database and application via *shared memory* instead of costly pipes or files. On the other hand, to save data model conversion costs between front-end and back-end, a *common data model* has to be established for the whole system. This second aspect of tight coupling is satisfied by the basing of the whole LILOG-DB on the Feature Term Data Model, which is really implemented on the level of data structures. The first aspect of the problem, integrated memory management, will be discussed below.

5.2.2 Intelligent Memory Management

A severe drawback of loosely coupled systems is their bad behavior with respect to memory management. In the worst case, both logic application and database try to get as much memory as they can; and if the communication rate between application and database is high, this will yield high paging rates that decrease the performance of the system. This effect is strengthened if costly pipes are employed to pass data at the interface. To overcome these effects, the memory management of a real tightly coupled system should be able to do two things:

1. It has to be able to communicate data between logic programs and the database kernel via shared memory.

2. It should be capable of balancing the load between logic program and database. That means that there has to be an integrated memory management for the whole system.

Strongly related to the "kernel" memory management is the management of intermediate results. For the support of natural language dialog systems, the notion of *specialization queries* has some relevance. The natural language specialization query sequence

> "Which Italian restaurants are in Trier?"
> "Which of them are cheap?"
> "Which of these are close to my dwelling?"

illustrates that our system has to be able to keep track of former queries and/or intermediate results to give adequate answers to the current one. The consequence is that an intelligent query/intermediate-result management component has to be attached to the memory manager.

Such query management can avoid much duplicate work in query processing. It additionally supports the concept of *query forms* allowing the user to tell the system which kind of queries shall be most efficiently supported.

5.2.3 Rule System Management and Sort Lattice Processing

In larger knowledge representation applications, the rule system and indeed the sort lattices themselves can be very large. When much memory is needed for logic computation and query processing, they may not even completely fit into main storage. Therefore, secondary storage of rule systems and sort lattices becomes a theme. The main question is how to divide rule systems and sort lattices into portions so that the system can guarantee, maybe by intelligent prefetching of such portions, that the relevant part of the rule system/sort lattice is always in main memory.

However, the work on these problems is still not yet completed. The current version of LILOG-DB assumes sort lattices and rule systems to be permanently in main storage.

5.2.4 Sophisticated Optimization

Our two approaches to cutting down the inefficiency of recursive query processing, rule rewriting and intelligent selection of recursive query processing strategies, can be seen as sophisticated optimization techniques.

We feel a strong need for powerful optimization tools in our system since in the absence of the level of information about the data that for example relational systems have, the existing information has to be exploited optimally to obtain efficient query processing schemas.

Some consequences of this basic principle are outlined here:

1. In the query processor, we have established a strict separation between the operators of the algebra and the algorithms implementing them, so that the EFTA optimizer can choose the most efficient algorithm by inspecting the database statistics and the operator tree.

2. An algebraic optimizer uses about 70 optimization rules to push constants through the query trees, eliminate redundant operations, exploit common subexpressions and transitivities, etc.

3. All EFTA operators are evaluated lazily, so that information not needed for further processing is never generated, thus avoiding redundant work.

4. At each stage of query processing, the schema of an ft-set is used to find a compact main storage representation of the intermediate results.

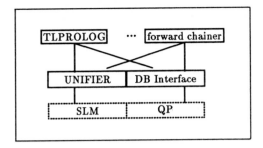

Figure 10: General architecture of the LPS

5.2.5 Extensibility

LILOG-DB is built in the spirit of much work that has been done in recent years on so-called *extensible* DBMS. The idea behind that work is to find database architectures and define standard interfaces to these modules such that DBMS can be easily augmented by user-defined modules, data types, and operators that incorporate the requirements of a certain application.

Extensibility ideas are present on all levels of design and implementation of LILOG-DB:

1. The sort concept allows for the definition of user-defined data types, which are utilized by the system's logic operations (e.g., order-sorted unification) as well as to derive efficient data representations.

2. As previously discussed, the algebra is extensible, i.e., it can "learn" user-defined operations.

3. The storage management can handle so-called *long fields* (i.e., uninterpreted byte vectors) which can be used to represent arbitrary new data structures (e.g., pictorial data), and there are standard interfaces that allow the system to incorporate new access paths.

The presentation of the LILOG-DB toolkit in the following section shows how these principles are realized on the level of implementation.

6 The LILOG-DB Toolkit

6.1 The Logic Programming System

The intention behind the design of the LPS of LILOG-DB is the support of logic programming with access to the LILOG-DB database.

There is a variety of logic programming mechanisms that are used in knowledge based systems, and it would be impossible to support them all. So, the target of our design is to provide a prototype collection of mechanisms that can serve as a toolbox for the encoding of inference engines with efficient database access.

Most of the inference engines reported in the literature are written in languages like LISP or, like the LEU2 inference engine, in Prolog; and so it is a natural decision to include a Prolog implementation, TLPROLOG (see (Ludwig 1989)), into the LPS.

Although the implementation of TLPROLOG contains some interesting features such as

```
function unify(x,y: term): boolean
{

Sx = x->sort; Sy = y->sort;

Sxy = glb(Sx,Sy);

if ( Sxy = NIL ) return(false);

if ( x is variable )
  instantiate x to y;
  goto sortcheck;

if ( y is variable )
  instantiate y to x;
  goto sortcheck;

if ( x->tag != y->tag ) return(false);

/* =g= stands for ground equality, i.e., equality in the absense of variables */

switch ( x->tag ) {
  case integer : if ( x->integer_value =g= y->integer_value ) goto sortcheck;
  case symbol  : if ( x->symbol_value  =g= y->symbol_value  ) goto sortcheck;
  case set     : if ( x->set_value     =g= y->set_value     ) goto sortcheck;
  case functor : if (      x->name = y->name
                      and x->arity = y->arity  ) {
                 i := 1;
                 while ( i <= x->arity ) {
                    if ( not unify ( x->args[i], y->args[i] ) )
                        return(false);
                    else
                        i := i + 1;
                 }
                 goto sortcheck;
               };
               return(false);
  case list    : if ( x =g= [] ) return( y =g= [] );
                 if ( y =g= [] ) return( x =g= [] );
                 let ( x = [ Hx | Tx ] , y = [ Hy | Ty ] ) in
                    if ( unify(Hx,Hy) and unify(Tx,Ty) ) goto sortcheck;
  case tuple   : forall features name:value1 in x
                    if exists feature name:value2 in y
                        if ( not unify(value1,value2) )
                            return(false);
                 goto sortcheck;
  }
return(false);

sortcheck: return( sort_check(x,Sxy) );
}
```

Figure 11: A naive unifier for the full FTDM

- Rule-goal graphs as the data structure on which resolution is performed,

- A macro mechanism allowing the emulation of different Prolog dialects,

- A data representation based on the structure sharing principle,

it shall not be further discussed here since so much has been written about Prolog implementations.

Besides a backward chaining capability such as that of TLPROLOG, a fully developed inference engine can be assumed to require a forward chainer, as most expert systems and the LEU2 inference engine do. While the kernel implementation of TLPROLOG is completed, a forward chainer is still under development.

The general architecture of the LPS is depicted in Fig. 10. As can be seen there, all inference tools (even the ones that are not yet written) rely on a single unifier, the FTDM-unifier.

A pseudo-code description of this unifier (Fig. 11) shows what services the unifier requires from the SLM:

- The determination of the *glb* of two sorts,

- The sort-check operation $t \in den(s)$?

Our inferencing tools supply embedded FLL queries at the DB interface and receive the answers. How these queries are processed is shown in Fig. 12, and will now be discussed in some detail.

6.2   The Query Processor

In the first sections of this paper we presented the data model and the languages of LILOG-DB and described their interrelations: TLPROLOG serves as a host language for embedded database operations formulated in FLL (i.e., FLL is embedded in TLPROLOG); FLL queries are compiled to our database algebra EFTA.

This *compilation* of FLL queries is an important part of query processing in LILOG-DB, which shall now be described in some depth.

The single aim of the query processor is to find a correct answer as quick as possible. There is a variety of methods to achieve this goal, including

- Algebraic transformations,

- Fast algorithms,

- Intelligent algorithm selection,

- Storage and representation techniques.

We will give examples for the application of each of these techniques.

The main steps of query processing are illustrated in Fig. 12. The Query Processor receives an FLL query and optimizes the recursive structure of the corresponding program using *rule rewriting*. The rule rewriter returns a *modified query*. This modified FLL query and the rewritten program are used by the FLL Compiler to generate an equivalent EFTA query. After an algebraic optimization of the EFTA query, a query-evaluation plan (QEP) is generated, i.e., the best algorithms implementing the algebra operations and the order of their application are selected. This QEP is then evaluated against the database.

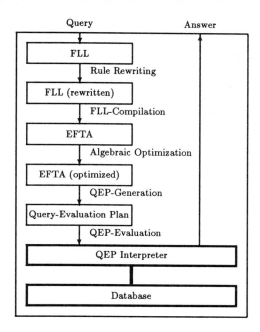

Figure 12: Processing of embedded FLL queries

6.2.1 Rule Rewriting

Rule rewriting techniques for global optimization of first-order database programs written in languages like DATALOG or LDL have been investigated by many authors in recent years.

Their main application is the field of recursive query processing. Let us use the simplest of the well known methods for illustration. The *magic sets* technique, for a given query ?- $ancestor(john, X)$. , rewrites the program

$$ancestor(X, Y) :- \quad parents(X, Y).$$
$$ancestor(X, Y) :- \quad parents(X, Z),\ ancestor(Z, Y).$$

to the program

$$magic\_ancestor^{bf}(john).$$
$$magic\_ancestor^{bf}(Z) :- \quad magic\_ancestor^{bf}(X),\ parent(X, Z).$$

$$ancestor^{bf}(X, Y) :- \quad magic\_ancestor^{bf}(X),\ parents(X, Y).$$
$$ancestor^{bf}(X, Y) :- \quad magic\_ancestor^{bf}(Z),\ parents(X, Z),\ ancestor^{bf}(Z, Y).$$

and modifies the query to

$$?\text{-}\ ancestor^{bf}(john, X).$$

So, what magic sets do is the following:

1. The binding pattern[7] of the query is determined. In our case, it is bf since in the query

    $$?\text{-}\ ancestor(john, X).$$

---

[7]Mostly called *adornment* in the literature.

the first argument is *bound* and the second one is *free*.

2. Then, from the original rules for *ancestor* and this binding pattern, a so-called *magic predicate* *magic_ancestor^{bf}* is computed. This predicate derives all *possible* ancestors of john.

3. The predicate *magic_ancestor^{bf}* is used to modify the original predicate *ancestor* so that at any stage of the bottom-up computation the join of *parent* and *ancestor* is restricted to the tuples that are possible ancestors of *john*.

The aim of magic sets – and rule rewriting in general – is to restrict the search space of recursive rule applications by precomputing the set of possible solutions in a *restriction predicate* and insert this into the original rules. *The essence of rule rewriting is the optimization of the recursive structure of an FLL program with respect to a given query.*

In the following, we will show how standard rule rewriting techniques can be enhanced to cope with the order-sortedness of FLL. We will do this by first performing a *type rewriting step* for type restrictions of the variables of a program, and then performing a *rule rewriting step* as described above.

The assumption under which our rewriting regime works is that for our type discipline some relations between the types – such as equivalence, subsumption or disjointness – can be derived. In (Ludwig 1991b), it is shown that for a large subclass of sort specifications equivalence, subsumption and disjointness of sorts are decidable. This class can be sketched by two restrictions:

- no use of *quantified constraints* like *forall x in□ : ...*

- restricted use of *hassort*-conditions.

The details can be inspected in (Ludwig 1991b). So, we know that for a large subclass of sort specifications s_1, s_2, we can decide for the sets $den(s_1)$, $den(s_2)$ of ground terms denoted by s_1, s_2, whether

1. $den(s_1) = den(s_2)$

2. $den(s_1) \subseteq den(s_2)$

3. $den(s_1) \cap den(s_2) = \emptyset$

So, we can introduce the notion of a *sort relation graph*, into which for each sort node we enter

- edges to the highest sort nodes to which it is disjoint (dotted lines),

- edges to the lowest sorts which subsume it.

A sort relation graph basically is a sort lattice, augmented by additional edges as described above. A sort relation graph for the declarations

$$
\begin{array}{lll}
\textit{sort nations} & = & \{\, us, british, german \ldots \}. \\
\textit{sort new\_world} & = & \{\, us, australian \ldots \} \textit{ isa nations.} \\
\textit{sort old\_world} & = & \{\, british, german \ldots \} \textit{ isa nations.} \\
\textit{sort european} & = & \{\, british, german \ldots \} \textit{ isa old\_world.} \\
\textit{sort asian} & = & \{\, chinese, indian \ldots \} \textit{ isa old\_world.} \\
\textit{sort eurasian} & & \textit{ isa european, asian.} \\
\textit{sort african} & = & \{\, egyptian, libyan \ldots \} \textit{ isa old\_world.} \\
\textit{sort american} & = & \{\, us, mexican \ldots \} \textit{ isa new\_world.} \\
\textit{sort oceanian} & = & \{\, australian, kiwi \ldots \} \textit{ isa new\_world.}
\end{array}
$$

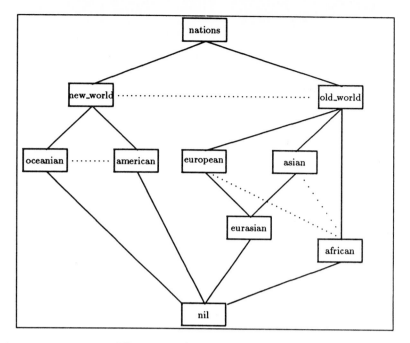

Figure 13: A sort relation graph

is depicted in Fig. 13. The following will show how we use sort relation graphs to rewrite the sort restrictions of logic programs.

For a sort relation graph, we can define two relations

$s_1 < s_2 :\Leftrightarrow$ There exist subsumption edges $s_1 \rightarrow \ldots \rightarrow s_2$.

$s_1 \,\tilde{\cap}\, s_2 :\Leftrightarrow$ There exist two sorts s_x, s_y with $s_1 < s_x$, $s_2 < s_y$ and a disjointness edge $s_x \leftrightarrow s_y$.

While $s_1 < s_2$ guarantees $den(s_1) \subseteq den(s_2)$, $s_1 \,\tilde{\cap}\, s_2$ guarantees $den(s_1) \cap den(s_2) = \emptyset$. We will use these notions to define a query-independent rule transformation which is local, i.e., considers each rule separately.

The type rewriting step basically employs two rules:

1. Reject rules with incompatible sort restrictions.

2. For rules with multiple (compatible) sort restrictions, select the strongest one.

A simple example for a rule with inconsistent sort restrictions is

$transatlantic\_country(X)$:- $country(X.european), country(X.american)$.

From our sort relation graph, we obtain $european \,\tilde{\cap}\, american$. Thus these two sorts are disjoint, the rule is inconsistent and should be rejected or (at least!) not evaluated.

For the rule

$$p(X) :\text{-} q(X.european), r(X.eurasian).$$

we know that $eurasian < european$ and can replace $q(X.european)$ by $q(X.eurasian)$ and push the sort restriction into the head of the rule:

$$p(X.eurasian) :\text{-} q(X.eurasian), r(X.eurasian).$$

Both the rejection of rules inconsistent with the sort declarations and the selection of the strongest possible sort restrictions avoid the incorporation of irrelevant terms in intermediate results, thereby speeding up query processing.

In our concept of rule rewriting, the type-rewriting step is performed once for the whole program, while the traditional rewriting step with techniques like magic sets is done for each query separately. A later extension of this concept might incorporate additional type-rewriting rules into the query-dependent part of the procedure.

6.2.2 Compilation of FLL Programs to EFTA

Our query compiler from FLL to EFTA will use a two-phase approach: in a first phase, we will compile the FLL program as a whole to a set of query-independent *EFTA-templates*; the second phase only consists of searching the relevant templates for a query and pushing the constants into them.

Only the second phase has to be performed at runtime, i.e., it is query-dependent. That means that we do as much as possible only once at compile-time of the FLL programs (instead of doing it again for every query) and as little as possible at query-evaluation time.

Our motivational remarks suggest that an EFTA-template is just a template of an operator-tree for EFTA-query-evaluation into which possible constants can be inserted at runtime. Thus, when a query is read, only two operations will have to be performed in the second phase of our algorithm:

- The relevant parts of the EFTA-templates have to be fetched.

- The constants of the query have to be pushed into the template to obtain a plan for efficient query evaluation.

A schema of compilation can be visualized as in Fig. 14. The precompilation phase reads an FLL program, and translates it into an EFTA-template-graph. The second phase uses this graph and a given query to construct an EFTA-operator-tree, which can then be submitted to the LILOG-DB query processor for evaluation against the database.

Decomposition of Programs: The notion of *stratification* of first-order programs with negation has been introduced to describe when the use of negation in programs is safe, i.e., produces predictable and unique results.

The stratification restriction basically states that negation should only be used to refer to an "already known" relation. A consequence is that *no negation can be used through recursion*. This is because, according to the fixpoint semantics of first-order programs, recursive predicates are computed by successively applying them to the input and the previously computed intermediate results until no more solutions are generated. Negation through recursion would therefore access incomplete intermediate results and thereby violate the "already known" restriction.

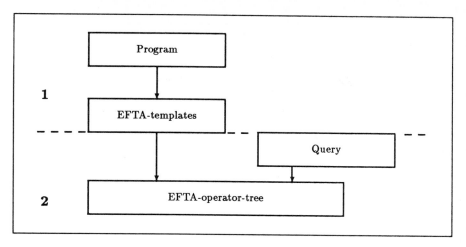

Figure 14: Schema of two-phase compilation

For a stratified program, there always exists at least one *layering* that assigns levels to the predicates so that for each rule

$$p :\!\!- \ldots not\, q \ldots$$

it is guaranteed that the level of q is lower then the level of p, i.e., negation always accesses lower levels of the layering.

Since our system compiles stratified programs, we can thus see an FLL program as a set of layers, where each layer is a set of one or more partitions (a partition is the set of clauses with the same name and arity defining a predicate).

For the sample program

> /* base-predicate: street */
> $street(X,Y) :\!\!- \langle source : X, dest : Y \rangle \, in\_ft\_set \, STREET$
>
> /* derived-predicate: way */
> $way(X,Y) :\!\!- street(X,Y).$
> $way(X,Y) :\!\!- way(X,Z), way(Z,Y).$

we can give a graphic representation of this structure as a *layered partitioned rule-goal-graph (LPRGG)*. In the LPRGG, so-called *partition-IDs* are visualized as pointers from subgoals to partitions (see Fig. 15).

Partitions of an LPRGG are represented by small rectangles and the name of the partition is printed in **boldface**. There are links from a partition-node to each node (depicted by an oval) representing one of its rules, and pointers from each rule to each of its subgoal-nodes.

We will now briefly sketch how the first phase of the FLL compiler converts an LPRGG to an EFTA-template-graph.

Phase 1 – Constructing an EFTA-template-graph: The main operational difference between the evaluation of FLL programs and the interpretation of EFTA expressions is that the control flow of FLL programs is implicitly described by variables, while it is explicitly encoded in EFTA expressions

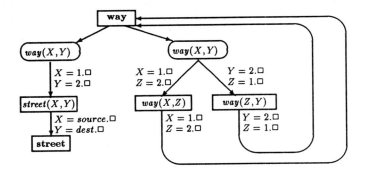

Figure 15: An LPRGG with variable-path equations

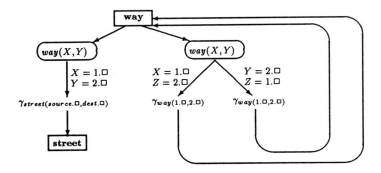

Figure 16: After the compilation of the single subgoals

by the use of paths.

So, the main task of the FLL compiler is to map a control flow managed via variables to a control flow directed by paths. As can be seen in Fig. 15, we label the rule-goal links and the goal-rule links of the LPRGG by equations of the form

$$VARIABLE = PATH$$

which contain information on which variable corresponds to which path in the accessed node.

Phase 1 first translates each subgoal of each rule separately, converting it to a γ-expression in which each variable of the subgoal is replaced by its corresponding path (see Fig. 16).

As depicted in Fig. 17, the compiled subgoals of each rule are then joined. As can be seen there, a rule is now no longer linked to each of its subgoals, but to the result of constructing a join including all compiled subgoals.

The final step of phase 1 is that the rule-heads are compiled to γ-expressions. The resulting EFTA-template-graph is depicted in Fig. 18. It contains incomplete EFTA expressions, since not all their arguments are given by EFTA expressions: some of them are encoded as references to partitions.

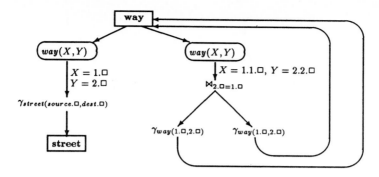

Figure 17: After the join of the subgoals in the rule

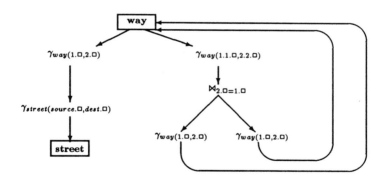

Figure 18: The resulting EFTA-template graph

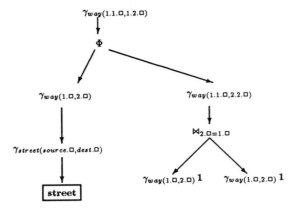

Figure 19: The resulting EFTA-operator-tree for the query $way(X, Y)$

They will be resolved in phase 2 of FLL compilation.

Phase 2 – Query Compilation: While the first phase of compilation is performed only once for an FLL program, the second phase is activated for each new query. As depicted in Fig. 14, phase 1 of FLL compilation constructs an EFTA-template-graph from an FLL program. This graph and the query are the input for phase 2, which constructs an EFTA-operator-tree.

This construction basically cuts the parts which are irrelevant for the query out of the EFTA-template-graph and inserts the constants of the query into the remaining templates. Roughly speaking, a template is irrelevant for a query iff it belongs to a partition that is never reached during the traversal of the EFTA-template-graph which is initiated by the query, or if it has a constant at a position where the query has a different constant.

The query compilation then inserts the constants of a query at the right places, and links the relevant EFTA-templates together to a single EFTA-operator-tree, using union- and closure-operators as "glue". Details of the construction can be found in (Ludwig 1990b) and are not given here.

Figure 19 shows the EFTA-operator-tree that is constructed for the EFTA-template-graph of Fig. 18 when the query

   ?- $way(X,Y)$.

arises.

Although a first version of it runs in our system, the compiler is still not complete; the two most important extensions to be implemented are the inclusion of built-in predicates such as $=$ and $<$ into the compilation and the incorporation of a safety check. While the first task is relatively simple, the second one will require some more conceptual work.

The compiler does not perform any optimization. The reason is that the compiler is embedded into two optimizers. On the top level, a rule rewriting component performs the global semantic optimization, while conventional local optimization is performed on EFTA-operator-trees.

Our approach has two mayor advantages. Firstly, a speed-up of query processing can be achieved by performing the query-independent part of compilation only once and minimizing the work that has to be done at runtime for a given query. Secondly, it allows for incremental compilation. In other words: there is a very simple correspondence between rule-goal-graphs (the input of precompilation) and EFTA-template-graphs, so that updates of the input program can be easily translated to updates of the EFTA-template-graph.

6.2.3 Algebraic Optimization

In the rule rewriting phase of query processing, we optimize the recursive structure of an FLL program with respect to a given query. The FLL compiler then generates an EFTA-operator-tree for the query, where recursion in FLL is mapped to the closure-operator Φ.

The experience with relational systems shows that such a tree, even if parsed from a relational query directly supplied by the user, normally is far from being the best (and often is not even a good) operator tree for the query. In other words: there usually exist semantically equivalent operator trees for a query which can be more efficiently evaluated.

This argument is even stronger for operator trees that are not directly parsed but automatically generated by a compiler, as in our case. However, research for relational systems has shown that this problem can be overcome by intelligent use of algebraic transformations.

In (Ludwig 1988c), we have shown that this holds for EFTA too. Since we have optimized the recursive structure in the rule rewriting phase, the task of algebraic optimization reduces to the efficiency-oriented transformation of the nonrecursive part of the query, i.e., we do not further optimize the closure-operator Φ, but restrict ourselves to equivalence transformations of its arguments.

These equivalence transformations implement some basic principles that should guarantee effective query processing:

- Eliminate redundant operations,

- Evaluate common subexpressions only once,

- Perform operations that decrease the sizes of intermediate results as early as possible,

- Combine multiple operations to one single operation wherever possible.

These principles yield a number of techniques that are briefly sketched in the following.

Exploitation of Transitivities in Conditions: For a γ-operator $\gamma_{if\ c\ then\ ..\ else\ ..}$ we can exploit transitivities in the condition-part c in two ways.

Constant propagation reduces the number of path-applications that have to be performed during the evaluation of c. A path that is known to be equal to a constant can be replaced by that constant.

Let $op \in \{=, <, >, \ldots\}$ be a valid operator inside a condition and $path, path' \in P$ be paths. Then

$$(path\ op\ path')\ and\ (path' = const)\ \Leftrightarrow\ (path\ op\ const)\ and\ (path' = const)$$

If θ is a transitive binary condition-operator such as $>$, $=$, $\leq$, etc., this transitivity can be exploited to eliminate redundant conditions:

$$A \,\theta\, B \ \text{ and } \ B \,\theta\, C \ \text{ and } \ A \,\theta\, C \ \Leftrightarrow \ A \,\theta\, B \ \text{ and } \ B \,\theta\, C$$

Pushing γ-Expressions down: Possibly the most important thing in optimizing relational algebra or EFTA queries is the downward propagation of selections, following the rule: the earlier the selections are performed, the smaller are the intermediate results and the faster is the execution.

A sample equation shows how to push a γ through the binary operators of EFTA:

$$\gamma_{c_1('1'.p)\,and\,c_2('2'.q)}\,(A \times B) \ \Leftrightarrow \ \gamma_{c_1(p)}\,(A) \ \times \ \gamma_{c_2(q)}\,(B)$$

Combining γ-Applications: In relational algebra, chains of selections (respectively, projections) can be combined to one single selection (respectively, projection). A main design aim for EFTA was to preserve this property in its whole strength for the γ-operator because of its important potential for optimization. We will illustrate how such a combine-transformation for the γ-operator can be performed. The benefit of these combine-transformations is that two scans of sets can be replaced by one more complex scan, saving disk accesses. The example

$$\gamma_{if\ 1.\square>2.\square\ then\ f(1.\square)\ else\ f(2.\square)}\ \gamma_{<3.\square,4.\square,5.\square>}\ R$$
$$\Leftrightarrow \ \gamma_{if\ 3.\square>4.\square\ then\ f(3.\square)\ else\ f(4.\square)}\ R$$

illustrates that the basic task to perform here is the replacement of the paths in the outer γ-expression.

Elimination of Redundant Operations One of the standards of relational algebra optimization is that a (lossless) join followed by projections only on non-join attributes can be dropped. Similar eliminations of redundant operations generating information that will soon be "forgotten" by the following steps of evaluation are given in the following.

Cross-products followed by non-trivial projections are redundant and can be eliminated.

$$\pi_{'1'.p}\,(f_1 \times f_2) \ \Leftrightarrow \ \pi_p(f_1)$$
$$\pi_{'2'.p}\,(f_1 \times f_2) \ \Leftrightarrow \ \pi_p(f_2)$$

A set-difference diminishing A by a restriction of A can be transformed to an application of the negated restriction to A.

$$A - (\gamma_c\,A) \Leftrightarrow \gamma_{not\ c}\,A$$

If A has n entries and the implementation of $-$ cannot use indexes or a sorting of A, this rule decreases the effort for the difference-computation from $O(n^2)$ to $O(n)$ (see below).

For the elimination of redundant unions and differences we can use the idempotency rules

$$A \cup A \Leftrightarrow A$$
$$A \cup (B - A) \Leftrightarrow A \cup B$$
$$A - (A \cup B) \Leftrightarrow \emptyset$$

A Cost-Oriented Ordering of EFTA Operations: We conclude our considerations with a summarizing table of EFTA operators and their costs[8]:

---

[8] n, m are the sizes of the ft-sets involved.

Operator	execution time	size of result
γ	n	n
$-$	$n \times m$	n
nest	n^2	n
unnest	n	n
$\cup$	$n \times m$	$n + m$
$\bowtie$	$n \times m$	$n \times m$

Operations of a retrieval algebra are normally performed bottom-up. Thus the size of the result of the evaluation of the current operator is the dominating criterion in our cost model because it determines the speed and the size of results of upper-level operator evaluations while the speed of the evaluation of the current operator determines nothing at all on the upper level.

Intuitively we can expect that *nest* and "$-$" produce results that are smaller than their input-sets while *unnest* and $\cup$ expand them. Considering that fact, we split our table into four different levels and choose an optimization strategy that (if possible) pushes operations of level i through operations of level j iff $i < j$, using the rules given above (and many more !):

Level	Operator	execution time	size of result
0	γ	n	n
1	$-$	$n \times m$	n
	nest	n^2	n
2	*unnest*	n	n
	$\cup$	$n \times m$	$n + m$
3	$\bowtie$	$n \times m$	$n \times m$

A sketch of the optimizer is given in Fig. 20. More material about optimization rules and the strategy of the optimizer can be found in (Ludwig 1988c).

Optimization in the presence of Extensibility The theory of EFTA has been developed in (Ludwig 1988b-c). Except for algebraic optimization of queries, it remains the same for XFTA. However, the problem of algebraic optimization deserves further study.

Some rules which are employed by our optimizer with respect to γ expressions are given in Fig. 21. There is a problem with these rules when evaluable functions come in:

- Optimization rules that rely on the fact that arguments of function symbols are uninterpreted must not be applied in the presence of evaluable function symbols. For example

$$\gamma_{1.\square} \, \gamma_{head(\square)} \, \{[f(1), f(2), f(3)], [f(4), f(5), f(6)]\}$$

would be naively optimized to

$$\gamma_\square \, \{[f(1), f(2), f(3)], [f(4), f(5), f(6)]\}$$

and then to

$$\{[f(1), f(2), f(3)], [f(4), f(5), f(6)]\}$$

When *head* is an interpreted function symbol standing for a function delivering the first element of a list, we instead have

$$\gamma_{1.\square} \, \gamma_{head(\square)} \, \{[f(1), f(2), f(3)], [f(4), f(5), f(6)]\}$$
$$\Rightarrow \quad \gamma_{1.\square} \, \{f(1), f(4)\}$$
$$\Rightarrow \quad \{1, 4\}$$

```
function optimize( x : fta_tree ) : fta_tree ;
var help1, help2 : fta_tree ;
var son1, son2 : fta_tree ;

function is_gamma( x : fta_tree ) : boolean;
(* returns true iff x denotes a γ_operation *)
function numsons( x : fta_tree ) : integer;
(* returns the number of son nodes of x *)

function eliminate_redundancies( x : fta_tree ) : fta_tree ;
(* applies rules to eliminate redundancies at the top level
of x and returns the resulting tree *)
function eliminate_all_redundancies( x : fta_tree ) : fta_tree ;
(* applies eliminate_redundancies recursive descent to the whole tree x *)
function push( x : fta_tree ) : fta_tree ;
(* applies rules to push operations of lower level through
operations of upper level and returns the resulting tree *)
function combine( x : fta_tree ) : fta_tree ;
(* applies rules to combine subsequent γ – applications *)
function optimize_gamma( x : fta_tree ) : fta_tree ;
(* performs the internal optimization of γ – expressions *)

begin
if x is a leaf then return(x)
else begin
    help1 := eliminate_all_redundancies(x);
    help2 := empty_tree;
    while (help1 ≠ help2) do begin
        help2 := help1;
        if is_gamma(help1) then begin
            son1 := son(help1);
            if is_gamma(son1) then
                help1 := combine(help1);
            help1 := push(optimize_gamma(help1));
            help1 := eliminate_redundancies(help1);
        end(*if*)
        if numsons(help1) = 1 then
            help1.son := optimize(help1.son);
        else begin
            help1.left_son := optimize(help1.left_son);
            help1.right_son := optimize(help1.right_son);
        end(*else*)
    end(*while*)
end(*else*)
return(help);
end(*optimize*)
```

Figure 20: Sketch of an algebraic optimizer for EFTA

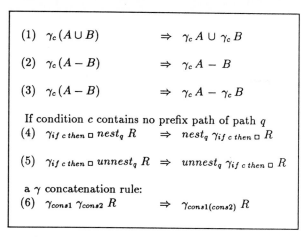

$$(1) \quad \gamma_c(A \cup B) \qquad \Rightarrow \quad \gamma_c A \cup \gamma_c B$$

$$(2) \quad \gamma_c(A - B) \qquad \Rightarrow \quad \gamma_c A - B$$

$$(3) \quad \gamma_c(A - B) \qquad \Rightarrow \quad \gamma_c A - \gamma_c B$$

If condition c contains no prefix path of path q

$$(4) \quad \gamma_{if\ c\ then\ \square}\ nest_q\ R \quad \Rightarrow \quad nest_q\ \gamma_{if\ c\ then\ \square}\ R$$

$$(5) \quad \gamma_{if\ c\ then\ \square}\ unnest_q\ R \ \Rightarrow \ unnest_q\ \gamma_{if\ c\ then\ \square}\ R$$

a γ concatenation rule:

$$(6) \quad \gamma_{cons1}\ \gamma_{cons2}\ R \qquad \Rightarrow \quad \gamma_{cons1(cons2)}\ R$$

Figure 21: Some γ optimization rules of EFTA

Although this problems occurs, it does not really affect the design of the algebraic optimizer: One has to simply avoid the mentioned rules from firing in the case of evaluable functions. However, an in-depth investigation of query optimization in the case of user-supplied extension functions remains a problem for future work.

6.2.4 Construction of the Query Evaluation Plan

After finishing the algebraic optimization, the Query Processor has to construct a *query evaluation plan (QEP)* (Gehlen 1989). A QEP is represented as a directed tree whose nodes contain information on:

- algorithms implementing the EFTA-operators of the query,

- algorithms of low-level operators, such as duplicate elimination, scans, and writes to temporary ft-set;

  At the conceptual level each EFTA-operator computes a set of terms (without duplicates). Since duplicate-elimination is an expensive operation, we omit this operation in the implementation of the EFTA-operators. Thus, we need an explicit duplicate-elimination algorithm, which is represented as a special node in the QEP.

- ft-sets stored on secondary storage or in main memory,

- additional refinements of query-processing such as pipelining, and

- the descriptions of the conceptual schemas of intermediate result sets.

Two nodes A and B of the QEP are connected by a directed edge from A to B if the result terms of B are used as input terms of A. The QEP is directly constructed from the EFTA-operator tree: For each node n in the EFTA-operator-tree there has to be generated a node in the QEP referencing to n and pointing to the succeeding QEP node. For example, Fig. 22 shows the QEP for the EFTA-operator tree in Fig. 23(c). Dashed boxes represent EFTA-operators and solid boxes represent QEP-nodes. The $\bowtie$-operation is evaluated by the hybrid-hash join-algorithm. Since duplicates may be generated

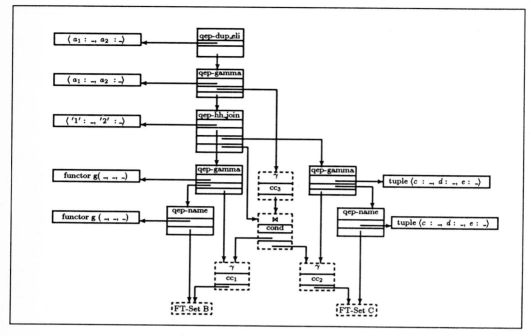

Figure 22: Query Evaluation Plan

during evaluation of the QEP, a duplicate elimination has to be performed at the end of evaluation. We use '_' for marking the positions in the internal schema which at evaluation time contain a pointer to the corresponding term in the result-table.

In a first step during construction of the QEP we use the sort information of the existing ft-sets involved in the EFTA-operator tree for bottom-up computing the sort information of the inner nodes of the tree.

Computation of Intermediate Result Schemas: We demonstrate the advantage of using sort information during query processing (Maier, Ley, Gehlen 1991). The exploitation of sort information may lead to:

- simplification of EFTA expressions;
- compact representation of intermediate result terms.

As mentioned earlier, we use sort specifications as conceptual schemas. In LILOG-DB the computation of conceptual schemas is performed by the *Sort Lattice Manager (SLM)*.

Starting with conceptual schemas of stored data, sort information for each node in the EFTA-operator tree is computed. The Query Processor passes the names of the basic ft-sets to the SLM. The SLM computes the conceptual schema by accessing the conceptual schema via the Term Manager and returns a schema pointer to the QEP.

The evaluation of inner nodes results in intermediate sets. Conceptual schemas of these intermediate results are computed bottom-up starting with the leaf sorts. To compute the schema of an inner node n, three steps are performed:

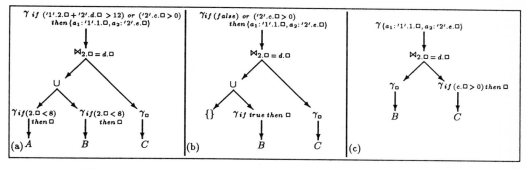

Figure 23: Semantically equivalent representations of an EFTA query

(1) Let n_e be the EFTA expression of n. If n_e contains type- and structure conditions, which can be pre-evaluated against the input schemas of n, we get a simplified EFTA expression n'_e.

(2) The overall syntactic structure of the result-terms of an EFTA expression is determined by the top-level operator. It is extracted into a *schema template*. (Considering a join-operation, all result terms are tuples of arity 2 with feature names '1' and '2', both features being mandatory.) The input schemas of n are inserted into the template corresponding to n'_e. The result is a conceptual schema for n.

Then constraints, satisfied by all result terms, are derived from n'_e. They refine the conceptual schema. For example, in the $\bowtie$-expression $A \bowtie_{1.\square=2.\square} B$ the path $1.\square$ (respectively $2.\square$) corresponds to A (respectively B). All result terms satisfy the constraint '1'.$1.\square$ = '2'.$2.\square$.

(3) The conceptual schema is then optimized. Redundant and irrelevant constraints are discarded.

The following example illustrates the steps during schema computation. Consider the query given by the EFTA-operator tree shown in Fig. 23(a). The query refers to the ft-sets A, B and C, which satisfy the following sort specifications:

$$\begin{aligned}
\text{sort } S_{0,A} \ &= \ \text{functor} \quad \text{f(symbol, integer)} \\
&\quad \text{with} \qquad 2.\square > 9.
\end{aligned}$$

$$\begin{aligned}
\text{sort } S_{0,B} \ &= \ \text{functor} \quad \text{g(symbol, integer, symbol)} \\
&\quad \text{with} \qquad 2.\square < 5.
\end{aligned}$$

$$\begin{aligned}
\text{sort } S_{0,C} \ &= \ \text{tuple} \quad \langle \text{ c: integer, d: integer, e: symbol } \rangle \\
&\quad \text{with} \qquad d.\square < 5.
\end{aligned}$$

The conceptual schema $S_{1,A}$ of the leftmost γ-operator γ_1 is computed as follows:

(1) Evaluate condition $2.\square < 8$ against sort $S_{0,A}$ of A; Simplify γ_1 to {};

(2) Generate an empty schema template;

(3) Add the constraint $2.\square < 8$ to $S_{1,A}$;
Detect the inconsistency in $S_{1,A}$ ($2.\square < 8$ and $2.\square > 9$);
Assign sort *nil* (denoting the empty set) to $S_{1,A}$.

The schema computation of the other inner nodes is performed similarly: $S_{1,B}$ is equal to $S_{0,B}$, since the condition $2.\square < 8$ is redundant in presence of the constraint $2.\square < 5$ of $S_{0,B}$. Thus, we get:

sort $S_{1,A} = $ nil.

sort $S_{1,B} = S_{0,B}$.

sort $S_{1,C} = S_{0,C}$.

The conceptual schema of the ∪-node is:

sort $S_2 = S_{1,A}$ or $S_{1,B}$.

which is optimized to:

sort $S_2 = S_{1,B}$.

The sort S_3 of the ⋈-node is given by the ⋈-template, the constraint '1'.2.□ = '2'.d.□ and the input schemas S_2 and $S_{1,C}$:

sort S_3 = tuple $\langle$ '1': S_2, '2': $S_{1,C}$ $\rangle$
  with '1'.2.□ = '2'.d.□.

Finally, the conceptual schema of the top γ-operator is computed:

sort S_4 = tuple $\langle$ a_1: symbol, a_2: symbol $\rangle$.

The domains of the features are given by the domains of '1'.1.□, respectively '2'.e.□.

The advantages of schema computation during query-processing are twofold:

1. A cross-analysis of EFTA-operator tree and database schemas during schema computation may lead to a *query simplification*.

   For each node of an EFTA-operator tree, containing EFTA conditions, checks against its input schemas are performed. The input schemas code information common to all input terms. If a condition is fulfilled for all input terms, we replace it by *true*. If no input term satisfies the condition, it is replaced by *false*. For example, the γ-subquery $\gamma_{if(2.\square<8)\,then\,\square}\,B$ of Fig. 23(a) is simplified to $\gamma_{if\,true\,then\,\square}\,B$, because the schema of B states that the condition 2.□ < 8 is satisfied for all terms of B.

   If a query obviously leads to an empty result set, as in the case of the leftmost γ-operator of Fig. 23(a), the corresponding subtree to this subquery is replaced by a node representing the empty set.

   Figure 23(b) shows a simplified EFTA-operator tree: It results from the applications of step (1) during schema computation. The simplification of the top γ-operator needs some explanation: The conceptual schema of the ⋈-operator contains the constraints '1'.2.□ < 5 originating from the sort of B and '2'.d.□ < 5 originating from the sort of C. Combining these constraints, the arithmetic expression evaluates to *false*. If the EFTA query has been simplified during schema computation a further algebraic optimization step can be started. Figure 23(c) shows the resulting EFTA-operator tree. The condition '2'.c.□ > 0 of the top γ-operator is pushed downwards.

   The query simplification based on schema computation leads to a significant speed-up of query evaluation.

2. During query evaluation the main memory available for intermediate results will be exhausted earlier if we repeatedly store data identical for all terms. The natural solution to this problem is to store common data only once. Therefore, information actually used for compact representation is extracted from conceptual schemas and stored in *internal schemas*, which are exploited

$$C(QEP) = \sum_{i=1}^{number\ of\ QEPnodes} (w_{I/O_i} * cost_{I/O_i} + w_{R/W_i} * cost_{R/W_i} + w_{CPU_i} * cost_{CPU_i})$$

with :

w_{I/O_i}	=	cost to read/write one page;
w_{R/W_i}	=	cost to read/write one term in main − memory;
$cost_{I/O_i}$	=	number of pages having to be read/written according to node i;
$cost_{R/W_i}$	=	number of terms having to be read/written in main − memory according to node i;
w_{CPU_i}	=	cost of one instruction;
$cost_{CPU_i}$	=	number of instructions according to node i;
$cost_{CPU_i}$	=	$cost_{compare_i} + cost_{hash_i} + ...;$
$cost_{compare_i}$	=	cost to compare two terms;
$cost_{hash_i}$	=	cost to compute the hash − value of one term;

Figure 24: A sketch of the hybrid cost model

for a *compact representation of terms* both in main memory and on secondary storage (see Sect. 6.3).

In general, there is more than one algorithm implemented for each EFTA operator. Thus an EFTA expression typically has many possible QEPs. The EFTA-operator tree encodes the ordering of the operators while the QEP additionally describes *how* the evaluation can be done efficiently.

Finding the optimal QEP is generally NP-complete in the number of ft-sets involved and thus computationally intractable (Ibaraki, Kameda 1984). Therefore heuristics are necessary for reducing the search space of possible QEPs to the search space with reasonably efficient QEPs. In determining such a QEP, we need an adequate cost model which enables the Query Processor to estimate the cost for executing one QEP. The task is to choose a QEP with "almost" minimal costs.

Cost Model: We assume that large main-memory capacities are available. Hence, most of the query processing takes place in main memory, once the needed ft-sets are read from disk. Whereas cost models in traditional database management systems mainly regard disk I/O time, we also have to stress other cost factors such as the number of data comparisons and the amount of data movement (Lehman, Carey 1986). Instead of read/write costs per page (I/O), the processing costs per term now form the basic cost unit.

The cost estimation for a particular QEP is performed by first computing the costs of the individual operations from bottom to top and by then summing up these costs. The cost of an individual operation is essentially dependent on the number and the average sizes of the terms of the operands. Accurate prediction of these values is a prerequisite for our query optimization. It is based on statistical information in the data dictionary maintained by the Term Manager.

If the size of the ft-sets exceeds the size of main memory, we additionally have to consider I/O costs. Thus, we have developed a hybrid cost model regarding both disk-based factors and main-memory factors. A sketch of how the costs of a QEP are determined is given in Fig. 24.

Join Processing: One of the more expensive operations is the join. For instance, if we choose a join generating a large intermediate result, we have to temporarily store a large number of terms. For example, assume that for the expression[9]

$$\gamma_{2.1.\square} (R_1 \bowtie (R_2 \bowtie R_3))$$

R_1, R_2, R_3 each contain 1000 terms and the left join's selectivity is 0.001 (the selectivity of a join is the number of terms of its result divided by the product of the numbers of terms of the source

---

[9]The conditions are omitted in this example.

ft-set) while the right one's is 0.1. Then the evaluation of $R_2 \bowtie R_3$ will compute an intermediate result with 100000 terms, and $R_1 \bowtie (R_2 \bowtie R_3)$ will generate 100000 terms too. If we use the (semantically equivalent) expression

$$\gamma_{2.1.\square} ((R_1 \bowtie R_2) \bowtie R_3),$$

the size of the intermediate result is 1000 terms and we save the memory for the storage of 99000 terms.

A *join-expression* is an EFTA expression whose operators are joins. In traditional database applications, queries requiring more than 10 joins are considered improbable (Krishnamurthy, Boral, Zaniolo 1986). However, logic-based languages like FLL typically contain many rules which, translated into EFTA, correspond to expressions with considerably more than 10 joins. For an EFTA expression which involves n ft-sets by applying the exhaustive search approach[10] (Selinger et al. 1979), the number of possible QEPs is $O(2^n)$. Therefore, we see the infeasibility of the exhaustive search approach and the need for an efficient join-preprocessing.

Currently the join-preprocessing is devided into two phases:

1. During the first phase, we perform a *reordering* of the join-expression in a way that the size of the intermediate results is minimized. Starting with the input join-expression, we build the *join-connection graph (jcg)* whose nodes are marked with the names of the involved ft-sets. For ft-set A n_A is the number of the terms in A and d_A is the average sizes of the terms in A. An edge e_{AB} between nodes A and B is labeled with the join-condition c_{AB} and the selectivities σ_{AB} of the join between A, B. The values n_A (n_B) and d_A (d_B) of the ft-sets are taken from the data dictionary. Having built the *jcg*, join-reordering takes place. The essential steps of the reordering algorithm are shown in Fig. 25. An example of join-reordering is given in Fig. 26.

   The stepwise reordering of the join-expression is shown in Fig. 26. In the upper row the incremental transformations from the input join-expression to the optimized join-expression are shown. The corresonding *jcg*s are sketched in the lower row starting with the original *jcg* in the leftmost column.

2. The *selection* of the join-algorithm is done in the second phase using a *join-classification schema (jcs)*. In this phase an efficient algorithm is selected for each individual join. The selection can be divided into two steps.

   The possible algorithms are first preselected depending on the actual join-condition. For example, a hash-based join-algorithm (see below) cannot be applied to a join between A and B if the join-condition does not have the pattern

   $$a_1.\square = b_1.\square \text{ and } \dots \text{ and } a_n.\square = b_n.\square$$

   where $a_i.\square$, $b_i.\square$ are paths in A, B, i.e., if the join-condition is a conjunction of path-equations.

   This preselection restricts the set S of possible algorithms to a subset S' of algorithms which actually can be applied. If S' contains only one element e, then e is selected, otherwise the *jcs* has to be used.

   In the *jcs* the join-algorithms are ordered according to their expected costs. The costs are a weighted sum of I/O cost and CPU cost. At the moment we use the ordering of Fig. 27c. The representation of the *jcs* implies that the algorithm has lower costs, being higher in the order. It is planned to incorporate some more join-algorithms.

---

[10]By exhaustive search, we mean the unbounded search traversal of the whole search space.

Procedure: join-reordering

Input: join-connection graph jcg of a join-expression je

Output: join-expression je' which is the result of the reordering phase

```
join-reordering(jcg)
begin
      while number of nodes in jcg greater 1
            for each edge e_{ij}
                  compute the result size s_{ij} of the join between i and j:
                  s_{ij} := (d_i * n_i + d_j * n_j) * σ_{ij};
                  /* performance can be increased by marking the edges which changed
                     during selection process */
            choose e_{ij} with minimal s_{ij};
            generate the join-expression je' with i and j as leaves and c_{ij} as root;
            if number of edges between i and j is 1
                  merge i and j to a new node X;
                  decrement the number of nodes by 1;
                  for each edge e_{jk}
                        e_{Xk} := e_{jk};
            else
                  decrement the number of edges between i and j by 1;
                  rename i to X;
            delete edge e_{ij};
            for each edge e_{ik}
                  e_{Xk} := e_{ik};
            n_X := n_i * n_j * σ_{ij};
            d_X := s_{ij} / n_X;
            for each e_{Xj}
                  compute σ_{Xj};
                  modify the paths in c_{Xj} by adding '1' resp. '2';
      return( je');
end.
```

Figure 25: An algorithm for join-reordering

Given the following join-expression:
$$(A \bowtie_{a_1.\square = b_1.\square} B) \bowtie_{'2'.b_2.\square = '2'.c_2.\square} (A \bowtie_{a_2.\square = c_1.\square} C)$$

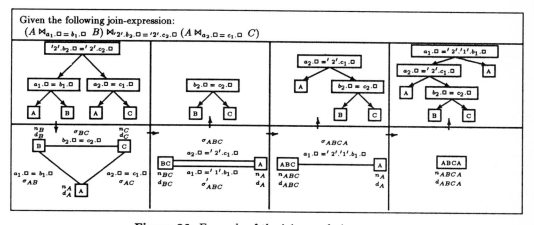

Figure 26: Example of the join-reordering process

Procedure: nested-loop-join	Procedure: sort-merge-join	
Input: ft-sets A, B; join-condition jc	**Input:** ft-set A with n number of terms in A, ft-set B with m number of terms in B and join-condition jc	**Notation:** n = number of terms in A; m = number of terms in B;
Output: result set rs	**Output:** result set rs	**Complexities:**

nested-loop-join(jc,A,B)
 begin
   rs := $\emptyset$;
   for each $a \in A$
     for each $b \in B$
       if eval-condition(jc,a,b) = 0
         rs := rs $\cup \{\langle '1' : a , '2' : b \rangle\}$;
   return(rs);
 end.
	sort-merge-join(jc,A,B)
	 begin
	   rs := $\emptyset$; i := 1 ; j := 1;
	   sort A on join-path concerning A;
	   sort B on join-path concerning B;
	   while i $\leq$ n and j $\leq$ m
	     if eval-condition(jc,a_i,b_j) < 0
	       i := i + 1;
	     else
	       if eval-condition(jc,a_i,b_j) = 0
	         rs := rs $\cup \{\langle '1' : a_i , '2' : b_j \rangle\}$;
	       j := j + 1;
	   return(rs);
	 end.
		hash-based:
		 $O(\max\{n, m\})$
		
		 is cheaper than
		
		 sort-merge:
		 $O(\max\{n * \log n, m * \log m\}$
		 $+ \max\{ n , m \})$
		
		 is cheaper than
		
		 nested-loop:
		 $O(n * m)$

a) nested-loop join	b) sort-merge join	c) join-classification schema

Figure 27: Nested-loop join, sort-merge join, complexities of joins

In the second step, heuristic rules are applied in order to recognize special cases in which a more efficient evaluation is possible, e.g., if it is known that the input ft-sets are sorted on the join-paths and the join-condition has the pattern mentioned above, the sort-merge join (Blasgen, Eswaran 1977) (see Fig. 27b) will be selected instead of the hash-based algorithm although the hash-based join generally is in a higher position according to the order of Fig. 27c.

If the join-condition consists of a conjunction of equality-conditions, we can choose the hash-based algorithm (DeWitt, Gerber 1985), (Nakayama, Kitsuregawa, Takagi 1988) which is introduced in Fig. 28.

The partitioning of a set is determined by a hash-function h_1 which computes the hash-value v according to the terms at the join-paths and normalizes v depending on the number of partitions. The position of a term in a hash-table is determined by a hash-function h_2 normalizing v depending on the size of the hash-table. The function *eval-condition* is applied in order to evaluate a condition on two terms a, b. The value 0 is returned if the condition is fulfilled.

If neither the hash-based nor the sort-merge join-algorithm are applicable, we have to evaluate the join-expression by the naive nested-loop algorithm (Gotlieb 1975) (see Fig. 27a).

Selection and Description of Algorithms: As stated above, for each EFTA operator in an EFTA expression we have to select an efficient algorithm. All information used in the selection process comes from either the EFTA expression or the data dictionary.

In the following we concentrate on the description and selection of closure algorithms. Namely we describe a seminaive (differential) fixpoint computation scheme for arbitrary safe Horn clause programs.

The naive approach is usually described as follows:

Procedure: hash-based-join

Input: join-condition jc and two input ft-sets A, B

Output: result set rs

```
hash-based-join(jc, A, B)
begin
    rs := ∅;
    partitioning A into A₁, ..., Aₙ with hash-function h₁(jc);
    partitioning B into B₁, ..., Bₙ with hash-function h₁(jc);
    for each i ∈ {1, ..., n}
        for each a ∈ Aᵢ
            store a in hash-table T using hash-function h₂(jc);
        for each b ∈ Bᵢ
            compute hash-value hv for b using hash-function h₂(jc);
            if T(hv) contains terms
                for each term t in T(hv)
                    if eval-condition(jc,t,b) = 0
                        rs := rs ∪ { ⟨ '1': t , '2': b⟩ };
        reset T;
    return( rs );
end.
```

	B_1	B_2	$\cdots$	B_{n-1}	B_n
A_1	X				
A_2		X			
$\vdots$			$\ddots$		
A_{n-1}				X	
A_n					X

The explicit join operation is performed involving A_i, B_i (see matrix). The costs of the hash-based join are mainly dependent of the size of the larger ft-set:

$O(\max\{\text{size}(\text{FT-Set}_1),\text{size}(\text{FT-Set}_2)\})$

Figure 28: Hash-based join-algorithm and its processing cost

naive_transitive_closure
$$for\ i := 1\ to\ n\ do$$
$$a[i] := e[i];$$
$$\Delta[i] := e[i];$$
$$while\ (\Delta[1] \cup \ldots \cup \Delta[n] \neq \emptyset)\ do$$
$$\quad for\ i := 1\ to\ n\ do$$
$$\quad\quad \Delta[i] := c[i] \bowtie (sg_1 \bowtie sg_2 \cdots \bowtie sg_n) - a[i];$$
$$\quad\quad a[i] := a[i] \cup \Delta[i];$$

By performing three transformation steps, we obtain an equivalent algorithm which is far more efficient than the one given above.

Applying a basic theorem of Balbin and Ramamohanarao (Balbin, Ramamohanarao 1987), we have the following formulation of the transitive closure algorithm:

semi_naive_transitive_closure
$$for\ i := 1\ to\ n\ do$$
$$a[i] := e[i];$$
$$\Delta[i] := e[i];$$
$$while\ (\Delta[1] \cup \ldots \cup \Delta[n] \neq \emptyset)\ do$$
$$\quad for\ i := 1\ to\ n\ do$$
$$\quad\quad \Delta[i] := c[i] \bowtie (\ \Delta sg_1 \bowtie sg_2 \cdots \bowtie sg_n$$
$$\quad\quad\quad\quad \cup \ \cdots$$
$$\quad\quad\quad\quad \cup\ sg_1 \bowtie \cdots sg_{n-1} \bowtie \Delta sg_n) - a[i];$$
$$\quad\quad a[i] := a[i] \cup \Delta[i];$$

In a second step we reduce the number of joins needed to compute the expression

$$\Delta sg_1 \bowtie sg_2 \bowtie sg_3 \bowtie \cdots \bowtie sg_n$$
$$\cup \quad sg_1 \bowtie \Delta sg_2 \bowtie sg_3 \bowtie \cdots \bowtie sg_n$$
$$\cup \quad sg_1 \bowtie sg_2 \bowtie \Delta sg_3 \bowtie \cdots \bowtie sg_n$$
$$\vdots$$
$$\cup \quad sg_1 \bowtie sg_2 \bowtie sg_3 \bowtie \cdots \bowtie \Delta sg_n .$$

This expression is the central part of the formulation of our algorithm after applying the theorem of Balbin and Ramamohanarao.

Figure 29 shows a straightforward evaluation method for the above "union" and an enhanced evaluation strategy using common subexpression elimination (CSE for short). Using CSE reduces the number of necessary join operations from $n^2 - n$ to $4n - 6$.

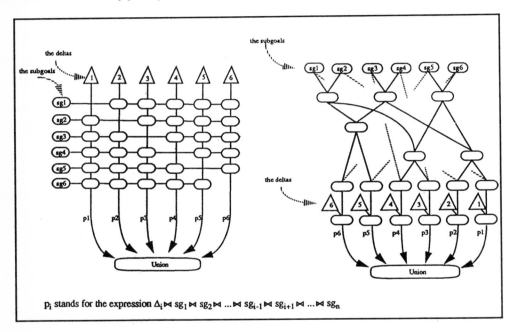

Figure 29: Evaluation of the "union" for $n=6$ subgoals (left: straightforward, right: using CSE)

In (Ludwig, Benzschawel, Gehlen 1991), we present an algorithm computing a variant of this join computation scheme for an arbitrary number n of subgoals. During a pre-compilation phase the join scheme will be computed and stored into an internal representation for further use by the query processor.

Reducing the number of joins does not automatically reduce the number of tuples that have to be compared [11]. One of the most important parameters for comparing main-memory based closure algorithms is the number of tuple compares needed to compute the final result.

Up to now, each node in the CSE-graph represents a join operation of the two incoming nodes. By performing a third step, in the following we replace each join-node by a more complex construction, involving some storage capability for memorizing intermediate results of previous iteration steps.

---

[11]In some cases we can get the opposite because we loose the possibility of freely reordering the join operations to reduce the size of intermediate results.

Without this modification these tuples would be computed again in each iteration. Figure 30 describes the algorithm by using a graphical representation of the CSE-graph.

To refer to the storage capability of a node, we assign to each node of the CSE-graph two data containers: the "res_cont" contains all intermediate results computed so far up to the previous iteration; the "delta_cont" contains all tuples computed at the actual iteration step.

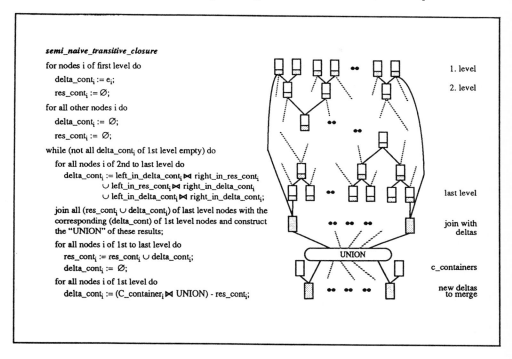

Figure 30: Algorithm and CSE-scheme with storage capabilities

The improvement of the third transformation, the inter-iteration duplicate-work-avoiding-method, is based on the distributive law for join expressions:

$$(res\_cont \cup delta\_cont)_i \bowtie (res\_cont \cup delta\_cont)_j$$
$$= \ (res\_cont_i \bowtie res\_cont_j)$$
$$\cup (delta\_cont_i \bowtie res\_cont_j)$$
$$\cup (res\_cont_i \bowtie delta\_cont_j)$$
$$\cup (delta\_cont_i \bowtie delta\_cont_j)$$

Considering the previous iteration step from the viewpoint of any other iteration (except the first), the expression

$$res\_cont_i \bowtie res\_cont_j$$

has already been evaluated before. Our algorithm has stored this sub-expression as an intermediate result and thus avoids computing it a second time. Inside the actual iteration step only the remaining three sub-expressions have to be evaluated. Usually the saved part is the most expensive one in view of the number of tuple compare operations, which is the most important parameter in the context of performance aspects.

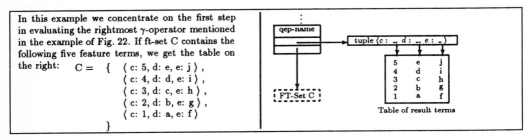

In this example we concentrate on the first step in evaluating the rightmost γ-operator mentioned in the example of Fig. 22. If ft-set C contains the following five feature terms, we get the table on the right: $C = \{$ ⟨ c: 5, d: e, e: j ⟩ , ⟨ c: 4, d: d, e: i ⟩ , ⟨ c: 3, d: c, e: h ⟩ , ⟨ c: 2, d: b, e: g ⟩ , ⟨ c: 1, d: a, e: f ⟩ $\}$

Figure 31: Internal representation of result terms

6.2.5 Interpretative Evaluation of QEP

After the QEP generation is finished, the QEP can be executed by the run-time system. The run-time system uses a bottom-up, set-oriented strategy:

Starting at the leaves of the QEP, the Query-Processor gets the permanently stored terms at the one-term-at-a-time interface between Query-Processor and Term Manager (TM) converted into a pointer structure representation well suited for main-memory processing.

The temporary terms resulting from the evaluation of an operator are stored in main memory using an efficient internal representation that avoids redundant information. Every result term is collected in a table. The complete term is built only when necessary. Figure 31 shows the internal representation of the intermediate result for the query of Fig. 22.

To avoid unnecessary storage of intermediate results we have implemented a *pipeline concept*. It supports the direct passing of single result-terms from one operator to the next. Pipelining avoids the expensive handling of temporarily generated ft-sets. The application of pipelining is restricted to operators processing their input *memoryless*(e.g., γ-operator), i.e., to operators which read each input-term only once.

The γ-operator supports the application of a conditional constructor to an ft-set. To address subterms in a term we defined the concept of paths including the path application. If a given path is repeatedly used as a subpath, then the evaluation requires the repeated application of p. To avoid this inefficient realization of the conditional constructor cc, we have developed the so-called *path-tree concept*, which guarantees that each subpath p is evaluated at most once per term. The path-tree is constructed as a part of the QEP.

First we initialize the root of PT_{cc} by the path end symbol $\square$. Successively we integrate all paths in the PT_{cc}. If an element e of a path p does not already exist in the tree, we generate a node n representing e and draw a directed edge from the parent of e to e. The parent of a node is either the root of PT_{cc} if the first element a of the path $a.x.\square$ is integrated or the direct predecessor a of the path $a.b.x.\square$ if b is integrated. Every node n of PT_{cc} is able to store a pointer to the subterm corresponding to the subpath p' which is represented in n.

Figure 32 shows an algorithm for the evaluation of a path-tree. The procedure *eval-node(N,T)* computes a subterm T' of term T by evaluating T with the path element which is represented in N.

The following example illustrates the construction and evaluation of a path-tree (see Fig. 33).

Example: For the γ-expression

$$\gamma_{if\ 1.2.1.\square\ hassort\ functor\ and\ 1.3.\square\ hasarity\ 2\ then\ [1.2.\square, 1.3.1.\square, 1.3.2.\square]}\ A$$

the corresponding path-tree is depicted in Fig. 33a. Evaluated against the term

563

```
Procedure: eval-path-tree

Input: path-tree PT_cc and term T.

Output: evaluated path-tree PT_cc.

eval-path-tree( PT_cc, T)
begin
        value of the root of PT_cc := T;
        if root of PT_cc has descendant N
                PT_cc := subtree of PT_cc with root N;
                T':= eval-node(N,T);
        if T' is a term
                eval-path-tree( PT'_cc, T');
        N' := child of root of PT_cc;
        while (root of PT_cc has child N' which is not evaluated)
                PT''_cc := subtree of PT_cc with root N';
                T'':= eval-node(N',T);
                if T'' is a term
                        eval-path-tree( PT''_cc, T'');
                N'' := next child of root of PT_cc;
        return( PT_cc);
end.
```

Figure 32: A simple algorithm for path-tree evaluation

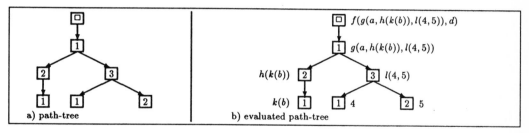

Figure 33: Illustration of a path-tree and an evaluated path-tree

$$f(g(a, h(k(b)), l(4, 5)), d),$$

it yields the tree in Fig. 33b. The result $[h(k(b)), 4, 5]$ of the γ-expression is then computed by applying the conditional constructor.

First measurements show that the path-tree concept enhances the performance of the evaluation of a conditional constructor between 25 and 50 % compared to the naive approach.

This brief explanation of the path-tree concept shows that sophisticated query evaluation techniques can significantly improve efficiency. Other techniques not further discussed here include a lazy evaluation schema for QEPs, etc.

6.3   The Term Manager

The kernel of every database system has to store its objects on secondary memory devices. The data objects of LILOG-DB are feature terms of any structure. Relational database systems divide their secondary memory into data containers, called relations or tables, which may only hold normalized objects of identical structure. In the introduction we argued that this approach is inadequate for our area of applications and would necessitate the very inefficient decomposition of complex data objects. In the sequel we described a data model, data manipulation and description languages and sophisticated query processing strategies to meet the demands of knowledge based systems for variably structured complex objects.

Our approach of processing complex objects without decomposition can only be successful if we uncomprisingly implement it over the complete storage hierarchy. The *Term Manager*[12] (TM), described in this section, performs the mapping between the feature terms of FLL and TLPROLOG and the byte sequences stored on disk.

The role of the TM in LILOG-DB can be compared to that of the Relational Storage System in System R (Astrahan et al. 1976), with normalized relations being replaced by ft-sets holding complex feature terms. We already mentioned in Sect. 4.3 that all feature terms stored in an ft-set have to satisfy the sort of the ft-set, which means that the traditional first normal form schemas are replaced by sorts. Ft-sets may be composed of data elements that differ considerably in their individual structure, and individual terms may even contain substructures not completely described by the schema.

To treat such terms, we have to give up the separation of type information stored in the data dictionary and values stored in data files. As in traditional database systems, we store properties that are common to all elements of an ft-set in the ft-set's data dictionary entry to avoid expensive redundancy on the disks. But contrary to the traditional approach, the records which represent elements of an ft-set are not only composed of atomic values, but also include the type information missing in the data dictionary entry. This potential to arbitrarily divide information into a common part and a part which varies from element to element is one of the most distinctive properties of the LILOG-DB Term Manager.

Our experimental work with the Term Manager has two focal points:

- We have to advance traditional data base storage technology to achieve efficiency competitive with traditional storage managers despite our increased flexibility.

- We have to generalize access path mechanisms to treat our flexible data formats.

In this overview, we restrict the discussion to these two points. But first we shall sketch the architecture of the Term Manager and its relations to other subsystems of LILOG-DB.

Architecture

In Fig. 34 the main users of the Term Manager are drawn as dashed boxes:

- The *Query Processor* (6.3) is the primary source of requests for the Term Manager. Usually it handles all user queries and updates. During the compilation and optimization phases, queries are decomposed to the Query Evaluation Plan (QEP), a DAG with operators as nodes. The Term Manager is responsible for the application of γ-operators to ft-sets, the Query Processor coordinates the execution of QEPs and provides implementations for the remaining EFTA-operators.

- The *Sort Lattice Manager* (6.5) is linked by a two-way interface to the TM:

---

[12]In former publications the Term Manager was called *Fact Manager* (Ley, Walter 1990). We renamed it to make clear that it is also suitable for the persistent storage of rules (with 'frozen' variables).

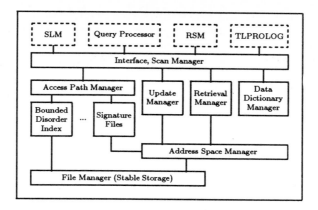

Figure 34: Term Manager architecture

- The SLM uses the TM to store sort specifications, constraints and sort lattices into persistent ft-sets.
- The TM calls the SLM to get sorts as schemas for ft-sets.

From the TM's point of view the Sort Lattice Manager is a specialized part of the Data Dictionary Manager. Treating sort lattice management as an independent architectural unit makes it possible to combine the TM with different SLM implementations adjusted to different areas of application. The interface used by the TM to get a sort is very simple and may be realized by very different SLM-architectures; the SLM itself uses the same TM interface as the Query Processor.

- The *Rule System Manager* (6.5) is responsible for persistent rule sets. It uses the Term Manager as a high-level secondary storage interface.

- For experimental work we provided *TLPROLOG* with a direct interface to the TM. This interface is useful for simple applications, which use only γ-operators, and for testing the TM without interference from the FLL-compiler or the Query Processor.

The Term Manager is not a monolithic fixed part of software, but a toolbox for experiments with different solutions for the storage structures and the access paths. The architecture is extensible on different levels:

- The expressibility of the TM's query sublanguage may be upgraded by XFTA-functions and composed XFTA-functions introduced above.

- Application-dependent access path mechanisms may be added to accelerate retrieval.

- All major components of the TM may be replaced by alternative implementations with slightly different functionalities. For example, it is possible to replace the file system interface component (File Manager) by a pure main-memory storage manager or by a mixed main-memory / secondary-memory storage manager.

In Fig. 34 the TM's main components are drawn as solid boxes:

- The *Interface and Scan Manager* is responsible for the central control of the TM. It administers scan control blocks, which hold short-lived state information such as cursors and file descriptors.

- The state of the persistent data base is described by meta-information stored in a collection of special ft-sets called the data dictionary. The *Data Dictionary Manager* provides buffered access to this information.

- The heart of the TM is the *Retrieval Manager*. It gets terms in their compact secondary storage representation, applies the γ-operator to filter out the required answer set and transforms these terms to the main memory representation.

- The complementary task is performed by the *Update Manager*. It controls the insertion, deletion or modification of terms and guarantees consistency between the access paths and the stored data.

- Access path implementations are interfaced by the *Access Path Manager*. Until now we have implemented the Bounded Disorder Index Method as well as the signature files discussed below.

- Data and access path records of arbitrary length are mapped to physical blocks by the *Address Space Manager* (ASM). It extends the traditional TID concept[13] for long records. If a record does not fit into a disk block, ASM uses a B*-tree like storage structure similar to the storage techniques of EXODUS (Carey et al. 1986) or Gemstone (Maier, Stein 1986).

- The Term Manager is built upon the *File Manager*. The File Manager has a simple block-oriented interface, and includes a disk block buffer and a recovery manager. All operating system dependencies are hidden in the File Manager, which maps LILOG-DB files to files of the underlying operating system. The prototype of the File Manager is built on the top of the UNIX file system, but advanced versions may use lower-system interfaces. The File Manager is used by the ASM and access paths which have block-oriented organizations.

Schemas

A relational schema consists of a list of attributes and their corresponding domains. The domains are restricted to built-in types like integer, real or string. Numbers usually have fixed-size representations; strings may be variably sized within system-dependent limits. Most relational database systems use an obvious mapping of tuples to secondary memory records: they simply concatenate the attribute representations and precede variably sized fields by their length or a pointer to the next field. Interpretation of such records is quite simple. To access a certain attribute value the system reads either at a fixed offset position in the record or it traces a short chain of length fields to find the actual offset. The instructions for this field-level access and the record layout are derived from the conceptual schema by simple hard-coded algorithms.

The conceptual schema of a LILOG-DB ft-set is given by a sort. We have shown above that sorts are a very powerful tool to model complex conceptual entities. A sort specification is composed of a sort description, a constraint expression, and an isa-list of super-sorts, whose properties are inherited. Sort specifications may be defined recursively, they may describe variants by disjunctions, or they may even be incomplete.

So sort specifications of LILOG-DB are much more expressive than conceptual schemas of the relational model or of the different flavors of nested relational models (Abiteboul, Fischer, Schek 1989), (Schek et al. 1990), (Dadam et al. 1986). Even in object-oriented database systems, incomplete schemas are exceptional (Zhu, Maier 1987). The very high expressiveness of sorts is an

---

[13]A TID is a record's secondary memory address composed of a block number and the record's position number in the block. TIDs are not sensitive to changes of the record sizes, because they are implemented by an indirect addressing technique.

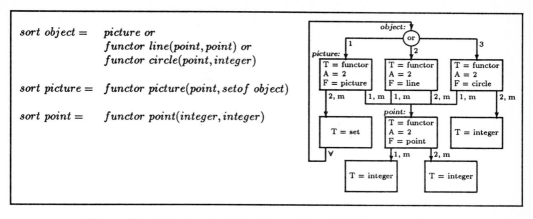

Figure 35: A simple sort declaration and the derived internal schema

advantage for conceptual modeling, but it makes the mapping of terms to secondary memory records less obvious and more difficult than in relational systems.

Most examples of sort specifications given above contain a lot of information about the syntactic structure of their terms. To cover the whole range from the traditional databases with their underlying "filing card paradigm" to databases which do not restrict the structure of their objects without a sharp decline of performance, the TM always tries to minimize the type information to be stored in the individual records. The alternative would be to give up the use of the conceptual schema to compact the representation and to store the database objects in a "self-descriptive" manner; that means the stored terms could be interpreted by a parser similar to that of a Prolog system. If we do not have any common type information about our objects, we have no choice but to use this method, which is complementary to traditional records with a fixed layout. However, the observation which triggered our work is that many applications handle objects that are less uniform than "filing cards", but for which enough type information is known to be of value to improve their representation.

To obtain satisfactory efficiency over the wide range of schemas given by the sort formalism, new techniques for field-level interpretation of records are necessary. Sort specifications are too complex for direct interpretation, as performed in the relational case. The extraction of structure information from complex constraints and from inherited sorts in large sort lattices may be prohibitively expensive. Only a subset of this information may be useful for compacting term representation without yielding excessive processing overhead. Contrary to many traditional implementations, we therefore materialize the *internal schema* and invest some cpu-time in extracting it from the conceptual schema. The internal schema is designed to facilitate fast processing on the field level. It does not contain all structure information hidden in the conceptual schema, but it is the result of a trade-off between fast field-level operations and compactness. For very large databases compactness is itself a goal to limit wasted disk space, and for all database systems it is desirable to minimize the amount of disk blocks to be read for a query. On the other hand, complex-object database kernels tend to be cpu-bound, and our first performance measurements indicated naive field access implementations as a bottle neck.

Our internal schemas are a restricted class of *and-or-graphs*, which can be interpreted efficiently. At or-nodes the decision which branch is to be taken is always possible by looking at the direct successors, which means that we do not need a deep backtracking mechanism. Figure 35 shows a complex sort declaration and an internal schema extracted from it. And-nodes are drawn as boxes, or-nodes as circles. And-nodes carry atomic type information like term-tags (T=integer, symbol,

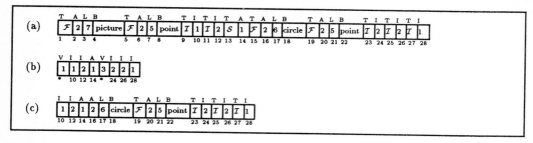

Figure 36: Representations of the term $picture(point(1,2), \{circle(point(2,2),1)\})$

functor, ...), arities (A= ...), functor-names (F= ...) and atomic values (I= ..., R= ..., S= ...). The arrows rooted in and-nodes are marked by argument position numbers (or names for tuples) and a flag which indicates them as optional or "must". Subschemas which are used for all successors of an and-node have the label "∀". Arrows beginning at or-nodes are enumerated consecutively.

In the example all information from the sort declarations is stored in the internal schema. But that is not always possible:

- Negated constraints are of little value to compact term representation; they cannot be written into the internal schema.

- Relational conditions such as $<$, $\leq$, $\geq$, and $>$ are not exploited, either.

- Constraints with an ∃-quantifier are "forgotten".

- Conditions of the type $path_1 = path_2$ cannot be represented in our internal schema.

To minimize the amount of type information which cannot be stored in the internal schema, the conceptual schema is normalized in the first step of the transformation procedure. Inherited sorts are unfolded, negations are "pushed down" as far as possible, constants are propagated, etc. This normalization is similar to the algebraic optimization of EFTA expressions. But the main differences between these two rule based transformation modules are the sets of formulas treated (e.g., constraints may be quantified) and the kinds of transformation: only equivalence transformations should be applied to EFTA expressions, but to fit into the internal schema formalism, some transformations to weaken the constraints are applied.

Term representation

To illustrate the use of internal schemas for term representation, we have sketched three records in Fig. 36. All records are representations of the term $picture(point(1,2), \{circle(point(2,2),1)\})$. The record in Fig. 36(a) is the "self-descriptive" representation, in Fig. 36(b) we used the schema shown in Fig. 35, and in Fig. 36(c) the schema

$$sort\ pic = \quad functor\ picture(point, set\ of\ term)$$
$$with\ forall\ X\ in\ 2.\Box : X.\Box\ hassort\ functor$$

was used. We assume that tags ($\mathcal{I}$nteger, $\mathcal{F}$unctor, $\mathcal{S}$et, $\mathcal{L}$ist, ...) are represented by a one-byte field (T). For arities (A) and lengths (L) the field width is one byte if the values are less than 128 and

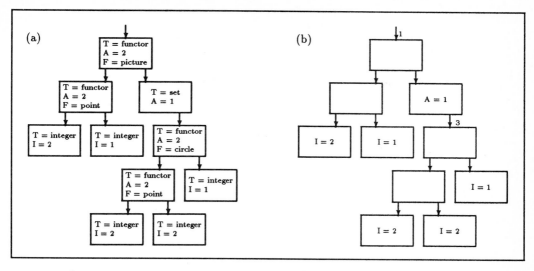

Figure 37: Tree representation of $picture(point(1, 2), \{circle(point(2, 2), 1)\})$

four bytes if they are ≥ 128. Integers (I) and Reals (R) are represented by four-byte fields. Byte fields (B) for functor names and atoms are variably sized. With these field formats, the record in Fig. 36(a) has a length of 62 bytes and the records in 36(b) and 36(c) have lengths of 23 and 40 bytes respectively. This significantly reflects the amount of type information contained in the three internal schemas used in the example.

Feature terms can be represented by trees. In Fig. 37(a) we use the same style as in our internal schema figure to draw the example term. The record of Fig. 36(a) is the result of a simple depth-first traversal of this tree. To use an internal schema, we have to traverse the term and the schema synchronously. We start at the root of the term and at the starting-label "object" in the schema. The first node visited in the schema is an or-node. We have to decide which of its direct descendants matches the current term node. We remember the number of the matching schema node by annotating the arrow leading to the current term node (see Fig. 37(b)). Next we delete all information from the term node which is common to the current schema and-node and to the term-node. For each descendant the same procedure is repeated until the entire term has been processed. The result is the tree shown in Fig. 37(b). It contains only information not stored in the internal schema. The record in Fig. 36(b) is the linearization of this tree by a depth-first traversal. Record 36(c) is calculated in the same manner with the pic-schema. The built-in sort *term*, used in this schema, is a simple method to describe incompleteness. It just says: there is no type information available – switch to the self-descriptive mode. Other kinds of incompleteness are expressed by quantifiers and by "open" tuple sorts.

The way we used internal schemas in the example above suggests describing them as finite automata. The class of automata we have chosen for internal schemas are known as root-to-frontier tree automata (Gécseg, Steinby 1984). The kernel of the update manager is a tree automaton which produces compact linear term representations. The Retrieval Manager is not simply the inverse automaton, but additionally has the ability to apply a conditional constructor to the retrieved terms. This approach of combining the tasks is much more efficient than a naive concatenation of an internal schema automaton and a conditional constructor automaton. A major challenge is to develop very efficient implementation techniques for this class of complex automata. We are currently investigating suitable compilation methods.

Access Paths

A major motivation to store terms using a compact representation is to find a query's answer set with as few disk block reads as possible. The other standard technique to minimize disk block reads is to introduce access paths. Access paths are suited for queries which reference only a small portion of the terms in an ft-set. For large ft-sets it is inefficient to get the terms matching a query by a sequential scan over the whole ft-set. If similar query patterns are used very often, it makes sense to store some redundant data structures that help to locate the answer sets with less disk block reads. Access paths can be seen as precomputed answers of a kind. But to be useful they should not be specialized to support a fixed query only. There should be some parameters by which access paths are adaptable to classes of queries.

The tuples of a conventional relation only differ in their attribute values. For a 1NF relation with attributes $A = \{a_1, \ldots, a_n\}$, an access path may be defined for a single attribute a_i (single-attribute index) or a set $A_I \subseteq A$ of attributes (multi-attribute index). An *exact match index* requires values for all attributes in A_I to be specified in a search operation. *Partial match indices* support search operations for subsets of A_I to be specified. Indices which allow intervals as search conditions are called *range indices* or *partial range indices*, respectively. Relational database systems usually support exact match indices and range indices. Partial match indices and partial range indices have been studied intensively in the literature, but they are not yet standard in commercial database systems.

For conventional database systems, it is often a problem to decide which access path mechanisms should be supported in addition to the standard techniques to get a satisfactory performance. In the database literature, hundreds of access path algorithms for very specialized applications have been proposed. The complex and variant structures of the terms in our ft-sets even extend the range of choice because it is now possible to index on such structure patterns as arities, types, etc. in addition to values.

Because the Term Manager should be adaptable to different areas of applications and we want to use it for experiments to collect knowledge about typical access patterns and the behavior of access paths, it has to be *extensible* in respect to access path mechanisms.

In our architecture, the Access Path Manager provides an interface which is operational for a large class of single ft-set access path mechanisms. These should use the services of the Address Space Manager or the File Manager. In LILOG-DB, like in most relational systems, access paths are stored separately from the data. The data records are referenced by their TIDs.

The Access Path Manager interface is implemented by a table of pointers to functions like the UNIX device driver interface (Bach 1986). There are four groups of services a new access path mechanism has to provide:

- There have to be functions to create and delete indices and to insert, update, and retrieve index entries.

- Indices have to be described in the data dictionary. A new index mechanism usually needs a new data dictionary format to store its internal parameters. Because our Data Dictionary Manager is able to handle variably structured meta-information, it is possible to hide the interpretation of access path descriptions in the access path implementation. The Data Dictionary Manager just has to store and to retrieve the descriptions. This makes the meta-information part of our access path interface very simple but universal.

- Access paths are useless if the Query Processor does not know how to use them. Access paths should be able to indicate which parts of a query they can deal with and to estimate the costs

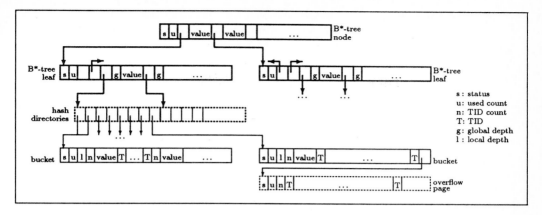

Figure 38: Bounded Disorder Index

of this retrieval operation. Our interface includes calls to test index applicability and to get statistics necessary for index selection.

- The last group of services includes miscellaneous calls such as initialization and test procedures. To test the access paths implemented so far, we used the TLPROLOG built-in predicate interface.

For our Term Manager prototype we have implemented a Bounded Disorder Method access path and a Signature File access path. The first method is an exact match index which supports range queries, the second method is a very flexible partial match index. In the sequel we shall describe these access path implementations.

Bounded Disorder Index: The only access path mechanisms used in many existing database systems are B*-trees, which are quite suitable for exact match queries as well as for range queries. The number of disk block reads necessary to search for a particular record is determined by the height of the B*-tree. The height is a function logarithmic in the number of the B*-tree entries. For realistic databases, the height is at least in the range of 3 to 4. Usually, it is not possible to keep the entire tree or at least all inner nodes in main memory.

On the other side, dynamic hashing methods achieve high performance; they need only one or two disk accesses per exact match query, but they can neither access keys sequentially nor answer range queries efficiently.

Lomet recently proposed the Bounded Disorder Method (Lomet 1988), which tries to combine the advantages of B*-trees and dynamic hashing. The idea of the Bounded Disorder Method is to obtain a coarse partition of the key range by a B*-tree and to use a dynamic hashing method inside of these intervals. The leaf entries of such a B*-tree point to large record containers instead of single records. Thereby the B*-tree is reduced to a size suitable for keeping completely in main memory. The number of disk accesses per exact match query becomes constant as for dynamic hashing. In contrast to most dynamic hashing methods, an approximate order of the keys is preserved, i.e., only a 'bounded disorder' is introduced.

We have implemented a Bounded Disorder Method access path in our Term Manager prototype, because it has some very promising properties:

- Flexibility: In our implementation the maximum number of disk blocks used for one interval is a parameter specified at index creation time. If intervals are limited to one disk block, the algorithm degenerates into a classical B*-tree access path.

- The Bounded Disorder Method supports range queries: only intervals which intersect with the search range have to be considered.

- If a sorted answer is required, the sorting algorithm may take advantage of the coarse ordering of the index, i.e., each interval is processed separately.

- Join algorithms and algorithms for duplicate elimination may utilize the partitioning of the key range too. The Term Manager Interface makes the partition limits visible to the Query Processor.

In Fig. 38 we have sketched the storage structure of our Bounded Disorder Index implementation. The upper part of the index is a B*-tree and the lower parts are directories and buckets for extensible hashing. Overflow pages may become necessary, but only for secondary indices with very long TID-lists corresponding to values which have a low selectivity.

To characterize a Bounded Disorder Index, we have slightly generalized the notion of an attribute set A_I. The attributes used for indexing may be positioned inside of complex terms. Attribute names are therefore replaced by paths. Our indices are not restricted to values stored in terms. We can define indices over values computed by XFTA-functions and by the EFTA-builtins 'hassort' and 'hasarity', which means we include structure information in the term properties which can be indexed. The index specification

    create bdo_index name_children on person
    attributes   value_of name.last.□,
                 eval count(children.□)

which builds a BDO-Index over person names and the number of children computed by the aggregate function count, gives an idea of the flexibility achieved by our approach.

Signature File: B*-trees and Bounded Disorder indices are only useful if we know the pattern of queries for an application very well. In this case we can very efficiently support the application by creating selective indices on the most frequently queried attributes and properties. The second indexing mechanism we have included in our Term Manager prototype is less selective, but more universal. Our Signature File implementation supports a variable number of term properties per index entry (Ley 1991):

    create sig_index keyword_index on papers
    attributes all argsof keyword.□ : value_of □

The universal quantifier "all argsof", used in this example, enumerates all arguments of the keyword list to be included in the signature. Contrary to Bounded Disorder indices, a term to be considered for a Signature File is not required to have all properties described in the index specification.

The main idea of the Signature File access path method (Faloutsos 1985) is to generate a file with very abridged versions of the terms, which is called 'signature file'. For a query, first the signature file is scanned. All terms for which it is evident that they are not matched by the query are filtered out by this scan. Only for the remaining entries do the long versions have to be loaded and examined. Signature File indices always return a superset of the desired answer. The main problems with Signature Files are:

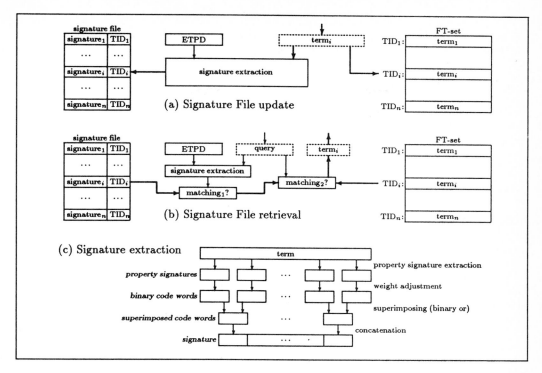

Figure 39: Signature File operations

- The choice of term properties: If too many properties are included, the signatures become too long. If only a few properties included, the signature file is only useful for a small set of query patterns.

- The coding of the selected properties: The properties should be coded as compactly as possible, but the loss of information should be as small as possible to keep the Signature File selective. Superimposed Coding is a very popular coding technique (Roberts 1979). Hash values of the properties are 'or-ed' on bit level to get a code word. In our prototype we use a combination of superimposed coding and concatenation of codewords.

- The organization of the signature file: Sequential scans over the whole signature file are only feasible for small databases. Large signature files need access paths themselves. Multilevel signature files are currently a field of extensive research (Deppisch 1989). We will implement a multi-level organisation in a future version of our Access Path Manager.

In Fig. 39 the Signature File method is illustrated in more detail. If a new term is stored in the indexed ft-set, a signature is calculated for this term (Fig. 39a). This signature extraction is controlled by the index description, which is part of the meta-data stored in the data dictionary. The new term signature and the TID are written to the signature file.

To prepare a retrieval scan, the same signature extraction algorithm is applied to the query (Fig. 39b). All signatures are read from the signature file and compared with the query's signatures. The TIDs of matching signatures point to candidates for the query's answer set. Only these candidates have to be loaded and checked against the query.

Figure 39c shows the signature extraction process. For all properties of the term which are indexed, a property signature is calculated by some hash functions. The property signatures are converted to binary code words with pre-defined length and weight, by using a pseudo-random generator. This weight adjustment reduces the loss of information in the next step, where binary code words are superimposed. To preserve information for terms with many properties, we limit the number of binary code words used to form a superimposed code word, i.e., we get a set of superimposed code words. These are concatenated to form the signature.

For queries the property signature extraction and the weight adjustment are the same as for terms. The binary code words are the leaves of an and/or tree representing the query. This and/or tree is tested against the term signatures to filter out non-matching terms.

Further Work

In this short overview, we have only sketched the architecture of the Term Manager, its data storage structures and access path mechanisms. The first prototypes of the Term Manager are operational. The results of initial performance evaluations indicate that it was worth the effort to build a new database kernel for our complex and variably structured objects and not to decompose them to conventional records or tuples, but the implementation techniques used in the Retrieval Manager still need some improvement. We are currently investigating compilation techniques to avoid the expensive interpretation of internal schemas and γ-operator-conditions. Furthermore we hope to obtain empirical results on the practicability and areas of application of our access paths. We have to develop cost models and mechanisms for index selection and data storage structure design (Selinger et al. 1979). Other important areas for research may be the necessary expressiveness of update operations and their efficient implementation, the physical clustering of ft-sets and indices, and the reorganization of complex object databases.

6.4   The Sort Lattice Manager

Sorts are a central concept throughout LILOG-DB. On the LPS-level they permit a cognitively adequate structuring of our term-universe, the specification of integrity constraints, the compact formulation of problems, and the early recognition of logical faults in the problem statement. By replacing the standard unification algorithm by order-sorted unification, resolution steps can be saved, thus speeding up inferencing. Each sort restriction attached to an FLL-variable is compiled to a *hassort* EFTA-condition, serving as a filter during query processing. In the database back-end, a sort lattice is used as the conceptual schema. Information about the syntactic structure that is common to all terms of a sort is extracted from the sort lattice into so-called internal schemas and exploited for compact storage of ft-sets. In addition, during query optimization schemas for intermediate results are computed and exploited for query simplification and for a more compact representation of the intermediate results during query evaluation.

In LILOG-DB, the management of sorts has been centralized into the Sort Lattice Manager (SLM). Thus sort specifications are stored only once and all parts of LILOG-DB use and manipulate sorts in a uniform way. Data modeling information is only accessible via the SLM. All other LILOG-DB modules only know that each universe of discourse is structured by sorts but they lack knowledge about the type of the structure (flat, hierarchical, lattice) and the constraints that can be attached to sorts. This handling of sorts as abstract data types facilitates to map data modeling concepts of different knowledge based systems to our sort concept, which in turn is necessary if the LILOG-DB toolbox is used to construct a back-end for an existing knowledge based system. (In the context of *LEU2* the ontology written in L_{LILOG} has to be mapped to a LILOG-DB sort lattice.)

In order to provide the other LILOG-DB modules with sort information, the SLM offers the following services:

- Elementary management tasks such as insertion, deletion and retrieval of sorts.

- Computation of the *glb* (*greatest lower bound*, i.e., the greatest common subsort) and the *lub* (*least upper bound*, i.e., the smallest common supersort) of two sorts.

- A sort-check ($t \in den(s)$?). (Sort-checks are used in the LPS and QP to test whether a term is an element of the denotation of a sort and in the Term Manager to check whether a term which has to be inserted in an ft-set satisfies the schema of the ft-set.)

- Consistency checks such as a check for non-empty denotations and a check to confirm that a structure given by isa-relations forms a lattice.

- Persistent storage of sort lattices.

- Management of internal schemas.

- Computation of schemas for intermediate results of query processing.

Our sort concept allows us to impose very complex constraints on sorts. Together with the fact that sort lattices in our application scenario can be very large (hundreds of sorts and more are possible) this causes new requirements for sort lattice management. In the following, we discuss the problems of fast *glb*-determination, and efficient computation of sort-checks, and consistency checking and we also present our solutions. Finally we discuss techniques for updating sort lattices.

We will only give a limited discussion of other SLM services here:

- To achieve persistency, a sort lattice is mapped to several (system-) ft-sets. Isa-relations **are** stored separately since for some operations on sort lattices (e.g., *glb*-computation) knowledge about the internal structure of sorts is not needed.

- For each sort *s* used as a schema of an ft-set, the information about the structure that is common to all terms of sort *s* is extracted from the specification of *s* and coded into a catalog called the internal schema. Only the variant parts of terms are stored, i.e., internal schemas lead to a compact storage of ft-sets. Internal schemas for intermediate results processed during the evaluation of a query are computed too (see Sect. 6.2.4).

- For a presentation of schema computation during query optimization see Sect. 6.2.4.

6.4.1 Computation of Glbs

Since it is a part of the unification procedure, the computation of the *glb* of two sorts has to be performed very frequently. Thus it is highly desirable to perform this computation in constant time, no matter how large the stored sort lattices are. To achieve this goal, the SLM computes the *glbs* of all pairs of sorts at compile time and stores them in a matrix (in fact only the upper triangle matrix is used, since $glb(s_1, s_2) = glb(s_2, s_1)$ *and* $glb(s, s) = s$). Such *glb*-matrices can also be found in EPOS (Huber, Varsek 1987).

Since the storage of *glbs* in a matrix requires quadratic space, the storage costs for large sort lattices become unacceptably high. To reduce this storage overhead, large sort lattices are split into smaller parts (so-called SL-components) in a way that the *glb* of two sorts belonging to different

SL-components always is the sort *nil*, and thus need not be stored. If necessary, SL-components can be split further. It should be clear that in the latter case the *glb* of two sorts belonging to different SL-components may be different from *nil*. Nevertheless, further splitting has to be done in a way that (roughly speaking) for each two different SL-components sl_1, sl_2 there is a single *glb* for all pairs $(s_1 \in sl_1, s_2 \in sl_2)$.

For each SL-component, a matrix is computed that contains the *glb* for each pair of sorts belonging to this component. Additionally, a "super-matrix" is generated, containing an entry for each pair of SL-components.

Heuristics for splitting sort lattices into components are described in (Maier 1989). The splitting process depends on two parameters *min* and *max* ranging over the desired component sizes. Considering the sort lattice of Fig. 40 and assuming *min = 3* and *max = 10*, first all isa-relations concerning *nil* and *term* are deleted. The lattice falls apart into a collection of components. Component c_2 is still too large. Deleting all isa-relations concerning the single top-element *being* of c_2 leads to three subcomponents. In order to avoid large super-matrices, small components (being sons of the same "father component") are collected into larger ones. Component c_1 results from such a merging step.

Figure 41 shows the corresponding matrices. In total 40 glb-entries are stored, whereas in a single (triangle) matrix 105 entries are required.

For sort lattices containing static knowledge about the structure of the world that is not updated at run time, the computation of the matrices is done at compile-time. In this case the performance of an algorithm for computing the *glb* of two sorts belonging to the same SL-component is of secondary importance. A simple algorithm for *glb*-computation proceeds as follows: Starting with two given sorts, the lattice is searched down in layers until all "first lower bounds" are reached. The *glb* is the lower bound with the highest number according to a topological sorting of the sorts (supersorts having a higher number than their subsorts). Figure 42 shows an example.

All preceding remarks concerning *glb*s are by analogy true for *lub*s. *Lub*s are especially needed in order to support generalization. Generalization is the operation complementary to unification and is used in many applications together with it (Knight 1989).

As far as we know, only in (Aït-Kaci et al. 1989) are comparable techniques for efficient determination of *glb*s and *lub*s presented. In (Aït-Kaci et al. 1989) sort-lattice elements are mapped to binary codewords encoding information about the lower bounds. Each *glb* is determined by two codewords. If n is the number of sorts in the lattice, then in contrast to our approach (constant time by using *glb*-matrices) the time for computing a *glb* is logarithmic in n. (Other operations like *lub*-computation are more expensive, although there is no precise information about this.) In both cases the storage costs are quadratic in n (but we need sort-identifiers instead of bits). The two approaches have in common the splitting of large sort lattices into smaller parts, using easily extensible heuristics for their computation.

6.4.2   Sort-Checks

In the following, "performing a sort-check" means testing whether or not a term t (taking instantiations of variables into account) is element of the denotation of a sort s.

A naive check whether a term t belongs to a sort s first tests whether t satisfies the sort-description part and the constraint part of the specification of s. Then – starting with the sorts listed in the isa part of the specification of s – the sort-lattice is traversed and the sort-descriptions and constraints of all supersorts of s are checked successively. (Each sort inherits all properties of its supersorts.)

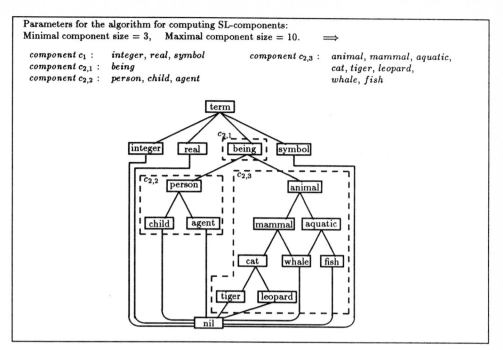

Parameters for the algorithm for computing SL-components:
Minimal component size = 3,   Maximal component size = 10. $\implies$

$component\ c_1$: $integer,\ real,\ symbol$ $component\ c_{2,3}$: $animal,\ mammal,\ aquatic,$
$component\ c_{2,1}$: $being$ $cat,\ tiger,\ leopard,$
$component\ c_{2,2}$: $person,\ child,\ agent$ $whale,\ fish$

Figure 40: A Sort lattice and its SL-components

super-matrix:

	c_1	$c_{2,1}$	$c_{2,2}$	$c_{2,3}$
c_1		*nil*	*nil*	*nil*
$c_{2,1}$	*term*		$c_{2,2}$	$c_{2,3}$
$c_{2,2}$	*term*	*being*		*nil*
$c_{2,3}$	*term*	*being*	*being*	

glb/lub-matrix for c_1:

	in	re	sy
in		nil	nil
re	term		nil
sy	term	term	

glb/lub-matrix for $c_{2,2}$:

	pe	ch	ag
pe		ch	ag
ch	pe		nil
ag	pe	pe	

glb/lub-matrix for $c_{2,3}$:

	an	ma	aq	ca	ti	le	wh	fi
an		ma	aq	ca	ti	le	wh	fi
ma	an		wh	ca	ti	le	wh	nil
aq	an	an		nil	nil	nil	wh	fi
ca	an	ma	an		ti	le	nil	nil
ti	an	ma	an	ca		nil	nil	nil
le	an	ma	an	ca	ca		nil	nil
wh	an	ma	aq	ma	ma	ma		nil
fi	an	fi	aq	an	an	an	aq	

(*glbs* are stored in the right upper corner of the matrix, *lubs* in the left lower corner;
term and *nil* need not to be stored in a component.)

Figure 41: *Glb/Lub* matrices for the sort lattice of Fig. 40

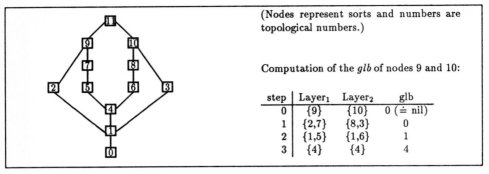

(Nodes represent sorts and numbers are topological numbers.)

Computation of the *glb* of nodes 9 and 10:

step	Layer$_1$	Layer$_2$	glb
0	{9}	{10}	0 ($\doteq$ nil)
1	{2,7}	{8,3}	0
2	{1,5}	{1,6}	1
3	{4}	{4}	4

Figure 42: An example for *glb*-computation

This is inefficient, mainly for two reasons.

- Constraints of subsorts are often specializations of supersort constraints.

  sort being   =   tuple $\langle$ age: integer, children: setof being $\rangle$
             with   age.□ < 300.

  sort person   =   tuple $\langle$ age: integer, children: setof person $\rangle$
             with   age.□ < 130 and forall X in children.□: X.age.□ = age.□
             isa   being.

  A naive sort check tests all constraints attached to a sort and all constraints inherited from its supersorts, not considering that it may be superfluous to test a supersort constraint, because more special subsort constraints have already been tested. Such redundancies can be avoided by determining at sort lattice definition time for each sort a minimal set of constraints that have to be checked and by restricting the checking procedure to this minimal set.

  The same is true for sort-description parts.

- Since structuring a universe of discourse by sort lattices is usually a very complex process, not accomplished by a single person but by a team, it is hard to avoid redundant information in sort lattices. (The current sort lattice of the LEU2 system has more than 500 sorts and is designed by a group of knowledge engineers.)

  The recognition of redundancy is complicated by the possibility of formulating semantically equivalent constraints in syntactically different ways: For example, concerning the connection of constraints, laws like commutativity, associativity and distributivity are valid and comparison operators in conjunctively connected constraints are transitive. Many constraints code implicit type- and existence-restrictions (e.g., the constraint *(age.□ < 18)* is only satisfied if *(□ hassort tuple and □ has age and age.□ hassort integer)* is true).

  A sort lattice manager should not demand redundancy avoidance, but eliminate redundancy itself.

Since sort checking is part of the unification procedure as well as part of EFTA query evaluation and of integrity checking, it has major influences on the performance of LILOG-DB. Naive sort checks have to be replaced by more efficient ones.

Our first step towards more efficient sort checking is to collect for each sort all constraints relevant for sort checking and to optimize these constraints subsequently. In more detail, for each sort s_i the following substeps are performed:

1. The sort description of s_i is converted into semantically equivalent constraints. This reduces sort checking to constraint checking.

2. The new constraints are conjunctively connected with the old ones.

3. The resulting constraints are algebraically optimized.

4. The optimized constraints are propagated to each subsort of s_i, that is conjunctively connected with the subsort constraints.

For sort *being* given above, the sort description part

   tuple ⟨ age: integer, children: setof being ⟩

is converted into

   (□ hassort tuple) and
   (not (□ has age) or age.□ hassort integer) and
   (not (□ has children) or (children.□ hassort set and forall X in children.□: X.□ hassort being))

and the resulting constraints for *being*

   □ hassort tuple and
   (not (□ has age) or age.□ hassort integer) and
   (not (□ has children) or
       (children.□ hassort set and forall X in children.□: X.□ hassort being)) and
   age.□ < 300

are optimized to

   age.□ < 300 and
   (not (□ has children) or
       (children.□ hassort set and forall X in children.□: X.□ hassort being))

and propagated to sort *person*.
For sort *person*, the complete constraint

   age.□ < 300 and
   (not (□ has children) or
       (children.□ hassort set and forall X in children.□: X.□ hassort being)) and
   □ hassort tuple and
   (not (□ has age) or age.□ hassort integer) and
   (not (□ has children) or
       (children.□ hassort set and forall X in children.□: X.□ hassort person)) and
   age.□ < 130 and forall X in children.□: X.age.□ < age.□

is optimized to

   age.□ < 130 and
   children.□ hassort set and forall X in children.□: (X.□ hassort person and X.age.□ <
   age.□).

For reasons of space we will cut the presentation of steps 1 and 3 (see (Maier 1991)). During optimization, constraints are converted into a constraint normal form, constants are propagated,

```
satisfies_constraint_person(t: term) : boolean
/* tests whether a term belongs to the denotation of sort person */

var    p1: term;      /* value of the application of path age.□ */
       p2: term;      /* value of the application of path children.□ */
       vp1: term;     /* value of the application of path X.age.□ */
       x1: term;      /* corresponds to variable X */

begin
    /* subconstraint age.□ < 130: */
    if (t is a tuple with feature age) p1 := value of this feature;
    else return "false";
    if (not (p1 < 130)) return "false";

    /* subconstraint children.□ hassort set: */
    if (t is a tuple with feature children) p2 := value of this feature;
    else return "false";
    if (not (p2 is a set)) return "false";

    /* subconstraint forall X in children.□: (X.□ hassort person and X.age.□ < X.□): */
    if (p2 is not a complex term) return "false"
    for each subterm ti of p2 do
        x1 := ti;
        /* X.□ hassort person: */
        if (satisfies_constraint_person(x1) == "false") return "false";
        /* X.age.□ < age.□ */
        if (x1 is a tuple with feature age) vp1 := value of this feature;
        else return "false";
        if (vp1 ≥ p1) return "false";
    return "true"
end
```

Figure 43: Compiled sort check for sort *person*

trivial subconstraints are evaluated and implicit type restrictions and transitivity relations are taken into account.

Reducing sort checking to checks of optimized constraints speeds up inference, query evaluation and integrity checking. However, the *interpretative* check of optimized constraints can be further improved:

- The input of an interpretative constraint check consists of a constraint and a term. In a first step the structure of the constraint has to be determined and, depending on the type of the structure (conjunctively connected subconstraints, quantified constraint, ...), the constraint check is called recursively for sub-constraints. However, since the structure of the constraint is already known at sort lattice definition time, structure determination and recursive calls of subconstraint checks are superfluous. (The same argument is valid for path evaluations.)

- An interpretative constraint check evaluates paths and subconstraints independently of former path and subconstraint evaluations.

    - When checking the constraint

        age.□ < 130 and
        children.□ hassort set and
        forall X in children.□: (X.□ hassort person and X.age.□ < age.□)

the path $age.\square$ is evaluated once during the test of $age.\square < 130$ and once for each children ($X.age.\square < age.\square$).

- The check of

$$(not\ c1\ and\ c2)\ or\ (c1\ and\ c3)$$

can lead to two checks of subconstraint $c1$. Even in optimized constraints multiple appearances of subconstraints are possible.

Therefore we compile constraints into constraint-specific functions, avoiding the shortcomings of the interpretative approach listed above. The recursive examination of constraint structure is replaced by iterative code. Different subconstraints and paths of a constraint are numbered and the results of their evaluations are stored in variables. Figure 43 shows the constraint check function for sort *person*.[14]

In Fig. 44, the steps towards efficient sort checking procedures are summarized. A detailed description of the optimization and compilation of constraints can be found in (Maier 1991).

6.4.3 Consistency Checks

Our notion of consistency checks covers all checks that are performed during sort lattice updates in order to maintain the underlying semantics of the sort lattice. In the following we discuss four types of consistency checks:

- When a new sort is added, it is tested whether its denotation is non-empty, i.e., whether it has a proper place in the taxonomic hierarchy and whether the specification itself contains no contradictory constraints. Sorts with an empty denotation are called inconsistent.

  We handle inconsistency detection as a special case of constraint optimization, namely the reduction of an inconsistent constraint to the constraint *false*. For each sort to be added, all constraints relevant for sort checking are computed and the discussed optimization techniques are applied. For example, this allows rejecting the insertion of a sort *working_child*

sort working_child	with	age.$\square \leq 17$
	isa	worker.

  into a sort lattice where the constraint

  $$age.\square > 18$$

  is attached to sort *worker*.

  However, in LILOG-DB the detection of inconsistent sorts is undecidable since the subsumption of sorts is undecidable and the equivalence

  $$den(s_1) \subseteq den(s_2) \iff$$
  $$den(s) = \{\ \}\quad where\ s\ is\ specified\ by\quad sort\ s = (s_1\ and\ (not\ s_2)).$$

  holds.

---

[14]In order to check whether a term containing non-instantiated variables belongs to sort *person*, the function has to be adapted: if a non-instantiated variable is involved in a path application, the value *maybe* is returned (a later instantiation may violate the corresponding subconstraint(s)).

582

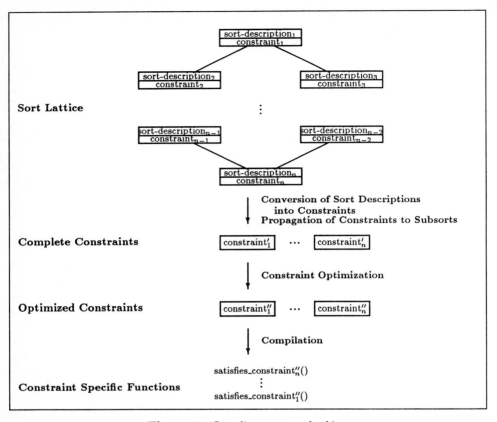

Figure 44: Speeding up sort checking

The undecidability of subsumption can be shown as follows:[15] In (Schmidt-Schauß, 1989) it is proved that even for a sublanguage of KL-ONE, consisting of expressions built by concept- and role-symbols using the operations *conjunction of concepts, value-restriction of roles* and *role value maps restricted to "="*, subsumption is undecidable. Since the conjunction of sorts, the value-restriction of features, and constraints concerning the equality of features are expressible in our sort specification language, it is clear that subsumption in LILOG-DB is undecidable as well. (Note that concept-symbols can be replaced by sort-names and role-symbols by the names of our – potentially set-valued – features.) Nevertheless, we expect that the impact of this theoretical result will be negligible in practice.

- To check whether a set of isa-relations forms a lattice, the SLM first checks the given structure for acyclicity, for connectivity and for the existence of a single sort having no subsorts (*nil*) and a single sort having no supersorts (*term*). These partial checks enable an early rejection of ill-formed structures. They can be done in time linear in the number of isa-relations. Next the *glb/lub*-matrices are computed. Whenever for a pair of sorts either no *glb* or no *lub* can be found the computation stops with result *no lattice*.

- The SLM provides a check of cross-references between sorts. It demands for each reference sort the existence of a sort specification, and rejects the deletion of a sort as long as there are any references to it.

- In order to avoid inconsistencies in ft-sets when updating a sort lattice, sorts used in conceptual schemas are marked. As soon as marked sorts are affected by an update, a protocol between SLM and Term Manager is activated. The deletion of a marked sort is forbidden. "Harmless" sort lattice updates such as adding a feature-description to a sort generally lead to updates of the corresponding internal schema, but can nevertheless be tolerated. Adding a supersort to a sort used as conceptual schema is usually a problem, while adding new subsorts does not involve any problems.

6.4.4 Impact of Sort-Lattice Updates on SLM Algorithms

In extreme cases, updates of a sort lattice may lead to a recomputation of all *glb*-matrices. An example is the insertion of an isa-relation between *person* and *mammal* into the sort-lattice of Fig. 41. In contrast, inserting a sort

$$\textit{sort senior} \quad \textit{with age}.\square > 60 \quad \textit{isa person}.$$

has only local effects (in Fig. 41 only $c_{2,2}$ is concerned). If updates with global effects occur frequently at run time, the recomputation overhead becomes unacceptable. For such application scenarios the computation of matrices can be switched off and the *glb*s are recomputed each time they are demanded.

Optimization and compilation of constraints are time-consuming operations. But usually they have to be done only once at data modeling time and the importance of efficient sort checking for the performance of LILOG-DB justifies them. But, depending on the frequency and type of sort lattice updates, constraint optimization and compilation may get unreasonable:

---

[15]In (Ludwig 1991b) we describe a decidable sublanguage of our language for describing sorts. Unlike (Schmidt-Schauß, Smolka 1989), where decidability is achieved through absence of role-inclusions, respectively agreements, and unlike (Smolka 1988), where it is achieved through limitation of (non-set-valued !) features, our approach is to disallow constraints referring to sorts standing lower or on the same level in the sort-taxonomy.

- Especially during rapid prototyping, sort lattice updates can be frequent and naive sort checking is preferable.

- For application scenarios in which higher sort lattice levels are static but lower hierarchy levels are often updated, it is recommendable to restrict compilation and optimization to more general sorts and otherwise to use naive sort checking.

Note that optimization and compilation of constraints can be done incrementally and that schema evolution is not excluded.

Most consistency checks are time-consuming too. A LILOG-DB user can switch between automatic and demand-driven calls of consistency checks.

Since sorts are used as conceptual schemas, dynamic updates may not only require recompilation of *glb*-matrices and sort checks, but also require costly checks, respectively updates, of the secondary storage representation of terms in order to avoid inconsistencies in ft-sets. An important question is whether a static structuring can be achieved in realistic applications. A closer look at the LILOG application scenario shows that the higher levels of the sort lattice encoding its ontology can in fact be assumed to be static.

6.5 The Rule System Manager

Integrating deductive capabilities within a database management system requires the development of a rule definition language. Like FLL (see Sect. 2.2.2), most of the rule definition languages used in deductive database systems are extensions of *DATALOG*, a first-order-logic retrieval language facilitating set oriented database processing.

A non-recursive set of *DATALOG* rules (i.e., a *DATALOG* program) can be translated to a relational algebra program. In LILOG-DB we distinguish between a query-independent and a query-dependent part of the translation process: A program consisting of (uncompiled) FLL-rules is compiled into an EFTA-template-graph (see Sect. 6.2). Given a query, an EFTA-template-graph in turn is compiled into a QEP. The Rule System Manager (RSM) supports the management of any programs represented at one of these compilation levels.

In order to evaluate an FLL query, only the corresponding QEP has to be evaluated (if necessary the QEP has to be constructed from the corresponding EFTA-template-graph).

Not all inference strategies that are used in knowledge based systems can be analogously compiled and thus efficiently executed inside a database system. This is especially true for languages based on *Prolog*, where the order of rules is relevant and the result of a query is generated one tuple at a time. Opposed to this, the relational algebra is nonprocedural and the efficiency of query evaluation in (relational) database systems relies on a bottom-up, set-oriented strategy.

Therefore, we decided to implement the interface between the *Prolog* interpreter included in our logic programming front end and the database system at the FLL-level. The rules stated at the FLL-level can be executed via the RSM. All other rules have to be processed on top of the database system. However, in both cases, rule management includes persistent storage of rules and the provision of a language allowing qualified retrieval of rules (depending on some given criteria, e.g., all rules containing a literal *way* with arity 2 and arbitrary sign). In the following subsection we discuss these tasks.

Considering the control strategies of inference machines, rules are logically interconnected by numerous semantic relationships.[16] At the start of our work, we hoped to design an RSM that is able to directly support resolution machines by adequately computing and exploiting information about semantic relationships between rules. Knowledge about semantic relationships is especially useful to improve the storage of rules and to provide the inference engine with hints about which rules are suitable to continue the current inference process. However, though we are sure about the potential benefits of an inference-engine-supporting RSM, we realize that the techniques needed are far beyond the current state of the art. There are still a lot of problems to solve and we have not yet reached the targets we aimed at. In the subsections following the next one, except one, we discuss how semantic relationships can be exploited to improve and complement rule storage and rule retrieval. The section about rule system management ends with some considerations about the architecture of a full-scale RSM.

Rule Retrieval

The RSM uses the Term Manager and the Query Processor for storing and retrieving rules: A rule is mapped to an FTDM term and stored persistently via the Term Manager (programs are mapped to ft-sets). The retrieval language in turn is mapped to our algebra EFTA and queries are evaluated by the Query Processor.

To map standard rule retrieval queries like

> which rules of program p_1 contain   a positive literal unifying with *compile_constraint(X, Y)* and a negative literal unifying with *write(X)*

to a semantically equivalent EFTA-query the RSM takes advantage of the extensibility of EFTA. It uses an evaluable function that checks existentially quantified conditions. Without such an evaluable function the query above cannot be formulated adequately in EFTA. EFTA itself does not allow us to express that within a rule-term there is a subterm (literal-term) with certain characteristics. If a rule is split into FTDM-terms such that for each literal an FTDM-term is stored, it is possible to state semantically equivalent queries, but the splitting leads to an inefficient evaluation. The number of I/O operations increases, and when evaluating search criteria of the form

> *literal_condition*$_1$ and *literal_condition*$_2$,

where *literal_condition*$_i$ is a condition concerning literal characteristics, superfluous operations are performed: Normally *literal_condition*$_2$ has only to be checked for rule-terms satisfying *literal_condition*$_1$. But when working with literal-terms one has to evaluate *literal_condition*$_2$ for all literals since a rule is qualified even if two different literals of it satisfy *literal_condition*$_1$ and *literal_condition*$_2$ respectively. Alternatively, one can find out the rules that correspond to the literals satisfying *literal_condition*$_1$ and evaluate *literal_condition*$_2$ restricted to the literals of these rules. After that, one still has to find out which rules correspond to the result literals and to construct the rule-terms.

Computing and Exploiting Semantic Rule Relationships

An important characteristic of the application scenario of LILOG-DB is that knowledge bases consist of extraordinarily large numbers of rules. Since during an inference process usually only parts of a rule system are actually needed, it does not make sense to load the complete rule system into primary storage. Hence it is preferable to load only a certain amount of rules into a *limited buffer*.

The time required to read a rule from hard disk is dominated by the seek time (time needed

---

[16]We call two rules *semantically related* if they have some characteristics in common enforcing them to be frequently used together in inference processes (e.g., if they have complementary literals that are unifiable).

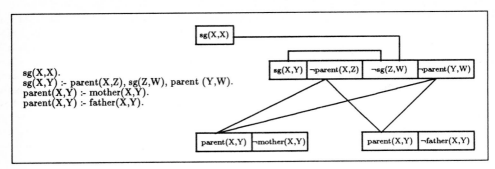

Figure 45: A Prolog program and the corresponding RGG

to move the head to the correct track) and by the latency time (time needed until the head is over the correct sector), but not by the time actually required to transfer the data. Therefore, it is efficient to keep semantically connected rules in nearby sectors on the same track and to swap in/out larger parts (so-called clusters) at a time.

Since the *swapping of clusters* includes the reading of rules probably needed in the near future, this also implements a *prefetching strategy*.

In order to estimate which rules are used together in inference steps, inference strategies have to be simulated at compile time. The RSM has to *compute rule-connectivity-values* reflecting the probability that two rules are needed in the same inference process.

For the LPS inference engines, rule-connectivity-values will be computed on the basis of so-called RGGs (Rule-Goal-Graphs).[17] An RGG reflects possible orders of rule applications independent from a concrete resolution strategy. It is constructed as follows. For each literal a literal-node is created. The literal-nodes of a rule are combined to rule-nodes. Two literal-nodes are connected by an edge if the literals belonging to them are complementary and unifiable, i.e., for each pair of literals that can be used together in a resolution step, an edge is created (see Fig. 45).

RGGs only provide information on which rules may potentially be used together, but how the search space is actually traversed – especially in case of tuple-oriented inference engines processing top-down using a backtracking mechanism – depends on the queries. If unification fails, backtracking must be performed and inferencing proceeds using some rule which may not be directly connected to the previously processed rule. Thus the probability that a unification between two literals connected by RGG-edges fails influences rule-connectivity-values.

Compared to using no rule-connectivity-values, even simple strategies lead to an essential improvement of rule-retrieval and decrease main storage usage. Simple strategies are the clustering of rules with the same head predicate, the clustering of rules mutually calling each other (so-called recursive cliques) and – considering inference engines traversing their search-space by depth-first-search – the assignment of high rule-connectivity-values not only to rules directly connected in the RGG, but also to rules soon reached by depth-first-search.

Given rule-connectivity-values, a rule-system can be split into clusters such that the sum of the resulting cluster connectivity values is minimized, i.e., there remains only a small probabability that two adjacent inference steps use rules of two different clusters. (A *cluster connectivity value* is

---

[17]An RGG as described here is identical with a connection graph ((Kowalski 1975), (Stickel 1986), (Bläsius, Bürckert 1987)), used as a static structure. We name it RGG because of its special use in other LILOG-subsystems (TLPRO-LOG, FLL-Compiler)

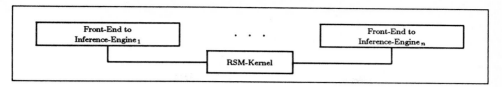

Figure 46: RSM architecture

the sum of the rule-connectivity-values between rules of the two clusters considered.)[18]

For inference engines not working on Horn clauses, not based on input-resolution or switching between different inference strategies, the approach of using the edges of an RGG as a basis for the computation of rule-connectivity-values is not applicable. RGGs become very complex and it cannot be guaranteed that after a rule r was used for a resolution step, a rule connected with r through edges will be used for the next step.

This is especially true for the inference engine in work for the LEU2-system. It does not work with Horn clauses, but with more complex and more expressive structures. In the long run the LEU2 inference engine will even support uncertainty and vagueness. A lot of practical experience will be needed in order to develop techiques for automated determination of semantical relationships between rules for such inference engines.

The qualified retrieval of rules needed by inference engines is either based on some condition concerning rules or on some condition concerning semantic relations in which the rules are involved. A rule condition is usually given at the beginning of an inference process in order to retrieve a starting rule and possibly all alternatives. A condition concerning semantic relations is then used for the retrieval of the next rules needed in the inference process. In this case the inference engine should be provided with an annotated list of rules suitable for continuing the inference process. The rule list can be built according to unification relations given, e.g., by an RGG. The annotations concern things like expected costs and probability of success. A computation of costs and probabilities can be done based on information about the number of matching facts and via an examination of the data-flow between subgoals of a rule (see (Smith 1989), (Ludwig et al. 1989)).

RSM Architecture

Taking our application scenario into account, the set of inference engines to be supported cannot be limited (compare Sect. 6.1). This raises the necessity to design an extensible RSM: We split the RSM into an inference engine-independent kernel and inference engine-dependent front-ends (see Fig. 46).

The kernel provides storage management and set-oriented retrieval of rules (i.e., retrieval of all rules satisfying a given search criterion). It can receive rule-connectivity-values by a front-end and exploit them for storage management.

In the front-ends, the computation of rule-connectivity-values, the classification of rules according to their significance for the continuation of inference processes and the adjustment of strategy parameters concerning storage management takes place. For inference engines working on a rule-normal-form different from that used by the RSM, the mapping has to be done by the corresponding front-end. The same holds for application-specific rule-retrieval languages. In order to support the

---

[18]The problem to split a rule-system into clusters (given rule-connectivity-values) can be considered abstractly as the problem to partition a graph with attributed edges such that the sum of the attribute values of the edges lying in the cut is minimized. Efficient standard heuristics do exist.

implementation of front-ends, the RSM provides tools for the computation of rule-connectivity-values and an abstract data type for rules.

The tighter the coupling between the inference engine and the RSM, the more efficiently the RSM-services can be implemented. Tight coupling includes the use of a common term-representation, the transfer of data via shared memory, and the handling of compiled rules. The latter is especially useful in order to provide an efficient support of set-oriented inference, as implemented by the FLL-part of the LPS.

Although in the literature single aspects of rule-management with DB-methods ((Rothermel 1988), (Böttcher, Beierle 1989), (Sellis, Roussopoulos 1988), (Cheiney, Maindreville 1989), (Smith 1989)) are described, we do not know of any approach to rule management suitable for different inference engines and attacking all management tasks sketched above. It is a non-trivial task to develop such an approach, especially because the determination of semantic relations between rules is largely dependent on the inference engine. A future problem is to make an RSM "learn" an inference strategy given by the user.

7 Contribution to LEU2

Until now, we have described LILOG-DB as a standalone system providing interfaces for upper-level inference engines. We now want to give a brief sketch of how the services of LILOG-DB, as described in other chapters of this book, are interfaced with the rest of the LEU2 system.

The abstract interface between LEU2 and LILOG-DB is the L_{LILOG}-ADT (Bollinger et al. 1989), a set of PROLOG predicates for the storage and retrieval of, for example, axioms, literals, and so on, of L_{LILOG}. It provides a uniform interface for the administration of L_{LILOG} expressions in the whole LEU2 system.

Two oversimplified calls to L_{LILOG}-ADT predicates may give a flavor of how it is used:

1. *create_knowledge_base*($kb1, temporary$) creates a temporary knowledge-base named $kb1$. This can now be filled with L_{LILOG} expressions.

2. *add_sort*($stuttgart, cities, geography$) declares an L_{LILOG} sort with name *stuttgart* in the knowledge-packet *cities* of the knowledge-base *geography*.

Figure 47 shows the architectural embedding of the L_{LILOG}-ADT implementation.

The implementational basis is the LILOG-DB database system (**1**). To be able to implement the L_{LILOG}-ADT functionality, we first had to interface LILOG-DB to Quintus-Prolog. This Quintus-Prolog/LILOG-DB Interface (**2**) has been implemented using the Foreign Function Interface of Quintus-Prolog. It basically provides a surface syntax for calls to the LILOG-DB query processor (whose language is EFTA) in terms of the Quintus-Prolog term syntax.

This surface has been used to write the L_{LILOG}-ADT predicates (**3**) L_{LILOG}-ADT is not intended to be used by LEU2 programmers directly. Instead, it serves as a tool for the LEU2 Inference Engine (**4**), and the user – i.e., the upper levels of LEU2, (**5**) – should access it only through calls to the inference engine.

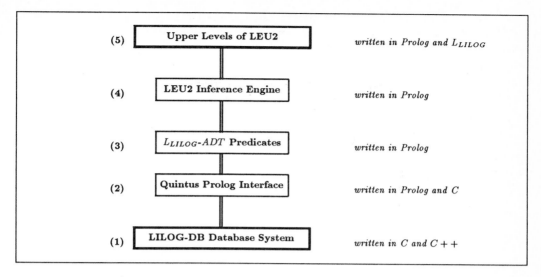

Figure 47: Architecture of the L_{LILOG}-ADT implementation

8   Conclusion

We have given a survey of the basic concepts of LILOG-DB, a deductive database system designed for the support of knowledge based systems, especially in the context of natural language processing.

The *Feature Term Data Model* of LILOG-DB has been presented, which allows complex object aggregation using the constructors *functor*, *list*, *set* and *feature-tuple*. With the introduction of feature-tuples, we have incorporated a facility to realize the open world assumption on data. While functors and lists come from the first-order logic foundation of our system, the introduction of general sets is a reaction to the impossibility of imposing any normal form in the relational algebra sense on a general purpose next generation DBMS. This aspect makes the efficient exploitation of existing knowledge about the application data, given by the schemas, an essential part of our implementation. Schemas in LILOG-DB are given by sort specifications, and may be variant, recursive or incomplete.

Three *languages* working on the FTDM have been presented. While TLPROLOG is used for the specification of inferencing tasks on data, embedded database queries can be formulated in the first-order based deductive database language FLL, which essentially is a DATALOG successor extended to the FTDM. FLL queries are translated to the database algebra EFTA, which can be seen as within the tradition of relational algebra, but allows arbitrary nesting of complex objects and has a closure operator.

The languages of LILOG-DB are completely implemented, in *C* on the *IBM UNIX* dialect *AIX*. The implementation of LILOG-DB has five major components that have been presented in this overview.

The *Logic Programming System* (LPS) currently includes TLPROLOG and a prototype of a Connection Graph Resolver. It is intended to provide sophisticated tools for the (logic) programming of knowledge representation applications.

The *Query Processor* covers the main memory processing of EFTA queries on the database, including a compiler from FLL to EFTA, so that two database front-ends currently exist, one for EFTA and one for FLL.

The access to the database is performed by the *Term Manager*. The efficiency-oriented processing of sort lattices and rule systems is done by the *Sort Lattice Manager* and the *Rule System Manager*, the latter one being not yet fully implemented.

Some of the main principles of our approach shall be repeated here. The most important one is that knowledge representation applications especially in the context of natural language processing do not allow for restricted normal forms, and not even for fully specified schemas. The resulting principle is that the system has to cope with *incomplete and variant information on complex objects*, and exploit it optimally. The consequence of this principle has been the design and implementation of *sophisticated optimization tools* (Rule Rewriter, EFTA optimizer, TM schema-handler), specially tuned managers for rule systems and sort lattices and an "intelligent" memory management.

Another basic principle is the *tight coupling* between logic programming and database querying, realized via the support of the same data-model throughout the whole system, and shared memory communication between application and database.

Finally, LILOG-DB is an *extensible database system*, which can be easily adapted to the needs of different applications by means of user-defined operators and types.

In the previous section, we have discussed our contribution to the LEU2 system. We achieve a semi-tight coupling between the LILOG-DB database system and the rest of LEU2 by using the C-Interface of Quintus Prolog. The database services can then be accessed via the L_{LILOG}-ADT, which provides an L_{LILOG}-style view on our database.

A focus of current work in the final stages of the LILOG project is given by the careful study of how our database kernel is used in LEU2; we are currently benchmarking the system with respect to the query patterns occuring in this environment. However, this work is in its early stages. The final chapter on LILOG-DB, an in-depth discussion of practical experiences, remains to be written.

References

Abiteboul, S., Fischer, P. C., Schek, H.-J. (eds.) (1989): Nested relations and complex objects in databases. Springer, Berlin, Heidelberg, New York, Lecture Notes in Computer Science, Vol. 361

Aït-Kaci, H. (1986): An algebraic semantics approach to effective resolution of type equations. Theor. Computer Science, Vol. 45, 293–351

Aït-Kaci, H. et al. (1989): Efficient implementation of lattice operations. ACM Transactions on Programming Languages and Systems, Vol. 11, 115–146

Astrahan, M. M. et al. (1976): System R: Relational approach to database management. ACM Transactions on Database Systems, Vol. 1, 97–137

Bach, M. J. (1986): The design of the UNIX operating system. Prentice-Hall, Englewood Cliffs, NJ

Balbin, I., Ramamohanarao, K. (1987): A generalization of the differential approach to recursive query evaluation. The Journal of Logic Programming, Vol. 4, 259–262

Bancilhon, F. (1986): Naive evaluation of recursively defined relations. In: Brodie, M., Mylopoulos, J. (eds.): On Knowledge Base Management Systems, Springer-Verlag, Berlin, Heidelberg, New York, pp. 165–178

Bancilhon, F., Ramakrishnan, R. (1986): An amateur's introduction to recursive query processing strategies. In: Proc. ACM SIGMOD Conf., Washington D.C., ACM Press, 16–52

Batory, D.S. et al. (1988): GENESIS: An extensible database management system. IEEE Transactions on Software Engineering, Vol. 14, 1711–1730

Beeri, C., Nasr, R., Tsur, S. (1988): Embedding ψ-terms in a Horn clause logic language. In: Proc. 3rd Int. Conf. on Data and Knowledge Bases, Jerusalem, Morgan Kaufmann Publishers, Inc., pp. 347–359

Bläsius, K.-H., Bürckert, H.-J. (eds.) (1987): Deduktionssysteme. Oldenbourg Verlag, München (in German)

Blasgen, M. W., Eswaran, K. P. (1977): Storage and access in relational data bases. IBM Systems Journal, Vol. 6, 363–377

Bollinger, T. et al. (1989): The interface specification of the LILOG inference engine II. IWBS paper, IBM Germany, Stuttgart

Böttcher, S., Beierle, C. (1989): Database support for the PROTOS-L system. IWBS Report 71, IBM Germany, Stuttgart

Carey, M. J. et al. (1986): Object and file Management in the EXODUS extensible storage database system. In: Proc. VLDB Conf., Kyoto, Morgan Kaufmann Publishers, Inc., pp. 91–100

Carey, M., DeWitt, D.J. (1987): An overview of the EXODUS project. IEEE Database Engineering Vol. 10, Special Issue on Extensible Database Systems, No. 2

Cheiney, J. P., Maindreville, C. (1989): Relational storage and efficient retrieval of rules in a deductive DBMS. In: Proc. IEEE Data Engineering Conf., Los Angeles, Computer Society Press, Inc., pp. 644–651

Codd, E. F. (1972): A relational model for large shared data banks. Communications of the ACM, Vol. 13, 377–387

Colby, L. S. (1989): A recursive algebra and query optimization for nested relations. In: Proc. ACM SIGMOD Conf., ACM Press, pp. 273–283

Dadam, P. et al (1986): A DBMS prototype to support extended NF² relations: An integrated view on flat tables and hierarchies. In: Proc. ACM SIGMOD Conf., Washington D.C., ACM Press, pp. 356–367

Deppisch, U. (1989): Signaturen in Datenbanksystemen. Dissertation, TH Darmstadt (in German)

DeWitt, D., Gerber, R. (1985): Multiprocessor hash based join algorithms. In: Proc. VLDB Conf., Stockholm, Morgan Kaufmann Publishers, Inc., pp. 151–164

Faloutsos, C. (1985): Access methods for text. ACM Computing Surveys, Vol. 17, 49–74

Gécseg, F., Steinby, M. (1984): Tree automata. Akadémiai Kiadó, Budapest

Gehlen, E. (1989): EFTA Query processing in LILOG-DB. IWBS Report 98, IBM Germany, Stuttgart

Gotlieb, L. R. (1975): Computing joins of relations. In: Proc. ACM SIGMOD Conf., ACM Press, pp. 55–63

Huber, M., Varsek, I. (1987): Extended Prolog for order-sorted resolution. In: Proc. IEEE Symposium on Logic Programming, San Francisco, Computer Society Press, Inc., pp. 34–43

Ibaraki, T., Kameda, T. (1984): On the optimal nesting order for computing n-relation joins. ACM Transactions on Database Systems, Vol. 9, 482–502

Knight, K. (1989): Unification: A multidisciplinary survey. ACM Computing Surveys, Vol. 21, 93–124

Kowalski, R. (1975): A proof procedure using connection graphs. Journal of the ACM, Vol. 22, 572–595

Krishnamurthy, R., Boral, H., Zaniolo, C. (1986): Optimization of nonrecursive queries. In: Proc. VLDB Conf., Kyoto, Morgan Kaufmann Publishers, Inc., pp. 128–137

Lehman, T. J., Carey, M. J. (1986): Query processing in main memory database management systems. In: Proc. ACM SIGMOD Conf., Washington D.C., ACM Press, pp. 239–250

Ley, M. (1991): Implementierung von Signatur-Dateien in LILOG-DB. Forthcoming IWBS Report (in German)

Ley, M., Walter, B. (1990): Ein Datenbankkern zur Speicherung variabel strukturierter komplexer Objekte. Springer-Verlag, Berlin, Heidelberg, New York, Informatik Forsch. Entw., Vol. 5, 188–201 (in German)

Lomet, D. B. (1988): A simple bounded disorder file organization with good performance. ACM Transactions on Database Systems, Vol. 13, 525–551

Ludwig, T. (1988a): FLL: A first-order language for deductive retrieval of feature terms. IWBS Report 57, IBM Germany, Stuttgart

Ludwig, T. (1988b): EFTA: An algebra for deductive retrieval of feature terms. IWBS Report 58, IBM Germany, Stuttgart

Ludwig, T. (1988c): Algebraical optimization of FTA-expressions. IWBS Report 59, IBM Germany, Stuttgart

Ludwig, T. (1989): The design and implementation of TLPROLOG. IWBS Report 103, IBM Germany, Stuttgart

Ludwig, T. et al. (1989): LILOG-DB: database-support for knowledge-based systems. In: Proc. BTW, Zürich, Springer-Verlag, Berlin, Heidelberg, New York, Informatik-Fachberichte, Vol. 204, pp. 176–195

Ludwig, T. (1990a): A brief survey of LILOG-DB. In: Proc. IEEE Data Engineering Conf., Los Angeles, Computer Society Press, Inc., pp. 420–427

Ludwig, T. (1990b): Compilation of complex DATALOG with stratified negation. In: Proc. of the 8th British National Conference on Databases, York, Pitman, pp. 85–107

Ludwig, T. (1991a): Query processing in LILOG-DB: What it is and where it goes. In: Proc. BTW, Kaiserslautern, Springer-Verlag, Berlin, Heidelberg, New York, Informatik-Fachberichte, Vol. 270, pp. 271–287

Ludwig, T. (1991b): Order sorted unification with constraints. Forthcoming IWBS Report

Ludwig, T., Walter, B. (1991): EFTA: a database retrieval algebra for feature-terms. Data and Knowledge Engineering, Vol. 6, 125–149

Ludwig, T., Benzschawel, S., Gehlen, E. (1991): Differential closure computation for general Horn-clause queries. Submitted for publication

Maier, A. (1989): Sort-Lattice management in LILOG-DB. IWBS Report 99, IBM Germany, Stuttgart

Maier, A., Ley, M., Gehlen, E. (1991): Sort Processing in a Deductive Database System. IWBS Report 154, IBM Germany, Stuttgart

Maier, A. (1991): Optimierung und Compilation von Sorten-Constraints in *LILOG-DB*. Forthcoming IWBS Report (in German)

Maier, D., Stein, J. (1986): Indexing in an object-oriented DBMS. in: Proc. International Workshop on Object-Oriented Database Systems, Pacific Grove, CA, Computer Society Press, Inc., pp. 171–182

Minski, M. (1975): A Framework for Representing Knowledge, in: Winston, P. (ed.): The Psychology of Computer Vision, McGraw Hill

Nakayama, M., Kitsuregawa, M., Takagi, M. (1988): Hash partitioned join method using dynamic destaging strategy. In: Proc. VLDB Conf., Los Angeles, Morgan Kaufmann Publishers, Inc., pp. 468–478

Przymusinski, T. (1988): On the declarative semantics of deductive databases and logic programs. In: Minker, J. (ed.): Foundations of Deductive Databases and Logic Programming, Morgan Kaufmann Publishers, Inc., pp. 193–216

Roberts, C. S. (1979): Partial match retrieval via the method of superimposed coding. In: Proceedings of the IEEE, Vol. 67, pp. 522–528

Rothermel, K. (1988): An effective method for storing and retrieving PROLOG clauses from a relational database. In: Proc. 3th Int. Conf. on Data and Knowledge Bases, Jerusalem, Morgan Kaufmann Publishers, Inc., pp. 255–268

Robinson, J. A. (1965): A machine-oriented logic based on the resolution principle. Journal of the ACM, Vol. 12, 23–41

Schek, H.-J. et al. (1990): The DASDBS project: objectives, experiences, and future prospects. IEEE Transactions on Knowledge and Data Engineering, Vol. 2, 25–43

Schek, H., Weikum, G. (1991): Erweiterbarkeit, Kooperation, Föderation von Datenbanksystemen. In: Proc. BTW, Kaiserslautern, Springer-Verlag, Berlin, Heidelberg, New York, Informatik-Fachberichte, Vol. 270, (in German), pp. 38–71

Schmidt-Schauß, M. (1989): Subsumption in KL-ONE is undecidable. In: Proc. 1st Int. Conf. on Principles of Knowledge Representation and Reasoning, Morgan Kaufmann Publishers, Inc., pp. 421–431

Schmidt-Schauß, M., Smolka, G. (1989): Attributive concept descriptions with unions and complements. IWBS Report 68, IBM Germany, Stuttgart

Schwarz, P. et al. (1986): Extensibility in the Starburst database system. In: Proc. International Workshop on Object-Oriented Database Systems, Pacific Grove, CA, Computer Society Press, Inc., pp. 85–92

Selinger, P. et al. (1979) Access path selection in a relational database management system. In: Proc. ACM SIGMOD Conf., Boston, ACM Press, pp. 23–34

Sellis, T., Roussopoulos, N. (1988): Deep compilation of large rule bases. In: Proc. 2nd Int. Conf. on Expert Database Systems, Vienna, Va, Benjamin/Cummings Publishing, Inc., pp. 525–549

Shieber, S. (1986): An introduction to unification-based approaches to grammar. CLSI Lecture Notes, Vol. 4, Stanford University, CA

Smith, D.E. (1989): Controlling backward inference. Artifical Intelligence, North Holland, Vol. 39, 145–208

Smolka, G. (1988): A feature logic with subsorts. IWBS Report 33, IBM Germany, Stuttgart

Stickel, M.E. (1986): An introduction to automated deduction. In: Springer-Verlag, Berlin, Heidelberg, New York, Lecture Notes in Computer Science, Vol. 232, 75–132

Stonebraker, M. (1987): Extending a database system with procedures. ACM Transactions on Database Systems, Vol 12, 350–376

Tsur, S., Zaniolo, C. (1986): LDL: A logic-based data language. In: Proc. VLDB Conf., Kyoto, Morgan Kaufmann Publishers, Inc., pp. 33–41

Zhu, J., Maier, D. (1987): Abstract object in an object-oriented data model. Technical Report No. CS/E 87-015, Oregon Graduate Center, OR, Beaverton

Chapter 3

Spatial Knowledge

The present chapter contains a series of papers that provide an insight into the current research activities carried out within the project LILOG-Raum (LILOG-Space) at the University of Hamburg. In order to show how LILOG-Raum is embedded within the LILOG framework, the topics of some subprojects will briefly be described as follows (for a broad overview see the introduction to this volume by Rollinger and Herzog): At the IBM Scientific Centre (Institute for Knowledge-Based Systems, IWBS), the knowledge representation language L_{LILOG}, based on an order-sorted variant of first-order predicate logic that takes LILOG's specific needs into account, is being developed, as well as the inference engine processing L_{LILOG} (see Sect.2.1 of this volume). Furthermore, IWBS takes global responsibility for the semantic analysis of German, the generation of natural language texts, and the knowledge engineering component. There have been strong interactions with each of these research groups.

In Hamburg, the topic of the subproject LILOG-Raum is the representation and processing of spatial knowledge enabling a cognitively adequate meaning analysis of spatial expressions of German. It is our aim to make a contribution to cognitive science by taking into account methods and results of cognitive linguistics and cognitive psychology and by striving for a cognitively adequate formal theory of spatial knowledge.

The lexical classes under investigation within this theoretical framework are local and directional prepositions, verbs of motion and position, and dimensional adjectives. These categories are analyzed with respect to their syntactic, semantic, and conceptual properties. To ensure an adequate treatment of the flexibility of natural language expressions, we assume a model of meaning representation consisting of two levels, a *semantic* and a *conceptual level*. The semantic level specifies the grammatically determined part of meaning. Semantic structures are systematically related to syntactic structures and guarantee the compositional construction of meaning representation. At the conceptual level, semantic structures are interpreted with respect to a specific context and available conceptual knowledge, e.g., knowledge about the constitution of objects, characteristic courses of events, causal connections, etc. Thus with respect to spatial expressions, the semantic component of LEU/2 (see Sect. 1.4) is supplemented with a conceptual component.

One of the purposes of the conceptual level is to provide the language-independent fundamental concepts that spatial knowledge is based on. To guarantee an appropriate representation and processing of spatial concepts, we assume that the conceptual level consists of a propositional as well as a non-propositional component, yielding a hybrid representation system. The propositional component consists essentially of facts and rules stated in the knowledge representation language L_{LILOG} and an ontology defining all of the concepts that facts and rules deal with. The non-propositional *depictional* component is concerned with pictorial, sketch-like representations of spatial knowledge. This component makes use of the notion of mental images developed within cognitive psychology. The tentative, but complete formalization and integration of pictorial representations within a complex knowledge representation system facilitates an examination of the notion of *mental images*, which are, for the most part, otherwise informally characterized. This research process will give rise to an improved approximate formalization of mental images which might in turn form the starting point for new research, thus resulting in intensive and productive cooperation between cognitive science and computer science.

In the first contribution, Habel argues the case for a hybrid representation system and outlines the architecture of the spatial knowledge representation component within the LILOG system. The specific problems that a natural language system concerning space has to deal with are discussed and a general account for the processing of spatial expressions is given. Habel sketches the way the subsequent contributions are embedded within this framework.

The contribution of Pribbenow demonstrates how phenomena of localization of objects and situations are treated within LILOG-Raum. In particular, Pribbenow discusses the way relevant information is extracted from natural language expressions, processed by the propositional component and then passed to the depictional component. Emphasis is placed on the way commonsense knowledge can be taken into account when determining the localization of entities, and how this kind of knowledge interacts with other knowledge sources. Pribbenow proposes different types of rules *selection rules* and *priorization rules* to cope with this task. Thus, this section also gives a sketchy description of the interaction between the LILOG inference engine and the special purpose component for solving spatial problems via depictions.

The next two sections are concerned with special issues of propositional processing. Maienborn shows how the distinction between a semantic and a conceptual level can be exploited to give a systematic explanation for the optionality of the local argument of verbs of motion and position. Beyond this specific problem, this section also demonstrates the necessity for an integrated view of semantic and conceptual processing. Carstensen/Simmons focus on the conceptual level. They present a general framework for dimensional designation of objects based on so-called *object schemata*.

Interestingly, object schemata, which were originally designed as conceptual foundation of dimensional adjectives, also turn out to be relevant for the interpretation of the optionality of the local argument of verbs of motion and position. Thus different linguistic categories, like dimensional adjectives and verbs of motion and position, which behave very differently at the semantic level, access the same basic concepts at the conceptual level. In our opinion, this finding underscores the strength of the semantic approach we have chosen.

Finally, Khenkhar presents the depictional representation system developed within LILOG-Raum in order to deal with sketch-like spatial knowledge. The formal properties of *cell matrices*, the concrete representational format, are discussed, and problem solving strategies by means of imagination and inspection processes over depictions are outlined.

The papers collected here each work out one specific aspect of the many-sided problem field of spatial knowledge. Together, they give some insight into our approach towards a theory of natural language reference to space. More detailed descriptions are given in further papers to be found in the bibliography.

We wish to thank all contributors to this chapter for their cooperation even during the final stages of implementing the LILOG prototype. Thanks to Geoff Simmons for his untiring struggle with our attempts to approximate the English language. Special thanks are due to Elke Jäger for transferring our manuscripts into TeX format.

Christopher Habel/Claudia Maienborn

Processing of Spatial Expressions in LILOG

Christopher Habel

1 Remarks on the Representation of Spatial Knowledge

Knowledge representations are of central importance in natural language processing systems because they are the source and goal of communicative processes and, moreover, because they are the basis of reasoning processes, see Fig. 1. This means that knowledge representations are the building blocks from which internal models of the external world are constructed.[1]

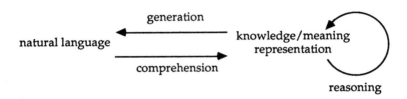

Fig. 1: The centrality of knowledge representations

The comprehension process, which is shown in Fig. 1 as one step, can be subdivided into two phases: in a first step a semantic representation is constructed, and in a second step a conceptual representation, which has to be integrated into the system's knowledge base via inferential processes, is built up from the semantic representation.

As the topic of this paper (and the other papers of this volume) is mainly the *processing of spatial knowledge*, we focus on the latter and keep the former, which is discussed in detail in Geurts (1990), in the background.

This view – sketched above – is a variant of two-level semantics as proposed by Bierwisch/Lang (1989): Our specific extension of *two-level semantics* especially concerns the interaction of two types – or formats – of knowledge representation used and needed for processing spatial concepts.

The system of knowledge representation determines what can be spoken or thought about. From this it follows that the capacity of the representation formalisms, for instance the storing, manipulation and acquisition of the entities and structures of the representation language, determines the capacity of a knowledge-based system, especially a system processing natural language. The main topic of the present paper (and this volume) involves a special field of knowledge representation, namely the way that *spatial knowledge* can be represented and processed adequately, and the specific problems of building semantic representations from spatial expressions of a natural language and reasoning about them.

---

[1]The external world is not assumed to be *the real world*. Fictional worlds are also a source for building internal, i.e., mental, models. Since the status of internal models is not the main topic of the present paper, I merely refer to Johnson-Laird (1983) and Habel (1986).

There are several reasons for focusing on this particular field of spatial knowledge: one of them is its "ubiquity". This can be appreciated best by considering where spatial knowledge is of importance. The answer is: (almost) everywhere, because human behavior (and therefore communication, planning , etc., as well) is grounded in space and time. The consequence should be that any natural language processing system needs an adequate capacity to process spatial expressions.

Representation of spatial knowledge as a subject of investigation is also of particular relevance because here we find the intersection of two relevant fields of information processing abilities, namely of language processing and of image processing, see Fig. 2.

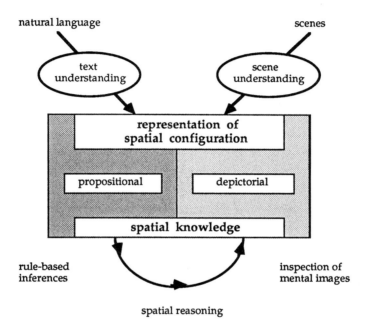

Fig. 2: The central position of spatial representations[2]

An information processing system equipped with both language and image understanding abilities will above all be organized in such a way that analog information used in the process of image understanding can be related to the propositional representations emerging from language processing or prior knowledge in a well defined way.

I hypothesize (cf. Habel 1987) that non-propositional representations, which I – like Kosslyn (1980) – call *depictorial* (see below) are produced from linguistic inputs as well. I am convinced that non-propositional representations are relevant for text understanding (cf. Habel 1987). Furthermore, the research field *representation and processing of spatial knowledge* is a field where the interaction of cognition and perception plays an important role. Cognition-oriented and computational linguists as well as researchers in Artificial Intelligence may regard this as justification for intensive research on this subject matter.

---

[2]Habel (1987) contains this figure and an extended argumentation for a dual-coding theory (see below).

Before we discuss some properties of such non-propositional representations in detail, we give a sketchy argument for depictorial representations in language processing. The brief example (1) concerning locations induced by spatial prepositional phrases gives evidence for the usefulness of depictorial representations.

(1) (a) Das Zentrum der Stadt liegt auf der rechten Rheinseite. Oberkassel liegt jenseits des Rheins.
         [The center of the city is situated on the right bank of the Rhine. Oberkassel is situated on the other side.]

     (b) Sie kommen aus der Bismarckstraße. Die Straße des 17. Juni liegt jenseits des Ernst-Reuter Platzes.
         [You are on Bismarckstrasse. The Strasse des 17. Juni is on the other side of Ernst-Reuter Square.]

     (c) Sie kommen aus der Bismarckstraße. Die Straße des 17. Juni liegt jenseits des Spring-brunnens.
         [You are on Bismarckstrasse. The Strasse des 17. Juni is on the other side of the fountain.]

For the texts in (1) *mental images*, forming an internal representation, depicted by sketches in Fig. 3a-c, may be assumed.[3]

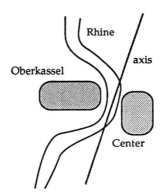

Fig. 3a: The city of Düsseldorf and the river Rhine

The core of the prepositional concept 'jenseits' ('beyond', or 'on the other side') is characterized by the fact that the objects denoted in the jenseits-PP – in our example the Rhine, Ernst-Reuter Square or the fountain – induce a path-like object (an axis) which is the basis for building an spatial situation with on the one side and on the other side. Since axes are genuinely spatial concepts, a spatial representation format should be considered for the representation of jenseits-PPs.

In the text (1a) the 'jenseits'-axis is induced by the path-like object Rhine. In cases like this a propositional analysis would also be possible and unproblematic. Assuming a three-place relation *JENSEITS* leads to the representation

---

[3]Mental images and mental maps are explained more extensively below. Some problems of detailing such maps can be seen clearly in the example; certainly the depiction will not be so detailed that the exact form of the square and the exact path of river are "coded" in this knowledge entity (at least not usually, i.e., for an average speaker/hearer).

JENSEITS('Center', 'Oberkassel', 'Rhine')

The conceptual symmetry of 'jenseits'-constellations can be formalized by

If $JENSEITS(x, y, z)$ then $JENSEITS(y, x, z)$

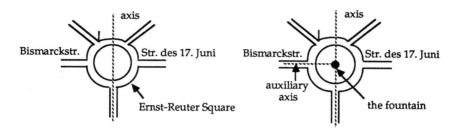

Fig. 3b: Ernst-Reuter Square I   **Fig. 3c:** Ernst-Reuter Square II

The examples (1b) and (1c) are little bit more problematic. What is the other side of a circle? Since circles are genuinely without sides (from an axiomatic as well as from a propositional point of view) an intuitive, image-like idea of the circle is needed: a mental image. The same problem holds with respect to the "other side of a point-like object", here the fountain. (Note that the fountain is conceptualized as point in comparison with the diameter of Ernst-Reuter Square, which is 130 meters.) The direction of the ingoing Bismarckstrasse can used as auxiliary axis to construct the 'jenseits'-axis in question.

In Habel (1990) it is demonstrated how the meanings of two spatial prepositions, namely <u>um</u> (<u>around</u>) and <u>an</u> (<u>on/at</u>), are distinguished by means of genuinely spatial concepts, in this case the concept of a closed loop.

As can be seen in Fig. 2, we can imagine two clearly distinguished formats of representation for the processing of spatial knowledge: first, a format of propositional representation; second, a non-propositional format, that of depictorial representations. It is not uncontroversial which role analog representations play in cognitive processes. This discussion among philosophers and cognitive psychologists, called the imagery debate[4], centers on the question whether *mental images*, which are also called *pictorial notions* or *mental pictures*, exist, i.e., if they are cognitively real or if they are epiphenomena, as Pylyshyn (1981) asserts. A contribution to this debate (from an AI point of view) is Habel (1990).

If a combination of propositional and depictorial representations is assumed, then corresponding approaches – following Paivio – are regarded as *dual coding* theories (cf. Paivio 1983). In the remainder of this paper, we follow the line of dual-coding theories, thus presupposing a hybrid representation system based on propositional as well as depictorial representations. This line of thinking is justified, since the assumption of the existence of non-propositional, depictorial representations in cognitive processes or in mental models bridges the gap between cognition and perception.

---

[4]Cf. N. Block (ed., 1981).

At this state of the discussion, some short remarks (cf. Habel 1989) on image-like representations may be appropriate. Following Kosslyn (1980, p.33), I assume that depictions occur in an internal spatial medium, which provides the material that mental images are formed from. This internal spatial medium is a theoretical entity just as propositional representation languages are theoretical entities. For example, it is possible to use cell matrices[5] for a concrete realization of this abstract entity. Such matrices, which are rectangular arrays on a discrete raster, can only be approximations of real depictions, i.e., mental images in the human mind.

2 Processing Spatial Expressions

The internal representation on the level of semantic and conceptual representations are expressions of the representation language L_{LILOG}. L_{LILOG} is an order-sorted language developed especially for the purpose of language processing. It is strongly oriented to the idea of the KL-ONE family and to formal logics (cf. Pletat/von Luck 1990).

2.1 Processing of Spatial Knowledge

The main goal of processing spatial expressions is to localize objects or situations (events, processes) in space. This process of localization is the topic of Pribbenow's paper in this volume. Here we merely sketch the general problem of localization. The following three subdomains of the ontological system are of prime importance:

D $\sim$ the domain of objects
E $\sim$ the domain of events (situations)
LR $\sim$ the domain of locations, i.e., the space of local regions.

In the class LR of local regions there exist regions of different types; some regions are enriched by further structure, especially by concepts as *orientation*. *Paths* for example are specific regions with orientation (cf. Habel 1990).

The two domains D and E, on the one hand, and LR, on the other, are connected by a (time-dependent and context-sensitive) mapping

(3a) $REG : D \cup E \rightarrow LR$

which assigns to an object or an event x its characteristic region $REG(x)$. In the following we mainly consider the case of object localization. (Note that – in principle – we permit event or situation localization, too.)

Let us assume a general relation of local inclusion

(3b) $LOC : LR \times LR \to BOOL,$

which can be interpreted as follows

$LOC(x, y) \quad \sim \quad$ the region x is locally included in the region y.

This system of concepts is similar to that of Bierwisch (1988, p.17ff.).[6] Based on these notations the structure of the meaning of spatial expressions can be represented; for example the meaning of spatial prepositions is given by

(4) $\lambda y \lambda x (LOC(REG(x), PREP^*(y))) \quad x, y$ variables on D

where $PREP^*$ is a *region-generating* mapping

(3c) $PREP^* : D \to LR,$

associated with the prepositional concept $PREP$.[7] The notation introduced here shall be exemplified by the NP

the city on the river.

The river denotes the *reference object* (RO), which determines the frame of localization, the city refers to the object to be located (LO). The spatial relation between the two objects (on the level D)

(5a) $ON(LO, RO)$

induces a relation on the LR-level:

(5b) $LOC(REG(LO), ON^*(RO))$

The general structure of the relation between the levels of objects and locations is depicted in **Fig. 4**:

Fig. 4: The relations between objects and their locations

(Not that because of the canonical type of the relationship between LO and $REG(LO)$ we sometimes use a relational notation as in (5a) with respect to locations, i.e., objects of the

---

[6]Note that the terminology is different, especially with respect to LOC. Since Bierwisch sees local inclusion as set-theoretical inclusion, he does not use a specific relation like LOC. His "loc" corresponds to the REG used in the present paper.

[7]This approach to the analysis of spatial prepositional phrases is a modification of Wunderlich/Herweg (to appear) and Herweg (1989). Habel/Pribbenow (1988) describe the concept of region-generating processes in detail.

domain LR. This usage is only a simplification, which can always be transformed into a fully precise expression of type (5b).)

In (4) and (5) we have used a traditional logic-oriented notation. In L_{LILOG} notation the result of the semantic construction would be (with respect to the localization induced by the spatial PP):

(5c) $lok(LO, reg)$, with $reg = ON^*(RO)$

where LO gives the located object described by <u>the city</u> and RO the reference object introduced by <u>the river</u>. Based on this L_{LILOG} formula, the conceptual processing is executed. Two types of rules, namely *selection* rules and *priorization* rules, formalized in L_{LILOG}, elaborate the meaning of the spatial expression (as represented in (5c)). The spatial disjointness of LO and RO could be the result of such elaboration processes. One specific task of these rules is to *trigger* processes in the *depictorial component*. (The rule-based processes are described in detail by Pribbenow in this volume.)

The depictorial component, as described in Khenkhar (this volume), is based on the concept of *cell matrices*, which can be assumed as approximative realizations of depictions. In depictions, two basic types of processes have to be considered:

- *imagination processes*, which build up cell matrices, i.e., image-like representations, out of propositional representations (such as 5c)) or out of other depictions (e.g., in the search processes for possible regions), and

- *inspection processes*, which analyze cell matrices with respect to a verification task given by the propositional component. For example, if the inference machine of the system tries to verify (5c) the inspection of relevant cell matrices can be delegated to the depictorial component as subtask.

From this a sketchy architecture of the spatial subcomponent can be deduced:

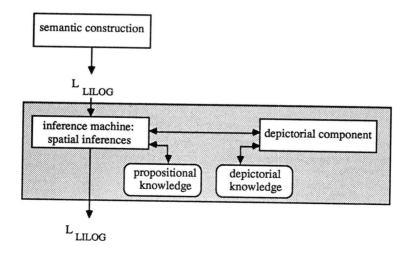

Fig. 5: The spatial component in the LILOG system

2.2 Constructing L_{LILOG}-Representations from Spatial Expressions

In the process of constructing a semantic representation from natural language expressions as well as in the generation of natural language output from internal representations, some specific aspects of spatial expressions have to be taken into consideration. In the following we give a sketchy description of two problem areas, namely the optionality of local arguments and the treatment of some spatial adjectives.

Local verbs, especially verbs of motion, require a local argument on the level of semantic interpretation, i.e., the level of L_{LILOG}-expressions. (Note that these local arguments are the basis of the localization process mentioned in Sect. 2.1.) As Maienborn (1990, and in this volume) shows, there exist cases in which the local argument seems to be optional

Rita is sitting.

and others in which the local argument seems to be obligatory

* Rita puts the book.

As the examples demonstrate, it is not suitable to require the local argument to be obligatory on the syntactic level. If the local argument were optional in principle, the characterizing property of local verbs would be missing. Thus the relevant question is: What is the level on which the local argument is obligatory? As Maienborn demonstrates, some general principles, e.g., the existential binding of local arguments and its conceptual interpretation, solve the conflict between the syntactic level, in which local arguments are facultative, and the semantic/conceptual level, in which spatial arguments are obligatory for verbs of position and motion.

This analysis and these principles are used in the semantic construction process leading to an L_{LILOG}-representation containing for example a path argument for verbs of motion.

The analysis of local verbs often makes use of the gestalt and position properties of spatial objects; e.g., a blanket requires a 'laying' constellation whereas a table (normally) is involved in a 'standing' constellation. Similar information (knowledge) is necessary for an adequate processing of dimensional adjectives like high, deep, long. The basic concept for an adequate theory of dimensional adjectives is that of *object schemata* (cf. Lang 1987, Lang/Carstensen 1989, Lang/Carstensen/Simmons 1991). In this volume, Carstensen and Simmons outline the realization of this approach as part of the spatial component of the LILOG system. On the one hand, the conceptual lexicon for objects contains knowledge about the dimension properties of the objects in question, e.g., with respect to the axes; on the other hand, the entries for adjectives (in the conceptual lexicon) contain constraints on the dimension properties of the objects which can be modified by these adjectives.

In the present paper we merely sketch the usefulness of this approach with respect to the generation of natural language descriptions. Let us assume that our system contains information about a pole, namely that its extension is 20 m with respect to the natural, i.e., maximal, axis. Now we consider two different cases, one in which the pole is located in a horizontal position, one in which it is located in a vertical position (Fig. 6).

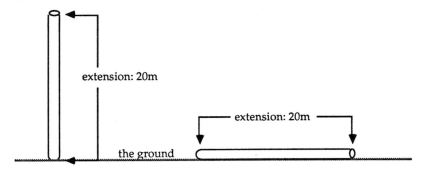

Fig. 6: The pole: vertical vs. horizontal position

Let us assume too that the knowledge of the system – as result of cognitive or perceptual processes – contains information about the objects, the pole and the ground, properties of these objects concerned, namely (the extension of the pole) and the relation between the objects (the mode of position). The task of the generation component is to choose the appropriate lexical entries, i.e., the verb of position and the dimensional adjective. The decision with respect to specific verbs and adjectives is carried out on the basis of inferential processes. The result generated should be:

> The 20m high pole is standing on the ground.
> The 20m long pole is lying on the ground.

In a similar way, object schemata are used in the processes of semantic construction and conceptual analysis of spatial expressions (cf. Carstensen/Simmons, in this volume).

3 Summary

Spatial expressions lead to specific problems in the analysis and synthesis of natural language utterances as well as in conceptual processing. For an adequate solution, (at least) three general areas of investigation arise:

- Specific entries in different levels of the lexicon, e.g., with respect to the roles of local verbs, object schemata (gestalt and position properties) for nouns, and constraint schemata for dimensional adjectives.

- A set of (propositional) inference rules (formalized in L_{LILOG}) with respect to spatial concepts. These inference rule are the basis of the localization process. Especially, they trigger the processes of the depictorial component. Furthermore, inferential processes are used for the analysis of predicative and adjective concepts.

- A representation formalism for a depictorial, i.e., quasi-analogical, treatment of spatial knowledge. The depictorial component is subdivided into an imagination and an inspection part.

An adequate analysis of spatial expressions (with respect to all of these three areas) is needed for any high-quality analysis of natural language expressions.

References

Bierwisch, M. (1988): On the grammar of local prepositions. In: M. Bierwisch, W. Motsch, I. Zimmermann (eds.): Syntax, Semantik und Lexikon. Akademie-Verlag (studia grammatica 29), Berlin, pp. 1-65

Bierwisch, M., Lang, E. (eds.) (1989): Dimensional Adjectives: Grammatical Structure and Conceptual Interpretation. Springer-Verlag, Berlin, Heidelberg, New York

Block, N. (ed.) (1981): Imagery. MIT Press, Cambridge, MA

Codd, E. F. (1968): Cellular Automata. Academic Press, New York

Geurts, B. (ed.) (1990): Natural Language Understanding in LILOG: An Intermediate Overview. IWBS Report 137, IBM Deutschland, Stuttgart

Habel, Ch. (1986): Prinzipien der Referentialität. Springer-Verlag, Berlin, Heidelberg, New York

Habel, Ch. (1987): Cognitive Linguistics: The Processing of Spatial Concepts, ATALA (Association pur le Traitement Automatique des Langues), 28, 21-56. Also as: LILOG Report 45, 1988, IBM Deutschland, Stuttgart

Habel, Ch. (1990): Propositional and depictorial representations of spatial knowledge: the case of path-concepts. In: R. Studer (ed.): Natural Language and Logic. Lecture Notes in Artificial Intelligence, Vol. xx. Springer-Verlag, Berlin, pp. 94-117. Also as: Report FBI-HH-M-171/89, University of Hamburg 1989

Habel, Ch., Pribbenow, S. (1988): Gebietskonstituierende Prozesse. LILOG Report 18, IBM Deutschland, Stuttgart

Herweg, M. (1989): Ansätze zu einer semantischen Beschreibung topologischer Präpositionen. In: Ch. Habel, M. Herweg, K. Rehkämper: Raumkonzepte in Verstehensprozessen. Niemeyer, Tübingen, pp. 99-127

Johnson-Laird, P.N. (1983): Mental Models. Cambridge University Press, Cambridge, UK

Kosslyn, S. (1980): Image and Mind. Harvard University Press, Cambridge, MA

Lang, E. (1989): The semantics of dimensional designation of spatial objects. In: M. Bierwisch, E. Lang (eds.), pp. 263-417

Lang, E., Carstensen, K. U. (1989): OSKAR: Ein PROLOG-Programm zur Modellierung der Struktur und der Verarbeitung räumlichen Wissens. In: D. Metzing (ed.): GWAI-89. Springer-Verlag, Berlin, Heidelberg, New York, pp. 234-243

Lang, E., Carstensen, K. U., Simmons, G. (1991): Modelling Spatial Knowledge on a Linguistic Basis: Theory-Prototype-Integration. Springer-Verlg, Berlin, Heidelberg, New York

Maienborn, C. (1990): Position und Bewegung: Zur Semantik lokaler Verben. IWBS Report 138, IBM Deutschland, Stuttgart

Paivio, A. (1983): The Empirical Case for Dual Coding. In: J. Yuille (ed.): Imagery, Memory and Cognition. Erlbaum, Hillsdale, NJ, pp. 307-332

608

Pletat, U., von Luck, K. (1990): Knowledge Representation in LILOG. In: Bläsius, K.H., Hedtstück, U., Rollinger, C.-R. (eds.) (1990): Sorts and Types in Artificial Intelligence. Lecture Notes in Artificial Intelligence, Vol. xx. Springer-Verlag, Berlin, Heidelberg, New York, pp. 140-164

Pylyshyn, Z. (1981): The imagery debate: analogue media versus tacit knowledge. Psychological Review, 88, 16-45

Wunderlich, D., Herweg, M. (to appear): Lokale und Direktionale. In: A. v. Stechow, D. Wunderlich (eds.): Handbuch der Semantik. de Gruyter, Berlin

Phenomena of Localization

Simone Pribbenow

1 Introduction

1.1 Aspects of Localization

When you look at travel or city guides, you will find a large number of expressions whose goal is to give the reader sufficient information about the location of objects of the real world. Of great importance for tourists are descriptions of the site of important buildings, monuments, squares and other sights, e.g.:

(1) Die Kunstakademie ist in der Eiskellerstraße untergebracht.
[The academy of arts is located on Eiskellerstrasse.]

Another class of spatial descriptions is formed by the location of events like famous festivals or sporting events

(2) Unsere Besichtigungstour fand in der Düsseldorfer Altstadt statt.
[Our sightseeing tour took place in the old part of Düsseldorf.]

But there is also a need to locate motions, for example the path or route

(3) Wir gehen durch das Museum. [We are walking through the museum.]

the source or goal,

(4) Der Rundgang beginnt in der altägyptischen und geht bis zur modernen Abteilung.
[The trip starts at the old Egyptian department and ends at the modern art department.]

or even the direction of a motion

(5) Wir fahren nach Frankreich. [We are going to France.]

The first two of these examples describe *static localizations* of objects (expression (1)) or situations[1] (expression (2)). In the static case the entities involved are unmoving or their motion is not relevant in the current context. The next three sentences express *dynamic localizations* of the route (expression (3)), source and goal (expression (4)), or the direction of a path (expression (5)). A complete path consists of a source, goal and one or more route entities. For a mathematical definition of path concepts see Habel (1989). In most cases, the path is induced by a passive or active motion. But it is worth mentioning that objects of a special elongated form such as streets and rivers (example (6)) or a collection of objects forming a line (example (7)) can also induce an abstract path:

---

[1]'Situation' is used as the general term for process, event and state.

(6) Die neue Eisenbahnlinie führt von Hamburg nach München.
[The new railway line runs from Hamburg to Munich.]

(7) Früher standen zahlreiche alte Weiden um den Teich im Stadtpark.
[Long ago there were many old willows around the pond in the city park.][2]

    In order to process all the examples above in the same way, a uniform treatment of these different kinds of localization is needed. A further examination of other text classes shows that spatial localization does not only occur in travel guides; it is a ubiquitous phenomenon. Therefore the discussion to follow is not limited to the domain of travelling and sightseeing, but can be seen as a contribution to the research on natural language processing in general.

1.2 A General Form for Localization Expressions

Before we consider the processing of spatial descriptions, the different forms of their surface structure are of interest. The examples given in (1) to (7) use prepositions to express the location of entities or spatial details of paths. Deictic expressions[3] can be used to give static localizations:

(8) Hier stand das alte Schloß. [The old castle stood here.]

Adverbs provide another way to describe localization, especially directions:

(9) Wir fahren heute südwärts. [Today we travel southward/south.]

For an adequate treatment of all these different expressions, we assume an interpretation process consisting of two levels: the *semantic* and the *conceptual* level, as proposed by Bierwisch/Lang (1987).[4] In the following discussion, we explain the conceptual interpretation in detail. The semantic interpretation that is carried out by the component doing linguistic analysis will only be given by example. For each localization fact, the semantic interpretation extracts a resulting expression consisting of three parts:

- the entity to be located, called the *located entity* or *LE* for short,

- the entity building the basis of the localization, called the *reference object* or *RO* for short,[5]

- the *spatial relation REL* holding between RO and LE.

    In the case of expressions containing prepositional phrases, the spatial relation REL is induced by the preposition itself, while the reference object RO is formed by the internal object

[2]This example is taken from Habel (1989).

[3]Note that German possesses a system of spatial deixis divided into three parts: hier, da, dort, in contrast to the English system consisting of only two expressions: here, there. For a detailed discussion of the German system of primary deixis see Ehrich (1982).

[4]This proposal is not limited to the domain of localization expressions, but is used for other classes like nouns, adjectives, and others as well. Maienborn (in this volume) applies the theory of Bierwisch/Lang to the treatment of verbs of position and movement, Carstensen/Simmons (in this volume) to that of dimensional adjectives.

[5]A collection of alternative terms for 'located entity' or 'reference object' can be found in Retz-Schmidt (1988).

of the prepositional phrase. In deictic expressions, the reference object has no direct linguistic counterpart; it is given implicitly by the *origo*[6] of the deictic relation. The deictic expression itself induces the localization relation REL. The same result observed for deictic expressions holds for adverbial phrases. In all forms of surface structures the third entity, the located object, is not marked explicitly in the text. It has to be extracted from the rest of the sentence. Maienborn (1990) gives a technical description of the processing necessary to compute the three components LE, RO and REL. The result of the analysis is an instantiation of the semantic localization predicate `Lok_sem`[7]:

```
Lok_sem (le:LE, reg:P, context:K).
```

It states that in the situational context K, the entity LE is located with respect to the (abstract) region P, which is described by the reference object RO and the relation REL. The parameter K denotes the situation to which the localization belongs, thus serving as a connection to the temporal component and describing features of the situational context. We leave the parameter K in the predicates and rules for reasons of completeness, but will ignore it in the remainder of this paper.

This predicate forms the interface between the semantic and the conceptual level of analysis. Before going into further details of the conceptual processing, we give two examples of the propositions passed over to the rule-based interpetation carried out by the inference engine. For the first sentence (1) the linguistic analysis extracts the propositions under (1').

(1) Die Kunstakademie ist in der Eiskellerstraße untergebracht.
     [The academy of arts is located on Eiskellerstrasse.]

(1') `Lok_sem (le:r_academy_of_arts, reg:P, context:K)`   with
         `refobject (P) = r_eiskellerstraße`
         `regtype (P)   = 'in'`

The located entity, the internal object `r_academy_of_arts`, is induced by the thema of the 'locate'-situation, the academy of arts[8]. The region under consideration is described by two features. `refobject` denotes the reference object, here the internal object `r_eiskellerstraße` corresponding to the natural language expression Eiskellerstraße. The region type, `regtype`, is given by the constant 'in'.[9] The semantic analysis of the first dynamic localization (see example (3)) results in (3').

(3) Wir gehen durch das Museum.
     [We are walking through the museum.]

---

[6]The origo of an expression depends on the concrete situation of the utterance. Normally the spatial aspect of the origo is the location of the speaker or hearer. For a further description of the term 'origo' see Bühler (1934).

[7]Expressions written in the font `Typewriter` correspond to technical terms like predicates, sorts, and so on used in the ontology or the rules in the LILOG-prototype. For a better understanding I mostly take the English equivalents. In those cases, the German terms really used by the system are given in brackets.

[8]I underline words or phrases taken from natural language (German or English).

[9]Note that this is not the preposition in, but the spatial relation corresponding to this preposition. As shown in the next example of dynamic localization, there is not always a one-to-one relation between prepositions and spatial relations.

(3') Lok_sem (le:route(path$_{we}$), reg:P, context:K)   with
      refobject (P) = r_museum
      regtype (P)   = 'in'

The LE is given by the route of the path induced by the people corresponding to <u>we</u>. The RO is the internal object for the museum, and the region type is the same as in the static example. For analysing expressions without an explicit RO, like deictic or adverbial expressions, a good candidate for the reference object must be computed from the locations in focus to fill the feature refobject.

2 Conceptual Processing

2.1 The General Process

The overall goal of conceptual processing – independent of the kind of natural language expression under analysis – is to construct an internal model (for the system) of the situation described in that expression. The final model shows the result of the process of text understanding; it can be used to answer questions, as prior knowledge for the analysis of the following texts and for similiar tasks.

In the processing of spatial expressions, this model should contain as much information as possible about the spatial situation described in these expressions. To obtain such a comprehensive model of space, two steps are necessary:

- the spatial expression is represented by means of primitive concepts and operators. The most important concepts in the spatial context are REGION/AREA[10] [REGION/GEBIET] and PATH [WEG]. Examples for relevant relations are that of localization LOK(LE,G,K) and contact between two entities Contact [Kontakt]. Functions are needed to select conceptualizations and parts of objects such as hollow_space [hohlraum] or front [vorderseite], to name two examples.

- the isolated knowledge entities are integrated into (conceptual and episodic) prior knowledge. Therefore, the consistency of the total knowledge must be checked,[11] and implicit knowledge is to be made explicit by inference processes. The status of the inferred knowledge can be certain or default (uncertain information, potentially overwritable).

The result of these two steps is a comprehensive model of the spatial situation described by the analysed expressions. The result is computed and represented in a hybrid system consisting of a propositional and a pictorial subsystem (see Habel's paper in this volume). In the LILOG prototype, the propositional formalism consists of facts and rules involving the predicates and functions mentioned and the spatially relevant parts of the ontology describing primitive concepts in the form of sorts. The pictorial formalism corresponds to the DEPIC-2D system (see Khenkhar's

---

[10]Regions are semantic entities of abstract character; while areas are the corresponding refined and pictorial explicated objects on the conceptual level.

[11]See Pribbenow (1988) for a proposal of the special processes needed for that task in the spatial domain.

paper in this volume). Their interaction is controlled by the inference machine via control operators (see Pletat's paper in this volume). Both subsystems make use of *referential objects, RefOs* for short (for the underlying theory of referentiality see Habel (1986)). So knowledge about objects is commonly accessible to rules as well as to depictions.

The interpretation of a spatial expression is therefore a task involving both formalisms. First the propositional system transforms the expression into conceptual entities like the concepts, relations and functions mentioned above. If the creation of a depiction seems appropriate the result of the process is passed to the depictorial component. In an *imagination*, a new depiction is computed (or an old one modified) by interpreting the propositional terms with pictorial processes. Afterwards, the results of both systems together can be used to infer further knowledge, prove consistency, or answer questions.

Inside the described hybrid system, the conceptual semantics of a concrete Lok_sem proposition is determined by the corresponding *localization area*. From a technical point of view, this entity is an internal referential object (RefO) with both propositional and depictorial features. It functions as a *search domain*, a term first described by Miller/Johnson-Laird (1976). Therefore each area object forms an important part of the resulting (spatial) model of the text analysis. The creation of a localization area requires:

- the definition of the area and its depictorial interpretation (if appropriate),

- the specialization of the defined area by means of priorization.

The first task is carried out by *selection rules*, the second by *priorization* or *delimitation* rules.

2.2 Selection Rules

One of the simplest rules defines the area constituted by a Lok_sem proposition with the region type 'bei', as it is induced by a natural language expression using the preposition bei. The German preposition bei[12] involves the direct surroundings of the reference object RO, and selects what we call the *exterior region* [Außenregion] of the RO. This region is similiar to the *region of interaction* proposed by Miller/Johnson-Laird (1976). Examples of other works on the semantics of bei can be found in Wunderlich (1982) who uses a topologically defined *äußere Umgebung* [external surroundings], and in Herweg (1989) who describes a *proximale Außenregion* [proximal exterior region].

The rule processing a bei-expression, (R1), is based on the described semantics of the preposition. The only premise is the result of the linguistic analysis, an instantiation of the Lok_sem predicate. The entry point EP indicates that this expression is the trigger for R1 and thus the rule is only used for forward inference. The possible instantiations of the variables are restricted by the sorts given in the head of the rule. They prevent RO and LE from being entities that cannot serve as depictionable objects like situations, ideas or other abstract concepts. The conclusion of the bei-rule consists of two parts:

---

[12]There is no exact English counterpart to bei. Similiar prepositions are at and near.

- The creation of the referential object G denoting the localization area corresponding to the analysed expression, with its defining feature filled in as exterior_region(RO,LE). The term exterior_region is taken from the semantics of the preposition; its two variables RO and LE are required by the depictorial component to compute the concrete form and extent of the depiction for area G. The control operator genrefo triggers the creation of a new RefO with sort AREA [GEBIET] if no internal RefO exists which has exactly the same definition in the same context.

- The conceptual semantics of the analysed expression is given by the predicate LOK(LE,G,K). Each concrete instantiation is stored as a fact concerning the localization of LE. The control operator depic_obl indicates that the following term is always (obligatorily) passed to the pictorial component DEPIC-2D, which creates the depiction based on that localization fact.

```
R1 forall   LE, RO : DEPICOBJECT,
            P  : REGION,
            K  : CONTEXT,
            G  : AREA;
    EP  Lok_sem(le:LE, reg:P, context:K)
        and refobject (P) = RO
        and regtype (P) = 'bei'
   →
    genrefo(G, and (definition:exterior_region (ro:RO,le:LE),
                    refobject:RO))
    and depic_obl LOK(le:LE, area:G, context:K).
```

Very similiar to R1 is the rule for the preposition an, which uses the term narrow_exterior_region [enge-außenregion] instead of exterior_region for representing the semantics of the preposition.[13] More interesting are the selection rules associated with prepositions allowing intrinsic as well as deictic use, for example vor [in front of], hinter [behind], links [to the left]. To analyze the deictic use, an additional point of reference is needed in order to compute the part of the RO that is construed as the front, back, or left side, etc. This point is normally the location of the speaker or hearer. The intrinsic use of these prepositions presupposes the existence of a front, back, etc., inherent to the object. The rules for those prepositions contain a mechanism that decides between the deictic and the intrinsic use. The intrinsic reading is favored if the reference object RO has the intrinsic side in question and if the context of the analyzed expression does not suggest the deictic use as it does in special text classes, or if deixis was used in the preceding sentences. Whether an intrinsic side of an entity exists can be determined by means of augmented object schemata described in Lang/Carstensen (1990) (see also Lang/Carstensen/Simmons (1991), Carstensen/Simmons (this volume)).

Another interesting group of prepositions are those that involve the concept of an interior_region [innenregion] like in [in] for both static and dynamic localization or durch [through] which involves a path or route through the interior of the reference object. The selection process interpreting these prepositions has to cope with the functional aspect of containment, which requires an adequate part of the RO as a container for the located entity. As an illustration consider the following examples:

---

[13]English counterparts to an are at and on depending on the context. The concept narrow_exterior_region implies that the extent of the resulting area is smaller than that of the area induced by the exterior_region associated with bei. Contact is focused if the preposition appears as an argument of contact verbs.

(10) a. der Riß im Haus [the crack in the house]
  b. die Frau im Haus [the woman in the house]
  c. das Haus in der Stadt [the house in the city]

In (10a), the crack is in the building's material referred to as substantial_parts [feste_Teile]; in (10b) the woman is located in the interior of the house referred to as hollow_space [hohlraum]. The house itself forms a part of the city, so in (10c) it is necessary to refer to the reference object as an (idealized) whole, which we call silhouette [silhouette].

The selection rules for the class of prepositions depending on the interior_region concept have to find the conceptualization of the RO that is suited to the requirements of the particular LE. If such a conceptualization exists then the predicate Can_contain (in-conceptualization(RO), LE) [kann_beinhalten (in-Konzeptualisierung(RO),LE)] can be verified.

This vocabulary is sufficient to formulate the selection rule for the static preposition in. Here we use a meta-level form to avoid writing a new rule for every possible in-conceptualization. In the domain in question, the three relevant conceptualizations are hollow_space, silhouette, and substantial_parts as described above. In the following rule (R2), we use the term in_space as a meta-variable for these three conceptualizations of RO.

```
R2 forall   LE, RO : OBJECT,
            P  : REGION,
            K  : CONTEXT,
            G  : AREA;
   EP  Lok_sem (le:LE, reg:P, context:K)
       and refobject (P) = RO
       and regtype (P) = 'in'
       and Can_contain (ro:in_space(ro:RO), le:LE)
   →
   genrefo(G, and(definition:interior_region(ro:in_space(ro:RO),
                  refobject:RO))
   and depic_obl LOK(le:LE, area:G, context:K).
```

To verify the Can_contain clause in the premise, special rules like R3 are needed. This rule expresses that concrete objects, sorted as OBJECT, are able to contain entities like cracks, tears, fissures, etc., subsumed by the sort GAP. R3 is used to handle expressions like (10a).

```
R3 forall LE : GAP,
          RO : OBJECT;
   EP  Can_contain (ro:substantial_parts (ro:RO), le:LE).
```

Another way of dealing with different situations involving in can be found within the framework of prototype theory. This kind of prepositional semantics based on *use types* has been worked out by Herskovits (1985) for English prepositions for an implementation see Hays (1987) and by Hottenroth (1986) for the French preposition dans [in].

In spite of the differences between the rules discussed for the different prepositions, the main purpose of selection rules is the creation of the internal area object corresponding to the localization expression (see Sect. 2.1). This area RefO is ready for a depictorial interpretation by means of an *imagination* process (for a detailed description see Khenkhar (this volume)). To compute this area entity, each rule makes use of the semantics of the analysed preposition, attributes of the reference object RO, for example those relevant to the choice between deictic or intrinsic use, and the (functional) interaction between reference and located entity. The derived knowledge is certain; counterfacts will cause an inconsistency (see Pribbenow (1988)).

2.3 Priorization Rules

As mentioned in Sect. 2.1, priorization or delimitation rules are employed to specialize the areas constructed by selection rules. As before, the rules are used to infer constraining knowledge, while the depictorial component represents this information explicitly by modifing the pictorial area object in consideration. The two most important sources of priorization knowledge are

- *typical locations* for the located object,

- *competing objects* with respect to the reference object.

The typical locations of an object category are those places where representatives of that category normally can be found. Consider two localizations concerning the same reference object:

(11) a. das Haus in der Straße [the house on the street]
     b. das Auto in der Straße [the car in the street]

(11a) and (11b) give priority to different parts of the reference object <u>Straße</u> [street]. A house is typically sited beside the street's lanes and sidewalks, whereas cars normally are parked or moving in these lanes. Therefore, these parts of the street have the highest priority as the actual location of the house or the car. It seems helpful to store them as typical locations for the categories of buildings or vehicles.

Competing objects have the opposite effects on areas. These are objects lying in the proximal surroundings of the reference object that are as large, significant, visible, i.e., as salient as the reference object itself. Thus a competing object can play the role of a landmark for the localization of LE as well as the primary RO. So the localization area induced by a competing object sets limits on the current area based on the reference object. Thus the effect of a competing entity is to produce negative priorization concerning parts of the primary localization area.

Before presenting a rule that realizes priorization, I will mention another kind of delimitation that is used implicitly in the depictorial component without being triggered by rules. If an area that depends on any kind of `exterior_region` or `narrow_exterior_region` (like localizations using <u>bei</u>, <u>an</u>, <u>vor</u>, <u>links</u>, etc.) is to be represented depictorially, the pictorial component has to make a decision about the extent of this area. It holds that the larger and more salient the RO, the larger the extent of the area. The same is true of the size of LE. That is the reason why RO and LE form the two arguments of each exterior region. Without knowledge about the size and relevance of these two objects, the depictorial component cannot create a pictorial area object at all.

Thus delimitation takes place implicitly in every computation of areas defined by exterior region concepts. It is based on information about the typical size and relevance of objects that the depictorial component obtains from ontological features of object categories or from individual facts. This delimitation process is not necessary for interior_region concepts, because the form and the extent of the resulting area is determined by the relevant part of the concrete reference object, e.g., the existing hollow spaces, substantial parts, and so on.

The influence of typical locations is reflected by the rule R4, which is triggered by the existence of a localization fact LOK (LE,G,K). The rule tries to verify whether a typical location for entities of the object category of the LE exists, and whether an instantiation of this typical location is part of the area under consideration. The first constraint is described by the predicate TypLok(LE,R), the abbreviation of *typical location* [Typischer Aufenthaltsort], which selects those kinds of areas abstracted to the definition of an area R that can serve as typical location for objects belonging to the category of the LE. The existence of such a part within the given area is proved by the predicate Overlap [Überlappen]. If necessary, the predicate is evaluated on the depictorial level which is indicated by the control operator depic_opt with opt standing for an optional use of the depictorial component.

The result of a rule application proceeds in two steps. First, the role Priorization [Priorisierung] of the area RefO G is filled in with the pertinent area definition R, and second, a tuple < area/area definition > is sent to the depictorial subsystem with the request to modify the area G with respect to region R. To indicate that most but not all of the possible LE can be found inside the typical location R, a default quantifier o_default is used (see Pletat (this volume)). This quantifier induces a default status to the whole rule. Results inferred by such a rule can be withdrawn by new facts.

```
R4 forall    RO :  DEPICOBJECT,
             G  :  AREA,
             R  :  GEBREGION,
             K  :  CONTEXT;
   o_default  LE :  DEPICOBJECT;
   EP LOK (le:LE, area:G, context:K)
      and TypLok (le:LE, typlokdef:R)
      and depic_opt (Overlap(typlokdef:R, area:G))
   →
   Priorization (area:G, typlokdef:R)
   and depic_obl (Modify(area:G, typlokdef:R)).
```

What is needed additionally are rules that describe typical locations of object categories, like the following rule R5. This rule states that buildings are normally sited in the narrow exterior region of the street "kernel" (lanes and sidewalks), in other words beside the street kernel.

```
R5 forall B : BUILDING,
          S : STREET;
   EP TypLok (le:B, typlokdef:narrow_exterior_region(ro:S, le:B)).
```

The process of computing the effects of competing objects will not be explained in detail, because the rules are analogous to that given for the computation of typical locations except that they use a delimitation predicate.

All of the described priorizations or delimitations, whether given explicitly by rules or used implicitly within the depictorial component, are used to specify the area entity under consideration, in order to yield a better search domain. The processes given by priorization rules require an area object as a basis for their work. The knowledge used in the priorization process involves typical attributes of object classes like typical locations, typical size or relevance, etc. This kind of information is called *commonsense knowledge*, and although people use this knowledge all the time, it has only default status. Concrete contradictory facts overwrite this uncertain information without causing any inconsistency as they do in interaction with facts derived by selection rules.

3 Conclusions

3.1 Interaction of Rule-Based and Depictorial Processes

The basic ideas underlying the interaction between the propositional and the depictorial subsystem involved in the process of analyzing localization expressions were outlined in the previous section. The rules compute the conceptual primitives that correspond to the analyzed expression. The resulting area object is represented by the pictorial component DEPIC-2D, which explicates the form and the extent of the area by computing its depiction. Based on that result, the two subsystems together compute the priorizations that can be made to refine the area in order to produce a good search domain.

The analysis of the interpretation process shows how the rules of the propositional system are used to derive *constraints* that are explicated by the depictorial subsystem. Only the pictorial component can access the current spatial relations of the objects involved, including relations that are not mentioned explicitly in the text. The latter property shows why depictions are useful for dealing with competing objects and typical locations.

The various advantages induce a natural distribution of the tasks arising in the treatment of spatial knowledge between the two subsystems.[14] For question-answering tasks, there is a simple maxim for deciding what formalism should be used for what kind of question:

The more complex the question, the more suitable the depictorial formalism.

If a fact given by the input text is all that is needed to generate the answer, it is not necessary to use a depictorial component. It would be easier to retrieve the necessary fact from the data base. But if the question depends on a spatial relation not mentioned in the input or calls for a complex task like route descriptions, then the properties of the pictorial formalism relieves us from using a huge number of propositional rules. If an answer exists, the pictorial component can find it by simply "looking" at the depictions using an *inspection* process.[15]

---

[14]A detailed discussion can be found in Pribbenow (1990). It contains a definition for the notion of *complexity* used in the following maxim.

[15]A comparision of propositional and pictoral deduction processes can be found in Lindsay (1988).

3.2 Summary

The conceptual semantics of each localization expression, i.e., each triple consisting of a spatial relation (for example given by a preposition), a reference object (the internal argument of the prepositional expression or the origo in deictic expressions) and the entity to be located, is given by an *area constituting process* [Gebietskonstituierender Prozeß](see Habel/Pribbenow (1988)). The area constituting process computes the corresponding area using constraints determined by the semantics of the spatial relation, the features of the two entities involved, and available information about the spatial environment. The result is an instantiation of a LOK-fact that indicates the location of the located entity LE in the computed area G. The area object will be represented and processed on both the propositional and the depictorial component. Note that sometimes the part or the conceptualization of the located entity has to be inferred before it is possible to assert the LOK-fact. This is especially important for dynamical localization, where an underlying (abstract) path is involved in the location.

References

Bierwisch, M., Lang, E. (eds., 1987): Grammatische und konzeptuelle Aspekte von Dimensionsadjektiven. Akademie-Verlag, Berlin

Bühler, K. (1934): Sprachtheorie. Fischer, Jena

Ehrich, V. (1982): Da and the system of spatial deixis in German. In: J. Weissenborn, W. Klein (eds.): Here and There. Benjamin, Amsterdam/Philadelphia, pp. 43-63

Habel, Ch. (1986): Prinzipien der Referentialität. Springer-Verlag, Berlin, Heidelberg, New York

Habel, Ch. (1989): Propositional and Depictorial Representations of Spatial Knowledge: The Case of Path-Concepts. Report FBI-HH-M-171/89, University of Hamburg

Habel, Ch., Pribbenow, S. (1988): Gebietskonstituierende Prozesse. LILOG Report 18, IBM Deutschland, Stuttgart

Hays, E. (1987): A Computational Treatment of Locative Relations in Natural Language. Report MS-CIS-87-31, LINC LAB 58, University of Pennsylvania

Herskovits, A. (1985): Semantics and pragmatics of locative expressions. Cognitive Science, 9, 341-378

Herweg, M. (1989): Ansätze zu einer semantischen Beschreibung topologischer Präpositionen. In: Ch. Habel, M. Herweg, K. Rehkämper (eds.): Raumkonzepte in Verstehensprozessen. Niemeyer, Tübingen, pp. 99-127

Hottenroth, P. (1986): Die Semantik lokaler Präpositionen. Ein prototypensemantisches Modell für die französische Präposition dans mit einer Analyse der Beziehungen zwischen der Präposition und den Objektbezeichnungen in den Präpositionalsyntagmen. Habilitation thesis, University of Konstanz

Lang, E., Carstensen, K.-U. (1990): OSKAR - A Prolog Program for Modelling Dimensional Designation and Positional Variation of Objects in Space. IWBS Report 109, IBM Deutschland, Stuttgart

Lang, E., Carstensen, K.-U., Simmons, G. (1991): Modelling Spatial Knowledge on a Linguistic Basis: Theory-Prototype-Integration. Springer-Verlag, Berlin, Heidelberg, New York

Lindsay, R. (1988): Image and inference. Cognition, 29, 229-250

Maienborn, C. (1990): Lokale Verben und Präpositionen: Semantische und konzeptuelle Verarbeitung in LEU II. IWBS Report 119, IBM Deutschland, Stuttgart

Miller, G., Johnson-Laird, P. (1976): Language and Perception. Cambridge University Press, Cambridge, MA

Pribbenow, S. (1988): Verträglichkeitsprüfungen für die Verarbeitung räumlichen Wissens. In: W. Hoeppner (ed.): Proc. GWAI-88, Springer-Verlag, Berlin, Heidelberg, New York

Pribbenow, S. (1990): Interaktion von propositionalen und bildhaften Repräsentationen. In: Ch. Freksa, Ch. Habel (eds.): Repräsentation und Verarbeitung räumlichen Wissens. Springer-Verlag, Berlin, Heidelberg, New York

Retz-Schmidt, G. (1988): Various views on spatial prepositions. AI Magazine, 9/2, 95-105

Wunderlich, D. (1982): Sprache und Raum. Studium Linguistik, 12, 1-19 and 13, 37-59

Verbs of Motion and Position:
On the Optionality of the Local Argument

Claudia Maienborn*

1 Theoretical Background

The present article on the optionality of the local argument of verbs of motion and position[1] is based on a view of semantics which is assumed in cognitive linguistics and is characterized basically by the assumption of a modularly organized mental representation system. According to Bierwisch and Lang (cf. Bierwisch 1982, 1983; Lang 1985; Bierwisch/Lang 1987, 1989) two levels of representation are involved in the process of reconstructing the meaning of natural language expressions: a *semantic level*, which belongs to the language system, and a language-independent *conceptual level*. The semantic level specifies the grammatically determined part of meaning. That is, semantic structures are systematically related to syntactic structures and guarantee the compositional construction of meaning representation. At the conceptual level, semantic structures are interpreted with respect to context and available conceptual knowledge, e.g., knowledge about the constitution of objects, characteristic courses of events, and causal connections. Within this framework, meaning is understood as the result of integrating the semantic and the conceptual meaning components. This "two-level semantics", as it is often called, is intended to capture both: the grammatically relevant structure as well as the conceptual foundation of semantic entities.[2] The concrete form of interaction between the semantic and the conceptual level of representation is deeply influenced by the specific requirements of the domain of investigation.[3] Besides the already existing works concerning nouns (Bierwisch 1982, 1983), symmetric predicates (Lang 1985), dimensional adjectives (Bierwisch/Lang 1987, 1989), local prepositions (Herweg 1989), and temporal conjunctions (Herweg 1990), the optionality of the local argument of verbs of motion and position seems to be a promising starting point for an elaboration of the interface between the semantic and the conceptual level with respect to the specific requirements of the local verb system.

2 Semantic Structure of Local Verbs

I consider the local adverbial occurring together with a local verb as being a syntactic complement of the verb. That means that the local adverbial has the semantic status of an argument. In German there is no single clear criterion for distinguishing complements from adjuncts. Nonetheless, several of the proposed criteria can be integrated into a relatively reliable heuristic, which in the

---

*I wish to thank Carola Eschenbach, Christopher Habel, and Michael Herweg for discussion and comments. Special thanks to Geoff Simmons for checking my English.

[1]The class of German verbs of motion and position or local verbs, as I will also call them, includes verbs of motion, e.g., gehen, laufen [to walk, to run], verbs of position, e.g., stehen, sitzen, liegen [to stand, to sit, to lie], an local causatives, e.g., stellen, setzen, legen [to put, to set, to lay].

[2]See especially Bierwisch/Lang (1987, 1989) for a detailed motivation and a discussion of a parallel approach to cognitive semantics which assumes just one level of representation, i.e., the conceptual level, as postulated by Jackendoff (1983, 1987).

[3]See Habel (this volume) for an outline of a representation system designed for spatial knowledge.

case of local verbs assigns the local adverbial the status of a complement. Therefore, the local argument distinguishes the class of local verbs from other verb classes.

The internal semantic structure of local verbs consists mainly of two components[4]: a *relation of localization*, which holds between an individual and a spatial entity, i.e., a place or path, and a *predicate of mode*. The relation of localization represents the localization of the individual denoted by the external argument relative to the place or path denoted by the local argument. Verbs of position instantiate a static version of the relation of localization, whereas verbs of motion instantiate a dynamic variant. The predicate of mode represents the specific position or motion associated with each verb, i.e., the idiosyncratic meaning component that allows for the distinction between verbs of position like stehen, sitzen, hocken, knien, kauern [to stand, to sit, to squat, to kneel, to crouch] or verbs of motion like gehen, rennen, laufen, schleichen, kriechen [to walk, to race, to run, to creep, to crawl]. Using predicate logic with λ-abstraction as representation formalism, the semantic structure of verbs of position and motion is given with (1) and (2) respectively.[5]

(1) $\lambda p \, \lambda x \, [LOC \, (x, p) \, \& \, MOD_{POSITION} \, (x)]$

(2) $\lambda w \, \lambda x \, [MOVE \, (x, w) \, \& \, MOD_{MOTION} \, (x)]$

LOC stands for the static relation of localization, *MOVE* stands for the dynamic variant, and $MOD_{POSITION}$ and MOD_{MOTION} represent the modes of position and motion respectively; x is a variable over individuals, p a variable over places, and w a variable over paths.

The identification of the structural complexes on which the mode of position or motion is based takes place at the conceptual level, because a structural analysis of the different modes has to rely on conceptual knowledge, e.g., knowledge about the properties of gestalt and position of objects and the restrictions imposed on combinations with local verbs (see Lang/Carstensen 1989, 1990). By means of the semantic predicate for the mode of position or motion, the language system has access to the corresponding conceptual structures, but it is not involved in the task of elaborating the different modes. Thus, the predicate of mode figures within the language system as a semantic label for a complex of conceptual structures.

The efficiency of the "two-level semantics" model relies crucially on the interaction between the two levels of representation. It is only this interaction between the semantic and the conceptual level which ensures an adequate treatment of the flexibility of natural language in referring to conceptually mediated states of affairs. One kind of interaction consists in conceptually specifying semantic entities as illustrated in the case of the predicate of mode. Semantic entities are related to conceptual structures and are therefore conceptually grounded (see, e.g., Pribbenow's paper in this volume). The system of local verbs indicates further forms of interaction, which shall be reconstructed in the following from the analysis of the semantic and conceptual aspects of the phenomenon of the optionality of the local argument.

[4]See Maienborn (1990a) for a detailed discussion of the semantics of local verbs and Maienborn (1990b) for its realization within the LILOG project.
[5]For the purposes at hand the semantic structure given in (1) and (2) is slightly simplified, ignoring the verbs' referential argument.

3 Optionality of the Local Argument

Sentences like (3) and (4), which are grammatical in spite of the lack of the local argument, are generally used to show that the local argument of verbs of motion and position is optional. But verbs of position like <u>wohnen</u> [to live][6], <u>lehnen</u> [to lean], or local causatives like <u>stellen</u> [to put], <u>legen</u> [to lay] enforce the realization of their local argument (see (5) and (6)).

(3) a. Rita sitzt. [Rita is sitting.]
     b. Rita steht. [Rita is standing.]
     c. Rita kniet. [Rita is kneeling.]

(4) a. Rita geht. [Rita is walking.]
     b. Rita läuft. [Rita is running.]
     c. Rita humpelt. [Rita is limping.]

(5) a. * Rita wohnt. [Rita is living.]
     b. * Rita lehnt. [Rita is leaning.]

(6) a. * Rita stellt das Buch. [Rita puts the book.]
     b. * Rita legt die Decke. [Rita lays the blanket.]

At first glance, local verbs seem to behave unsystematically with respect to the optionality of the local argument, preventing a uniform characterization. With this observation in mind, it is generally decided to treat the optionality of the local argument as verb-specific, i.e., to decide for each local verb individually, if the presence of the local argument is required or not. Such a solution to the problem of optionality is by no means satisfactory, because it stipulates an unsystematic behavior of local verbs just in connection with their local argument, the characteristic feature that distinguishes them from other verb classes. Under this approach, a systematic explanation of the relation between verbs of motion and position and their local argument turns out impossible.

The strategy of treating the optionality of the local argument for each verb individually fails completely to explain varying judgements on the variation of the external argument (see (7) and (8)).

(7) a. Rita liegt in ihrem Bett.   Rita liegt.
        [Rita is lying in her bed.]   [Rita is lying.]
     b. Das Buch liegt auf dem Tisch.   ? Das Buch liegt.
        [The book is lying on the table.] [The book is lying.]
     c. Der Teppich liegt im Flur.   ?? Der Teppich liegt.
        [The carpet is lying in the hall.] [The carpet is lying]
     d. Das Zimmer liegt im Erdgeschoß. * Das Zimmer liegt.
        [The room is (lies) in the ground floor.] [The room lies.]

(8) a. Rita steht vor dem Haus.   Rita steht.
        [Rita is standing in front of the house.] [Rita is standing.]
     b. Das Buch steht auf dem Tisch.   ? Das Buch steht.
        [The book is standing on the table.] [The book is standing.]

---
[6]The German verb <u>wohnen</u> is characterized by a local component which has to be specified by the local argument. For example: <u>Rita wohnt in Stuttgart.</u> [Rita is living in Stuttgart.] Therefore, the English <u>to live</u> is not the exact translation of <u>wohnen</u> (cf. the French verb <u>habiter</u>).

c. Das Haus steht am Stadtrand. [The house is (standing) on the outskirts of the town.]	?? Das Haus steht. [The house is standing.]
d. Der Wald steht auf der Anhöhe. [The wood is (stands) on the hill.]	* Der Wald steht. [The wood stands.]

Sentences (7) and (8) show that the lack of the local argument triggers different degrees of acceptability. Moreover, sentences like (9) and (10) indicate that judgements can switch completely if a modal adverb turns up.

(9) a. * Das Zimmer liegt. [The room lies.]
     b.   Das Zimmer liegt ruhig. [The room is (lies) quiet.]

(10) a. * Der Wald steht. [The wood stands.]
     b.   Der Wald steht schwarz und schweiget...
          [The wood stands black and silent.]
          (Matthias Claudius: Der Mond ist aufgegangen)

The examples (7) – (10) show the impossibility of formulating a global statement about the optionality of the local argument of verbs of motion and position. It is not the case that the lack of the local argument is either permissible or ruled out; it is judged with varying degrees of acceptability. In the following, an explanation of the phenomenon of optionality will be outlined by making use of the specific principles and properties of the semantic and the conceptual level of representation. It is intended to capture both – the degrees of acceptability as well as the underlying regularity within the relation between local verbs and their local argument.

4 Interaction between Semantic and Conceptual Structures

A crucial assumption of cognitive linguistics concerns the modularity of the mental representation system. For the representation of meaning, three modules within the whole system are of primary interest: the syntactic, the semantic, and the conceptual module. Each of these modules has its own set of well-formedness conditions mirroring inherent regularities. Therefore, syntactic, semantic, and conceptual well-formedness conditions can be distinguished and considered separately with respect to their contribution to a global judgement of well-formedness. Syntactic and semantic well-formedness conditions are language-specific restrictions, and thus constitute the basis on which grammaticality is judged. As to the phenomenon of optionality of the local argument, a closer look at the different dimensions of well-formedness will clarify the reasons for the degrees of acceptability.

From a syntactic point of view, the PP-complement of verbs of motion and position is always optional. There are no syntactic principles which could explain why sentence (11a) is grammatical, but sentence (11b) is ungrammatical. Both sentences are syntactically well-formed. The " * ", which marks ungrammaticality, has to be motivated elsewhere.

(11) a.   Rita steht. [Rita is standing.]
     b. * Der Wald steht. [The wood stands.]

In the same vein, differently instantiated semantic or conceptual features of individual verbs belonging to the syntactic paradigm of local verbs can influence syntactic well-formedness. Again, there are no syntactic reasons for the ungrammaticality of (12c,d) in contrast to the grammaticality of (12a,b).

(12) a. Rita sitzt. [Rita is sitting.]
     b. Rita hockt. [Rita is squatting.]
     c. * Rita wohnt. [Rita is living.]
     d. * Rita lehnt. [Rita is leaning.]

At the syntactic level, local verbs are treated uniformly: the PP-complement is always optional. Degrees and limitations of acceptability due to a missing local argument are not caused by syntactic principles.

What about the problem of optionality at the semantic level? Arguments are anchored in the semantic structure of verbs. The internal verb structure specifies function-argument relations, and each argument variable is instantiated by the semantic contribution of the corresponding argument. Thus, the internal argument structure of a verb mirrors its external combinatorial behavior. If an argument required by the verb is not supplied by its structural environment, the corresponding internal argument variable cannot be saturated. As a consequence, meaning composition is incomplete, leaving a semantically defective structure that violates the semantic well-formedness conditions. This means that a flexible treatment of the argument requirements of a verb at the semantic level is ruled out, because it implies an illegitimate modification of the verb's semantic structure. Therefore, the local argument is semantically indispensible for verbs of motion and position. If it is not provided by a local PP, the corresponding place or path variable of the relation of localization remains unsaturated.

With respect to the optionality of the local argument of verbs of motion and position a conflict arises: syntactic well-formedness conditions tolerate the lack of the local argument, while semantic well-formedness conditions force its presence. One solution to this problem is the contextual reconstruction of the local argument. The missing local argument is reconstructed from the linguistic or extralinguistic context, and the corresponding place or path variable within the verb's semantic structure is instantiated by the resulting constant.

(13) a. Ich muß um 10 Uhr in der Uni sein.
       [I have to be at the university at ten o'clock.]
     b. Fährst du mich?
       [Can you give me a lift?]

(14) a. Morgen bin ich im Institut.
       [I will be at the institute tomorrow.]
     b. Kommst du auch?
       [Will you come, too?]

In sentences (13) and (14), sentence (a) provides a local specification, which can be used to reconstruct the missing local argument of sentence (b). Additional operations can become necessary during the reconstruction process, as in the case of sentences (13) and (14), where a place specification has to be converted into a path specification in order to fit the requirements of the verb of motion <u>fahren</u> [to drive] and <u>kommen</u> [to come], respectively. Similarly constructed texts with verbs of position (see (15)) or local causatives (see (16)) show, however, that the contextual reconstruction of the local argument apparently occurs only within certain limits. The sentences (a) of (15) and (16) provide a local specification which could be used to reconstruct the local argument of the sentences (b). Nonetheless, this option cannot be taken: the contextual reconstruction is blocked.

(15) a. Ich habe das Buch ins Fach gelegt.   b. * Es liegt immer noch.
      [I've laid the book on the shelf.]   [It is still lying.]

(16) a. Das Sofa soll an die Wand.   b. * Stellst du es?
      [The sofa should be put by the wall.]   [Could you place it?]

The question as to which regularities this behavior is based on cannot be discussed here, particularly because it is not an inherent problem of local verbs. An explanation of the restrictions governing the use of contextual reconstruction must be integrated into a general theory of lexical ellipsis. Here it should be emphasized only that contextual reconstruction of the local argument, just in the case of verbs of motion, can systematically remove the discrepancy between syntactic and semantic requirements. In all other cases, contextual reconstruction turns out to be a rather marginal phenomenon.

5 Existential Binding of the Local Argument

A strategy for removing the discrepancy between syntactic and semantic well-formedness conditions, which is valid for the whole class of local verbs, consists of existentially binding the local argument. If a semantic argument is not realized syntactically, the corresponding argument variable can be regarded as existentially bound. In this case, the meaning composition of the VP can be continued and a violation of semantic well-formedness conditions is prevented. Thus, the syntactically sanctioned optionality of the local argument of verbs of motion and position at the semantic level is taken into account by an existential binding of the place or path variable.

I regard the existential binding of an argument as an instrument that is used at the semantic level in order to avoid a semantic defect. Such a precaution calls for motivation and interpretation. In the case of verbs of motion and position, we are faced with the questions: what kind of interpretation should be given to the existential binding of a local argument, and how is the sentence meaning influenced? I take the abstraction from the location as starting point for a conceptual interpretation of the existential binding of the local argument. If the local argument remains unspecified, an abstraction from the concrete location takes place, because the concrete location is judged to be irrelevant within the utterance situation, independently of whether it is known or not. With respect to the two components of the semantic structure of local verbs – relation of localization, and mode of motion or position – the abstraction from the location causes a defocusing of the relation of localization. It only says that the individual is localized, but not where it is localized. Instead, the mode component is under focus.

The interpretation of the existential binding of the local argument as an abstraction from location requires that it is possible to focus the mode of motion or position, and that it can be given an interpretation within the utterance situation. Mode focusing is admissible only if the individual affected has several possible positions in space. In this case, one position can be singled out and contrasted from all other potential positions. This is exactly what mode focusing achieves. If an individual lacks any variability of potential positionings, such a contrast turns out to be impossible. Thus, the individual affected has to meet certain conceptual conditions, so that mode focusing is admissible and the existential binding of the local argument is legitimate.

Lang (1987) develops the notion of *object schemata* as a proposal for codifying the gestalt and position properties of objects.[7] Object schemata contain information about the movability of objects, alternative positionings, and canonical positions. Thus, they provide the kind of knowledge that has to be consulted when checking an object's potential positionings and movements. From the object schemata of human bodies, closets or bottles of wine, for example, it can be inferred that the corresponding objects can take up the mode of position associated with liegen [to lie], as well as the mode of position associated with stehen [to stand]. Thus in these cases, the prerequisite of mode focusing, namely the existence of alternative potential positionings, is fullfilled; therefore, the focusing of one mode of position selected from the spectrum of possibilities can take place (see (17) – (19)). On the other hand, the object schemata of objects like rooms or mountains do not allow any alternative positionings, so mode focusing is conceptually inadmissible, and the existential binding of the local argument is therefore ruled out (see (20)).

(17) a. Rita steht.   b. Rita liegt.
         [Rita is standing.]   [Rita is lying.]

(18) a. Der Schrank steht.   b. Der Schrank liegt.
         [The closet is standing.]   [The closet is lying.]

(19) a. Die Weinflasche steht.   b. Die Weinflasche liegt.
         [The bottle of wine is standing.]   [The bottle of wine is lying.]

(20) a. * Das Zimmer liegt. [The room lies.]
      b. * Der Berg steht. [The mountain stands.]

Varying degrees of acceptability observed for the absence of the local argument of verbs of motion and position reflect the plausibility of mode focusing within an utterance context. If the utterance context supports the contrast of position or motion modes, high degrees of acceptability are obtained. For example, if a move of house is taken as the utterance context of (21), the sentences are accepted without any objection.

(21) a. Der Teppich liegt. [The carpet is lying.]
      b. Der Schrank steht. [The closet is standing.]
      c. Die Lampe hängt. [The lamp is hanging.]

A move of house can be characterized by the achievement of a final state which is defined by the normal or desired position of the furniture. Thus, the core of a move of house consists of the contrast between two states of position, a marked final state and an initial state defined by the negation of the final state. This contrast can be exploited when anchoring the mode focusing. In the same way, an earthquake as utterance context of (22) can establish a contrast of states of position. In contrast to its extremely limited acceptability relative to a neutral context (see (8c)), sentence (22) is absolutely acceptable when judged with respect to an utterance context that establishes a contrast of position modes.

---

[7]See also Lang/Carstensen/Simmons (1991) and Carstensen/Simmons (this volume) for an introduction to the theory of object schemata and its application within the LILOG project.

(22) Das Haus steht. [The house is standing.]

When judging the acceptability of a sentence which lacks a local argument, the utterance situation has to match a context-independent basic schema, which provides a contrast between states of position or motion and thus motivates mode focusing. If an utterance situation supplies such a motivation, the sentence is accepted without restrictions. If an utterance situation matches the basic schema only partially or not at all, acceptability is appropriately reduced. From this point of view, acceptability judgements concern exclusively conceptual meaning aspects of natural language expressions. Degrees of acceptability observed in connection with local verbs cannot be traced back to properties inherent to the language system; i.e., they do not reflect syntactic or semantic irregularities within the class of local verbs, but are triggered at the conceptual level.

When judging sentences (21) and (22), it is knowledge about the utterance context which allows the contrast of position modes. The motivation of mode focusing takes place at the conceptual level. At the semantic level, phase quantifiers like schon [already] and noch [still] establish a change from one phase to the complementary one (see Löbner 1989). In combination with local verbs, phase quantifiers determine a transition from one phase of position or motion into the complementary phase of position or motion. Therefore, phase quantifiers establish the contrast required by the mode focusing at the semantic level (see (23)). The only conceptual prerequisite is that the object can take up different positions (see (24)).

(23) a. Der Teppich liegt schon. [The carpet is already lying.]
      b. Die Lampe hängt noch. [The lamp is still hanging.]
      c. Das Auto fährt noch nicht. [The car cannot be driven yet.]
      d. Das Haus steht immer noch / nicht mehr / schon wieder.
         [The house is still standing / no longer standing / standing again.]

(24) a. * Hamburg liegt längst an der Elbe.
         [Hamburg lies at the Elbe for a long time.]
      b. * Der Berg steht schon wieder.
         [The mountain is standing again.]

Knowledge about the utterance context consulted when judging the acceptability of sentences (21) and (22) does the same job as phase quantifiers in (23). The only difference is that phase quantifiers induce the contrast potential semantically, so that judgments are not subject to any degrees of acceptability, whereas in (21) and (22), the contrast potential has to be provided by the conceptual level. In this case success and therefore acceptability of the sentence depends on the suitability of the utterance situation.

Besides the possibility of establishing complementary phases of position or motion given with phase quantifiers, the language system can also express contrastive relations between modes of position or motion. In the sentences under (25) concurrent modes are explicitly contrasted. In the sentences under (26), where a local verb is combined with a modal adverb, a contrast to combinations with concurring modal adverbs is established.

(25) a. Das Buch steht nicht, es liegt. [The book isn't standing, but lying.]
    b. Rita wohnt nicht, sie residiert. [Rita isn't living, but residing]
    c. Rita geht nicht, sie schleicht. [Rita isn't walking, but creeping.]
    d. Soll ich die Weinflaschen legen oder stellen?
       [Should I lay the bottles of wine down or set them up?]
    e. Soll ich den Karren schieben oder ziehen?
       [Should I push the cart or pull it?]

(26) a. Das Zimmer liegt ruhig. [The room lies quiet.]
    b. Rita sitzt aufrecht. [Rita is sitting upright.]
    c. Rita wohnt schön. [Rita is living nicely.]
    d. Rita läuft schnell. [Rita is running quickly.]
    e. Der Schrank steht quer. [The closet stands crooked.]

The combination of a local verb with a modal adverb supplies a greater potential for contrast, which the conceptual level can exploit when checking the conceptual conditions imposed by the existential binding. The contrast potential of the mode of a local verb like liegen [to lie] consists of the complementary mode 'NOT-LIE', as well as all contrastive modes like 'STAND', 'SIT', etc. Due to the combination with a modal adverb, contrast potential is increased by the contrast potential of the modal adverb. This is the reason for the differing judgements observed in (9) and (10). When a modal adverb enters the scene, new possible positionings are introduced which justify mode focusing. In sentence (26a), mode focusing and therefore existential binding of the local argument is admissible, because the modal adverb ruhig [quiet] establishes a contrast to an alternative situation where the room is not quiet, i.e., Das Zimmer liegt nicht ruhig.

6 Summary

The strict distinction of a language-specific and a conceptual level of meaning representation facilitates a systematic access to the optionality of the local argument of verbs of motion and position. The apparently unsystematic behavior of local verbs can be traced back to systematic principles of the semantic and the conceptual system. The mechanism of existentially binding an argument provides the language system with a remedy for the conflict between the syntactic level, where the local argument is optional, and the semantic level, where the local argument is indispensible. The conceptual prerequisite for the use of this mechanism is that the focusing of the mode of position or motion, which is initiated by the existential binding of the local argument, can be conceptually motivated. This presupposes a contrast between alternative modes. Phase quantifiers, modal adverbs, and explicit contrasts establish the required contrast of modes already at the semantic level itself. If the contrast of modes is introduced only at the conceptual level, degrees of acceptability reflect how well the conceptual conditions are met by the utterance context.

A semantic analysis which does not go beyond the abstraction from location as interpretation of the existential binding of the local argument would specify the meaning of the last sentence in (27) as an assertion that the speaker walked to an unspecified place sometime in the past; such an analysis is not convincing.

(27) " Es ist schon sechs Jahre, da ich nicht mehr in Wien lebe, und auch viele Jahre vorher war ich nicht mehr im Museum." "So? Ich bin oft dort herumgegangen, auch vor diesem Bild bin ich gestanden. Ja, *gegangen* bin ich, früher einmal."

Arthur Schnitzler (1900): Frau Berta Garlan

[" It has been six years now since I lived in Vienna, and I had not been to the museum for many years before." " Is that so? I have often walked around there, and I have stood before this picture, too. Yes, I walked, long ago."]

An adequate semantic analysis of this sentence presupposes an interpretation of the mechanism of existential binding as focusing of the mode associated with gehen [to walk], and signals the necessity of conceptually motivating the use of this semantic mechanism. Without involving any knowledge about the specific utterance situation, consulting only linguistic knowledge, the conceptual knowledge codified in object schemata, and knowledge about the principles of interaction between the semantic and the conceptual level, it can be stated that the mode of motion associated with gehen [to walk] which the speaker used in the past is contrasted with an alternative mode of motion predominant at the utterance time. This semantic-conceptual meaning framework is filled up depending on the utterance situation. In the case of (27), the speaker in the utterance situation is known to be paralyzed at the utterance time, and therefore mode focusing is conceptually motivated. It should be stressed that the burden of justifying the existential binding of the local argument is carried not only by pragmatic considerations concerning a specific utterance situation, but also by the context independent semantic-conceptual meaning structure, which paves the way for context dependent interpretation.

References

Bierwisch, M. (1982): Formal and lexical semantics. Linguistische Berichte, 80/82, 3-17

Bierwisch, M. (1983): Semantische und konzeptuelle Repräsentationen lexikalischer Einheiten. In: R. Ruzicka, W. Motsch (eds.): Untersuchungen zur Semantik. Akademie-Verlag (studia grammatica 22), Berlin, pp. 61-99

Bierwisch, M., Lang, E. (eds.) (1987): Grammatische und konzeptuelle Aspekte von Dimensionsadjektiven. Akademie-Verlag, Berlin (studia grammatica 26/27)

Bierwisch, M., Lang, E. (eds.) (1989): Dimensional Adjectives: Grammatical Structure and Conceptual Interpretation. Springer-Verlag, Berlin, Heidelberg, New York

Herweg, M. (1989): Ansätze zu einer semantischen Beschreibung topologischer Präpositionen. In: Ch. Habel, M. Herweg, K. Rehkämper (eds.): Raumkonzepte in Verstehensprozessen, Interdisziplinäre Beiträge zu Sprache und Raum. Niemeyer, Tübingen, pp. 99-127

Herweg, M. (1990): Zeitaspekte. Die Bedeutung von Tempus, Aspekt und temporalen Konjunktionen. Deutscher Universitäts-Verlag, Wiesbaden

Jackendoff, R. (1983): Semantics and Cognition. MIT Press, Cambridge, MA

Jackendoff, R. (1987): The status of thematic relations in linguistic theory. Linguistic Inquiry, 18: 3, 369-411

631

Lang, E. (1985): Symmetrische Prädikate: Lexikoneintrag und Interpretationsspielraum. Eine Fallstudie zur Semantik der Personenstandslexik. Linguistische Studien, Reihe A, Arbeitsberichte 127, 75-112

Lang, E. (1987): Semantik der Dimensionsauszeichnung räumlicher Objekte. In: M. Bierwisch, E. Lang (eds.), pp. 287-458

Lang, E., Carstensen, K.-U. (1989): OSKAR - ein PROLOG-Programm zur Repräsentation der Struktur und Verarbeitung räumlichen Wissens. In: D. Metzing (ed.): GWAI-89: 13th German Workshop on Artificial Intelligence. Springer-Verlag, Berlin, Heidleberg, New York, pp. 234-243

Lang, E., Carstensen, K.-U. (1990): OSKAR - A Prolog Program for Modelling Dimensional Designation and Positional Variation of Objects in Space. IWBS Report 109, IBM Deutschland, Stuttgart

Lang, E., Carstensen, K.-U., Simmons, G. (1991): Modelling Spatial Knowledge on a Linguistic Basis: Theory - Prototype - Integration. Springer-Verlag, Berlin, Heidleberg, New York

Löbner, S. (1989): Wahr neben falsch. Habilitationsschrift, University of Düsseldorf

Maienborn, C. (1990a): Position und Bewegung: Zur Semantik lokaler Verben. IWBS Report 138, IBM Deutschland, Stuttgart

Maienborn, C. (1990b): Lokale Verben und Präpositionen: Semantische und konzeptuelle Verarbeitung in LEU II. IWBS Report 119, IBM Deutschland, Stuttgart

Why a Hill Can't be a Valley:
Representing Gestalt and Position Properties of Objects with Object Schemata

Kai-Uwe Carstensen, Geoff Simmons*

Introduction

What, one might ask, is the difference between a hill and a valley? There must be a crucial one if we believe our intuition and agree with the objection registered by Lewis Carroll's Alice:

> "When you say 'hill'," the Queen interrupted, "*I* could show you hills, in comparison with which you'd call that a valley."
> "No, I shouldn't," said Alice, surprised into contradicting her at last: "a hill *can't* be a valley, you know. That would be nonsense—" [1]

When, one might ask further, does such a difference become important for a text comprehension system?

In this paper we want to argue that an answer to both questions is provided if one considers the use of *dimensional adjectives* with respect to the object nouns:

(1) a. high hill
     b. deep valley
     c. *high valley
     d. *deep hill

The examples in (1) show

- that these adjectives are sensitive to gradable *gestalt* and *position* properties of spatial objects in that they *designate* respective object axes as distinctive *dimensions*

- that the representation of these features is relevant for a text comprehension system as the expressions in (1) are natural language expressions which such a system should accept or reject.

Obviously we need an adequate semantic theory of dimensional adjectives which is related to our perception-based knowledge of objects and their spatial contexts.

In the following we present the core of such a theory (developed by Lang 1989a) which treats *dimensional designation* of spatial objects and in which the relevant object features are

*Our thanks to Ewald Lang for his meticulous scrutiny and valuable advice.

[1] Lewis Carroll, Through the Looking Glass. In: M. Gardner (ed.), The Annotated Alice. Penguin Books Ltd.: Harmondsworth, Middlesex 1987, p. 207.

comprised in structures called *object schemata*. We then describe some extensions of the theory gained by working with OSKAR[2] (Lang/ Carstensen 1989, 1990) and outline the realization of this theory in the representational formalism of LILOG (cf. Lang/ Carstensen/ Simmons 1991).

1 Overview: Relevant Aspects of Dimensional Designation

Before we describe Lang's theory in some detail we have to elaborate on the need for a sophisticated semantics of dimensional adjectives (DAdjs). Why not simply annotate object concepts with features for height, length, shortness, etc.? A few remarks shall be made to answer this question:

First, there can be no one-to-one relation between DAdjs and object features as some of the former constitute pairs of antonyms, i.e., opposites on a scale belonging to only one object feature (long / short → length). This kind of *polarity* is a general linguistic phenomenon (cf. good / bad) that should not be directly represented in object concepts.

Second, there is a distinction to be made between *object constitutive* and *contextually induced* properties which has to be accounted for in a principled and consistent way. For example, while both hills and towers are high by default, (only) towers can be said to be long (when they are lying down); while poles and streets are always long, (only) poles can be said to be high in certain contexts; poles cannot be deep and spherical objects can neither be deep nor high.

Third, there is no way to avoid modeling the gestalt properties of an object, as DAdjs can denote different object extents according to the context in which they are used (see the illustration below). For the same reason, such a referential access to an object model is necessary to allow for quantification of the respective object extents, i.e., *graduation* of the DAdjs as in the board is 40cm wide.

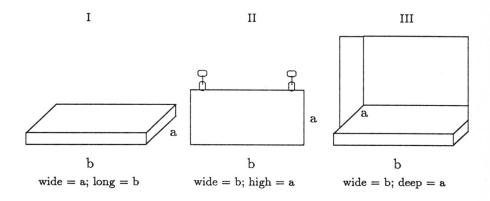

I	II	III
wide = a; long = b	wide = b; high = a	wide = b; deep = a

---

[2]OSKAR is the acronym of *O*bjekt-*S*chemata zur *K*onzeptuellen *A*nalyse *R*äumlicher Objekteigenschaften (Object schemata for the conceptual analysis of spatial properties of objects) – a Prolog-program developed by Ewald Lang and Kai-Uwe Carstensen.

2 Dimensional Designation of Objects

2.1 General Framework

The semantics of dimensional adjectives concerns the following group of words:

(2) a. lang - kurz   breit - schmal   dick - dünn
         long - short $\begin{Bmatrix} \text{wide} \\ \text{broad} \end{Bmatrix}$ - narrow   thick - thin

    b.   hoch - niedrig   tief   flach
         high - low   deep   shallow

    c.   weit - eng   d. groß - klein
         $\begin{Bmatrix} \text{wide} \\ \text{broad} \end{Bmatrix}$ - narrow $\begin{Bmatrix} \text{big - small} \\ \text{large - small} \\ \text{tall - short} \end{Bmatrix}$

According to Lang, these adjectives refer to *axes* of a spatial object, which are determined and qualified by its gestalt and position properties, thereby designating them as *dimensions* of that object. Leaving out the details, the simplified schema of the semantic form of DAdjs is the following:

(3) $[[\text{QUANT DIM } x] = \text{VAL}^3]$

QUANT and DIM represent the two relevant semantic components of a DAdj, i.e., the graduation and the dimensional designation component, respectively. QUANT is a semantic prime for a scaling operation which assigns a scale value to some spatial object x relative to a dimension d (which again is the value of DIM x). DIM is a variable for a limited set of constants (MAX, SUB, DIST, VERT, OBS, ACROSS, see below), which are to be interpreted as functions yielding d.

This approach to the semantics of dimensional designation adheres to the paradigm of cognitive linguistics (cf. Bierwisch / Lang 1987, 1989)[4], where the modularity of cognitive behavior is explicitly reflected within the semantic theory for natural language expressions by taking into account the interaction of the various cognitive systems and subsystems. One aspect of this is the interaction of the grammar G (the language system embodying linguistic knowledge) and the conceptual system C, which is intermodally accessible and therefore serves as a mediator between language and perception.

Theoretically, G is said to be in an *inherent* relationship with C, i.e., G contains parameters which are instantiated by structures of C. Since semantic representations like (3) constitute the interface between G and C, the constants mentioned above function as parameters (so-called

---

[3]According to Bierwisch 1989, VAL itself has the internal structure $[v \pm c]$ where v is a norm or comparison value, c is the difference of the scale value from v, and $\pm$ is a variable for the operations + and − which yield the different polarities of the DAdjs.

[4]Note that within this approach the meaning of an expression is characterized by the interaction of two different representational levels: the *semantic* and the *conceptual* level. See Maienborn (this volume) for some aspects of this interaction. In the case of DAdjs, (3) corresponds to the semantic level.

Dimensional Assignment Parameters (DAPs)), and are instantiated by their corresponding conceptual values (so-called *Dimensional Assignment Values* (DAVs)). The latter can be viewed as those features of object concepts that represent prominent gestalt and position properties. Therefore, they are said to be *perceptually based* and *conceptually categorized* whereas the DAPs are *conceptually motivated* but *grammatically coded*, which means that the way DAPs are couched in lexical expressions allows for certain differences among languages (such as groß versus tall, large, big).

With this two-level semantic approach, we are able to model the (in)validity of the following inferences, which differ from grammatically coded converses (as for example, x is longer than y $\longleftrightarrow$ y is shorter than x):

(4) a. The pole is 20m high/tall $--$ >   The pole is 20m long
    b. The tower is 20m high/tall $-/-$ >   *The tower is 20m long

It is not within lexical semantics but on the conceptual level where the inferences in (4) come out to be valid or not. This is to be realized by rules that determine which DAP of a DAdj can be instantiated by which conceptual DAV. Obviously, the same holds for the interpretation of *the hill is deep and *the valley is high and for the aforementioned distinction between object constitutive and contextually induced spatial properties.

Note that with this approach, the semantics of natural language expressions is more than just a subdiscipline of linguistics; it has a well defined interface to other cognitive sciences and therefore can be accessed, discussed, used and applied in the area of AI. Additionally, the primitives of the semantic representation no longer constitute a symbol system in its own right – and can only be interpreted in terms of the system itself – (as in the Katz/Fodor Semantic Marker framework). Rather, they are anchored in the various cognitive modules, ultimately being connected to the external world.

2.2 Gestalt and Position Properties of Objects

According to Lang, the categorization of percepts as spatial objects can be described by two interacting sets of principles: the so-called *Inherent Proportion Schema* (IPS) which defines the gestalt properties of an object and the so-called *Primary Perceptual Space* (PPS) which defines, among others, a system of axes within which the gestalt properties of an object can be interpreted as position properties.

The relevant principles underlying the IPS include those responsible for

- the *delimination* of an object against the background,

- the perception of *symmetry axes* (which are referred to by DAdjs) and

- *axial disintegration* (how possible symmetry axes can be discerned: a brick has three disintegrated axes while a ball only has one integrated axis),

- *salience/prominence* (how axes are ordered within an object according to their size, yielding a *proportion schema* of the object) and

- *penetrability* (which accounts for the different ranges of the DAdjs thick and wide / weit)

We can now list and give an interpretation for the DAPs of the DAdjs relating to *gestalt properties* of objects:

MAX identifies the maximal disintegrated axis of some object x, which in turn presupposes that there is exactly one such axis of x available (long / short).

SUB identifies either a non-maximal disintegrated third axis (cf. thick board) or an integrated axis forming the diameter of a circular section (cf. thick pole).

DIST identifies an object axis perceived as inside diameter of a hollow body (cf. wide hole).

The PPS, an internal model of how we reconstruct external physical space on the basis of perceptual information from upright walk, equilibrum and eye level, is defined by the following three axes:

- the *Vertical* axis (ubiquitous and constant)
- the *Observer* axis
- the *Horizontal* axis (dependent on, i.e., defined by orthogonality to, the other two axes)

An object, then, is assigned a *position property* if one of its axis extensions defined by IPS is redefined by being projected onto an axis of the surrounding space as determined by PPS. Here are the corresponding DAPs:

VERT selects exactly that disintegrated axis of an object which coincides with the Vertical of PPS (high / low).

OBS identifies any disintegrated axis of an object which coincides with the Observer axis of PPS (deep).

Additionally, there is the parameter ACROSS which selects an axis dependent on another axis that is identified by either MAX or VERT or OBS (wide /breit - narrow /schmal).[5] Taken together, VERT and OBS can be used to describe how objects are *oriented* and *perspectivized*, respectively. Not surprisingly, DAVs are simply names representing the clusters of conditions defining the range of the DAPs. [6] Together with (representations of) the other gestalt properties described above, the DAVs are arranged into complex structures called *object schemata*.

---

[5]Due to this inherent relativity there is no object constitutive DAV for ACROSS.

[6]To distinguish them from the DAPs, DAVs are written in small letters: max, sub, dist, vert, obs, etc. The DAV ∅ represents an unspecified disintegrated axis of an object and can be regarded as the 'landing site' for the contextual DAPs VERT, OBS and ACROSS. There is another DAV, diam, which conceptually fills a lexical gap regarding dimensional designation – although it has no adjectival counterpart it might correspond to expressions like has the diameter of.

2.3 Object Schemata

Very generally, object schemata (OS) are designed as matrices with rows and colums. The columns, called *sections*, contain relevant information about the *axes* of an object which can be designated by DAdjs. They are arranged according to the decreasing order of the axis extents, thereby modeling the *proportion* of that object. In the first row, the general gestalt properties are encoded: the *dimensions* of the object are named by the constants a, b and c, *boundedness* of an axis is represented by (the scope of) '< ... >' and the *integratedness* of an axis is represented by (the scope of) '(...)'. The second row contains the primary ('object constitutive') DAVs, the third row – divided by a horizontal bar – the contextually induced DAVs.

(5) 'tower'   'pole'   'high pole'
  < a   (b   c) >   < a   (b   c) >   < a   (b   c) >
   max   sub   <u>max   sub</u>   <u>max   sub</u>
   <u>vert</u>   vert

The OS in (5) illustrate the similarity in the gestalt of towers and poles. Note that towers have a *canonical* vertical orientation while the orientation of a pole must always be contextually induced. This leads us back to the interaction of DAPs and DAVs, i.e., the interpretation of DAPs with respect to an OS: DAPs can either *identify* (cf. <u>long</u> <u>pole</u>) or *specify* (cf. <u>high</u> <u>pole</u>) a DAV in an OS. *Compatibility conditions*, which emerge from the inherent relationship between the *gestalt* and *position properties* determine possible OS and possible interpretations, while ruling out, for example, natural language expressions like (1 c, d) as ill-formed.

Finally, just a glimpse at the OS in (6) and (7) suffices to confirm Alice's suspicion that there is no simple way to compare hills and valleys, and proves that there is more to gestalt and position properties than 'height' and 'depth' features in object concepts.

(6) 'hill'   (7) 'valley'
  < (a   b)   c >   < a   b   c >
     diam   vert   max ∅   vert
                                            obs

3 OSKAR

The Prolog program OSKAR, developed in the 'rapid-prototyping' style, was originally intended to be a means for testing the theory of dimensional designation with respect to consistency (no incorrect designations) and completeness (exhaustive applicability to spatial objects). This was achieved, and it turned out to be a useful procedure for discovering some minor points to be improved. To name just two examples, *inherent* orientation and perspectivation had to be explicitly represented as additional DAVs, and *canonical* and *fixed* orientation had to be distinguished.

On the other hand, the aspect of 'sidedness' of objects was taken into account from the beginning, in that information about objects' constitutive ('intrinsic') or contextual ('deictic') sides became part of the OS. This gave rise to a number of possibilities and new ideas for representing conceptual knowledge inside and outside the theory of dimensional designation:

a) Procedures for a principled simulation of *position variation* of objects were developed, i.e., the axis- and side-related aspects of 'tilting' and 'turning' were represented;

b) Contextual specification was redefined as a device for specifying an object's reference to the PPS (i.e., *positioning* or *perspectivising* an object): with this, 'setting upright' and 'laying down' could be identified as subtypes of the positioning of objects;

c) *Position properties* like those addressed by expressions like <u>stands</u>, <u>lies</u>, <u>upsidedown</u>, <u>reversed</u> were represented;

d) Moreover, the *movability* of an object was found to be a prerequisite for position variation and the position properties listed in c). The movability features of an object (immobile and movable) thus derive from the structure of the entries of the OS at issue.

The Prolog prototype OSKAR, having implemented, supplemented and tested the theoretical foundation (cf. Lang/ Carstensen 1989, 1990), provides us with a specification for integrating dimensional designation and positional variation into LILOG (cf. Lang/ Carstensen/ Simmons 1991).

4 Dimensional Designation and Positional Variation in LILOG

The integration of Lang's theory of dimensional designation and positional variation into the LILOG system proceeds in two steps:

(I) The theory must be realized in L_{LILOG}, the representational formalism of the LILOG system. With OSKAR as a prototype, this is a relatively straightforward process.

(II) The integration into LILOG must account for a number of new issues that are directly affected by dimensional designation, such as:

    (a) Mechanisms of *inheritance* that regulate the relationship between OS defined for classes of objects and OS assigned to individual RefOs.

    (b) A treatment of *context* and context change.

    (c) A realization of the scalar function QUANT (cf. (3) above), to be integrated into the *semantic form* of scalar adjectives.

In the remainder of this article, we will focus on the first of these two steps: the implementation of dimensional designation and positional variations in the representation language L_{LILOG}. It will be necessary to make decisions about the representation of inheritance and context dependence; problems related to the semantics of DAdjs and verbs of position will be remarked on briefly.[7]

---

[7]The syntax assumed in this paper for the language L_{LILOG} is implemented in the LEU/2 prototype; its semantics is loosely based on the specification in Pletat/von Luck 1989.

5 OS and Object Ontology in L_{LILOG}

Object schemata (OS) categorize objects into classes with respect to their gestalt and position properties; we will exploit the feature logic of L_{LILOG} to reconstruct OS in LILOG. In L_{LILOG}, spatial objects are classified as subsorts of the sort OBJECT, distinguishing them from other kinds of entities like events. We will represent the gestalt and position properties for subsorts of OBJECT (e.g., HILL, VALLEY) by taking OS as complex feature structures. The sort declarations will define object constitutive OS information that is assumed by default for each object in a class; thus the ontology specifies the gestalt properties and canonical position properties for each class of spatial objects. However, because the interpretation of OS of some particular object within a class is context dependent, we will realize the assignment of the pertinent OS to a specific object by means of a temporally-indexed L_{LILOG} function (see Sect. 6).[8]

We begin by defining DAPs and DAVs in L_{LILOG}. As one might expect, these are just atoms collected in a special sort called DIMDESIGNATION, which in turn is a subsort of the sort SPATIALCONCEPT, an extremely general and unspecified sort that merely serves to keep theoretical notions of spatial knowledge separate from everything else in the sort lattice.[9]

```
(8) sort DimDesignation < SpatialConcept;
        atoms   max, vert, sub, dist, obs, across, imax,
                ivert, iobs, diam, empty.
```

The values prefixed with "i" are the DAVs mentioned in Sect. 3 that represent "inherent" orientation and perspectivation, and empty corresponds to ∅. The L_{LILOG} sort OBJECT has a feature has_default_schema, which is of the sort OBJECTSCHEMA. Thus a portion of our sort declaration for OBJECT is:[10]

```
(9) sort Object < SpatialEntity;
        features has_default_schema :   Objectschema,

            ...
```

The sort OBJECTSCHEMA is also a subsort of SPATIALCONCEPT; its features specify a dimensionality (an integer between 1 and 3) and a list of entities of the sort SECTION:[11]

```
(10) sort Objectschema < SpatialConcept,
        features  dimensions : [1..3],
                  sections   : List_of_Sections.
```

---

[8]A note on typography: names of sorts will be given in SMALL CAPS in the running text; names of features and any portion of L_{LILOG} code will be written in the text font Typewriter.

[9]Having DAVs and DAPs in the same sort is a technical expedient (it facilitates unification). It is up to the knowledge engineer to see to it that DAPs and DAVs are not confused (for example, across can only be contextually induced, and thus cannot appear in the ontology).

[10]We will elaborate on the "default" status of this OS in Sect. 6. Lang describes the notion of a "basic schema" (Grundschema), which is not reflected in this paper. Lang's basic schemata treat problems of proportional variation within an object class, which are important to our treatment of inheritance in L_{LILOG}. Due to lack of space, we will not comment further on this point (cf. Lang 1987, 1989 a,b, Lang/ Carstensen 1990, Lang/ Carstensen/ Simmons 1991).

[11]A list in L_{LILOG} is inductively defined as in PROLOG; a list is either a special object called the "empty list" (represented in L_{LILOG} with the constant nil), or it consists of a feature head, which can be of any sort, and a feature rest, which is another list.

The **sections** feature of an OS in LILOG represents the disintegrated or integrated axes of an object (written in (5)-(7) above as "a", "b", "(a b)", etc.). At this level we have very little information about object axes; things get interesting when we look at the sort declaration for SECTION itself:

```
(11) sort Section < SpatialConcept;
     features   number_of_dims : [1..3],
                davs           : List_of_Davs,
                degree         : SpatialDegrees.
```

The sort SECTION defines the content of a section of an OS as shown in (5)-(7) above. In the ontology, the feature **davs** is assigned a list of the object-constitutive primary entries of an OS; contextually induced DAVs may be appended to the list in the course of processing a text (cf. the second and third rows of (5)-(7) above).

The feature **number_of_dims** specifies the number of dimensions taken up by the axis represented by a section, thus indirectly representing the axis' integratedness. Finally, the feature **degree** relates the object axis to an entity of the sort SPATIALDEGREES, which may in turn be used in a realization of the function QUANT given in (3) above (cf. Sect. 7).

Given these sort definitions, we can define the OS of an object class by assigning appropriate values to feature paths in the sort declaration for that class. Returning to our familiar examples, we can now give a portion of the sort declarations for HILL and VALLEY (somewhat simplified for expository economy), which are the L_{LILOG} counterparts to (6) and (7) above (would Lewis Carroll have been startled, or intrigued?).

```
(12) sort hill < and (Object,
             has_default_schema :
               and(dimensions :   {3},
                  <sections head> :
                    and( number_of_dims   :   {2},
                         <davs head>      :   {diam},
                         <davs rest>      :   {nil}),
                  <sections rest head>    :
                    and( number_of_dims   :   {1},
                         <davs head>      :   {vert},
                         <davs rest>      :   {nil}),
                  <sections rest rest>    :   {nil})).
```

```
(13) sort valley < and (Object,
                has_default_schema :
                  and(dimensions :  {3},
                      <sections head> :
                        and( number_of_dims     :   {1},
                              <davs head>        :   {max},
                              <davs rest>        :   {nil}),
                        <sections rest head>    :
                        and( number_of_dims     :   {1},
                              <davs head>        :   {empty},
                              <davs rest>        :   {nil}),
                        <sections rest rest head> :
                        and( number_of_dims     :   {1},
                              <davs head>        :   {obs},
                              <davs rest head>   :   {vert},
                              <davs rest rest>   :   {nil}),
                        <sections rest rest rest> :   {nil})).
```

6   Inheritance and Context Dependent Assignment of Object Schemata

The sort declarations in (12) and (13) define context-invariant gestalt properties and canonical position properties of objects. But as shown in Sect. 1, dimensional designation is context dependent, and thus so is the processing of OS; in particular, this concerns the assignment of *positional properties and variations* to individual objects. When an object enters discourse, the OS determined by its sort is assumed; for example, if a tree is mentioned in a text, we assume that the tree is standing (and hence that the OS appropriate for vertical orientation is valid) unless we have explicit evidence to the contrary. If the object undergoes a manipulation in its position, or if the assumption about its position is explicitly contradicted, then a new OS', based on the original OS and appropriate to the new position, is assigned to that object.

To cope with the context dependence and default status of OS in LILOG, we will create RefOs of the sort OBJECTSCHEMA in L_{LILOG}, which are assigned to objects by means of the temporally indexed L_{LILOG} function has-os. This function has the following arguments and sortal restrictions:

(14) function has-os(O:Object, T:Interval) → Objectschema.

When a RefO of the sort OBJECT is introduced into discourse, it is assumed by default to be assigned an OS that is identical with its default schema. Modifications of that initial OS may be due to positional specification (e.g., the pole is 2m tall entails the pole's upright position), or positional change (e.g., the tree has been felled entails the loss of the tree's canonical verticality). Both result in an OS' reflecting the object's new position; in the latter case, the OS' is associated with a new temporal index.

In declaration (14), INTERVAL is the sort of temporal intervals. Temporal intervals are the entities proposed for LILOG for the treatment of tense and aspect (cf. Eberle 1988, 1989). In order to see how we arrive at a value for the argument T in has-os, we must take a closer look at verbs that are related to the positional properties of objects. In the LILOG proposal for the semantics of *verbs of position*, stehen, liegen, sitzen, etc. (stand, lie, sit, etc.) are classified as *static*; stellen, legen, setzen, etc. (put / place, lay, set, etc.) as their *causative* derivatives (cf. Maienborn 1990). In addition to specifying a local argument and tense and aspectual information, the meaning of each of these verbs determines a *mode of position* – a characteristic relation between the object's axes and the Vertical and/or Observer axis of the surrounding space, as reflected in the occurrence of vert and/or obs in the object's OS.[12]

For the static verbs, the mode of position is realized as an evaluation of matching conditions with the OS of the object in question. Now it is clear that the OS reflecting a certain static position is constant for a certain object just as long as that object remains in that position. This means that the temporal index T for the usage of a static verb coincides with the index T associated with the object's position.

The causative verbs (legen, etc.) indicate a change of state, for which a new OS' is created and assigned to the object with a new temporal index T'. The new OS' reflects the resulting mode of position valid at T' (e.g., liegen). The modification of OS accounting for positional variation is implemented in OSKAR (cf. Sect. 3), and these procedures are easily adapted as L_{LILOG} rules. The treatment of temporal intervals is determined entirely by the analysis of tense and aspect for the verbs in question. Thus we have a context-dependent assignment of OS to objects that makes use of temporal information inferred by the LILOG system. We can treat references to periods of time when different OS were valid for a given object. Consider the sentence:

(15)   While the tree was still standing, it was 5m tall.

If the tree is lying on the ground "now" (t_0), this implies that the dimensional designation tall, which is applicable at some t_i before t_0, is no longer acceptable at t_o.

7 Dimensional Designation and Scalar Functions

Now that we have seen how object schemata are defined for object sorts and bound to RefOs in L_{LILOG}, we can take a very brief look at the proposed implementation of the process of dimensional designation in L_{LILOG}. As described in Sect. 2, dimensional designation is a process by a which a DAP is interpreted for a given object in a given context; a DAV in the OS of that object in the given context must be identified or specified, thus locating the axis of the object that has been designated. Borrowing the terminology of OSKAR, we will call this process the *evaluation* of a DAP. Since we have added a temporal index in LILOG as a contextual property, we will assume that evaluation is also dependent on a temporal location; that is, a DAdj will be evaluated with respect to the temporal information of the sentence in which it is uttered.

We now define in L_{LILOG} a function eval_DAP. The evaluation of this function starts a set of L_{LILOG} rules that identify or specify a DAV in the given OS, and return the section representing the axis that is designated by the DAP, much as this was done in OSKAR.

---

[12]This characterization of the OS that are associated with the modes of position is slightly oversimplified. See Lang/ Carstensen 1990 and Lang/ Carstensen/ Simmons (1991) for details.

```
(16) function eval_DAP(DAP:DimDesignation, OS:Objectschema)
                           → Section.
```

The function eval_DAP, together with the feature degree on SECTION, allows us to account for sentences like (17) and (18):

(17)   This hill is 10m high.
(18)   This hill is higher than that hill.

We will assume a theory of DAdjs as *degree adjectives*. In such a theory, sentence (17) may be treated by assigning a measurement value to a degree, and sentence (18) may be treated by placing the degrees of height of the mentioned objects in an ordering relation. There are quite a few theories of this kind on the market (cf. Bierwisch 1989 or von Stechow 1985). We can produce a LILOG representation that is amenable to all of these theories by interpreting the feature degree as a scalar function.

Leaving out the details, the essence of the lexical interpretations of DAdjs in such a theory is the QUANT function given in (3) above. If we add a temporal index T to that function, then we can define a LILOG interpretation for QUANT as follows:

```
(19) forall X:Object, DIM:DimDesignation, T:Interval,
            D:Degree;
     QUANT (DIM, X, T)= D
     ↔
     has-os(X, T) = OS
     and
     degree(eval_DAP(DIM, OS)) = D.
```

This means that the scale value assigned to an object extent for a DAP DIM at T is equal to the value of the feature degree for the OS section returned by eval_DAP.

In this paper, we have briefly outlined a three-step process that begins with linguistic theory, which is then confirmed and enhanced in a specific technical prototype (OSKAR), and is finally integrated into a comprehensive knowledge representation system (LILOG). All in all, the insights thus gained and rendered in formal representation may well account for the core of the conditions and principles organizing human knowledge of spatial objects.

References

Bierwisch, M. (1989): The semantics of gradation. In: M. Bierwisch, E.Lang (eds.), pp. 71-261

Bierwisch, M., Lang, E. (eds.) (1987): Grammatische und konzeptuelle Aspekte von Dimension-sadjektiven. Akademie-Verlag, Berlin, (studia grammatica 26/27)

Bierwisch, M., Lang, E. (eds.) (1989): Dimensional Adjectives: Grammatical Structure and Conceptual Interpretation. Springer-Verlag, Berlin, Heidelberg, New York

Eberle, K.(1988): Eine Prolog-Theorie für zeitliche Beziehungen zwischen Ereignissen. LILOG Report 14, IBM Deutschland, Stuttgart

Eberle, K.(1989): Quantifikation, Plural, Ereignisse und ihre Argumente in einer mehr-sortigen Sprache der Prädikatenlogik erster Stufe. IWBS Report 67, IBM Deutschland, Stuttgart

Lang, E. (1987): Semantik der Dimensionsauszeichnung räumlicher Objekte. In: M. Bierwisch, E. Lang (eds.), pp. 287-458

Lang, E. (1989a): The semantics of dimensional designation of spatial objects. In: M. Bierwisch, E. Lang (eds.), pp. 263-417

Lang, E. (1989b): Primärer Orientierungsraum und inhärentes Proportionsschema: Interagierende Kategorisierungsraster bei der Konzeptualisierung räumlicher Objekte. In: Ch. Habel, M. Herweg, K. Rehkämper (eds.): Raumkonzepte in Verstehensprozessen. Interdisziplinäre Beiträge zu Sprache und Raum. Niemeyer, Tübingen

Lang, E., Carstensen, K.-U. (1989): OSKAR - ein PROLOG-Programm zur Repräsentation der Struktur und Verarbeitung räumlichen Wissens. In: D. Metzing (ed.): GWAI-89. 13th German Workshop on Artificial Intelligence. Springer-Verlag, Berlin, Heidelberg, New York, pp. 234-243

Lang, E., Carstensen, K.-U. (1990): OSKAR - A Prolog Program for Modelling Dimensional Designation and Positional Variation of Objects in Space. IWBS Report 109, IBM Deutschland, Stuttgart

Lang, E., Carstensen, K.-U., Simmons, G. (1991): Modelling Spatial Knowledge on a Linguistic Basis: Theory - Prototype - Integration. Springer-Verlag, Berlin, Heidelberg, New York

Maienborn, C. (1990): Position und Bewegung: Zur Semantik lokaler Verben. IWBS Report 138, IBM Deutschland, Stuttgart

Pletat, U., von Luck, K.(1989): Knowledge Representation in LILOG, IWBS Report 90, IBM Deutschland, Stuttgart

von Stechow, A. (1985): Comparing semantic theories of comparison. In: Journal of Semantics 3, 1-77

Object-Oriented Representation of Depictions on the Basis of Cell Matrices

Mohammed Nadjib Khenkhar

Introduction

In this contribution, a depictional approach for the representation and processing of spatial knowledge is presented. The spatial structures of objects are represented in the form of depictions corresponding to their locations relative to one another. Depictions are representation structures for sketch-like spatial knowledge. Therefore, a depiction is of the same nature as a sketch and is imprecise with respect to the metrical properties of the object to be represented. In contrast to this, the topological properties occurring in depictions conform to those of the spatial structures of the objects that are represented. The present approach is based on the concept of the quasi-analog representation medium *cell matrix* (Kosslyn 1980; Habel 1987, 1988; Khenkhar 1988, 1989, 1990). Depictions are, therefore, realized by cell matrices. The cells (the elements of the matrix), contain (among other things) information concerning the spatial structures of the objects to be represented. The basic processes which are the pre-requisites for the imagination and inspection processes of depictions are defined on the basis of the neighbor cell relations and neighbor cell patterns defined in the cell set. The following sections present the representation structures required for this depictional approach: the cell, the depiction and the map. An example is used to show in a quasi-analog format how spatial problems may be solved by means of the imagination and inspection processes.

1 Cell

In the depictional representation system described in this paper, cells are the representation structure which the more complex representation structures – the depictions – are based upon. The cell structure depends on the processes of imagination and inspection which are carried out on the cell structure and the depictions. The cell structure defined in the following is a first proposal for the development of a depictional representation system, which can be implemented and used for experiments. If required it may be modified or extended by the addition of further attributes. In this approach, both the cells and the depictions have a frame-oriented representation. The first proposal for the cell structure is as follows:

CELL:

in-depic	:	$< DEPIC^+ >$
part-of	:	$< RefO^+ >$
coordinates	:	$< Z \cdot Z >$
evaluation	:	$< (aspect \cdot value)^+ >$
status	:	$< (RefO \cdot \{certain, possible, arbitrary\})^+ >$

By means of the attribute 'in-depic', each cell is assigned uniquely to the depiction in which it appears. In this approach, the spatial structure of a Referential Object (Habel 1986), such as the form of a certain crossing, is represented by a structured set of cells based on the defined neighbor cell relations. The RefO 'CROSSING: r2' (the notation '<S>: r2' is similar to that of L_{LILOG} and denotes the RefO 'r2' of the sort 'S' – in L_{LILOG} notation the RefO is followed by the sort) is assigned to a cell set which is intended to depict the topological structure of the crossing so as to provide an adequate representation of some of its spatial properties. In cases where several Referential Objects within one depiction may be represented along with their positions relative to one another, one individual cell may be assigned to one or several Referential Objects. The attribute 'part-of' is intended to be used for this assignment. With the attribute 'coordinates', one cell is marked uniquely within one depiction. Furthermore, the coordinates of one cell make it possible – according to the rule of the neighbor cell relations – to determine the coordinates of the neighbouring cells. By means of the attribute 'evaluation', the various assignments of a cell to several Referential Objects are evaluated. This type of evaluation is intended to deal with the aspect of imprecise descriptions of positions and the vagueness of spatial expressions as they occur in natural language. Although these evaluations resemble the truth degrees of fuzzy logics (Zadeh 1965), they must actually be distinguished from them because they are supposed to contribute to the solution of specific aspects of vagueness (Khenkhar 1988).

Another very important attribute of a cell is the attribute 'status'. The attribute value 'certain' expresses that the corresponding cell is an element of those spatial points or cells the corresponding Referential Object 'certainly' takes up in space. Possible locations of Referential Objects are represented by cells which have the status 'possible' (e.g., the 'at-area' in the expression at the crossing in the sentence the multi-storey building at the crossing). Those cells which are to represent an arbitrary assumption as to the location of a Referential Object are given the attribute value 'arbitrary'. Consider the following two sentences: the school lies behind the small lake and the playground lies before the small lake. Nothing is mentioned about the speaker's position, and yet it can be deduced from the two sentences that the school lies opposite the playground provided the speaker's position was the same when the two sentences were uttered.

2 Depiction

In this section, the structure of depictions is presented. Their structure is based on the cell structure proposed above. The structure of the depictions also depends on the processes operating on them. It must be designed in such a way that all processes running on the depiction level must have access to all information they need in an efficient way. Another aspect which exerts a great influence on the development of the depiction structure is the representation of prototypical objects (Rosch 1975). In the present approach, it is assumed that there is one prototype for each of the object sorts. Such a prototype may be a specific Referential Object of the given sort. In the following, the expression *prototypical depiction* is introduced for the depiction of the prototype of a sort. Thus, each RefO of a specific sort may have one default-like prototypical depiction, i.e., the depiction the sort's prototype has. For the representation of individual spatial structures of objects, the representational structure depiction (DEPIC) is used. The prototypical depictions of objects are also represented by the same representational structure. Since the prototype of a sort represents a specific Referential Object, its depiction may be coded in the same way as all other depictions of other objects in DEPIC. Prototypical depictions will be used during a problem solution process when no other specific or exact information as to the spatial structure of an individual object is available. In such cases, it is assumed by default that the object under consideration has a depiction similar to that of the prototype. The first definition of the internal structure of a depiction allows for graphical or sketch-like representations of spatial relationships and is as follows:

DEPIC:
RO	:	< RefO >
components	:	< parts >
representation	:	total | section
perspective	:	bird's eye view | frontal
resolving-power	:	$< N \cdot N >$
scale	:	$< N \cdot E >$
centre	:	$< Z \cdot Z >$
occupied-cells	:	$< RefO \cdot CELL^+ >$

The value ranges of the individual attributes of a depiction are not yet fully specified here. To facilitate understanding of the individual attributes, let us consider a simple example. In this example, the spatial structure of a certain channel with the name Rhein-Marne-Kanal is represented according to the depictional approach presented here (see Fig. 1). Furthermore, the portion of the propositional part of the knowledge which establishes the relationships between the Referential Object 'Rhein-Marne-Kanal' and its depictionally represented spatial structure is introduced. The relations 'prototypical-depiction' (assigning to each RefO its prototypical depiction), 'depiction' (assigning to each RefO its individual depiction) and 'depict' (assigning to each RefO all maps in which it is depicted with other objects) establish the connections between the propositional and the depictional knowledge. The representational structure MAP will be discussed below. At this point, it must be mentioned that all statements of sizes occurring in the examples introduced in the following (e.g., those which are mentioned under the attribute 'scale') are only to be considered with the greatest care. It is our aim to fill in only relative sizes with which we can *estimate* the distances between objects within one depiction fairly well. This does not exclude rough estimations.

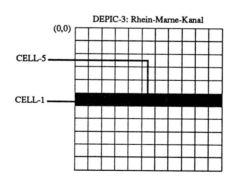

Fig. 1

CHANNEL: r1
name	:	Rhein-Marne-Kanal
...		
loc	:	AREA: r17
prototypical-depiction	:	DEPIC-0
depiction	:	DEPIC-3
depict	:	MAP-7

DEPIC-3

RO	:	CHANNEL: r1
components	:	CHANNEL: r1
representation	:	section
perspective	:	bird's eye view
resolving-power	:	(11, 11)
scale	:	(50, m)
centre-coord	:	(5, 5)
occupied-cells	:	(CHANNEL: r1, {cell−1, ..., cell−11})

One instance of an occupied cell is shown in the following:

CELL-1

in-depic	:	DEPIC-3
part-of	:	CHANNEL: r1
coordinates	:	(0, 5)
evaluation	:	(CHANNEL: r1, 10)
status	:	(CHANNEL: r1, certain)

The internal representation of the RefO 'CHANNEL: r1' thus contains the following important information:

- In 'loc', there is the RefO 'AREA: r17', which represents the area in which the RefO 'CHANNEL: r1' is located.

- The attribute 'prototypical-depiction' contains the appropriate prototypical depiction of a channel.

- The contents of the attribute 'depiction' (DEPIC-3) represents the individual depiction of the Rhein-Marne-Kanal.

- The attribute 'depict', contains several MAPs (in this example MAP-7) in which the RefO is represented depictionally (see below).

3 Map

For the representation of several objects including their spatial relationships to one another, another depictional representation structure called MAP, which is structured in a slightly different manner, is used. Thus it is possible, for instance, for an object with its entire surroundings to be represented depictionally in one MAP. All objects located in the surroundings of this object are entered in the MAP. If required, it is possible to inspect the surroundings of the object – the inspection processes will be discussed later – and thus all surrounding objects can be *read* from the MAP. In a MAP, areas in which specific objects are located can also be represented depictionally. Thus it is possible, by means of an appropriate area overlapping function, to determine the spatial relations of positions between objects within one MAP. It can be seen from this that there is a relationship between a MAP and a mental map in the sense of Downs and Stea (1982).

If one imagines the internal representation of a mental map as a net with edges and nodes, one can easily imagine that certain nodes in this net are associated with MAPs which represent the surroundings of the corresponding nodes depictionally. In these surroundings, the so-called *landmarks* are located. In a MAP, a set of propositionally represented facts concerning the spatial relations between objects are represented depictionally. This is where it differs considerably from the system SPAM by McDermott and Davis. In the fuzzy map of SPAM, spatial relations are coded in a propositional form (McDermott and Davis 1984).

In principle, the processes running on a MAP, such as that of imagination and inspection, are different from the processes of propositionally oriented systems. For the solution of spatial problems, a depictional system certainly needs a smaller set of primitive processes running on depictions. In contrast to this, I think the solution of spatial problems in a propositional system will be more difficult to handle since the concept of the spatial context gets lost in propositional coding, whereas it exists explicitly in the depictional representation. When changes are made in the propositional knowledge basis, for instance, by replacing one specific spatial relation by another, it may under certain circumstances be very difficult to realize all the consequences of such a change. The correctness of all spatial relations between the objects involved in the change and all the other objects must be examined. In artificial intelligence, this problem is known under the name of the *frame problem* (McCarthy and Hayes 1969). In a depictional system, things are completely different because *erasing* the depiction of a certain object within a MAP and *drawing* it at a different place in the same MAP does not present any difficulties at all for the depictional system. The object moved has simply changed its position, and thus automatically has a new position with respect to other objects within the same MAP (Khenkhar 1988). When required, the new positional relations may simply be *read* by means of the inspection processes. The structure of MAP is defined as follows:

MAP
ROs	:	$< RefO^+ >$
perspective	:	bird's eye view | frontal
resolving-power	:	$< N \cdot N >$
scale	:	$< N \cdot E >$
occupied-cells	:	$< (RefO \cdot CELL)^+ >$

The representation structure MAP has the same quasi-analog representation medium *cell matrix* as DEPIC. Therefore, MAPs are also depictions which can represent several objects according to their positional relationships in a depictional format. When several objects and their spatial relations to one another are represented in a MAP, their individual depictions are used (they are coded in the representation structure DEPIC).

4 Problem Solving by Means of Imagination and Inspection

In this section, the two main processes of a depictional representation system are explained using an example of problem solving. The example should also illustrate several aspects of how such a system might function when solving spatial problems. The spatial problem consists of making a decision as to whether or not a certain object, a museum, lies on a certain street. The depictional system already knows that the museum is at the corner 'Schulstr./Hafenstr.' A short definition of the problem runs as follows:

- given: at(MUSEUM: r70, CORNER: r7)

- question: on(MUSEUM: r70, STREET: r71)

To begin with, the fact 'at(MUSEUM: r70, CORNER: r7)' is transformed into the depictional representation. For this purpose, the fact is forwarded to the depictional component by means of the inference engine (Bollinger et al. in this volume). In depictional representation the spatial relations of the given fact are represented in a depictional manner by means of the imagination process (Fürnsinn et al. 1984; Khenkhar 1988). In order to achieve this, a map MAP-1 is generated in which the objects ('corner', 'Schulstr.' and 'Hafenstr.') and the area 'r77' in which the museum is located are marked (see Fig. 2 and Fig.3).

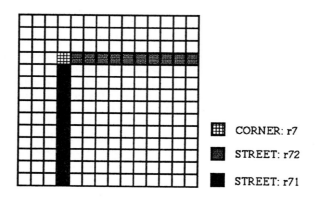

⊞ CORNER: r7

▦ STREET: r72

■ STREET: r71

Fig. 2

The following internal structures result from the depictional interpretation of the fact by means of the imagination process.

CORNER: r7

    name   :   Schulstr./Hafenstr.

    ...

    loc   :   —

    prototypical-depiction :   DEPIC−1

    depiction   :   —

    depict   :   MAP−1

STREET: r71

    name   :   Schulstr.

    ...

    loc   :   —

    prototypical-depiction :   —

    depiction   :   —

    depict   :   MAP−1

STREET: r72
    name   :   Hafenstr.
    ...
    loc   :   —
    prototypical-depiction :   —
    depiction   :   —
    depict   :   MAP−1

AREA: r77
    ...   :   —
    depict   :   MAP−1

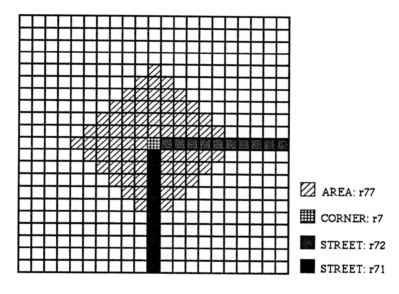

AREA: r77

CORNER: r7

STREET: r72

STREET: r71

Fig. 3

In imagination processes, the prototypical knowledge about the spatial size of objects plays a crucial role. In order to generate the area in which the museum is located, it is necessary to have the prototypical depiction of a corner. The prototypical depiction of a corner is assigned to the sort CORNER. When generating MAP-1, it is the cells of the corner Schulstr./Hafenstr. that are marked first. For this purpose, the above-mentioned prototypical depiction of the corner is accessed (see Fig. 2). In this paper, we will not discuss the interaction between the propositional and the depictional representation. A proposal as to how such an interaction could function is made in Pribbenow (1990).

After the imagination of the objects in MAP-1, area 'r77', the location of the museum, is generated. The imagination processes used for this purpose are based on the concept of *area-constituting processes* (Habel and Pribbenow 1988). Several sizes, such as the spatial size of the reference object (here, the RO is the corner) and of the entity to be localized (here, the LE is the museum) exert a strong influence on the spatial structure of the generated areas formed in this way. The cells of the area 'r77' are detemined and marked as follows:

The neighbor cells of the individuals cells of the corner 'r7' are determined according to the defined neighbor cell relation pattern. Theoretically, any type of neighbor cell relation pattern can be used. In MAP-1, the 4-neighbor cell pattern was used. Fig. 4 shows what the result would be like if the 8-neighbor cell pattern was used.

All cells of area 'r77', in which the museum is located are determined according to the same principle, i.e., by generating the neighbor cells of those cells which had already been determined previously and they computing their neighbor cells again. This process terminates when a certain limit is reached – a limit which depends on the LE (here: the museum) and on the neigbor cell relation pattern. The result of all imagination processes that were necessary for the transformation of the fact 'at(MUSEUM: r70, CORNER: r7)' into the depictional representation are coded in MAP1 as shown in Fig. 3. All cells of one object have the same graphical pattern. Different objects in one map also have different graphical patterns. The facts occurring in the question mentioned above may now be examined by means of inspection processes, using an inspection component. An inspection process is a type of *top view* on the generated areas in the depictions. It is used for the determination of certain spatial relationships (Fürnsinn et al 1984, Khenkhar 1988).

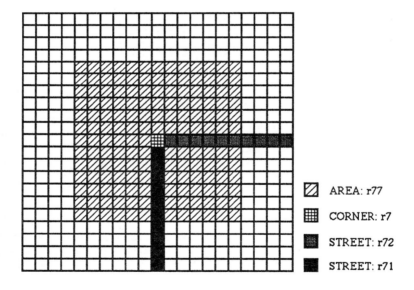

Fig. 4

In order to perform inspection processes, the area 'r99' is generated according to the principle described above by means of an imagination process. The area 'r99' is the one that occurs in the question. It must be decided whether or not the museum lies on 'Schulstr.'. The area 'on-Schulstr.' is the object 'r99'. For the imagination of this area, all cells of the object 'r71' (Schulstr.) in are examined, since 'Schulstr.' occurs as RO in the question. The result of the imagination process of the area 'r99' can be seen in Fig. 5.

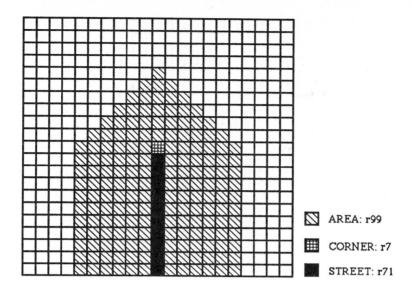

AREA: r99

CORNER: r7

STREET: r71

Fig. 5

It is now possible to inspect the two areas 'r77' (fact) and 'r99' (question) with respect to their overlapping relationship. First of all the intersection area of the two areas involved is generated. The ratio of the sizes of the intersection area and the area 'r77' (fact) is of crucial importance for answering the question.

The following three cases may occur:

- The ratio equals 1. That is, the intersection area and the area 'r77' cover each other exactly and are equal. In this case the question may be answered *yes*.

- The ratio equals 0. That is, the area 'r99' and the area 'r77' do not overlap. In this case the question may be answered *no*.

- The ratio equals a number X, greater than 0, smaller than 1 (0<X<1). That is, the two areas 'r77' and 'r99' do overlap in an intersection area that is a partial area of area 'r77'. In this case, the question may not be answered unequivocally. One sensible interpretation of this number X may be defined as follows:

The number X represents the degree of certainty for a positive answer. In other words, the higher the number X, the more certain it is that the answer to the question will be positive. According to the principle described above, the depictional component may now answer the question *yes* since the intersection area equals the area 'r77' (see Fig. 6).

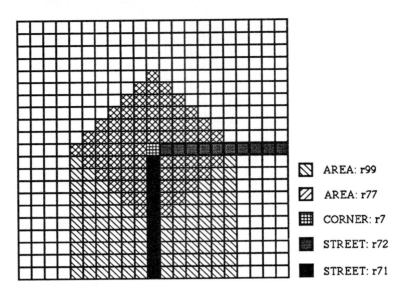

Fig. 6

In the example given above, the solution of a spatial problem was presented using a yes/no-question. If the problem is of a different nature as is the case when wh-questions are to be answered, the depictional system can do with a simpler strategy. For instance, the answer to the question What lies on Schulstr.? can be supplied by the system in a simple manner. First of all, the system imagines the 'on-area' 'r20', which occurs in the wh-question. The 'on-area' is generated in a way that is similar to the way it was generated in the above example. The difference to the previous case consists in the fact that the size of the 'at-area' is not influenced by the object to be localized (Habel and Pribbenow 1988). The next step in seeking an answer to the question consists in searching the 'at-area'. Each cell belonging to the 'at-area' is investigated in order to find out which RefOs it belongs to. The set of the RefOs thus found represents those objects which are located on Schulstr.

Summary

In this contribution, a depictional approach for the representation and processing of spatial knowledge was presented. The approach is based on the concept of the quasi-analog representation medium *cell matrices*. A neighbor cell relation is defined on the cell set of a cell matrix, which the further concepts are then based upon. That is why all facts coded in this representation format are, with respect to the neighbor cell relation, represented in an analog format. Using this approach, it is possible to represent sketch-like spatial knowledge by means of depictions. This knowledge can be processed with the aid of the processes of imagination and inspection. Due to a lack of space, these types of processes were only briefly discussed in this contribution. This holds also for the strategies of problem solving of such a depictional representation system which may achieve more adequate results by taking advantage of the depictional representation. The interaction of the propositional and the depictional component of an entire system of representation and processing of spatial knowledge has not been elaborated here. This subject is discussed in Pribbenow (1990).

References

Downs, R., Stea, D. (1982): Kognitive Karten. Die Welt in unseren Köpfen. UTB Harper and Row

Fürnsinn, M., Khenkhar, M. N., Ruschkowski, B. (1984): GEOSYS - Ein Frage-Antwort-System mit räumlichen Vorstellungsvermögen. In: C.-R. Rollinger (ed.): Probleme des Textverstehens. Ansätze der Künstlichen Intelligenz. Niemeyer, Tübingen

Habel, Ch. (1986): Prinzipien der Referentialität. Untersuchungen zur propositionalen Repräsentation von Wissen. Springer-Verlag, Berlin, Heidelberg, New York

Habel, Ch. (1987): Cognitive Linguistics: The Processing of Spatial Knowledge. ATALA (Association pour le Traitement Automatique des Languages), 28, 21- 56. Also as: LILOG Report 45, 1988, IBM Deutschland, Stuttgart

Habel, Ch. (1988): Prozedurale Aspekte der Wegplanung und Wegbeschreibung. In: H. Schnelle, G. Rickheit (eds.): Sprache in Mensch und Computer. Westdeutscher Verlag. Also as: LILOG Report 17, 1987, IBM Deutschland, Stuttgart

Habel, Ch. (1988): Repräsentation räumlichen Wissens. In: G. Rahmstorf (ed.): Wissensrepräsentation in Expertensystemen. Springer-Verlag, Berlin, Heidelberg, New York. Also as: Fachbereich Informatik, Uni. Hamburg, Mitteilung 153

Habel, Ch. (1989): zwischen-Bericht. In Ch. Habel, M. Herweg, K. Rehkämper (ed.): Raumkonzepte in Verstehensprozessen. Interdisziplinäre Beiträge zu Sprache und Raum. Niemeyer, Tübingen, pp. 37-69

Habel, Ch., Pribbenow, S. (1988): Gebietskonstituierende Prozesse. LILOG Report 18, IBM Deutschland, Stuttgart

Khenkhar, M. N. (1988): Vorüberlegungen zur depiktionalen Repräsentation räumlichen Wissens. LILOG Report 19, IBM Deutschland, Stuttgart

Khenkhar, M. N. (1989): DEPIC-2D: Eine Komponente zur depiktionalen Repräsentation und Verarbeitung räumlichen Wissens. In: D. Metzing (ed.): GWAI-89: 13th German Workshop on Artificial Intelligence. Springer-Verlag, Berlin, Heidelberg, New York

Khenkhar, M. N. (1990): Eine objektorientierte Darstellung von Depiktionen auf der Grundlage von Zellmatrizen. In: Ch. Freksa, Ch. Habel (eds.): Repräsentation und Verarbeitung räumlichen Wissens. Springer-Verlag, Berlin, Heidelberg, New York

Kosslyn, S. M. (1980): Image and Mind. Harvard University Press, Cambridge, MA

McCarthy, J., Hayes P. (1969): Some philosophical problems from the standpoint of artificial intelligence. In: B. Meltzer, D. Michie (eds.): Machine Intelligence. Edinburgh University Press

McDermott, D., Davis E. (1984): Planning routes through uncertain territory. Artificial Intelligence, 22, 107-156

Pribbenow, S. (1988): Verträglichkeitsprüfungen für die Verarbeitung räumlichen Wissens. In: Hoeppner, W. (ed.): GWAI-88. 12th German Workshop on Artificial Intelligence. Springer-Verlag, Berlin, Heidelberg, New York

Pribbenow, S. (1990): Interaktion von propositionalen und bildhaften Repräsentationen. In: Ch. Freksa, Ch. Habel (eds.): Repräsentation und Verarbeitung räumlichen Wissens. Springer-Verlag, Berlin, Heidelberg, New York

Rosch, E. (1975): Cognitive representations of semantic categories. Journal of Experimental Psychology, 104, 192-233

Zadeh, L. A. (1965): Fuzzy sets. Information and Control, 8, 338-353

Chapter 4

Generating Natural Language

Natural language generation has always been viewed as the "poor cousin" of natural language analysis. One of the reasons is that fairly simple matching techniques for answering questions could be used that led to an overall acceptable performance, but the main reason is that the reader is a human being who is very cooperative and tries to interpret even the most cryptic utterance of a system in a sensible way. This situation changed and language generation became a research area when the simple techniques proved to be inflexible and hence hardly adaptable to the different demands of the host systems. The interest in modeling human language production grew also.

The problems worked on in language generation are aspects of determining content and form of a text, where "text" ranges from one sentence to a paragraph. Hence, issues of text planning, text coherence, and language as a communicative means are in focus. On the other hand, people from the area of language analysis working in generation focus on mechanisms for generating language in formal grammar systems and start working on bidirectional grammars, ones that can be used for analysis and generation. Slowly, research efforts in these two areas are coming closer together and influencing each other.

In the following three contributions the underlying philosophy and the capabilities of the LILOG generation component are described in detail. In the first contribution differences and similarities of analysis and generation are expanded further and the architecture of the LILOG generation component is introduced. Some of the problems of integrating the generation component into a text understanding system are then discussed.

In the second contribution, we address the problem of generating paragraphs from the representations that have been built by the understanding process. Therefore, the planning mechanism, the plan library and the intermediate text structure representation is discussed, which might be viewed as the starting point for developing a revision component.

In the third contribution we describe the formulator, which is the component that takes a formal description of a sentence as input and produces correctly inflected German sentences. First, the interfaces to other components of the LILOG system are described, thus showing the restrictions whithin which the component was implemented. Then the control structure of the formulator and its algorithms are discussed. Finally, some of the problems that stem from integrating this component into the environment of the LILOG system are critically reviewed.

Hans-Joachim Novak

Integrating a Generation Component into a Natural Language Understanding System

Hans-Joachim Novak

1 Introduction

So far we have seen that the main goal of the LILOG project is to build a text understanding system. Therefore the emphasis of the research is on linguistic formalisms for the representation of linguistic knowledge, grammar formalisms and their implementation, and knowledge representation and inference.

Generation in LILOG started as a question-answering component in order to verify what the system had understood, but soon it developed its own impetus and proceeded along the lines of text generation. The aim of the project is to construct internal representations of the incoming short texts. In the generation subproject we aim at answering questions about these short texts and also at generating them from their internal representations. In the LILOG scenario the generation component is able to answer four different kinds of question:

1. yes/no questions

2. wh-questions

3. route questions

4. general questions like "What do you know about X?", where X is a sight in the city of Düsseldorf.

In order to answer the first two kinds of questions we rely heavily on the capabilities of the inference engine. Parsing of the questions yields an Extended Discourse Representation Structure (EDRS) which is translated into an L_{LILOG}-formula that can be submitted to the inference engine. The proof of such a formula can either yield a negative result, i.e., no proof found, or yield instances for the variables of the formula. In the latter case the task of the generation component lies in rendering a natural language description of these instances. The descriptions can range from simple noun or prepositional phrases to complete sentences, if, for instance, a when-question has been asked that can only be answered by referring to a reference event.

The task of generating route descriptions is currently performed by a specialized component that has been developed by our project partners at Hamburg University. A modified A* algorithm is used to find the optimal path between the given start and end point. The modification is such that the optimal path between A and B is not the shortest one but the one that can be described with a minimal number of direction changes.

The fourth kind of question, finally, needs the full capacity of the generation component. In this case we first have to decide *what* we want to say and then *how* we want to say it. Therefore, we have devised a planning component that takes a communicative goal as input and produces paragraph-length texts. This component is the topic of the contribution following this one.

In the remainder of this contribution we focus on the integration of the generation component into the text understanding system LEU/2. First, we take a close look at the similarities and differences between analyzing and generating language. Then we present the architecture of the generation component motivating the design decisions for the planning component that is described in the next contribution. Finally, we discuss the integration of the component into the system environment of LEU/2.

2 Natural Language Analysis and Generation

Often the argument is put forth that generation is the inverse of analysis, even more so, since we have grammar formalisms that allow the declarative representation of grammatical knowledge which is thus direction-independent. Although it seems to be the case that the only difference between parsing and generation lies in the nature of the input, I will argue that there are more differences that have to be taken into account and that the view of parsing has to be broadened before we can use the same grammars and lexicons for parsing and generation.

Viewed from a coarse-grained level both tasks seem to be similar, namely functions mapping utterances to meanings and vice versa. However, in comprehension some of the linguistic knowledge may be ignored, whereas its use cannot be avoided in generation. (Russell, Warwick, Carroll 1990) argue that there is an asymmetry between parsing and generation with unification grammars. One asymmetry they disclose stems from the different processing directions. In parsing we start with a string of words, and no matter whether the processing is bottom-up or top-down, the basis for selecting grammar rules is information associated with words in the lexicon. In generation we start with a semantic description, and there is no guarantee in general that the constituents of the input structure correspond to words. Generally, the semantic representation and the lexical items are not related directly but rather by intermediate syntactic rules, any one of which is able to manipulate the representation. The correct identification of a lexical item is not possible in generation without considering the syntactic rules which may intervene.

Another asymmetry brought forth by (Russell, Warwick, Carroll 1990) concerns the constraints that have to be imposed on a unification grammar in order to be able to generate with it. As they formulate it (p. 206): "Grammatical analyses developed in a purely parsing environment cannot always be transferred straightforwardly into a format suitable for generation." I will not go into detail here but refer the reader to the article. I want to put forth another, more basic asymmetry between comprehension and generation that is usually not seen from the point of view of a grammar formalism or a grammatical theory.

This is the more principled asymmetry of the processes as known from the monitoring experiments done in psycholinguistics. It has been shown in many experiments (for a discussion of some of them and an excellent book on speaking see (Levelt 1989)) that speakers can monitor their own speech: both their internal speech, before it was uttered, and their overt speech, in the same way as they listen to interlocutors. Monitoring is used to detect and sometimes correct errors before uttering them and also for corrections after something wrong has been uttered. This process shows the principled asymmetry between comprehension and generation: generation makes use of the comprehension component whereas comprehension does not need the generation component. Whether this asymmetry bothers us depends on our view of the comprehension and generation task. If we are concerned primarily with the structure and the regularities of language and its formalization then we can neglect this asymmetry. If our interest is mainly in language as one means of communication and do we want to model communication on our machines then this difference is important to us, as we should also find it in our models. It is only recently that we see a growing concern among researchers in the different fields of computational linguistics, artificial

661

intelligence and psycholinguistics to develop models that are based on the view of language as a means of communication. The demands of generation can help us broaden our view also for research in comprehension.

Sixteen years ago Bertram C. Bruce (Bruce 1975) argued that there are no real differences in the tasks of comprehension and generation; every task that has to be performed in generation has its counterpart in comprehension. Although I regard this as basically true, it does not reflect our current research in terms of the problems being worked on. In generation the problems of what to convey to the user and how to do this as well as work on lexical selection are the major problems. In comprehension the development of formalisms for the encoding of grammatical theories, the incorporation of semantics into the theories, and efficient parsing algorithms are in the mainstream of work. Let us briefly consider two examples of processes to motivate Bruce's claim that for every task there is a corresponding one on the other side of the fence. Consider the generation task of deciding which information to include in an utterance. The corresponding task in comprehension would be to identify the selectivity involved in saying exactly this much and representing it instead of abstracting from it. Consider lexical selection in generation. The counterpart would be to draw conclusions from the fact that this particular expression was used instead of alternative ones. Generally, the claim is that whenever a process is used in generation it has effects which may be discernible, interpretable and significant (see also (Mann 1987), p. 230). Presently, the state of the art in comprehension is far away from incorporating the above mentioned processes, but it should not stay like this! The primary reason for this lack is our poor notion of what exactly constitutes a context and how to represent it.

To end this section on generation and analysis, we shift our attention to another area, namely knowledge representation. There are two main reasons why research efforts in analysis and generation are apart from each other. The first is that the foci of research are naturally far away from each other. In generation the tasks are to select and decide what and how to say things, in analysis the task is to deliver a semantic description of an almost arbitrary input of the user. The second reason is that the formal descriptive mechanisms for analysis are far better developed because we abstract from intentions, speech acts and plans, which are very hard to formalize in a way that can be handled by inference techniques (but see (Cohen, Morgan, Pollack 1990) for progress in this area). Unfortunately, generation always starts with an intention to communicate something, and breaks this intention down to a speech act to be uttered and further down to either a declarative, interrogative or imperative sentence modus.

Knowledge representation nowadays is solidly grounded in logic, namely first-order predicate logic, possibly with some extensions such as, for instance, a sort concept as in L_{LILOG}. We thus have for every syntactic expression in our logic a formal semantic expression. Once we have proved the deduction theorem for our logic we know that we can conduct a proof in our formal system either syntactically or semantically. It is now interesting to see that we express the semantics of our natural language syntax in the syntax of our formal system. We then make inferences by use of the syntax of the formal system. In generation we have to take the results of these inference steps and try to give them an interpretation such that we can build a syntactic structure in our natural language again, although the relation between natural language syntax and formal syntax is not quite clear. Remember that the formal syntax is the natural language semantics that abstracts from several of the issues that have to be dealt with in generation (intention and speech acts for instance). We need far more groundwork in knowledge representation of the kind of (Cohen, Levesque 1990a; Cohen, Levesque 1990b) before we can represent more semantic relations that are necessary for generation.

3   The Architecture of the Generation Component

Viewing the generation component as a black box shows us its two main components (see Figure 1). It is triggered by an incoming question EDRS, does its work and yields as output a list of

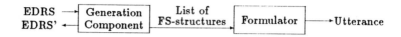

Figure 1: A first sketch of the generation component

FS-structures. FS-structures are expressions of a formal sentence description language that fully specifies a constituent or a sentence (examples thereof are given in the section on the formulator). The second output of the generation component is an EDRS' for the generated answer or utterance. This is necessary in order to refer anaphorically to objects, for instance in follow up questions that have been uttered by the system. FS-structures are the input to the formulator, our front-end surface generator which yields correctly inflected German sentences[1]. Of course, FS-structures can specify partial sentences, for instance just an NP with a restrictive relative clause or a genitive attribute. Generally speaking, more can be specified in an FS-structure and can be dealt with by the formulator than the generation component can construct from the underlying representations. We thus have a powerful tool for the generation of correctly inflected surface strings; we need not take care of all the details of morphology and syntax in the generation component and can concentrate on deciding what to say and how we want to say it. Other front-end generators similar to our formulator that are also not embedded in a formal grammar theory are for instance SUTRA (Busemann 1988), FREGE (Emele 1987), or for English MUMBLE and MUMBLE-86 (McDonald 1983; McDonald, Meteer 1988). Our formulator shares with them a clearly defined input specification that fully determines the utterance to be generated.

Naturally, there are also disadvantages associated with this architecture. The major one is that we do not use the same grammar for analysis and generation. The generation grammar is encoded in the formulator whereas the analysis grammar is encoded in the lexicon. The major drawbacks are first, the discrepancy between what can be analyzed and what can be generated, and second, that our formulator does not have an explicit grammar but rather a procedurally encoded one. Just recently we began to enhance our linguistic representation formalism by typed feature structures that allow us to make type inferences, and we plan to look at questions of control structure in order to come closer to the goal of a real bidirectional grammar system that does not need two grammars.

Two reasons led to the above architecture. The first is that we decided early in the project to implement a component like the formulator in order to be independent of changes of the grammar formalism that then actually took place as a change from CUG to HPSG. The second reason is that we wanted to concentrate on the selection and text planning tasks, and doing research in this area as well as in generation in a unification based paradigm with HPSG would have meant overestimating our capacity.

---

[1]The formulator itself is described in detail in the third article in this chapter.

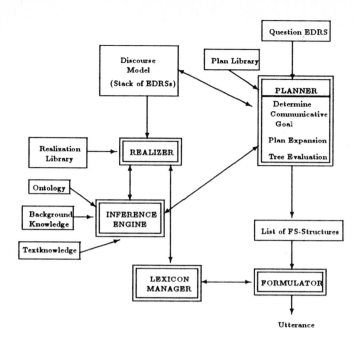

Figure 2: The generation component

Let us now look at the generation component in more detail (see Figure 2)[2].

In order to answer one of the four different question types the planner is called with the question EDRS. By using predefined plans (plan library) and the inference engine it determines *what* to answer, and by calling the realizer with its realization library it also decides *how* to structure the answer. The output of the planner is a list of FS-structures, giving the internal format of the answer that can be further processed by the formulator to yield an utterance. As a side effect of answering a question the discourse model is updated by adding the EDRS structure for the answer to it.

The realizer accesses the discourse model, for instance to decide whether an entity should be pronominalized, and uses the inference engine to access the ontology, the background knowledge, and the text knowledge that has been built by the understanding process. It is the component that provides by means of the realization library the mapping between the concepts in the knowledge base and possible syntactic structures needed to realize them in language. It also has access to the lexicon through the lexicon manager, as it needs to know, for instance, the roles that a verb can take in order to build the corresponding FS-structures.

The realizer and the planner are the two components that build the input to the formulator and are described in detail in the next article in this chapter. Here we give an overall view of the generation component and therefore describe the planner's tasks a little more. The planner analyzes the incoming EDRS and determines the communicative goal. At present, we distinguish four communicative goals corresponding to the four question types, namely:

---

[2]The rightmost arrows denote the major data flow from the question EDRS to the utterance. Double rectangles stand for processes and normal ones for data structures. Arrows between processes denote changes in control and exchange of data structures. Arrows pointing from data structures to processes denote the reading of data, arrows in the other direction the writing of data.

1. answer_y/n(question)

2. answer_wh(question)

3. describe(route)[3]

4. describe(object)

In the second step, plans of the plan library are triggered by the communicative goals. There are two kinds of plans, primitive ones and complex ones. Primitive plans cannot be further expanded but they can be executed immediately. A primitive plan to answer a yes/no question includes a call to the inference engine to prove the proposition in question. The inference engine is called with the L_{LILOG} expression corresponding to the question EDRS and yields either instances for the variables of the L_{LILOG} expression or an expression denoting that it could not find an answer. Assuming it found an answer, then the instances are either atoms, refos (reference objects), or skolem constants that have to be verbalized. According to the type of instance, the realizer decides how to verbalize them by means of the realization library (the mapping functions from the conceptual representations to linguistic structures). For instance, if the realizer gets a refo that denotes an object it tries to generate a noun phrase or a pronoun describing the object. Noun phrase generation follows the strategy of uniquely characterizing the object such that it cannot be mixed up with another one currently in the discourse model. Hence, noun phrases can become quite complex, by the use of restrictive relative clauses.

The complex planning case arises when the communicative goal is describe(object). Here the user wants to get information about an object without specifying any concrete demands (remember that the original question is "What can you tell me about X?"). In this case a complex plan, describe(X), is triggered which is itself composed of plans that we call domain plans, as they describe which information should be included in a paragraph describing a sight, for instance how to access the object, its location, its entry price, something about its history, etc. The plan expansion is done by a hierarchical expansion planner (Sacerdoti 1975) the same way that Hovy uses this mechanism to do RST-planning (Hovy 1988) (see also (Kreyß, Novak 1990) for a description of the algorithm). The planning process stops when all composite plans have been expanded to primitive ones. The result is a tree structure with nodes that are plan names and leaves that are primitive plans, i.e., action statements to say things. The last step then is to traverse the tree for possible reorganizations, determine sentence boundaries and finally build the FS-structures.

Plan expansion can be viewed as content planning and tree evaluation as planning *how* to say things. We have structured the intermediate tree level according to Meteer's notion of a "text structure" (Meteer 1990) and employ some of the heuristics of (Scott, de Souza 1990) for establishing the final structure of the text. The rules according to which sentence boundaries are determined and the rules deciding which adjuncts to incorporate into a sentence are still research topics.

After this introduction of the generation component we now turn to the integration of the component into the system LEU/2.

---

[3]The communicative goal to generate a route description is currently not handled by our planner but by a separate component that has been devised by our project partners at Hamburg University. Their component also yields FS-structures. To incorporate new plans in our planner such that it can also generate the route descriptions is a goal that at the time of writing of this article has not yet been achieved.

4 The Generation Component in the Environment of LEU/2

No generation component can be seen as an isolated component. It has interfaces to almost all other components of the system in which it resides. Looking again at Figure 2, we see that in our case there are interfaces to all the knowledge sources of the system via the inference engine, to the lexicon via the lexicon manager (but see the article on the formulator concerning the lexicon), and to the discourse model which is a stack of EDRS structures. The reasons for building our own grammar have already been discussed above.

Which components largely influence the generation capabilities? The two major components are the knowledge representation and the discourse model. In a text generation system the discourse model need not be as fully developed as for instance in a dialogue system, and instead one often finds a set of default assumptions about the possible audience. The discourse model in those cases mainly helps to keep track of what the system already said and therefore to enable pronominal references and to avoid uttering propositions already known to the hearer or inferable by him or her. If we aim at a question-answering system that can also generate cooperative responses, we pose high demands on the analysis component and the discourse model, as cooperative responses often necessitate speech act and plan recognition (see (Allen 1983; Carberry 1983; Carberry 1988; Litman, Allen 1987)) as well as recognizing presuppositions in order to deal with them effectively (see (Kaplan 1983)). The task of reacting appropriately to user misconceptions about the system's knowledge poses yet further requirements on the analysis component and the knowledge representation (see (McCoy 1986; McCoy 1987)).

In the LILOG system (LEU/2) the generation component is used to verify the system's understanding abilities. Only by asking questions we can find out what the system understood and inferred. The overall commmunicative situation for this task resembles an examination rather than an information seeking. As we did not aim at a dialogue system we neglect issues of speech act and plan recognition and also do not handle user misconceptions. It was an aim of generation to be able to generate the short texts that are the input of LEU/2 from their underlying representations.

Let us again consider the tasks of the generation component and see what interaction with the other components of LEU/2 are necessary to accomplish them. The tasks are question answering, giving route descriptions, which is currently done by another component, and giving descriptions of objects of interest such that small paragraphs are generated that resemble the original short texts.

In order to answer questions access to the system's knowledge and rules is needed. This is achieved by use of the inference engine. The question EDRS is translated into an L_{LILOG} formula that is to be proven by the inference engine which itself can use all available rules. In the cases of constituent questions and yes/no questions that can be answered positively the answers are straightforward and only require noun phrase or prepositional phrase generation except when a "when" question has been asked. In this case sentences sometimes have to be generated that describe the reference event. Problems arise if we want to answer cooperatively a yes/no question in the negative case:

User: Is the Hetjensmuseum in Schulstraße?
System: No, it is in Hafenstraße.
System: No, the Gallery of Art is in Schulstraße.

The above examples exemplify that we need a notion of focus in order to make the distinction between the two possible answers. Currently, no such notion is delivered by the analysis component. One way out of this problem is to generate as answer:

System: No, the Hetjensmuseum is in Hafenstraße but the Gallary of Art in in Schulstraße.

In order to come up with these answers we need to be able to modify the L_{LILOG} formula that is submitted to the inference engine such that the yes/no question in the negative case is answered as a constituent question. The user interface of the inference engine allows us to do exactly this. This interface to the inference engine is very powerful and has been designed to meet our needs (Bollinger et al., in this volume). At present, we do not handle overgeneration, but the necessary mechanisms are available so that it can be incorporated in the future.

One of the things being done when generating a noun or prepositional phrase is word choice. From the inference engine we get an instance of a variable and the sort of the variable, i.e., its meaning as defined in the formal knowledge representation by attributes belonging to or inherited by the sort. The sort name together with the attributes now has to be translated into a word or a natural language expression. One of the shortcomings of our system is the fact that there is a one-to-one correspondence between sorts and words to simplify lexical selection (see (Reiter 1990a; Reiter 1990b) for the problems of doing lexical selection in a KL-ONE based knowledge representation).

Let us now come to the second task, text generation. First, we look at the representational basis for this task. Analyzing the short texts we consider in LILOG leads to a representation of the propositional content of the texts. Therefore an event-centered representation is built for each sentence in the EDRS format. Pronominal references to objects introduced earlier are resolved, and finally the EDRS of a complete short text is translated to L_{LILOG}. This translation triggers forward inferences such that besides the event-centered representation we also have an object-centered one. The idea behind this mechanism is that if several sentences predicate certain things about an object it is part of the understanding process to group these predications around the object. This leads naturally to the fact that some of the attributes of an object, namely those that originally stem from another event, can only be verbalized as a sentence or a subclause. Consider the following sentence of a short text:

Die Kreuzherrenkirche, die im 15. Jahrhundert erbaut wurde, ...
The Kreuzherrenkirche which was built in the 15th century, ...

This phrase is represented in L_{LILOG} as follows:

```
refo r_erbauen: ERBAUEN.
refo r_kreuzherrenkirche: Kirche
refo r_erbau_zeit: ZEIT
...
axiom ax_1
patiens (r_erbauen)  = r_kreuzherrenkirche and
temporal (r_erbauen) = r_erbau_zeit
...
```

The following axiom directly links the reference object r_kreuzherrenkirche to the time it was built:

```
axiom ax_2
forall E: ERBAUEN,
       G: GEBAEUDE,
       Z: ZEIT;
EP  temporal (E) = Z and
    patiens (E)  = G
    -->
    entstehung (G,Z).
```

EP is the entry point of the rule, i.e., the literal that is evaluated first. As it points to one of the premises of the rule, the rule is a forward inference. The rule leads to an additional attribute for the reference object r_kreuzherrenkirche, namely:

entstehung(r_kreuzherrenkirche, r_erbau_zeit).

Later verbalization of such an attribute is done by the realizer using realization plans.

During analysis no other coherency relation besides pronominal reference is analyzed. Therefore, these relations are captured in the predefined plans that describe possible structures of descriptive paragraphs and are used by the generation process. Generally, planning in the generation component is done outside the logical formalism of the LILOG system as our knowledge representation system does not allow for modeling and reasoning about intentions and beliefs, which is a notoriously hard problem.

Using the above example representation, I would like to point to another interface problem. The temporal phrase "in the 15th century" is represented as a role, the value of which is another refo. Thus the preposition used in the phrase has been resolved as one that can denote temporal information. Generating the temporal adjunct implies generating the appropriate preposition again. From an analysis point of view, one would not encode in the lexicon the prepositions that have to be used with certain nouns in order to use them as temporal phrases, but generation requires this. This information does not belong in the ontology, i.e. build different sorts for temporal nouns according to the prepositions they take, but seems to be highly idiosyncratic and should be encoded in the lexicon. At present, it is encoded in the realization plans.

Finally, I want to point out different conceptions of what constitutes an ontology and what the requirements for using it are. Common understanding is that the ontology contains and defines the terminology the system knows about, like a KL-ONE TBOX. The formal apparatus to define concepts is given by the representation language but it has to be used by the people modeling the world of discourse. Modeling knowledge depends on its later use - just think about the granularity of the representations. Modeling knowledge in order to talk about it later is one requirement which is different from that of modeling knowledge in order to draw generally applicable inferences in a certain domain. To be more concrete, two sorts ARTEFACT and NATURAL-THING might be relevant in one domain, but the distinction is irrelevant for language use, where the distinction should be PERSON and NON-PERSON as this distinction is grammatically relevant. From a generation point of view, we want to find in an ontology language-relevant distinctions. This is not always true in the LILOG ontology and our realization plans try to capture some these distinctions. Ultimately, we aim at a level of representation like an upper model (Bateman 1990) that only captures language-relevant distinctions and is connected to a more task-oriented ontology.

Generally, in a large project like LILOG the common understanding about each other's problems in performing different tasks grows while working on them. As such, the experience of building this large AI system with so many different features and integrating the different components into one system was definitely worthwhile. It led many people to a larger understanding of what it means to understand *and* to generate language and drew the different research areas closer together.

References

Allen, J. F. (1983): Recognizing intentions from natural language utterances. In: Brady, M., Berwick, R. C. (eds.): Computational Models of Discourse. MIT Press, Cambridge, Mass., chapter 2, pp. 107–164

Bateman, J. A. (1990): Upper modeling: organizing knowledge for natural language processing. In: Proceedings of the 5th International Workshop on Language Generation, Dawson, PA., pp. 54–61

Bruce, B. C. (1975): Generation as social action. In: Theoretical Issues in Natural Language Processing-1 (TINLAP), Cambridge, Mass., pp. 64–67

Busemann, S. (1988): Surface transformations during the generation of written german sentences. In: McDonald, D. D., Bolc, L. (eds.): Natural Language Generation Systems. Springer, Berlin, New York, pp. 98–165. Symbolic Computation

Carberry, S. (1983): Tracking user goals in an information-seeking environment. In: Proceedings of the 3rd AAAI, Washington

Carberry, S. (1988): Modeling the user's plans and goals. Computational Linguistics 14(3), 23–37

Cohen, P. R., Levesque, H. J. (1990a): Intention is choice with commitment. Artificial Intelligence 42(3)

Cohen, P. R., Levesque, H. J. (1990b): Performatives in a rationally based speech act theory. In: Proceedings of the 28th Annual Meeting of the ACL, Pittsburgh, Pennsylvania, University of Pittsburgh, pp. 79–88

Cohen, P. R., Morgan, J. L., Pollack, M. E. (eds.) (1990): Intentions in Communication. System Development Foundation Benchmark Series. A Bradford Book, MIT Press, Cambridge, MA.

Emele, M. (1987): Frege–Ein objektorientierter FRont-End-GEnerator. In: Morik, K. (ed.): GWAI-87. 11th German Workshop on Artificial Intelligence, Berlin, New York, Springer, pp. 64–73. IFB Bd. 152

Hovy, E. H. (1988): Planning coherent multisentential text. In: Proc. 26th Annual Meeting of the ACL, pp. 163–169

Kaplan, R. M. (1983): Co-operative response from a portable natural language system. In: Brady, M., Berwick, R. C. (eds.): Computational Models of Discourse. MIT Press, Cambridge, Mass., pp. 167–208

Kreyß, J., Novak, H.-J. (1990): The textplanning component pit of the lilog system. In: Proc. 13th International Conference on Computational Linguistics, pp. 431–433

Levelt, W. J. M. (1989): Speaking: From Intention to Articulation. A Bradford Book, MIT Press, Cambridge, MA.

Litman, D. J., Allen, J. F. (1987): A plan recognition model for subdialogues in conversations. Cognitive Scinece 11, 163–200

Mann, W. C. (1987): What is special about natural language generation research. In: Wilks, Y. (ed.): Theoretical Issues in Natural Language Processing. New Mexico State University, Las Cruces, NM., pp. 206–210

McCoy, K. F. (1986): The romper system: Responding to object-related misconceptions using perspective. In: Proceedings of the 24th Annual Meeting of the Association for Computational Linguistics, New York, pp. 97–105

McCoy, K. F. (1987): Contextual effects on responses to misconceptions. In: Kempen, G. (ed.): Natural Language Generation. Martinus Nijhoff, Dordrecht, chapter 3, pp. 43–54

McDonald, D. D., Meteer, M. W. (1988): From water to wine: Generating natural language text from today's applications programs. In: Proceedings of the Second Conference on Applied Natural Language Processing, Austin, Texas, pp. 41–48

McDonald, D. D. (1983): Natural language generation as a computational problem: An introduction. In: Brady, M., Berwick, R. C. (eds.): Computational Models of Discourse. MIT Press, Cambridge, Mass.

Meteer, M. W. (1990): The "generation gap" the problem of expressibility in text planning. Phd thesis, published as bbn report no. 7347, Bolt, Beranek and Newman Inc.

Reiter, E. B. (1990a): Generating appropriate natural language object descriptions. Tr-10-90, Center for Research in Computing Technology, Harvard University, Cambridge, MA. PhD Thesis

Reiter, E. B. (1990b): A new model for lexical choice for open-class words. In: Proceedings of the Fifth International Natural Language Generation Workshop, Dawson, Pa., pp. 23–30

Russell, G., Warwick, S., Carroll, J. (1990): Asymmetry in parsing and generating with unification grammars: Case studies from elu. In: Proc. of the 28th Annual Meeting of the ACL

Sacerdoti, E. D. (1975): A structure for plans and behaviour. North-Holland, Amsterdam

Scott, D. R., de Souza, C. S. (1990): Getting the message across in rst-based text generation. In: Dale, R., Mellish, C., Zock, M. (eds.): Current Research in Natural Language Generation, London, San Diego, New York, Boston, Academic Press, pp. 47–73

From Knowledge Structures to Text Structures

Zuzana Dobeš and Hans-Joachim Novak

1 Introduction

In this paper we will be concerned with the actual machinery of the generation component. We will describe the various tasks that take place between the time the control module hands over a fully specified question EDRS to the generation component and an appropriate response is generated submitting the information asked for within the EDRS. The generator planner upon receiving an EDRS initiates a number of subtasks such as determining the appropriate communicative goal that leads to responding to the question encoded in the EDRS. Once the goal is determined, an appropriate plan is selected which is capable of carrying out the goal. While carrying out the plan, other plans may be included through a recursive expansion mechanism, which are then attached to an appropriately structured plan tree. The resulting plan tree is then evaluated by the component whose task is to transform the tree into a sequence of requests to the realizer. The realization component has the task of constructing a formulator template (i.e., an FS-structure) from this specification, which ultimately results in the output sentence or constituent string satisfying the query.

2 Overview

We begin our discussion by providing some background information about the generator planner, and the theory which motivated its design in the initial stage. We point out some of the problems that we came across when designing the interface of the planning component with the realization component. As these components were developed separately and are responsible for very different sets of tasks, the bridging of these components was relatively difficult and introduced an assortment of problems. These problems are commonly faced by generation systems. They can be handled through the use of various techniques; we will discuss the approach that we chose to take.

We will likewise discuss the planning algorithm and the decisions that need to be made at the various stages of planning, together with the control mechanism by which plans are evaluated, expanded, and incorporated into an evolving plan. We will also discuss to some detail the kind of structure, the *plan tree* that results from the planning process, and the properties of the representation used to encode all the information.

When a plan can no longer be broken down into a series of sub-goals, it is called a primitive plan or plan element. Such non-decomposable plan elements result in a primitive planning step, or action, which is executed by the realization component. Such a realization step can be rather shallow, that is, simply classify the plan element into its *realization type*, or it may involve evaluation through a series of realization phases resulting in an actual formulator template when the full discourse context is available and may be taken into account.

Last, we explain how the resulting plan tree is evaluated and broken down into a series of realization requests. During this phase the entire plan tree may be used to determine realization choices. This includes determining what constitutes a single sentence, what can be coordinated, what can be embedded, what can be pronominalized and so on. These tasks vary in difficulty, for while it is extremely difficult to determine exactly what and how much can go into a single sentence, there are a number of good algorithms which can be used to help us decide in most cases when to pronominalize.

3   The Development of the Generation Component

The development of the generation component has involved a number of persons who have worked on various parts of it over the past few years. Through each phase we have learned more and more about the interactions of the various submodules both within the generation component and within the LILOG system as a whole, and have used this knowledge to shape the design of the system.

Initially the system simply responded to simple user queries by mapping values of attributes directly into strings. Then as the user queries became more complicated and the formulator was fully implemented and ready to use, work began on improving the overall design of the realization component. A more systematic modular way of mapping concepts and plan elements into templates was designed and implemented.

3.1   Development of the Planner

At the same time a planning mechanism needed to be designed which could deal with more general queries about object descriptions. That is, it was not enough in these cases to simply resort to the inference engine to retrieve attributes of objects and realize them. What results in this case are entire paragraphs, and putting such extended texts together requires knowledge about what makes text coherent and understandable.

The planning mechanism that was chosen for our system was influenced in part by ideas from RST (Rhetorical Structure Theory) (Mann, Thompson 1988). This theory proposes a set of relations which can describe units of text, where a unit can comprise paragraphs or sequences of sentences down to clause-sized chunks of text. A piece of text is said to be coherent if it can be characterized by a single overreaching relation, and if all the parts of the text which spans this relation are also decomposable into relations by a recursive process, down to the level of clauses.

Though this work has been primarily used for the analysis of text, it has recently been effectively elaborated on and extended for work in generation (Hovy 1988; Hovy, McCoy 1989; Moore, Paris 1988). RST relations can be viewed as plans which are recursively expanded by a top-down hierarchial planning mechanism. So while RST-analysis of text is concerned with recognizing relations and breaking them down into finer-level relations, in the generation planning task we are concerned with creating coherent texts by recursively creating a plan tree by a process which maintains coherency and relevancy between all the elements of a plan as they are created and attached to the resulting plan tree.

Our system at this time makes use of only a limited set of relations from RST theory, for example *elaboration* and *background*, but expands on several of the relations which have to do with extension, and elaboration of domain concepts, i.e., concepts in the domain of discourse in LILOG. We do not use many of the other relations characteristic of an RST planner, because these require finer representations of knowledge within the user model which we do not have yet. But the basic mechanism by which such relations could be specified and included in our system has been designed and implemented.

3.2 Planning Problems

At the end of the initial phase of design we had an RST based planner capable of planning the content of paragraphs corresponding to simple user queries. We also had a generator capable of realizing sentences and single constituents from knowledge structures. The natural next step was to connect these two components. In trying to bridge these components we ran into many of the problems in paragraph planning (see (Hovy 1990)) which are still considered to be unsolved. This includes above all the general topic of delimiting and organizing sentence content. So the second phase of designing and implementing resulted in extending the existing planning component so as to promote a clearer and more natural interface to the realization component.

One of the initial problems we had was that the output of the planning process was such that the inner nodes of the plan tree were simply names of relations like *elaborate* in the example below, and the leaves were domain concepts. A simplified sample plan tree is shown below. The knowledge which is used to instantiate the plans is shown first, then the plan tree. The first plan makes use of object-centered knowledge, where an attribute stellt_aus of the first plan element r_kunstsammlung was used to derive the second plan element r_bilder. The second example uses an event-centered representation to derive the tree. The event r_umfassen which has two attributes, thema and objekt, was used to instantiate the plan.

refo r_kunstsammlung : KUNSTSAMMLUNG.
refo r_bilder : BILD+.

axiom ax_1
stellt_aus(r_kunstsammlung) = r_bilder.

would be represented as follows in a plan:

```
tree(features(r_kunstsammlung),      ! the top level plan
       tell(r_kunstsammlung),        ! the plan arguments
       tell(r_bilder))
```

and the following knowledge:

refo r_umfassen : UMFASSEN.
axiom ax_2
thema (r_umfassen) = r_kunstsammlung.
objeckt (r_umfassen) = r_bilder.

results in the following plan:

```
tree(features(r_kunstsammlung),      ! the top level plan
       tell(r_kunstsammlung),        ! the plan arguments
       tree(tell(r_umfassen),
            tree(elaborate(r_umfassen),   ! the new plan
                 tell(r_kunstsammlung),   ! the plan arguments
                 tell(r_bilder)))))
```

There were problems realizing the information from such plan trees, because of several points outlined below:

1. All information about the sort of the plan element that the planner derived during the planning process is lost. Some of this information is very useful for the realizer in deciding how to realize the plan element.

2. All the information about how a plan element was derived is lost. For instance, if a plan element resulted from the fact that it was the value of a particular attribute, knowing this kind of information is also useful for realizing it.

3. All information about the structure of complex objects, which must be derived in most cases, is lost because it is spread out over several plans without showing the way the pieces of the structure are connected. Complex objects include events, whose arguments we would like to keep together so that it is easy to map into clauses.

4. At the level of plan structures all information is lost as to how the elements of a plan relate to the plan as a whole. A single plan may introduce plan elements which simply support the relation, for instance by additional information besides those which define the primary plan arguments. This kind of information may also help in realization decisions. Supporting information is more likely to be expressed as embedded constituents, while plan arguments are candidates for top-level sentence constituents.

3.3   The Generation Gap

The essence of the problem was that since planners are usually designed to operate at the level of content and topic structure, they are not equipped to handle information in such a way as to preserve certain kinds of information that may help in the task of realization. It is certainly the case that a tight coupling of planning and realization would be ideal, but it would increase the complexity of the planning component tremendously. What we therefore need is a kind of compromise. We need a way of representing and handling the information at the plan level such that we first of all do not lose any information, and secondly that allows us to encode all that is possible about the general structure of the resulting plan without increasing the complexity of the planner.

When the planner is not able to influence how plans are realized, and when there is no inbuilt mechanism to assure that the plans the planner constructs are realizable in the first place we run very quickly into what is called in the generation community the problem of the "generation gap". Meteer's thesis addresses this problem directly (Meteer 1990a), and calls for the introduction of a new representational level called the "text structure" which is encoded using abstract linguistic resources (Meteer 1990b), with the goal of producing structures which ensure expressibility. The abstract linguistic resources which the text structure representation keeps track of are constituency, semantic types of constituents, and the structure of constituents.

So our primary task in the second stage of designing the planner was to come up with techniques by which the planner's output could be enhanced, to include information about the final text structure. The planner must have access to information about the kind of constituents that plan elements map into, the structural relationships between elements of a constituent, and how sentence boundaries are established.

The knowledge that is required to make these kinds of decisions comes from a variety of sources. First, we must establish knowledge about the entities in our domain, how they are structured in the knowledge base, how this structure can be appropriately mapped into plan elements, and how plan elements can be mapped into sentence-level constituents. As soon as we know, for instance, information about a plan element's type we have some information about how this information can be elaborated on and what kind of elaborations can occur. Each kind of elaboration can be attached to the existing plan tree in such a way that we can be sure that for the most part the resulting plan structure is realizable. The plan element type thus plays a double role. First, it determines further planning, i.e., whether the planner should look for more information to say about this object or entity, or whether it is for instance a value of some attribute about which nothing more can be said. Second, the type determines how the element should be realized, thus ensuring that all plan elements are realizable. Currently we represent plan element types as tuples consisting of the sort and the realization type of an element, e.g., [MUSEUM, Object]. Ultimately we aim at generalizing from these structures to what Meteer calls "semantic types". So by defining appropriate "types" for plan elements and providing an appropriate mechanism by which plan structures evolve, we are maximizing the use of plan resources and can be sure our plans are realizable.

4 Text Structure

The text structure representation was designed to handle information in a uniform way through all levels of processing by the generator. Constituents at all levels can be represented with the same underlying mechanism. The building blocks of the Meteer text representation provide us with two basic "types" of structures. These structures correspond to relations that hold between concepts, and are represented by trees. These include *kernel* and *composite* trees. Each type tells us two kinds of information, first how a parent node and its children are related to one another, and how the particular tree may be expanded. The kernel tree is represented as *head—argument*, that is, a "head" element, along with a list of "arguments", corresponds to a predicate argument structure. It has the property that the head element cannot be modified, that is, new arguments cannot be added to it, and only the arguments themselves can be elaborated. The *composite—matrix, adjunct* structure links up a dominant element, along with its dependent elements. The *composite—coordinate* structure links up elements of equal status (see (Meteer 1990a) for more detail). This distinction is meant to capture the general notions of *parataxis*, and *hypotaxis* (see (Halliday 1985)).

We have adopted a similiar representation scheme within our planner, though we use it in a different way, reflecting the fact that we use it in a completely different planning and generation environment. For instance, Meteer's text planner uses the context provided by the text structure to guide the planning process ((Meteer 1990a), Chap. 6). Our planner, on the other hand, is an RST based planner, which uses RST-like relations and schemas to guide the planning process.

In summary, we make use of the text structure representation in several ways: as an intermediate representation by way of which the planner and the knowledge base exchange information, for representing plan choices, and finally for post-plan processing, in which sentences are delimited and organized.

We now turn to the planner, and describe the structure of plans and how a plan tree is assembled.

5 The Planner

The top level of the planner instantiates plans corresponding to the communicative goal that has been determined by analyzing the incoming EDRS. This layer of the planner accesses *coop-plans* for the communicative goals answer_y/n and answer_wh. These plans contain calls to the inference engine to find the answer and in a later stage call realization plans to build the FS-structure for the formulator. This layer also triggers the top plan, which is a complex one, for the communicative goal

describe(X) which expands into domain plans, i.e., plans that take the structure of the concrete domain and its representation into account, and into realization plans, i.e., plans mapping domain concepts onto language.

The result of the planning process in all cases is a plan tree. The plan tree consists of a tree structure whose root node is simply a plan element specifying the kind of element that the node holds, or the kind of element described in the tree structure which is attached to it at its branches when the element is complex. For complex nodes to which an entire tree is attached, information about the structural relationship of the parent node to the attached children is also specified.

The simplest kind of plans that can be triggered are plans corresponding to requests for realizing a specific concept. In this case a coop plan simply instantiates a primitive *tell* plan which calls the top-level realization routines to evaluate and classify the realization class of the concept. The result in this case is a simple plan tree with no internal nodes but only leaves corresponding to the partially completed realization specification.

Actions appear as follows, where **r_region** is a domain concept corresponding to a spatial region with the realization type **raumregion**:

*action(*tell(r_region),
      body: generate_value_np(r_region,raumregion,?Output),
      input: Type == ?Value,
      output: ?Output,
      requirements: ?Value == [value,raumregion]*)*.

This results in the following initial text structure:

[[[matrix,head],$VALUE$:raumregion,object:r_region],
   [[arg,simple],$ATTRIBUTE$:praep,in]
   [[arg,simple],$ATTRIBUTE$:refobject,object:r_palace]].

This can then be translated into the following structure that contains a partially evaluated object, namely **r_palace**.

[[[matrix,head],[pp]]
   [[arg,simple],[$PREP$,[word,in]]],
   [[arg,simple],[$HEAD$,[instance,r_palace]]]]

In the last stage of realization this r palace can be fully evaluated into the following structure, as it stands just prior to formulator template construction, and which corresponds to the phrase: *In dem Palais.*

[[pp],
   [$PREP$,[word,in]],
   [$HEAD$,[word,Palace],[DET:det_def,NUM:sg]]]

More complex plans such as one to describe some object have to be recursively expanded and evaluated, which results in a complex plan tree whose leaves correspond to partially evaluated realization specifications as above. In this case the planning decisions involved are more complicated as they include determining how much information is to be included in the description, and determining the relevancy of existing knowledge to the description based on what the user assumes or has been told already. The content and structure of the plan trees that are created are therefore driven by factors such as coherency, and relevancy of knowledge.

The planner starts with a communicative goal. The output of the planning process is a tree whose inner nodes are text structures with descriptions of the relations that connect the node to its children. The leaves are text structures corresponding to the elements that are to be realized. The planner matches the current goal with plans that can achieve the goal. The requirements of the plan are tested, the plan's subgoals are determined, and the plan tree is appropriately extended to include the new plans. Next, all the subgoals of this plan are put on an agenda, which contains all the goals that remain to be processed. A new goal is then chosen from the agenda, and processing continues until the agenda is empty.(See (Hovy 1988), for the general topic of RST based planning, and (Hovy 1989) and (Kreyß, Novak 1990) for how it is applied within LILOG).

5.1   The Plan Library

Plans are represented as relations or collections of relations called schemas (Mann, Thompson 1988). There are different levels of abstraction involved in the definition of plans. The top level consists of a few RST relations. These are broken down to relations that reflect the structure of the L_{LILOG} knowledge base. For example, the relation *elaborate* specializes into domain relations such as *part_whole*, *process_step*, and *set_member*. The following example is the plan for elaborating a part_whole relation:

*plan(*elab_pw(N),
     nucleus: N,
     satellite: S,
     nucleus_requirements: [],
     satellite_requirements: [],
     joint_requirements: and([plan_domain_map(part_whole(N,S)),
                              not(bel(hoerer,part_whole(N,S)))],
     nucleus_growth_point: [],
     satellite_growth_point: features(S)*)

A relation holds between two parts, called the nucleus and satellite, which after being realized correspond to two sucessive pieces of text. As we have said, these pieces of text can correspond to parts of a paragraph, that is, multiple sentences, down to clause sized constituents. We also allow our plans to cover information below the clause level, and this means that the pieces of text may not necessarily follow each other. Also, there is often no precise order of the nucleus and satellite prescribed until the realization phase.

The nucleus and satellite requirements encode criteria which must hold before the relation is instantiated by the planner, and inserted into the plan tree. Requirements may check whether an domain concept is of a certain type, or whether an attribute can be found for the concept.

Growth_points allow the addition of further information, again by the use of plans.

There are also primitives associated with information in the "user model", which include requests to check whether a particular piece of knowledge is known to the user or not. For instance, if a user believes a fact to be true then there is no need to inform her of it. The concept of a user model has not been fully expanded in our system but clearly such a model is a vital element to any planner.

We also make use of planning schemas (in the flavor of (McKeown 1985)) which are represented as a pre-defined collection of RST relations. A schema corresponds to a plan, to satisfy a complex goal, which is initiated by the incoming EDRS, for instance a request to describe entities, or to provide informative responses to constituent, and yes/no questions. The top level of the planner inspects EDRS structures of a user query, and determines which schema is the most appropriate for responding to it. Such a schema is multi-nuclear, and has no growth points associated with it. Here is an example schema:

*schema(*describe(N),
nucleus: background(N),elaborate(N),enable(N),
nucleus_requirements: NR*).*

The plan tree is expanded according to the particular configuration of the nucleus and satellite and their selected growth point plans. The plan may consist of one or more nuclei, or a nucleus with one or more satellites. The nucleus and satellite can be simple or complex, depending on whether it has growth points attached to it or not.

In terms of text structure representation, a default structure is established for each of the possible plan configurations. A plan consisting simply of a nucleus and a satellite is encoded as a *composite—matrix-adjunct* structure with the composite node as the schema/relation, the nucleus as *matrix*, and the satellite as an *adjunct*. The default *coordinate* structure is used for relations or domain elements, *list* for unlike relations (as is the case in domain schemas). We also have *sequence* for temporally or spatially related domain elements, as well as *conjunction* and *disjunction*. Growth point plans are treated as *adjuncts* to the parent plans they are associated with.

We now briefly discuss how constituents and constituent structures are determined within our planner/generator model, which serve as the means by which text structures are defined.

6   Determining Constituents

The planner retrieves relevant knowledge via plan based access primitives, so-called domain plans. This knowledge is represented as a text structure corresponding to a plan element. Within such a structure, all the elements which are subject to plan-level elaboration must be represented as separate constituents. So a single plan element may introduce more than one constituent, such as is the case with events. Some of these constituents may be accessed by the planner to make further planning decisions.

Now there is a problem that we face at this point, mainly concerning the kind of plan elements that our planner permits. Plan elements in our system are not restricted to clause-sized chunks of information, or events. Relations such as *elaboration, enhancement,* or *extension* need not necessarily hold between "clauses" but possibly between a clause and one or more of its constituents (Halliday 1985). The planner may apply relations to concepts such as *Museums, The opening times of museums,* or *The availability of parking spaces.* In each case, constituents that arise do not necessarily correspond to clause sized units. Elaborating a *Museum* may result in an attribute specification such as *The museum exhibits paintings,* where the "exhibiting" or the "paintings" may still be elaborated upon. So all the arguments of an event, or an attribute specification which the planner can further elaborate on, must be identifiable within the text structure that is built. Using the text structure representation allows us to perform finer-level constituent planning, as well as enabling us to represent information in a form which is useful for later stages of generation. So constituent planning at the plan level requires that knowledge access primitives determine the appropriate granularity of concepts within the text structure which is built.

On the other hand, RST clearly assumes that text spans are of some minimal size, mainly clauses, and is in essence a theory about the way clauses combine. Clearly the presence of constituents below the level of a clause, such as modifiers, should also play a role in planning text messages, and knowledge in a *real* knowledge base is certainly not always represented in clause-sized chunks. Planning strategies which integrate techniques for planning at the level of the clause as well as below the clause level need to be worked out in greater detail.

7 Determining Constituent Structure

Constituent structure gives us the ability to represent text structure phenomena such as coordination, and subordination, as well as information about obligatory or optional arguments of constituents. For example, an event is represented as a *composite* structure with one or more parts; a *matrix* holds the subcategorized arguments of the verb corresponding to the event, and the other arguments are represented as *adjunct* structures corresponding to all the adjuncts associated with the event. A noun group is itself also a *composite* structure, consisting of a core element, as *matrix*, along with its modifiers, represented as *adjuncts*.

While many of the decisions concerning constituency can be taken at the time of planning, other decisions must be taken at a later stage, by a component which has access to the entire plan. In fact we want to prevent the planner from making decisions about the text structure which are hard to undo. We do not want to commit prematurely to a particular organization of the text structure, which may not end up being the best choice, in light of the completed plan. On the other hand, for reasons of efficiency, we do not simply want to shift the problem of sentence organization to another level of the generator.

A short example will demonstrate the point. Here are several ways of expressing the same set of concepts.

(1) *The museum is closed this year. It is being restored.*

(2) *The museum is closed this year, because it is being restored.*

(3) *Because the museum is being restored, it is closed this year.*

(4) *The museum, which is being restored, is closed this year.*

The text representation of (1), (2) and (3) are nearly identical in this case. A *matrix* holds the "closed" event, and the "restore" event is represented as an *adjunct*. This exemplifies the fact that the text structure representation does not specifically encode the notion of a sentence-level constituent. The precise notion of what constitutes a sentence must be derived by some external means. Nor does the text structure specify information about the order of clauses, explaining why (2) and (3) correspond to the same text structure.

(4), however, corresponds to an entirely different text structure, one in which the "restore" event is an adjunct of the element corresponding to the "museum" object, which is itself an argument of the "closed" event. So the "restore" event can be realized either as a modifier to an object entity, in the form of an embedded clause, or as a subordinate clause, or as a separate sentence.

In general, decisions concerning embedding are made at a later stage. Since such clauses need not necessarily be rhetorically related to the clause they are embedded in, we have more choices at a later stage as to where we attach them. Likewise, coordination can pose some problems. If the relation is a *LIST* schema, with several elements on the same level but not temporally connected as in a *SEQUENCE* schema, the planner may *coordinate* the elements immediately. But the coordination may be over entire propositions or over one or more of its terms. What this amounts to is the problem of aggregation (Hovy 1990). Again we make the most conservative choice, and simply coordinate at the top level, and perform the task of grouping these elements at a later stage. In summary, the representation that is chosen is the one from which the maximal number of possible expressions could be derived without a lot of difficulty.

8 The Realizer

Once the planner invokes a plan element, action control is given to external realization routines. The realizer decides, based on the kind of plan element type that is usually determined at planning time, what kind of realization choices it has. The decision about pronominalization, for instance, must be postponed until a later time, when the complete utterance is entirely planned out.

8.1 Building Realization Specifications

There are primitives which create fully specified text structures from information determined by the realization routines. Each realization text structure has the following form:

1. Content Type specification: The content type encodes information about a reference object's specific realization type.

2. Structure Type specification: The structure type gives the generator information about what kind of structures are attached to it.

3. Structure Body: The body of a structure may be simple or complex. A simple one contains constants, literals, or reference objects, complex ones contain other realization text structures.

As a structure is further evaluated it is mapped into a particular constituent type, such as a noun phrase, a prepositional phrase, a clause and so on. Each of the constituent types may then further specialize into more specific types such as simple noun phrases or complex noun phrases with modifiers such as restrictive relative clauses, or simply adjectives.

At this time we have classified many of the entities of the LILOG sort hierarchy, their properties, and the kinds of concepts they can be a part of (e.g., what kinds of events an entity can participate in), into categories useful for planning and generation. We are following loosely the categories specified in the UPPER MODEL (Bateman 1990), as well as those of Meteer (Meteer 1990a). This classification is based on a combination of semantic and linguistic criteria. Plan level entities correspond to *schemas* and *relations*, and domain concepts are characterized as different types of *entities*, *events*, *attributes* and *qualities*.

8.2 Entities

Entities are subdivided into two basic types. First we have a general category of *values* and *objects*. Values correspond to knowledge base entities which have a well defined structure and correspond to concepts of size, shape, location, and time. They may also correspond to a span of time, or a range of quantities.

Values concerned with time or mass have the attributes of unit, value, and optionally dimension. Locations are encoded as special structures which include information about the spatial preposition binding the spatial concept – which is computed in the semantic phase. For the realization of the different types of units, for instance, *km*, *sec*, and *centuries*, special realization routines have been developed.

8.3 Events

Events map into the four types *achievements, activities, states* and *accomplishments.* Event types are associated with the verb, by which the event is introduced in the text. However since a given verb may be used to express various event types the classification is dynamic and not static. An event semantics component is used to classify events and how they are interconnected together. The generator has the difficult problem of determining all the relevant arguments of the event and how these are mapped onto case roles of the verb, and the proper tense and voice to use. The planner must also determine how a given event type can and cannot be elaborated on by the planner.

We now give an example of a text structure and the corresponding realization text structure.

The sentence *The Keramiksammlung unfaßt zehntausend Objekte* is encoded by the following text structure:

```
[[[matrix,head],$EVENT$:Umfassen],
    [[arg,simple],$ROLE$:thema,object:r_sammlung],
    [[arg,simple],$ROLE$:objekt,[set,unknown_members]:r_objects]]
```

The text structure is then converted to the following realization text structure by the realizer. The structure is shown as it stands at the time just prior to templates construction:

```
[[clause],
    [$ROLE$:thema,
        [np,simple],
            $HEAD$,[word,Keramiksammlung],[DET:det_def,NUM:sg]]
    [$ROLE$:objekt,
        [np,modifier],
            $HEAD$,[word,Objekt],[DET:none,NUM:pl]
            $MOD$,[attr]
                $ATTR$,[word,10000]]
    [$PRED$,[word,umfassen],
        [TENSE:present,
         VOICE:active,
         MOOD:indicative,
         SENTENCE_TYPE:declarative]]]
```

The next example first shows the structure of knowledge in L_{LILOG} for an "umfassen" (contain) event and the corresponding text structure as it has been built by instantiating a plan.

refo r_hm : MUSEUM.
refo r_hma : AUSTELLUNG.
refo r_umfassen : UMFASSEN.
refo r_bild : BILD+.

axiom ax_1
sammlung (r_hm) = r_hma.

axiom ax_2
thema (r_umfassen) = r_hma.
objeckt (r_umfassen) = r_bilder.

```
tree([[top,composite],$RELATION$:elab_pw,object:r_hm],
    tree([[matrix,simple],$NUCLEUS$:elab_pw,object:r_hm]),
    tree([[adjunct,composite],$SATELLITE$:elab_pw,object:r_hm],
        tree([[matrix,head],$ATTRIBUTE$:sammlung,object:r_hm],
            tree([[argument,simple],$ATTR_OBJECT$,object:r_hm]),
            tree([[argument,simple],$ATTR_VALUE$,object:r_hma])),
        tree([[adjunct,composite],$RELATION$:elaborate,object:r_hma],
            tree([[matrix,simple],$NUCLEUS$:elaborate,object:r_hma]),
            tree([[adjunct,composite],$SATELLITE$:elaborate,object:r_hma],
                tree([[matrix,head],$EVENT$:r_umfassen]
                    tree([[argument,simple],$ROLE$:thema,object:r_hma]),
                    tree([[argument,simple],$ROLE$:objekt,object:r_bilder])))))))
```

We note that this plan does not give us precise realization constraints. With appropriate modifications it may correspond to a sentence or a complex noun phrase. The decision as to which is chosen cannot be determined until the plan is completed. Examples of three possible realizations which are possible for this plan are discussed below.

The first corresponds to a noun phrase, concerning the object r_hm. The top level nucleus would result in a noun phrase in realization as it is a simple named object, some museum, say the Hetjensmuseum. The satellite matrix plan would then play the role of a noun phrase modifier when it is attached to this nucleus. The adjunct of the satellite would be attached to the satellite matrix as a modifier since it is concerned with r_hma which is an argument of the satellite matrix.

The second way to realize the plan would be to break it down into two clauses. One would be over the matrix of the satellite, and the other the adjunct of the satellite. In this case the nucleus is dropped since its content appears as an argument of the satellite matrix.

The third way, which is the preferred way, is one in which one single sentence results. Here the satellite matrix must be made into a genitive noun phrase construction, and this noun phrase must be substituted for the thema argument of the r umfassen event, since they both correspond to the same object mainly r_hma.

- The Hetjensmuseum, which has an exhibition that contains paintings,..

- The Hetjensmuseum has an exhibition. The exhibition contains paintings.

- The Hetjensmuseum's exhibition contains paintings.

9 Plan Tree Evaluation

In (Scott, de Souza 1990) a number of heuristics are suggested which may be employed by the planner as a means for establishing the structure of the final text. The paper argues that quality text can be produced if the process in charge of realizing plans is made sensitive to the plan's structure and the effects that various syntactic constructions have on our ability to comprehend the underlying plan relations.

We apply these heuristics to the text structures that are created in the planning phase. The representation of these structures is convenient for doing the kind of processing that is required. The general heuristics of keeping rhetorical relations together in the text, and creating one sentence out of every relation, are already partially encoded in our structures.

The general problem of combining clauses to form complex sentences is accomplished using clause structuring techniques of embedding, hypotactic coordination and paratactic coordination. These are precisely the kinds of distinction that we are able to encode in the text structure representation. So we have a convenient means by which to translate heuristics of this kind into actions corresponding to text structure revisions.

Heuristics concerned with the general topic of sentence complexity, also need to be applied at the post-planning phase. Decisions must be made on the basis of incomplete specifications of constituents, which are not available until realization time. Our component, at this time, does not have access to the kind of linguistic or semantic criteria that are required for applying heuristics concerned with constituent realization such as: *Syntactically simple expressions of embedding are to be preferred over more complex ones.* In addition, an attribute which can be represented as an adjective rather than as a clause may be preferred, according to complexity criteria, over more complex constituents. An adjective does not change the complexity of the clause in which it stands, if we measure it by a factor such as "number of embeddings". We leave these kinds of decisions to the generator/realization component.

Furthermore, our system is not designed to take back decisions made by the planner. This implies that we cannot employ replanning strategies should the realization component reject a structure as being "too complex". If, however, a text structure becomes too complex according to certain "complexity" criteria, then the structure can be revised using revision strategies that operate on text structures to simplify the structures appropriately.

In the example shown below, we have a small plan to describe some church. Sentence (A) corresponds to an elaboration of the location of the church, and in sentence (B) the location is further elaborated upon. The last three sentences (C-E) correspond to the church's history.

- (A) *The XX Church lies in the old part of the town.*

- (B)*It is located at the corner of Ratinger Street and Ursulinen Street.*

- (C)*It housed office space from 1803 to 1968.*

- (D)*It has served as a catholic parish since 1968.*

- (E)*It was built in the 15th Century.*

This initial text structure results from using the rule: one sentence per relation, including relations stemming from growth points. This can be improved as follows. First (B) can be inserted as an embedded clause of (A) as it modifies the location. (C) and (D) may be coordinated together as an ordered sequence to form (2). This leaves one remaining "unattached" clause having to do with history. This is embedded into (A) resulting in the final text shown in (1).

- (1) *The XX Church, which was built in the 15th Century, lies in the old part of the town, on the corner of Ratinger Street and Ursulinen Street.*

- (2)*From 1803 it was used as office space and since 1968 it has served as a catholic parish.*

To demonstrate that clearly this problem involves some tough decisions, we show some of the optional ways of structuring the same text that must have been rejected in order to come up with (1) and (2) above. Let us assume that we start with three sentences, one containing (A) and (B), and the second containing (C) and (D), and one containing (E). These correspond to the elements that have been pre-structured at the plan level. Leaving (E) alone results in a "dangling" sentence, so this requires us to reject some of the structures shown below. The last is rejected on grounds of "complexity". Still other choices must be simply rejected on grounds of coherency, a constraint which is difficult to define in a general way.

1. (1) *The XX Church lies in the old part of the town, on the corner of Ratinger Street and Ursulinen Street.*
   (2) *From 1803 it was used as office space and since 1968 it has served as a catholic parish.*
   (3) *It was built in the 15th Century.*

2. (1) *The XX Church, which from 1803 was used as office space and since 1968 has served as a catholic parish, lies in the old part of the town, on the corner of Ratinger Street and Ursulinen Street.*
   (2) *It was built in the 15th Century.*

3. (1) *The XX Church lies in the old part of the town, on the corner of Ratinger Street and Ursulinen Street.*
   (2) *From 1803 the XX Church, which was built in the 15th Century, was used as office space and since 1968 it has served as a catholic parish.*

4. (1) *The XX Church, which was built in the 15th Century and which was used from 1803 as office space and has served since 1968 as a catholic parish, lies in the old part of the town, on the corner of Ratinger Street and Ursulinen Street.*

Clearly the problem of deciding which construction to choose is complex, and rules about sentence complexity, style, and coherency are required. A discourse-level grammar capable of monitoring systematically the way text structures are revised at this stage is clearly required. Since in our model we have shifted many of these hard problems onto the post-planning phase, we must concern ourselves with the complexity of this component. One way to simplify the task of post-planning is to concentrate on specifying the full range of resources that may be utilized by the planner, in coming up with representations that are useful for text revision.

10   Outlook

In this contribution we have looked more closely into the generation component, and the way it has developed over time. The generation component was developed with the idea in mind that enhancing the capabilities of the component should simply involve expanding on the various libraries, and not on manipulating data and control structures, which require knowledge about programming concepts. Though this does not seem to be a problem for the planner and the realizer, it is not as straightforward for the intermediate stage as we are not completely certain of all the factors that may play a role in text structuring. Determining sentence boundaries is a hard problem. It is hard to say whether we want to design a smarter realization component which, for instance, is capable of "rejecting" certain choices for sentences and then doing replanning on its own, or if the tree evaluation component should be given this task. In conclusion, we have made use of what we feel are some interesting ideas that have developed in generation in recent years and have begun to integrate them into the generation component.

References

Bateman, J. A. (1990): Upper modeling: organizing knowledge for natural language processing. In: Proceedings of the 5th International Workshop on Language Generation, Dawson, PA., pp. 54–61

Halliday, M. A. K. (1985): An Introduction to Functional Grammar. Edward Arnold, London

Hovy, E. H., McCoy, K. F. (1989): Focusing your rst: A step toward generating coherent multi-sentential text. In: 11th Annual Conference of the Cognitive Science Society, Ann Arbor, Michigan

Hovy, E. H. (1988): Planning coherent multisentential text. In: Proc. 26th Annual Meeting of the ACL, pp. 163–169

Hovy, E. H. (1989): Notes on dialogue management and text planning in the lilog project. unpublished working paper, IBM Deutschland GmbH, Institute for Knowledge Based Systems, Postfach 80 08 80, 7000 Stuttgart 80

Hovy, E. H. (1990): Unresolved issues in paragraph planning. In: Dale, R., Mellish, C., Zock, M. (eds.): Current Research in Natural Language Generation. Academic Press, London, pp. 17–45

Kreyß, J., Novak, H.-J. (1990): The textplanning component pit of the lilog system. In: Proc. 13th International Conference on Computational Linguistics, pp. 431–433

Mann, W. C., Thompson, S. A. (1988): Rhetorical structure theory: Toward a functional theory of text organization. Text 8(3), 243–281

McKeown, K. R. (1985): Text Generation: Using Discourse Strategies and Focus Constraints to Generate Natural Language Text. Cambridge University Press, Cambridge

Meteer, M. W. (1990a): Abstract linguistic resources for text planning. In: Proceedings of the Fifth International Natural Language Generation Workshop, Dawson, Pa., pp. 62–68

Meteer, M. W. (1990b): The "generation gap" the problem of expressibility in text planning. Phd thesis, published as bbn report no. 7347, Bolt, Beranek and Newman Inc.

Moore, J. D., Paris, C. L. (1988): Constructing coherent text using rhetorical relations. In: 10th Cognitive Science Conference, Montreal, Canada

Scott, D. R., de Souza, C. S. (1990): Getting the message across in rst-based text generation. In: Dale, R., Mellish, C., Zock, M. (eds.): Current Research in Natural Language Generation, London, San Diego, New York, Boston, Academic Press, pp. 47–73

The Formulator

Birgit Wendholt

1 Introduction

This paper presents the concepts, the environment and the implementation of the Formulator and describes the linguistic phenomena it processes. The Formulator builds surface representations of German utterances out of a semantics-based input structure. Grammar rules and syntactic processes are contained in the code. Neither the input structure nor the computation is affected or directed by a grammar formalism.

The paper consists of two main parts. The first part, Sect. 2, introduces the environment of the Formulator to point out certain restrictions within which it has been implemented. The conceptual part of the environment consists of an interface language, the "Formale Satzbeschreibungssprache" (FSS) (Dotzek 1989), that provides the Formulator with a semantic based specification of German utterances and thus defines the subject of the program. In this context, aspects of the interface to the planner are discussed. The remaining parts constitute the programming environment of the Formulator. The STUF-ADT (Dörre, Raasch 1991) was to be applied to represent and manipulate instances of the FSS. A morphology component, the TLM (Two-Level Morphology) (see Steffens and Schiller, in this volume), performs the inflectional processes on words. Finally, a lexicon that provides the Formulator with inherent grammatical properties of single words is presented. The components are introduced by means of their underlying concepts or their interface definition to the Formulator.

The second part, Sect. 3, deals with the program, its implementation and the linguistic data it produces. Different layers of the implementation are demonstrated: a declarative layer, where the data structures of the Formulator are defined and preprocessed, and a procedural layer that implies the control structure of the Formulator. The section closes with a collection of linguistic phenomena and some selected examples.

2 Environment of the Formulator

Section 2.1 deals with the requirements of the planner on an interface language to the Formulator convenient to the architecture of the generation component. It introduces the role concept of the FSS and points out the contributions of a semantics-based input structure to the planner. Finally, the representational means are outlined and some of the trade-offs between generality of input and performance aspects are discussed.

Section 2.2 briefly overviews aspects of the STUF-ADT and its application in the Formulator. It becomes obvious that combining a merely restricted input structure with the functionality of the STUF-ADT creates conflicts when accessing graph structures.

Section 2.3 deals with the interface to the TLM. Consistent data structures facilitate communication between the modules. The aim of isolating morphological and syntactic processes was accomplished except for the verb class. Some examples illustrate how interface specifications for verbs and the one-word domain of the TLM affect verb treatment in the Formulator. The only solution to overcome such inconsistencies, presupposing the TLM architecture, appears to be a separate morpho-syntax component.

Section 2.4 discusses problems with a lexicon common to both analysis and generation. Repercussions of a unification grammar on lexical coding are pointed out and contrasted to generation requirements. Incompatible demands on the lexicon enforce the development of a specific generation lexicon.

2.1 The FSS and the Interface to the Planner

When designing the generation component, decisions were made to separate processes determining style and contents of utterances from those of syntactic realization. The planner is responsible for stylistic information such as pronominalization, topicalization, sentence type, different kinds of modification and sentence content described in terms of semantic roles. The Formulator's task is to produce syntactic realizations out of semantic input. It has to apply grammar rules, to build morphological graphs with sufficient inflectional features and to guarantee the requirements of linear precedence. Therefore an interface has been devised to:

- directly map semantic categories onto corresponding terms of an input language,

- abstract from dependencies of syntactic or grammatic origin (government and agreement phenomena, tense forming processes, ...),

- abstract from linear precedence requirements, both on sentence and constituent level,

- map semantically motivated dependencies onto hierarchical structures,

- be independent of internal data structures in the Formulator.

The first four topics are accomplished in an augmented version of the FSS. The FSS consists of a set of thematic and syntactic roles with no order restrictions. Thematic roles are due to the case frame theory (Fillmore 1968) and correspond to the semantic categories the planner gets out of DRS structures and the text knowledge. Normally these roles denote reference objects (refos), thus mapping of planning entities becomes very direct. Since typical verb argument roles (agent, patient, theme, ...) are supplied on the same level as adjunct roles (local, time, ...) planning is independent of their syntactic meaning. Furthermore each role may be highly structured. Thematic roles, which imply noun phrases, are typical candidates for different kinds of modifications as there are adjectives, genitive attributes, appositions, prepositional phrases and sentential types as relative- and subclauses as well as infinitive constructions. The FSS provides modifier labels for each of these items, which can also be nested. To cover all sorts of modifications, syntactic roles had to be introduced into the FS terminology, since some arguments of a noun do not correspond to thematic roles and determine restricted realizations. The input to the Formulator is a fully specified FS structure which contains the baseform of the lexical items to be used, the determiner type and number for nouns, and sentence modus, genus verbi, tense and mood for verbs. Besides this information many different kinds of modifications can be specified.

The requirement to use the STUF-ADT affected the underlying data structures of the Formulator. Instances of the FSS are encoded as feature graphs. FS roles denoting a linguistic item are mapped onto features, simple values onto atomic values of graphs. A high-level STUF mechanism, the template mechanism, enables the definition of an interface which abstracts from internally manipulated graphs. The templates can be provided with an arbitrary number of arguments and allow recursive nesting.

Therefore FS structures could be directly translated into templates. The template names correspond to roles, and the arguments are either atomic values or again templates that represent substructures in the FSS. Their macro characteristic supports further processes in the Formulator. Just at the time of defining, the resulting graphs could be augmented with structural constraints and prepared for later access to morphological details. Figure 1 gives a good impression of the degree of abstraction of templates and points out prestructuring aspects.

```
input:     np(Museum,sg,det_def,attr(renovieren,past_part)).

internal: [ morph : [ root : Museum
                      syncat : noun
                      agr : _1 [ number : sg
                                 person : 3 ]]
            det : morph : [ root : det_def
                            syncat : pronoun
                            agr : _1 ]
            mod : attr : morph : [ root : renovieren
                                   syncat : past_part
                                   agr : _1 ]]
```

Figure 1: Template and internal representation of the utterance "das renovierte Museum"

There are nevertheless some disadvantages in using templates for the interface. The order of arguments of the input in Figure 1 is fixed. To overcome order constraints, all arguments would have to be realized as templates denoting the corresponding structure. This solution was rejected, because the expansion of deeply nested input structures is expensive. The templates are static data. Their arity and structure is fixed at definition time. Thus the programmer is urged to periodically update the set of definitions.

In conclusion, we enable the planner to abstract from syntactic processes and grammar requirements by defining a semantics-based interface language the FSS. The syntactic information which is required in FS structures depends on discourse context and style considerations. A high-level interface is provided by use of the template mechanism. The planner can abstract from order requirements. This holds for the sentence level. However, a certain order is stipulated by the inner structure of constituents.

2.2 STUF-ADT

The STUF-ADT is a unification formalism implemented as abstract datatype. The underlying datatype, the feature graph, is equipped with all typical attributes demanded in unification formalisms, especially the option to define reentrancies. The feature graphs have three levels of representation: definition, intermediate and internal representation.

On the definitional level one can design simple graphs and macro graphs called templates. Simple graphs may be named. The STUF compiler replaces the names by their definitions. Thus simple graphs cannot be referenced by their name in other structures. However, template names are preserved during compiling. Only a second translation phase substitutes graph definitions for identifiers in all locations at which they occur. The STUF-ADT allows templates to be parameterized with an arbitrary number of arguments. Parametric templates consist of two parts. The left part, the header of the template, contains its name and arguments. The right part is the definition of the template that contains variables which are identical to the arguments of the header. Instantiation of templates means binding the arguments of the template header and thus the variables in the definition to actual values. These values might be either templates or atomic values.

The intermediate level results from compiling graph definitions. Its data structure is clearly arranged by means of logical terms. Efficient primitives admit dynamical graph production, omitting the defining phase. Both aspects determine this level as the one for constructing more complex graphs with predefined contents.

A second phase translates the intermediate graphs into internal counterparts. The internal representation provides the datatype for the ADT primitives. These are unification, access to embedded graphs by definite paths (sequence of features) and testing.

The STUF-ADT is applied in the Formulator as follows. Parameterized templates constitute the interface to the planner. They are additionally used to organize input graphs, separate morphologically relevant data from process-directing entries, and introduce structural equivalences (reentrancies) to encode agreement phenomena. Instantiated templates are expanded and deliver the graphs for manipulation in the Formulator. Unification is used to augment graphs with information either derived by grammar rules or retrieved from the lexicon. Further on, unification is used to establish reentrant structures dynamically. Some identity relations between substructures of roles cannot be predefined in parametric templates, since the affected roles have still to be computed. To give an example, imagine an instance of the FSS which represents a sentence. One of the first steps of the program is to establish subject-verb agreement. No information about the corresponding subject role is available in the input structures. The argument roles of the verb and possible cases are determined by accessing the lexicon. Other processes consider the genus verbi attribute of the verb to identify the actual subject role. This role serves as parameter to predicates which construct graphs that encode sharing structures for person and number features by means of intermediate predicates. Combined test and access primitives allow a check for available substructures. However, this approach is only applicable for a definite set of features, and only efficient for very small sets. Partial information is extracted from the graphs, atomic information to trigger dependent processes, complex information to reduce the context of processing (from sentence level to constituent level) or to submit complete graphs to the TLM.

The STUF-ADT provides access primitives for graph contents but none for graph structure. One can only get information out of graphs when provided with the features involved. The FSS allows arrangements for all possible subsets of the roles available. Therefore the Formulator does not possess a definite access sequence to cover the different input configurations. It has to determine the set of roles involved for each input graph. Since STUF does not provide methods to retrieve features, graphs temporarily have to be interpreted as normal Prolog structures in order to compute the input-dependent subset of roles.

In conclusion, templates are a good means to define the interface to the planning component, and to prestructure graph content. Unification and reentrancy options support inheritance phenomena in a grammar. To manipulate the FS structures, access primitives to determine graph structure are required. However, STUF does not support such aspects of access. This results in a nonuniform use of the abstract datatype.

2.3   Interface to the TLM

The TLM is a separate module for the analysis and generation of inflected word forms. It enables the Formulator to abstract from inflectional instances of a lexical item and to use one representative, the baseform, which itself serves as an item for lexical access. The TLM has a collection of defined feature graph types building the interface to the Formulator. Each of them represents the structure and content for one word class and relies on the terminology of the underlying TLM theory. Further on we refer to these types as morph graphs.

The grammar processes of the Formulator compute specific word class attributes, such as syntactic category and inflectional features, considering the syntactic context of a single word. The values are inserted into partially specified morph graphs by means of unification. Complete graphs are locally delivered to the TLM. "Locally" suggests that a category is accessed only once. Applying grammar rules and triggering the morphology is done in one phase. The TLM returns the inflected lexical item which is stored and annotated with its syntactic category for later linear ordering. This procedure guarantees a clear distinction of syntactic from morphological areas of work. However, verbs appear as a word class which enforces exceptional treatment and imposes inherent morphological knowledge on the Formulator. One reason is the specification of verbal morph graphs. It requires the decomposition of a verb into root and prefix form and the provision of the characteristic of the prefix (it is separable or non-separable). The other reason is connected with the TLM's architecture, which restricts the domain of morphology to single word processing. Syntactic items spreading over more than one word, like *discontinuous verb forms* and *to-infinitive* constructions, require special treatment which in both cases is affected by morphological attributes: for the first instance knowledge about auxiliaries is required, and for the second the prefix type of the verb has certain effects. The following notes will support the above theses.

German verbs with a separable prefix behave exceptionally when they occur in the middle field of a sentence and bear the tense markers *present* or *past* and mood *active*. The prefix is detached from the root and realized as an independent item. Since the morphology only deals with single words, the input for "anfangen" with attributes present active (the remaining ones are displayed in Figure 2) results in the inflected form "fängt". The prefix has been separated and thrown away.

```
[ root : fangen
  prefix : [ root : an
             separable : yes
             attached : no ]
  tense : present
  mood : active
  syncat : finite_verb
  agr : [ num : sg
          pres : 3 ]]
```

Figure 2: A sample input to TLM for verbs

To raise another objection, consider that the Formulator is only provided with the baseform "anfangen" in its input. To produce the graph in Figure 2 it has to retrieve the specific decomposition of the verb, which is an inherent morphological property. It even has to know the kind of prefix to determine whether the prefix is realized as a single lexical item. Similar phenomena can be observed concerning *to-infinitive* constructions. It depends on the characteristic of the prefix where the lexical item "zu" appears on the surface. For a verb with a separable prefix, "zu" is realized between prefix and root ("anzufangen"), otherwise "zu" appears as single item in front of the verbal infinitive form. Correct syntactic structures can only be evaluated when the Formulator knows first, that certain infinitives require a "zu" and second, what kind of prefix is available. To close with some remarks about discontinuous verb forms, consider how verbs are supplied to the

Formulator, as graphs which contain the baseform and among others, tense and voice markers for the verb. As soon as passive voice or tenses "higher" than past appear, discontinuous verb forms result, a set of one finite form and further infinite items. The item set is computed by means of rules, whereas some tenses require that the specific verb-dependent auxiliary is available. In parallel, a morph graph for each item is built and submitted to the morphology.

The inconsistencies described above are typical for verbs, since in all cases numerous lexical items correspond to one syntactic structure. For prefix verbs these are root and detached prefix, for *to-infinitives* the infinitive and the item "zu", for discontinous verb forms the single items. A morpho-syntax component which has access to syntactic rules and morphological attributes could handle mutual interferences and serve as a candidate for other morpho-syntactic phenomena, e.g., coordinated compound nouns that share one part as in the phrase "Flanier und Einkaufsstraße".

2.4 Lexicon

The lexicon often becomes a bottleneck in systems which do both analysis and generation. A high degree of reusability can be obtained by pursuing a "uniform strategy". The semantic results of the analysis serve as input structures to the syntactic generation module. However, this affects the degree to which the planning module is admitted to abstract from linguistic knowledge. Besides processing a conceptual structure it has to consider representations which are determined by a certain grammar formalism. Therefore "asynchronous strategies" are often chosen. The semantic structures of the syntax module of the generation component and the ones produced by the analysis component differ in content and organization. Such a decision may have far-reaching effects on possible common lexicons. To become more precise, problems with the LEU2 lexicon are discussed, since analysis and generation are candidates for the second strategy. First the lexical requirements of the Formulator are introduced; second the applicability of a lexicon influenced by a unification grammar is examined.

The semantics-based approach of the Formulator implies that no grammatical properties of words are directly available in the input data. However, they are needed to complete inflectional features for the ongoing morphological processes, as gender for nouns, declination classes for adjectives and case determined by verbs and prepositions. Furthermore, grammatical qualities determine types of syntactic constructions as verbs determine infinitives or kinds of subclauses, indispensible reflexive markers or expletives. In a lexically based approach, as chosen for the generation component, these properties have to be determined by lexical access.

The analysis component of the LEU2 system relies on a HPSG-like grammar formalism (see the paper by Kiss in this volume). It is a lexicalized approach, where lexical coding directly depends on concepts of the grammar as well as on processing with a unification formalism. The effects are so serious that such a lexicon becomes inadequate for generation.

First of all coding is too implicit, especially for the grammatical properties of verbs. Neither the way the arguments are accessible nor the way coreferences between arguments and their syntactic case are established in the lexicon graphs suit generation needs. Figure 3 shows the entry for the verb "besitzen" in a lexicon as it has been proposed by the analysis component. Details that do not contribute to the explanation are omitted.

Such representations cause two problems. First, before accessing the lexicon no information about the subset of thematic roles which qualify as argument roles for the specific verb is available in the Formulator. Second, the thematic roles and their corresponding case attributes are related implicitly by techniques of variable sharing. To compute the thematic roles involved, one has to violate the notion of STUF as abstract datatype. Since STUF does not provide access primitives for features, the argument roles "thema" and "patiens" can only be retrieved when the appropriate

```
[ syntax :
   local :
     [ subcat : [ syntax : local : head : case : acc
                  sx : cond : _3 ]
       subj : [ syntax : local : head : case : nom
                  sx : cond : _2 ]
   sx : cond : [ thema : _2
                  patiens : _3 ]]]
```

Figure 3: An excerpt from the lexicon graph for "besitzen"

subgraph is interpreted as a normal Prolog data structure. Furthermore, to get the attached cases one has to perform a four-step extract-and-testing procedure.

A second objection refers to a too-rich encoding. Syntactic categories are represented by means of attribute schemes in order to generalize over category classes which are admitted in a certain syntactic context. Generation, however, only needs atomic identifiers for the category. Decisions about how to distribute constituents are based on other considerations. Finally, since the lexicon is only indexed by base forms it does not support access by sorts, which the planner retrieves from the ontology. Sorts have to be mapped onto word representations in order to be processed by the morphology.

As one possible solution for the above problems we created a separate generation lexicon, a plain structure that allows indexing by sorts and baseforms. Figure 4 displays the general scheme for verb entries in the generation lexicon and one instantiation for the verb "besitzen".

```
genlex(VerbSort,VerbAtom,verb,VerbSubcatAndMorInfo)

VerbSubcatAndMorInfo :=
  [ { rolecasemapping(RoleCat,Surface,Rolename) },
    aux(Auxiliar)
    mor(RootTempl,PrefixTempl) ]

  Rolecat : np, pp, inf, vp, expl, refl
  Surface : case or status indicator
  Rolename : a thematic role label

genlex('Besitzen',besitzen,verb,
       [ rolecasemapping( np, nom, thema ),
         rolecasemapping( np, acc, patiens ),
         aux( haben ),
         mor( root(sitzen) , nonsep(be) ) ]
```

Figure 4: Verbal scheme in the generation lexicon and sample entry

This lexicon allows unique encoding of all kinds of verb arguments. Noun and prepositional roles are mapped onto corresponding cases, the same holds for reflexive pronouns, and infinitives are mapped onto their governed status (Bech 1955; Bech 1957). The verb argument structures are made explicit, such that the attached roles can be accessed directly. Morphological entries are motivated by several reasons which have been discussed in the section dealing with the TLM interface. Lexicon entries for the remaining classes are much simpler. Nouns are encoded with gender, quantifiers and pronouns with possible effects on the declination class of adjectives, prepositions appear with a list of cases they govern, and all of them are annotated with category identifiers and sort names.

The lexicons of the analysis and the generation component cover all the words that appear in the LEU2 sample texts, but do not provide a basic vocabulary. However, a text understanding system meant to support a dialogue with different users should be able to deal with unknown words (words that are not available in the system's lexicon). The task of providing valid lexicon structures for unknown words is performed by a lexicon manager component by means of a lexical database. Severe problems due to the classification of verbs along the lines of argument structure and semantic content have currently restricted the domain of unknown word resolution to word classes such as noun, adjective, etc. The extension of a system lexicon exclusively triggered during parsing time implies that the generation only succeeds with words formerly detected by the lexicon manager. In the current version of the generation component, accessing the lexicon for grammatical attributes of words is performed in two steps. Starting the access with primitives adapted to the entries in our lexicon either returns with the required structures or turns to calling the lexicon manager to determine them among the temporarily stored entries.

In conclusion, lexical entries in the analysis lexicon are highly affected by the underlying HPSG-like formalism. Implicit information, complex coding of categories and single indexing require a separate generation lexicon. The Formulator needs lexical information to collect inflectional patterns for further morphological processes and for determining special kinds of syntactic constructions.

3 The Formulator

The following subsections deal with the implementation of the Formulator and the kinds of linguistic phenomenon the Formulator can process. The first subsection shows how the template mechanism of the STUF-ADT contributes to further processing. The second subsection overviews the control structure of the Formulator and continues with some details about the programming of selected syntactic constructions and grammar phenomena. The third one supplies a complete list of the linguistic phenomena the Formulator deals with and some input examples for more complicated instances. Some remarks about additional work to be done on certain phenomena conclude the section.

3.1 Defining Versus Processing

As mentioned in the section about the STUF-ADT, the template mechanism supports the Formulator's tasks of imposing grammatical constraints on the input structures (by introducing path equations to satisfy agreement requirements) and produce adequate data for the TLM (by distinguishing final morphological attributes from entries that trigger syntactic or grammatical processes). That is, a well considered definition of template graphs makes several aspects of processing obsolete. To be more precise, we outline the benefits of the template mechanism for the definition of noun phrases. Consider the graph definition for a nounphrase with a specifier and a modifier argument that is supposed to be instantiated with an adjective phrase in the following example.

```
np(_Root,_Num,_Det,_Mod) :=
     [ morph : [ root : _Root
```

```
            syncat : noun
            agr : [ number : _Num
                    person : '3' ] ]
    det : morph : [ root : _Det
                    syncat : pronoun ]
    < det morph agr > = < morph agr >  ].
```

_Mod = adjective phrase:

```
attr(_Root,_Syncat) :=
    [ mod : attr : morph : [ root : _Root
                             syncat : _Syncat ]
      < mod attr morph agr > = < morph agr > ].
```

The path equations in the example constitute identical *agr* structures for the noun, the determiner and the adjectives and thus ensure that *agr* features specified for the noun available for the determiner and the adjective. To generalize, the processes in the Formulator only have to provide the *agr* values for lexical heads of phrases, since their dependent elements simply inherit the data. For the second aspect consider the path labels in the template definition. One part of the properties required by the morphology for certain word classes is concentrated under definite and unique paths. This facilitates both the augmentation with further computed values and the access to the relevant morphological data submitted to the TLM.

3.2   Implementation

The following principles underlie the design of the Formulator. Grammar and morphology are treated in parallel and by one traversal of the original input structures. Role labels trigger corresponding processes. As there is no explicit grammar directing the flow of control, a bottom-up strategy is needed which is almost independent of role order. Nonlocal phenomena such as case and status government, determination of declination classes, and subject-verb agreement impose preferences on role sets. In all cases, each role is processed in a recursive depth-first manner. That is, one role has been completely formulated with respect to the grammar, the morphology, and the linearization when control turns to the remaining ones. Formulating divides up into two phases both on sentence and constituent level; the first deals with the grammar and the morphology, whereas the second one contributes to linear precedence requirements. These principles provide the background for understanding the overall control structure.

The Formulator is provided with a sequence of ordered pairs which are evaluated iteratively. The first element of each pair denotes the type of utterance, the second its content, supplied as instantiated template. Type markers such as *complex*, *np*, *pp*, or role identifiers trigger corresponding processes and thus define different starting points for the Formulator. The omission of type markers implies the input to undergo certain tests to identify the available structure. The following steps are performed:

1. The instantiated templates are expanded, resulting in internal graph representations. If the type was *complex*, a sentence structure or a sequence of constituents is assumed. In a first step all roles engaged are collected and the existence of verbs is checked. If there is one, case and state assignment as well as subject-verb agreement is established, and each label triggers a corresponding predicate. Otherwise, if no verb entry is supplied, processing starts with the available role types.

2. Computing the surface representation for each role involves several aspects of evaluation:

- Subgraphs of the input structure representing a role contain base forms, each denoting one syntactic category. The base forms are used to access grammatical attributes of words of the lexicon. Some of the attributes are used to augment the subgraphs with inflectional values. Others determine inflectional values or the constituent type of the word's arguments.

- Agreement requirements between lexical heads and their arguments, specifiers or complements are fulfilled, both for simple and coordinated structures.

- Syntactic processes such as tense forming, coordination, handling of ellipsis and formulating embedded structures are performed. Embedded structures are evaluated recursively, starting again by identifying available roles.

- Morph graphs are delivered to the TLM before returning from category level, and resulting word forms are recorded with their category marker for ongoing linearization.

- Special linear precedence rules apply to noun and adjective phrases.

The original graph is temporarily augmented with various kinds of information in the local environment of categories or roles, where the extensions of the graph are performed on copies of its substructures. Thus, those kinds of extensions contributing solely to requirements of a local context are suppressed for the embedding graph levels of the local context.

3. Finally, linear precedence rules (lp rules) apply to sentence level and produce a nonstipulated order of constituents.

The overview of the control structure gives only a preliminary view of how linguistic phenomena are treated. The remainder of this subsections provides some details concerning case assignment, agreement, discontinuous verbforms, infinitival complements and coordination, and further introduces the principles of the *lp rules* that apply on sentence level.

3.2.1 Processing Linguistic Phenomena

Case is a grammatical feature of words that indicates their syntactic function. It depends on verbs, prepositions, nouns and even adjectives. The Formulator only deals with the first three types of governing case. Assigning case to arguments of verbs depends on the value of its voice attribute. If it is specified as active then the relation of argument roles and their surface case is simply taken from the lexicon. If it is specified as passive then this relation undergoes several transformations. The nominative case is assigned to the role which is encoded as direct object in the lexicon (the role which normally bears accusative case). The former nominative role may be realized as by-phrase. Verbs without direct objects are treated as exceptions. The syntactic subject is realized as expletive, but the semantic subject (the role that normally bears nominative case) determines number and person features of the verb. Prepositions provide the Formulator with a collection of possible cases they govern. A definite case can only be determined by the role context the preposition appears in. Concerning nouns, the syntactic role *poss* triggers the assignment of genitive case.

Agreement is defined as formal correspondence of syntactically related complexes concerning grammatical features (gender, case, ...). The German language requires agreement in person and number between subject and verb, and agreement in case, number and gender between 1) subject and predicative noun, 2) attributive adjective, certain pronouns, determiner and noun, and 3) noun and apposition. It is implemented by means of sharing structures. These are either introduced in the template definitions or dynamically produced with the help of intermediate primitives of the STUF-ADT. The second case applies to subject-verb agreement, since the subject has still to be identified as one of the roles of the FS structures. It has to be one of the arguments of a verb and depends on the value of the voice feature. Once the role bearing subject properties has been fixed it parameterizes the processes to impose the required agreement structure on the graph.

The representation for verbs in the FS structures consists of the verb's baseform and additional grammatical features (tense, voice, ...). The Formulator contains a rule system which is able to produce verb complexes, which are syntactic realizations of all possible combinations of the grammatical features. The rules are triggered one after another by single grammatical features of the verb or the type of sentence available. Besides realization of single words they set processes to deal with two classes of discontinuous verb forms. The first class comprises the verbs with detached prefixes. The second class consists of all tensed verb forms built analytically by means of auxiliaries.

Verbs or nouns may have valency for infinitive complements. Infinitive complements of verbs fall into two classes. They may become rather complex. Infinitives are reduced sentential structures which lack the subject argument of the verb. Consider the sentence "Die Teilnehmer beschließen, [am nächsten Tag einen längeren Ausflug in die Stadt zu unternehmen]". The brackets mark the boundaries of a complex infinitive construction. Presupposing that it is a reduced sentence, its formulation becomes straightforward. The same case-assigning processes as for sentences apply to the arguments of the verb, except one specialty: the subject role is deliberately omitted. The lp rules are implemented very generally, as they have to deal with arbitrary parts of sentences. Therefore no problems arise concerning linearization of infinitive constructions.

Coordination frequently causes difficulties in theoretical linguistics. Therefore coordination in the Formulator is only based on an intuitive notion of combining elements of a linguistic structure. The Formulator deals with coordination on sentence, constituent (noun phrases, verb phrases, ...) and category level (noun, adjective, ...). Inflectional features (case, number, gender, ...) are distributed over the participants in the complex structure by means described in the paragraphs above. The coordination of structures lying between category and constituent or constituent and sentence level is not supported except for one application, coordinated sentences whose predicates share one argument role.

3.2.2   Principles of the lp Rules

The lp rules compute the constituent order of sentences. Sentences are not only meant to be main clauses, but may be subclauses, infinitival complements or simply collections of adjunct roles. The lp rules are directed by two kinds of parameters. The items *front, middle, last,* which belong to the first type, denote the position of the verb in a sentence. The second kind comprises role labels denoting a constituent to become topicalized. The rules are sensitive to noun and pronoun indicators, since in some cases pronouns that substitute a noun phrase affect the nonstipulated constituent order. The rules were taken from the SUTRA system (Busemann 1988). Basically SUTRA contains binary rules that for each single constituent determine its position relative to the remaining constituents. The implementation was done by Zuzanna Dobeš.

3.3   Linguistic Coverage

The Formulator was faced with different kinds of sentences and complex constituent structures determined by the original sample texts which were proposed at the beginning of the LEU2 project. At sentence level it deals with *complex* sentences (main and subclauses), infinitives, reduced sentences and topicalization. On the constituent level it deals with complex noun and adjective phrases and modified verb phrases. Noun phrases can be modified with adjective phrases, pre- or postnominal genitives, relative clauses, subclauses or infinitives, and may be supplemented by prepositional phrases or appositions. Furthermore, different kinds of specifiers are supported, such as articles, certain pronouns or quantifiers. Pronouns that substitute for a noun phrase, and ellipses, are also treatable. Adjective phrases can appear with adverbial or nominal as well as prepositional modifications and rely on both adjectival or participial bases. Finally, verb phrases with infinitival or sentential modifications are produced. Nearly all constituent and sentence structures can be coordinated.

The following examples form only a subset of the phenomena mentioned above. One criterion for selecting exactly these examples was to show the more complicated constructions.

3.3.1 Samples of Performance

The first three examples deal with different kinds of modification of noun phrases. The first shows how relative clauses, genitive attributes and appositions are supplied and recursive aspects of noun phrases. The second illustrates a complicated relative clause. The noun the relative pronoun refers to was formerly a genitive attribute of the noun "Hälfte". The final example outlines a nested attribute modification.

```
sent(pred(entstehen,past,active),
     thema(np('Gebaeude',sg,det_def,
              mod(
               rel_s(patiens(relpro),
                     instrument(mit,np(Fassade,sg,det_indef,
                                       mod(attr(geschungen)))),
                     pred(versehen,present,z_passive))))),
     praed(np(Werk,sg,blank,
              mod(
               poss(np('Architekt',pl,det_def,
                       mod(
                        attr(Kopenhagen),
                        app(coord(np(Dissing),
                                  np(Weitling)))))))))).
```

"Das Gebäude, das mit einer geschwungenen Fassade versehen ist, entstand als Werk der Kopenhagener Architekten Dissing und Weitling."

```
sent(pred(umfassen,present,active),
     thema(np('Sammlung',sg,det_def)),
     object(np('Bild',number(180),
               mod(
                rel_s(poss_by(rel_pro),
                      s_adv(etwa),
                      thema(np('Haelfte',sg,det_def)),
                      pred(stammen,present,active),
                      source(von,np(Paul_Klee))))))).
```

"Die Sammlung umfaßt 180 Bilder, von denen etwa die Hälfte von Paul Klee stammt."

```
np('Bronzeplastik',sg,det_def,
   mod(attr(hoch,adj,
            mod(np('Meter',number(4)))),
       dir_app('Habakuk'),
       poss(np(Bildhauer,sg,det_def,
               mod(dir_app('Max Ernst')))))).
```

"die 4 Meter hohe Bronzeplastik Habakuk des Bildhauers Max Ernst,"

The next examples deal with phenomena on sentence level. The first shows the input for a sentence with a time role as topic element. The second gives an example of a reduced sentence. Reduced sentences lack the subject and the inflected verb, but contain participles and other particles of the verb form. The third example contains the input for a complex sentence (main- and subclause) with an embedded infinitive clause, and the final example supplies the input for a more complicated coordinated structure.

```
sent(pred(machen,active,past),
     time(nach,np('Projektsitzung',sg,det_def,
                  mod(lokal(an,np('Montag',sg,det_def)),
                      attr(anstrengen,past_part)))),
     agens(np('Teilnehmer',pl,det_def,
              mod(poss(np('Workshop',sg,det_def))))),
     thema(np('Ausflug',sg,det_def)),
     goal(in,np('Innenstadt',sg,det_def,
                mod(attr('Duesseldorf'))))))
```

"Nach der anstrengenden Projektsitzung am Montag machten die Teilnehmer des Workshops einen Ausflug in die Düsseldorfer Innenstadt."

```
sent(pred(beginnen,past,active,inf(regnen)),
     sub_s(junctor(kaum),
           pred(ankommen,past_perfect,active),
           agens(np_el(Teilnehmer,pl,det_def)))).
```

"Kaum angekommen, begann es zu regnen."

```
sent(agens(np(man)),
     sub_s(junctor(nachdem),
           agens(np(man)),
           pred(essen,past_part,active),
           patiens('Kleinigkeit',sg,det_def)),
     pred(beschliessen,past,active,
          inf(pred(einkehren,uninflected),
              time(kurz),
              goal(in,np('Koe-Bistro',sg,blank,
                         mod(prae_poss('Lili')))),
              lokal(in,np(Ecke,sg,det_def,mod(dir_app('Koe/Bahnhofstrasse'))))))))
```

"Nachdem man eine Kleinigkeit gegessen hatte, beschloß man kurz in Lili's Kö-Bistro an der Ecke Kö/Bahnstraße einzukehren."

```
sent(agens(quantifier(einige)),
    coord(vp(pred(machen,past,active),
            thema(np('Abstecher',sg,det_indef)),
            goal(zu,np('Schadowplatz',sg,det_def)))),
         vp(pred(besichtigen,past,active),
            thema(np('salinenbrunnen,sg,det_def)),
            lokal(dort)))).
```

"Einige machten eine Abstecher zum Schadowplatz und besichtigten dort den Salinenbrunnen."

3.4   Further Work

In the previous parts of this section, reduced sentence constructions such as infinitives and the one supplied as an example were examined. This class of syntactic phenomena, however, contains further instances. One of them, the complex participle construction, usually appears as noun modifier substituting a relative clause. Consider the phrase "an beiden Seiten [der von dicht stehenden Bäumen gesäumten] Königsallee" which has been taken from the LEU2 sample texts. Processes dealing with participle constructions can be derived from the rules for infinitives extended with inflectional parts.

The German language contains numerous adverbial expressions to denote directions. Some of them such as *südlich, nördlich, . . .* behave similarly to nouns, as they allow a number of different modifications. As an example consider the phrase "wenige Meter südlich der Kirche", again taken from the sample texts. Two changes are required to deal with the complex expressions. First, we have to generalize over the currently assumed lexical heads of constituents in argument and adjunct roles to nouns and adverbials and thus to review the definition of noun phrase templates. Second, further processes dealing with the inner structure of the adverbial expression have to be developed.

The last phenomenon concerns coordinated compound nouns whose composites share the final noun, that has to be dropped from all but one element for stylistic reasons. Consider the coordinated phrase "Flanier und Einkaufsstraße" where the final noun "Straße" of the first compound has been elided. The Formulator is supposed to support the processes of a morpho-syntax component yielding the correct surface representations of the coordinated phrase, as it is the only component which knows about syntactic structures that may determine destructive morphological processes.

4   Criticism

One of the effects of a unification formalism on the underlying datatype is that it hardly supports collection-like data structures or, therefore, primitives to manipulate them. Consider the characteristics of the FS structures, which are collections of nested associated pairs with a key (rolename) and a value (the substructure encoding the content of the role). To support the representation and processing of the FS structures, the following properties of an abstract datatype are required: 1) representational means for nested associated pairs and primitives to access the keys, the values and whole pairs, 2) the possibility to define keys several times with different values. Simulating the collections of associated pairs by the STUF-ADT only covers a subset of the above requirements, as it gives a representation for nested structures and one primitive to access values by means of definite keys. We neither have information available on the participants in the structure on one recursive level (access to keys or pairs), nor are we allowed to have multiple definitions of keys with incompatible values. The consequences of the first restriction has been discussed in the section on the environment of the Formulator. To point to the consequences of the second restriction, consider the phrase *Nach der anstrengenden Projektsitzung am Montag unternahmen die Teilnehmer am Dienstag einen Ausflug.* (" After the exhausting project meeting on Monday went the participants on Tuesday on an excursion.") The underlined parts denote different time roles on the same sentence level. Since multiple use of one role frequently appears in a language as a stylistic means to contrast aspects of the sentence content, feature graphs constrain the very subject of the generation component, i.e., the generation of adequate linguistic expressions. Inherent properties of the abstract datatype of the STUF-ADT severely affect the representational power for a language specification as proposed by the FSS. It should be examined whether the problems are to be solved with a language strictly based on a grammar theory or, alternatively, with a general semantics-based specification that abstracts from the level of sentential constituents.

References

Bech, G. (1955): Studien über das Deutsche Verbum Infinitum I, Vol. 35 of Det Kongelige Danske Videnskabernes Selskab, Historisk-filologiske Meddelelser. Munksgaard, Köbenhavn

Bech, G. (1957): Studien über das Deutsche Verbum Infinitum II, Vol. 36 of Det Kongelige Danske Videnskabernes Selskab, Historisk-filologiske Meddelelser. Munksgaard, Köbenhavn

Busemann, S. (1988): Surface transformations during the generation of written german sentences. In: McDonald, D. D., Bolc, L. (eds.): Natural Language Generation Systems. Springer, Berlin, New York, pp. 98–165. Symbolic Computation

Dörre, J., Raasch, I. (1991): The Stuttgart Type Unification Formalism. IWBS Report 168, IBM Wissenschaftliches Zentrum, Institut für wissensbasierte Systeme, Postfach 80 08 80, 7000 Stuttgart 80

Dotzek, K. (1989): Spezifikation einer formalen Satzbeschreibungssprache zur Generierung syntaktischer Strukturen im Rahmen der kategorialen Unifikationsgrammatik. Technical report, Institut für Informatik, Universität Stuttgart, Azenbergstraße 12, 7000 Stuttgart 1

Fillmore, C. J. (1968): The case for case. In: Bach, E., Harms, R. T. (eds.): Universals in Linguistic Theory. Holt, Rinehart and Winston, New York

Chapter 5

LEU/2

This chapter is dedicated to the implemented text understanding system LEU/2. Starting from different angles, we shall take a look at what actually happens when all the ideas and theories presented in the previous chapters meet the implementation level.

The first article, "Constructing a Context for LEU/2" argues that for the process of text understanding it is essential to take into account the imbedding scenario of the text understanding task. After presenting a general outline of the scenario chosen for implementation, the reader will be given an idea of the specification efforts required in order to get a well-performing system – hard work, indeed!

The second paper describes "The Text Understanding System LEU/2" from the user's point of view. Without having to sit down in front of the terminal, you will learn something about what you can do with this system and about the kinds of interfaces used therein. Moreover, the article presents typical dialogues and sample screens and provides an overview of the architecture.

Finally, "The Trace of Building a Large AI System" addresses the problems arising in the implementation process. Due to the given project constraints, we had to cope with essential problems arrising in fields such as *designing large systems*, *creating AI prototypes*, and *doing distributed software development* on top of trying to solve the ones specific to our project. The article describes the suggested solutions and how they worked "in reality".

Although all of the three papers describe one special system, LEU/2, the outlined ideas certainly will be of interest for any attempt to implement other, more or less related systems.

Andreas Arning

Constructing a Context for LEU/2

K. von Luck, T. Pirlein

Abstract

The meaning of text is strongly determined by its context. The clarification of meaning therefore implies the elaboration of the context in which the text understanding task is going to run. The elaboration of the context results in our case in a scenario which determines the decisions for the domain of LEU/2. So to present the domain for LEU/2 first the selection criteria have to be discussed. After this an elaboration of a part of the domain is exemplified by explaining the metamorphosis of a text from the first attempt to the final form, which serves as the input of LEU/2. The modifications are seen and discussed as indices for the competence of LEU/2 in the last part of the paper.

1 The Selection of the Domain

The LILOG system is a text understanding system based on different knowledge bases. Up to the present, no general knowledge bases are available for these kinds of systems.[1] Therefore, a domain of discourse was chosen for LILOG which was rich enough for a wide range of phenomena yet small enough to be handled effectively within LILOG.

The domain chosen for LEU/2 is textual information about sightseeing tours in a large German city (Düsseldorf). The task for LEU/2 is to understand this textual information and in order to prove successful understanding answer limited questions about topics mentioned in the texts. More specifically, there are no efforts within the LILOG project in the research areas of consulting systems (i.e., expert systems with limited expertise) or natural language dialogue systems – including user models, dialogue strategies and dialogue coherence. This implies the restriction of the domain to common sense knowledge necessary for the tasks of text understanding and question answering.

To limit the scope of questions (in the sense of simulating a realistic, not a real dialogue[2]) the following story was constructed:

A group of people is assembled for a one-week workshop in Düsseldorf. One afternoon is scheduled for a walk in the city center. LEU/2 should be used for providing information about the city center of Düsseldorf.

Again, this scenario restricts the domain again in some relevant directions. Some examples of these kinds of restrictions are the following:

- Since the scenario implies only walking (but no driving), it is only the city center of Düsseldorf which has to be represented.

---

[1] For a discussion see [Klose, Luck 91].
[2] For that distinction see, e.g., [Bobrow et al. 77].

- Since the scope of the walk covers just one afternoon (but not an evening with visits to theaters, cinemas or nightclubs), only certain kinds of objects of interest have to be taken into account.

- Since the information is designed for people participating in a workshop, special interests (say, of children, or typical holiday affairs) can be excluded.

- Since we are not dealing with a consulting system, no elaboration is needed with regard to knowledge about – relative – rankings of the different attractions.

- Travel or hotel information does not have to be represented here, since the (theoretical) participants are considered to have accommodation and travel reservations already.

In order to acquire the information necessary for this domain, several travel agencies and information centers were asked for suitable information for planning such an afternoon. Additionally, some travel guides were analyzed. To complete the information source, some specific information was obtained by telephone (e.g., missing opening hours) and by visiting the city center of Düsseldorf (e.g., style of food in some restaurants).

In a second phase, the incoming information was classified and the ultimate scope of information about the city center was chosen. For the purpose of serving as the source for a text understanding system, the information was coded in textual form. Three different kinds of text were produced in order to reduce the risk of constructing special-purpose procedures only suited for just one text:

1. The semantic content of the first type of text can be characterized as more or less object-oriented clusters of information with a certain number of relevant data items like the kind of object, location and opening time. An example of this kind of textual information is:

   > Die Kunstakademie, die 1773 aus einer Zeichenschule entstand, ist in einem aus der Gründerzeit stammenden Gebäude in der Eiskellerstraße untergebracht. Es wurde 1879 nach den Plänen des Architekten Riffart errichtet. Das Gebäude, das durch seine breiten Vorbauten auffällt, wurde 1945 restauriert. ...
   >
   > [Originating from a drawing school in 1773, the academy of art is located in a (Gründerzeit) building in Eiskellerstraße, designed by the architect Riffart and build in 1879. The building with its striking broad front section was refurbished in 1945. ...]

2. The second typical text is a more elaborate version of a proposed walk through a part of the city center of Düsseldorf. Its style is typical for specific travel guides and for example introduces a couple of problems like 'pseudo-agents' in 'Our stroll along ...' or spatial relations coded as temporal relations like 'After leaving the place at the top you can see the church at the next corner.'. An example of this type of text looks like the following:

   > Die etwa 1 km lange, meist nur "Kö" genannte Königsallee, Düsseldorfs elegante Einkaufs- und Flanierstraße, verläuft in nordsüdlicher Richtung vom Corneliusplatz zum Graf–Adolf–Platz. Zwischen den beiden Fahrbahnen liegt der alte, flache Stadtgraben.
   > Die Allee wurde 1804 angelegt. Zunächst hieß sie Mittelallee. Später hieß sie Kastanienallee, ehe sie im Jahre 1851 ihren heutigen Namen erhielt.
   > An beiden Seiten der von dicht stehenden Bäumen gesäumten Königsallee reihen sich Geschäftshäuser und Verwaltungsbauten aneinander. Exklusive Geschäfte, Restaurants und Terrassencafes findet man an der Ostseite der Kö.
   > Wir beginnen unseren Bummel über die Königsallee am Hofgarten. Die unterirdische Kö-Passage führt uns von hier zu dem am Nordende der Kö gelegenen, rechteckigen Corneliusplatz. ...

[Düsseldorf's Königsallee – conventionally called the "Kö" – a quite elegant avenue for shopping and strolling, stretches between Corneliusplatz in the north and Graf–Adolf–Platz in the south. Between its two roadways runs the old, flat moat.
The avenue was build in 1804. First, it was called Mittelallee. Later, it was renamed Kastanienallee, and in 1851 it was given its present name.
Along the Königsallee, which is tightly bordered by trees, one finds a row of office and shop buildings. Exquisite shops, restaurants, and coffee houses are located on the Kö's eastern side.
Our stroll along the Königsallee takes its point of departure at the Hofgarten. From there, the underground Kö-passageway leads us to the rectangular-shaped Corneliusplatz at the Kö's northern end. . . .]

3. The third text describes an – artificial – event, which took place in Düsseldorf:

In der ersten Maiwoche fand in Düsseldorf der große LILOG-Workshop statt. Nach der anstrengenden Projektsitzung am Dienstag machten die Teilnehmer des Workshops am Mittwoch einen Ausflug in die Düsseldorfer Innenstadt. Der Bus brachte sie von ihren Hotels am Rhein in rund 30 Minuten zum Hofgarten. Kaum waren sie angekommen, begann es zu regnen, trotzdem unternahmen sie einen etwa einstündigen Spaziergang durch den Park. . . .
[The big LILOG workshop took place during the first week of May. After the exhausting project meeting on Tuesday, on Wednesday the participants took off for an excursion into Düsseldorf's city center. The bus picked them up at their hotels by the Rhine and took them to the Hofgarten in about thirty minutes. Hardly had they arrived there, when it started to rain, but they nonetheless took a walk through the park for about one hour. . . .]

The chosen question mainly focuses on the sequential event structure of the story; information about single objects and their relations only serve as a kind of background knowledge:

q: Wann begann es zu regnen ?
[When did it start to rain ?]
a: Nachdem die Gruppe im Hofgarten angekommen war.
[After the group had arrived at the Hofgarten.]

In addition to this information, a part of the city map was represented by coding it manually into a street graph. A couple of prototypical items of spatial information about objects were coded by hand as well (see the papers by [Habel 91] and [Khenkhar 91]).

Whereas in the first prototype of the LILOG system a pre-existing text was selected which served as an inflexible textual base, in the second prototype an additional phase was added to check the textual information for LEU/2. This check-up was carried out with various aspects such as morphology, grammar, etc., in mind in order to reduce difficulties within the working bases for the system.[3] This procedure reduces ad hoc solutions within the system to cover the texts and opens the possibility of explaining the system's competence to outside observers by showing the deleted or modified parts of the texts. So for an evaluation of the system the metamorphosis of the texts is one of the relevant sources, as we will show later.

After consolidating the textual input, the scope of the domain was – to some extent – frozen. To 'understand' the texts in some depth, the system should be able to perform inferential tasks

---

[3]The main sources of problems with given texts were the modules for handling the syntax, semantics and inference on background knowledge; easier problems arose e.g., from the morphology or the generation modules.

upon the textual information. The next step was to clarify these inferential tasks. Thus, this step pinpoints the level of text understanding. In part, this step resulted in the answers to the questions

- What are the concepts you are interested in ?
- What is the knowledge about these concepts ?

in the form of a collection of question/answer pairs, which the system is expected to deal with adequately on the basis of the given textual information and the background knowledge.

After the final assembly of the different text parts, the evaluation of their adequacy for the given task was important. Therefore, a set of clusters necessary for text understanding had to be identified and collected. A cluster is a set of highly interconnected concepts having only a relatively small number of relations to the concepts of other clusters.[4] Other separations might be possible and those chosen need only give some hints as to the appropriatness of the text corpus. The clusters are as follows:

Space: Here, features of entities are sketched which depend on spatial attributes, like shape, orientation and dimensions.

Entities such as objects (see below) and their location in the city center of Düsseldorf are often mentioned in the texts of LEU/2. In the texts of type 2 and 3, for example, the Königsallee is described from north to south.

Objects: Classes of objects appearing in the texts are:

persons, animals, plants (trees in an avenue or park), sights (fountains, memorials,..), buildings (museum,..), institutions (church, city hall,..), abstract objects (entrance fees,..), cultural objects (arts,..), etc.

Qualities, Quantities and Measuring Scales: Objects have qualities like size, weight, color, etc., spaces have a volume, a content, etc. All these features should be expressable in a form independent of their objects. Aspects of vagueness in the texts like the relativeness of measurements ('a large man' vs. 'a large church') are also important in the texts.

Changes, Time and Events: Considering that the world is changing, there should exist a possibility, to express situations located in (the dimensions) space and time: excursions, bus driving and others are examples out of the texts.

Moreover, it is necessary to introduce pure time-concepts for definitions, such as a calender or the expression of relations between time intervals for expressions like 'after having a lunch they went to the church'.

Energy and Motion: Reconstructing events means, among other things, differentiating between the cases of initiating and keeping alive this event: does the event happen by itself ('rain') or is it to be initiated? The distinction between these two cases enables us to differentiate the following changes of location: the active 'walking'-event and the passive 'driving'-event.

Assemblies and Material: Physical objects are often made of parts assembled together in some way: they can consist of one simple material, such as a 'sculpture of bronze' or consist of many separate parts where each part is a seperate object as well. Examples in the texts are fronts or floors of buildings.

---

[4]The identification of clusters is motivated by [Hayes 79] but differs slightly.

Emotions and Mental States: Mental and internal states or emotions have to be defined with regard to the existence of persons. The examples in the texts involve 'tiredness' or 'anger'.

All the clusters mentioned above are necessary to reconstruct the chosen texts. Thus, the limitations given through the scenario are not essential but only needed to restrict the quantitative complexity of the model (see the paper [Klose, Luck 91]).

2   The Metamorphosis of a Text

As already indicated, in this section the metamorphosis of a text will serve as an example for detecting strengths and weaknesses of the actual implementation of LEU/2. We started at end of 1988 with a text about the Kreuzherrenkirche taken from a tourist guide, which had the following original form:

> Die Kreuzherrenkirche liegt an der Ecke Ratinger Straße und Ursulinengasse. Die 1443 durch den damaligen Herzog nach Düsseldorf gerufenen Kreuzherren erbauten sie als Klosterkirche vor den Toren der Stadt. Die Besonderheiten der gotischen Hallenkirche sind ihre zwei parallelen Schiffe, die in dieser Form am Niederrhein relativ selten sind.
>
> [The crusaders' church is located at the intersection of Ratiner Straße and Ursulinengasse. Called to Düsseldorf by the duke in 1443, the crusaders built it as a cloister outside the city walls. The parallel naves which in this form are quite rare in the Niederrhein area are peculiar to the gothic church.]

The first modifications concerned two aspects. On the one hand, difficult syntactical constructs such as the copula '... Schiffe, die ... selten sind ...' [... naves which ... are rare ...] and sentences based on participle constructions such as '... nach Düsseldorf gerufenen Kreuzherren ...' [... crusaders, which were called to Düsseldorf ...] were replaced by easier ones. On the other hand, content-oriented modifications like the replacement of 'herzoglichen Erbauer der Kirche' [ducal architects of the church] by the more interesting phrase 'katholische Pfarrkirche' [Catholic parish church].

Around July 1989, the modifications resulted in the following text:

> Die Kreuzherrenkirche, die im 15. Jahrhundert als Kloster des Kreuzherren-Konvents erbaut wurde, befindet sich an der Ecke Ratinger Straße/Ursulinengasse. Ab 1803 beinhaltete das Bauwerk Büros, und seit der Restaurierung im Jahre 1968 wurde es als katholische Pfarrkirche genutzt. Besonderheit der gotischen Hallenkirche sind ihre beiden parallelen Schiffe.
>
> [Built as a cloister of the crusaders' convent in the 15th century, the crusaders' church is located at the intersection Ratinger Straße / Ursulinengasse. From 1803 on, the building comprised offices, and it has been used as a catholic parish church since its restoration in 1968. The parallel naves are peculiar to the gothic hall church.]

Because of problems in, e.g., handling adjectives in an adequate way as well as some problems in the inference component concerning temporal relationship additional modifications were made.[5] The latest version, dating from the end of 1990, resulted in:

---

[5]For examples of such modifications see the next section.

Die gotische Kreuzherrenkirche, die im 15. Jahrhundert erbaut wurde, befindet sich an der Ecke Ratingerstraße und Ursulinengasse. Ab 1803 beinhaltete das Bauwerk Büros. Die Kirche besitzt parallele Schiffe.

[The gothic crusaders' church, built in the 15th century, is located at the intersection of Ratinger Straße and Ursulinengasse. From 1803 on, the building comprised offices. The church is endowed with parallel naves.]

LEU/2 is able to handle questions about this text and generate answers like:

Q: Wo befindet sich die Kreuzherrenkirche ?
[Where is the Kreuzherrenkirche located ?]

A: An der Ecke Ratinger Straße, Ursulinengasse.
[At the corner of Ratinger Straße and Ursulinengasse.]

Q: Wann wurde die Kreuzherrenkirche errichtet ?
[When was the Kreuzherrenkirche constructed ?]

A: Im 15 Jahrhundert.
[In the 15th century.]

Q: Welche Kirche wurde im 15. Jahrhundert erbaut ?
[Which church was constructed in the 15th century ?]

A: Die Kreuzherrenkirche.
[The Kreuzherrenkirche.]

3 Conclusion

A couple of modifications were made not only of this text about the Kreuzherrenkirche, but of all the other texts as well. Most of the modifications were induced by the demand to keep the system clean from ad hoc solutions for special natural language constructs. As an example of the modifications made, a part of the diary of the text about the Kreuzherrenkirche is given below, starting from the first version of this text and ending at the final one:

- 'liegt an der Ecke' replaced by 'befindet sich an der Ecke'
  Reason: 'liegen' is ambiguous in the context of buildings

- 'Die 1443 ... erbaute' replaced by 'im 15. Jahrhundert'
  Reason: was not reconstructable

- 'durch den damaligen Herzog nach Düsseldorf gerufenen Kreuzherren erbauten sie als Klosterkirche vor den Toren der Stadt' deleted
  Reason: too difficult to capture the meaning of ('Toren der Stadt', 'gerufenen')

- 'Die Besonderheiten der ...' deleted
  Reason: problems with the semantics of 'besonders'

- 'Hallenkirche' deleted
  Reason: modeling is uninteresting from content view

- ... die in dieser Form am Niederrhein relativ selten sind.'
  Reason: too hard to capture the meaning of 'relativ', 'selten' and 'in dieser Form'

- 'Kirche ... Bauwerk' added
  Reason: anapher resolution, in contrast to church as institution

- 'beinhaltet das Bauwerk Büros' added
  Reason: modeling of spatial inclusions

As you can see from this example, the performance of a system like LEU/2 is determined by the different components that are part of the system. A *very* sketchy picture of the architecture of LEU/2 is given in Figure 1, showing a typical kind of cascaded architecture for a natural language understanding system.[6]

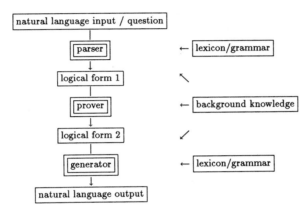

Figure 1: Sketch of the architecture of LEU/2

There were a couple of deletions of text caused by one of the components where the text was manageable by all the other components. These deletions give hints of theoretical and/or practical difficulties with the specific component. A set of modifications were caused by at least one component to include phenomena which were intended to serve as examples of theoretical and/or practical work, but these modifications had to be agreed upon by – almost – all other components.

One of the frequent reasons for modification and one of the most discussed topics in the field of text understanding is the separation between semantic knowledge – coded mainly in the lexicon – on the one hand and common sense knowledge or world knowledge on the other. During the conception and implementation of the modules in our prototype, this discussion was reflected by a considerable flexibility in the division of functions between semantic analysis and inferential processes.

During the integration, descriptive parts of linguistic theories had to be completed with procedural or functional aspects. Typical misfits appeared each time it was clear *what should be expressed* within certain modules (like morphology or syntax), but still unclear *how to proceed* from one module to the next. In the ideal case, this allowed the conclusion that there were incompatibilities between the levels of linguistic analysis corresponding to the respective modules.

One of these phenomena is the identification of adjectival passive constructions versus regular verbs as given in the following example:

---

[6]For a more precise impression of the system's architecture see [Herzog, Rollinger 91].

Das Museum wird um 11 Uhr geöffnet.

[The museum will be opened at 11 a.m.]

Das Museum ist von 9 bis 15 Uhr geöffnet.

[The museum is open from 9 a.m. to 3 p.m.]

According to Vendler's classification, 'open' should be categorized as an event in the first sentence and, combined with 'to be' in the second case, as a state. The integration of the modules showed that none of the system components was able in the first run to deliver this differentiation – in this case, the reason was the incompatibility between unsorted unification grammars and the necessity to overwrite default values.

Because we included such material, these texts served as an excellent basis for discussions between representatives of different theories, who were forced to cooperate by integrating their specific approaches into **one** running system. The elaboration of the context chosen for the LEU/2 in this explicit form made clear several limits and deficiencies of particular theories. On the other hand, the semantics outlined by the sharp contextual limits made this approach feasible in setting the specifications for LEU/2. Given the present state of affairs in artificial intelligence, this seems for us to be the only way to construct an integrated natural language understanding system, which is – of course – in contrast to approaches like [Lenat et al. 90] and [Barnet et al. 90]

References

[Barnet et al. 90] J. Barnett, K. Knight, I. Mani, E. Rich (1990): Knowledge and Natural Language Processing. *Comm. of the ACM*, 33(8):50-71.

[Bobrow et al. 77] D. G. Bobrow, R. M. Kaplan, M. Kay, D. A. Norman, M. Thompson, T. Winograd (1977): GUS: a frame-driven dialog system. *Artificial Intelligence*, 8:155–173.

[Habel 91] C. Habel. In this volume.

[Hayes 79] P. J. Hayes (1979): The naive physics manifesto. In D. Michie (ed.): *Expert Systems in the Microelectronic Age*, Edinburgh University Press.

[Herzog, Rollinger 91] O. Herzog, C.-R. Rollinger. In this volume.

[Khenkhar 91] M. Khenkhar. In this volume.

[Klose, Luck 91] G. Klose, K. v. Luck. In this volume.

[Lenat et al. 90] D. B. Lenat, R. V. Guha, K. Pittman, D. Pratt, M. Shepherd (1990): CYC: Toward programs with common sense. *Comm. of the ACM*, 33(8):30-49.

The Text Understanding System LEU/2

Jan Wilms

The concepts of a text understanding system as described in the previous chapters have been implemented in LEU/2, the second 'LILOG Experimentier Umgebung' (LILOG Experimental Environment). This Experimental Environment is used for development work as well as for experiments and to demonstrate the capibilities of the system. The version of LEU/2 described here is 2.4, the version that was shown to the public at Hanover CeBIT trade fair 1991. Therefore not all features of the final version as of end 1991 are discussed here in detail.

For development the engineering environments for linguists (see the paper by J.Dörre in Sect. 1.1 of this book) and for knowledge engineers (see the paper by M.Börkel in Sect. 2.2) have been implemented. For a description of LILOG-KE, the LILOG Knowledge Engineering Environment, also see [Seiffert, Wilms]. These development environments may be used stand alone or together with the complete system. If run with the complete system, they may also be used to inspect intermediate results.

For experiments the behavior of LEU/2 can be modified in a number of ways. The mode of processing can be determined by changing user-defined options like the parsing strategy, the search strategy and calculi used by the inference engine, search depth for forward or backward chaining, and so on. A configurator allows one to specify which modules to use. This is true for program modules as well as for parts of knowledge bases. In this way, it is possible, for example, to experiment with different variants of the parser, the morphology module, or the database management module, or one can use an alternate lexicon or another set of background knowledge rules. By the time when this was written, we only were able to perform part of the experiments that we plan to do. So there is more work under way.

The rest of this paper will describe how we demonstrate that LEU/2 is actually able to comprehend the meaning of texts. Due to the large number of features in LEU/2, it is not possible to cover all of them. So we will focus on some of them to give an idea of how LEU/2 understands texts. As LEU/2 deals with German texts, all examples here are shown in German, but we do provide English translations. The command language of the system, e.g. for all messages issued by the processes, is English. The current version of the system reads texts from travel guides about the city of Düsseldorf (see also the paper by K.v.Luck and T.Pirlein in this chapter) like the following:

Im Palais Nesselrode ist das Hetjensmuseum, das 1909 eröffnet wurde, untergebracht. Es befindet sich an der Ecke Schulstraße und Hafenstraße. Die Keramiksammlung umfaßt zehntausend Objekte. Der Eintritt der Ausstellung, die von 10 Uhr bis 17 Uhr geöffnet ist, beträgt 2 DM. [1]

When this text is read in, it is processed and a representation of its content is stored in the system's text knowledge base. So let us for the rest of this chapter assume that this text, which

---

[1]Nesselrode Palace houses the Hetjens Museum, which was opened in 1909. It is located at the corner of Schulstrasse and Hafenstrasse. The ceramics collection of the museum contains ten thousand items. Admission to the exhibit, which is open from 10 a.m. until 5 p.m., costs 2 DM.

is only one of many sample texts, has been read by the system. When using LEU/2, we do not of course have to use this specific formulation of the text. Much more than this, we can express the same thing in many different ways. If, for example, we read in an alternate version of the text like:

Die Keramiksammlung des Hetjensmuseums, das sich an der Ecke Schulstraße und Hafen-straße befindet, umfaßt zehntausend Objekte. Es ist im Palais Nesselrode untergebracht. Die Ausstellung hat von 10 Uhr bis 17 Uhr geöffnet. Der Eintrittspreis des Museums beträgt 2 DM.[2]

the system will react by saying:

Ja, das war mir bereits bekannt.   (Yes, I knew this already.)

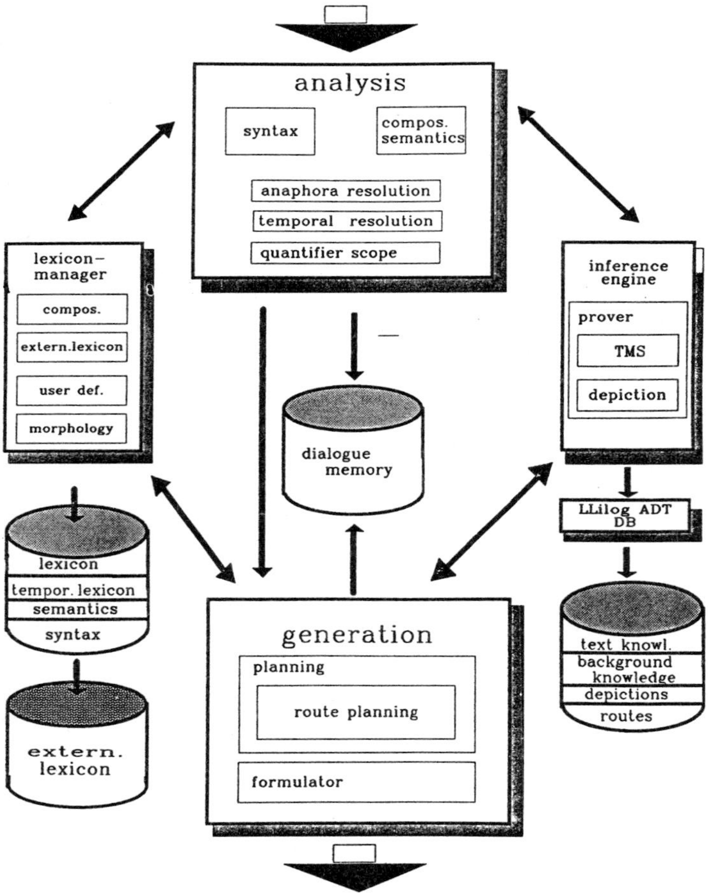

Figure 1: Architecture of LEU/2

---

[2]The ceramics collection of the Hetjens Museum, which is located on the corner of Schulstrasse and Hafenstrasse, contains ten thousand items. It is housed in Nesselrode Palace. The exhibit is open from 10 a.m. until 5 p.m. Admission to the museum is 2 DM.

So this is also a first indication that the system actually did understand both texts, which enabled it to conclude that the alternate text did not contain any new information. In the next step, one would let the system answer questions that humans would normally be able to answer, given that they have read the text. If, for example, we ask the system:

Wann hat das Hetjensmuseum geöffnet?　　　(When is the Hetjens Museum opened?)

it will answer:　　Von 10 Uhr bis 17 Uhr.　　　(From 10 a.m. to 5 p.m.)

The answer is evident to anyone who has read the text, but explicitly the text only gives the opening times of the exhibition. So the system must figure out that the exhibition is the exhibition of the ceramics collection, that the ceramics collection is part of the museum and that, whenever the exhibition is opened, presumably the museum will be open too - a fairly complex task of resolving anaphorically definite noun phrases, which relies on fairly sophisticated knowledge representation and reasoning.

In a live demonstration of the system, one can watch the system going through the four major steps which are performed to handle a question: Syntactic Analysis, Semantic Analysis, Knowledge Processing, and Language Generation. To give the reader a rough idea, we give a diagram of the system's architecture here (see Figure 1). Basically these four steps correspond to the first four chapters of this book. So no further explanation should be necessary here. In this way many questions can be answered by the system. Some examples of questions with their answers are shown in Figure 2.

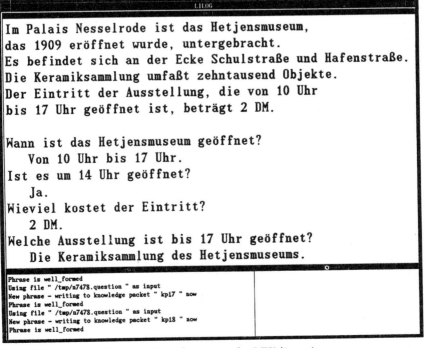

Figure 2: Sample screen of a LEU/2 session

Some of the questions can only be understood appropriately if the discourse is considered. The second question [3], for example, only makes sense following a previous mention of the Hetjens Museum (like the first one), so the 'es' ('it') can be related to the Hetjens Museum. And the third[4] requires a discourse referent, because only then can 'the admission' be interpreted in the intended fashion as 'admission to the Hetjens Museum'[5].

In the next step we demonstrate, how the system can generate text. As an application we choose the description of ways from one point to another, which in our city domain can be used to tell the ways to sights. However in real applications it might be used for explanation components (of expert systems etc.). Finding a path is done based on knowledge about part of the city map of Düsseldorf, but this is not the point of interest here. If we put the question 'Wie komme ich von der Müller Schlösser Gasse zum Eiskellerberg?'[6], ('Müller Schlösser Gasse' and 'Eiskellerberg' are the names of two streets in Düsseldorf) the system would reply by giving the following description:

Gehen Sie zum Stiftsplatz! Gehen Sie über den Stiftsplatz schräg nach rechts! Biegen Sie dann links in die Lambertusstraße ein! Biegen Sie an der nächsten Ecke rechts in die Altestadt ein! Gehen Sie die Altestadt und die Ratinger Straße entlang! Biegen Sie an der dritten Ecke scharf links in die Mühlengasse ein! Gehen Sie durch die Mühlengasse bis zur nächsten Ecke! Da ist dann der Eiskellerberg. [7]

One may observe, that the formulation the system chooses is quite adequate. The phrases 'schräg nach rechts' or 'scharf links' are used rather than simply 'rechts' or 'links', if this helps to distinguish the way. Moreover 'durch die Mühlengasse' may only be used because it is a 'Gasse' (lane).

At this point we can also show how knowledge from new text can be used in answering questions. For example we could ask 'Wie komme ich vom Marktplatz zur Opernstube?'[8] where 'Opernstube' is the name of a restaurant whose location is not known to the system. The answer would therefore be 'Der Anfangspunkt ist unbekannt.'[9]. However if we provide new information by reading in the sentence 'Die Opernstube befindet sich an der Rheinstraße.'[10] and ask the question, then the system is able to find out in a first step where the Opernstube is located, and in a second step construct and describe a path from Marktplatz to that location:

Gehen Sie in das Schloßufer! Gehen Sie das Schloßufer entlang, bis zum Burgplatz! Gehen Sie über den Burgplatz links! Biegen Sie dann schräg nach rechts in die Marktstraße ein! Gehen Sie immer die Marktstraße entlang! An der Rheinstraße ist dann die Opernstube. [11]

---

[3]Is it open at 2 p.m.?

[4]How much is the admission?

[5]Which exhibit is open until 5 p.m.?

[6]How do I get from the Müller Schlösser Gasse to the Eiskellerberg?

[7]Go to Stiftsplatz. Go across the Stiftsplatz diagonally to the right. Turn left into Lambertusstrasse. Turn right at the next corner into Altestadt. Go along Altestadt and Ratinger Strasse. Take a sharp left at the third corner into Mühlengasse (Mühlen Lane). Go through Mühlengasse to the next corner. There is the Eiskellerberg.

[8]How to I get from the Marktplatz to the Opernstube?

[9]The starting point is unknown.

[10]The Opernstube at the Rheinstrasse.

[11]Go into the Schlossufer street. Go along the Schlossufer street as far as the Burgplatz. Go across the Burgplatz to the left. Bear right into Marktstrasse. Keep going along Marktstrasse. At the Rheinstrasse is the Opernstube.

LEU/2 is also able to deal with words, which cannot be found in the system's lexicon (see the paper by W.Emde in Sect. 1.3 of this book). For Example, let a text be read in containing the sentence 'Das Software-Museum wurde 1986 eröffnet.'[12]. The compound 'Software-Museum' of course cannot be found in the system's lexicon. So the lexicon manager trys to analyze it with one of four steps, the third of which is successful here. The trace of these steps for 'Software-Museum' is shown below.

Unknown word: Software-Museum

Searching for entry in temporary lexicon ..
No entry in temporary lexicon!

Searching for a synonym which is known ..
Can not build lexical entry using a synonym

Trying to decompose word ...
Decomposed as Software - Museum
New concept: #Software-Museum inserted as sub-concept of: Museum !
Decomposition successful

continuing calling process ...

At the end of this process lexical information derived from the second part of the composite noun ('Museum') together with information on the meaning (concept) of the word (here: #Software-Museum) is inserted in the temporary lexicon and provided to the calling process, i.e. the parser. On the next occurence of the word, it can (in the first step) be looked up successfully in the temporary lexicon, thus avoiding repeated analysis.

```
'Software-Museum' :=
    'MOR_NOUN',
    'NOUN_TEMP'(norm,'ART'),
    'GENDER'(neut),
    'NOUN_SX'(@('#Software-Museum',sorts))
```

For this composite noun the concept was created dynamically as a subconcept of the sort 'Museum', i.e. the new sort was inserted into the ontology below 'Museum'. Figure 3 on the next page shows an excerpt of the LILOG ontology (as displayed by the browser of the KE tools) showing the dynamically acquired concept '#Software-Museum' and its inherited roles and features.

---

[12]The software museum was opened in 1986.

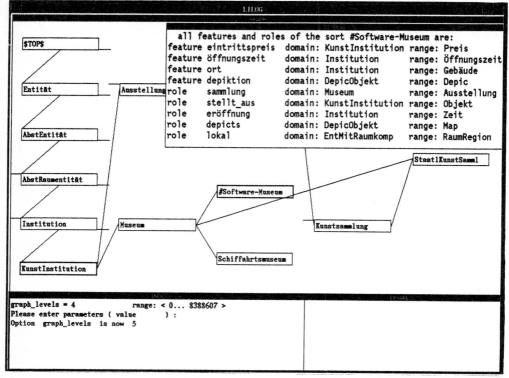

Figure 3: Excerpt of the LILOG ontology showing a dynamically acquired concept

In a LEU/2 working session some intermediate results can be displayed. Just for illustration we will give some types of result here. Others, like feature structures, the ontology, or displays of depictions (imagination and inspection) are not fit to be printed in a book but should rather be inspected dynamically on the screen. So we renounce showing those here and encourage the reader to try to view the LEU/2 video [Video] or a live demonstration of the LEU/2 system. Intermediate results given on the following two pages below are for the first sentence of the 'Hetjens' text quoted above: 'Im Palais Nesselrode ist das Hetjensmuseum, das 1909 eröffnet wurde, untergebracht.'

Intermediate results of the syntactic analysis, which can be inspected by the user cover amongst other things the chart, the parse tree, and the feature structure (see the previously mentioned paper by J.Dörre in Sect. 1.1).

The intermediate result of the semantic module is the EDRS of the sentence, as shown on the next page.

```
% EDRS :

REFLIST:  drfnt52  drfnt53  drfnt54  drfnt55  drfnt56  drfnt57  drfnt58

REFO: drfnt52   SORTS : Unterbringen
   Attributes:   lokal: drfnt53
                 patiens: drfnt55
   Lfeatures:    temp: present
                 det: state
REFO: drfnt53   SORTS : RaumRegion
   Attributes:   inlokspec: drfnt54
   Lfeatures:    det: anon
REFO: drfnt54   SORTS : Palais
   Attributes:   name: Palais_Nesselrode
   Lfeatures:    det: def
REFO: drfnt55   SORTS : Museum
   Attributes:   name: Hetjensmuseum
   Lfeatures:    number: sg
                 gender: neut
                 det: def
REFO: drfnt56   SORTS : Eroffnung
   Attributes:   patiens: drfnt55
                 temporal: drfnt57
   Lfeatures:    temp: past
                 det: event
REFO: drfnt57   SORTS : Zeit
   Attributes:   intempspec: drfnt58
   Lfeatures:    det: anon
REFO: drfnt58   SORTS : Jahr
   Attributes:   einheit: jahr
                 zahlenwert: n1909
                 jhr: n1909
   Lfeatures:    det: def

DEPENDENCIES:
   drfnt54 < drfnt53        drfnt53 < drfnt52
   drfnt56 < drfnt55        drfnt55 < drfnt52
   drfnt58 < drfnt57        drfnt57 < drfnt56
```

The drfntnn used in the EDRS are dynamically created IDs of discourse referents, some of which are pretty printed below. They are inserted in the knowledge base as Reference Objects, e.g.:

```
Showing attribute values of refo drfnt58 of sort Jahr
   in kbs: know_base(demotextkb_1,[kp12])
      feature jhr: 1909
      feature zahlenwert: 1909
      feature einheit: jahr
```

The pretty-print of the L_{LILOG} fact constructed from the EDRS (i.e., the sentence) as inserted in the knowledge base is:

```
axiom ax_inf_74 in demotextkb_1-kp12
        jhr(drfnt58)=1909
    and zahlenwert(drfnt58)=1909
    and einheit(drfnt58)=jahr
    and intempspec(drfnt57,drfnt58)
    and temporal(drfnt56)=drfnt57
    and patiens(drfnt56)=drfnt55
    and name(drfnt55)=Hetjensmuseum
    and name(drfnt54)=Palais_Nesselrode
    and inlokspec(drfnt53,drfnt54)
    and patiens(drfnt52)=drfnt55
    and lokal(drfnt52,drfnt53)  .
```

Additionally some facts inferred by forward chaining during the step of knowledge processing are inserted into the knowledge base. One example for the sentence above is:

```
axiom ax_inf_86 in demotextkb_1-kp12
forall      K:Kontextvektor
            T:EntMitZeitkomp
    Lok(def:innenregion(ro:hohlraum(ro:drfnt54)),
                gebiet:refo_inf_10,
                kontext:K,
                le:drfnt55,
                ro:drfnt54,
                temp:T)  .

Showing attribute values of refo refo_inf_10 of sort Gebiet
   in kbs: know_base(demotextkb_1,[kp12])
        feature definition: innenregion(ro:hohlraum(ro:drfnt54))
        feature refobjekt: drfnt54
        role le_objekt: drfnt55
```

LEU/2 was completely implemented in Quintus Prolog (2.4 and 3.1) on IBM workstations running AIX (PS/2-70, PS/2-80, RT6150, RS6000). The database interface is implemented in C, the user interface is based on XWindows and OSF/Motif (AIXWindows). Demonstrations of LEU/2 can be given on any of the machines mentioned above, preferably on RS6000s of course.

References

[Seiffert, Wilms] R. Seiffert, J. Wilms. LIKEET, the LILOG Knowledge Engineering Environment and Tools. In J. H. Griesser, ed., *IBM ITL Conference on Expert Systems*, IBM, 219-223, 1990.

[Video] Video-Tape. LILOG - Linguistics and Logic in Text Understanding. IKBS, IBM Germany GmbH, 15 min., 1990.

The Trace of Building a Large AI System

Andreas Arning

"The more you plan, the more you are hit by coincidence.
So don't you plan too much but save your head to manage the chaos."
(traditional)

Abstract

This is a report about the successful development of a complex natural language understanding system. It describes the difficulties that were faced when planning, implementing, and finishing this project. After outlining the planned proceeding, it is described what really happened during the realization, in other words: the problems *expected* are compared to the problems *experienced*. Finally, those topics and details are discussed which were helpful and thus responsible for the success of the project, and experiences transferable to other projects are emphasized.

1   Introduction

The following report describes the development of a complex AI system, namely a natural language understanding system. It is not meant to describe completely all the technical details like the paper (Knuth 89) (which is worth reading): since in our case, many more people have been involved, more emphasis is put on the problems that are caused just by this fact, like coordination and version control.

The message of this paper is **not** *"If you do it this way you will succeed"*, but much more *"That's the way we did it, and in our special case, we got a success instead of a catastrophe"*. There are some ideas that can be reused for other projects, and others which just worked in our special case. So keep in mind that the following doesn't describe the **class** of successful implementations but just **one instance**.

2   Project Description

2.1   Goals

The LILOG project was established to do research on text understanding using methods of linguistics and logic.

For two reasons, the implementation of prototype systems plays an important role in the project. First of all, creating an integrated system including parser, inference engine, and generation module, as well as lexicon and background knowledge, serves as a focal point. It forces the scientists involved to talk to each other and to restrict themselves to theories that really work.

On the other hand, a successful prototype might become the very first version of a successful program product one day; although this system was designed as a workbench for the scientists to test and validate different theoretical approaches, nevertheless additional motivation was created by the fact that there was a fixed deadline when the system was supposed to be reviewed by higher management, in order to check out further application fields.

Thus the experimental text understanding system LEU/2 (LILOG Experimentier Umgebung[1]) was planned and implemented, the process which is described in this paper.

2.2 Constraints

For building the LEU/2 system, the following conditions were given:

Scenario

In order to test the implemented theories with a realistic kind of application, machine-readable text about sightseeing tours was chosen as domain for the text understanding system. Moreover, a mode was to be provided to type in NL questions, which are also to be answered by the system in NL, a feature that can help to verify that the text is understood. Just the definition of the scenario has been likewise a complex process; see the paper by G. Klose and T. Pirlein in this chapter.

People/Staff

The project is run in cooperation with 5 German universities, each of them covering interesting topics at state-of-the-art level. About 60 people were supposed to contribute to the system, half of them in one location, the other half spread over the universities. More information about the organizational details is given in the introduction of this book by C. Rollinger and O. Herzog.

Time

Given the fact that we wanted to have a running system long before the end of the project in December 1991, but on the other hand to have enough time to create nontrivial solutions, 15 months seemed appropriate for implementation including integration and test. Due to late delivery of the required system software, the implememtation could not be started before April 1989, although some conceptual ideas and data structures could be worked out in advance. So midyear 1990 was assigned as realistic target date (although everybody was told to aim for the first quarter 1990, see below).

Environment

The development was done completely on workstations, with everybody having his/her own workstation. Coordination, integration, and about half of the development work happened in the main location, but the rest was spread over 5 other locations in all parts of West Germany. Unfortunately, for security reasons there was no facility to log in remotely across the locations. However, source code could be sent not only by diskette but also via electronic mail.

3 Planning

For the duration of this section, we jump back in time some months and participate in the planning phase. In order to emphasize that this is the view from before implementation, the section is written throughout using future tense instead of past tense.

---

[1]LILOG Experimental Environment

3.1 The Ideal Case

Let us see what the optimal development process should look like. When several people work on different components, it would be nice if at the end all the components could be plugged together and make up a running system. But nobody would claim this to be the ideal case rather than an illusion, because in any reasonably complex software development project, a substantial part of the development capacity is necessary to coordinate the components and to establish appropriate interfaces between the components.

Large Systems: Dependencies

When planning the schedules for a complex system, it comes to mind as an almost trivial fact that the appropriate modules have to be ready and tested when they are needed to develop other modules. This is valid also when developing systems other than software, but it is not quite as simple as it sounds: see Sect. 5.3.

Software Systems: Version Control

In the ideal case of producing software, building the system is a monotonic process: all modules evolve stepwise until they have their full functionality, working all the time properly together without regressions. In reality, however, the ideal case seems like "an almost monotonic process" which is done "without major regressions". You do not get this for free but you (and your staff) have to respect several rules. Examples follow:

- Try to be upward compatible (a well known rule). In other words: make sure that everything that works[2] using version n of one module will also work using version $n+1$. This implies that you try not to change names or data structures unless absolutely necessary. This in turn implies that much effort should be spent on interface and data definitions in an early phase of the project.

- If you change the semantics of one procedure's parameter list, you should also change the procedure's name[3], to make sure that all callers of this procedure become aware of this change. In order to fulfill the following rule as well, it can be helpful to support the old procedure, too, for an intermediate time interval and maybe make it cause some kind of warning.

- When changing one module, do not force another module to have to change at the same time. Otherwise you cannot reset single modules to older versions, a fact that can cause you severe regression problems.

A prerequisite for this of course is a solid version control, since you can create almost arbitrarily many additional problems, if there is any confusion about the different versions of one module.

AI Systems: Prototyping

For an experimental research system as described here, often there is no complete specification in the beginning, since one goal of the implementation is to find out what can be realized and thus what the actual specification will be. This problem is well known, and there are several strategies to handle

---

[2]Unless it relies on a bug.
[3]At least if the changes cannot be found by the syntactical checks in use.

it, see (Budde 84) and (Boehm 86). According to the terminology used here, our goal is to build an *explorative* prototype, and the *spiral model* seems to be the appropriate approach. But there are major differences even between the modules to be implemented: On the one hand we have to build straightforward components such as the window interface, where the specifications are well known in the beginning. On the other hand, we plan a hybrid inference engine and a hybrid knowledge base in order to process depictional knowledge[4] as well as propositional knowledge, where we cannot rely on other people's experiences. Thus it is difficult to apply a method off the shelf and we have to find our own way.

Special Case: Distributed Development

Given the fact that in our case the development will be done in a distributed manner, it would be ideal if this could be done without additional overhead problems. This becomes easier, the more the tasks can be modularized such that different locations can work quite independently between the nevertheless necessary synchronization points.

The Ideal Case: Conclusio

All these requirements lead to the milestone concept often applied in software development:

- definition of the task

- definition of the modules

- definition of the data structures

- implementation

- test

Note that in our situation this is still an idealized model, because it is not possible to define the task in detail in the beginning, and because the definition of the modules cannot really be separated from the definition of the data structures. But more than in other software development projects it seems to be important to make all definitions and specifications concrete by forcing ourselves to do an implementation as early as possible. Hence, even before the definition of the data structures eventually used, any implementer has to provide a "dummy" version of his/her module, which allows us to *start* with the integration of the modules rather then to *end* the development process with the integration. This procedure has several advantages:

- The fundamental design decisions are forced to be done soon. This is the typical advantage as known from other top-down methods.

- Having code, you have a very precise specification; some "irrelevant" details that turn out to be relevant can be detected in an early stage.

- Having the specification not just machine-readable but machine-processable, you will detect more mismatches than if you have it just in paper form: the papers will not bite each other, but the code does.

- The effort you have to make to integrate the pieces has to be made anyway. But starting early, you may detect severe errors also very early, when the repair is still quite cheap.

---

[4]See Chap. 3 of this book.

3.2 Likely Disasters

Instead of waiting for catastrophes to occur, let us try to foresee what can go wrong – and thus what will go wrong. For any of these problems, we consider in advance possible **preventions** (to avoid it), **solutions** (action to solve the problem, once it has occurred), and **fall-back strategies**. A fall-back strategy (FBS) will normally consist of going back one step and trying to solve the problem at another level, maybe accepting losses in functionality or speed.

Later on we will evaluate whether this list was complete, or rather what else happened, see Sect. 5 below.

Now, extracted from experiences in other software projects and previous prototypes, here are the possible problems, as visible in the beginning, together with the supposed solutions.

Single component not ready in time

Prevention: nothing special, but the milestone checkpoints will help to detect this in an early stage.

Action: analyze why; maybe get support for the component from the writer of another component.

FBS: use older version or even dummy version of this component.

Many components not ready in time

Prevention: assign time buffers at the beginning (but avoid the name "time buffer").

Action: if it is necessary to relax a deadline, do it before it is too late, to keep it serious.

FBS: if your time buffer is exhausted, either strip target version or signal a delay in timing to all people affected.

Severe interface/interaction problems between modules

Prevention: milestone concept.

Action: try to uncover the most-difficult-to-fix problems first (Top Down Problem Handling).

FBS: if not solvable inside the existing modules, create additional module to bridge the gap.

Response time problems

Prevention: (try to) guarantee compatibility to more powerful (future) hardware.

Action: locate bottlenecks; have tuning specialist optimize code or even algorithms.

FBS: for test purposes: recycle or preprocess intermediate results; for demo purposes: use several machines, explain things using one machine while the other machines are busily working; paging problems: see "storage space problems" below.

Storage space problems

(Due to gigabytes of virtual storage in our environment, this will not be a hard limit but just result in extensive paging.)

Prevention: maximum storage configuration, at least for the heavily used machines.

Action: find space-wasting parts and try to save some space; use stripped versions for testing where possible; take space-expensive parts out of store and use database techniques (indexing).

FBS: overnight processing; patience.

Distributed development not working

Prevention: "emergency-off" switch (bypass) for every component which is not developed in the main location; introduce *one* technically competent contact person in every outside location to keep cross-location traffic effective.

Action: no special action (analyze why and try to solve problems).

FBS: concentrate development in one location; invite single persons from other locations for up to several months.

3.3   Milestones and Dates as Planned Originally

Table 1 gives the project's several deadlines, called milestones. Between two milestones there will be 3 months, except between 0th and 1st, where we assign one extra month because of vacation time. The milestone numbers will be referenced in the following sections.

Note that in an experimental prototype like the planned one, there is not really a sharp line between bug fixes and functional enhancements, but after the "ready" deadline is be reached, major changes may be rejected if they seem at all risky. On the other hand, for a non-commercial product the time from a "tested and debugged" version to a "polished" one can be shortened or even truncated, thus we have a time buffer for unforeseen events, but please do not tell it to the staff!

Milestone#	Target, Comment	Target Date
0.	**Dummy version** A complete version of the planned system, but just consisting of empty boxes. This is used to test the calling of the different modules of each other. The data structures passed are allowed to be empty lists at this stage.	5/89
1.	**Intermediate version** A refined version of the dummy version: now real data structures have to be exchanged between the modules. But the output of any module may still be independent of its input, e.g., the module is allowed to return identical data on each call. The processing inside the module may also be faked arbitrarily.	9/89
2.	**Ready** All components have their desired target functionality. From now on, no functional enhancements may be done, just bug fixes.	12/89
3.	**Tested and debugged** System ready. Just some time is needed for polishing and evaluation of the system's behaviour in all the different situations.	3/90
4.	**Demo version** (date planned but not published) System polished.	6/90
5.	**Demo**	7/10/90

Table 1: The milestones

4 Implementation

Here, some technical details about the implemented LEU/2 system are given. For more information about the complete system, see the paper by J. Wilms in this chapter. If you are interested in special components and the theories they are based on, you will find information in other chapters of the book.

Implemented Components

Table 2 gives some raw information about the several modules. $STUF$ and L_{LILOG} denote special formalisms developed in this project, and $KLoC$ is a shorthand for "1000 lines of code".

Module	written in:	Size	Remarks
Scanner	Prolog	0.4 KLoC	
Lexicon Manager	Prolog	5.5 KLoC	**developed externally**
TLM Programs	Prolog	3 KLoC	Two Level Morphology
TLM Data	*STUF*	6 KLoC	
NL Parser	Prolog	1.5 KLoC	**developed externally**
Syntax	*STUF*	(7.5 KLoC)	HPSG Syntax
Semantics:			
compositional	*STUF*	(7.5 KLoC)	Size together with Syntax
non-compositional	Prolog	7 KLoC	
Inference Engine	Prolog	29 KLoC	without Depiction module
Depiction module	Prolog	14 KLoC	spatial reasoning component for the inference engine, **developed externally**
Knowledge Base:			
ontology	L_{LILOG}	5 KLoC	
propositional rules	L_{LILOG}	1 KLoC	
depictional rules	L_{LILOG}	1.5 KLoC	**developed externally**
Data Base System	C	70 KLoC	**developed externally**
	Prolog	5 KLoC	
NL Generation	Prolog	26 KLoC	
Linguistic Workbench	Prolog	7 KLoC	Ported from DOS to AIX
Supervisor	Prolog	23 KLoC	
Window System	Prolog	9.5 KLoC	
L_{LILOG} Compiler for	C	3 KLoC	Including Parser Generator
knowledge base	Prolog	6.5 KLoC	for Parsers in Prolog
STUF Compiler for	C	0.2 KLoC	Parser Generator reused
lexicon data	Prolog	7.5 KLoC	from L_{LILOG} compiler

Table 2: The modules. This table illustrates that quite different types of modules had to be combined in one system: some of them have a rather experimental character while others are based on well-established theories.

System Software and Hardware

LEU/2 is running in Prolog under AIX. The development was done almost completely on PS/2 machines, all of them having 10 MB or even 16 MB of main storage; in the meantime it has also started working on newer machines (RS/6000).

For version management, a system similar to SCCS with minor enhancements was used, in order to have available logs and facilities for switching arbitrarily to backlevel versions. File transfer inside the main location was done via local area network, by using commands optimized for ease of use. File transfer across the locations was done generally by sending diskettes around[5], but in urgent cases programs were sent via email, since in the external locations not all of the workstations were connected to the mailing network.

---

[5]Of course this is not the state of the art, but at least it increases motivation not to send untested versions.

Headcounts

Almost 60 people participated in the project. But while some of them just worked on the theories, only 32 supplied real code – in terms of higher management:

- 18 professionals
- 5 guest scientists
- 9 students (part time)

Time

Since it was more important to meet the planned content rather than the planned deadline for each milestone, the deadlines were relaxed as soon as they turned out to be unrealistic. The milestones, as they were shifted eventually:

0.	Dummy version:	5/89		
1.	Intermediate version:	11/89	(instead of	9/89)
2.	Ready:	3/90	(instead of	12/89)
3.	Tested and debugged:	6/90	(instead of	3/90)
4.	Demo version:	6/90		
5.	Demo	7/10/90		

5 After Implementation: Taking Inventory

5.1 Reconsidering the "Ideal Case"

Dependencies

Although we tried to have tools and prerequisite modules ready and tested as they were needed, this did not work in one case: The linguistic workbench had to be ported from DOS to AIX / X-Windows. This turned out to be a redesign instead of just a straightforward porting or reimplementation task, a fact which caused a delay of several weeks in shipment. Because of this, syntax and compositional semantics had to be developed in another environment than all the other components, requiring additional integration efforts.

Besides this problem, some tools/modules turned out to be quite buggy when we started to use them. This was a problem which was not foreseen, and thus will be discussed in the subsection "Unpredicted Problems" below.

Version Control

Upward compatibility for every component was almost met. Even the change of module names (which normally would have needed a synchronized version switch in several modules) was straightened by using adapter modules.

Indeed there were no real regression problems. Almost all bugs detected were also found in previous versions.

One problem arose when two people agreed by telephone to drop the first parameter in a certain function definition. After this, one of them assumed this function to have three parameters while the other one assumed four. This was not a problem caused by the telephone equipment, since it turned out that the people had been talking about the same module but in a different version. But it was not so much a lack in version control as rather a psychological problem: when integrating the second milestone, the parameter list of the module had been changed, in order to fit together with the other ones, and then sent back to the owner. Although being told to do so, the owner had not replaced his own version by the "official" one, because in the meantime he had made further changes in his version – the classical "lost update" problem as known from the database field.

Prototyping

Problems arose when two research topics depended on each other (Two Level Morphology and HPSG Syntax); it would have been better if one of them had been left unchanged and doing service for the other, instead of having moving targets in two related components.

Although the milestone concept was quite helpful, the granularity of the milestones did not seem to be fine enough. This will also be discussed below in the subsection "Unpredicted Problems".

Distributed Development

Trying to get the distributed development done without overhead problems: due to clear interface descriptions between internal and external modules, this worked satisfactorily, maybe because the critical module interfaces were all at one location. Some extraordinary shipments to the external locations were useful to provide the external locations with newer module versions; one version in every 4 months would have inhibited work.

In the final laps, however, each location sent out a person for single days. This might have been avoided if remote login had been possible.

5.2 Reconsidering the "Likely Disasters"

Single component not ready in time

Severe problem: the Prolog parts of semantics module. The dummy for this module was not usable without endangering the system's functionality, and there was no other older version. On the other hand, the skill needed to do this job was not widespread, since it required knowledge in compositional semantics as well as experience in writing Prolog code. Thus it was a major problem to find a person to get this done, and it was not fixed until the person responsible for compositional semantics began also to program Prolog. The planned fall-back strategy wouldn't have worked here!

Many components not ready in time

Due to major interface mismatches in the first and second milestone (see next topic) the integration consumed much time. Thus the following milestones were shifted according to the delays: The 2nd milestone was slipped from 9/89 to 11/89. Delay now: 2 months. For the same reason, the 3rd milestone was slipped from 12/89 to 3/90. Delay now: 3 months.

Severe interface/interaction problems between modules

Interface problems occurred in the early phase of the project: The integration of the first version took 2 months including redesign meetings. On the other hand, this work was very valuable, since it was a quite cheap way to fix high-level design mismatches, a process which is usually very expensive.

Integration of the second milestone version took as long as 3 months, although it covered most of the integration work for LEU/2.

All further versions of the several modules could be integrated into the system quite easily in a plug-in-like way, since everybody could test his new versions inside the integrated version of the previous milestone.

One interface, however, turned out to be an intersection rather than an interface; this too has to be discussed in the subsection "Unpredicted Problems".

Response time problems

Motivated while waiting for slow or even creeping system parts, some effort was spent on optimization of single components. This added up to a performance better than estimated in the beginning of the project.

- parser tuned by owner (factor 3)

- linguistic workbench tuned by owner (factor 4)

- inference engine tuned by owner (to avoid duplicate axioms, factor 2-5 in special cases)

- tuning specialist:

  - tuned morphology (new strategy, factor 10)
  - tuned semantics module (code review; small improvement only)
  - tuned inference engine (code review; improvement in special cases)
  - redesigned subsumption checker (using bit vectors and precomputing; factor 1000-10000)

- Faster hardware (factor 3) used for demos

- Moving to even faster hardware (factor 5) now.

Storage space problems

Did not occur, since up to 16 MB main storage were used where necessary.

Distributed development not working

As mentioned in Sect. 5.1, there were no major problems imposed by the distributed development. In one location, however, there were two different technical areas: first the spatial reasoning component of the inference engine (Prolog coding) and second one part of the Knowledge Engineering activities (writing of rules); the technical contact person at this location though felt competent and thus responsible for the Prolog activities only.

The "Emergency-off" switches were implemented in 3 out of 4 external modules[6]. Fortunately they didn't become necessary to keep the system running, although they are valuable now to examine system behavior running or bypassing these modules. The 4th externally developed module, however, is the parser, which, in our classical architecture, is required for all the following processing and thus cannot be bypassed without losing functionality completely. But this component is a compact module, and the second milestone did already have the functionality to serve as final version.

5.3   Unpredicted Problems

Interface Problem

It was expected that two linguistic modules – the development of syntactic and semantic data – would have to be done in cooperation. But two other modules turned out also to be Siamese twins instead of separable modules: semantic data and knowledge base. This might have been a severe handicap for the complete development process and did work *only* because of extensive communication between the module owners, some of them linguists and others knowledge engineers.

This problem could have been foreseen with a better knowledge of the components involved, but even after doing the project, a solution seems not to be easy.

Planning Problem

Although the "early integration policy" turned out to be effective, well-accepted, and thus successful, the crew involved experienced a gap between the first two milestones as described in Sect. 3.3. Between milestone 0 (specify who calls whom) and milestone 1 (pass real data) there was missing a milestone "0.5", to specify the information passed without having to specify the data structure formats. This is why some data structures specified in milestone 1 had to be respecified again, as they didn't contain all the information needed.

This problem didn't occur for some of the module interfaces[7], because some of the implementers sat down and specified the superset of information which ever might have to flow between their modules. This resulted in a very stable interface between these modules without the need for respecification. But since not all people involved did this on their own, it might have been better to prescribe this step explicitly.

Planning Error

Although in general all tools were labelled as ready on schedule, some of them were not usable at all at this time, due to bugs and bad performance as well as specification/implementation mismatches. Note that this is *not* a problem just for lack of testing efforts, but rather on principle: the usability of a tool often cannot be determined before confronting it with real use.

This should not have been an unpredicted problem.

---

[6]Lexicon Manager, Depiction module, Data Base System.
[7]For example, Generation module and Inference Engine.

6 Discussion

6.1 Result Assessment

Rating the outcome of the project, it can be said that all targets were reached: the LEU/2 system was existing at the committed date with planned functionality. Almost 240,000 lines of code are running together properly. The development was achieved by creating an evolving series of versions without regression problems. After giving very successful demos to several experts, now the system is used by many people for experimenting and doing further research. Hence in the following the term "success" will be used occasionally instead of "result".

6.2 Reasons for the Result

Since the project did run quite well, let us consider the details that might have contributed to the success, structured into technical, organizational, and psychological aspects.

Technical

At any time, an accurate version control has had an important status in the developing process of LEU/2. This was considered to be indispensable in order to save the way back to previous versions whenever it might become necessary – a fact which is especially important when the integrating person cannot really judge the quality of fixes, because the knowledge of many specialists cannot be subsumed by one person's knowledge. Thus, bad fixes could be taken back immediately without knowing the internal details. Moreover, since much emphasis was put on keeping to the rules regarding version control (see Sect. 3.1), switching to newer or older versions could generally be done component-wise. This also helped to avoid the panic experienced in previous projects: "Oops, today we have nothing that works, and we cannot reproduce yesterday's version...".

When testing a certain bug fix, there is no discussion that the bug should disappear when applying the fix. But it is valuable to verify that the bug is *still there* when you remove that certain fix again, just to be sure that the proposed test is really of probative value, trying other tests if needed. Using this method, a few bad fixes could be rejected at once.

At this point I would like to admit that despite all the official rules and deadlines, based on experiences throughout the project, different people were treated differently when it came to bringing in "last-minute changes" before important deadlines: especially some people, known for their "downward compatibility"[8] changes, were not allowed to make changes in the last several weeks.

Organizational

As mentioned above, the implementers were directed to deliver code already in the early phases of the project. This forced specifications to be very concrete for every milestone. The use of an easy motto for each of the milestones helped to improve the acceptance of the milestone concept. Thus integration was started very early, which allowed us to find out the major misalignments very soon, namely while integrating the "dummy version". On the other hand, this also gave a first feeling for how seriously further deadlines (milestones) would be taken, still in time to admonish the people appropriately. And finally, having a first version very early helped to improve the motivation, as the

---

[8]What did not work before the fix, was guaranteed not to work after, either.

crew could already see a first running system. Furthermore, this first reference version was even the first primitive fall-back version, at least for single components.

When coordinating the work of many people at several locations, it is not possible just to travel around, in order to see whether there are any problems anywhere. Instead of polling for problems, it was much more effective to have the staff members signal their problems; this sounds almost too trivial to mention, but one shouldn't forget to encourage them to report any problem right away.

Very helpful for the progress of the project was the idea to consult an external expert for AI architectures, who reviewed our plans in an early stage. Without knowing all the details, he could give us several hints on the methodological layer.

Psychological

Although some people temporarily had doubts about the success of the project, they were prohibited from starting any culpability discussions, which might have caused loss of motivation and cooperation. Instead, they were put off until the end of the implementation, and at the end, this discussion was not necessary at all.

Doing a software development project with research people, you have to find an acceptable way between too many programming guidelines on one side and chaos on the other side. Even simple programming style requirements can be felt to be a burden. Thus, after requesting a guy to give an error message in a certain program part instead of just letting the program abort, this was the newly invented and proudly presented error message:

```
hello out there, here's your favorite error message again ...
```

But at any time it was clear that the *staff people* were the experts, not the *coordinator*. Thus the coordinator's offer "I bet 5 marks that your module can't handle this sentence"[9] resulted in a loss of money but maybe in a gain of motivation.

As much as possible, the attempt was made to take unnecessary work off the staff people's shoulders. A simple example: The way the people delivered their version diskettes was recommended but not forced; since there are ways more than a dozen to write to a diskette[10], it would have made receiving the files easier to require one standardized format. But it seemed better to implement a diskette normalizer rather than to prescribe the people one guideline too many and to reject a diskette because of its format.

Staff

The factor mostly difficult to influence, however, was the capability of the crew. But here we had luck: the motivation was very high, and although not all of them were software development professionals, they were brilliant scientists and at least open for implementation needs.

6.3   Applicability To Other Projects

So what can be learned from this? Beneath all implicit or explicit hints given so far, the two most portable experiences shall be emphasized.

---

[9]Yes, the module *could* handle the sentence.

[10]For example, tar, backup, cpio, cpio -C, mount, doswrite, cat, ... combined with high/low density.

Being Friends With Reality - Part 1

Planning a project like this, you need a time buffer for unforeseen events. This seems to be trivial, but you have to defend this "no man's land" against two parties: on the one hand, often it may be hard to assign a time frame while you cannot say what it is really for, and to justify this to higher management. On the other hand, you have to forbid your staff to relax plans and rely on this extra amount of time.

The reward for doing this: First of all, you are in time even if you are late. Secondly, it is easier to convince someone that he is late, when the due date is in the past rather than in the future.

Being Friends With Reality - Part 2

As a professional software developer you prefer the stable, tested solution to the first, untested implementation of a brand-new theory, see (Knuth 90); as a scientist maybe you do not. This can be a serious problem if you want to build a large system, especially if two highly experimental modules interface with each other. So it is a nontrivial step in planning the implementation to make the staff used to software development needs.

Given task T and a machine M, assume that there are three approaches to solve it:

(a) an algorithm that needs 1 second on machine M

(b) an algorithm that needs 10000 hours on machine M

(c) an algorithm which never terminates

Make sure that your crew recognizes a *big* difference between solution (a) and (b), and a *small* difference between (b) and (c), although from the theoretical point of view the difference between (a) and (b) is the irrelevant one – since there are no time constraints for a Turing machine[11]. Indeed some of the implementers didn't think that way but had to learn this during the project.

References

Herzog, O., et al. (1986): LILOG - Linguistic and Logic Methods for the Computational Understanding of German. LILOG Report 1b, IBM Deutschland, Stuttgart

Knuth, D.E. (1989): The errors of TeX. Software – Practice and Experience, 19(7), 607-685

Knuth, D.E. (1990): The future of TeX and Metafont. TeXMaG 5, Electronic Magazine, editor: Neil Burleson (NABTEXM@VENUS.TAMU.EDU)

Boehm, B.W. (1986): A spiral model of software development and enhancement. ACM SIGSOFT Software Engineering Notes, 11(4)

Budde, R. et al. (1984): Approaches to prototyping. Springer-Verlag, Berlin, Heidelberg, New York

Floyd, C. (1984): A systematic look at prototyping. In: Budde, R. et al. (eds.): Approaches to prototyping, Springer-Verlag, Berlin, Heidelberg, New York

[11]Except in a "busy beaver" competition.

List of Contributors

Jürgen Angele, Universität Karlsruhe, Inst. für Angew. Informatik und formale
   Beschreibungsverfahren, Postfach 6980, 7500 Karlsruhe 1

Andreas Arning, IBM Deutschland GmbH, WT WZ IWBS 7000-75, Postfach 80 08 80,
   7000 Stuttgart 80

Stefan Benzschawel, Universität Trier, Informatik, Postfach 38 25, 5500 Trier

Prof. Dr Karl-Hans Bläsius, Caspar-Olevian-Str. 61, 5500 Trier

Dr. Toni Bollinger, IBM Deutschland GmbH, WT WZ IWBS 7000-75, Postfach 80 08 80,
   7000 Stuttgart 80

Manfred Börkel, IBM Deutschland GmbH, WT WZ IWBS 7000-75, Postfach 80 08 80,
   7000 Stuttgart 80

Dr. Peter Bosch, IBM Deutschland GmbH, WT WZ IWBS 7000-75, Postfach 80 08 80,
   7000 Stuttgart 80

Prof. Dr. Wilfried Brauer, Technische Universität München, Institut für Informatik, Postfach 20 24 20
   8000 München 2

Kai-Uwe Carstensen, Universität Hamburg, Fachbereich Informatik WSV, Bodenstedtstr. 16,
   2000 Hamburg 50

Zuzana Dobes, IBM Deutschland GmbH, WT WZ IWBS 7000-75, Postfach 80 08 80, 7000 Stuttgart 80

Jochen Dörre, Universität Stuttgart, Institut für Maschinelle Sprachverarbeitung, Computerlinguistik
   Kepplerstr. 17, 7000 Stuttgart 1

Kurt Eberle, Universität Stuttgart, Institut für Maschinelle Sprachverarbeitung, Computerlinguistik
   Kepplerstr. 17, 7000 Stuttgart 1

Dr. Werner Emde, Universität Osnabrück, FB 7, Projekt LILOG, Sedanstr. 4, 4500 Osnabrück

Gregor Erbach, Universität des Saarlandes, Computerlinguistik, Bau 17, Im Stadtwald 15,
   6600 Saarbrücken 11

Dieter Fensel, Universität Karlsruhe, Inst. für Angew. Informatik und formale Beschreibungsverfahren
   Postfach 6980, 7500 Karlsruhe 1

Barbara Gängler, Universität Bielefeld, AG Wissensbasierte Systeme, Technische Fakultät
   Universitätsstr. 25, 4800 Bielefeld 1

Erich Gehlen, Universität Trier, Informatik, Postfach 38 25, 5500 Trier

Peter Gerstl, IBM Deutschland GmbH, WT WZ IWBS 7000-75, Postfach 80 08 80, 7000 Stuttgart 80

Drs. Bart Geurts, Universität Tilburg, ITK, P.O. Box 90153, 5000 LE Tilburg, Holland

Dr. Helmar Gust, Universität Osnabrück, FB 7, Studiengang CL+KI, Sedanstr. 4, 4500 Osnabrück

Prof. Dr. Christopher Habel, Universität Hamburg, Fachbereich Informatik WSV, Bodenstedtstr. 16 2000 Hamburg 50

Dr. Otthein Herzog, IBM Deutschland GmbH, WT WZ IWBS 7000-75, Postfach 80 08 80, 7000 Stuttgart 80

Prof. Dr. Siegfried Kanngießer, Universität Osnabrück, FB 7, Studiengang CL+KI, Postfach 44 69 4500 Osnabrück

Mohammed Khenkhar, Universität Hamburg, Fachbereich Informatik WSV, Bodenstedtstr. 16 2000 Hamburg 50

Tibor Kiss, IBM Deutschland GmbH, WT WZ IWBS 7000-75, Postfach 80 08 80, 7000 Stuttgart 80

Gudrun Klose, IBM Deutschland GmbH, WT WZ IWBS 7000-75, Postfach 80 08 80, 7000 Stuttgart 80

Dr. Esther König, Kyoto University, Department of Electrical Engineering, Yoshida-Honmachi, Sakyo-ku Kyoto 606, Japan

Dieter Landes, Universität Karlsruhe, Inst. für Angew. Informatik und formale Beschreibungsverfahren Postfach 6980, 7500 Karlsruhe 1

Dr.Dr. sc. Ewald Lang, Bergische Universität Wuppertal, FB 4 , Sonderforschungsbereich 282 "Theorie des Lexikons" , 5600 Wuppertal 1

Michael Ley, Universität Trier, Informatik, Postfach 38 25, 5500 Trier

Prof. Dr. Godehard Link, Universität München, Seminar für Philosophie, Logik und Wissenschaftstheorie Ludwigstr. 31/I, 8000 München 22

Prof. Dr. Peter Lockemann, Universität Karlsruhe, Institut für Informatik II, Postfach 69 80, 7500 Karlsruhe 1

Sven Lorenz, Universität Stuttgart, Institut für Maschinelle   Sprachverarbeitung Computerlinguistik Kepplerstr. 17, 7000 Stuttgart 1

Dr. Kai v. Luck, IBM Deutschland GmbH, WT WZ IWBS 7000-75, Postfach 80 08 80, 7000 Stuttgart 80

Petra Ludewig, Universität Osnabrück, FB 7, Projekt LILOG, Sedanstr. 4, 4500 Osnabrück

Thomas Ludwig, Universität Trier, Informatik, Postfach 38 25, 5500 Trier

Claudia Maienborn, Universität Hamburg, Fachbereich Informatik WSV, Bodenstedtstr. 16 2000 Hamburg 50

Albert Maier, Universität Trier, Informatik, Postfach 38 25, 5500 Trier

Dr. Rolf Mayer, IBM Deutschland GmbH, WT WZ IWBS 7000-75, Postfach 80 08 80,
7000 Stuttgart 80

Dr. Bernhard Nebel, DFKI, Stuhlsatzenhausweg 3, 6600 Saarbrücken 11

Susanne Neubert, Universität Karlsruhe, Inst. für Angew. Informatik und formale
Beschreibungsverfahren, Postfach 6980, 7500 Karlsruhe 1

Dr. Hans-Joachim Novak, IBM Deutschland GmbH, WT WZ IWBS 7000-75, Postfach 80 08 80,
7000 Stuttgart 80

Thomas Pirlein, IBM Deutschland GmbH, WT WZ IWBS 7000-75, Postfach 80 08 80,
7000 Stuttgart 80

Dr. Udo Pletat, IBM Deutschland GmbH, WT WZ IWBS 7000-75, Postfach 80 08 80, 7000 Stuttgart 80

Simone Pribbenow, Universität Hamburg, Fachbereich Informatik WSV, Bodenstedtstr. 16
2000 Hamburg 50

Ingo Raasch, IBM Deutschland GmbH, WT WZ IWBS 7000-75, Postfach 80 08 80,
7000 Stuttgart 80

Mechthild Rickheit, Universität Osnabrück, FB 7, Projekt LILOG, Sedanstr. 4, 4500 Osnabrück

Prof. Dr. Claus-Rainer Rollinger, Universität Osnabrück, FB Sprach- und Literaturwissenschaft,
Arbeitsbereich CL und KI, Postfach 4469, 4500 Osnabrück 1

Rob A. van der Sandt, IBM Deutschland GmbH, WT WZ IWBS 7000-75, Postfach 80 08 80,
7000 Stuttgart 80

Anne Schiller, IBM Deutschland GmbH, WT WZ IWBS 7000-75, Postfach 80 08 80, 7000 Stuttgart 80

Prof. Dr. Peter H. Schmitt, Universität Karlsruhe, Inst. für Logik, Komplexität und Deduktionssysteme
Postfach 6980, 7500 Karlsruhe 1

Prof. Dr. Helmut Schnelle, Ruhr-Universität Bochum, Sprachwissenschaftliches Institut,
Postfach 10 21 48, 4630 Bochum 1

Hinrich Schütze, CSLI, Ventura Hall, Stanford University, Stanford, CA 94305-4115, USA

Roland Seiffert, IBM Deutschland GmbH, WT WZ IWBS 7000-75, Postfach 80 08 80,
7000 Stuttgart 80

Geoff Simmons, Universität Hamburg, Fachbereich Informatik WSV, Bodenstedtstr. 16,
2000 Hamburg 50

Prof. Dr. Gerd Smolka, DFKI, Stuhlsatzenhausweg 3, 6600 Saarbrücken 11

Petra Steffens, IBM Deutschland GmbH, WT WZ IWBS 6900-52, Wilkensstr. 1a, 6900 Heidelberg 1

Prof. Dr. Rudi Studer, Universität Karlsruhe, Inst. für Angew. Informatik und formale
Beschreibungsverfahren, Postfach 6980, 7500 Karlsruhe 1

738

Prof. Dr. Ipke Wachmuth, Universität Bielefeld, AG Wissensbasierte Systeme, Technische Fakultät
Universitätsstr. 25, 4800 Bielefeld 1

Prof. Dr. Bernd Walter, Universität Trier, Informatik, Postfach 38 25, 5500 Trier

Birgit Wendholt, IBM Deutschland GmbH, WT WZ IWBS 7000-75, Postfach 80 08 80,
7000 Stuttgart 80

Birgit Wesche, IBM Deutschland GmbH, WT WZ IWBS 7000-75, Postfach 80 08 80, 7000 Stuttgart 80

Jan Wilms, IBM Deutschland GmbH, WT WZ IWBS 7000-75, Postfach 80 08 80, 7000 Stuttgart 80

Lecture Notes in Artificial Intelligence (LNAI)

Lecture Notes in Computer Science